FREE MONEY TO GET A BETTER HOME

by

Matthew Lesko

and

Mary Ann Martello

Researchers
Cindy Owens, Jean Neuner,
Bev Matson, Chelsea Noble, Dixie St. John

Production
Beth Meserve

Marketing
Kim McCoy

Support
Mercedes Sundeen

Cover
Ray Holland

FREE MONEY TO GET A BETTER HOME, Copyright 2003 by Matthew Lesko and Mary Ann Martello. All rights reserved. Printed in the United States of America. Published by Information USA, Inc., P.O. Box E, Kensington, MD 20895; {www.lesko.com}.

Clip art used in this publication © Dynamic Graphics, Inc.; Totem Graphics; One Mile Up; Tech Pool; Image Club Graphics, Inc.; and Corel Corp.

FIRST EDITION

Library of Congress Cataloging-in-Publication date
    Lesko, Matthew
    Martello, Mary Ann

Free Money To Get A Better Home

ISBN # 1-878346-67-9

Most books by Matthew Lesko are available at special quantity discounts for bulk purchases for sales promotions, premiums, fund-raising or educational use. Special books or book excerpts also can be created to fit specific needs.

For details, write Information USA, Special Markets, Attention: Kim McCoy, P.O. Box E, Kensington, MD 20895; or 1-800-797-7811, Marketing; {www.lesko.com}.

TABLE OF CONTENTS

Free Money To Get A Better Home
Buy A House, Fix Up A House Or Become A Real Estate Millionaire

Uncle Sam's Housing Offices 16

County Housing Programs   258

City Housing Programs   272

More Nonprofit Housing Programs   314

More Free Money And Help For Homeowners and Renters   321

FREE MONEY TO GET A BETTER HOME

BUY A HOUSE, FIX UP A HOUSE OR
BECOME A REAL ESTATE MILLIONAIRE

Forget the stock market, precious metals or even trading cards, Invest in the one sure thing that is certainly a lot more profitable and will give you a lot more pleasure on a day-to-day basis than any other investment that you can think of … real estate.

Each year the government gives out $329 billion in over 4,000 different money programs that you can use to:
➡ buy your first home,
➡ move up to a bigger home,
➡ make your current home nicer,
➡ pay your rent, security deposit or mortgage, or
➡ become a real estate investor

These programs come in all shapes and sizes and are in thousands of different agencies. But once you learn the system, you will see how you, too, can tap into little-known government programs where you can apply to get:
➡ $6,000 for closing costs
➡ $7,000,000 to develop townhouses
➡ $27,000 to makeover your bath and kitchen, or
➡ $750,000 to buy a farm or ranch

Millions Are Eligible But Fail To Apply

Over 12 million people a year are using government real estate programs, but there are still tens of millions more who are eligible and are not applying because they do not know that these programs are available. I recently read an announcement from one government program that gives a $3,500 grant to families to fix up their home. The government estimates that 20 million people who are eligible for this money fail to apply. Are you one of these people? $3,500 is nothing to walk away from.

But you can't apply if you don't know about the program. Information is power. With the right information you can do the things you always wanted to do. You can solve those problems that are nagging at your life. But you have to know all your options. This is really a case of what you don't know can hurt you.

★ Why borrow $20,000 from the bank at 5% or 6% interest to fix up your kitchen if you can use a government program that will give you the money free or at 0% interest?

★ Why cancel your summer vacation because you need the money to paint your house when you can get a $7,000 grant from a local government agency to paint your house?

★ Why give up your dream of buying a $1.5 million apartment building because every bank is laughing at you, when you can turn to a government office that will co-sign your bank loan for you to make sure you get the money?

★ Why continue to pay rent just because you live paycheck to paycheck and can't come up with the down payment and closing costs, when there are programs from government offices and nonprofit organizations that will give you the down payment and closing costs for free.

Remember that with these 4,000 programs that give out money for real estate, not one of them have money to advertise that they are giving this money away. The only government money program that advertises is the Lottery. Lotteries are really state government tax collection programs.

Where Does This Money Come From?

The simple answer is YOU. For the most part these are your tax dollars at work. The Legislative branch of government passes laws that institute programs they think are important. They then tell the Executive branch to carry out the programs and collect the taxes to pay for them. The way to change a program is through the Legislative Branch. That is your elected representative, like your Congressman or Senator. Never yell at a government agency if you think a program is unfair and it should be changed. You will only frustrate yourself. Go through your elected official, as they are the people who make the laws that change the programs.

So, when you use these programs you are really getting your tax dollars back.

Where Are The Agencies?

All the programs are not in Washington. It's a complex maze of programs throughout the country. If it was not so complicated, I don't think we'd be in business. All government information about the programs is public information to you, to me or to anyone else. So, if all the programs were in Washington, then most people could easily figure out the main agencies that have these programs and forget about spending money on a book. But these programs are not set up that way.

- For some programs, the money originates in Washington and is handed out to consumers directly from Washington
- For others, the money originates in Washington and is handed out to consumers through state agencies, local agencies and nonprofit organizations
- For some, the money originates at the state and local level and is handed out to consumers at the state and local level or through nonprofit organizations
- And for others, the money originates from private, non-government, funding sources and is handed out through nonprofit organizations

People With Bad Credit and Millionaires Are Eligible

It sounds crazy. But remember, this is the government. A lot of things in the government do not make sense. I gave up trying to make sense out of everything the government does. My job is big enough just trying to report what programs actually exist.

With so many programs, no one can say that you have to have specific requirements in order to get government money for real estate. Every program has different requirements. Some programs require you to have enough capital to show you can pay for all the other expenses you are going to incur, because they are only going to give you money for part of the project and they want to make sure you have money for the other part. Other programs require that you have no money at all, because these programs want to get homes to people who would normally not have one. And other programs just give out money because they are trying to solve a certain problem we have in our society, like making sure young families have homes, improving homes for seniors, making sure all homes are free of lead paint, or making sure your vacation homes are weatherized

There are even programs for real estate investors who are in financial trouble from running their buildings. Remember, most government programs have been established to give people money who normally can't get it elsewhere.

Don't try to figure out why these programs are there. Just start applying to them.

Apply To As Many Programs As You Can

Don't worry about how many programs you can apply for, If you see a program that you think might work for you, apply to it. If you apply to 50 programs and everyone gives you the money, that is a wonderful problem to have. Only worry about it after it happens. Not before.

Sure there are some programs that give money for specific reasons, and if you get accepted from two separate places you will have to refuse one of the offers. For example, you may apply to more than one program that offers grants for down payments or closing costs, or money to add a new addition to your home. If more than one gives you the money, it will be a happy day in your life to have to turn down one of those agencies. Don't worry about it. It's a nice problem to have. Worry more about where you are going to apply for the money.

Get Your Money In The Morning

This may actually happen with some programs. There are organizations who are set up to give out emergency money to fix up your home or to pay your rent or mortgage. Their mission requires them to operate quickly. But in 4,000 programs,this is very rare. A few weeks is actually fast for these programs. It may even take a few months.

There are many people who say that a few months is a long time and they would rather not apply for the money. I say this is nonsense. If this is a long time for you, then maybe you should not apply for the money. But I guarantee you that in the world of money, a few months is no time at all to wait for someone who is going to give you $200,000 to buy a home. I bet you can't even remember what you did for the last few months.

One-Page Applications

This is not unreasonable at all. Many of the government programs that give out grants really don't need a lot of financial information because, unlike a bank, they are not worried if you don't pay the money back. They don't want it back. It's free money.

Sure, some of the programs may require a 10 page application if you are planning to build a village of town houses or buy a hotel. But the size of the application should never concern you. "Size does not matter." The important thing is getting the money. It should not matter if the application is 50 pages long. If someone is going to give you $500,000 to do what you want to do in life, it is stupid not to put in the time it takes to fill out the application, even if it takes a week. Where else are you going to get $500,000 for a week's work?

What's In The Book?

We have attempted to catalog as many programs as possible to save you the time and money of doing it yourself. I always felt that if the world had one idiot like me who was willing to do all the hard work of locating these programs, then the rest of the country could take advantage of the research and would not have to do any of the hard work themselves. This is a lot better than having everyone in the country digging up the programs for themselves.

The book concentrates on the following areas:
- Federal money programs
- State money programs
- County and City money programs
- Nonprofit organizations

We Don't Have It All

It's impossible for any one publication, database or anything else, to be able to collect everything in the universe on a given subject. I know I'm biased, but I certainly believe that we are the best people in the world for collecting information on government money programs. I also know that we cannot possibly get every single program that is available.

One problem is that programs come and go. Our world is changing every second. It is a big complex society we are living in, and people are making decisions all throughout the day that make subtle or big changes which affect the contents of this book. Budgets keep changing. Priorities keep changing. People keep changing. Offices keep changing.

A bigger problem is that the world of free money is enormous. Preparing a book for a national audience makes us excellent at identifying national and state programs. But truthfully, it is sometimes beyond our capabilities to completely cover all local, county and nonprofit programs. First of all, if we did collect all these programs in the country, you would not be able to pick up the book. There are thousands and thousands of local communities in the United States and each of them can have 5 to 50 programs. Fifty times 5,000 would be 250,000 programs. We would never finish researching

Our goal is to arm you with knowledge. We want to show you the money, but you are going to have to do a little work yourself.

You Have To Do A Little Work Too

Our research staff has put in about 7 man-years of work to collect the information in this book. And as you read above, we have left some of the local work for you. Because it is impossible to collect every local program from the thousands of communities available, we want to give you all the best sources for locating these money programs yourself. And we also give you the information for finding any new national and state programs that were not available at the time we were researching the book.

Here's where to go:

Catalog Of Federal Domestic Assistance
Anyone selling you information about federal programs on real estate has to get the information from this source. It's printed every six months by the federal government, and is the major source of all federal programs. You can do a free search identifying all the federal real estate programs by going on the web to {http://www.cfda.gov}. The book is also available in almost every public library and for sale from the U.S. Government Printing Office {www.gpo.gov}

Your State Housing Authority
Every state has offices that provide financing for buying and fixing up homes and for real estate investing. Call your State Capitol Operator located in your state capital, or go to {http://www.govengine.com/} and look for your state housing office for information about all their programs.

Your City and County Governments
Contact your city and county officials. Almost every local jurisdiction has money for housing and real estate. Many have money for closing costs, down payments, repairs and even rental assistance. It will take some effort but it's worth the time. You can also locate your local and county government offices on the web at {http://www.govengine.com/localgov/index.html}.

Local and National Nonprofit Organizations

There are thousands of nonprofits groups that help homeowners and real estate investors. They can be groups that offer down payment money, closing cost money and even free technical assistance. It may take a considerable amount of time to find them all. Your local library can be of help or your local elected officials listed below.

Your Elected Officials

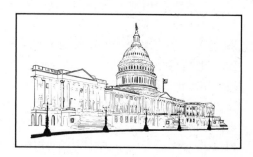

Your elected representatives are in the business of seeing how they can help you locate money, services or anything else you need. They all have people on their staff whose job it is to help you so you will vote for their boss. This is why politicians are always getting re-elected. If they do a favor for you, you will vote for them forever, no matter what they do.

- You have one congressman and two senators at the federal level. You can contact all three.
- You have more than one elected official in your state capital.
- You also have an elected representative at your city and county level.

Contact them all. They are all getting a government salary to help you and they all have access to different resources. The worst that can happen is that more than one person solves your problem. If you need help finding them go to {http://www.govengine.com/}. Your local public library can also tell you how to contact them.

Other places

Housing Counseling Center Locator, 800-569-4287 or 800-217-6970 or {http://www.hud.gov/offices/hsg/sfh/hcc/hcc_home.cfm}

For help identifying more money programs, contact the Office of Community Planning and Development at 800-998-9999 or {http://www.comcon.org}.

Another good starting place to get free help identifying free government programs and services is the Federal Information Center at {http://www.pueblo.gsa.gov/}, or call 1-800-FED-INFO.

It Doesn't Matter If It Sounds Like You Don't Qualify

You are going to find programs that excite you at first and then when you read further it seems that you will not qualify. Or you will gather more information on a program in this book and you will run into some phrase or sentence in the description that makes you feel you do not have a chance. You may encounter things like:

- "all the money is given out by June 30th" and it is already September 1
- "the money is only for people who live in the country" and you live in the city
- "the money goes to nonprofit organizations" and you are not one
- "you have to come up with 20% of the money for the project" and you don't have any
- "the money is only for people who live in Minnesota" and you live in New Jersey
- "the money is for people making less than $60,000/yr" and you make $70,000

Don't look at phrases like these as impassable boulders that stand in your way of getting the money you need. In reality, they can simply be small pebbles in the road that you may not even feel at all. But if you don't follow up, you will never know.

Here's what I've seen happen in each of these situations:

1) *"all the money is given out by June 30th"*: The end of the accounting year for most government agencies is September 30, but the agency can start giving out more money beginning October 1, and you can be the first in line. I think you can wait another 30 days for your money.

2) *"the money is for people who live in the country:"* That may be so. But it will still pay to get the details of the program to see if there is something in the description that was not obvious to others. A young man in Boston was trying to get money from a program that gave money for teenage entrepreneurs that lived in the country. He lived in Boston. When he got the materials, it said that it was for people in the country, but the description also said that it was for people who wanted to start lawn mowing businesses. That is wanted he wanted to do and he convinced the office that he was qualified. Government officials, or for that matter anyone, do not know everything. Get the facts and find out for yourself.

3) *"the money is for nonprofits"*: for about $100 in fees you can become a nonprofit. Just call up the IRS and your state capital and ask for the office that registers nonprofit organizations. Fill out the paperwork. Don't worry. You'll do it wrong. Send it in anyway. And they will send it back telling you how you messed up and then you will correct your mistakes. Another way to solve the problem is to find a local nonprofit, like a community college, church, or community group. Tell them you would like to use their name to apply for a bunch of money and that you will give them 15% if you get the money. They have nothing to lose, and everything to gain.

4) *"you have to come up with 20% of the cost of the project"*: There is always more than one way to come up with the extra money other than having the cash in your pocket. Some programs allow you to provide services or equipment that you already have as part of your 20%. You may be able to use your sweat as your contribution. The fact that you will work for free in helping to get the house built or the refurbishing done is worth something. You can call yourself a general contractor or just a handyman who pounds in the nails. Or you may need equipment, like the use of a car, to get the project done. This can be your car, which you already have and can count as a percentage of the project.

5) *"the money is only for people in Minnesota"*: Contact them anyway. It's likely that if this is a unique program, then the program administrators will be aware of similar programs around the country that do the same thing. People doing similar work around the country have a tendency to organize and share information on how they are doing. We are one of the best organized countries in the world. If there are ten people in the country doing the same thing, they will start an association, a newsletter, and have annual meetings.

6) *"the money is for people making less than $60,000"*: We all know that rules are made to be broken and many bureaucrats who hand out money have the power and authority to break the rules. It is easier for them to bend a few rules if they like you or they like your project. Or they may be having trouble giving away all their money this year, and you are one of the best ideas they have seen. Remember, bureaucrats are human too. They have feelings. Like all of us, unless they are having a bad day, their instinct is to help. Always give them a chance to see if they can help.

They May Not Have Money But They Do Have Info

This is very important to remember when you are identifying programs that may or may not be of help to you. Remember, the easiest thing to do is to look at a program and determine that it is not for you so you don't have to do any more work.

This is not the way important things will happen to you. You have to follow up on programs even though they do not seem perfect at first glance. Remember you are looking for help. You are looking for ideas. You are even looking for more programs than are in this book. The people involved in handing out money are the best people to help you get on the road to your money. They are in the business. Also remember, the description of the program may even be wrong.

Don't cut yourself out of an opportunity. Follow up on every potential program that you encounter.

Failure Is Your Friend

The name of the game in getting money is failure. Sounds stupid, but it's true. It is unlikely that you are going to buy this book and make one phone call and get a check in the mail next Tuesday. Sure you would like it to happen. And I would love to see it happen to you. It actually does happen to some people, and those are the people that I put in my infomercials. So if this happens to you, make sure you call me and I'll put you in my next show.

If this is a new process for you, what is more likely to happen is that after your first, your second, or maybe even your 15th call, you still don't have the money you are seeking. How long it takes will depend on many things, some of which you have no control over.

Learning any new process requires failure. If you are not failing, then you are not learning anything. Watch kids who learn to walk. I remember when my kids started, and that was 20 years ago. My boy would crawl over to the living room coffee table and pull himself up to the table edge. He would take one step and then fall on his butt. He would do that over and over again. Eventually he would be able to take two steps and then fall on his butt and crawl back and pull himself up on the coffee table again. He did that 100 times to learn how to walk across the room. Maybe our family is a bunch of slow learners.

Now, just think if I was doing my job as a protective parent and told my son not to try walking because he was going to fall on his butt. If I did that, I'd be pushing him around in a wheelchair today.

Learning how to get money, or doing anything else you want to do in life, is like learning to walk. You have to fall down a whole bunch of times before you get it right. So if you are not failing, you're not learning. SO GO OUT THERE AND FAIL.

This Book Is Out Of Date

Sorry to disappoint you. But I have to warn you of the truth. In our modern society, it is virtually impossible to expect to include every program possible and have every item completely accurate. The problem is that the world is too big and it is always changing. Every day programs are coming and going. Every day people change their address, phone number and websites. It is just a fact that these things happen in our modern society.

But remember, if a listing in this book leads you to a non-working number or website, it does not necessarily mean that the program is gone. In all likelihood it is still there but has changed a little bit since we completed our search. Here are some tricks you can try to locate the program:

➡ call the information operation and ask for the telephone number for the agency listed in the program description

➡ search the web for the agency name in any of the web search engines like {www.dogpile.com} or {www.google.com}

➡ contact the Federal Information Center at {http://www.pueblo.gsa.gov/}, or call 1-800-FED-INFO. This is a free service that will help you locate a federal government agency

➡ go to {www.govengine.com} on the web for a listing of most federal, state and local government agencies

➡ contact your federal, state or local elected official. They all have staff people that will help you find what you need at any level of government

11 Steps For Getting The Money You Need

Step #1: Review The Book

It is important to go through the entire book. You don't have to read everything, but you have to at least review the title of every entry. Place a check mark on those entries that you feel MIGHT be of some interest to you. You can also place a post-it note on the edge of the page or turn down the corner of the page so you can easily return to it.

Step #2: Assign A Grade To Likely Programs

Two grades can be enough. But it must be at least two. Read each entry in detail and place either an "A" or "B" next to the entry. Using a "1" or "2" is also good. The higher grade should identify those entries that seem more likely and the lower grade should identify programs that are a little less likely but are "maybes."

Step #3: Follow Up Immediately

As you probably guessed from reading the step above, you should now go back and contact all your "A" list programs first. Leave your "B" list programs for a later round. You want to tackle the most obvious first . You can start digging deeper later, but you may not have to. I know it sounds like an obvious choice, but some people get overwhelmed with so many places to go to. This prioritizes the process for you.

Step #4: Contact the Agency Directly

This is a must. Do not assume that you know everything about the program just by reading the description in the book. You have to get the details before you make the decision if this is a program for you. You can contact the agency in any of four ways:

- by telephone,
- by email,
- by website, or
- in person

You may even want to do a combination. You can go to the website and review their programs, then call and ask for specifics. But remember, even if you get details about a specific program on the web, be sure you contact the agency by phone or email to ensure you have the complete information. Like printed material in books, a lot of material on the web can also be out of date or even misleading.

Step #5: Be Careful What You Ask For

Your initial contact with an agency should be friendly. Many people are intimidated to

contact any government agency. Remember, you don't have to know what you are talking about, because most of the bureaucrats don't know what they are talking about either. This is the government, remember. Your best approach is to try to be as inclusive as possible in your initial contact. Try not to say things that can get you a "no" answer right off the bat. For example, don't let the first words out of your mouth be:

"Hi, I want a grant to buy a townhouse. Will you give me one?

This can get the door closed on you right away when in fact there may be lots of money sitting there waiting for you. The bureaucrat answering the phone may not be aware of any grant programs because he just started working there a few weeks ago and does not know all the programs. Or he may not be aware of any money that says "townhouse" on the label. He will look down his list for the word "townhouse" and tell you that there is no money available. The government may be offering other kinds of money that don't have the name "grant" attached to it, but it means the same thing. They may be offering money in the form of "direct payments" or under a program called "loans," but in fact you never have to pay back the money if you live in the house for more than three years. That's just as good as a grant

You can miss a lot by trying to be very specific. The problem is that most people in the government don't even know what is available. By being specific, the official can find an easier way to tell you "no" and send you on your way. You'll be happy, because this is what you sort of expected anyway, and the official will be happy because he doesn't have to do any more work. It is much better to start with something like:

"Hi. I'm trying to get a description of all the money programs that are available for housing or real estate."

You want the official to stretch her imagination and try to come up with a complete list for you. When you get a complete descriptive listing, review it in close detail and call the office back and tell them all the programs for which you would like to apply.

Step #6: Don't Leave Empty Handed

If after reviewing all their programs you decide that they have nothing for you, you have one more important thing to do before you move on. Call up one of the program officers and tell them about your search. See if they are aware of any programs that may suit your needs, or if they know of other agencies that have ANY kind of financial assistance for housing and real estate.

These people are in the business and are likely to attend meetings and conventions where other people like them from other agencies who hand out money also attend. They are on the front line of the housing money market and will likely know other people who do this work.

Step #7: Apply, Apply, Apply

Keep going through this process and keep applying to as many programs as possible. Apply even if people tell you that you have a very small chance of getting the money. Apply even if they tell you that you "may" not be qualified. When you hear terms like "may" or "small chance," this still means that you do have a chance, and that is all you need.

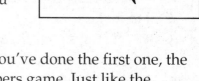

Don't worry about filling out so many applications. Once you've done the first one, the rest are pretty much the same. The whole process is a numbers game. Just like the lottery, you have to play to win.

Step #8: No Application Is A Problem

No matter how easy the application may appear you are likely to encounter some difficulty with at least one question. But this is not a real problem, as there is plenty of help.

The best way to handle this is to call the office giving out the money and ask to speak to a "program officer" for the program to which you are applying. These are the people who are directly involved in handing out the money. Be blunt and tell them that you "have no idea what they are talking about in question #6 on the application." You are probably not the first person in the world who had trouble with that question. The office probably realizes it is confusing, but didn't have money in the budget to reprint the forms.

If for some reason you are not getting help directly from the office giving out the money, you can always contact the office of your elected official. This is your Congressman or Senator at the federal level, your state elected official for state programs, and your councilman or mayor at the local level. They all have people on their staff whose job it is to solve problems that taxpayers are having with the government.

Step #9: See What A Winning Application Looks Like

You can always contact the office who is giving out the money and ask to see a copy of a winning application from someone who got the money last year. This is your money the government is handing out and you have a right to see how they are spending it. If the agency is not helpful in getting you an application, ask to speak to their Freedom Of Information Act Office. Every federal agency and most state agencies have such offices. They can tell you where to send your request to make sure that it is handled properly. This procedure could take a few weeks or even months, so be careful if you are looking for something in a hurry.

Step #10: It's Important To Be A Nag

We all hate to be nags. But it is important because a piece of paper can get lost so easily in a mountain of paperwork.

- Call to make sure they sent out your application.
- Call to make sure they received your application.
- Call to make sure you know when you will be notified if you are accepted.
- Call a few days after the notification date if you have not heard anything yet.

It may be uncomfortable at times, but the squeaky wheel does get attention.

Step #11: Success and Failure are Both Good

If you get the money, call. Make sure you thank them and ask all the stupid questions you think are necessary to know when, where, and how you are going to get your money.

If your application is rejected, be sure you call anyway. This is the only way you may learn the truth about why you did not get the money. Ask how soon you can apply again. They may be accepting applications every month and too many people applied last month. You always have to keep learning how and why organizations give out money, and by being an applicant you are in a wonderful position to ask.

Life Isn't Easy But It Can Be Fun

Remember, you have nothing better to do than to try to improve your life. And you can have a great time doing it. When you call these agencies, they are not going to have professional comics answering the telephone giving you a laugh a minute as they shower you with all the information you need to get a wad of cash. They are just people like you and me trying to get through the day and do a decent job. But you can create fun for yourself and make the process a wonderful experience if you don't take yourself so seriously.

Make the whole process a game. Tell the bureaucrats things like:
- "I have no idea what you are doing."
- "I bought a book from some crazy guy about getting money for housing."
- "I'm scared as hell about filling out any government application."

Talk like this disarms people. The more natural and honest you are about what you are doing, the more people can relate to you, and the more fun you will have.

I believe that everyone in life is basically scared as hell and has no idea what the hell they are doing. So it's fun if you tell people you're scared and don't know what you are doing. It relaxes them and they can start enjoying you. You are no longer a threat. That's when you can really start having fun. And life is too short not to have funnnnnnnnnn.

Matthew Lesko

Uncle Sam's Housing Offices

The U.S. Department of Housing and Urban Development (HUD) is our Federal government's effort to address the housing needs of our country. They have designed programs for renters, homeowners, and investors, all with the goal to provide safe and stable homes for all. For many of these programs, you need to contact your state or local HUD office. Some, like the Section 8 vouchers, will pay part of your rent or mortgage for those families meeting income requirements. Other programs provide loan guarantees to help lending institutions feel more comfortable in creating mortgages.

For those programs where you need to apply through a HUD or FHA approved lender, a website at {http://www.hud.gov/ll/code/llplcrit.html} was designed to help you search for a lender in your area. A listing of HUD offices is located on page 360.

For those interested in Multi-Family housing programs, we have also included the Multi-Family Hubs at the end of the section. Forms and regulations for the Multi-Family programs can be found at {www.hudclips.org}. You can search for Handbooks and Regulations in the Library section and Forms in the Forms area. Search Tip: type in the word Section and the number to find the forms — i.e. Section 213. The Handbook number is listed on the bottom of the Forms document to help you in finding the correct Handbook.

Many of the programs include a five digit number in the description. The number refers to the Catalog of Federal Domestic Assistance, which is a publication that lists all the government money programs. You can search the catalog online at {www.cfda.gov}, and it is also available in most public libraries.

For more information or to learn about different programs you can contact:

U.S. Department of Housing and Urban Development
451 7th St., SW
Washington, DC 20410
202-708-1112
www.hud.gov

Rural Housing Service
U.S. Department of Agriculture
Room 5037, South Building
14th Street and Independence Ave., SW
Washington, DC 20250
202-720-4323
www.rurdev.usda.gov

Bureau of Indian Affairs
Office of Tribal Services
MS 4660 MIB
1849 C St., NW
Washington, DC 20240
202-308-3667
www.doi.gov/bureau-indian-affairs.html

U.S. Department of Veterans Affairs
Washington, DC 20420
202-273-7355
800-827-1000
www.va.gov

U.S. Department of Housing and Urban Development (HUD) Programs

Moving To Opportunity

Moving to Opportunity for Fair Housing (MTO) is a 10-year research demonstration that combines tenant-based rental assistance with housing counseling to help very low-income families move from poverty-stricken urban areas to low-poverty neighborhoods. One of the advantages that tenant-based rental assistance has over subsidized housing projects and public housing is that it allows the recipient to choose modestly priced private housing in neighborhoods that can offer ample educational, employment, and social opportunities. Five public housing authorities (Baltimore, Boston, Chicago, Los Angeles, and New York City) administer this demonstration project.

Households chosen for the demonstration's experimental group receive housing counseling and vouchers for rental housing in areas with less than 10 percent poverty. For more information contact your local HUD office (starting on page 360) or check out the program online at {www.hud.gov}.

Let The Government Help You Buy Your Home

Home ownership vouchers assist first-time homeowners with their monthly home ownership expenses. The home must pass an initial housing quality standards inspection conducted by the Public Housing Agency (PHA) and an independent home inspection before the PHA may approve the purchase by the family.

PHAs may choose to administer a home ownership program, but are not required to do so. The PHA may impose limits on the size of this program, or limit use of the option to certain purposes. However, PHAs must provide home ownership assistance when required as a reasonable accommodation to a family with a disabled person.

There are low-income requirements. The qualified monthly income of the family who will own the home must not be less than the Federal minimum hourly wage multiplied by 2,000 hours (currently $10,300). Except in the case of an elderly household or a family with a disabled person, welfare assistance is not counted in determining whether the family meets this requirement. There may be other eligibility requirements. (14.871 Section 8 Housing Choice Vouchers).

If you are interested in applying for a voucher, contact the local public housing agency (starting on page 365) or HUD office near you (starting on page 360); or check out the program online at { www.hud.gov/offices/pihprogramcs/hcv/index.cfm}.

Money to Buy, Fix Up Or Refinance A Home

Did you find a great house that is need of repair? Rather than get a mortgage for the house and another for the rehab, you can combine them into one with the U.S. Department of Housing and Urban Development's (HUD) 203(k).

Section 203(k) insures mortgages covering the purchase or refinancing and rehabilitation of a home that is at least a year old. A portion of the loan proceeds is used to pay the seller, or, if a refinance, to pay off the existing mortgage, and the remaining funds are placed in an escrow account and released as rehabilitation is completed. The cost of the rehabilitation must be at least $5,000.

Section 203(k) insurance enables home buyers and homeowners to finance both the purchase (or refinancing) of a house and the cost of its rehabilitation through a single mortgage, or to finance the rehabilitation of their existing home. Section 203(k) insured loans can finance the rehabilitation of the residential portion of a property that also has nonresidential uses; they can also cover the conversion of a property of any size to a one- to four-unit structure. Applications must be submitted to the local HUD Field Office through an FHA approved lending institution. 8,000 homes took advantage of this funding. The budget for this program is $900,000,000. (14.108 Rehabilitation Mortgage Insurance 203k). For more information contact your local HUD office (starting on page 360) or check out the program online at {www.hud.gov/improvements/index.cfm}.

$48,000 To Buy A Mobile Home

For those in the market for a manufactured home, the U.S. Department of Housing and Urban Development (HUD) has a guaranteed loan program to help insure mortgage loans made by private lending institutions to finance the purchase of a new or used manufactured home. The program insures lenders against loss from default on loans of up to $48,600. The program is authorized under Title I. 865 people used this funding last year. The budget for this program is $71,000,000. (14.110 Manufactured Home Loan Insurance-Financing Purchase of Manufactured Homes as Principal Residences of Borrowers).

For more information contact your local HUD office (starting on page 360) or check out the program online at {www.hud.gov}; or Home Mortgage Insurance Division, U.S. Department of Housing and Urban Development, 451 7th St., SW, Room 9272, Washington, DC 20410; 202-708-2121; {www.hud.gov/progdesc/manuf13.cfm}.

$2,000,000 To Build or Rehabilitate Condominiums

With their amenities and ease of maintenance, condominiums can offer some households an appealing alternative to traditional home ownership. Under Section 234(d), HUD insures mortgage loans made by private lenders to finance the construction or rehabilitation of condominium projects. Section 234(d) insures mortgages issued to developers of condominium projects for 10-40 years or three-quarters of the property's remaining economic life, whichever is less. The maximum amount of the mortgage varies according to the size of the unit and the type of structure. There are also loan-to-replacement cost limits and debt service limits.

To be eligible for HUD insurance, a condominium project must contain at least four dwelling units. The units may be in detached, semi-detached, row, walk-up, or elevator structures. (14.112 Mortgage Insurance for Construction or Substantial Rehabilitation of Condominium Projects 234d).

For more information contact your local HUD office (starting on page 360) or check out the program online at {www.hud.gov}; or Home Mortgage Insurance Division, U.S. Department of Housing and Urban Development, 451 7th St., SW, Room 9272, Washington, DC 20410; 202-708-2121; {www.hud.gov/progdesc/condo14.cfm}.

$277,000 To Help Purchase a 2-4 Family Unit

The government wants you to own a home, so they have created this great mortgage insurance program. Down payment requirements can be low; many closing costs can be financed; and some fees are limited.

Through this program, HUD's Federal Housing Administration (FHA) insures mortgages made by qualified lenders to people purchasing or refinancing a home of their own. FHA's mortgage insurance programs help low- and moderate-income families become homeowners by lowering some of the costs of their mortgage loans. FHA mortgage insurance also encourages lenders to make loans to otherwise creditworthy borrowers and projects, by protecting the lender against loan default on mortgages for properties that meet certain minimum requirements--including manufactured homes, single-family and multifamily properties, and some health-related facilities. (14.117 Mortgage Insurance-Homes 203B).

For more information contact your local HUD office (starting on page 360), contact the FHA Mortgage Hotline at 1-800-HUDSFHA, or check out the program online at {www.hud.gov/buying/insured.cfm}.

$300,000 For People Whose Homes Were Hurt By A Disaster

If you lost your home due to a major disaster, the U.S. Department of Housing and Urban Development (HUD) has developed a program to help you get back into a home. They even made it easier by requiring no down payment. The borrower is eligible for 100 percent financing, including closing costs.

Through Section 203(h), the Federal Government helps victims in Presidentially designated disaster areas recover by making it easier for them to get mortgage loans and become homeowners or reestablish themselves as homeowners. Section 203(h) program allows the Federal Housing Administration (FHA) to insure mortgages made by qualified lenders to victims of a major disaster who have lost their homes and are in the process of rebuilding or buying another home. (14.119 Mortgage Insurance- Homes for Disaster Victims 203h).

For more information contact your local HUD office (starting on page 360), contact the FHA Mortgage Hotline at 1-800-HUDSFHA, or check out the program online at {www.hud.gov/buying/insured.cfm}.

Money For Low to Moderate Income Families Hurt by a Disaster or Urban Renewal

One of the many barriers facing low- and moderate-income home buyers is that lenders have often regarded mortgage loans for comparatively small amounts as unprofitable, the servicing and other administrative costs were thought to outweigh the potential profits. This program increases home ownership opportunities for low- and moderate-income families by insuring small mortgage loans and thus reducing the lender's risk. Traditionally, this program has been targeted to assist displaced persons, although it is used in other situations as well.

This program insures mortgage loans made by private lenders to finance the purchase, construction, or rehabilitation of low-cost, one- to four-family housing. (14.120 Mortgage Insurance- Homes for Low and Moderate Income Families 221d2). For more information contact your local HUD office (starting on page 360), contact the FHA Mortgage Hotline at 1-800-HUDSFHA, or check out the program online at {www.hud.gov/buying/index.cfm}.

$200,000 To Help Purchase A Home On 2.5 Acres

Are you looking to buy or build a home on property in a rural area? Through Section 203(i) HUD's Federal Housing Administration (FHA) insures mortgages made by qualified lenders to individuals purchasing homes in outlying areas, where lack of a normal market could make resale in case of default difficult. FHA's mortgage insurance programs help low- and moderate-income families become homeowners by lowering some of the initial costs of their mortgage loans.

FHA mortgage insurance also encourages lenders to make loans to otherwise creditworthy borrowers. Insured loans may be used to finance the purchase of proposed, under-construction, or existing one-family housing, or new farm housing on 2 1/2 or more acres adjacent to an all-weather public road. 1,300,000 loans were made through this program. The budget for this program is $139,000,000,000. (14.121 Mortgage Insurance- Homes in Outlying Areas 203i). For more information contact your local HUD office (starting on page 360), contact the FHA Mortgage Hotline at 1-800-HUDSFHA, or check out the program online at {www.hud.gov}.

Money for Homes in Urban Renewal Areas

Do you want to purchase or rehabilitate a home in an urban renewal area? Many lenders are reluctant to extend mortgages in these circumstances. One of the many barriers facing low- and moderate-income home buyers is that lenders have often regarded mortgage loans for comparatively small amounts as unprofitable, the servicing and other administrative costs were thought to outweigh the potential profits.

This program increases home ownership opportunities for low- and moderate-income families by insuring small mortgage loans and thus reducing the lender's risk. This program insures mortgage loans made by private lenders to finance the purchase, construction, or rehabilitation of low-cost, one- to four-family housing. (14.122 Mortgage Insurance- Homes in Urban Renewal Areas 220). For more information contact your local HUD office (starting on page 360), contact the FHA Mortgage Hotline at 1-800-HUDSFHA, or check out the program online at {www.hud.gov/offices/hsg/mfh/progdesc/progdesc.cfm}.

$100,000 To Buy or Fix Up Houses In Older Areas Of A Town

Many people want to buy homes in older areas where lenders are reluctant to loan for the home purchase. Section 223(e) provides mortgage insurance to enable people to purchase or rehabilitate housing in older, declining urban areas.

Section 223(e) can be used only to supplement other HUD mortgage insurance programs. HUD's Federal Housing Administration (FHA) administers mortgage insurance programs that help low- and moderate-income families become homeowners by lowering some of the initial costs of their mortgage loans. (14.123 Mortgage Insurance- Housing in Older, Declining Areas 223e).

For more information contact your local HUD office (starting on page 360), contact the FHA Mortgage Hotline at 1-800-HUDSFHA, or check out the program online at {www.hud.gov}.

$1,000,000 For Investors to Develop Co-Ops

The U.S. Department of Housing and Urban Development has created a program to encourage the building of cooperative apartments. Section 213 insures mortgage loans to facilitate the construction, substantial rehabilitation, and purchase of cooperative housing projects. Each member shares in the ownership of the whole project with the exclusive right to occupy a specific unit and to participate in project operations through the purchase of stock.

Section 213 enables nonprofit cooperative housing corporations or trusts to develop or sponsor the development of housing projects to be operated as cooperatives, and also allows investors to provide good quality multifamily housing to be sold to nonprofit corporations or trusts upon completion of construction or rehabilitation. 170 units were developed last year. (14.126 Mortgage Insurance-Cooperative Projects 213).

For more information contact your local HUD office (starting on page 360) or check out the program online at {www.hud.gov/offices/hsg/mfh/progdesc/progdesc.cfm}; or Office of Multifamily Housing Development, U.S. Department of Housing and Urban Development, Washington, DC 20410; 202-708-1142.

$10,000 To Buy Your House From Long Term Ground Lease

For those homeowners whose homes are on long-term ground leases, there is a program to help you buy your home. The U.S. Department of Housing and Urban Development (HUD) has a loan guarantee program to help finance the purchase of the home. (14.130 Mortgage Insurance-purchase by Homeowners of Fee Simple Title From Lessors 240). For more information contact your local HUD office (starting on page 360) or check out the program online at {www.hud.gov}.

$60,000 for Renters, Homeowners or Investors to Improve Their Property

Help exists for those that want to improve their homes. Under Title I, HUD insures lenders against most losses on home improvement loans. The Federal Housing Administration (FHA) makes it easier for consumers to obtain affordable home improvement loans by insuring loans made by private lenders to improve properties that meet certain requirements.

This is one of HUD's most frequently used loan insurance products. Title I loans may be used to finance permanent property improvements that protect or improve the basic livability or utility of the property--including manufactured homes, single-family and multifamily homes, nonresidential structures, and the preservation of historic homes. The loans can also be used for fire safety equipment. 7,562 people improved their homes through this program. The budget for this program is $109,000,000. (14.142 Property Improvement Loan Insurance For Improving All Existing Structures and Building of New Nonresidential Structures Title I).

For more information contact your local HUD office (starting on page 360), contact the FHA Mortgage Hotline at 1-800-HUDSFHA, or check out the program online at {www.hud.gov/offices/hsg/sfh/title/ti_home.cfm}; or call HUD Customer Service for brochure and list of lenders at 800-767-7468.

Government Backed Graduated Mortgage Payments

Don't think you have enough money to afford mortgage payments? Section 245 enables a household with a limited income that is expected to rise to buy a home sooner by making mortgage payments that start small and increase gradually over time. Section 245 insures mortgages for first-time (and other) buyers who have low and moderate incomes--and who thus cannot meet standard mortgage payments--but who expect that their income will increase substantially in the next 5-10 years.

Potential homeowners who are considering using a graduated-payment mortgage to purchase a home must remember that their monthly payments to principal and interest will increase each year for up to 10 years, depending on which of five available plans they select. (14.159 Section 245 Graduated Payment Mortgage Program). For more information contact your local HUD office (starting on page 360), contact the FHA

Mortgage Hotline at 1-800-HUDSFHA, or check out the program online at {www.hud.gov}.

$100,000 To Help Buy A Mobile Home and A Mobile Home Lot

Sometimes banks charge a very high interest for a manufactured home and lot, but the U.S. Department of Housing and Urban Development (HUD) offers a loan guarantee program to make it more affordable. This program insures mortgage loans made by private lenders to buyers of manufactured homes and the lots on which to place them.

Title I insurance may be used for loans of up to $64,800 for a manufactured home and lot and $16,200 for a lot only. The lot must be appraised by a HUD-approved lender. The dollar limits for combination and lot loans may be increased up to 85 percent in designated high-cost areas. The maximum loan term is 20 years for a single-module home and lot, 25 years for a multiple module home and lot, and 15 years for a lot only. 1,500 homes used this program last year. The budget for this program is $52,000,000. (14.162 Mortgage Insurance-combination and Manufactured Home Lot Loans Title I).

For more information contact your local HUD office (starting on page 360) or check out the program online at {www.hud.gov/offices/hsg/sfh/title/ti_home.cfm}; or call HUD Customer Service at 800-767-7468 for brochure.

$200,000 To Help Buy A Home In An Area Affected By A Base Closing

Buying a home in an area hurt by defense cutbacks can be difficult. The U.S. Department of Housing and Urban Development (HUD) offers the 238c program to help families undertake home ownership in military impacted areas.

HUD insures lenders against loss on mortgage loans. These loans may be used to finance the purchase of proposed, under construction, or existing one- to four-family housing, as well as to refinance indebtedness on existing housing. (14.165 Mortgage Insurance-Homes-Military Impacted Areas 238c). For more information contact your local HUD office (starting on page 360) or check out the program online at {www.hud.gov}.

Money to Buy A Home Using Increased Equity Payments

There is help for those on limited incomes. Section 245(a) enables a household with a limited income that is expected to rise to buy a home sooner by making mortgage payments that start small and increase gradually over time. The increased payments are applied to reduce the principal owed on the mortgage and thus shorten the mortgage term.

Section 245(a) works by helping first-time buyers and others with limited incomes—particularly young families, who expect their income to rise but may not yet be able to handle all of the up front and monthly costs involved in home buying—to tailor their mortgage payments to their expanding incomes and buy a home sooner than they could with regular financing. However, this program adds an innovative twist to this basic product: growing equity mortgages (GEMs) enable the homeowner to apply scheduled increases in monthly payments to the outstanding principal balance of their mortgage and thereby to considerably shorten the term of the mortgage. This reduced term and the faster repayment of principal make GEMs more attractive to lenders and investors than other fixed-rate investments. (14.172 Mortgage Insurance- Growing Equity Mortgages GEM).

For more information contact your local HUD office (starting on page 360) or check out the program online at {www.hud.gov}.

Uncle Sam Will Co-Sign An Adjustable Rate Mortgage

Here is a way to start with a low monthly mortgage rate. Section 251 insures home purchase or refinancing loans with interest rates that may increase or decrease over time, enabling consumers to purchase or refinance their home at a lower initial interest rate. Under this FHA-insured mortgage product, the initial interest rate and monthly payment are low, but these may change during the life of the loan. FHA uses 1-year Treasury Constant Maturities Index to determine interest rate changes. The maximum amount the interest rate may increase or decrease in any one year is 1 percentage point.

Over the life of the loan, the maximum interest rate change is 5 percentage points from the initial rate. Down payment requirements can be low. Many closing costs can be financed. 100,000 loans will be available this year. (14.175 Adjustable Rate Mortgages). For more information contact your local HUD office (starting on page 360), contact the

FHA Mortgage Hotline at 1-800-HUDSFHA, or check out the program online at {www.hud.gov}.

Reverse Mortgages For Seniors

Stop being house rich, but cash poor. The Home Equity Conversion Mortgage program enables older homeowners to withdraw some of the equity in their home in the form of monthly payments for life or a fixed term, or in a lump sum, or through a line of credit.

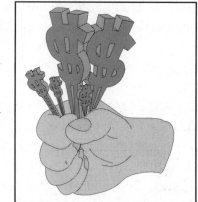

The Home Equity Conversion Mortgage Program (HECM) can enable an older home owning family to stay in their home while using some of its built up equity. The program allows such a household to get an insured reverse mortgage-a mortgage that converts equity into income. Because older persons can be vulnerable to fraudulent practices, the program requires that persons receive free reverse mortgage housing counseling from a HUD-approved reverse mortgage counseling agency before applying for a reverse mortgage. FHA insures HECM loans to protect lenders against loss if amounts withdrawn exceed equity when the property is sold. HECM can be used by homeowners who are 62 years of age and older. 15,000 loans will be made this year. (14.183 Home Equity Conversion Mortgages 255).

For more information contact your local HUD office (starting on page 360) or check out the program online at {www.hud.gov/offices/hsg/sfh/hecm/hecmhome.cfm}.

Money to Make Your Home Energy Efficient

The Energy Efficient Mortgages Program (EEM) helps home buyers or homeowners save money on utility bills by enabling them to finance the cost of adding energy-efficiency features to new or existing housing as part of their FHA-insured home purchase or refinancing mortgage. The cost of the energy improvements and estimate of the energy savings must be determined by a home energy rating system (HERS) or an energy consultant. Up to $200 of the cost of an energy inspection report may be included in the mortgage.

EEM can be used to make energy-efficient improvements in one- or two-unit existing and new homes. The improvements can be included in a borrower's mortgage only if their total cost is less than the total dollar value of the energy that will be saved during their useful life. The cost of the improvements that may be eligible for financing as part of the mortgage is either 5 percent of the property's value (not to exceed $8,000) or $4,000—whichever is greater. For more information contact your local HUD office (starting on page 360) or check out the program online at {www.hud.gov/offices/hsg/sfh/eem/eemhome.cfm}.

Money For Members Of The Armed Services

Section 222 enables members of the Coast Guard and National Oceanic and Atmospheric Administration on active duty to purchase a home that is partially subsidized by the respective service.

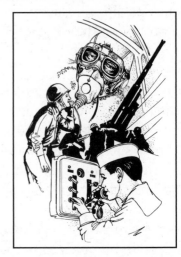

Section 222, allows the Department of Transportation (DOT) and the Department of Commerce (DOC) to pay the FHA mortgage insurance premium on behalf of service members on active duty under their jurisdictions. The mortgages may finance single-family dwellings and condominiums insured under standard HUD home mortgage insurance programs. For purchasers with a mortgage insured under Section 222, premiums are paid by DOT if the purchaser is in the Coast Guard or by DOC if she/he is an employee in the National Oceanic and Atmospheric Administration, as long as active duty status continues while she/he owns the home.

The Department of Defense has suspended its participation in this program. For more information contact your local HUD office (starting on page 360), contact the FHA Mortgage Hotline at 1-800-HUDSFHA, or check out the program online at {www.hud.gov}.

Home Ownership For Everyone

HOPE I helps low-income people buy public housing units by providing funds that nonprofit organizations, resident groups, and other eligible grantees can use to develop and implement home ownership programs. Home ownership can be one key to self-sufficiency for low-income families, building assets for families and stability and pride for neighborhoods. HOPE I grants can be used to fund a wide range of home ownership activities that help public housing residents develop the skills, the resources, the partnerships, and the strategies they will need to buy their housing units, including:
  ★ economic development planning, including job training and other activities that promote economic self-sufficiency for potential home buyers.
  ★ financial assistance to home buyers, including interest rate buy-downs and down payment assistance.

★ rehabilitation of properties.
★ relocation of residents who elect to move.
★ administrative costs; legal fees, and architectural and engineering work.
★ replacement housing and replacement reserves.
★ resident and home buyer counseling and training.

HOPE I Program Fact Sheet available from the Resident Initiatives Clearinghouse, 1-800-955-2232. For more information contact your local HUD office (starting on page 360) or check out the program online at {www.hud.gov}.

Buy Your Public Housing Unit

Do you live in a public housing unit that you would like to purchase? The Section 5(h) home ownership program offers Public Housing Agencies (PHA) a flexible way to sell public housing units to low-income families.

Section 5(h) helps low-income families purchase homes through an arrangement that benefits both the buyer and the public housing agency (PHA) that sells the unit. Section 5(h) works for PHAs as well: it permits public housing authorities to sell individual units and developments that may, due to their location or configuration, no longer be efficient to operate--while HUD continues to service the debt. Current residents of the units offered for sale have preference to purchase them.

See Fact Sheet: Section 5(h), available from the Resident Initiatives Clearinghouse, 1-800-955-2232. For more information contact your local HUD office (starting on page 360) or check out the program online at {www.hud.gov}.

Money to Build or Rehabilitate A Trailer Home Park

For those who want to own a trailer park, the U.S. Department of Housing and Urban Development has a loan guarantee to encourage lenders to help with financing. Section 207 Program insures mortgage loans to facilitate the construction or substantial rehabilitation of multifamily manufactured home parks. Section 207 promotes the creation of manufactured home communities by increasing the availability of affordable financing and mortgages. 571 units used this program last year. The budget for this program is $13,200,000. (14.127 Mortgage Insurance- Manufactured Home Parks 207).

For more information contact your local HUD office or check out the program online at {www.hud.gov}. For more information contact your local HUD office (starting on page 360), contact the FHA Mortgage Hotline at 1-800-HUDSFHA, or check out the program online at {www.hud.gov/offices/hsg/sfh/eem/eemhome.cfm}; or Office of Multifamily Development, U.S. Department of Housing and Urban Development, Washington, DC 20410; 202-708-1142.

Money to Buy a Hospital

The Federal Housing Administration helps hospitals access affordable financing for capital projects. You can use the money for construction financing, refinancing, modernization, remodeling, equipment, or expansion. To be considered for insurance, a hospital must meet certain minimum eligibility requirements. For example, it must be principally an acute care hospital and properly licensed. (14.128 Mortgage Insurance-Hospitals 242).

For more information contact your local HUD office (starting on page 360), contact the FHA Mortgage Hotline at 1-800-HUDSFHA, or check out the program online at {www.hud.gov}; or Office of Insured Health Care Facilities, U.S. Department of Housing and Urban Development, Washington, DC 20410; 202-708-0599; {www.hud.gov/progdesc/hlthprog.html}.

Money to Buy A Nursing Home

Many investors and developers are looking at building senior care facilities to accommodate the needs of this growing population. Section 232 insures mortgage loans to facilitate the construction and substantial rehabilitation of nursing homes, intermediate care facilities, board and care homes, and assisted-living facilities. Section 232/223(f) allows for the purchase or refinancing with or without repairs of existing projects not requiring substantial rehabilitation. Section 232 insures mortgage loans to facilitate the construction and substantial rehabilitation of nursing homes, intermediate care facilities, board and care homes, and assisted-living facilities. Section 232/223(f) allows for the purchase or refinancing with or without repairs of existing projects not requiring substantial rehabilitation. Facilities must accommodate 20 or more residents who require skilled nursing care and related medical services, or those who while not in need of nursing home care, are in need of minimum but continuous care provided by licensed or trained personnel.

Assisted living facilities and board and care homes are also eligible and must contain a minimum of five accommodations or units. (14.129 Mortgage Insurance- Nursing Homes, Intermediate Care Facilities and Board and Care Homes 232). For more information contact your local HUD office (starting on page 360), contact the FHA Mortgage Hotline at 1-800-HUDSFHA, or check out the program online at {www.hud.gov/offices/hsg/sfh/eem/eemhome.cfm}; or Office of Multifamily Development, U.S. Department of Housing and Urban Development, Washington, DC 20410; 202-708-1142; forms can be found at {www.hudclips.org}.

Money to Buy Your Co-op

If you would like to buy a co-op, then the U.S. Department of Housing and Urban Development will assist you with a loan guarantee. They want to make available, good quality, new housing for purchase by individual members of a housing cooperative. (14.132 Mortgage Insurance-Purchase of Sales-Type Cooperative Housing Units 213 Sales). For more information contact your local HUD office (starting on page 360) or check out the program online at {www.hud.gov}; forms can be found at {www.hudclips.org}.

$150,000 To Purchase A Condominium

If you would like to buy a condominium but don't have the money, never fear. The U.S. Department of Housing and Urban Development has a program that insures the loan for a person who purchases a unit in a condominium building.

One of the many purposes of FHA's mortgage insurance programs is to encourage lenders to make affordable mortgage credit available for non-conventional forms of ownership. Condominium ownership, in which the separate owners of the individual units jointly own the development's common areas and facilities, is one particularly popular alternative. Insurance for condominiums, such as is provided through Section 234(c), can be important for low- and moderate-income renters who wish to avoid being displaced by the conversion of their apartment building into a condominium. The program insures a loan for as many as 30 years to purchase a unit in a condominium building—which must contain at least four dwelling units and can be detached or semidetached, a rowhouse, a walk-up, or an elevator structure. 82,000 people used this program last year. The budget for this program is $14,000,000,000. (14.133 Mortgage Insurance-Purchase of Units in Condominiums 234c).

For more information contact your local HUD office (starting on page 360), contact the FHA Mortgage Hotline at 1-800-HUDSFHA, or check out the program online at {www.hud.gov/buying/index.cfm}.

Money For Investors, Builders And Developers To Refinance Their Projects

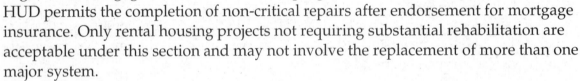

If you would like to purchase an apartment building, the U.S. Housing and Urban Development will help. Section 207/223(f) insures mortgage loans to facilitate the purchase or refinancing of existing multifamily rental housing. These projects may have been financed originally with conventional or FHA insured mortgages.

Properties requiring substantial rehabilitation are not eligible for mortgage insurance under this program.
HUD permits the completion of non-critical repairs after endorsement for mortgage insurance. Only rental housing projects not requiring substantial rehabilitation are acceptable under this section and may not involve the replacement of more than one major system.

Insured mortgages may be used to purchase or refinance existing multifamily housing projects consisting of 5 or more units. (14.134 Mortgage Insurance-Rental Housing; 14.155 Mortgage Insurance or Refinancing of Existing Multifamily Housing Projects). For more information contact your local HUD office (starting on page 360), contact the FHA Mortgage Hotline at 1-800-HUDSFHA, or check out the program online at {www.hud.gov/offices/hsg/mfh/progdesc/progdesc.cfm}; or Office of Multifamily Development, U.S. Department of Housing and Urban Development, Washington, DC 20410; 202-708-1142; forms can be found at {www.hudclips.org}.

$5,000,000 For Investors to Develop Housing For Seniors, Moderate Income Families And People With Disabilities

Section 221(d)(3) and 221(d)(4) insures mortgage loans to facilitate the new construction or substantial rehabilitation of multifamily rental or cooperative housing for moderate-income families, elderly, and the handicapped. Single Room Occupancy (SRO) projects may also be insured under this section.

Both programs assist private industry in the construction or rehabilitation of rental and cooperative housing for moderate-income and displaced families by making capital more readily available. Insured mortgages may be used to finance the construction or rehabilitation of detached, semidetached, row, walkup, or elevator-type rental or cooperative housing containing 5 or more units. 39,000 were developed using this program. The budget for this program is $4,380,000,000. (14.135 Mortgage Insurance-Rental and Cooperative Housing for Moderate Income Families and Elderly 221d3 and 221d4). For more information contact your local HUD office (starting on page 360), contact the FHA Mortgage Hotline at 1-800-HUDSFHA, or check out the program online at {www.hud.gov/offices/hsg/mfh/progdesc/progdesc.cfm}; or Office of Multifamily Development, U.S. Department of Housing and Urban Development, Washington, DC 20410; 202-708-1142; forms can be found at {www.hudclips.org}.

Money For Investors and Nonprofits To Develop Housing For Seniors

The elderly and disabled often find it difficult to find appropriate and affordable housing. The Section 231 insures mortgage loans to facilitate the construction and substantial rehabilitation of multifamily rental housing for elderly persons (62 or older) and/or persons with disabilities.

Insured mortgages may be used to finance the construction, rehabilitation, and purchase of detached, semidetached, walk-up, or elevator type rental housing designed for elderly occupancy or handicapped individuals consisting of eight or more rental units. (14.138 Mortgage Insurance- Rental Housing for the Elderly 231). For more information contact your local HUD office (starting on page 360), contact the FHA Mortgage Hotline at 1-800-HUDSFHA, or check out the program online at {www.hud.gov/offices/hsg/mfh/progdesc/progdesc.cfm}; or Office of Multifamily Development, U.S. Department of Housing and Urban Development, Washington, DC 20410; 202-708-1142.

Money to Develop Rental Housing In Urban Areas

Good quality rental housing in urban renewal areas is hard to find. Section 220 insures loans for multifamily housing projects in urban renewal areas, code enforcement areas, and other areas where local governments have undertaken designated revitalization activities. Section 220 insures lenders against loss on mortgage defaults. Section 220 provides good quality rental housing in urban areas that have been targeted for overall revitalization. 499 units used this program last year. (14.139 Mortgage Insurance-Rental Housing in Urban Renewal Areas 220 Multi-family).

For more information contact your local HUD office (starting on page 360), contact the FHA Mortgage Hotline at 1-800-HUDSFHA, or check out the program online at {www.hud.gov/offices/hsg/mfh/progdesc/progdesc.cfm}; or Office of Multifamily Development, U.S. Department of Housing and Urban Development, Washington, DC 20410; 202-708-1142.

$2,000,000 To Fix Up Multifamily Units

Want to improve your multi-family rental housing? Section 241(a) insures mortgage loans to finance repairs, additions, and improvements to multifamily rental housing and health care facilities with FHA insured first mortgages or HUD-held mortgages.

Insured mortgages finance repairs, additions, and improvements to multifamily projects, group practice facilities, hospitals, or nursing homes already insured by HUD or held by HUD. Major movable equipment for insured nursing homes, group practice facilities, or hospitals may be covered by a mortgage under this program. 937 units were repaired last year. The budget for this program is $15,000,000. (14.151 Supplemental Loan Insurance-Multifamily Rental Housing 241a).

For more information contact your local HUD office (starting on page 360), contact the FHA Mortgage Hotline at 1-800-HUDSFHA, or check out the program online at {www.hud.gov/offices/hsg/mfh/progdesc/progdesc.cfm}; or Office of Multifamily Development, U.S. Department of Housing and Urban Development, Washington, DC 20410; 202-708-1142.

$4,000,000 To Build or Fix Up Housing For Seniors

Sometimes the elderly need more than just a place to live. The Section 202 program helps expand the supply of affordable housing with supportive services for the elderly. It provides very low-income elderly with options that allow them to live independently but in an environment that provides support activities such as cleaning, cooking, transportation, etc.

The program is similar to Supportive Housing for Persons with Disabilities (Section 811). HUD provides interest-free capital advances to private, nonprofit sponsors to finance the development of supportive housing for the elderly. The capital advance does not have to be repaid as long as the project serves very low-income elderly persons for 40 years. 6,830 units used this program last year. The budget for this program is $783,286,000. (14.157 Supportive Housing For The Elderly 202).

For more information contact your local HUD office (starting on page 360) or check out the program online at {www.hud.gov/offices/hsg/mfh/progdesc/progdesc.cfm}; or Office of Housing Assistance and Grants Administration, U.S. Department of Housing and Urban Development, Washington, DC 20410; 202-708-2866; {www.hud.gov/progdesc/2eldrl14.cfm}; forms can be found at {www.hudclips.org}.

Money To Finance Coop Buildings

The purpose of FHA's mortgage insurance programs is to encourage lenders to make mortgage credit available to borrowers who would not otherwise qualify for conventional loans on affordable terms (such as lower income families and first-time home buyers) and to residents of disadvantaged neighborhoods (where mortgages may be hard to get).

Section 203(n) helps with a financing structured to meet the needs of persons who are buying a corporate certificate and occupancy certificate, the instruments that enable them to own a share of and live in a cooperative housing project. The program insures a loan to purchase an apartment in a residential cooperative--which can be a detached or semidetached building, a rowhouse, or a multifamily building. (14.163 Mortgage Insurance- Single Family Cooperative Housing 203n). For more information contact your local HUD office (starting on page 360), contact the FHA Mortgage Hotline at 1-800-HUDSFHA, or check out the program online at {www.hud.gov}.

Money to Developers In Financial Trouble

Sometimes buildings fall into disrepair. The U.S. Department of Housing and Urban Development has a program that provides loans to restore or maintain the physical and financial soundness, to assist in the management and to maintain the low-to moderate-income character of certain projects assisted or approved for assistance under the National Housing Act or under the Housing and Urban Development Act of 1965.

Flexible Subsidy funds can be lent to eligible projects in an amount based on the project's total needs. It may be used to correct physical deficiencies resulting from deferral of regular maintenance; to reduce deficiencies in replacement reserve funds; and to fund operating deficits. Eligible owners are nonprofits, with existing loans from HUD under the Section 202 program. Public bodies do not qualify for this program. (14.164 Operating Assistance For Troubled Multifamily Housing Projects).

For more information contact your local HUD office (starting on page 360) or check out the program online at {www.hud.gov/offices/hsg/mfh/progdesc/progdesc.cfm}; or Office of Housing Assistance and Grants Administration, U.S. Department of Housing and Urban Development, Washington, DC 20410; 202-708-2866.

$500,000 If You Can't Make A Profit On Your Apartment Building

There is help for those whose multifamily mortgages are insured by HUD. Section 223(d) helps avoid insurance claims on HUD-insured multifamily mortgages by insuring separate loans to cover operating losses. Section 223(d) insures two-year operating loss loans that covers operating losses during the first 2 years after completion (or any other 2-year period within the first 10 years after completion) of multifamily rental projects with a HUD-insured first mortgage. (14.167 Mortgage Insurance- Two Year Operating Loss Loans, 223d).

For more information contact your local HUD office (starting on page 360) or check out the program online at {www.hud.gov/offices/hsg/mfh/progdesc/progdesc.cfm}; or Office of Multifamily Development, U.S. Department of Housing and Urban Development, Washington, DC 20410; 202-708-1142.

$1,000,000 To Build or Fix Up Housing For People With Disabilities

HUD provides funding to nonprofit organizations to develop rental housing with the availability of supportive services for very low-income adults with disabilities, and provides rent subsidies for the projects to help make them affordable. The Section 811 program allows persons with disabilities to live as independently as possible in the community by increasing the supply of rental housing with the availability of supportive services.

The program also provides project rental assistance, which covers the difference between the HUD-approved operating costs of the project and the tenants' contribution toward rent. HUD provides interest-free capital advances to nonprofit sponsors to help them finance the development of rental housing such as independent living projects, condominium units and small group homes with the availability of supportive services for persons with disabilities. 1,859 units used this program. The budget for this program is $250,515,000. (14.181 Supportive Housing For Persons With Disabilities 811).

For more information contact your local HUD office (starting on page 360) or check out the program online at {www.hud.gov/offices/hsg/mfh/progdesc/progdesc.cfm}; or Office of Housing Assistance and Grants Administration, U.S. Department of Housing and Urban Development, Washington, DC 20410; 202-708-2866; forms can be found at {www.hudclips.org}.

Money To Help Rid Low-Income Housing Of Drug Related Crime

For those who own low-income housing, drug related problems may plague their development. HUD has put together a program to help reduce or eliminate drug-related crime and related problems in and around the premises of federally assisted low income housing. They want to encourage owners of such housing to develop a plan for addressing the problems of drug-related crime and they offer grants to help owners carry out their plans. Money can be used for increased security, training of tenant patrols, drug intervention activities and drug treatment programs. (14.193 Federally Assisted Low-Income Housing Drug Elimination).

For more information contact your local HUD office (starting on page 360) or check out the program online at {www.hud.gov}; or Office of Housing Assistance and Grants Administration, U.S. Department of Housing and Urban Development, Washington, DC 20410; 202-708-2866.

$400,000 To Help Operate A Homeless Shelter

The Supportive Housing Program is designed to develop supportive housing and services that will allow homeless persons to live as independently as possible. Eligible applicants are States, units of local government, other governmental entities such as PHAs, and private nonprofits.

Transitional housing is one type of supportive housing used to facilitate the movement of homeless individuals and families to permanent housing. Basically, it is housing in which homeless persons live for up to 24 months and receive supportive services that enable them to live more independently. The supportive services may be provided by the organization managing the housing or coordinated by them and provided by other public or private agencies. Transitional housing participants receive supportive services that enable them to live more independently. Housing placement assistance must be part of any transitional housing program.

Permanent housing for homeless persons with disabilities is another type of supportive housing, as is safe havens for homeless individuals with serious mental illness currently residing on the streets who may not yet be ready for supportive services. 2,581 applications were received for this program. The budget for this program is $742,246,000. (14.235 Supportive Housing Program). For more information contact your local HUD office (starting on page 360) or check out the program online at {www.hud.gov/offices/hsg/mfh/progdesc/progdesc.cfm}; or Office of Special Needs Assistance Programs, Community Planning and Development, U.S. Department of Housing and Urban Development, 451 7th St., SW, Washington, DC 20410; 202-708-4300.

Money To Rid Low-Income Housing of Drug Related Crime

Low-income housing units can be effected by drugs and crime. To combat this problem, the U.S. Department of Housing and Urban Development (HUD) offers a grant program called the New Approach Anti-Drug Program (formerly Safe Neighborhood Grants Program). This program uses a comprehensive, coordinated neighborhood/community-based approach to eliminate drug-related and other crime problems on the premises and in the vicinity of low-income housing, which may be privately or publicly owned and is financially supported or assisted by public or nonprofit private entities. Some eligible activities include increased security, enhancing the investigation and prosecution of drug-related crimes, and development of capital improvements directly relating to enhancing security. (14.312 New Approach Anti-Drug Grants).

For more information contact your local HUD office (starting on page 360) or check out the program online at {www.hud.gov}; or Program Analysts, Office of Housing Assistance and Grant Administration, U.S. Department of Housing and Urban

Development, 451 7th St., SW, Room 6146, Washington, DC 20410; 202-708-2866, ext. 5787; Super-NOFA Information Center at 800-HUD-8929.

Loans to Investors, Builders, Developers of Affordable Housing

Here is another innovative mortgage insurance and reinsurance product to help increase the amount of affordable housing available. Section 542(b) encourages the development and preservation of affordable housing. The program provides insurance and reinsurance for multifamily housing projects whose loans are originated, underwritten, serviced, and disposed of by a Qualified Participating Entity (QPE) and/or its approved lenders. (14.189 Qualified Participating Entities Section 542b).

For more information contact your local HUD office (starting on page 360) or check out the program online at {www.hud.gov/offices/hsg/mfh/progdesc/progdesc.cfm}; or Office of Multifamily Development, U.S. Department of Housing and Urban Development, Washington, DC 20410; 202-708-1142.

$7 Million For Investors, Builders and Developers To Build Houses And Apartments

For those interested in working with a Housing Finance Agency to develop low-income housing, here is a mortgage insurance program for you. Section 542(c) enables the U.S. Department of Housing and Urban Development (HUD) and State and local housing finance agencies (HFAs) to provide new risk-sharing arrangements to help those agencies provide more insurance and credit for multifamily loans. Section 542(c) provides credit enhancement for mortgages of multifamily housing projects whose loans are underwritten, processed, serviced, and disposed of by HFAs. HUD and HFAs share in the risk of the mortgage.

Eligible mortgagors include investors, builders, developers, public entities, and private nonprofit corporations or associations may apply to a qualified HFA. 55 projects were funded last year. (14.188 HFA Risk Sharing Pilot Program). For more information contact your local HUD office (starting on page 360) or check out the program online at {www.hud.gov/offices/hsg/mfh/progdesc/progdesc.cfm}; or Office of Multifamily Development, U.S. Department of Housing and Urban Development, Washington, DC 20410; 202-708-1142.

Money to Build Or Renovate Single Room Occupancy Units

Although they receive no Federal rental subsidies, single room occupancy apartments are often in need. Section 221(d)(3) and 221(d)(4) program insures mortgage loans for multifamily properties consisting of single-room occupancy (SRO) apartments. It is aimed at those tenants who have a source of income but are priced out of the rental apartment market.

SRO projects generally require assistance from local governing bodies or charitable organizations in order to reduce the rents to affordable levels. Although SRO housing is intended for very low-income persons, the program does not impose income limits for admission. Insured mortgages may be used to finance construction or substantial rehabilitation of projects consisting of five or more one room SRO units, with no more than 10 percent of the total gross floor space dedicated to commercial use (20 percent for substantial rehabilitation projects). Each SRO apartment can have its own kitchen or bathroom facilities, or these facilities may be shared by several apartments. Apartments can be designed to allow for more than one occupant. The budget for this program is $2,600,000. (14.184 Mortgage Insurance for Single Room Occupancy Projects).

For more information contact your local HUD office or check out the program online at {www.hud.gov/offices/hsg/mfh/progdesc/progdesc.cfm}; forms can be found at {www.hudclips.org}.

Money to Pay for Help

Do you see residents who are in need of help? If you provide Section 8 (or Section 202) housing to low-income people, you can apply for grant funds to provide support services to the elderly or disabled residents. The goal is to keep these people in their own homes as long as possible by providing supportive services as needed. This service provider can offer case management services, monitor the assistance the residents receive, and act as an advocate for the resident in dealing with community service providers. (14.191 Multi-family Housing Service Coordinators)

For more information contact your local HUD office (starting on page 360) or contact Office of Housing Assistance and Grants Administration, Office of Multifamily Housing

Programs, Department of Housing and Urban Development, Washington, DC 20410; 202-708-2866; {www.hud.gov/progdesc/8coord.cfm}.

Keep Rent Affordable

Housing subsidy contracts are expiring on thousands of privately owned multifamily properties with federally insured mortgages. Many of these contracts set rents at amounts higher than those of the local market. As these contracts expire, the Market-to-Market program will reduce rents to market levels and will restructure existing debt to levels supportable by these rents. If you own Section 8 housing, then you are eligible to apply for this program. (14.197 Multifamily Assisted Housing Reform and Affordability).

For more information contact your local HUD office (starting on page 360) or check out the program with Charles Williams, Director, Office of Multifamily Housing Assistance Restructuring, Suite 4000, 1280 Maryland Ave., SW, Washington, DC 20024; 202-708-0001; {www.hud.gov/omhar}.

$2,500,000 To Provide Housing For AIDS Patients And Their Families

Want to help those who are suffering from AIDS? The Housing Opportunities for Persons with AIDS program provides funds for a variety of services including: counseling, information and referral services; acquisition, rehabilitation, and conversion of property to provide housing and services; new construction of housing; short-term rent, mortgage, and utility payments to prevent homelessness; supportive services such as health, mental health, day care, nutrition services, and more; operating costs for housing; and much more. HOPWA funds have helped many  communities establish strategic AIDS housing plans, better coordinate local and private efforts, fill gaps in local systems of care, and create new housing resources. In assisting low-income persons who are living with HIV or AIDS and their families avoid homelessness, grantees have provided for a wide-array of housing, social services and program planning and development activities undertaken in connection with health-case, AIDS Drug Assistance and other support offered through community-wide efforts. The budget for this program is $300,000,000. (14.241 Housing Opportunities for Persons with AIDS (HOPWA)).

For more information contact your local HUD office (starting on page 360) or check out the program with David Vos, Director, Office of HIV/AIDS Housing, Community Planning and Development, Department of Housing and Urban Development, 451 Seventh St., SW, Room 7212, Washington, DC 20410; 202-708-1934; 800-877-8339; {www.hud.gov/offices/cpd/aidshousing}.

$4,000,000 For Your Nonprofit To Help People Buy Homes

By investing in a little sweat equity, future homeowners can help make their dream a reality. The Self-Help Homeownership Opportunity Program provides funds to nonprofit organizations that have experience in providing self-help housing homeownership programs. Money can be used for land acquisition and infrastructure improvements and may not exceed $10,000 per dwelling. 2,900 homes were built last year using these funds. The budget for this program is $65,000,000. (14.247 Self-Help Homeownership Opportunity Program-SHOP).

For more information contact Office of Affordable Housing Programs, Community Planning and Development, Department of Housing and Urban Development, 451 7th St., SW, Washington, DC 20410; 202-708-2684; {www.hud.gov/progdesc/cpdindx.html}.

$450,000 To Make An Apartment Building Assisted Living

If you are a nonprofit and own a multi-family housing development for seniors and the disabled, you are eligible to apply for funds to convert some or all of the dwelling units into an Assisted Living Facility (ALF) for the frail elderly. These facilities are designed to accommodate the frail elderly and people with disabilities who can live independently but need assistance with activities of daily living. ALFs must provide support services such as personal care, transportation, meals, housekeeping, and laundry. The funds can cover the cost of the conversion, but the supportive services much be provided by the owners either directly or through a third party. 761 units were converted last year through this program. (14.314 Assisted Living Conversion for Eligible Multifamily Housing Projects (ALCP)).

For more information, contact your local HUD office (starting on page 360) or contact Office of Grant Policy and Management, Department of Housing and Urban Development, Room 6138, 451 Seventh Street, SW., Washington, DC 20410; 202-708-3000; {www.hud.gov/offices/hsg/mfh/progdesc/alcp.cfm}.

Help People Keep Their Homes

Sometimes money is tight and people get into a financial mess. You can help them straighten out their finances and keep their homes by providing counseling to homeowners, homebuyers, perspective renters, and tenants. Grants are available to HUD-approved local housing counseling agencies, HUD approved national and regional intermediaries, and to State housing finance agencies. Grants provide a variety of housing counseling services, including single family home buying, homeownership, mortgage default, HECM, rental, and rental delinquency under HUD and other programs. (14.169 Housing Counseling Assistance Program).

For more information contact your local HUD office (starting on page 360) or Program Support Division, Office of Insured Single Family Housing, Department of Housing and Urban Development, 451 7th Street, SW, Washington, DC 20410; 202-708-0317; {www.hud.gov/offices/hsg/sfh/hcc/hcc_home.cfm}.

$10,000 Grant to Make Your Home Healthier

A healthy home environment is essential, especially for children. The purpose of the Healthy Homes Initiative is to develop, demonstrate and promote cost effective, preventive measures to correct multiple safety and health hazards in the home environment that produce serious diseases and injuries in children. This program focuses on demonstration projects that implement housing assessment, maintenance, renovation, and construction techniques to identify and correct housing-related illness and injury risk factors. Eligible  applicants include: not-for-profit institutions, for-profit firms (for-profit firms are not allowed to profit from the project), and State and local governments. Purchase of property or medical treatment costs are not eligible for funding. The budget for this program is $10,000,000. (14.901 Healthy Homes Initiative Grants).

For more information contact your local HUD office (starting on page 360) or contact Ms. Ellen Taylor, Planning and Standards Division, Office of Healthy Homes and Lead Hazard Control, Department of Housing and Urban Development, 451 Seventh Street,

SW, Room P3206, Washington, DC 20410; 202-755-1785, extension 116; {www.hud.gov/offices/lead}.

Buy A HUD Foreclosed Multi-Family Property

The U.S. Department of Housing and Urban Development sometimes needs to sell multifamily housing projects that are owned by the Department or are subject to a mortgage held by the Department. The property can be sold with tenant-based Housing Choice Vouchers provided to eligible tenants. The property can also be sold with a grant for the rehabilitation of the property if the new owners meet certain requirements. The multi-family housing project can also be sold to the highest bidder. (14.199 Multifamily Property Disposition).

To learn about possible foreclosure sales, contact a Realtor or Marc Harris, Department of Housing and Urban Development, Office of Housing, Multifamily Housing Programs, Office of Asset Management, Room 6160, 451 7th Street, SW., Washington, DC 20410; 202-708-0614, extension 2680; {www.hud.gov/progdesc/multindx.cfm}.

Get A $100,000 Home For $1 Plus Fix Up Money

That's right, only $1. Single family homes that are acquired in foreclosure actions by the Federal Housing Administration (FHA) are eligible for sale to local governments across the nation for $1 plus closing costs when the properties have been listed for at least six months and remain unsold. Local governments buying HUD properties for $1 plus closing costs may sell or rent them to low- and moderate-income families, to first-time homebuyers, or to groups that will use the properties to provide services such as child-care centers, domestic abuse shelters, job training centers, etc. Not a bad deal for a buck! 1,200 were sold last year through this program. (14.313 Dollar Home Sales).

For more information contact your local HUD office (starting on page 360) or contact Asset Management and Disposition Division, 451 7th Street, SW, Washington, DC 20410; 202-708-1672; {www.hud.gov/offices/hsg/sfh/reo/reo_home.cfm}.

50% Discount For Law Enforcement Officers To Buy A Home

It may seem incredible, and it is. The U. S. Department of Housing and Urban Development (HUD) wants to make American communities stronger and to build a safer nation. Public safety improves when police officers live in a neighborhood. The

Officer Next Door (OND) program helps make this goal a reality by making homeownership faster and more affordable for Law Enforcement Officers.

Law enforcement officers may purchase HUD-owned single unit properties located in designated revitalization areas at a 50 percent discount off list price. You must be a full-time, sworn law enforcement officer who is "employed full-time by a Federal, state, county or municipal government; or a public or private college or university." Officers must agree to occupy homes as their sole residence for a period of 3 years. The officer must also agree to execute a second mortgage and note in the name of the Department for an amount equal to the 50 percent discount. This zero interest note will gradually decrease over the 3-year mandatory residence period until it reaches zero. Should the officer leave the home before the 1st anniversary of occupancy, 90 percent of the discounted amount will be due to HUD. Departure before the 2nd anniversary of occupancy will require a 60 percent repayment, and departure before the 3rd anniversary of occupancy will require a 30 percent repayment of the discounted amount.

Officers must certify initially, and once annually, for each year of the occupancy term, that he/she continues to own and live in the home as a sole residence, and that no other residential real estate is owned. OND property is listed at the following website {http://www.hud.gov/offices/hsg/sfh/reo/homes.cfm} and sold exclusively over the Internet. Properties are single family homes located in revitalization areas. Properties available through the program are marked with a special Office Next Door button. Bids are awarded once each week. Your bid must be the amount of the list price. You may submit your bid directly or utilize the services of a real estate broker. Winning bids are randomly selected by computer. The winning bid is posted each week on the web site where you made your bid.

You may also buy a home from a government agency or a nonprofit organization that bought the home from HUD. When an agency or nonprofit buys the house, HUD expects the full discount to be passed on to you. . To make a HUD home even more affordable, you may apply for an FHA-insured mortgage with a downpayment of only $100 and you may finance all closing costs. If the home you want to purchase needs repairs, you may use FHA's 203(k) mortgage program. 7,352 law enforcement officers took advantage of this program last year. The total value of the homes was $367,600,000. (14.198 Officer Next Door Sales Program).

Contact your local HUD office (starting on page 360) or check out the program online at {www.hud.gov/offices/hsg/sfh/hsgsingle.cfm}. Information is also available from the HUD HELP line at 800-569-4287.

$5,000,000 to Start A Homeless Shelter

Many people have no place to call home, and states, cities, and nonprofits work to fill the gap. The Emergency Shelter Grant Program provides funds for programs designed to improve the quality of emergency shelters and transitional housing for the homeless, make available additional shelters, meet the costs of operating shelters, and provide essential social services to homeless individuals. States, cities, and counties can receive funds, and then these fund can be distributed to nonprofits. 365 grants were made last year through this program. The budget for this program is $150,000,000. (14.231 Emergency Shelter Grants Program ESG).

For more information contact your local HUD office (starting on page 360) or John Garrity, Director, Office of Special Needs Assistance Programs, U.S. Department of Housing and Urban Development, 451 7th St., SW, Room 7262, Washington, DC 20410; 202-708-4300; {www.hud.gov/offices/cpd/homeless/programs/esg/index.cfm}.

Money to Pay Mortgages, Rents, Or Utility Payments In Emergencies

Funds are available for food and feeding related expenses, such as transportation of food and food preparation and serving equipment. Money can also be used for mass shelter and rent/mortgage and/or utility assistance for one month only. The Emergency Food and Shelter funds are to be used in obviously emergency situations, and is to provide food and shelter to those in need. 11,000 agencies used these funds. The budget for this program is $140,000,000. (83.523 Emergency Food and Shelter National Board Program- Emergency Food and Shelter).

For more information contact Curtis Carleton, Federal Emergency Management Agency, Preparedness, Training and Exercises Directorate, Washington, DC 20472; 202-646-4535; or Sharon Bailey, Director, Emergency Food and Shelter Program, 701 North Fairfax Street, Suite 310, Alexandria, VA 22314; 703-706-9660; {www.fema.gov}.

Grants To Pay Rents For People With Disabilities Or Chronic Illnesses

The Shelter Plus Care Program provides rental assistance, in connection with supportive services funded from sources other than this program, to homeless persons with disabilities (mentally ill, chronic alcohol or drug problems, or AIDS) and their families. The rental assistance can be through tenant-based, sponsor-based, project-based, or single room occupancy. States, local governments, or public housing agencies can apply for the funds. The budget for this program is $251,000,000. (14.238 Shelter Plus Care).

For more information contact your local HUD office (starting on page 360) or John Garrity, Director, Office of Special Needs Assistance Programs, U.S. Department of Housing and Urban Development, 451 7th St., SW, Room 7262, Washington, DC 20410; 202-708-4300; {www.hud.gov/progdesc/cpdindx.html}.

Money For Housing Research

Housing issues and programs change as needs change, and research is required to find out what works best. The U.S. Department of Housing and Urban Development offers research funds to researchers, research organizations, state and local governments, academic institutions, and nonprofits. The funds are to carry out research, demonstration and program evaluation and monitoring projects of high priority and pre-selected by

the Department to improve the operations of the Department's programs. The majority of PD&R's funds are awarded through competitive procurement solicitations or Interagency Agreements with other Federal Agencies. A limited number of cooperative agreements are awarded to offerors of unsolicited solicited research proposals that meet the strategic objectives of the Department of Housing and Urban Development. (14.506 General Research and Technology Activity).

For more information contact Assistant Secretary for Policy Development and Research, Department of Housing and Urban Development, 451 7th Street SW., Washington, DC 20410. Attention: Budget, Contracts, and Program Control Division; 202-708-1796; {www.huduser.org}.

Help the Hispanic Community

Grants are available to help Hispanic-Serving Institutions of higher education (HSIs) expand their role and effectiveness in addressing community development needs in their localities, including neighborhood revitalization, housing, and economic development. Only nonprofit institutions of higher education are eligible for funds. Some examples of funded project include a microenterprise center for bilingual child care providers, a youth center, and renovation of a space that will hold a comprehensive culinary arts program. (14.514 Hispanic-Serving Institutions Assisting Communities).

For more information contact Armand Carriere in the Office of University Partnerships, Office of Policy Development and Research, 451 7th Street SW., Washington, DC 20410; 202-708-3061, extension 3181; {www.hud.gov/grants}.

Local Colleges Get Money to Fix Up Your Home

Money is available to assist Historically Black Colleges and Universities (HBCUs) expand their role and effectiveness in addressing community development needs in their localities, including neighborhood revitalization, housing, and economic development. The HBCU program also encourages greater citizen participation in the local/neighborhood planning process. Some examples of funded projects include: forming a partnership with the local YWCA to provide transitional housing for homeless and battered single women, and women with children, in order to teach them self-sufficiency; supporting neighborhood revitalization strategies in three blighted areas; developing a micro revolving loan program; and establishing a computer learning center at a public housing facility. Funds are only available to Historically Black Colleges and Universities. The budget for this program is $10,000,000. (14.520 Historically Black Colleges and Universities Program).

For more information contact Ophelia Wilson, Office of University Partnerships, Office of Policy Development and Research, Dept. of Housing and Urban Development, 451 7th Street, SW., Washington, DC 20410; 202-708-3061, extension 4390. Fax: 202-708-0309; {www.oup.org}.

$3 Billion In Grants To Fix Up Homes In Cities

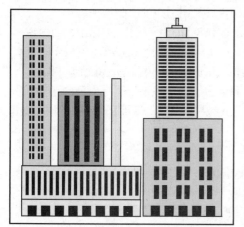

Community Development Block Grant money is available to metropolitan cities to help them provide decent housing and expand economic opportunities for low to moderate income residents. Recipients may undertake a wide range of activities directed toward neighborhood revitalization, economic development, and provision of improved community facilities and services. Entitlement communities develop their own programs and funding priorities as long as programs/activities conform to the statutory standards and program regulations. In addition, CDBG funds may be used to pay for public services within certain limits. Recipients may contract with other local agencies or nonprofit organizations to carry out part or all of their programs. Community-based development organizations may carry out neighborhood revitalization, community economic development or energy conservation projects to further achieve the national objectives of the CDBG program. Recipients may provide assistance to microenterprises or other for-profit entities when the recipient determines that the provision of such assistance is appropriate to carry out an economic development project. All eligible activities must either benefit low- and moderate-income persons, aid in the prevention or elimination of slums or blight, or meet other community development needs having a particular urgency. 1,034 were repaired last year. The budget for this program is $3,037,000,000. (14.218 Community Development Block Grants/Entitlement Grants).

For more information contact Entitlement Communities Division, Office of Block Grant Assistance, Community Planning and Development, 451 7th Street, SW., Washington, DC 20410; 202-708-1577; {www.hud.gov/offices/cpd/index.cfm}.

$5 Million In Grants To Fix Up Homes In Small Towns

The Small Cities Program provides funding for the development of viable urban communities by providing decent housing, a suitable living environment, and expanding economic opportunities, principally for persons of low and moderate income. Small Cities develop their own programs and funding priorities. It could be acquisition, rehabilitation or construction of certain public works facilities and improvements, clearance, housing rehabilitation, code enforcement, direct assistance to facilitate and expand homeownership among persons of low and moderate income, relocation payments and assistance, administrative expenses, economic development, completing existing urban renewal projects, and certain public services with some restrictions. Neighborhood-based nonprofit organizations, local development corporations, Small Business Investment Companies, or other nonprofit organizations serving the development needs of nonentitlement areas may act as subgrantees to carry out neighborhood revitalization or community economic development projects. This program is only available to three counties in Hawaii. The budget for this program is $5,889,800. (14.219 Community Development Block Grants/Small Cities Program (Small Cities)).

For more information contact State and Small Cities Division, Office of Block Grant Assistance, Community Planning and Development, Department of Housing and Urban Development, 451 7th Street, SW., Washington, DC 20410; 202-708-1322; {www.hud.gov/offices/cpd/about/cpd_programs.cfm}.

Help to Get The Money

The money is there, but sometimes it is hard to find. The Community Development Block Grants/Special Purpose Program is designed to help States, units of general local government, Indian tribes and areawide planning organizations to plan, develop and administer local Community Development Block Grant programs. Assistance may be used to transfer skills and knowledge in planning, developing and administering the Community Development Block Grant programs  from those individuals and institutions which possess them to eligible block grant entities and affiliated CDBG participants which need them. Project activities show how they will increase the effectiveness with which eligible block grant communities can use CDBG funds to meet community development national and local program objectives. May take several forms, such as the provision of written information, person-to-person exchange, seminars, workshops or training sessions. Those eligible include States, units of general local government, Indian tribes, areawide planning organizations, groups designated by such governmental units to assist them in carrying out assistance and qualified groups. (14.227 Community Development Block Grants/Special Purpose).

For more information contact Office of Management and Technical Assistance, Community Planning and Development, Department of Housing and Urban Development, 451 7th St., SW., Washington, DC 20410; 202-708-3176; {www.hud.gov/progdesc/cpdindx.html}.

Money to Buy Or Fix Up Houses In The Pacific Islands Or The Virgin Islands

Community Development Block Grant funds provide community development assistance to the Pacific Islands of American Samoa, Guam, the Northern Mariana Islands, and the Virgin Islands in the Caribbean. Funds have been used for housing rehabilitation, infrastructure and public facilities development, and/or improvements, economic development initiatives, microenterprise/small business creation and/or assistance, and first-time home buyer assistance. The budget for this program is $7,000,000. (14.225 Community Development Block Grants/Special Purpose Grants/Insular Areas).

For more information contact Office of Block Grant Assistance, Community Planning and Development, Department of Housing and Urban Development, 451 7th St., SW, Washington, DC 20410; 202-708-1322; {www.hud.gov/offices/cpd/about/cpd_programs.cfm}.

$570,000,000 For Local Communities to Fix Up Your House

Section 108, the loan guarantee provision of the Community Development Block Grant program, is one of the most potent and important public investment tools that HUD offers to local governments. It allows them to transform a small portion of their CDBG funds into federally guaranteed loans large enough to pursue physical and economic revitalization projects that can renew entire neighborhoods. Such public investment is often needed to inspire private economic activity, providing the initial resources or simply the confidence that private firms and individuals may need to invest in distressed areas. Section 108 loans are not risk-free, however; local governments borrowing funds guaranteed by Section 108 must pledge their current and future CDBG allocations to cover the loan amount as security for the loan. Activities eligible for funds include economic development activities, acquisition of real property, rehabilitation of publicly owned property, construction of public works, and more. Units of general local government are eligible for funds. (14.248 Community Development Block Grants-Section 108 Loan Guarantees (Section 108)).

For more information contact Financial Management Division, Room 7180, Community Planning and Development, Department of Housing and Urban Development, 451 7th Street, SW., Washington, DC 20410; {www.hud.gov/offices/cpd/about/cpd_programs.cfm}.

Help For Native Alaskans and Hawaiians

Alaska Native Institutions (ANIs) of higher education and Native Hawaiian Institutions (NHIs)of higher education can enhance their role and effectiveness in addressing community development needs in their localities, including neighborhood revitalization, housing, and economic development, by applying for this grant program. Cities, counties, towns, and villages can benefit from this program. (14.515 Alaska Native/Native Hawaiian Institutions Assisting Communities).

For more information contact Armand Carriere in the Office of University Partnerships, Office of Policy Development and Research, 451 7th Street, SW., Washington, DC 20410; 202-708-3061, extension 3181; {www.oup.org}.

Grants For Special Projects

Section 108, the loan guarantee provision of the Community Development Block Grant program, is one of the most potent and important public investment tools that HUD offers to local governments. It allows them to transform a small portion of their CDBG funds into federally guaranteed loans large enough to pursue physical and economic revitalization projects that can renew entire neighborhoods. In order to help public entities eligible under the Section 108 Loan Guarantee program carry out economic development projects authorized by Section 108, grant assistance is available to enhance the security of loans guaranteed under the Section 108 program or improve the viability of projects financed with loans guaranteed under the Section 108 program. This is only for qualified Brownfields projects. Units of local government are eligible to apply for this program. (14.246 Community Development Block Grants/Economic Development Initiative (Section 108)).

For more information contact Lisa Peoples, Economic Development Specialist, Office of Economic Development, Community Planning and Development, 451 7th Street, SW., Washington, DC 20410; 202-708-0614, extension 4456; {www.hud.gov}.

Help for Public Housing

Revitalization Grants enable Public Housing Agencies (PHA) to improve the living environment for public housing residents of severely distressed public housing projects through the demolition, substantial rehabilitation, reconfiguration, and/or replacement of severely distressed units; revitalize the sites on which severely distressed public housing projects are located and contribute to the improvement of the surrounding neighborhood; lessen isolation and reduce the concentration of low-income families; build sustainable mixed-income communities; and provide well-coordinated, results-based community and supportive services that directly complement housing redevelopment and that help residents to achieve self-sufficiency, young people to attain educational excellence, and the community to secure a desirable quality of life.

HOPE VI Demolition Grants enable PHAs to expedite the demolition of obsolete and/or severely distressed public housing units. Any subsequent new construction or revitalization of any remaining units must be funded from other resources. Up to 15 percent of a grant may be used for Community and Supportive Services programs. Only Public Housing Agencies operating public housing units are eligible to apply. (14.866 Demolition and Revitalization of Severely Distressed Public Housing (HOPE VI)).

For more information contact Assistant Secretary for Public and Indian Housing, Deputy Assistant Secretary for Public Housing Investments, Office of Urban Revitalization, Department of Housing and Urban Development, Washington, DC 20410; 202-401-8812; {www.hud.gov/hopevi}.

Money for Public Housing

The Capital Fund provides funds annually to Public Housing Agencies (PHAs) for capital and management activities, including modernization and development of public housing. The funds may be used for the development, financing and modernization of public housing developments and for management improvements. The funds may not be used for luxury improvements, direct social services, costs funded by other programs, and ineligible activities as determined by HUD on a case-by-case basis. Only Public Housing Agencies are eligible to apply for funds. (14.872 Public Housing Capital Fund (CFP)).

For more information contact Assistant Secretary for Public and Indian Housing, 451 7th St., SW, Washington DC 20410; 202-708-0950; {www.hud.gov/progdesc/pihindx.html}.

50% Discount For Teachers K-12 To Buy A Home

The Teacher Next Door Initiative is designed to strengthen America's communities by encouraging public and private school teachers to live in low and moderate income neighborhoods. Teachers (State-certified in grades Kindergarten through 12th grade) may purchase HUD-owned single unit properties located in designated revitalization areas at a 50 percent discount off list price. Teachers must agree to occupy homes as their sole residence for a period of 3 years. The teacher must also agree to execute a second mortgage and note in the name of the Department for an amount equal to the 50 percent discount. This zero interest note will gradually decrease over the 3-year mandatory residence period until it reaches zero. Should the teacher leave the home before the 1st anniversary of occupancy, 90 percent of the discounted amount will be due to HUD. Departure before the 2nd anniversary of occupancy will require a 60 percent repayment, and departure before the 3rd anniversary of occupancy will require a 30 percent repayment of the discounted amount.

Teachers must certify initially, and once annually, for each year of the occupancy term, that he/she continues to own and live in the home as a sole residence, and that no other residential real estate is owned. The Teacher Next Door program is limited to a specialized group. To be eligible for this program, participants must be employed full-time by a public school, private school, or federal, State, county, or municipal educational agency as a state- certified classroom teacher or administrator in grades K-12. In addition, eligibility requires participants to certify that they are employed by an educational agency that serves the school district/jurisdiction in which the home they are purchasing is located. 2,700 teachers took advantage of this program last year. The budget for this program is $137,000,000. (14.310 Teacher Next Door Initiative).

For more information contact Asset Management and Disposition Division, 451 7th Street SW, Washington, DC 20410; 202-708-1672; {www.hud.gov/offices/hsg/sfh/reo/reo_home.cfm}.

Free Help to Complain to A Mobile Home Manufacturer

Manufactured home construction and safety standards have been established to protect the quality, durability, safety and affordability of manufactured homes; to facilitate the availability of affordable manufactured homes and to increase home ownership for all Americans; to provide for the establishment of practical, uniform, and, to the extent possible, performance-based Federal construction standards for manufactured homes; to encourage innovative and cost-effective construction techniques for manufactured homes; and to protect residents of manufactured homes with respect to personal injuries and the amount of insurance costs and property damages in manufactured housing. Designs of homes are reviewed for compliance, and homes are inspected during construction by HUD-approved third-party inspection agencies. Consumers receiving defective homes have recourse, ranging from the right to be notified that their home contains a defect, to correction by the manufacturer of serious defects and imminent safety hazards. Any purchaser of a manufactured home built on or after June 15, 1976, for residential use is automatically covered by the program. (14.171 Manufactured Home Construction and Safety Standards (Manufactured Housing)).

For more information contact Office of Single Family Housing (HU), Office of Consumer and Regulatory Affairs (HUC), Manufactured Housing and Standards Division (HUCM), Room 9152, Department of Housing and Urban Development, Washington, DC 20410; 202-708-6409; Fax: 202-708-4213; Toll-free consumer hotline (leave message only): 800- 927-2891; {www.hud.gov/progdesc/snglindx.html}.

More Money to Help Fair Housing

The government funds the Equal Housing Agency, but money is also available to develop, implement, carry out, or coordinate programs or activities designed to obtain enforcement of the rights granted by the Fair Housing Act or by substantially equivalent State and local fair housing laws. Financial assistance is provided for specialized projects conducted by State and local fair housing agencies certified by HUD as "substantially equivalent." Such projects are to obtain better administrative enforcement of equivalent State and local fair housing laws. All projects should strengthen and/or broaden the range of enforcement and compliance activities conducted by State and local agencies. (14.408 Fair Housing Initiatives and Administrative Enforcement Initiative Program (FHIP & AEI)).

For more information contact Lauretta A. Dixon, Director, FHIP/FHAP Support Division, Office of Programs, Office of Fair Housing and Equal Opportunity,

Department of Housing and Urban Development, 451 7th Street, SW., Room 5234, Washington, DC 20410; 202-708-0800, ext. 7051; {www.hud.gov/progdesc/fheoindx.html}.

Help People Learn Their Rights

Many people do not know what rights they have concerning housing issues. Financial assistance is provided for specialized projects conducted by public or private entities to inform the public concerning rights and obligations under the Fair Housing Act or State or local laws that provide rights and remedies for alleged discriminatory housing practices. State and local governments; public or private nonprofit organizations or institutions and other public or private entities that are formulating or carrying out programs to prevent or eliminate discriminatory housing practices are eligible for funds. (14.409 Fair Housing Initiatives Program (FHIP) Education and Outreach Initiative (FHIP & EOI)).

For more information contact Lauretta A. Dixon, Director, FHIP/FHAP Support Division, Office of Fair Housing and Equal Opportunity, Department of Housing and Urban Development, 451 7th Street, SW., Room 5224, Washington, DC 20410; 202-708-0800, ext. 7051; {www.hud.gov/progdesc/fheoindx.html}.

Nonprofits Can Help With Fair Housing

Money is available to nonprofits to develop, implement, carry out, or coordinate programs or activities designed to obtain enforcement of the rights granted by the Fair Housing Act or by State and local fair housing laws. Financial assistance is provided for projects conducted by private nonprofit fair housing enforcement organizations that are formulating or carrying out programs to prevent or eliminate discriminatory housing practices. Only private nonprofit fair housing enforcement organizations are eligible for funds. (14.410 Fair Housing Initiatives Program (FHIP) Private Enforcement Initiative (FHIP & PEI)).

For more information contact Lauretta A. Dixon, Director, FHIP/FHAP Support Division, Office of Fair Housing and Equal Opportunity, Department of Housing and Urban Development, 451 7th Street, SW., Room 5234, Washington, DC 20410; 202-708-0800, ext. 7051; {www.hud.gov/progdesc/fheoindx.html}.

Help Those In Need

Sometimes a roof over one's head is not enough. To address the needs of public housing residents, supportive services, resident empowerment activities and/or assisting residents in becoming economically self-sufficient are necessary. The primary focus of the program is on "welfare to work" and on independent living for the elderly and persons with disabilities. Grant funds may be used for both economic development and supportive services activities, organizational development, mediation, including the employment of service coordinators/case managers. Those eligible to apply include Public and Indian Housing (PHAs/IHAs), and Tribally Designated Housing entities (TDHEs), resident management corporations, resident councils or resident organizations (including nonprofit entities supported by residents). (14.870 Resident Opportunity and Supportive Services (ROSS)).

For more information contact Customer Services and Amenities Division, Office of Public and Assisted Housing Delivery, Public and Indian Housing, Department of Housing and Urban Development, Room 4224, 451 Seventh Street, SW., Washington, DC 20410; 202-708-4214; {www.hud.gov/progdesc/pihindx.html}.

Money For Teens To Learn To Build Or Fix Up Houses

Houses don't just happen. You can be involved teaching young adults the skills of the trade and meet the housing needs of others at the same time. The Youthbuild program provides funding assistance for a wide range of multi-disciplinary activities and services to assist economically disadvantaged youth. The opportunities are designed to help disadvantaged young adults who have dropped out of high school to obtain the education and employment skills necessary to achieve economic self-efficiency and develop leadership skills and a commitment to community development in low income communities. Another important objective of the Youthbuild program is to expand the supply of permanent affordable housing for homeless persons and members of low income and very low income families. By giving disadvantaged young adults participating in the program meaningful on-site training experiences constructing or rehabilitating housing as a community service, they are helping to meet the housing needs of homeless and low income families in their community.

Grant funds can be used to fund eligible educational and supportive services and activities composed of basic skills development, and counseling, referral and support services. Funds can also be used for architectural and engineering fees, construction, rehabilitation, acquisition, operating expenses and replacements reserves. Those eligible to apply for funds include public and private nonprofit agencies, state or local housing agencies, or state and local units of government. 1,533 units were built last year. The budget for this program is $65,000,000. (14.243 Opportunities for Youth- Youthbuild Program).

For more information contact Jackie Williams-Mitchell, Director, Office of Rural Housing and Economic Development, Department of Housing and Urban Development, 451 7th Street SW., Washington, DC 20410, Room 7137; 202-708-2290; {www.hud.gov/progdesc/cpdindx.html}.

$2,000,000 Grant To Provide Single Room Occupancy Units

There is a need in society today for Single Room Occupancy buildings. Grants are available to rehabilitate residential properties, so that when finished they will contain multiple single room dwelling units. Public Housing Agencies and private nonprofit organizations are eligible to apply for funds. The budget for this program is $15,561,000. (14.249 Section 8 Moderate Rehabilitation Single Room Occupancy).

For more information contact John D. Garrity, Deputy Director, Office of Special Needs Assistance Programs, Community Planning and Development, Department of Housing and Urban Development, Room 7262, 451 7th Street, SW., Washington, DC 20410; 202-708-4300; {www.hud.gov/progdesc/cpdindx.html}.

$5,000 To Get Rid Of Lead Paint In Your Home

Lead poisoning can be very dangerous, but even more so in children. Lead-Based Paint Hazard Control grants provide assistance to State, Tribal, and local governments in developing programs for the identification and control of lead-based paint hazards in privately-owned housing that is owned by or rented to low- or very-low income families. Objectives include: building the capacity necessary to eliminate lead-based paint hazards in all housing; preventing childhood lead poisoning; involving cooperation among all levels of government, the private sector, faith-based organizations, and community-based organizations; integration of lead- safe practices into other programs which will continue beyond the life of the grant; establishment of a public registry of lead-safe housing; and promoting job training, employment, and other economic lift opportunities for low-income residents of project neighborhoods. Applicants eligible for Hazard Control Grants are States, Tribes, or units of local government. 60,000 homes were tested and 36,000 were made safe through this program. The budget for this program is $100,000,000. (14.900 Lead-Based Paint Hazard Control in Privately-Owned Housing).

For more information contact Hazard Control Grants: Matthew E. Ammon, Director, Lead Hazard Control Grants Division, Office of Lead Hazard Control, Department of Housing and Urban Development, 451 Seventh Street, SW., Room P-3206, Washington, DC 20410; 202-755- 1785 ext. 158; {www.hud.gov/progdesc/leadindx.html}.

70% Discount On Rent

In order to best assist very low-income families in obtaining decent, safe, and sanitary rental housing. Vouchers are available to increase the housing choice for families. The Section 8 Rental Voucher Program provides housing assistance payments to participating owners on behalf of eligible tenant. Housing assistance payments are generally 70% of the rent with the family paying 30% of their income. Public Housing Agencies apply for these vouchers which are then given to low-income families. In 2003 there were 2,100,000 vouchers available. (14.871 Section 8 Housing Choice Vouchers).

For more information contact Office of the Public and Assisted Housing Delivery, Department of Housing and Urban Development, Washington, DC 20410; 202-708-0477; {www.hud.gov/progdesc/pihindx.cfm}.

Low Cost Flood Insurance

Through the National Flood Insurance Program, property owners may buy flood insurance at a premium rate that is generally lower than a normal actuarial rate. Maximum amounts for coverage are $35,000 for a single family home, $100,000 for all other residential structures, plus $10,000 per dwelling unit for contents. (83.100 Flood Insurance Program).

For more information contact Federal Insurance Administration, FEMA, Washington, DC 20472; 202-646-3429; 888-FLOOD29; {www.fema.gov}.

Nonprofits Can Buy HUD Foreclosures At 30% Off Fair Market Value

The U.S. Department of Housing and Urban Development (HUD) needs to do something with the properties they acquire through foreclosures. They sell many to interested buyers on a competitive basis, but they also sell to nonprofit organizations and local governments at a discount. These organizations can purchase the properties for 10-30% off the fair market value. The nonprofit or local government must agree that the home will be used in conjunction with a home ownership plan. (14.311 Single Family Property Disposition).

For more information contact Asset Management and Disposition Division, Office of Single Family Housing, U.S. Department of Housing and Urban Development, Washington, DC 20410; 202-708-1672; {www.hud.gov/offices/hsg/sfh/reo/reo_home.cfm}.

$500 Per Month To Help Pay Your Rent

In order to make good quality rental housing available to low-income families at a cost they can afford, the U.S. Department of Housing and Urban Development makes payments to owners of approved HUD-insured and non-insured multifamily rental housing projects to supplement the partial rental payments of eligible tenants. Assistance covers the difference between the tenant's payment and the basic market rental. The tenants payment is usually 30% of their income, the HUD pays the other 70%. Eligible sponsors include nonprofits or other investors. (14.149 Rent Supplements-Rental Housing for Lower Income Families) and (14.856 Lower Income Housing Assistance Program- Section 8 Moderate Rehabilitation (Section 8 Housing Assistance Payments Program for Very Low Income Families- Moderate Rehabilitation)) for Public Housing Agencies.

For more information contact Director, Office of Multifamily Housing Management, Department of Housing and Urban Development, Washington, DC 20410; 202-708-3730; {www.hud.gov/progdesc/multindx.cfm}.

Grants To Local Communities To Provide Money To Buy Or Fix Up Homes And To Pay Rent

Who needs affordable housing? More families than you think need help finding and paying for affordable housing. In general, under the HOME Investment Partnerships Program, HUD allocates funds to eligible State and local governments to strengthen public-private partnerships and to expand the supply of decent, safe, sanitary, and affordable housing. Participating jurisdictions may use HOME funds to help renters, new homebuyers or existing homeowners, with primary attention for very low-income and low-income families. As of September 30, 2002, 687,274 units were committed; 450,589 units were completed; and 83,939 families have received tenant-based rental assistance. (14.239 HOME Investment Partnership Program).

The HOME program is implemented through State and local governments called participating jurisdictions. Participating jurisdictions may be States or units of general local government, including consortia and urban counties. HOME participating jurisdictions have a great deal of flexibility in designing and managing their HOME programs. HUD's Office of Affordable Housing Programs Office administers the HOME program.

> HUD Office of Affordable Housing
> Office of Community Planning and Development
> 451 7th Street, SW
> Washington, DC 20410
> 202-708-2470
> TTY: 800-877-8339

To find which jurisdictions implement state or local HOME programs in your area and how these programs work, check the listings for your state.

HOME Program- HUD

Alabama
Ms. Barbara Wallace,
HOME/Tax Credit Coordinator
Housing Finance Authority
P.O. Box 230909
Montgomery, AL 36123

334-244-9200
Fax: 334-244-9214

Cities
City of Birmingham
Mr. Ronnie D. White
Program Director

Department of Community
Development
710 20th St., N., Room 700
Birmingham, AL 35203-2216
205-254-2312
Fax: 205-254-2628

City of Huntsville
Mr. Bill Taylor, Housing
Specialist
Division of Community
Development
120 E. Holmes Ave.
Huntsville, AL 35804
256-427-5400
Fax: 256-427-5431

City of Mobile
Mr. Steve Kohrman, Director
Mobile Housing Board
P.O. Box 1345
Mobile, AL 36633-1345
334-476-4165
Fax: 334-470-0582

City of Montgomery
Mr. George Stathopoulos, Chief
Department of Community
Development
P.O. Box 1111
Montgomery, AL 36101
334-241-2997
Fax: 334-241-4432

City of Tuscaloosa
Ms. Evelyn Young, Assoc. Dir.
Department of Community
Planning and Development
P.O. Box 2089
Tuscaloosa, AL 35401
205-349-0160
Fax: 205-349-0135

Counties
County of Jefferson
Mr. Robert Newbill, Supervisor
Department of Planning and
Community Development
805 22nd St., N.
Birmingham, AL 35203-2303
205-325-5761
Fax: 205-325-5095

Alaska
Ms. Carma Edith Reed, Planner
Alaska Housing Finance Corp.
P.O. Box 101020
Anchorage, AK 99510-1020
907-330-8275
Fax: 907-338-2585

Municipalities
Municipality of Anchorage

Ms. Lynn Taylor, Manager
Division of Housing and
Community Development
P.O. Box 196650
Anchorage, AK 99519-6650
907-343-4881
Fax: 907-343-6831

American Samoa
Mr. Ali'imau H. Scanlan,
Director
Department of Commerce
American Samoa Government
Pago Pago, AS 96799
684-633-5155
Fax: 684-633-4195

Arizona
Ms. Carol Ditmore, HOME
Coordinator
Department of Commerce
3800 N. Central Ave., Suite 1500
Phoenix, AZ 85012-1908
602-280-1365
Fax: 602-280-1470

Cities
City of Phoenix
Ms. Elizabeth DeMichael,
Manager
Department of Housing
251 W. Washington St., 4th Floor
Phoenix, AZ 85034-2218
602-262-4785
Fax: 602-534-1214

City of Tucson
Ms. Nancy Magelli, Project
Coordinator
City of Tucson
Department of Community
Services/Technical Services
P.O. Box 27210
Tucson, AZ 85726-7210
520-791-4132
Fax: 520-791-5648

Counties
County of Maricopa
Ms. Isabel McDougall, Director
Department of Community
Development
3003 N. Central Ave., Suite 1040
Phoenix, AZ 85012
602-240-2210
Fax: 602-240-6960

Consortia
Maricopa County Consortium
Mr. Jim Prante, HOME
Coordinator
Department of Community
Development
3003 N. Central Ave., Suite 1040
Phoenix, AZ 85012-2906
602-240-2210
Fax: 602-240-6960

Arkansas
Mr. Don Jackson, HOME
Program Manager
Arkansas Development Finance
Authority
P.O. Box 8023
Little Rock, AR 72203-8023
501-682-5900
Fax: 501-682-5859

Cities
City of Ft. Smith
Mr. Matt Jennings, Director
Department of Economic and
Community Development
P.O. Box 1908
Ft. Smith, AR 72902-1908
501-784-2209
Fax: 501-784-2462

City of Little Rock
Ms. Lisa Spigner, Housing
Manager
Housing and Neighborhood
Programs
500 W. Markham St.
Little Rock, AR 72201
501-371-6825
Fax: 501-399-3461

City of North Little Rock
Ms. Mary Bowman, Director
Community Development
Agency
P.O. Box 5868
North Little Rock, AR 72119
501-340-5342
Fax: 501-340-5345

City of Pine Bluff
Mr. Donald R. Sampson, Dir.
Department of Community
Development
200 E. Eighth Ave.
City Hall, Room 103

Pine Bluff, AR 71601
870-543-1820
Fax: 870-543-1821

California

Mr. Wayne Walker, Section
Chief
State of California
Department of Housing and
Community Development
P.O. Box 952054
Sacramento, CA 94254-2054
916-445-4782
Fax: 916-322-1560

Cities

City of Alhambra
Mr. Stanley Smalewitz, Housing
Manager
Division of Housing
111 S. First St.
Alhambra, CA 91801-3702
626-570-5037
Fax: 626-458-4201

City of Anaheim
Ms. Bertha Chavoya, Housing
Manager
Department of Community
Development
201 S. Anaheim Blvd., 2nd Floor
Anaheim, CA 92805
714-765-4340
Fax: 714-765-4331

City of Bakersfield
Ms. Trisha Richter, HOME
Coordinator
Department of Economic and
Community Development
515 Truxtun Ave.
Bakersfield, CA 93301
661-326-3765
Fax: 661-328-1548

City of Baldwin Park
Mr. Tad Mimura, Housing
Manager
Department of Community
Development
4141 N. Maine Ave.
Baldwin Park, CA 91706
626-869-7500
Fax: 626-337-2965

City of Bellflower
Ms. Margo Wheeler, Director
Department of Community
Development
16600 Civic Center Dr.
Bellflower, CA 90706
562-804-1424
Fax: 562-925-8660

City of Berkeley
Ms. Teri Piccolo, Planner
Department of Planning
2201 Dwight Way
Berkeley, CA 94704
510-644-6001
Fax: 510-644-8678

City of Burbank
Mr. Duane Solomon, HOME
Coordinator
Department of Redevelopment
and Housing
275 E. Olive Ave.
Burbank, CA 91502
818-238-5108
Fax: 818-238-5174

City of Chico
Mr. Dennis McLaughlin, Officer
P.O. Box 3420
Chico, CA 95927
530-895-4862
Fax: 530-895-4825

City of Chula Vista
Mr. Juan Arroyo, HOME
Manager
Department of Community
Development
276 Fourth Ave.
Chula Vista, CA 91910-2631
619-585-5722
Fax: 619-585-5698

City of Compton
Ms. Arlene W. Williams,
Director
Department of Economic and
Resource Development
205 S. Willowbrook Ave.
Compton, CA 90220
310-605-5580
Fax: 310-761-1419

City of Costa Mesa
Mrs. Muriel Ullman, Manager

City of Costa Mesa
Department of Redevelopment
and Housing
P.O. Box 1200
Costa Mesa, CA 92628-1200
714-754-5635
Fax: 714-754-5330

City of Davis
Ms. Jerilyn Cochran, Grants
Coordinator
Department of Community
Services
23 Russell Blvd.
Davis, CA 95616-3837
530-757-5691
Fax: 530-757-6628

City of Downey
Mr. Edward G. Velasco, Housing
Manager
Department of Community
Development
7850 Quill Dr.
Apollo Neighborhood Center,
Suite C
Downey, CA 90242
562-904-7167
Fax: 562-869-2810

City of El Cajon
Mr. James S. Griffin, Director
Department of Community
Development
200 E. Main St.
El Cajon, CA 92020
619-441-1741
Fax: 619-441-1743

City of El Monte
Ms. Martha Murillo, Housing
Director
Department of Community
Development
11333 Valley Blvd.
El Monte, CA 91731-3293
626-580-2070
Fax: 626-580-2293

City of Escondido
Ms. Susan Wurtzel, Housing
Manager
Division of Housing
201 N. Broadway
Escondido, CA 92025
760-839-4518
Fax: 760-839-4313

City of Fontana
Mr. Steven Pasarow, Project
Specialist
Department of Community
Development
8434 Wheeler St.
Fontana, CA 92335
909-350-6625
Fax: 909-350-6616

City of Fresno
Ms. Yvonne Quiring, Director
Department of Housing and
Neighborhood Development
2600 Fresno St., Room 3076
Fresno, CA 93721-3605
559-498-1282
Fax: 559-488-1078

City of Fullerton
Ms. Linda R. Morad,
Coordinator
Division of Development
Services
303 W. Commonwealth Ave.
Fullerton, CA 92832-1710
714-738-6878
Fax: 714-738-3110

City of Garden Grove
Ms. Allison Moore, Specialist
Department of Economic
Development
11222 Acacia Pkwy.
Garden Grove, CA 92840-5310
714-741-5140
Fax: 714-741-5136

City of Glendale
Ms. Beth Stochl, HOME
Coordinator
Department of Community
Development
141 N. Glendale Ave., Suite 202
Glendale, CA 91206
818-548-2060
Fax: 818-548-3724

City of Hawthorne
Ms. Mari Guerrero,
CDBG/HOME Coordinator
4455 W. 126th St.
Hawthorne, CA 90250-4482
310-970-7103
Fax: 310-970-7473

City of Huntington Beach
Mr. Steve Holty
Department of Economic
Development
2000 Main St., Fifth Floor
Huntington Beach, CA 92648-
2702
714-536-5542
Fax: 714-375-5087

City of Huntington Park
Mr. Clarence P. Williams,
CDBG/Coordinator
Department of Community
Development
6550 Miles Ave., Suite 145
Huntington Park, CA 90255-4302
323-584-6266
Fax: 323-588-4578

City of Inglewood
Ms. Pamela Thigpen, Grants
Manager
Department of Business and
Economic Development
One W. Manchester Blvd., Suite
700
Inglewood, CA 90301-1750
310-412-8800
Fax: 310-412-5188

City of Long Beach
Mr. David D. Lewis, Officer
333 W. Ocean Blvd., 2nd Floor
Long Beach, CA 90802
562-570-6879
Fax: 562-570-5921

City of Los Angeles
Mr. Walter Clark, Community
and Housing Program Manager
Department of Housing
111 N. Hope St.
Seventh Floor, Room 722
Los Angeles, CA 90012
213-367-9128
Fax: 213-367-9242

City of Lynwood
Mr. Donyea Adams, HOME
Coordinator
Department of Community
Development
11330 Bullis Rd.
Lynwood, CA 90262

310-603-0220
Fax: 310-639-6957

City of Merced
Mr. Lee Pevsner, Director
Department of Housing and
Transportation
678 W. 18th St.
Merced, CA 95340
209-385-6863
Fax: 209-725-8775

City of Modesto
Mr. Miguel Galvez, Associate
Planner
Division of Housing and
Neighborhoods
1010 10th St., Room 4300
Modesto, CA 95354-0825
209-571-5506
Fax: 209-544-3982

City of Montebello
Ms. Patty Castreye,
Administrator
Department of Economic
Development
1600 W. Beverly Blvd.
Montebello, CA 90640
323-887-1390
Fax: 323-887-1401

City of Monterey Park
Mr. Roger Grody, Coordinator
Department of Economic
Development
320 W. Newmark Ave.
Monterey Park, CA 91754
626-307-1385
Fax: 626-307-1467

City of Moreno Valley
Ms. Mary Lanier, Manager
Department of Community and
Economic Development
14177 Frederick St.
Moreno Valley, CA 92553
909-413-3453
Fax: 909-413-2210

City of Mountain View
Ms. Adriana Garefalos, Planner
Department of Community
Development
P.O. Box 7540
Mountain View, CA 94039

650-903-6306
Fax: 650-903-6474

City of National City
Mr. Paul Desrochers, Executive
Director
Department of Community
Development
140 E 12th St., Suite B
National City, CA 91950-3312
619-336-4250
Fax: 619-336-4286

City of Norwalk
Mr. Jesus Santeze, Specialist
Department of Housing and
Community Development
12700 Norwalk Blvd.
City Hall
Norwalk, CA 90650
562-929-5951
Fax: 562-929-5780

City of Oakland
Mr. Jeff Levin, Program
Manager
Community and Economic
Development Agency
250 Frank H. Ogawa Plaza, Fifth
Floor
Oakland, CA 94612
510-238-3502
Fax: 510-238-2226

City of Oceanside
Ms. Margarie Pierce, Assistant
Director
Department of Housing
300 N. Coast Hwy.
Oceanside, CA 92054-2824
760-966-4187
Fax: 760-966-4177

City of Ontario
Mr. Douglas Ford, Director
Department of Revitalization
316 E. E St.
Ontario, CA 91764
909-395-2006
Fax: 909-395-2288

City of Orange
Ms. Mary Ellen Laster, CDBG
and Housing Rehab Manager
Department of Economic
Development

230 E. Chapman Ave.
Orange, CA 92866
714-288-2580
Fax: 714-288-2598

City of Oxnard
Mr. Ernest Whitaker, Housing
Manager
Department of Housing
555 S. A St.
Oxnard, CA 93030
805-385-7400
Fax: 805-385-7416

City of Paramount
Mr. Jose Gomez, Director
Department of Finance
16400 Colorado Ave.
Paramount, CA 90723-5050
562-220-2200
Fax: 562-529-8497

City of Pasadena
Ms. Stella J. Lucero, HOME
Coordinator
Department of Housing and
Development
100 N. Garfield Ave., Suite 101
Pasadena, CA 91109
626-744-8300
Fax: 626-744-8340

City of Pomona
Mr. Cleve Jackson, HOME
Coordinator
P.O. Box 660
Pomona, CA 91769-0660
909-620-3761
Fax: 909-620-4567

City of Redding
Mr. Don Meek, Supervisor
Office of Community
Development
777 Cypress Ave.
Redding, CA 96001-2718
530-225-4121
Fax: 530-225-4126

City of Redwood City
Mrs. Debbi Jones-Thomas,
Housing Coordinator
Department of Housing Services
P.O. Box 391
Redwood City, CA 94064-0391

650-780-7290
Fax: 650-780-0128

City of Richmond
Ms. Harriette Langston,
Manager
Redevelopment Agency
330 25th St., Second Floor
Richmond, CA 94804
510-307-8147
Fax: 510-307-8149

City of Riverside
Ms. Tranda Drumwright,
Manager
Department of Housing and
Community Development
3900 Main St., Suite 500
Riverside, CA 92522-3717
909-826-5608

City of Rosemead
Ms. Lisa Baker, Grants
Coordinator
Department of Community
Development
8838 E. Valley Blvd.
Rosemead, CA 91770
626-569-2100
Fax: 626-307-9218

City of Sacramento
Ms. Vicky Cook, Manager
Sacramento Housing and
Redevelopment Agency
630 I St.
Sacramento, CA 95814-1834
916-440-1368
Fax: 916-498-1655

City of Salinas
Ms. Barbara Batyi, Community
Development Administrative
Supervisor
Department of Community
Improvement
200 Lincoln Ave.
Salinas, CA 93901
831-758-7206
Fax: 831-758-7215

City of San Bernardino
Ms. Peggy Eaeheco, Director
Economic Development Agency
201 N. East St., Third Floor
San Bernardino, CA 92401-1507

909-663-1044
Fax: 909-888-9413

City of San Diego
Mr. Joseph Correia, Manager
Housing Commission
1625 Newton Ave.
San Diego, CA 92113-1038
619-231-9400
Fax: 619-702-2189

City of San Francisco
Ms. Marcia Rosen,
Administrator
Department of Community
Development
25 Van Ness Ave., Suite 600
San Francisco, CA 94102
415-252-3177
Fax: 415-252-3140

City of San Jose
Mr. Alex Sanchez, Director
Department of Housing
Four N. Second St., Suite 1350
San Jose, CA 95113
408-277-4747
Fax: 408-277-3197

City of San Mateo
Mr. Robert R. Muehlbauer,
Manager
Division of Housing and
Economic Development
330 W. 20th Ave.
San Mateo, CA 94403-1338
650-522-7222
Fax: 650-522-7201

City of Santa Ana
Ms. Patricia Whitaker, Housing
Manager
Community Development
Agency
P.O. Box 1988
Santa Ana, CA 92702-1988
714-667-2224
Fax: 714-667-2225

City of Santa Barbara
Mr. Steven Faulstich, Supervisor
Department of Community
Development
630 Garden St.
Santa Barbara, CA 93102-1990

805-564-5461
Fax: 805-564-5477

City of Santa Clara
Mr. Jeffrey Pedersen, Manager
Division of Community Services
1500 Warburton Ave.
Santa Clara, CA 95050
408-615-2490
Fax: 408-248-3381

City of Santa Cruz
Mr. Eugene Arner, Manager
Department of Housing and
Community Development
809 Center St., Room 206
Santa Cruz, CA 95060-3826
831-420-6253
Fax: 831-420-6458

City of Santa Monica
Mr. Robert T. Moncrief, Manager
Division of Housing and
Redevelopment
1685 Main St., Room 212
Santa Monica, CA 90401
310-458-8702
Fax: 310-458-3380

City of Santa Rosa
Mr. David Gouin, Manager
Department of Housing and
Redevelopment
P.O. Box 1806
Santa Rosa, CA 95402-1806
707-543-3316
Fax: 707-543-3317

City of South Gate
Ms. Kathy Johnston, HOME
Coordinator
Department of Community
Development
8650 California Ave.
South Gate, CA 90280
323-563-9531
Fax: 323-567-0725

City of Stockton
Mr. Robert Bressani, Supervisor
Department of Housing and
Redevelopment
305 N. El Dorado St., Suite 200
Stockton, CA 95202
209-937-8278
Fax: 209-937-8822

City of Sunnyvale
Ms. Marilyn Roaf, Specialist
Department of Community
Development
P.O. Box 3707
Sunnyvale, CA 94088-3707
408-730-7442
Fax: 408-728-0711

City of Torrance
Ms. Donna R. Richardson,
Housing Administrator
3031 Torrance Blvd.
Torrance, CA 90503
310-618-5840
Fax: 310-618-2429

City of Vallejo
Mr. Gary Truelsen, Manager
Department of Community
Development
P.O. Box 1432
Vallejo, CA 94590
707-648-4393
Fax: 707-648-5249

City of Visalia
Ms. Mary-Alice Avila, Project
Manager
315 E. Acequia Ave.
Visalia, CA 93291
559-738-3414
Fax: 559-730-7031

City of Westminster
Ms. Gerry Gehres, Analyst
Department of Community
Development
8200 Westminster Blvd.
Westminster, CA 92683
714-898-3311
Fax: 714-898-8251

City of Whittier
Mrs. Anne O'Donnel-Ivarra,
Manager
13230 Penn St.
Whittier, CA 90602-1772
562-464-3380
Fax: 562-464-3509

Counties
County of Alameda
Ms. Linda Gardner
Housing Director
224 W. Winton Ave., Room 108

Hayward, CA 94544-1215
510-670-5404
Fax: 510-670-6378

County of Contra Costa
Ms. Kathleen Hamm, Program
Manager
Department of Community
Development
651 Pine St., Fourth Floor, N.
Wing
Martinez, CA 94553-0095
925-335-1253
Fax: 925-335-1265

County of Fresno
Mr. Jerry Rutz, Analyst
2220 Tulare St., Eighth Floor
Fresno, CA 93721-2104
559-262-4277
Fax: 559-488-3316

County of Kern
Mr. Mark A. Smith, Program
Manager
Department of Community
Development
2700 M St., Suite 250
Bakersfield, CA 93301-2370
661-862-5050
Fax: 661-862-5052

County of Los Angeles
Mr. Greg Kawczynski, HOME
Coordinator
Community Development Corp.
Two Coral Cir., Bldg. A
Monterey Park, CA 91755
323-838-7761
Fax: 323-890-8586

County of Orange
Ms. Pam Leaning, Assistant
Director
Department of Housing and
Community Development
1770 N. Broadway
Santa Ana, CA 92706-2642
714-480-2899
Fax: 714-480-2803

County of Marin
Mr. Roy Bateman, Coordinator
Community Development
Agency
3501 Civic Center Dr., Room 308

San Rafael, CA 94903-4157
415-499-6698
Fax: 415-499-7880

County of Riverside
Ms. Susan Wamsley, Assistant
Director
Economic Development Agency
3525 14th St.
Riverside, CA 92501-3813
909-955-8916
Fax: 909-955-6686

County of Sacramento
Ms. Vicky Cook, Program
Manager
Housing and Redevelopment
Agency
630 I St.
Sacramento, CA 95814-1834
916-440-1368
Fax: 916-498-1655

County of San Joaquin
Mr. Jonathan M. Moore, Deputy
Director
Department of Community
Development
1810 E. Hazelton Ave.
Stockton, CA 95205
209-468-3065
Fax: 209-468-3163

County of San Luis Obispo
Mr. Dana C. Lilley, Planner
Department of Planning and
Building
County Government Center
San Luis Obispo, CA 93408
805-781-5715
Fax: 805-781-5624

County of San Mateo
Mr. Tom Roberts, Director
Office of Housing
262 Harbor Blvd., Bldg. A
Belmont, CA 94002
650-802-5050
Fax: 650-802-5049

County of Santa Clara
Mr. Charles Chew, Program
Manager
County of Santa Clara
Department of Housing and
Community Development

1735 N. First St., Suite 265
San Jose, CA 95112-4511
408-441-0261
Fax: 408-441-0365

County of Santa Barbara
Ms. Susan Ruby, Manager
Department of Planning and
Development
P.O. Box 2219
Santa Barbara, CA 93120-2219
805-568-3521
Fax: 805-568-2289

County of Sonoma
Mr. Charles D. McGowan,
Specialist
Community Development
Commission
1440 Guerneville Rd.
Santa Rosa, CA 95403-4107
707-524-7500
Fax: 707-524-7557

County of Ventura
Ms. Loretta McCarty, HOME
Coordinator
800 S. Victoria Ave.
Chief Administrative Office,
L#1940
Ventura, CA 93009-1940
805-654-2876
Fax: 805-654-5106
Consortia

County of San Bernardino
Consortium
Ms. Julie Hemphel, Deputy
Director
Department of Housing and
Economic Development
290 N. D St., Sixth Floor
San Bernardino, CA 92415-0040
909-388-0800
Fax: 909-388-0820

County of San Diego
Consortium
Ms. April York, Temporary
Coordinator
Department of Housing and
community Development
3989 Ruffin Rd.
San Diego, CA 92123-1815
858-694-8724
Fax: 858-694-4871

Colorado

Mr. Pat Coyle, HOME Program
Manager
Division of Housing
1313 Sherman St., Suite 518
Denver, CO 80203
303-866-2033
Fax: 303-866-4077

Cities

City of Aurora
Mr. Michael G. Hilliard, Mgr.
Department of Community
Development
9801 E. Colfax Ave.
Aurora, CO 80010-2109
303-360-0053
Fax: 303-361-2989

City of Boulder
Mrs. Jan Oldham, Grants
Administrator
Department of Housing and
Human Services
P.O. Box 791
Boulder, CO 80306-0791
303-441-3157
Fax: 303-441-4368

City of Colorado Springs
Ms. Valerie Jordan, Manager
Department of Community
Redevelopment
P.O. Box 1575
Colorado Springs, CO 80901-
1575
719-385-5336
Fax: 719-578-6543

City of and County of Denver
Ms. Laurie Baker, Program
Specialist
Community Development
Agency
7111 E. 56th Ave.
Commerce City, CO 80022-1859
720-913-1540
Fax: 720-913-1800

City of Ft. Collins
Ms. Julie Smith, HOME
Administrator
Department of Planning
P.O. Box 580
Ft. Collins, CO 80522-0580

970-221-6595
Fax: 970-224-6111

City of Greeley
Ms. Terry McKellar, Community
Development Specialist
Department of Community
Development
1100 Tenth St., Suite 201
Greeley, CO 80631-3808
970-350-9781
Fax: 970-350-9895

City of Lakewood
Mr. Steven Gundel, HOME
Coordinator
Department of Housing
480 S. Allison Pkwy.
Lakewood, CO 80226
303-987-7599
Fax: 303-987-7821

Counties

County of Adams
Mr. Jim Rose, Office Manager
Office of Community Outreach
7111 E. 56th Ave.
Commerce City, CO 80022-2236
303-286-4175
Fax: 303-286-4166

County of Arapahoe
Mr. James M. Taylor, Director
Department of Housing and
Community Development
2009 W. Littleton Blvd.
Littleton, CO 80120
303-738-8060
Fax: 303-738-8069

County and City of Denver
Ms. Laurie Baker, Program
Specialist
Community Development
Agency
7111 E. 56th Ave.
Commerce City, CO 80022-1859
720-913-1540
Fax: 720-913-1800

County of Jefferson
Ms. Rebecca McLean, Program
Manager
Office of Community
Development
730 Simms St., Suite 300

Golden, CO 80401
303-271-4609
Fax: 303-271-4021

Consorita

City of Pueblo Consortium
Mr. Tony Berumen, Director
Department of Housing and
Community Development
P.O. Box 1427
Pueblo, CO 81002-1427
719-584-0830
Fax: 719-584-0831

Connecticut

Mr. Elliot Stone, HOME
Program Manager
Department of Economic and
Community Development
505 Hudson St.
Hartford, CT 06106
860-270-8168
Fax: 860-270-8055

Cities

City of Bridgeport
Mr. Les Gulyos, Manager
Department of Housing
45 Lyon Ter.
City Hall
Bridgeport, CT 06604
203-576-8143
Fax: 203-576-7135

City of Hartford
Mr. Jon Labelle, Project Manager
Department of Housing and
Community Development
Ten Prospect St., Third Floor
Hartford, CT 06103-2814
860-522-4888
Fax: 860-722-6630

City of New Britain
Mr. Kenneth A. Malinowski,
Director
Department of Municipal
Development
27 W. Main St., Suite 311
New Britain, CT 06051-4241
860-826-3330
Fax: 860-826-2682

City of New Haven
Ms. Regina Winters, Interim
Director

Office of Housing and
Neighborhood Development
165 Church St.
New Haven, CT 06510
203-946-7090
Fax: 203-946-4899

City of Stamford
Mr. Timothy R. Beeble, Director
Office of Community
Development
P.O. Box 10152
Stamford, CT 06904-2152
203-977-4864
Fax: 203-977-4775

City of Waterbury
Ms. Mary Welz-Schlosky,
Manager
Office of Community
Development
236 Grand St.
Chase Municipal Bldg., Room
222
Waterbury, CT 06702-1042
203-757-9621
Fax: 203-596-7977

Delaware
Mr. Jim M. Loescher, Manager
Delaware State Housing
Authority
18 The Green
Dover, DE 19901-3612
302-577-5001
Fax: 302-739-1118

Cities
City of Wilmington
Ms. Jane C.W. Vincent, Director
Department of Real Estate and
Housing
800 French St.
Louis L. Redding City-County
Bldg., Seventh Floor
Wilmington, DE 19801-3537
302-571-4057
Fax: 302-573-5588

Counties
County of New Castle
Ms. Charlotte Gilbert
Community Services
Coordinator
Department of Community
Development and Housing

800 N. French St.
Louis L. Redding City-County
Bldg.
Wilmington, DE 19801-3590
302-395-5600
Fax: 302-395-5592

District of Columbia
Ms. Gail Lyle, HOME Program
Manager
Department of Housing and
Community Development
801 N. Capitol St., N.W.
Washington, DC 20002
202-442-7200
Fax: 202-535-1955

Florida
Ms. Joyce Martinez
HOME Rental Administrator
State of Florida Housing and
Finance Corp.
227 N. Brounough St.
Suite 5000
Tallahassee, FL 32301-5026
850-488-4197
Fax: 850-488-9809

Cities
City of Clearwater
Mr. Michael Holmes, Manager
Department of Planning and
Development Services
P.O. Box 4748
Clearwater, FL 33758-4748
727-562-4032
Fax: 727-562-4037

City of Daytona Beach
Ms. Jennifer Thomas, Deputy
Director
Department of Community
Development
P.O. Box 2451
Daytona Beach, FL 32115-2451
904-258-3175
Fax: 904-947-3020

City of Ft. Lauderdale
Ms. Margarette Hayes,
Coordinator
Department of Economic
Development
101 N.E. Third Ave., Suite 200
Ft. Lauderdale, FL 33301-1965

954-468-1526
Fax: 954-468-1529

City of Gainesville
Mr. James A. Hencin, Manager
Block Grant Program
P.O. Box 490
Gainesville, FL 32602-0490
352-334-5031
Fax: 352-334-3166

City of Hialeah
Mr. Frederick H. Marinelli,
Director
Department of Grants and
Human Services
P.O. Box 110040
Hialeah, FL 33011-0040
305-883-8042
Fax: 305-883-5817

City of Hollywood
Ms. Jeannette M. Smith, Director
Division of Housing and
Community Development
P.O. Box 229045
Hollywood, FL 33022-9045
954-921-3271
Fax: 954-921-3365

City of Jacksonville/County of
Duval
Ms. Janet Hamer, Chief
City of Jacksonville/County of
Duval
Division of Housing Services
128 E. Forsythe St., Suite 500
Jacksonville, FL 32202-4011
904-630-7000
Fax: 904-630-3605

City of Lakeland
Ms. Nancy Bennett, Coordinator
Department of Community
Development
228 S. Massachusetts Ave.
Lakeland City Hall
Lakeland, FL 33801
863-603-6317
Fax: 863-603-6323

City of Miami/County of Dade
Mr. Rickert Glasgow, Director
City of Miami/County of Dade
Division of Community
Development

140 W. Flagler St., Suite 1000
Miami, FL 33130-1519
305-375-3418
Fax: 305-372-6304

City of Miami
Ms. Gwendolyn Warren,
Director
Department of Community
Development
444 S.W. Second Ave., Second
Floor
Miami, FL 33130
305-416-2088
Fax: 305-416-2090

City of Miami Beach
Mr. Miguell DelCampillo,
Housing Director
Division of Housing
1700 Convention Center Dr.
Miami Beach, FL 34102-1819
305-673-7260
Fax: 305-673-7772

City of Orlando
Ms. Lelia Allen, Bureau Chief
Department of Housing and
Community Development
400 S. Orange Ave., Sixth Floor
Orlando, FL 32801
407-246-2708
Fax: 407-246-2895

City of Pompano Beach
Mr. L. James Hudson, Director
Department of Housing and
Urban Improvement
P.O. Drawer 1300
Pompano Beach, FL 33061
954-786-4659
Fax: 954-786-4666

City of St. Petersburg
Ms. Stephane Lampe,
Coordinator
Department of Housing and
Neighborhood Improvement
P.O. Box 2842
St. Petersburg, FL 33701-2842
727-892-5563
Fax: 727-892-5397

City of Tallahassee
Ms. Martha Bentley, Supervisor

Department of Neighborhood
and Community Services
300 S. Adams St., B27
Tallahassee, FL 32301-1731
850-891-6540
Fax: 850-891-6597

City of Tampa
Mr. David Snyder, Assistant
Manager
Community Redevelopment
Agency
2105 N. Nebraska Ave.
Tampa, FL 33602-3616
813-274-7989
Fax: 813-274-7927

City of Hillsborough
Mr. Kevin McConnell, Director
Department of Community
Improvement
P.O. Box 1110
Tampa, FL 33619-4488
813-744-5557
Fax: 813-744-5777

City of West Palm Beach
Mr. Jerry Kelly, Community
Development Specialist
City of West Palm Beach
Department of Economic and
Community Development
P.O. Box 3366
West Palm Beach, FL 33402-3366
561-835-7300
Fax: 561-835-7348

Counties
County of Brevard
Ms. Rosa Reich, Planner
Department of Human Services
2725 Judge Fran Jamieson Way,
Bldg. B, Suite 106
Viera, FL 32940
321-633-2076
Fax: 321-633-2170

County of Broward
Ms. Sue Fejes, Assistant Director
Division of Community
Development
201 S. Andrews Ave., 2nd Floor
Ft. Lauderdale, FL 33301-1801
954-765-4910
Fax: 954-765-4919

County of Dade/City of Miami
Mr. Rickert Glasgow, Director
Division of Community
Development
140 W. Flagler St., Suite 1000
Miami, FL 33130-1519
305-375-3418
Fax: 305-372-6304

County of Duval/City of
Jacksonville
Ms. Janet Hamer, Chief
Division of Housing Services
128 E. Forsythe St., Suite 500
Jacksonville, FL 32202-4011
904-630-7000
Fax: 904-630-3605

County of Lee
Mr. Dennis Simon, Principal
Planner
Department of Human Services
P.O. Box 398
Ft. Myers, FL 33902-0398
941-656-7930
Fax: 941-656-7960

County of Palm Beach
Mr. John R. Batey, HOME
Coordinator
Department of Housing and
Community Development
3323 Belvedere Rd., Bldg. 501
West Palm Beach, FL 33406
561-233-3635
Fax: 561-233-3651

County of Pasco
Ms. Dianne W. Morris, Manager
Department of Community
Development
7530 Little Rd.
West Pasco Government Center,
Suite 340
New Port Richey, FL 34654
727-847-8970
Fax: 727-847-8021

County of Pinellas
Mr. Larry Yancey
Department of Community
Development
600 Cleveland St., Suite 800
Clearwater, FL 33755
727-464-8210
Fax: 727-464-8254

County of Polk
Ms. Nancy Sutton, Housing
Coordinator
Department of Housing and
Neighborhood Development
P.O. Box 9005
Bartow, FL 33831-9005
941-534-5244
Fax: 941-534-0349

County of Orange
Mr. Frantz Dutes, Asst. Mgr.
Department of Housing and
Community Development
525 E. South St.
Orlando, FL 32801-2817
407-836-4240
Fax: 407-836-4205

County of Volusia
Mr. John V. Angiulli, Manager
Continuum of Care
123 W. Indiana Ave.
De Land, FL 32720-4611
904-943-7039
Fax: 904-943-7011

Consorita
Escambia County Consortium
Mr. Randy Wilkerson, Exec. Dir.
Neighborhood Enterprise
Foundation, Inc.
P.O. Box 18178
Pensacola, FL 32523-8178
850-458-0466
Fax: 850-458-0464

Sarasota Consortium
Mr. Donald D. Hadsell, Director
Department of Community
Development
P.O. Box 1058
Sarasota, FL 34230-1058
941-316-1070
Fax: 941-316-1078

GEORGIA
Mr. Kevin Mac, Director
Dept. of Community Affairs
60 Executive Park, S., N.E.
Atlanta, GA 30329-2231
706-821-1797

Cities
City of Albany
Mr. Rudolph Goddard, Director

Department of Community and
Economic Development
230 S. Jackson St., Suite 315
Albany, GA 31701-2887
912-430-5283
Fax: 912-430-2737

City of Athens/Clarke County
Ms. Julie Brunner, Administrator
Department of Human and
Economic Development
P.O. Box 1868
Athens, GA 30603-1868
706-613-3155
Fax: 706-613-3158

City of Atlanta
Mr. Philip Smith, Director
Department of Planning,
Development and
Neighborhood Conservation
68 Mitchell St., S.W., Suite 1200
Atlanta, GA 30303-3520
404-330-6390
Fax: 404-658-7384

City of Augusta/County of
Richmond
Ms. Franciene Parham,
Administrator
Department of Community
Development
One Tenth St., Suite 430
Augusta, GA 30911
706-821-1797
Fax: 706-821-1784

City of Columbus/County of
Muscogee
Mr. Greg Clark, Chief
Division of Economic
Development
P.O. Box 1340
Columbus, GA 31902-1340
706-653-4487
Fax: 706-653-4486

City of Macon
Mr. Chester Wheeler, Director
Department of Economic and
Community Development
439 Cotton Ave.
Southern Trust Bldg.
Macon, GA 31201
912-751-7190
Fax: 912-751-7390

City of Savannah
Ms. Victoria Bertolozzi, Analyst
Neighborhood Planning and
Community Development/
Bureau of Public Development
P.O. Box 1027
Savannah, GA 31402-1027
912-651-6520
Fax: 912-651-6525

Counties
County of Clarke/City of
Athens
Ms. Julie Brunner, Administrator
Department of Human and
Economic Development
P.O. Box 1868
Athens, GA 30603-1868
706-613-3155
Fax: 706-613-3158

County of Clayton
Mr. Craig Goebeh, Director
Housing and Community
Development Program
136 South Main Street, Suite B
Jonesboro, GA 30236
770-210-5210
Fax: 770-210-5215

County of Cobb
Mr. W. Lance Crawford,
Director
Community Development
Program
127 Church St.
The Brumby Bldg. at Marietta
Station, Suite 270
Marietta, GA 30060
770-528-4630
Fax: 770-528-4613

County of DeKalb
Mr. Rick Herman, Director
Department of Community
Development
1807 Candler Rd.
Decatur, GA 30032-4162
404-286-3353
Fax: 404-286-3337

County of Gwinnett
Ms. Virginia McKinny
Community Development Block
Grants
P.O. Box 1750

Laurenceville, GA 30046-1750
770-822-5190
Fax: 770-822-5193

County of Muscogee/City of
Columbus
Mr. Greg Clark, Chief
Division of Economic
Development
P.O. Box 1340
Columbus, GA 31902-1340
706-653-4487
Fax: 706-653-4486

County of Richmond/City of
Augusta
Ms. Franciene Parham,
Administrator
Department of Community
Development
One Tenth St., Suite 430
Augusta, GA 30911
706-821-1797
Fax: 706-821-1784

Consortia
County of Fulton Consortium
Mr. Melvin Richardshon,
Assistant Director
Office of Environment and
Community Development
141 Pryor Street, SW, Suite 5001
Atlanta, GA 30303
404-730-8066
Fax: 404-730-8112

GUAM

Housing and Urban Renewal
Authority
Ms. Taling M. Taitano, Exec. Dir.
117 Bien Venida Ave.
Sinajana, GU 96926
671-477-9851
Fax: 671-472-7565

Hawaii

Ms. Sharyn Miyashiro
Acting Executive Director
Department of Business
Economic Development and
Tourism
677 Queen St., Suite 300
Honolulu, HI 96813
808-587-0641
Fax: 808-587-0600

Cities/Counties
City and County of Honolulu
Ms. Jean Tangi, Acting
Coordinator
Department of the Budget
530 S. King St.
Room 208
Honolulu, HI 96813-3018
808-523-4375
Fax: 808-527-6968

Idaho

Mr. Earl Cook, Grants Manager
Idaho Housing and Finance
Association
P.O. Box 7899
Boise, ID 83707-1899
208-331-4712
Fax: 208-331-4808

Cities
City of Boise
Mr. Jim Fackrell, Director
Division of Housing and
Community Development
1025 S. Capitol Blvd.
Boise, ID 83706
208-384-4158
Fax: 208-384-4195

Illinois

Ms. Mary Somrak-Arey
HOME Program Director
Illinois Housing Development
Authority
401 N. Michigan Ave., Suite 900
Chicago, IL 60611-4255
312-836-5364
Fax: 312-832-2176

Cities
City of Chicago
Mr. Nancy Pomes, Deputy
Commissioner
Division of Compliance and
Monitoring
318 S. Michigan Ave.
Chicago, IL 60604-4200
312-747-2608
Fax: 312-747-5023

City of Decatur
Reginald Fluker, Manager
Department of Neighborhood
Services
One Gary K. Anderson Plaza

Decatur, IL 62523-1196
217-424-2778
Fax: 217-424-2728

City of East St. Louis
Ms. Chris Anderson, HOME
Coordinator
CDBG Operations Corp.
301 River Park Dr., Third Floor
E. St. Louis, IL 62201-1201
618-482-6635
Fax: 618-271-8194

City of Evanston
Ms. Roberta Schur, Planner
Division of Planning
2100 Ridge Ave., Room 3900
Evanston, IL 60201
847-866-2928
Fax: 847-448-8120

City of Joliet
Mr. Robert Listner, Director
Division of Neighborhood
Services
150 W. Jefferson St.
Joliet, IL 60432
815-724-4090
Fax: 815-724-4118

City of Peoria
Ms. Pat S. Landes, Asst. Dir.
Department of Development
456 Fulton St., Suite 402
Peoria, IL 61602-1217
309-494-8605
Fax: 309-494-8680

City of Rockford
Ms. Vicki Manson,
Neighborhood Development
Coordinator
Department of Community
Development
425 E. State St.
Rockford, IL 61104-1014
815-987-5690
Fax: 815-967-6933

City of Springfield
Mr. Jan Sorenson, Grants
Coordinator
Office of Economic Development
231 S. Sixth St.
Springfield, IL 62701-1502

217-789-2377
Fax: 217-789-2380

City of Urbana
Mr. Michael J. Loschen, Grants
Coordinator
Department of Community
Development Services
400 S. Vine St.
Urbana, IL 61801
217-384-2335
Fax: 217-384-2367

Counties
County of DuPage
Mr. Phil Smith, Administrator
Department of Human Services
421 N. County Farm Rd.
Wheaton, IL 60187
630-682-7543
Fax: 630-682-7179

County of Lake
Mr. Vern Witkowski,
Community Development
Administrator
Department of Planning,
Building and Development
18 N. County St., Sixth Floor
Waukegan, IL 60085-4356
847-360-6495
Fax: 847-360-6734

County of Madison
Ms. Dorothy Hummel, HOME
Program Coordinator
Department of Community
Development
130 Hillsboro Ave.
Edwardsville, IL 62025-1955
618-692-6200
Fax: 618-692-7022

County of McHenry
Mr. John W. Labaj, Deputy
Director
Department of Planning and
Development
2200 N. Seminary Ave., Annex
Bldg. A
Woodstock, IL 60098
815-338-2040
Fax: 815-337-3720

County of Will
Mr. Ron Pullman, Director

Department of Community
Development
100 Manhattan Rd.
Farm Bureau Bldg.
Joliet, IL 60433-4060
815-727-2332
Fax: 815-727-2341

Consortia
Cook County Consortium
Mr. Ted Sucharski, HOME
Program Coordinator
Department of Planning and
Development
69 W. Washington Blvd., Suite
2900
Chicago, IL 60602-1304
312-603-1066
Fax: 312-603-9970

St. Clair County Consortium
Mr. David Van Toll, HOME
Program Coordinator
Division of Community
Development
19 Public Sq., Suite 200
Belleville, IL 62220-1624
618-277-6790
Fax: 618-236-1190

Indiana
Ms. Sheryl Sharpe
Community Development
Manager
Housing Finance Authority
115 W. Washington St.
Suite 1350, South Tower
Indianapolis, IN 46204-3413
317-232-7777
Fax: 317-232-7778

Cities
City of Anderson
Mr. Ron Harris, Deputy Director
Department of Community
Development
P.O. Box 2100
Anderson, IN 46018
765-648-6097
Fax: 765-648-5914

City of Bloomington
Ms. Doris Sims, Exec. Dir.
Department of Redevelopment
P.O. Box 100
Bloomington, IN 47402

812-349-3401
Fax: 812-349-3582

City of East Chicago
Mr. John D. Artis, Director
Department of Redevelopment
and Housing Authority
P.O. Box 498
East Chicago, IN 46312-0498
219-397-9974
Fax: 219-397-4249

City of Evansville
Ms. Brenda Taylor, Community
Development Specialist
Department of Metropolitan
Development
One N.W. Martin Luther King,
Jr. Blvd.
306 Civic Center Complex
Evansville, IN 47708-1831
812-436-7823
Fax: 812-436-7809

City of Ft. Wayne
Mr. Brian White, Community
Development Administrator
Department of Community and
Economic Development
One E. Main St.
City-County Bldg., Room 910
Ft. Wayne, IN 46802
219-427-2158
Fax: 219-427-1115

City of Gary
Ms. Letty Almodovar, Director
Department of Planning and
Community Development
475 Broadway
Third Floor, Suite 318
Gary, IN 46402-1239
219-881-5075
Fax: 219-881-5085

City of Hammond
Ms. Katrina Burns, Loan Officer
Department of Community
Development
649 Conkey St.
Hammond, IN 46324-3027
219-853-6371
Fax: 219-853-6334

City of Indianapolis
Mr. Jim Kaufman, Grants
Manager

Department of Metropolitan
Development/HOME Program
200 E. Washington St.
City County Bldg., Suite 1841
Indianapolis, IN 46204
317-327-5866
Fax: 317-327-5908

City of Lafayette
Ms. Aimee Dibble, Director
Department of Community and
Redevelopment
20 N. Sixth St.
Lafayette, IN 47901-1412
765-476-4510
Fax: 765-476-4513

City of Muncie
Mr. Jerry L. Thornburg, Director
Department of Community
Development
300 N. High St.
Muncie, IN 47305
765-747-4825
Fax: 765-747-4898

City of South Bend
Ms. Elizabeth Leonard, Director
Department of Community and
Economic Development
227 W. Jefferson Blvd.
County-City Bldg., Suite 1200
South Bend, IN 46601
219-235-9330
Fax: 219-235-9021

City of Terre Haute
Mr. Mike Kass, Administrator
Department of Redevelopment
17 Harding Ave.
City Hall, Room 301
Terre Haute, IN 47807
812-232-0018
Fax: 812-235-3652

Counties
County of Lake
Ms. Alverna Hooks, Deputy
Director
Department of Community
Development
2293 N. Main St.
Crown Point, IN 46307-1885
219-755-3232
Fax: 219-736-5925

Iowa
Ms. Anna Woolson, Team
Leader
Department of Economic
Development
200 E. Grand Ave.
Des Moines, IA 50309-1827
515-242-4825
Fax: 515-242-4809

Cities
City of Cedar Rapids
Mr. Dan Schmelzinger, Director
Department of Housing,
Building, and Zoning
1201 Sixth St., S.W.
Cedar Rapids, IA 52404-1256
319-286-5836
Fax: 319-286-5870

City of Davenport
Mr. Gregg Hoover, Director
Department of Community and
Economic Development
226 W. Fourth St.
Davenport, IA 52801-1308
319-326-7766
Fax: 319-328-6714

City of Des Moines
Mr. Bob Schulte, Director
Department of Housing and
Community Services
602 E. First St.
Des Moines, IA 50309-1881
515-237-1384
Fax: 515-237-1687

City of Iowa City
Mr. Steven Nasby, Community
Development Coordinator
Department of Planning and
Community Development
410 E. Washington St.
Iowa City, IA 52240
319-356-5230
Fax: 319-356-5009

City of Sioux City
Mr. Russell Kock, Administrator
Department of Community
Development
P.O. Box 447
Sioux City, IA 51102
712-279-6283
Fax: 712-279-6196

City of Waterloo
Mr. Richard W. Earles, Director
Department of Community
Development
620 Mulberry St., Suite 202
Waterloo, IA 50703
319-291-4429
Fax: 319-291-4431

Kansas
Ms. Barbara Cowdin, HOME
Program Director
Division of Housing
700 S.W. Harrison St., Suite 1300
Topeka, KS 66603-3755
785-296-4819
Fax: 785-296-8985

Cities
City of Kansas City
Mr. Brian Z. White, Program
Coordinator
Department of Housing and
Community Development
701 N. Seventh St.
Kansas City, KS 66101-3064
913-573-5100
Fax: 913-573-5115

City of Lawrence
Ms. Margene Swarts,
Community Development
Manager
Department of Housing and
Neighborhood Development
Six E. Sixth St.
Lawrence, KS 66044
785-832-3100
Fax: 785-832-3405

City of Topeka
Mr. Mark Stock, CDBG Program
Manager
Department of Housing and
Neighborhood Development
2010 S.E. California Ave.
Topeka, KS 66607
785-368-3711
Fax: 785-368-2546

City of Wichita
Mr. Mark Stanberry, HOME
Coordinator
Department of Human Services
332 N. Riverview St.
Wichita, KS 67203

316-268-4685
Fax: 316-268-4291

Counties
County of Sedgwick/ Central
Plains HOME Consortium
Mr. Bradley Snapp, Coordinator
Department of Community
Development
1540 N. Broadway, Suite 203
Wichita, KS 67214
316-383-7433
Fax: 316-383-8271

Consortia
Johnson County Consortium
Ms. Mary Scott, Director
Department of Housing
9305 W. 74th St.
Merriam, KS 66204
913-432-2174
Fax: 913-722-3296

Central Plains HOME
Consortium/County of
Sedgwick
Mr. Bradley Snapp, Coordinator
Department of Community
Development
1540 N. Broadway, Suite 203
Wichita, KS 67214
316-383-7433
Fax: 316-383-8271

Kentucky
Mr. Rob Ellis, CPD Director
Kentucky Housing Corp.
1231 Louisville Rd.
Frankfort, KY 40601-6156
502-564-7630
Fax: 502-564-6445

Cities
City of Covington
Mr. Howard Hodge, Director
Department of Housing and
Community Development
638 Madison Ave.
Covington, KY 41011-2422
606-292-2188
Fax: 606-292-2139

City of Lexington/County of
Fayette
Ms. Paula King, HOME
Coordinator

City of Lexington/County of
Fayette
Division of Housing and
Community Development
200 E. Main St., Sixth Floor
Lexington, KY 40507
606-258-3070
Fax: 606-258-3081

City of Louisville
Ms. Barbara Ferrell,
Administrator
Department of Housing and
Urban Development
745 W. Main St., Suite 300
Louisville, KY 40202-2675
502-574-4397
Fax: 502-574-4199

City of Owensboro
Mr. Keith Free, Associate
Director
Metropolitan Planning
Commission
P.O. Box 732
Owensboro, KY 42302-9003
270-687-8656
Fax: 270-687-8664

Counties
County of Fayette/City of
Lexington
Ms. Paula King
HOME Coordinator
City of Lexington/County of
Fayette
Division of Housing and
Community Development
200 E. Main St., Sixth Floor
Lexington, KY 40507
606-258-3070
Fax: 606-258-3081

County of Jefferson
Ms. Brenda White, Director
Division of Community
Development
810 Barret Ave., Sixth Floor
Louisville, KY 40204-1700
502-574-6550
Fax: 502-574-6912

Louisiana
Ms. Debra Washington, Program
Manager
Housing Finance Agency

200 Lafayette St., Suite 300
Baton Rouge, LA 70801
225-342-1320
Fax: 225-342-1310

Cities
City of Alexandria
Ms. Brenda Ray, Director
Department of Community
Development
P.O. Box 71
Alexandria, LA 71309-0071
318-449-5072
Fax: 318-449-5031

City of Baton Rouge
Mr. Al Gensler, Director
Department of Community
Development
P.O. Box 1471
Baton Rouge, LA 70821-1471
225-389-3039
Fax: 225-389-3939

City of Houma/Parish of
Terrebonne
Ms. Melanie VanBuren, HOME
Program Manager
Department of Housing and
Human Services
P.O. Box 6097
Houma, LA 70361
985-873-6892
Fax: 985-873-6880

City of Lafayette
Mr. Joe Bourg, Manager
Governmental and Business
Relations Division
P.O. Box 4017-C
Lafayette, LA 70502-4017
337-291-8411
Fax: 337-291-8415

City of Lake Charles
Mr. Mark Tizano, Planner
Department of Planning and
Economic Development
P.O. Box 900
Lake Charles, LA 70602-0900
337-491-1440
Fax: 337-491-1437

City of Monroe
Dr. James Tarver, Interim
Director

Division of Community
Development
P.O. Box 123
Monroe, LA 71201-0123
318-329-2256
Fax: 318-329-2845

City of New Orleans
Mr. John Roussell, Deputy
Director
Division of Housing and
Neighborhood Development
1340 Poydras St., Tenth Floor
New Orleans, LA 70112
504-299-4800
Fax: 504-299-4951

City of Shreveport
Mr. Larry Ferdinand, Director
Department of Community
Development
P.O. Box 31109
Shreveport, LA 71130-1109
318-673-5900
Fax: 318-673-5903

Parishes
Parish of Jefferson
Mr. Kim Thompson, Manager
Department of Community
Development Programs
1221 Elmwood Park Blvd., Suite
605
Harahan, LA 70123-2337
504-736-6262
Fax: 504-736-6425

Parish of Terrebonne/City of
Houma
Ms. Melanie VanBuren, HOME
Program Manager
Department of Housing and
Human Services
P.O. Box 6097
Houma, LA 70361
985-873-6892
Fax: 985-873-6880

Maine
Mr. Michael Martin, State of
Maine Housing Authority
353 Water St.
Augusta, ME 4338
207-626-4615
Fax: 207-626-4692

Cities
City of Portland
Mr. Roger Bondeson, Manager
Department of Housing and
Neighborhood Service
389 Congress St., Room 313
Portland, ME 04101-3509
207-874-8711
Fax: 207-756-8990

Northern Mariana Islands
Northern Mariana Islands
Housing Corp.
Ms. Mary Lou S. Ada, Executive
Director
Commonwealth Development
Authority
P.O. Box 502149
Saipan, MP 96950-2149
670-234-7145
Fax: 670-234-7144

Maryland
Ms. Vicky Semour
HOME Program Manager
State of Maryland
Department of Housing and
Community Development
100 Community Place
Crownsville, MD 21032-2025
410-514-7440
Fax: 410-987-4097

Cities
City of Baltimore
Mr. James R. Majors, Chief
Department of Housing and
Community Development
417 E. Fayette St., Suite 1036
Baltimore, MD 21202-3431
410-396-5590
Fax: 410-625-0830

Counties
County of Anne Arundel
Ms. Kathleen M. Koch, Executive
Director
County of Anne Arundel
Arundel Community
Development Services, Inc.
2660 Riva Rd., Suite 210
Annapolis, MD 21401
410-222-7600
Fax: 410-222-7619

County of Baltimore
Mr. Kevin M. Roddy, Grants
Administrator
Office of Community
Conservation
One Investment Place, Suite 800
Towson, MD 21204
410-887-6055
Fax: 410-887-5696

County of Montgomery
Ms. Luann W. Korona, Section
Chief
Department of Housing and
Community Affairs
100 Maryland Ave., Fourth Floor
Rockville, MD 20850
240-777-3600
Fax: 240-777-3653

County of Prince Georges
Mr. James M. Lyons, Manager
Department of Housing and
Community Development
9400 Peppercorn Place, Suite 120
Largo, MD 20774
301-883-5570
Fax: 301-925-4147

Massachusetts
Ms. JoAnn McGuirk
HOME Program Director
State of Massachusetts
Department of Housing and
Community Development
One Congress St., Tenth Floor
Boston, MA 2114
617-727-7824
Fax: 617-727-0532

Cities
City of Boston
Ms. Charlotte Golar Richie,
Director
Department of Neighborhood
Development
26 Court St.
Boston, MA 2108
617-635-0500
Fax: 617-635-0561

City of Brockton
Mr. Steven C. Cruz, Exec. Dir.
Redevelopment Authority
140 School St.
Brockton, MA 02302-3114

508-587-6085
Fax: 508-584-2362

City of Cambridge
Ms. Elsa Campbell, Manager
Department of Community
Development
57 Inman St.
Cambridge, MA 2139
617-349-4634
Fax: 617-349-4669

City of Fall River
Mr. Thomas McCloskey,
Executive Director
Community Development
Agency
P.O. Box 1711
Fall River, MA 02720-2107
508-679-0131
Fax: 508-679-0752

City of Fitchburg
Mr. David Streb, Coordinator
718 Main St.
Fitchburg, MA 01420-3182
978-345-1018
Fax: 978-342-0161

City of Holyoke
Mr. William H. Murphy,
Administrator
Office of Community
Development
20 Korean Veterans Plaza
City Hall Annex, Room 400
Holyoke, MA 01040-5036
413-534-2230
Fax: 413-534-2231

City of Lawrence
Mr. William Luster, Director
Department of Community
Development
225 Essex St., Third Floor
Lawrence, MA 1840
978-794-5891
Fax: 978-683-4894

City of Lowell
Mr. Jay Matthew Coggins,
Director
Division of Planning and
Development
50 Arcand Dr.
JFK Civic Center

Lowell, MA 1852
978-970-4252
Fax: 978-970-4262

City of Lynn
Mr. Charles J. Gaeta, Exec. Dir.
Lynn Housing Authority
Ten Church St.
Lynn, MA 1902
781-477-2800
Fax: 781-592-6296

City of Malden
Mr. Peter Garbaiti, HOME
Coordinator
Malden Redevelopment
Authority
200 Pleasant St., Room 621
Malden, MA 02148-4802
781-324-5720
Fax: 781-322-3734

City of New Bedford
Mr. Patrick Sullivan, Director
Department of Community
Development
608 Pleasant St.
New Bedford, MA 02740-6113
508-979-1500
Fax: 508-979-1575

City of Newton
Mr. Stephen D. Gartrell, Director
Department of Community
Development
1000 Commonwealth Ave.
Newton Center
Newton, MA 2159
617-552-7135
Fax: 617-965-6620

City of Peabody/North Shore
HOME Consortium
Mr. Kevin J. Hurley, HOME
Coordinator
Department of Community
Development
24 Lowell St.
City Hall
Peabody, MA 01960-5440
978-532-5000 Ext. 327
Fax: 978-531-9908

City of Quincy
Mr. Angelito Santos, Principal
Planner

Department of Planning and
Community Development
1305 Hancock St.
Quincy, MA 2169
617-376-1362
Fax: 617-376-1097

City of Somerville
Mr. Stephen M. Post, Executive
Director
Office of Housing and
Community Development
93 Highland Ave.
Somerville, MA 02143-1740
617-625-6000
Fax: 617-625-0722

City of Springfield
Ms. Kathleen Lindenburg,
Housing Director
Department of Community
Development
81 State St.
Springfield, MA 01103-1699
413-787-6500
Fax: 413-787-6515

City of Worcester
Mr. Stephen O'Neil, Director
Office of Planning and
Community Development
418 Main St., Suite 400
Worcester, MA 1608
508-799-1400
Fax: 508-799-1406

Consortia
Barnstable County Consortium
Mr. Edward Allard, Specialist
Cape Cod Commission
3225 Main St.
Barnstable, MA 2630
508-362-3828
Fax: 508-362-3136

North Shore HOME
Consortium/City of Peabody
Mr. Kevin J. Hurley, HOME
Coordinator
Department of Community
Development
24 Lowell St.
City Hall
Peabody, MA 01960-5440
978-532-5000 Ext. 327
Fax: 978-531-9908

Michigan

Mr. Bill Parker, Coordinator
State of Michigan
Housing Development
Authority
P.O. Box 30044
Lansing, MI 48909-7544
517-373-1462
Fax: 517-335-4797

Cities

City of Ann Arbor
Mr. Larry Friedman
Department of Community
Development
P.O. Box 8647
Ann Arbor, MI 48107-8647
734-994-2589
Fax: 734-994-2915

City of Battle Creek
Mr. Tim Parks, Coordinator
Department of Planning and
Community Development
P.O. Box 1717
Battle Creek, MI 49016-1717
616-966-3315
Fax: 616-966-3659

City of Bay City
Ms. Debbie Kiesel, Acting
Director
Department of Redevelopment
and Housing Services
301 Washington Ave.
Bay City, MI 48708
517-894-8153
Fax: 517-894-8220

City of Detroit
Ms. Leah Vest, Executive
Manager
Department of Planning and
Development
65 Cadillac Tower, Suite 1900
Detroit, MI 48226
313-224-3461
Fax: 313-224-9149

City of Flint
Ms. Karen Morris
Department of Community and
Economic Development
1101 S. Saginaw St.
Flint, MI 48502

810-766-7436
Fax: 810-766-7351

City of Grand Rapids
Mr. Thomas S. Syrek, Director
Department of Housing and
Community Development
300 Monroe Ave., N.W.
City Hall, Room 460
Grand Rapids, MI 49503-2206
616-456-3445
Fax: 616-456-4619

City of Jackson
Mr. Michael Sims, Assistant
Director
Department of Community
Development
161 W. Michigan Ave.
Jackson, MI 49201
517-768-4060
Fax: 517-768-5832

City of Kalamazoo
Ms. Peg Giem
Department of Community
Development
241 W. South St.
Kalamazoo, MI 49007-4796
616-337-8225

City of Lansing
Mr. Dennis Lysakowski
Division of Development
316 N. Capitol Ave., Suite D-2
Lansing, MI 48933-1234
517-483-4051
Fax: 517-483-6036

City of Muskegon
Mr. Will Griffin, Director
Department of Community and
Neighborhood Services
P.O. Box 536
Muskegon, MI 49443
231-724-6963
Fax: 231-726-2501

City of Pontiac
Ms. Ruth Steed, HOME Program
Administrator
Department of Community
Development
51000 Woodward Ave.
Pontiac, MI 48342-5015

248-857-5670
Fax: 248-857-5744

City of Port Huron
Ms. Mary Wrocklage
Department of Planning and
Community Development
100 McMorran Blvd.
Port Huron, MI 48060
810-984-9736
Fax: 810-982-7872

City of Saginaw
Mr. Robert Brown, Director
Department of Rehabilitation
and Block Grant Services
1315 S. Washington Ave., Room
210
Saginaw, MI 48601-2513
517-759-1530
Fax: 517-759-1756

City of Warren
Ms. Rosemary Furlong, Program
Coordinator
Department of Community
Development
29500 Van Dyke Ave.
Warren, MI 48093-6726
810-574-4687
Fax: 810-574-4685

City of Westland
Mr. James Gilbert, Director
Department of Community
Development
32715 Dorsey Rd.
Westland, MI 48185
734-595-0288
Fax: 734-595-1680

Counties

County of Genesee
Ms. Christine Keisling
Metropolitan Planning
Commission
1101 Beach St., Room 223
Flint, MI 48502
810-766-6549
Fax: 810-257-3185

County of Macomb
Mr. James Baumgartner,
Director
Department of Planning and
Economic Development

One S. Main St., Seventh Floor
Mt. Clemens, MI 48043
810-469-5285
Fax: 810-469-6787

County of Oakland
Ms. Karry Reith, Manager
Department of Community
Development
1200 N. Telegraph Rd.
Executive Office Bldg. 112,
Department 414
Pontiac, MI 48341-1043
248-858-0493
Fax: 248-858-5311

County of Wayne
Mr. James Constan, Program
Manager
Division of Community
Development
600 Randolph St.
Wayne County Bldg.
Detroit, MI 48226
313-224-6655
Fax: 313-224-7450

MINNESOTA

Mr. Jim Cegla
Federal Programs and Policy
Director
Minnesota Housing Finance
Agency
400 Sibley St., Suite 300
St. Paul, MN 55101-1941
800-657-3701
Fax: 651-296-8139

Cities
City of Duluth
Mr. Keith Hamre, Manager
Division of Community
Development and Housing
411 W. First St.
City Hall, Room 407
Duluth, MN 55802-1100
218-723-3357
Fax: 218-723-3400

City of Minneapolis
Mr. Ken Brunsvold, Director
Office of Grants and Special
Projects
350 S. Fifth St.
City Hall, Room 200
Minneapolis, MN 55415

612-673-2348
Fax: 612-673-3724

City of St. Paul
Mr. Ron Ross, Manager
Department of Planning and
Economic Development
25 Fourth St., W., 14th Floor
St. Paul, MN 55102-1634
651-266-6692
Fax: 651-228-3220

Counties
County of Dakota
Ms. Stephanie Newburg, HOME
Coordinator
Housing and Redevelopment
Authority
2496 145th St.
Rosemount, MN 55068
651-423-8117
Fax: 651-423-8180

County of Hennepin
Mr. Rod Waara, Director
Office of Planning and
Development
10709 Wayzata Blvd., Suite 260
Hopkins, MN 55305
612-541-7080
Fax: 612-541-7090

Consortia
St. Louis County Consortium
Ms. Nancy Larson
Department of Community
Development
227 W. First St.
Missabe Bldg., Room 901
Duluth, MN 55802-1202
218-749-9741
Fax: 218-725-5029

Mississippi

Ms. Deborah Franklin
Grants Management Manager
State of Mississippi
Division of Community Services
P.O. Box 24628
Jackson, MS 39225-4628
601-949-2250
Fax: 601-949-2230

Cities
City of Hattiesburg
Mr. Joe Strahan, Senior
Planner/Housing Coordinator

Department of Planning and
Community Development
200 Forest Street
City Hall
Hattiesburg, MS 39401
601-545-4598
Fax: 601-545-4592

City of Jackson
Mr. Leo Stevens, Director
Division of Development
Assistance
P.O. Box 17
Jackson, MS 39205-0017
601-960-2155
Fax: 601-960-2403

MISSOURI

Ms. Angela Campbell,
Administrator
Housing Development
Commission
3435 Broadway
Kansas City, MO 64111
816-759-6660
Fax: 816-759-6828

Cities
City of Columbia
Mr. John Fleck, Planner
Department of Planning and
Development
P.O. Box N
Columbia, MO 65205
573-874-7244
Fax: 573-874-7546

City of Independence
Mr. Herb Webb, HOME
Coordinator
Department of Community
Development
P.O. Box 1019
Independence, MO 64051
816-325-7425
Fax: 816-325-7400

City of Kansas City
Mr. John Tangeman, Director
City of Kansas City
Department of Housing and
Community Development
414 E. 12th St.
City Hall, 11th Floor
Kansas City, MO 64106
816-513-3000
Fax: 816-513-3011

City of Springfield
Mr. R. Charles Marinec, Grants
Administrator
Department of Planning and
Development
840 Boonville Ave.
Springfield, MO 65802
417-864-1038
Fax: 417-864-1881

City of St. Joseph
Mr. Gerald McCush, HOME
Coordinator
Department of Community
Development
1100 Frederick Ave.
City Hall, Room 405
St. Joseph, MO 64501
816-271-4646
Fax: 816-271-5365

City of St. Louis
Ms. Jill Claybour, HOME
Coordinator
City of St. Louis
Community Development
Agency
1015 Locust, Suite 1140
St. Louis, MO 63101
314-622-3400
Fax: 314-622-3413
Counties

County of St. Louis
Mr. Phil Minden, Housing Mgr.
Office of Community
Development
121 S. Meramec Ave.
St. Louis, MO 63105
314-615-8337
Fax: 314-889-3420

MONTANA
Ms. Connie Oustad
HOME Program Manager
Department of Commerce
P.O. Box 200545
Helena, MT 59620-0545
406-444-0092
Fax: 406-444-9774

Cities
City of Billings
Mr. John Walsh, Director
Department of Community
Development

P.O. Box 1178
Billings, MT 59103
406-657-8281
Fax: 406-657-8252

City of Great Falls
Ms. Kim Johnson,
CDBG/HOME Administrator
Department of Community
Development
P.O. Box 5021
Great Falls, MT 59403-5021
406-455-8407
Fax: 406-454-3181

NEBRASKA
Ms. Lara Huskey
Housing Coordinator
Office of Economic Development
P.O. Box 94666
Lincoln, NE 68509-4666
402-471-3759
Fax: 402-471-3778

Cities
City of Lincoln
Mr. Steve Werthmann, Manager
Department of Urban
Development
129 N. Tenth St.
Room 110
Lincoln, NE 68508
402-441-7864
Fax: 402-441-8711

City of Omaha
Mr. Mike Saklar, Director
Department of Planning
1819 Farnam St., Suite 1111
Omaha, NE 68183-1100
402-444-5150
Fax: 402-444-6140

NEVADA
Ms. Debbie Parra
Officer Department of
Commerce
1802 N. Carson St., Suite 154
Carson City, NV 89701-1215
775-687-4258
Fax: 775-687-4040

Cities
City of Reno
Ms. Linda Johnson, Housing
Administrator

Department of Community
Development
P.O. Box 1900
Reno, NV 89505-1900
775-334-2305
Fax: 775-334-2343

Counties
County of Clark
Mr. Michael J. Pawlak,
Administrator
Division of Community
Resources Management
P.O. Box 551212
Las Vegas, NV 89155-1212
702-455-5025
Fax: 702-455-5038

County of Lyon
Ms. Denise Cox
Public Information Contact
County of Lyon
Western Nevada Development
District
31 S. Main St.
Yerington, NV 89447
775-883-7333

NEW HAMPSHIRE
Mr. William Ray
Planner New Hampshire
Housing Finance Authority
Division of Planning and
Development
P.O. Box 5087
Manchester, NH 03108-5087
603-472-8623
Fax: 603-471-1043

Cities
City of Manchester
Mr. Samuel Maranto, City
Planner
One City Hall Plaza
Manchester, NH 03101-2018
603-624-6530
Fax: 603-624-6529

NEW JERSEY
Ms. Sheri Malnak, Administrator
State of New Jersey
Division of Housing and
Community Resources
P.O. Box 806
Trenton, NJ 08625-0806

609-984-8453
Fax: 609-984-8454

Cities

City of Atlantic City
Mr. Michael P. Toland, CDBG
Director
Department of Planning and
Development
1301 Bacharach Blvd.
Room 505, City Hall
Atlantic City, NJ 8401
609-347-5330
Fax: 609-347-5317

City of Camden
Mr. Louis Pastoriza, Clerk
Bureau of Grants Management
P.O. Box 95120
Camden, NJ 08101-5120
856-757-7000

City of East Orange
Ms. Lancie Marchan, Manager
Department of Policy, Planning,
and Development
44 City Hall Plaza
East Orange, NJ 07019-4104
973-266-5138
Fax: 973-674-2180

City of Elizabeth
Ms. Stephanie Welch, Secretary
Department of Community
Development
50 Winfield Scott Plaza
Elizabeth, NJ 07201-2408
908-352-8450
Fax: 908-352-2275

City of Irvington
Ms. Tonique Griffin, Public
Information Contact
Office of Community
Development and Planning
Civic Sq.
Municipal Bldg., Room 102
Irvington, NJ 07111-4518
973-399-6658
Fax: 973-399-0827

City of Jersey City
Ms. Elenor O'Malley, Manager
Office of Grants Management
30 Montgomery St., Room 404
Jersey City, NJ 7302

201-547-6910
Fax: 201-547-5104

City of New Brunswick
Ms. Carole Small-Lyons, HOME
Coordinator
Department of Planning,
Community and Economic
Development
390 George St.
New Brunswick, NJ 8901
732-745-5050
Fax: 732-545-2390

City of Newark
Mr. Basil Franklin, Director
Department of Economic
Development
920 Broad St., Suite 218
Newark, NJ 07102-2609
973-733-3682
Fax: 973-733-3769

City of Passaic
Ms. Sonya Dasilva, Assistant
Director
Department of Community
Development
330 Passaic St.
Passaic, NJ 07055-5815
973-365-5641
Fax: 973-365-5552

City of Paterson
Ms. Anna-Lisa Dopirak, Director
Department of Community
Development
125 Ellison St., Second Floor
Paterson, NJ 07505-1310
973-279-5980
Fax: 973-278-2981

City of Perth Amboy
Mr. Michael W. Keller, Director
Office of Economic and
Community Development
One Olive St., Second Floor
Perth Amboy, NJ 08861-4517
732-442-4000
Fax: 732-442-9274

City of Trenton
Ms. Rhonda Coe, Director
Department of Housing and
Development
319 E. State St., Third Floor

Trenton, NJ 08608-1809
609-989-3598
Fax: 609-989-4243

City of Vineland
Mr. Joseph Bullock
Community Development
Director
Department of Administration
P.O. Box 5108
Vineland, NJ 8360
856-794-4000
Fax: 856-794-6163

Counties

County of Atlantic
Mr. Stephen Lingle, Director
Department of Community
Development/Improvement
Authority
201 Shore Rd., Stillwater Bldg.
Northfield, NJ 8225
609-345-5838
Fax: 609-645-5931

County of Bergen
Ms. Lynn Bartlett-DeLuise,
HOME Coordinator
Department of Community
Development
25 E. Salem St., Room 601
Hackensack, NJ 07601-7021
201-646-3458
Fax: 201-487-0945

County of Burlington
Mr. Robert Schmidt, Public
Information Contact
Department of Economic
Development
795 Woodlane Rd.
Mount Holly, NJ 08060-1317
609-265-5072
Fax: 609-265-5500

County of Camden
Ms. Beth Pugh, Analyst
P.O. Box 100
Blackwood, NJ 08012-0100
856-374-6335
Fax: 856-374-6348

County of Essex
Ms. Maggie Benz, Coordinator
Division of Housing and
Community Development

50 S. Clinton St.
Fourth Floor, Suite 4300
East Orange, NJ 7018
973-395-8450
Fax: 973-395-8437

County of Gloucester
Ms. Diane Kirwan-Patterson,
Division Head
Office of Government Services
P.O. Box 337
Woodbury, NJ 08096-7337
856-384-6955
Fax: 856-384-6938

County of Hudson
Mr. Kathy Jacobs, Director
Division of Community
Planning
583 Newark Ave.
Jersey City, NJ 07306-2301
201-795-6186
Fax: 201-795-1903

County of Monmouth
Ms. Virginia A. Edwards,
Director
Community Development
Program
One E. Main St.
Hall of Records Annex
Freehold, NJ 07728-1255
732-431-7490
Fax: 732-308-2995

County of Ocean
Mr. Tony Agliata, Community
Development Director
Department of Planning
129 Hooper Ave.
Toms River, NJ 08753-7605
732-929-2054
Fax: 732-244-8396

County of Somerset
Ms. Rosalee Yurasko, Director
County of Somerset
Office of Community
Development
P.O. Box 3000
Somerville, NJ 08876-1262
908-231-7039
Fax: 908-707-4127

County of Union
Mr. President Carlisle, Housing
Coordinator

Division of Community
Development
Elizabethtown Plaza
Union County Administration
Bldg.
Elizabeth, NJ 7207
908-527-4227
Fax: 908-527-4901

Consortia
Hudson County Consortium
Ms. Kathy A. Jacob, HOME
Coordinator
Division of Community
Planning
583 Newark Ave.
Second Floor
Jersey City, NJ 07306-2301
201-795-6186
Fax: 201-795-1903

Mercer County Consortium
Mr. Keith Rick Johnson, Aid
Department of Housing and
Community Development
P.O. Box 8068
Trenton, NJ 08650-0068
609-989-6959
Fax: 609-989-0306

County of Middlesex
Consortium
Mr. John A. Sully, Executive
Director
Department of Housing and
Community Development
JFK Sq.
County Administration Bldg.
New Brunswick, NJ 8901
732-745-3519
Fax: 732-745-4117

Morris County Consortium
Ms. Helen Wolfmeyer, HOME
Coordinator
Division of Community
Development
P.O. Box 900
Morristown, NJ 07963-0900
973-285-6060
Fax: 973-285-6031

New Mexico
Ms. Terri Sais
Public Information Contact
State of New Mexico

Mortgage Finance Authority
P.O. Box 2047
Albuquerque, NM 87102-4147
505-843-6880
Fax: 505-243-3289

Cities
City of Albuquerque
Ms. Marti Luick, Manager
Department of Family and
Community Services
P.O. Box 1293
Albuquerque, NM 87106-1293
505-768-2871
Fax: 505-768-3204

City of Las Cruces
Mr. Don Fahrenkrog, Director
Department of Neighborhood
Development
575 S. Alameda Blvd., Room 231
Las Cruces, NM 88005
505-528-3105
Fax: 505-528-3102

New York
Public Information Office
38-40 State St.
Albany, NY 12207
518-473-2526

Cities
City of Albany
Ms. Patricia Hourigan, Public
Information Contact
Department of Housing and
Community Development
200 Henry Johnson Blvd.,
Second
Albany, NY 12210-2867
518-434-5240
Fax: 518-434-5242

City of Islip
Ms. Carole Carroll, Director
Community Development
Agency
15 Shore Ln.
Bay Shore, NY 11706
631-665-1185
Fax: 631-665-0036

City of Binghamton
Mr. Paul Nelson, Director
Office of Community
Development

38 Hawley St.
City Hall, Governmental Plaza,
Fourth Floor
Binghamton, NY 13901-3793
607-772-7028
Fax: 607-772-0508

City of Buffalo
Ms. Dawn Sanders, Director
Department of Neighborhood
Services
65 Niagra Sq., Room 313
Buffalo, NY 14202
716-851-4182
Fax: 716-851-4242

City of Elmira
Ms. Cheryl Schneider, HOME
Coordinator
Department of Business and
Housing Development
317 E. Church St.
City Hall Armory Annex
Elmira, NY 14901
607-737-5607
Fax: 607-737-5696

City of Babylon/Long Island
Housing Partnership
Ms. Patricia Bourne
Director
Town of Babylon/Long Island
Housing Partnership
Department of Community and
Economic Development
180 Oser Ave.
Hauppauge, NY 11788
631-434-9277
Fax: 631-434-9311

City of Jamestown
Ms. Jan Kurth, Grants
Coordinator
Community Development
Office/Urban Renewal Agency
200 E. Third St.
Municipal Bldg., Third Floor
Jamestown, NY 14701
716-483-7656
Fax: 716-483-7772

City of Mount Vernon
Ms. Carmen Sylvester, Director
Department of Planning and
Community Development
One Roosevelt Sq.

City Hall, Second Floor
Mount Vernon, NY 10550
914-699-7230
Fax: 914-699-1435

City of New Rochelle
Ms. Christine Magrin
Administrator
City of New Rochelle
Department of Development
515 North Ave.
City Hall
New Rochelle, NY 10801-3405
914-654-2184
Fax: 914-632-3626

City of New York City
Mr. Ted Gallagher, Planner
City of New York City
Department of Housing
Preservation and Development
100 Gold St.
New York, NY 10038
212-863-8061
Fax: 212-863-8067

City of Niagara Falls
Mr. Robert Antonucci, HOME
Coordinator
Office of Community
Development
P.O. Box 69
Niagara Falls, NY 14302
716-286-8800
Fax: 716-286-8809

City of Rochester
Mr. Robert M. Barrows,
Assistant Director
Department of Community
Development
30 Church St., Room 028B
Rochester, NY 14614-1290
716-428-6150
Fax: 716-428-6229

City of
Schenectady/Troy/Colonie
Consortium
Mr. Terrance Connelly, Deputy
Director
Department of Planning and
Economic Development
105 Jay St.
City Hall, Room 1
Schenectady, NY 12305

518-382-5147
Fax: 518-382-5275

City of Syracuse
Mr. James Laurenzo
Economic Development Chief
Department of Community and
Economic Development
201 E. Washington St., Room 612
Syracuse, NY 13202
315-448-8110
Fax: 315-448-8036

Mr. Paul Driscoll
Senior Urban Planner
Department of Community
Development
201 E. Washington St., Room 612
Syracuse, NY 13202
315-448-8726
Fax: 315-448-8720

Ms. Linda Delaney
Investor Housing Specialist
Department of Community
Development
201 E. Washington St., Room 612
Syracuse, NY 13202-1410
315-448-8713
Fax: 315-448-8705

City of Utica
Ms. Lori Calabrese, Housing Dir.
Office of Community
Development
One Kennedy Plaza
Utica, NY 13502-4236
315-792-0181
Fax: 315-797-6607

City of Watertown
Mr. Kevin Jordan
Public Information Contact
Development Authority of the
North Country
317 Washington St.
Watertown, NY 13601
315-785-2593

City of Yonkers
Mr. J. Stephen Whetstone,
Commissioner
Bureau of Community
Development
87 Nepperhan Ave., Suite 315
Yonkers, NY 10701-3892

914-377-6650
Fax: 914-377-6672

Counties
County of Erie
Mr. Tom Dearing, Coordinator
Department of Environment and
Planning
95 Franklin St., Room 1016
Buffalo, NY 14202
716-858-7256
Fax: 716-858-7248

County of Nassau
Mr. Donald J. Campbell,
Commissioner
Office of Housing and
Intergovernmental Affairs
250 Fulton Ave., Sixth Floor
Hempstead, NY 11550-3901
516-572-0880
Fax: 516-572-0889

Development Authority of the
North County
Mr. Kevin Jordan, Public
Information Contact
317 Washington St.
Watertown, NY 13601
315-785-2593

County of Orange
Mr. John Ebert, HOME
Coordinator
Department of Community
Development
223 Main St.
Goshen, NY 10924-2124
914-291-2424
Fax: 914-291-2430

County of Rockland
Mr. Michael Dolan, Director
Office of Community
Development
151 S. Main St., Suite 212
New City, NY 10956-3516
914-638-5646
Fax: 914-638-5157

County of Suffolk
Mr. Joseph T. Sanseverino,
Director
Department of Community
Development
P.O. Box 6100

Hauppauge, NY 11788-0099
631-853-5705
Fax: 631-853-5688

County of Westchester
Mr. William C. Brady, HOME
Coordinator
Department of Housing and
Community Development
148 Martine Ave.
County Office Bldg., Room 414
White Plains, NY 10601
914-285-4271
Fax: 914-285-9093

Consortia
Amherst Consortium
Ms. Susan Davida, Assistant
Planner
5583 Main St.
Williamsville, NY 14221-5409
716-631-7082
Fax: 716-631-7153

Colonie Consortium/City of
Schenectady/Troy
Mr. Terrance Connelly, Deputy
Director
Department of Planning and
Economic Development
105 Jay St.
City Hall, Room 1
Schenectady, NY 12305
518-382-5147
Fax: 518-382-5275

Dutchess County Consortium
Ms. Anne Saylor, Specialist
27 High St.
Poughkeepsie, NY 12601-1935
914-486-3600
Fax: 914-486-3610

Monroe County Consortium
Ms. Sandra H. Mindel, Specialist
Division of Community
Development
50 W. Main St., Suite 8100
Rochester, NY 14614-1225
716-428-2185
Fax: 716-428-5336

Onondaga County Consortium
Ms. Linda DeFichy,
Administrator

Department of Community
Development
421 Montgomery St.
1100 Civic Center
Syracuse, NY 13202
315-435-3558
Fax: 315-435-3794

North Carolina
Mr. Bill Dowse, Director
Housing Finance State Agency
P.O. Box 28066
Raleigh, NC 27611-8066
919-877-5622
Fax: 919-877-5701

Cities
City of Asheville
Mr. Sherman Fearing, Analyst
Division of Community
Development
P.O. Box 7148
Asheville, NC 28802-7148
828-259-5721
Fax: 828-259-5428

City of Charlotte
Mr. Stanley D. Watkins, City
Manager
Department of Neighborhood
Development
600 E. Trade St., Suite 200
Charlotte, NC 28202
704-336-3380
Fax: 704-336-2904

City of Concord
Mr. Steve Osborne, Community
Development Code Enforcement
Manager
Department of Community and
Economic Development
P.O. Box 308
Concord, NC 28026
704-786-6161
Fax: 704-795-0983

City of Durham
Ms. Ava Hinton, HOME
Coordinator
Department of Housing and
Economic Development
101 City Hall Plaza
Durham, NC 27701-3329
919-560-4570
Fax: 919-560-4090

City of Fayetteville
Mr. Michael E. McNair, HOME
Coordinator
P.O. Box 635
Fayetteville, NC 28302-0635
910-433-1590
Fax: 910-433-1592

City of Goldsboro
Ms. Linda Bullock, Coordinator
Department of Community
Development
P.O. Drawer A
Goldsboro, NC 27533
919-580-4317
Fax: 919-580-4315

City of Greenville
Ms. Alice Faye Brewington,
HOME Coordinator
Department of Planning and
Community Development
P.O. Box 7207
Greenville, NC 27835
252-329-4509
Fax: 252-329-4424

City of Lenoir/Hickory County
Consortium
Mr. Rick Oxford, Community
Development Administrator
Western Piedmont Council of
Governments
P.O. Box 9026
Hickory, NC 28603-9026
828-322-9191
Fax: 828-322-5991

City of High Point
Ms. Paulette Anderson,
Community Development
Administrator
Department of Community
Development and Housing
P.O. Box 230
High Point, NC 27261-0230
336-883-3349
Fax: 336-883-3355

City of Raleigh
Ms. Eileen B. Breazeale, Director
Department of Community
Development
P.O. Box 590
Raleigh, NC 27602-0590
919-857-4330
Fax: 919-857-4359

City of Rocky Mount
Ms. Vanessa McCleary,
Administrator
Department of Planning and
Development
P.O. Box 1180
Rocky Mount, NC 27802-1180
252-972-1101
Fax: 252-972-1590

City of Wilmington
Ms. Elizabeth Roheaugh, Interim
Director
Department of Housing and
Neighborhood Development
P.O. Box 1810
Wilmington, NC 28402-1810
910-341-7836
Fax: 910-341-7802

Counties
County of Cumberland
Ms. Thanena Wilson, Director
Department of Community
Development
P.O. Box 1829
Fayetteville, NC 28302-1829
910-323-6111
Fax: 910-323-6114

County of Orange
Ms. Tara L. Fikes, Director
Department of Housing and
Community Development
P.O. Box 8181
Hillsborough, NC 27278
919-245-2490
Fax: 919-644-3056

County of Wake
Mr. David Cristeal, Director
Division of Housing and
Community Revitalization
P.O. Box 550
Raleigh, NC 27602
919-856-5689
Fax: 919-856-5594

Consortia
Gastonia Consortium
Ms. Annie Thombs,
Administrator
Department of Community
Development
P.O. Box 1748
Gastonia, NC 28053-1748

704-866-6752
Fax: 704-864-9732

City of Greensboro Consortium
Ms. Linda Wilson, Manager
Department of Housing and
Community Development
P.O. Box 3136
Greensboro, NC 27402-3136
336-373-2349
Fax: 336-373-2153

Hickory County
Consortium/City of Lenoir
Mr. Rick Oxford, Community
Development Administrator
Western Piedmont Council of
Governments
P.O. Box 9026
Hickory, NC 28603-9026
828-322-9191
Fax: 828-322-5991

Surry County Consortium
Mr. Dennis Thompson, County
Manager
Office of the County Manager
P.O. Box 706
Dobson, NC 27017-0706
336-401-8201
Fax: 336-401-8217

Winston-Salem Consortium
Dr. Monica R. Lett, Director
Department of Housing and
Neighborhood Development
P.O. Box 2511
Winston-Salem, NC 27101-2511
336-727-8597
Fax: 336-727-2878

North Dakota
Mr. Mike Spletto, Program
Manager
Division of Community Services
600 E. Boulevard Ave.
Bismarck, ND 58505-0660
701-328-2094
Fax: 701-328-2308

Ohio
Mr. Les Warner
HOME Coordinator
Office of Housing and
Community Partnerships
P.O. Box 1001

Columbus, OH 43216-1001
614-466-2285
Fax: 614-752-4575

Cities
City of Akron
Mr. Warren R. Walfish, Manager
Department of Planning and
Urban Development
161 S. High St., Room 201
Akron, OH 44308-1626
330-375-2618
Fax: 330-375-2434

City of Canton
Mr. William E. McGeorge,
Director
Department of Planning and
Community Development
P.O. Box 24218
Canton, OH 44701-4218
330-489-3258
Fax: 330-580-2070

City of Cincinnati
Mrs. Connie Roesch, HOME
Coordinator
Dept. of Neighborhood Services
801 Plum St.
Cincinnati, OH 45202-1927
513-352-3735
Fax: 513-352-6113

City of Cleveland
Ms. Bobbie Peery, HOME
Coordinator
City of Cleveland
Department of Community
Development
601 Lakeside Ave., Room 302
Cleveland, OH 44114
216-664-4218
Fax: 216-420-7960

City of Columbus
Ms. Gail Gregory, Deputy
Director
Department of Trade and
Development
50 W. Gay St., Third Floor
Columbus, OH 43215-9040
614-645-6767
Fax: 614-645-6295

City of Dayton
Mr. David B. Sutton, Specialist

Department of Community
Development
101 W. Third St.
Dayton, OH 45401-1814
937-333-3870
Fax: 937-333-4281

City of East Cleveland
Mr. William Ellington, Director
Department of Community
Development
13601 Euclid Ave.
East Cleveland, OH 44112
216-681-2388
Fax: 216-681-2085

City of Hamilton
Ms. Carla Tipton, HOME/IDIS
Coordinator
Department of Planning
20 High St., Suite 207
Hamilton, OH 45011
513-868-5886
Fax: 513-867-7364

City of Lima
Mr. Richard Friensen, Public
Information Contact
Department of Community
Development
50 Town Sq.
Municipal Bldg.
Lima, OH 45801-4900
419-221-5147
Fax: 419-221-5214

City of Lorain
Mr. Sanford A. Prudoff, Director
Department of Community
Development
200 W. Erie Ave., Fifth Floor
Lorain, OH 44052-1606
440-246-2020
Fax: 440-245-9428

City of Mansfield
Ms. Cynthia Baker, Manager
Department of Community
Development
30 N. Diamond St.
Mansfield, OH 44902
419-755-9795
Fax: 419-755-9465

City of Springfield
Ms. Selena Singletary, Director

Department of Planning and
Development
76 E. High St.
Springfield, OH 45502-1214
937-324-7380
Fax: 937-328-3489

City of Toledo
Ms. Debra L. Younger, Director
Department of Neighborhoods
One Government Center, Suite
1800
Toledo, OH 43604
419-245-1400
Fax: 419-245-1413

City of Youngstown
Ms. Mary June Tartan, HOME
Coordinator
Community Development
Agency
Nine W. Front St., Room 205
Youngstown, OH 44503
330-744-0854
Fax: 330-744-7522

Counties
County of Cuyahoga
Mr. Paul Herdeg, Manager
Department of Development
112 Hamilton Ave., Fourth Floor
Cleveland, OH 44114
216-443-7260
Fax: 216-443-7258

County of Franklin/Mid Ohio
RPC
Ms. Tonya Sims, HOME
Ownership Project Director
Department of Community
Development
285 E. Main St.
Columbus, OH 43215
614-233-4181
Fax: 614-228-1904

County of Hamilton
Ms. Susan Walsh, Deputy
Director
Department of Community
Development
138 E. Court St., Room 507
Cincinnati, OH 45202
513-946-4802
Fax: 513-946-4919

County of Lake
Ms. Marianne Norman, Director
Planning Commission
125 E. Erie St.
Painesville, OH 44077
440-350-2339
Fax: 440-350-2740

County of Montgomery
Ms. Roberta E. Longfellow,
Housing Administrator
Department of Development
and Building Regulations
451 W. Third St., Tenth Floor
Dayton, OH 45422
937-225-4631
Fax: 937-496-6629

County of Stark
Ms. Beth Pearson, Chief
Regional Planning Commission
201 Third St., N.E., Suite 201
Canton, OH 44702-2298
330-451-7395
Fax: 330-438-0990

County of Summit
Ms. Donna Marcinek, Housing
Coordinator
Department of Development
175 S. Main St., Suite 207
Akron, OH 44308
330-643-2561
Fax: 330-643-2886

Consortia
County of Butler Consortium
Ms. Donna Everson
Administrator
Division of Community
Development
130 High Street, Sixth Floor
Hamilton, OH 45011
513-785-5391
Fax: 513-785-5723

Warren City Consortium
Mr. Alexander Bobersky, Acting
Director
Department of Community
Development
418 S. Main Ave.
Warren, OH 44481
330-841-2595
Fax: 330-841-2643

Oklahoma
Mr. Byron DeBruler, State
Contact
Oklahoma Housing Finance
Agency
P.O. Box 26720
Oklahoma City, OK 73126-0720
405-419-8137
Fax: 405-879-8820

Cities
City of Lawton
Mr. Jim Phillips, HOME
Coordinator
Department of Planning and
Community Development
206 S.W. Third St.
Lawton, OK 73501
580-581-3347
Fax: 580-581-3346

City of Norman
Ms. Linda Price, Manager
Department of Planning
P.O. Box 370
Norman, OK 73070-0370
405-366-5439
Fax: 405-366-5379

City of Oklahoma City
Mr. Curtis Williams
Department of Neighborhood
and Community Planning
420 W. Main St., Suite 920
Oklahoma City, OK 73102
405-297-2846
Fax: 405-297-3798

City of Tulsa
Mr. Roy Marshall, HOME
Coordinator
Department of Urban
Development
110 S. Hartford Ave., Suite 200
Tulsa, OK 74120-1816
918-596-2600
Fax: 918-699-3570

Consortia
Tulsa County Consortium
Ms. Claudia Ellingsworth
Brierre, Planner
Department of Community
Development
201 W. Fifth St., Suite 600
Tulsa, OK 74103

918-579-9431
Fax: 918-583-1024

Oregon
Ms. Betty Markey
HOME Program Manager
Department of Housing and
Community Services
1600 State St.
Salem, OR 97301-4246
503-986-2116
Fax: 503-986-2020

Cities
City of Salem
Mr. Maurice Anderson,
Coordinator
Department of Community
Development
555 Liberty St., S.E., Room 305
Salem, OR 97301
503-588-6173
Fax: 503-588-6005

Counties
County of Clackamas
Ms. Evelyn Harris
HOME Project Manager
Department of Community
Development
112 11th St.
Oregon City, OR 97045-1021
503-655-8591
Fax: 503-655-8563

County of Washington
Mr. Todd Adkins, Specialist
Department of Housing Services
111 N.E. Lincoln St., Suite 200L
Hillsboro, OR 97123-3082
503-846-4797
Fax: 503-693-4795

Consortia
City of Eugene Consortium
Ms. Linda L. Dawson, Manager
Department of Planning and
Development
99 W. Tenth Ave., Suite 240
Eugene, OR 97401-3038
541-682-5071
Fax: 541-682-5572

City of Portland Consortium
Ms. Martha McLennan, Director

Bureau of Housing and
Community Development
421 S.W. Sixth Ave.
Suite 1100-A
Portland, OR 97204
503-823-2386
Fax: 503-823-2387

Pennsylvania
Mr. Scott Dunwoody
HOME Coordinator
Department of Community and
Economic Development
Commonwealth Ave.
502 Forum Bldg.
Harrisburg, PA 17120
717-468-3065
Fax: 717-234-4560

Cities
City of Allentown
Ms. Heidi Baer, Coordinator
Department of Community
Development
435 Hamilton St.
Allentown, PA 18101
610-437-7761
Fax: 610-437-8781

City of Altoona
Mr. Carl Fisher, Manager
Department of Planning and
Community Development
1117 Ninth Ave.
Altoona, PA 16602
814-949-2470
Fax: 814-949-0372

City of Bethlehem
Mr. Tony Hanna, Director
Department of Community and
Economic Development
Ten E. Church St.
Bethlehem, PA 18018-6025
610-865-7085
Fax: 610-865-7330

City of Chester
Mr. David N. Sciocchetti, Acting
Executive Director
Economic Development
Authority
P.O. Box 407
Chester, PA 19016-0407
610-447-7850
Fax: 610-447-7856

City of Erie
Mr. David Deter, Manager
Department of Planning and
Development
626 State St.
Municipal Bldg., Room 404
Erie, PA 16501
814-870-1270
Fax: 814-870-1443

City of Harrisburg
Ms. Angela Smith, HOME
Coordinator
Department of Building and
Housing Development
Ten N. Second St.
Martin Luther King Jr.
Government Ctr., Suite 206
Harrisburg, PA 17101-1677
717-255-6480
Fax: 717-255-6421

City of Johnstown
Mr. Ronald Andrews,
Coordinator
Department of Community and
Economic Development
Main and Market Sts.
City Hall, Room 205
Johnstown, PA 15901
814-533-2056
Fax: 814-533-2111

City of Lancaster
Mr. Thomas A. Fields, Director
Department of Housing and
Community Development
P.O. Box 1599
Lancaster, PA 17608-1599
717-291-4730
Fax: 717-291-4713

City of Philadelphia
Mr. John Kromer, Housing
Director
Office of Housing and
Community Development
1234 Market St., 17th Floor
Philadelphia, PA 19107
215-686-9721
Fax: 215-686-9801

Urban Redevelopment
Authority of Pittsburgh
Division of Housing
200 Ross St., Tenth Floor

Pittsburgh, PA 15219-2069
412-255-6666
Fax: 412-255-6645

City of Reading
Mr. Eric Galosi, Director
Department of Community
Development
815 Washington St., Room 306
Reading, PA 19601-3690
610-655-6211
Fax: 610-373-2858

City of Scranton
Mr. Thomas J. Kane, HOME
Coordinator
Office of Economic and
Community Development
340 N. Washington Ave., Third
Floor
Scranton, PA 18503
570-348-4168
Fax: 570-348-4293

Borough of State College
Ms. Lu B. Hoover
118 S. Fraser St.
State College, PA 16801-3899
814-234-7109
Fax: 814-231-3082

Redevelopment Authority of
Washington County
Mr. Richard Galway, Specialist
Department of Community
Development
100 W. Beau St., Room 603
Courthouse Square Bldg.
Washington, PA 15301
724-228-6875
Fax: 724-228-6829

City of Wilkes-Barre
Mr. Frank Eick, Housing
Director
Office of Community
Development
40 E. Market St.
City Hall
Wilkes-Barre, PA 18711
570-208-4129
Fax: 570-208-4136

City of Williamsport
Ms. Mary Rucinski, Assistant
Director

Office of Economic and
Community Development
245 W. Fourth St.
City Hall
Williamsport, PA 17701
570-327-7511
Fax: 570-327-7509

City of York
Ms. Leigh Smith, Assistant
Division of Community Affairs
One Mark Way
York, PA 17401-1231
717-849-2264
Fax: 717-849-2329

Counties
County of Allegheny
Ms. Laura Richeson-Zinski
Housing Manager
Department of Economic
Development
425 Sixth Ave., Suite 800
Pittsburgh, PA 15219
412-350-1000
Fax: 412-350-1050

County of Beaver
Mr. Robert Dyson, Director
Office of Community
Development
699 Fifth St.
Beaver, PA 15009-1927
724-775-4711
Fax: 724-775-4117

County of Berks
Mr. Kenneth L. Pick, Director
Department of Community
Development
633 Court St., 14th Floor
Reading, PA 19601-3584
610-478-6325
Fax: 610-478-6326

County of Bucks
Mr. Gerard Pescatore
Department of Community
Development
1260 Almshouse Rd.
Neshaminy Manor Center
Doylestown, PA 18901
215-345-3842
Fax: 215-345-3865

County of Chester
Ms. Dolores Colligan
Office of Housing and
Community Development
P.O. Box 2747
West Chester, PA 19380-2747
610-344-6772
Fax: 610-344-5748

County of Delaware
Ms. Carol Murdock Catania,
Housing Coordinator
Office of Housing and
Community Development
600 N. Jackson St., Room 101
Media, PA 19063-2561
610-891-5425
Fax: 610-566-0532

County of Lancaster
Mr. David Brazina, HOME
Coordinator
Housing and Redevelopment
Authority
29 E. King St., Suite 316
Lancaster, PA 17602-2852
717-394-0793
Fax: 717-394-7635

County of Luzerne
Ms. Sandra Russell, Assistant
Director
Department of Community
Development
54 W. Union St.
Wilkes-Barre, PA 18701-1410
570-824-7214
Fax: 570-829-2910

County of Montgomery
Ms. Ivy Torres, Assistant
Director
Office of Housing and
Community Development
P.O. Box 311
Norristown, PA 19404-0311
610-278-3540
Fax: 610-278-3636

County of Westmoreland
Ms. Kathy Fetsko, HOME
Coordinator
Department of Planning and
Development
Two N. Main St.
Courthouse Square, Suite 601

Greensburg, PA 15601-1603
724-830-3616
Fax: 724-830-3611

County of York
Mr. M. Chris Rafferty,
Community Development
Coordinator
Planning Commission
100 W. Market St.
County Government Center
York, PA 17401-1231
717-771-9870
Fax: 717-771-9511

PUERTO RICO
Ms. Maria Nagron, Director
Department of Housing
Avenida Barbosa Num. 606
Apartado 21365
Rio Piedras, PR 928
787-274-2121
Fax: 787-763-0008

Cities
Municipio de Aguadilla
Ms. Daisy Caceres, HOME
Coordinator
Department of Federal Programs
P.O. Box 1008
Aguadilla, PR 605
787-891-3965
Fax: 787-891-3930

Municipio de Arecibo
Mr. Jaime Adames Cruz, HOME
Coordinator
P.O. Box 1086
Arecibo, PR 00613-1086
787-881-3946
Fax: 787-817-5881

Municipio de Bayamon
Mr. Angel Martinez, HOME
Coordinator
P.O. Box 2988
Bayamon, PR 960
787-269-3980
Fax: 787-786-1032

Municipio de Caguas
Ms. Carmen Berrios, HOME
Coordinator
Department of Housing
P.O. Box 7889
Caguas, PR 726

787-744-8833
Fax: 787-745-2250

Municipio de Carolina
Mr. Juan A. Cancel, Executive
Director
CADEN
P.O. Box 8
Carolina, PR 00986-0008
787-762-8686
Fax: 787-257-1008

Municipio de Guaynabo
Mr. Orlando Perez Delgado,
HOME Coordinator
Department of Housing
P.O. Box 7885
Guaynabo, PR 00970-7885
787-287-3334
Fax: 787-731-4160

Municipio de Mayaguez
Mr. Israel Alvares, HOME
Coordinator
Division of Housing
P.O. Box 447
Mayaguez, PR 00681-0447
787-834-1460
Fax: 787-833-0805

Municipio de Ponce
Mr. Miguel Mercado, Executive
Director
Department of Housing and
Federal Programs
P.O. Box 331709
Ponce, PR 00733-1709
787-840-9200
Fax: 787-841-0140

Municipio de San Juan
Ms. Eliana Echegoyen, Executive
Director
Department of Housing
P.O. Box 36-2138
San Juan, PR 00936-2138
787-722-8088
Fax: 787-725-7715

Municipio de Toa Baja
Ms. Norma Santiago, Director
Office of Planning and
Community Development
P.O. Box 51983
Toa Baja, PR 00950-1983
787-261-0244
Fax: 787-261-7930

RhodE IslaNd

Ms. Susan Bodington, Assistant
Director
Rhode Island Housing and
Mortgage Finance Corp.
44 Washington St.
Providence, RI 2903
401-457-1286
Fax: 401-457-1140

Cities
City of Pawtucket
Mr. Edward G. Soares, HOME
Program Manager
Department of Planning and
Redevelopment
175 Main St.
Pawtucket, RI 02860-4119
401-724-5200
Fax: 401-726-6237

City of Providence
Mr. Arthur Hanson, HOME
Director
Department of Planning and
Development
400 Westminster St.
Providence, RI 02903-3215
401-351-4300
Fax: 401-351-9533

City of Woonsocket
Ms. Rita Cicchitelli
Department of Planning and
Development
169 Main St.
Woonsocket, RI 02895-4379
401-767-9228
Fax: 401-766-9312

SouTh CaroliNa

Ms. Valerie M. Williams,
Director
Housing Finance and
Development Authority
919 Bluff Rd.
Columbia, SC 29201
803-734-2000
Fax: 803-253-6884

Cities
City of Charlseston
Ms. Patricia W. Crawford, Dir.
Department of Housing and
Community Development
75 Calhoun St.

Third Floor, Division 616
Charleston, SC 29401-3506
843-724-3766
Fax: 843-724-7354

City of Columbia
Mr. Richard J. Semon, Director
Department of Community
Development
P.O. Box 147
Columbia, SC 29217-0147
803-733-8315
Fax: 803-988-8014

City of Greenville
Mr. Thurman Norris,
Administrator
Department of Community
Development and Relations
P.O. Box 2207
Greenville, SC 29602
864-467-4570
Fax: 864-467-5735

Greenville County
Redevelopment Authority
Ms. Gwendolyn Kennedy,
Executive Director
301 University Ridge, Suite 2500
Greenville, SC 29601
864-242-9801
Fax: 864-232-9946

City of Spartanburg
Mr. Ed Memmot, Director
Department of Community
Development
P.O. Box 1749
Spartanburg, SC 29304
864-596-3560
Fax: 864-596-2680

Counties
County of Charleston
Ms. Henrietta Canty Woodward,
Director
Department of Community
Development
Two Courthouse Sq.
O.T. Wallace Office Bldg., Sixth
Floor
Charleston, SC 29401
843-958-3560
Fax: 843-720-2209

Consortia
Santee-Lynches HOME
Consortium
Mr. James T. Darby, Executive
Director
Regional Council of
Governments
P.O. Drawer 1837
Sumter, SC 29151
803-775-7381
Fax: 803-773-9903

South Dakota
Housing Development
Authority
Mr. Ron Wagner, Manager
Office of Planning and Housing
Development
P.O. Box 1237
Pierre, SD 57501-1237
605-773-5897
Fax: 605-773-5154

Cities
City of Sioux Falls
Mr. Randy Bartunek, Director
Department of Community
Development
224 W. Ninth St.
Sioux Falls, SD 57104-6407
605-367-7125
Fax: 605-367-8798

Tennessee
Ms. Jane Boles, Director
Housing Development Agency
404 James Robertson Pkwy.,
Suite 1114
Nashville, TN 37219-1505
615-741-3007
Fax: 615-532-5069

Cities
City of Chattanooga
Ms. Sandra Gober, Director
Office of Economic and
Community Development
100 E. 11th St., Room 101
Chattanooga, TN 37402
423-757-5133
Fax: 423-757-4851

City of Clarksville/County of
Montgomery
Mr. Ron Tedford, Director

Office of Community
Development
329 Main St.
Clarksville, TN 37040
931-645-7448
Fax: 931-645-7481

Jackson Housing Authority
Mr. David Ralston, Director
Office of Community
Development
125 Preston St.
Jackson, TN 38301
901-422-1671
Fax: 901-425-4617

City of Knoxville
Ms. Diana Gerard Lobertini,
Manager
Department of Community
Development
P.O. Box 1631
Knoxville, TN 37901-1631
865-215-2120
Fax: 865-215-2554

City of Memphis
Mr. Carl Reynolds,
Administrative Director
Department of Community
Development
701 N. Main St.
Memphis, TN 38107-2311
901-576-7300
Fax: 901-576-6555

City of Nashville/County of
Davidson
Mr. Paul Johnson, Assistant
Director
Metropolitan Development and
Housing Agency
P.O. Box 846
Nashville, TN 37202-0846
615-252-8508
Fax: 615-252-8559

Counties
County of Davidson/City of
Nashville
Mr. Paul Johnson, Assistant
Director
Metropolitan Development and
Housing Agency
P.O. Box 846
Nashville, TN 37202-0846

615-252-8508
Fax: 615-252-8559

County of Knox
Mr. Bill Niemeyer, Director
Development Corporation of
Knox County
601 W. Summit Hill Dr., Suite
200A
Knoxville, TN 37902-2011
865-546-5887
Fax: 865-546-6170

County of Montgomery/City of
Clarksville
Mr. Ron Tedford, Director
Office of Community
Development
329 Main St.
Clarksville, TN 37040
931-645-7448
Fax: 931-645-7481

County of Shelby
Mr. Jim Vasquez, Administrator
Department of Housing
1075 Mullins Station Rd.
Memphis, TN 38134
901-387-5700
Fax: 901-387-5708

Texas
Ms. Jeannie Arellano
HOME Program Manager
Department of Housing and
Community Affairs
P.O. Box 13941
Austin, TX 78711-3941
512-475-3109
Fax: 512-475-3287

Cities
City of Abilene
Mr. Kelly Cheek, Specialist
Office of Community and
Economic Development
P.O. Box 60
Abilene, TX 79604-0060
915-676-6383
Fax: 915-676-6242

City of Amarillo
Ms. Vicki Covey, HOME
Coordinator
Department of Community
Services

P.O. Box 1971
Amarillo, TX 79186-1971
806-378-3098
Fax: 806-378-9389

City of Arlington
Ms. Charmaine Pruitt, HOME
Coordinator
Department of Neighborhood
Services
P.O. Box 231
Arlington, TX 76011-0231
817-276-6730
Fax: 817-861-8097

City of Austin
Mr. Paul Hilgers, Director
Department of Housing and
Conservation
505 Barton Springs Road, Suite
600
Austin, TX 78704
512-499-3100
Fax: 512-499-3112

City of Beaumont
Mr. Richard Chappell, Director
Department of Community
Development
P.O. Box 3827
Beaumont, TX 77704-3827
409-880-3763
Fax: 409-880-3125

City of Brownsville
Mr. Ben Medina, Community
Development Coordinator
Department of Planning and
Community Development
P.O. Box 911
Brownsville, TX 78522-0911
956-548-6150
Fax: 956-548-6144

City of Bryan
Ms. Alsie Bond, Administrator
Department of Community
Development
P.O. Box 1000
Bryan, TX 77801-1000
409-779-5175
Fax: 409-779-5184

City of College Station
Mr. Randy J. Brumley, HOME
Coordinator

Department of Community
Development
P.O. Box 9960
College Station, TX 77840-9960
409-764-3778
Fax: 409-764-3785

City of Corpus Christi
Mr. Norbert Hart, Director
Community Improvement Corp.
P.O. Box 9277
Corpus Christi, TX 78469-9277
361-880-3010
Fax: 361-880-3011

City of Dallas
Ms. Mary Kay Vaughn, Director
Department of Community
Development
1500 Marilla St.
Six Delta N.
Dallas, TX 75201
214-670-5988
Fax: 214-670-0156

City of Denton
Ms. Barbara Ross, Community
Development Coordinator
Division of Community
Development
100 W. Oak St., Suite 208
Denton, TX 76201
940-349-7235
Fax: 940-383-2445

City of El Paso
Mr. Robert Soto, Administrator
Department of Community and
Human Development
Two Civic Center Plaza, Ninth
Floor
El Paso, TX 79901-1196
915-541-4639
Fax: 915-541-4370

City of Ft. Worth
Ms. Gloria Eurotas, Asst. Dir.
Department of Housing
1000 Throckmorton St.
City Hall Annex
Ft. Worth, TX 76102-6383
817-871-7540
Fax: 817-871-7328

City of Galveston
Mr. Sterling W. Patrick, Director

Department of Community
Development
P.O. Box 779
Galveston, TX 77550-0779
409-766-2101
Fax: 409-762-7079

City of Garland
Ms. Renee Ramey, Director
Division of Neighborhood
Services
P.O. Box 469002
Garland, TX 75046-9002
972-205-3321
Fax: 972-205-3303

City of Grand Prairie
Ms. Sherie L. Goin, Community
Development Manager
Department of Housing and
Community Development
P.O. Box 534045
Grand Prairie, TX 75053-4045
972-237-8166
Fax: 972-237-8187

City of Harlingen
Mrs. Diana R. Serna,
Coordinator
Department of Community
Development
P.O. Box 2207
Harlingen, TX 78551-2207
956-427-8735
Fax: 956-430-6691

City of Houston
Ms. Paulette Wagner, Grants
Manager
Department of Housing and
Community Development
P.O. Box 1562
Houston, TX 77251-1562
713-868-8300
Fax: 713-865-4113

City of Irving
Ms. Barbara Vanderloop,
Manager
Department of Community
Development
P.O. Box 152288
Irving, TX 75015-2288
972-721-4800
Fax: 972-721-4813

City of Killeen
Ms. Cinda Hayward, HOME
Coordinator
Division of Community and
Economic Development
P.O. Box 1329
Killeen, TX 76540-1329
254-501-7840
Fax: 254-526-3594

City of Laredo
Mr. Erasmo Villarreal, Director
Department of Community
Development
P.O. Box 1276
Laredo, TX 78040-1276
956-795-2675
Fax: 956-795-2689

City of Longview
Ms. Linda H. Strotheide,
Specialist
Department of Housing and
Community Development
P.O. Box 1952
Longview, TX 75606-1952
903-237-1235
Fax: 903-237-1254

City of Lubbock
Ms. Nancy J. Haney, Manager
Department of Housing and
Community Development
P.O. Box 2000
Lubbock, TX 79457-2000
806-775-2300
Fax: 806-775-3281

City of McAllen
Mr. Richard Montesdeoca,
Program Director
Department of Community
Development
P.O. Box 220
McAllen, TX 78505-0220
956-687-7238
Fax: 956-972-7253

City of Odessa
Mr. Michael Marrero, Program
Manager
Department of Community
Development
P.O. Box 4398
Odessa, TX 79760-4398
915-335-4820
Fax: 915-335-4817

City of Pasadena
Mr. Miles Arena, Administrator
Department of Planning
1211 Southmore Ave., Room 208
Pasadena, TX 77506-0672
713-475-7243
Fax: 713-477-1072

City of Port Arthur
Ms. Vivian Ballou,
Administrator
Department of Community
Development
P.O. Box 1089
Port Arthur, TX 77640-1089
409-983-8259
Fax: 409-983-8120

City of San Angelo
Ms. Teresa Special, HOME
Coordinator
City of San Angelo
Department of Community
Development
P.O. Box 1751
San Angelo, TX 76902-1751
915-657-4294
Fax: 915-658-6561

City of San Antonio
Ms. Ivy Taylor, Coordinator
Department of Housing and
Community Development
419 S. Main St., Suite 200
San Antonio, TX 78204
210-207-6614
Fax: 210-886-0006

City of Tyler
Ms. Donna Beddingfield, HOME
Coordinator
Department of Neighborhood
Services
P.O. Box 2039
Tyler, TX 75702-2039
903-531-1303
Fax: 903-531-1155

City of Waco
Ms. Dedri Brown, Community
Development Administrator
Planning and Community
Development Services
P.O. Box 2570
Waco, TX 76702-2570

254-750-5650
Fax: 254-750-1605

City of Wichita Falls
Mr. Michael Uriniack, HOME
Coordinator
Department of Housing and
Community Development
P.O. Box 1431
Wichita Falls, TX 76307-1431
940-761-7475
Fax: 940-761-8877

Counties
County of Bexar
Mr. Jesse Flores, HOME
Coordinator
Department of Housing and
Human Services
233 N. Pecos St., Suite 590
San Antonio, TX 78207
210-335-3708
Fax: 210-335-6788

County of Brazoria
Mr. David Lewis, CDBG
Administrator
Government Service Agency
9500 Forest Ln., Suite 408
Dallas, TX 75243
800-775-2633
Fax: 214-342-1896

County of Dallas
Mr. Rick Lossberg, Director
Department of Housing and
Community Development
411 Elm St.
Third Floor
Dallas, TX 75202-3301
214-653-7601
Fax: 214-653-6517

County of Ft. Bend
Ms. Marilynn Kindell, Director
Department of Community
Development
301 Jackson St., Suite 740
Richmond, TX 77469
281-341-4410
Fax: 281-341-3762

County of Harris
Mr. Bruce A. Austin, Director
Community Development
Agency

2727 El Camino St.
Houston, TX 77054
713-747-0132
Fax: 713-747-4274

County of Hidalgo
Mr. Anthony Covacevick,
Director
Urban County Program
100 E. Cano St., Second Floor
Edinburg, TX 78539-1356
956-318-2619
Fax: 956-383-5971

County of Tarrant
Ms. Patricia Ward, Director
Department of Community
Development
1509-B S. University Dr., Suite
276
Ft. Worth, TX 76107-6568
817-338-9129
Fax: 817-338-9136

Utah

Ms. Lauren Rayner, HOME
Coordinator
Division of Community
Development
324 S. State St.
Suite 500
Salt Lake City, UT 84111-2388
801-538-8650
Fax: 801-538-8888

Cities
City of Ogden
Mr. Aaron Wolfe-Bertling,
Manager
Neighborhood and Community
Development Agency
2484 Washington Blvd., Suite
211
Ogden, UT 84401
801-629-8940
Fax: 801-629-8902

City of Salt Lake City
Ms. Anita J. Short, Community
Development Planner
Division of Capital Planning and
Programming
451 S. State St., Room 406
Salt Lake City, UT 84111
801-535-7115
Fax: 801-535-6131

Counties
County of Salt Lake
Mr. Lynn J. Feveryear, Manager
Department of Housing and
Community Development
2001 S. State St.
Suite N2100, County
Government Center
Salt Lake City, UT 84190-0001
801-468-3246
Fax: 801-468-3684

Consortia
Utah Valley Consortium
Ms. Geo Drake, HOME
Administrator
Provo Redevelopment Agency
55 N. University Ave., Suite 215
Provo, UT 84601
801-852-6164
Fax: 801-375-1469

Vermont

Mr. David Weinstein, Director
Department of Housing and
Community Affairs
P.O. Drawer 20
Montpelier, VT 05620-0501
802-828-3250
Fax: 802-828-2928

Virginia

Ms. Charlene Sinclair, Financial
Officer
Department of Housing and
Community Development
501 N. Second St.
Jackson Center
Richmond, VA 23219-1321
804-371-7101
Fax: 804-371-7091

Cities
City of Alexandria
Mr. Bob Muderig, Public
Information Contact
Office of Housing
P.O. Box 178
Alexandria, VA 22314
703-838-4990
Fax: 703-706-3904

City of Charlottesville
Mr. William Warner, Program
Manager

Thomas Jefferson Planning
District Commission
P.O. Box 1505
Charlottesville, VA 22902
804-979-7310
Fax: 804-979-1597

City of Chesapeake
Ms. Elizabeth Allen, Loan
Officer
Redevelopment and Housing
Authority
P.O. Box 1304
Chesapeake, VA 23320
757-523-0401
Fax: 757-523-1601

City of Danville
Mr. Lars Laubinger
Public Information Contact
Department of Community
Development
P.O. Box 3300
Danville, VA 24543
804-799-5260
Fax: 804-797-8919

City of Hampton
Ms. Joan Kennedy, Director
Office of Neighborhood Services
22 Lincoln St.
Hampton, VA 23669
757-727-6460
Fax: 757-727-6074

City of Lynchburg
Mr. Keith Wright, Coordinator
Department of Community
Planning and Development
P.O. Box 60
Lynchburg, VA 24505-0060
804-847-1671
Fax: 804-845-7630

City of Newport News
Ms. Phyllis Hardy, Public
Information Contact
Redevelopment and Housing
Authority
P.O. Box 77
Newport News, VA 23607-0077
757-247-9701
Fax: 757-247-6535

City of Norfolk
Mr. David Young, Community
Development Director

Redevelopment and Housing
Authority
P.O. Box 968
Norfolk, VA 23501-0968
757-623-1111
Fax: 757-626-1607

City of Portsmouth
Mr. Bob Creecy, Director
Portsmouth Environmental
Services
801 Crawford St.
Portsmouth, VA 23704
757-393-8641
Fax: 757-393-5475

City of Richmond
Mr. David Ingross, Grants
Administrator·
Department of Planning and
Community Development
900 E. Broad St., Room 501
Richmond, VA 23219
804-646-6365
Fax: 804-646-6358

City of Roanoke
Mr. Frank Baretta,
HOME/CDBG Coordinator
Office of Grants Monitoring
541 Luck Ave., S.W., Suite 221
Roanoke, VA 24016
540-853-6003
Fax: 540-853-1252

City of Suffolk
Ms. Cynthia D. Rohes, Assistant
City Manager
Dept. of Management Services
P.O. Box 1858
Suffolk, VA 23439-1858
757-923-2085
Fax: 757-923-2091

City of Virginia Beach
Ms. Sharon Prescott,
Administrator
Dept. of Housing Development
2424 Courthouse Dr.
Municipal Center, Bldg. 18A
Virginia Beach, VA 23456-9083
757-426-5803
Fax: 757-426-5766

Counties
County of Arlington

Mr. Ken Aughenbaug, Team
Leader
Department of Economic
Development
2100 Clarendon Blvd., Suite 709
Arlington, VA 22201
703-228-3772
Fax: 703-228-3834

County of Chesterfield
Mr. Thomas Taylor, Director
Department of Community
Development
P.O. Box 40
Chesterfield, VA 23832
804-768-6056
Fax: 804-748-7549

County of Fairfax
Ms. Heather Davis, Public
Information Contact
Department of Housing and
Community Development
3700 Pender Dr., Suite 300
Fairfax, VA 22030-7444
703-246-5103
Fax: 703-246-5115

County of Henrico
Mr. Eric Leabough, Public
Information Contact
Department of Planning
P.O. Box 27032
Richmond, VA 23273
804-261-8248
Fax: 804-261-8256

County of Prince William
Ms. Mary Lively, Supervisor
Office of Housing and
Community Development
15941 Cardinal Dr., Suite 112
Woodbridge, VA 22191
703-792-7530
Fax: 703-792-4978

Virgin Islands

Ms. Janine Hector, Director
Housing Finance Authority
210-3A Altona
Frostco Bldg.
Saint Thomas, VI 802
340-772-3180
Fax: 340-775-7913

Washington

Mr. Doug Hunter
HOME Development Project
Manager
Dept. of County Development
P.O. Box 48300
Olympia, WA 98504-8300
360-753-4930
Fax: 360-586-5880

Cities
City of Bellevue
Mr. Dan Stroh, Director
King County
Consortium/Planning Division
P.O. Box 90012
Bellevue, WA 98009-9012
425-452-5255
Fax: 425-452-2814

City of Bellingham
Mr. David M. Cahill, Manager
Community Development
Division
210 Lottie St.
Bellingham, WA 98225-4009
360-676-6880
Fax: 360-738-7306

City of Bremerton
Ms. Deborah Peavler-Stewart,
Administrative Analyst
Department of Community
Development
286 Fourth St.
Bremerton, WA 98337
360-478-7996
Fax: 360-478-5278

City of Seattle
Mr. Richard Hooper, Director
Department of Human Services
618 Second Ave., Eighth Floor
Seattle, WA 98104-2232
206-684-0338
Fax: 206-233-7117

City of Spokane
Ms. Melora Sharts,
Administrator
Department of Community and
Economic Development
808 W. Spokane Falls Blvd.,
Room 650
Spokane, WA 99201-3339

509-625-6325
Fax: 509-625-6315

City of Tacoma
Mr. Ray Spadafore, Auditor
747 Market St.
Suite 1036
Tacoma, WA 98402-3794
253-591-5222
Fax: 253-591-5050

City of Yakima
Ms. Fran Eads, Specialist
112 S. Eighth St.
Yakima, WA 98901
509-575-6101
Fax: 509-575-6176

Counties
County of Clark
Mr. Pete C. Munroe,
CDBG/HOME Program
Manager
Department of Community
Services
P.O. Box 5000
Vancouver, WA 98666-5000
360-397-2130
Fax: 360-397-6128

County of Kitsap
Ms. Shirley Christensen,
Administrator
Department of Community
Development
614 Division St.
Port Orchard, WA 98366
360-337-7285
Fax: 360-337-4609

County of Pierce
Mr. Gary Aden, Administrative
Program Manager
Department of Community
Service
8815 S. Tacoma Way, Suite 202
Tacoma, WA 98499-4588
253-798-7038
Fax: 253-798-3999

County of Spokane
Mr. Tim Crowley, Specialist
721 N. Jefferson, Suite 200
Spokane, WA 99260-0190
509-477-4488
Fax: 509-477-2561

Consortia
King County Consortium
Ms. Linda Peterson, Manager
Housing and Community
Development Program
700 Fifth Ave., 37th Floor
Seattle, WA 98104-5037
206-296-8672
Fax: 206-296-0229

Longview Consortium
Ms. Julie Hourcle, Assistant
Planner
Department of Community and
Economic Development
P.O. Box 128
Longview, WA 98632-0128
360-577-3329
Fax: 360-577-4018

Tri-Cities HOME Consortium
Ms. Josie Woods, Specialist
P.O. Box 190
Richland, WA 99352
509-942-7595
Fax: 509-942-7764

West Virginia
Housing Development Fund
Mr. Carl R. Moore, Director
Department of Operations and
Program Development
814 Virginia St., E., Third Floor
Charleston, WV 25301
304-345-6475
Fax: 304-340-9943

Cities
City of Charleston
Ms. Zora Rogers, HOME
Supervisor
Mayor's Office of Economic and
Community Development
P.O. Box 2749
Charleston, WV 25330
304-348-8035
Fax: 304-348-0704

City of Charleston-Kanawha
County Consortium
Ms. Beth Cade, Asst. Director
Mayor's Office Economic and
Community Development
P.O. Box 2749
Charleston, WV 25301

304-348-8035
Fax: 304-348-0704

City of Parkersburg
Mr. Steve Brodsky, Director
Department of Development
P.O. Box 1627
Parkersburg, WV 26102
304-424-8542
Fax: 304-424-8464

City of Wheeling
Mr. Gary A. Lange, Community
Development Specialist
Department of Community
Development
1500 Chapline St.
City-County Bldg.
Wheeling, WV 26003
304-234-3701
Fax: 304-234-3605

Consortia
Cabell County Consortium
Mr. Bill Toney, Program Director
Office of Development and
Planning
P.O. Box 1659
Huntington, WV 25717
304-696-4458
Fax: 304-696-4465

City of Charleston-Kanawha
County Consortium
Ms. Beth Cade, Asst. Director
Mayor's Office Economic and
Community Development
P.O. Box 2749
Charleston, WV 25301
304-348-8035
Fax: 304-348-0704

Wisconsin
Ms. Mary Francis Fay-Troudt
HOME Program Manager
Division of Housing
P.O. Box 8944
Madison, WI 53708-8944
608-266-0288
Fax: 608-267-6917

Cities
City of Eau Claire
Ms. Carol Doyle, Executive
Director
Division of Housing

203 S. Farwell St.
Eau Claire, WI 54701
715-839-4943
Fax: 715-839-4939

City of Green Bay
Ms. Lori DeNault, Coordinator
Department of Community
Development
100 N. Jefferson St., Suite 608
Green Bay, WI 54301
920-448-3400
Fax: 920-448-3426

City of Kenosha
Mr. Jim Schultz, Director
Department of Neighborhood
Services and Inspections
625 52nd St., Room 100
Kenosha, WI 53140
262-653-4263
Fax: 262-653-4254

City of LaCrosse
Mr. John Florine, Community
Development Administrator
Department of City Planning
400 La Crosse St.
La Crosse, WI 54601
608-789-7512
Fax: 608-789-7318

City of Madison
Mr. Hickory R. Hurie,
Community Development
Grants Supervisor
Department of Planning and
Development
P.O. Box 2985
Madison, WI 53701
608-267-0740
Fax: 608-261-9661

City of Milwaukee
Mr. Skip Seager, President
Neighborhood Improvement
Development Corp.
841 N. Broadway
Milwaukee, WI 53202-3515
414-286-5618
Fax: 414-286-8667

City of Racine
Mr. Richard A. Linsmeier,
Director
Department of Planning
730 Washington Ave.
Racine, WI 53403
262-636-9151
Fax: 262-636-9298

Counties
County of Waukesha

Mr. Glen Lewinski, CDBG
Coordinator
Department of Community
Development
1320 Pewaukee Rd.
Waukesha, WI 53188
262-548-7921
Fax: 262-896-8510

Consortia
Milwaukee County Consortium
Mr. Gary Bottoni, HOME
Coordinator
Department of Housing and
Community Development
907 N. Tenth St.
Courthouse Annex, Room 310
Milwaukee, WI 53223-1442
414-278-4880
Fax: 414-223-8196

Wyoming
Ms. Cheryl Gillum, Director
Community Development
Authority
P.O. Box 634
Casper, WY 82602
307-265-0603
Fax: 307-266-5414

U.S. Department of Agriculture Programs

Dream of living in the country? Here's your chance to make it a reality. The Rural Housing Service (RHS) is an agency of the U.S. Department of Agriculture (USDA) and offers programs to assist individuals, developers and nonprofits. The goal is for you to live in a clean safe place. Programs include homeownership assistance, housing rehabilitation and preservation, rental assistance, farm labor housing and more. Typically these programs are limited to rural areas, usually having a population of no more than 20,000 people. Read on to see how you can make your dream a reality!

Many of the programs include a five-digit number in the description. The number refers to the Catalog of Federal Domestic Assistance, which is a publication that lists all the government money programs. You can search the catalog online at {www.cfda.gov}, and it is also available in most public libraries.

For more information or to learn about different programs, you can contact the Rural Housing Service of the U.S. Department of Agriculture at:

Rural Housing Service
U.S. Department of Agriculture
Room 5037, South Building
14th Street and Independence Ave., SW
Washington, DC 20250
202-720-4323
www.rurdev.usda.gov

$7,000 for a Bathroom/Kitchen

Money is available to help those in rural areas install basic services to make their homes more habitable. Grant funds may be used to connect service lines to a residence, pay utility hook-up fees, install plumbing and related fixtures, i.e. a bathroom sink, bathtub or shower, commode, kitchen sink, water heater, outside spigot, or bathroom, if lacking.

These grants are available to households who own and occupy the dwelling, and are available only in Arizona, California, New Mexico, and Texas. This program is called Individual Water and Waste Grants.

For more information contact your state, area or local Rural Development office or contact Single Family Housing, Direct Loan Division, U.S. Department of Agriculture, Washington, DC 20250; 202-720-1474; {www.rurdev.usda.gov}.

$200,000 to Buy or Fix Up Homes In the Country

The Farm Labor Housing Loan and Grant program provides capital financing for the development of housing for domestic farm laborers. 1% loans and grants are provided to buy, build, improve, or repair housing for farm laborers, including persons whose income is earned in aquaculture (fish and oyster farms) and those engaged in on-farm processing.

Funds can be used to purchase a site or a leasehold interest in a site; to construct housing, day care facilities, or community rooms; to pay fees to purchase durable household furnishings; and to pay construction loan interest. Loans are for 33 years at 1% interest, except as noted above. Grants may cover up to 90% of development costs. The balance may be a Farm Labor Housing Program loan. Funds may also be used to build, buy, improve, or repair labor housing and to provide related facilities.

1,500 units used this program last year. The budget for this program is $30,000,000 in loans and $15,000,000 in grants. (10.405 Farm Labor Housing Loans and Grants).

For more information on the Farm Housing Loans and Grants Program contact your state, area or local Rural Development office or contact Multi-Family Housing, U.S. Department of Agriculture, Washington, DC 20250; 202-720-1604; {www.rurdev.usda.gov}.

$15,000 Grant For Owners or Developers In Small Towns To Fix Up Their Homes

The Housing Preservation Grants program provides funds to repair or rehabilitate individual housing, rental properties, or co-ops owned and/or occupied by very low- and low-income rural persons. Housing Preservation Grant assistance is available from grantees to assist very-low and low-income homeowners to repair and rehabilitate their homes.

Assistance is also available to rental property owners to repair and rehabilitate their units providing they agree to make such units available to very-low and low-income families. Financial assistance provided by the grantee may be in the form of a grant, loan, interest reduction on commercial loans, or other comparable assistance. Those assisted must own very low- or low-income housing, either as homeowners, landlords, or members of a cooperative. 1,400 homes used this program last year. The budget for this program is $8,000,000. (10.433 Rural Housing Preservation Grants).

For more information on Rural Housing Preservation Grants contact your state, area or local Rural Development office or contact Multi-Family Housing, U.S. Department of Agriculture, Washington, DC 20250; 202-720-1600; {www.rurdev.usda.gov}.

$50,000 To Fix Up Your Home After A Natural Disaster

Was your home in the country hurt by a natural disaster? The Rural Housing Service assists homeowners to meet emergency needs resulting from a natural disaster. Money is only available to the extent that funds are not provided by the Federal Emergency Management Agency (FEMA).

Applicants must own and occupy the home in a rural area. Loan recipients must have sufficient income to repay the loan. Grant recipients must be 62 years of age or older and be unable to repay a loan for that part of the assistance received as a grant. The applicant's income for a loan may not exceed the very low-income limit. 990 homes were repaired using these funds. (10.444 Direct Housing — Natural Disaster Loans and Grants Section 504).

For more information contact your state, area or local Rural Development office or contact Single Family Housing, U.S. Department of Agriculture, Washington, DC 20250; 202-720-1474; {www.rurdev.usda.gov}.

$2,700 A Year For Rent

Can't afford rent or want to help those with limited incomes? Rural Rental Assistance Payments help people with very low and low incomes, the elderly, and persons with disabilities if they are unable to pay the basic monthly rent.

Tenants in Rural Housing contribute 30% of their adjusted income, and the Rural Housing Service pays the rest of the rental rate. Prospective tenants can contact their local rural housing office to see what apartments participate in this program. Landlords can contact the local Rural Housing office to learn how they can qualify to participate in this program.

For more information contact your state, area or local Rural Development office or contact Multi-Family Housing, U.S. Department of Agriculture, Washington, DC 20250; 202-720-1600; {www.rurdev.usda.gov}.

$27,500 In Grants And Loans To Fix Up Your Home

That is the amount of money you can get to repair your rural home through the Section 504 Rural Housing Repair and Loan program. These low interest long-term loans helped over 4,000 homeowners use this money to fix up their homes. This program is limited to very low income homeowners. The Very Low-Income Housing Repair program provides loans and grants to very low-income homeowners in rural areas to repair, improve, or modernize their dwellings or to remove health and safety hazards.

Grant funds are only available to homeowners aged 62 or older who cannot repay a Section 504 Loan. This includes repairs or replacement of heating, plumbing or electrical services, roof or basic structure as well as water and waste disposal systems, and weatherization. Loans of up to $20,000 and grants of up to $7,500 or more are available. Loans are for up to 20 years at 1 percent interest. A real estate mortgage is required for loans of $7,500 or more. Full title services are required for loans of $7,500 or more. Grant funds may be used only to pay for repairs and improvements resulting in the removal of health and safety hazards. A grant/loan combination is made if the applicant can repay part of the cost. Loans and grants can be combined for up to $27,500 in assistance. Applicants must own and occupy a home in a rural area; and be a citizen of the United States or reside in the United States after having been legally admitted for permanent residence or on indefinite parole. 10,000 homes used this program last year. The budget for this program is $60,000,000. (10.417 Very Low-Income Housing Repair Loans and Grants (Section 504 Rural Housing Loans Grants)).

For more information Director, Single-Family Housing Processing Division, Rural Housing Service, Department of Agriculture, Washington, DC 20250; 202-720-1474; {www.rurdev.usda.gov}.

$100,000 Direct Loans To Buy or Fix Up Homes In The Country

Want to buy a home in the country, but don't think you can afford it? Think again.

Rural Housing Service provides financing for individuals and families who cannot obtain credit from other sources to purchase homes in rural areas. Applications are received at USDA offices. Funds may be used to purchase suitable existing homes, new site build homes, approved modular units, and new manufactured units from an approved dealer/contractor. Funds may also be used to repair or remodel homes, or to make the home accessible and usable for persons who are developmentally disabled.

Loans may be made for up to 100% of the appraised value of the site and the home. Maximum repayment period is 33 years, or under certain conditions, 38 years. Downpayment is not required if your net assets do not exceed $7,500. Certain fees must be paid and you cannot currently own a home. Applicants for direct loans from RHS must have very low or low incomes. Very low income is defined as below

50 percent of the area median income (AMI); low income is between 50 and 80 percent of AMI; moderate income is 80 to 100 percent of AMI. Form required: *Uniform Residential Loan Application.* Over 17,000 homes were purchased through this program. The budget for the program is $1,076,998,750. (Section 502 Direct Loan Program- 10.410 Very Low to Moderate Income Housing Loans).

For more information contact your state, area or local Rural Development office or contact Single Family Housing, Direct Loan Division, U.S. Department of Agriculture, Washington, DC 20250; 202-720-1474; {www.rurdev.usda.gov}.

$105,000 Guaranteed Loan To Buy Or Fix A House

Through USDA's Guaranteed Rural Housing Loan Program, low and moderate income people can qualify for mortgages even without a down-payment. Loans may be for up to 100% of appraised value. Mortgages are 30-year fixed rate. Guaranteed loans can be made on either new or existing homes.

Homes must be located in rural areas (USDA can determine eligible areas). Home buyers make application with participating lenders. Applicants for loans may have an income of up to 115% of the median income for the area. Form required: Uniform Residential Loan Application. Bank determines what other forms you will need. Over 29,000 homes were purchased using this loan. The budget for this program is $3,136,429,000. (Section 502 Guaranteed Loan Program- 10.410 Very Low to Moderate Income Guaranteed Housing Loans).

Approved lenders under the Single Family Housing Guaranteed Loan program include:

- Any State housing agency;
- Lenders approved by:
    - HUD for submission of applications for Federal Housing Mortgage Insurance or as an issuer of Ginnie Mae mortgage backed securities;
    - the U.S. Veterans Administration as a qualified mortgagee;
    - Fannie Mae for participation in family mortgage loans;
    - Freddie Mac for participation in family mortgage loans;
    - Any FCS (Farm Credit System) institution with direct lending authority;
    - Any lender participating in other USDA Rural Development and/or Consolidated Farm Service Agency guaranteed loan programs.

For more information contact your state, area or local Rural Development office or contact Single Family Housing, Direct Loan Division, U.S. Department of Agriculture, Washington, DC 20250; 202-720-1474; {www.rurdev.usda.gov}.

Want To Help Build Your Country Home?

Here is a chance for you to put in some sweat equity and build the home of your dreams. The Section 502 Mutual Self-Help Housing Loan program is used primarily to help very low- and low-income households construct their own homes. The program is targeted to families who are unable to buy clean, safe housing through conventional methods.

Families participating in a mutual self-help project perform approximately 65 percent of the construction labor on each other's homes under qualified supervision. The savings from the reduction in labor costs allows otherwise ineligible families to own their homes.

If families cannot meet their mortgage payments during the construction phase, the funds for these payments can be included in the loan. Maximum repayment period is 33 years, or under certain conditions, 38 years. Applicants for direct loans from RHS must have very low or low incomes. Very low income is defined as below 50 percent of the area median income (AMI); low income is between 50 and 80 percent of AMI; moderate income is 80 to 100 percent of AMI. Form required: Uniform Residential Loan Application. (Section 502 Mutual Self-Help Loan Program- 10.410 Very Low to Moderate Income Housing Loans).

For more information contact your state, area or local Rural Development office or contact Single Family Housing, Direct Loan Division, U.S. Department of Agriculture, Washington, DC 20250; 202-720-1474; {www.rurdev.usda.gov}.

$1,000,000 To Purchase Or Fix Up Rental Housing

Rural Rental Housing Loans are direct, competitive mortgage loans made to provide affordable multifamily rental housing for very low-, low-, and moderate-income families; the elderly; and persons with disabilities. This is primarily a direct mortgage program, but its funds may also be used to buy and improve land and to provide necessary facilities such as water and waste disposal systems.

In new Section 515 projects, 95 percent of tenants must have very low incomes. In existing projects 75 percent of new tenants must have very low incomes. Very low-,

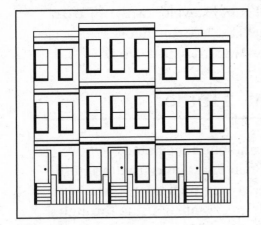

low-, and moderate-income families; the elderly; and persons with disabilities are eligible for tenancy of Section 515-financed housing. Very low income is defined as below 50 percent of the area median income (AMI); low income is between 50 and 80 percent of AMI; moderate income is capped at $5,500 above the low-income limit. Those living in substandard housing are given first priority for tenancy.

When rental assistance is used top priority is given to very low-income households. The program is adaptable for participation by a wide variety of owners. Loans can be made to individuals, trusts, associations, partnerships, limited partnerships, State or local public agencies, consumer cooperatives, and profit or nonprofit corporations. 6,600 units were built or repaired last year. The budget for this program is $50,000,000. (10.415 Rural Rental Housing Loans).

For more information contact your state, area or local Rural Development office or contact Multi-Family Housing, U.S. Department of Agriculture, Washington, DC 20250; 202-720-1600; {www.rurdev.usda.gov}.

Money To Build Rental Units

The Rural Housing Service guarantees loans under the Rural Rental Housing Guaranteed loan program for development of multi-family housing facilities in rural areas of the United States. Loan guarantees are provided for the construction, acquisition, or rehabilitation of rural multi-family housing. Occupants must be very-low-, low- or moderate-income households, elderly, handicapped, or disabled persons with income not in excess of 115% of the area median income. Very low income is defined as below 50 percent of the area median income (AMI); low income is between 50 and 80 percent of AMI; moderate income is capped at $5,500 above the low-income limit.

The average rent of all units is 30% of 100% of the median income of the surrounding area (adjusted for family size). The terms of the loans guaranteed may be up to 40 years, and the loans must be fully amortized. Rates of the loans guaranteed must be fixed, as negotiated between lender and borrower, within the RHS maximum established under the Notice of Fund Availability (NOFA). The rate is based on the 30-year Treasury Bond rate on the day prior to date of loan closing.

Maximum rent is 30 percent of 115 percent of median income, and average rent of all units is 30 percent of 100 percent of the median income adjusted for family size.

The program is limited to rural areas. Generally, communities are eligible if they have populations of not more than 10,000, nor more than 20,000 if there is a serious lack of mortgage credit. An applicant must be: A citizen of the United States or a legally admitted alien for permanent residence in the United States; a nonprofit organization such as a local government, community development group or American Indian tribe, band, group, or nation (including Alaskan Indians, Aleuts, Eskimos, and any Alaskan native village); or a for-profit corporation.

Eligible lenders are those currently approved and considered eligible by the Federal National Mortgage Association, the Federal Home Loan Mortgage Corporation, the Federal Home Loan Bank members, or the Department of Housing and Urban Development for guaranteed programs supporting multifamily housing. State Housing Finance Agencies may also be considered eligible lenders. Other lenders have the opportunity to enter into a correspondent bank relationship with approved lenders in order to participate in the program. 2,985 units were built last year. The budget for this program is $100,000,000. (10.438 Section 538 Guaranteed Rural Rental Housing Program).

For more information contact your state, area or local Rural Development office or contact Multi-Family Housing, U.S. Department of Agriculture, Washington, DC 20250; 202-720-1604; {www.rurdev.usda.gov}.

$400 Per Month To Help Pay Rent In Small Towns

The Rural Rental Assistance Payments are made to developers who operate low-income housing. These payments are used to reduce the rents paid by residents whose rents exceed 30 percent of their income. 43,750 families used this program last year. The budget for this program is $679,000,000. (10.427 Rural Rental Assistance Payments).

For more information contact Director, Multi-family Housing Portfolio Management Division, Rural Housing Service, Department of Agriculture, Washington, DC 20250; 202-720-1600; {www.rurdev.usda.gov}.

Money For Conserving the Water and Soil During an Emergency

Farmers often face natural disasters, like floods, hurricanes, or droughts. The Emergency Conservation Program provides assistance to rehabilitate eligible farmlands. These funds are made available without regard to a Presidential emergency disaster designation.

To be eligible the applicant must have suffered a natural disaster that if untreated would impair or endanger the land. Money can be used for debris removal, fence restoration, grading and shaping of farmland, water conservation, and more. (10.054- Emergency Conservation Program).

For more information contact your state or local Rural Development office or contact U.S. Department of Agriculture, Farm Service Agency, Stop 0513, 1400 Independence Ave., SW, Washington, DC 20250; 202-720-6221; {www.fsa.usda.gov}.

Money To Improve Your Water and Soil

The Conservation Reserve Program encourages farmers to plant long-term resource-conserving covers to improve soil, water, and wildlife resources. This is a voluntary program that offers annual rental payments, incentive payments, and annual maintenance payments for certain activities, and cost-share assistance to establish approved cover on eligible cropland. In addition the program encourages restoration of wetlands by offering a one-time incentive payment, and ther conservation practices are also eligible. (10.069- Conservation Reserve Program).

For more information contact your state or local Rural Development office or contact U.S. Department of Agriculture, Farm Service Agency, Stop 0513, 1400 Independence Ave., SW, Washington, DC 20250; 202-720-6221; {www.fsa.usda.gov}.

Loans to Help Your Country Property Recover From an Emergency

Disasters can strike at any time. The Farm Service Agency provides emergency loans to help producers recover from production and physical losses due to drought, flooding and other natural disasters. Emergency loan funds may be used to restore or replace essential property, any all or part of production costs associated with the disaster year, pay essential family living expenses, refinance certain debts, and more. Farmers and ranchers must have suffered at least a 30% loss of crop production or a physical loss to livestock, livestock products, real estate, or chattel property. (10.404-Emergency Loans).

For more information contact your state or local Rural Development office or contact U.S. Department of Agriculture, Farm Service Agency, Stop 0520, 1400 Independence Ave., SW, Washington, DC 20250; 202-720-1632; {www.fsa.usda.gov}.

Money For Farmers and Ranchers to Improve Water and Soil

Many farmers face serious threats to soil, water, and related natural resources. The Environmental Quality Incentives Program provides technical, financial, and educational assistance to address these concerns in an environmentally beneficial and cost-effective manner.

The program works primarily in priority areas where significant natural resource programs exist. All activities must be carried out according to a conservation plants. These plans are site-specific for each farm or ranch. The program offers incentive payments and cost sharing for these plans. (10.912- Environmental Quality Incentives Program).

For more information contact your state or local Rural Development office or contact Deputy Chief for Natural Resources, Conservation Programs, Natural Resources Conservation Service, U.S. Department of Agriculture, P.O. Box 2890, Washington, DC 20013; 202-720-1868; {www.nrcs.usda.gov}.

Money To Fix Up An Abandoned Coal Mine

Approximately 1.1 million acres exists of abandoned coal-mined land and are need of reclaiming. Money is available to protect people and the environment from the adverse effects of past coal mining practices, and to promote the development of soil and water resources of unreclaimed mined lands. (10.910- Rural Abandoned Mine program).

For more information contact your state or local Rural Development office or contact Deputy Chief for Natural Resources, Conservation Programs, Natural Resources Conservation Service, U.S. Department of Agriculture, P.O. Box 2890, Washington, DC 20013; 202-720-1873; {www.nrcs.usda.gov}.

$400,000 Grants To Build Homes In Small Towns

Help build affordable housing and businesses in rural areas. In order to expand the supply of affordable housing and access to economic opportunities in rural areas, grants are available that can be used for capacity building, and support for innovative housing and economic development activities for these programs. Local, rural, nonprofit organizations, community development corporations, Federally recognized Indian Tribes, State Housing Financing Agencies and State Community and Economic Development Agencies are eligible for funds. The budget for this program is $25,000,000. (14.250 Rural Housing and Economic Development).

For more information contact Jackie Williams-Mitchell, Director, Office of Rural Housing and Economic Development, Community Planning and Development 451 7th St., SW., Rm. 7137, Washington, DC 20410; 202-708-2290; {www.hud.gov/rhed.html}.

$750,000 To Buy A Farm

Farming is a difficult enterprise, subject to many uncontrollable variables. Loans are available to assist eligible farmers, ranchers, and aquaculture operators, including farming cooperatives, corporations, partnerships, and joint operations, through the extension of credit and supervisory assistance. Loans can be used so people can become owner-operators of not larger than family farms; make efficient use of the land, labor, and other resources; carry on sound and successful farming operations; and enable farm families to have a reasonable standard of living. Loan funds may be used to: enlarge, improve, and buy family farms; provide necessary water and water facilities; provide basic soil treatment and land conservation measures; construct, repair, and improve essential buildings needed in the operation of a family farm; construct or repair farm dwellings; and provide facilities to produce fish under controlled conditions. Those eligible to apply for the loan must be U.S. citizens or permanent residents, and have the necessary education and/or experience to operate a family farm. Assistance is authorized for eligible applicants in the 50 States, the Commonwealth of Puerto Rico, the Virgin Islands of the United States, Guam, American Samoa, the Commonwealth of the Northern Mariana Islands, and, to some extent, the Trust Territories of the Pacific Islands. 5,500 farms used this program last year. The budget for this program is $1,291,000,000. (10.407 Farm Ownership Loans).

For more information contact Department of Agriculture, Farm Service Agency, Director, Loan Making Division, Ag Box 0522, Washington, DC 20250; 202-720-1632; {www.fsa.usda.gov}.

Buy Some Land

In the country, land is often available, but tends to be offered in a large quantity. Funds are provided to assist public or private nonprofit organizations in providing sites for housing, to acquire and develop land in rural areas that will be subdivided as building sites and sold on a cost development basis to families eligible for low and very low income loans, cooperatives, and broadly based nonprofit rural rental housing applicants. Money can
also be used for water and sewer facilities, needed landscaping, walks, parking areas, and driveways. Repayment of the loan is expected within two years. Those eligible for loans include private or public nonprofit organizations that will provide the developed sites to qualified borrowers on a cost of development basis in open country and towns of 10,000 population or less and places up to 25,000 population under certain conditions. Assistance is available to eligible applicants in States, Puerto Rico, the Virgin Islands, Guam, and the Northern Marianas. (10.411 Rural Housing Site Loans and Self-Help Housing Land Development Loans (Section 523 and 524 Site Loans)).

For more information contact Director, Single-Family Housing Processing Division, Rural Housing Service, Department of Agriculture, Washington, DC 20250; 202-720-1474; {www.rurdev.usda.gov}.

$300,000 Grant To Help Families Build Part Of Their Own House

Funds are available in the form of Self Help Technical Assistance Grants that will provide financial assistance to qualified nonprofit organizations and public bodies that will aid needy very low and low-income individuals and their families to build homes in rural areas by the self help method. Any State, political subdivision, private or public nonprofit corporation is eligible to apply. Section 523 Grants are used to pay salaries, rent, and office expenses of the nonprofit organization. Pre-development grants up to $10,000 may be available to qualified organizations. Eligible organizations may use technical assistance funds to hire the personnel to carry out a technical assistance program for self-help housing in rural areas; to pay necessary and reasonable office and administrative expenses; to purchase or rent equipment such as power tools for use by families participating in self-help housing construction; and to pay fees for training self-help group members in construction techniques or for other professional services needed. Funds will not be used to hire personnel to perform any construction work, to buy real estate or building materials, or pay any debts, expenses or costs other than previously outlined for participating families in self-help projects. 98 grants were made last year. The budget for this program is $34,000,000. (10.420 Rural Self-Help Housing Technical Assistance (Section 523 Technical Assistance)).

For more information contact Director, Single-Family Housing Processing Division, Rural Housing Service (RHS), Department of Agriculture, Washington, DC 20250; 202-720-1474; {www.rurdev.usda.gov}.

Free Housing Counseling Services For Families In Small Towns

Many organizations want to help low-income rural families obtain adequate housing. These objectives can be accomplished through the establishment or support of housing delivery and counseling projects run by eligible applicants. Uses of grant funds may include: development and implementation of a program of technical and supervisory assistance; payment of reasonable salaries of professional, technical, and clerical staff actively assisting in the delivery of the project; payment of office expenses; payment of administrative costs; and payment of reasonable fees for necessary training. Technical and Supervisory Assistance Grants may be made to public or private nonprofit corporations, agencies, institutions, organizations, Indian Tribes, and other associations. The budget for this program is $1,687,543. (10.441 Technical and Supervisory Assistance Grants).

For more information contact Rural Housing Service (RHS), USDA, 14th Street and Independence Avenue SW., Washington, DC 20250; 202-720-1474; {www.rurdev.usda.gov}.

$20,000 Grant To Prepare A Loan Package For An Apartment Building

Getting the paperwork in order often takes time and skill. Grants are available to package single family housing applications for very low- and low-income rural residents who wish to buy, build, or repair houses for their own use and to package applications for organizations wishing to develop rental units for lower income families. Grants reimburse eligible organizations for part or all of the costs of conducting, administering, and coordinating an effective housing application packaging program. Eligible organizations aid very low- and low-income individuals and families in obtaining benefit from Federal, State, and local housing programs. Application packagers cannot charge a fee for their service. Eligible applicants include state or local governments, and private nonprofit organizations. The budget for this program is $700,000. (10.442 Housing Application Packaging Grants (Section 509 Grants)).

For more information contact Director, Single Family Housing Processing Division, Rural Housing Service, Department of Agriculture, Washington, DC 20250; 202-720-1474; {www.rurdev.usda.gov}.

Rural Development Offices

National Office
Rural Housing Service National Office
U.S. Department of Agriculture
Room 5037, South Building
14th Street and Independence
Avenue, S.W.
Washington, DC 20250
202-720-4323
http://www.rurdev.usda.gov/rhs/

National Centralized Servicing Center
1520 Market Street
St. Louis, Missouri 63103
800-414-1226

Alabama
Alabama USDA Rural Development State Office
Suite 601, Sterling Centre
4121 Carmichael Road
Montgomery, AL 36106-3683
334-279-3400

Fax: 334-279-3403
TDD/TTY: 334-279-3495

Area Offices
Contact the Area Office, listed below, serving your county for information on community facilities, business and industry, cooperatives, rural utilities, and/or multi-family housing programs.

AREA 1
USDA Rural Development
4890 University Square
Suite 3-G
P.O. Box 5267
Huntsville, AL 35814-5267
256-544-5795
Fax: 256-544-2158
Serving: Calhoun, Cherokee,
Clay, Cleburne, Colbert, DeKalb,
Etowah, Franklin, Jackson,
Lauderdale, Lawrence,
Limestone, Madison, Marshall,
Morgan, Randolph, St. Clair, and
Talladega Counties

AREA 2
USDA Rural Development
205 W. Adams Street
P.O. Box 2026
Dothan, AL 36302
334-793-7819
Fax: 334-793-2744
Serving: Autauga, Barbour,
Bullock, Chambers, Coffee,
Coosa, Dale, Elmore, Geneva,
Houston, Henry, Lee, Macon,
Montgomery, Pike, Russell, and
Tallapoosa Counties

AREA 3
USDA Rural Development
3831-B Palisades Drive
Tuscaloosa, AL 35405
205-553-1733, ext. 5
Fax: 205-553-5100
Serving: Bibb, Blount, Chilton,
Cullman, Fayette, Greene, Hale,
Jefferson, Lamar, Marion,
Pickens, Shelby, Sumter,
Tuscaloosa, Walker, and
Winston Counties

AREA 4
USDA Rural Development
213 East 1st Street
P.O. Box 517
Bay Minette, AL 36507
251-937-7350
Fax: 251-937-4984
Serving: Baldwin, Butler,
Choctaw, Clarke, Conecuh,
Covington, Crenshaw, Dallas,
Escambia, Lowndes, Marengo,
Mobile, Monroe, Perry,
Washington, and Wilcox
Counties

Local Offices
Contact the Local Office serving
your county for information on
our single family housing
programs.

USDA Rural Development
1504-B Hwy 31 S.
Bay Minette, AL 36507
251-937-3297, Ext. 4
Serving: Baldwin, Mobile,
Washington, and Counties

USDA Rural Development
1413-C Hillyer
Robinson Industrial Pkwy
Anniston, AL 36201
256-831-3067
Serving: Calhoun Cherokee
Cleburne Etowah, and Counties

USDA Rural Development
733 Logan Road
Clanton, AL 35045
205-755-5101, Ext. 4
Serving: Chilton, Bibb, and
Shelby Counties

USDA Rural Development
117 Neil Morris Road, Suite C
P.O. Box 646
Tuscumbia, AL 35674
256-383-4323, Ext. 4
Serving: Colbert, Franklin,
Lauderdale and, Lawrence
Counties.

USDA Rural Development
376 Southern Bypass
Andalusia, AL 36420
334-222-6528, Ext. 4
Serving: Covington, Butler,
Conecuh, Crenshaw, and
Escambia Counties.

USDA Rural Development
205 4th Avenue NE, Suite 103
Cullman, AL 35055
256-734-6471, Ext. 4
Serving: Cullman, Blount,
Jefferson, Walker, and Winston
Counties.

USDA Rural Development
1702 Hwy 123 South, Suite H
Ozark, AL 36360

334-774-4926
Serving: Dale, Coffee, Geneva,
and Pike Counties

USDA Rural Development
200 Main St. West, Suite 105
P.O. Box 1607
Rainsville, AL 35986
256-638-7423
Serving: DeKalb, Jackson, and
Marshall Counties.

USDA Rural Development
105 Gossom Switch Rd., Suite A
Wetumpka, AL 36092
334-567-2264, Ext. 4
Serving: Elmore, Autauga,
Coosa, Montgomery, and
Tallapoosa Counties.

USDA Rural Development
1849 Ross Clark Circle, Suite 1
Dothan, AL 36301-5331
334-793-2310, Ext. 4
Serving: Houston, Barbour, and
Henry Counties.

USDA Rural Development
145 Columbus Avenue
P.O. Box 737
Vernon, AL 35592
205-695-7622, Ext. 4
Serving: Lamar, Fayette, Marion,
and Pickens Counties.

USDA Rural Development
600 South 7th Street, Suite 1
Opelika, AL 36801
334-745-7638
Serving: Lee, Bullock, Chambers,
Macon, and Russell Counties.

USDA Rural Development
819 Cook Ave., N.W., Suite 150
Huntsville, AL 35801-5983
256-532-1677, Ext. 4
Serving: Madison, Limestone,
and Morgan Counties.

USDA Rural Development
334 Agricultural Drive
Hwy 21 South
Monroeville, AL 36460
251-743-2587, Ext. 4
Serving: Monroe, Choctaw, and
Clarke Counties.

USDA Rural Development
127 N. East Street
Room 204, Fed Bldg
Talladega, AL 35160
256-362-8210, Ext. 4
Serving: Talladega, Clay,
Randolph, and St. Clair
Counties.

USDA Rural Development
3831-C Palisades Dr.
Tuscaloosa, AL 35405
205-553-1733, Ext. 4
Serving: Tuscaloosa, Greene,
Hale, and Sumter Counties.

USDA Rural Development
Three Camden Bypass
P.O. Box 130
Camden, AL 36726
334-682-4116, Ext. 4
Serving: Wilcox, Dallas,
Lowndes, Marengo, and Perry
Counties.

Alaska

Rural Development State Office
800 West Evergreen, Suite 201
Palmer, AK 99645
907-761-7705
Fax: 907-761-7783

Bethel Area Office
311 Willow Building 3
PO Box 1869
Bethel, AK 99559
907-543-3858
Fax: 907-543-3855
Serving Bethel, Bristol Bay, and
Wade Hampton Counties

Dillingham Area Office
Kangiiqutaq Building
123 Main St
PO Box 1370
Dillingham, AK 99576
907-842-3921
Fax: 907-842-3922
Serving Dillingham County

Fairbanks Service Center
590 University Ave
Fairbanks, AK 99709-3661
907-479-4362
Fax: 907-479-6998

Serving North Slope, Denali,
Fairbanks North Star, Nome,
Northwest Arctic, Southeast
Fairbanks, Valdez-Cordova, and
Yukon-Koyukuk Counties

Kenai Area Office
110 Trading Bay Road
Suite 160
Kenai AK 99611
907-283-8732
Fax: 907-283-9667
Serving Aleutians East,
Aleutians West, Kenai
Peninsula, Kodiak Island, Lake
and Peninsula Counties

Nome Area Office
240 Front St, Room 106
PO Box 1569
Nome, AK 99762
907-443-6022

Sitka Area Office
204 Siganaka Way
Sitka AK 99835
907-747-4324
Fax: 907-747-4325
Serving Haines, Juneau,
Ketchikan Gateway, Prince Of
Wales-Outerketchikan, Sitka,
Skagway-Hoonah-Angoon,
Wrangell-Petersburg, and
Yakutat Counties

America Samoa, Hawaii and Western Pacific
See Hawaii

American Samoa Local Office
USDA Rural Development
Pago Plaza, Suite 203
P.O. Box 2447
Pago Pago, AS 96799-2447
011-684-633-1131
Fax: 011-684-633-4329

Arizona

USDA Rural Development
Rural Housing Program State
Office
3003 N. Central Ave., Suite 900
Phoenix, AZ 85012-2906
602-280-8755
Fax: 602-280-8879

Phoenix Area Office
Rural Development Manager
3003 N. Central Ave., Suite 900
Phoenix, AZ 85012-2906
602-280-8737
Fax: 602-280-8753

Casa Grande Local Office
115 East First Street, Suite A
Casa Grande, AZ 85222
520-836-1960, Ext. 4
Fax: 520-836-1297

Flagstaff Sub-Office
1585 South Plaza Way, Suite 120
Flagstaff, AZ 86001
928-774-2401, Ext. 5
Fax: 928-774-2780

Kingman Local Office
101 E. Beale St., Suite B
Kingman, AZ 86401
928-753-6181, 6182 Ext. 4
Fax: 928-753-3254

Holbrook Local Office
51 West Vista, Suite 5
Holbrook, AZ 86025
928-524-2771, 2887 Ext. 4
Fax: 928-524-6609

Nogales Local Office
2585 N. Grand Avenue, Suite 5
Nogales, AZ 85621
520-281-0221, 2498
Fax: 520-281-1460

Phoenix Local Office
3150 N. 35th Avenue, Suite 6
Phoenix, AZ 85017
602-353-0378 Ext. 4
Fax: 602-353-0906

Prescott Valley Local Office
8841 Florentine, Suite B
Prescott Valley, AZ 86314
928-759-9301 Ext. 3
Fax: 928-759-9284

St. Michaels Local Office
St. Michaels Professional Plaza
Hwy 264
P.O. Box 859
St. Michaels, AZ 86511
928-871-5038, Ext. 4
Fax: 928-871-4530

Safford Local Office
305 E. 4th Street
Safford, AZ 85546
928-428-0635 Ext. 4
Fax: 928-428-4284

Tucson Local Office
4650 N. Highway Dr., Suite 1
Tucson, AZ 85705
520-887-4505 Ext. 4
Fax: 520-888-1467

Willcox Local Office
658 North Bisbee Avenue
Willcox, AZ 85643
520-384-3529 Ext. 4
Fax: 520-384-2735

Yuma Local Office
2450 S. 4th Avenue, Suite 401
Yuma, AZ 85364
928-344-8902, Ext. 4
Fax: 928-341-1499

Arkansas

USDA Service Center State
Office
700 West Capitol, Room 3416
Little Rock, AR 72201-3225
501-301-3200
Fax: 501-301-3278

Batesville Service Center
490 E. College St.
Fed Bldg., Room 226A
Batesville, AR 72501
870-793-4164
Fax: 870-793-3175
Serving Cleburne,
Independence, Jackson, and
Sharp Counties

Bentonville Service Center
101 NE 3rd St
Bentonville, AR 72712-5390
479-273-2622
Fax: 479-273-3721
Serving Benton, Madison, and
Washington Counties

Camden Service Center
351 W Washington St., Suite 218
Camden, AR 71701-3901
870-836-2089
Fax: 870-836-8041

Serving Calhoun, Columbia,
Dallas, Ouachita, and Union
Counties

Clarendon Service Center
605 Madison St
Clarendon, AR 72029-2824
870-747-3431
Fax: 870-474-3617
Serving Arkansas, Monroe,
Phillips, and Prairie Counties

Conway Service Center
1111 Main St., Suite 221
Conway, AR 72032-5449
501-327-6509
Fax: 501-450-7748
Serving Conway, Faulkner,
Perry, and Van Buren Counties

Forrest City Service Center
107 W Cook St.
Forrest City, AR 72335-2730
870-633-3055
Fax: 870-630-0241
Serving Crittenden, Cross, Lee,
and St Francis Counties

Fort Smith Service Center
3913 Brooken Hill Dr.
Fort Smith, AR 72908-9289
479-646-8300
Fax: 479-646-2691
Serving Crawford, Franklin,
Logan, Scott, and Sebastian
Counties

Harrison Service Center
402 N Walnut St., Suite 127
Harrison, AR 72601-3621
870-741-8600
Fax: 870-741-2613
Serving Boone, Carroll, Marion,
Newton, and Searcy Counties

Hope Service Center
2510 N Hervey St.
Hope, AR 71801-8419
870-777-8800
Fax: 870-777-3284
Serving Hempstead, Lafayette,
Little River, Miller, and Nevada
Counties

Jonesboro Area Office
1306 Stone St

Jonesboro, AR 72401-4522
870-972-4720
Fax: 870-972-4762
Serving Craighead, Mississippi,
and Poinsett Counties

Malvern Service Center
220 Olive St., Suite 3
Malvern, AR 72104-3728
501-337-7381
Fax: 501-332-4185
Serving Clark, Garland, Hot
Spring, and Saline Counties

Melbourne Service Center
1107 Hwy 69 E
Melbourne, AR 72556
870-368-4413
Fax: 870-368-5505
Serving Baxter, Fulton, Izard,
and Stone Counties

Monticello Service Center
419 W Gaines St
Monticello, AR 71655-4723
870-367-8400
Fax: 870-367-5816
Serving Ashley, Bradley, Chicot,
Desha, and Drew Counties

Nashville Service Center
121 W Sypert St
Nashville, AR 71852-2431
870-845-4121
Fax: 870-845-2177
Serving Howard, Montgomery,
Pike, Polk, and Sevier Counties

Pine Bluff Service Center
100 E 8th Ave., Room 2603
Pine Bluff, AR 71601-5073
870-534-3200
Fax: 870-535-0236
Serving Cleveland, Grant,
Jefferson, and Lincoln Counties

Russellville Service Center
420 N Hampton Ave
Russellville, AR 72802-8240
501-968-3497
Fax: 501-968-5933
Serving Johnson, Pope, and Yell
Counties

Searcy Service Center
505 S Elm St

Searcy, AR 72143-6604
501-268-5866
Fax: 501-268-7153
Serving Lonoke, Pulaski, White,
and Woodruff Counties

Walnut Ridge Service Center
1100 W Main St
Walnut Ridge, AR 72476-1006
870-886-7791
Fax: 870-886-7552
Serving Clay, Greene, Lawrence,
and Randolph Counties

California

USDA Rural Development State
Office
430 G Street, #4169
Davis, CA 95616-4169
530-792-5800, ext 1
Fax: 530-792-5838

Region 1
Serving Butte, Clousa, Glenn,
Lassen, Modoc, Plumas, Shasta,
Siskiyou, Sutter, Tehama,
Trinity, Yolo and Yuba Counties.

Alturas Local Office
808 W. 12th St.
Alturas, CA 96101
530-233-4615

Oroville Local Office
150-D Chuck Yeager Way
Oroville, CA 95965
530-533-4401 ext. 4

Red Bluff Local Office
2 Sutter St., Suite. B
Red Bluff, CA 96080
530-527-1013 ext. 4

Redding Local Office
3179 Bechelli Ln., Suite. 109
Redding, CA 96002
530-246-5244 ext. 4

Willows Local Office
132 N. Enright Ave., Suite. C
Willows, CA 95988
530-934-4614 ext. 4

Yreka Local Office
215 Executive Ct., Suite B

Yreka, CA 96097
530-842-6123 ext. 4

Yuba City Local Office
1521-D Butte House Rd.
Yuba City, CA 95993
530-673-4347 ext. 4

Region 2
USDA Rural Development
777 Sonoma Avenue
E Street Annex
Santa Rosa, CA 95404
Serving Alameda, Alpine,
Amador, Calaveras, Contra
Costa, Del Norte, El Dorado,
Lake, Marin, Mendocino, Mono,
Monterey, Napa, Nevada,
Placer, Sacramento, San Benito,
San Francisco, San Joaquin, San
Mateo, Santa Clara, Santa Cruz,
Sierra, Solano, and Sonoma
Counties.

Auburn Local Office
251 Auburn Ravine Rd.
Suite 103
Auburn, CA 95603
530-885-7081 ext. 4

Elk Grove Local Office
9701 Dino Dr., Ste. 170
Elk Grove, CA 95624
916-714-1104 ext. 4

Eureka Local Office
5630 South Broadway
Eureka, CA 95503
707-442-6058 ext. 4

Salinas Local Office
744 LaGuardia St., Ste. A
Salinas, CA 93905
831-424-1036 ext. 4

Santa Rosa Local Office
777 Sonoma Avenue
E Street Annex
Santa Rosa, CA 95404-4731
707-526-6797

Stockton Local Office
1222 Monaco Ct., Ste. 19
Stockton, CA 95207
209-946-6455 ext. 4

Ukiah Local Office
405 S. Orchard Ave.
Ukiah, CA 95482
707-462-2916 ext. 4

Region 3
USDA Rural Development
4625 W. Jennifer #126
Fresno CA 93631
Serving Fresno, Inyo, Los
Angeles, Madera, Merced,
Riverside (W), San Bernardino,
Stanislaus, Tuolumne Counties.

Fresno Local Office
4625 W. Jennifer
Fresno, CA 93722
559-276-7494 ext. 4

Indio Local Office
82-901 Bliss Ave.
Indio, CA 92201
760-347-7658

Merced Local Office
2135 W. Wardrobe Ave, Suite A
Merced, CA 95349
209-723-3714 ext. 4

Modesto Local Office
3800 Cornucopia Way, Suite E
Modesto, CA 95358
209-491-9320 ext. 4

Victorville Local Office
17330 Bear Valley Rd., Suite 106
Victorville, CA 92392
760-843-6882

Region 4
Serving Imperial, Kern. Kings,
Orange, Riverside (E), San
Diego, San Luis, Obispo, Santa
Barbara, Tulare, and Ventura
Counties.

Bakersfield Local Office
1601 New Stine Rd., Ste. 280
Bakersfield, CA 93309
661-861-4221 ext. 4

El Centro Local Office
177 N. Imperial Ave.
El Centro, CA 92243
760-352-4418

Hanford Local Office
680 Campus Dr., Ste. D
Hanford, CA 93230
559-584-9209 ext. 4

Moreno Valley Local Office
22690 Cactus Ave., Ste. 280
Moreno Valley, CA 92553
909-656-6800

Santa Maria Local Office
920 E. Stowell Rd.
Santa Maria, CA 93454
805-928-9269 ext. 4

Visalia Local Office
3530 W. Orchard Ct.
Visalia, CA 93277
559-734-8732, ext. 4

Colorado

Rural Development State Office
Lakewood State Office
655 Parfet Street, Room E-100
Lakewood, CO 80215
720-544-2903
800-659-3656
TTY 720-544-2976

Alamosa Rural Development
Local Office
2205 State Street
Alamosa, CO 81101
719-589-5661 ext. 4
Fax: 719-589-0515

Burlington Rural Development
Local Office
111 So. 14th Street, Suite #2
Burlington, CO 80807
719-346-7699 ext. 4
Fax: 719-346-5523

Canon City Rural Development
Local Office
248 Dozier Avenue
Canon City, CO 81212
719-275-4465 ext. 4
Fax: 719-275-3019

Cortez Rural Development Local
Office
628 W. 5th Street
Cortez, CO 81321
970-565-8416 ext. 4
Fax: 970-565-8797

Craig Rural Development Local
Office
356 Ranney Street
Craig, CO 81625
970-824-3476 ext. 4
Fax: 970-824-7055

Fort Morgan Rural Development
Local Office
220 State Street
Fort Morgan, CO 80701
970-867-9419 ext. 4
Fax: 970-867-9410

Grand Junction Rural
Development Local Office
2754 Compass Drive, Suite #185
Grand Junction, CO 81506
970-242-4511 ext. 4
Fax: 970-241-2782

Greeley Rural Development
Local Office
4302 W. 9th Street Road
Greeley, CO 80634
970-356-8097 ext. 4
Fax: 970-351-0392

Hugo Rural Development Local
Office
318 5th Street
P.O. Box 218
Hugo, CO 80821
719-743-2408 ext. 4
Fax: 719-743-2701

Lamar Rural Development Local
Office
3501 So. Main, #C
Lamar, CO 81052
719-336-3437 ext. 4
Fax: 719-336-7958

Montrose Rural Development
Local Office
102 Par Place, #1
Montrose, CO 81401
970-249-8407 ext. 4
Fax: 970-249-5718

Rocky Ford Rural Development
Local Office
202 South 10th
Rocky Ford, CO 81067
719-254-7616 ext. 4
Fax: 719-254-4541

Trinidad Rural Development
Local Office
422 East 1st
Trinidad, CO 81082
719-846-3681 ext. 4
Fax: 719-846-0525

Wray Rural Development Local
Office
247 N. Clay, Suite 2
P.O. Box 405
Wray, CO 80758
970-332-3107 ext. 4
Fax: 970-332-9801

Connecticut
(Southern New England)
Rural Development State Office
451 West Street, Suite 2
Amherst MA 01002-2999
413-253-4300
Fax: 413-253-4347

Norwich Service Center
Serving Eastern Connecticut
238 West Town Street
Norwich, CT 06360
860-859-5218 Ext. 3004
Fax: 860-859-5223
Serving Windham and New
London Counties.

Windsor Service Center
Serving Western and Central
Connecticut
627 River Street
Windsor, CT 06790
860-688-7725 Ext. 4
Fax: 860-688-7979
Serving Tolland, Middlesex,
Hartford, Litchfield, New
Haven, and Fairfield Counties.

Delaware
Delaware USDA Rural
Development
4607 South DuPont Highway
Post Office Box 400
Camden, DE 19934
302-697-4300
Fax: 302-697-4390

Frederick Area Office
USDA Rural Development
92 Thomas Johnson Dr.
Suite 110

Frederick, MD 21702
301-694-7522, Ext. 5
Fax: 301-694-5840

Dover Local Office
USDA Rural Development
3500 South DuPont Highway
Dover, DE 19901
302-697-2600 Ext 4
Fax: 302-697-8259
Serving Kent and New Castle
Counties.

Georgetown Local Office
USDA Rural Development
Agricultural Service Center
408-A North DuPont Highway
Georgetown, DE 19947
302-856-3990 Ext 4
Fax: 302-856-4381
Serving Sussex County.

Florida/Virgin Islands

USDA Rural Development State
Office
4440 N.W. 25th Place
Gainesville, FL 32606
352-338-3402
Fax: 352-338-3405

Area 1
Crestview Area Office
932 N. Ferdon Blvd., Suite B
Crestview, FL 32536
850-682-2416
Serving Bay, Escambia, Holmes,
Okaloosa, Santa Rosa, Walton
and Washington Counties.

Milton Local Office
USDA, Agriculture Center
6275 Dogwood Drive
Milton, FL 32570
850-623-2441
Fax: 850-623-8012
Serving Escambia and Santa
Rosa Counties.

Defuniak Springs Local Office
732 N. Ninth Street, Suite A
DeFuniak Springs, FL 32433
850-892-3712
Fax: 850-892-6002
Serving Okaloosa and
Walton Counties.

Chipley Local Office
1424 Jackson Ave., Suite B
Chipley, FL 32428
850-638-1982
Fax: 850-638-9325
Serving Bay, Holmes and
Washington Counties.

Area 2
Marianna Area Office
2741 Pennsylvania Ave., Suite 5
Marianna, FL 32448
850-526-2610
Serving Calhoun, Columbia,
Franklin, Gadsden, Gulf,
Hamilton, Jackson, Jefferson,
Lafayette, Leon, Liberty,
Madison, Suwannee, Taylor and
Wakulla Counties.

Marianna Local Office
2741 Pennsylvania Ave., Suite 7
Marianna, FL 32448-4014
850-526-2610
Fax: 850-526-7534
Serving Calhoun, Gulf, Jackson
and Liberty Counties.

Quincy Local Office
2138 W. Jefferson St.
Quincy, FL 32351
850-627-6365
Fax: 850-627-7297
Serving Franklin, Gadsden, Leon
and Wakulla Counties.

Live Oak Local Office
10094 US 129 South
Live Oak, FL 32060
904-362-2681
Fax: 904-362-3375
Serving Columbia, Hamilton,
Jefferson, Lafayette, Madison,
Suwannee and Taylor Counties.

Area 3
Ocala Area Office
2303 N.E. Jacksonville Rd.
Suite 400
Ocala, FL 34470
352-732-7534
Serving Alachua, Baker,
Bradford, Citrus, Clay, Dixie,
Duval, Flagler, Gilchrist, Levy,
Marion, Nassau, Putnam,

Seminole, St. Johns, Union and
Volusia Counties.

Baldwin Local Office
260 U.S. 301 North
Baldwin, FL 32234
904-266-0088
Fax: 904-266-4858
Serving Baker, Bradford, Clay,
Duval, Nassau, St. Johns and
Union Counties.

Deland Local Office
1342-A South Woodland Blvd.
DeLand, FL 32720
904-734-2535
Fax: 904-736-9339
Serving Flagler, Putnam,
Seminole and Volusia Counties.

Ocala Local Office
2303 N.E. Jacksonville Road
Suite 300
Ocala, FL 34470
352-732-7534
Fax: 352-732-9728
Serving Alachua, Citrus, Dixie,
Gilchrist, Levy and Marion
Counties.

Area 4
Tavares Area Office
32245 David Walker Drive
Tavares, FL 32778
352-742-7005
Serving Brevard, DeSoto,
Hardee, Hernando,
Hillsborough, Lake, Manatee,
Orange, Osceola, Pasco, Pinellas,
Polk and Sumter Counties. Also
serves St. Croix, St. Thomas & St.
John, Virgin Islands

Bartow Local Office
1700 Hwy. 17 S., Suite 3
Bartow, FL 33830-6633
863-533-2051
Fax: 863-533-1884
Serving Desoto, Hardee and
Polk Counties.

Plant City Local Office
201 S. Collins Street, Suite 200
Plant City, FL 33566
813-752-1474
Fax: 813-754-7297

Serving Hillsborough, Manatee, Pinellas and Pasco Counties.

Tavares Local Office
32235 David Walker Drive
Tavares, FL 32778
352-742-7005
Fax: 352-343-6275
Serving Brevard, Hernando, Lake, Orange, Osceola and Sumter Counties.

Area 5
West Palm Beach Area Office
750 S. Military Trail, Suite J
West Palm Beach, FL 33415
561-683-2285
Serving Broward, Charlotte, Collier, Dade, Glades, Hendry, Highlands, Indian River, Lee, Martin, Monroe, Okeechobee, Palm Beach, Sarasota and St. Lucie Counties.

North Fort Myers Local Office
3434 Hancock Bridge Pkwy.
Suite 209-A
N. Ft. Myers, FL 33903-7005
941-997-7331
Fax: 941-997-7557
Serving Charlotte, Collier, Hendry, Lee and Sarasota Counties.

Okeechobee Local Office
454 N.W. Hwy. 98
Okeechobee, FL 34972
863-763-3345
Fax: 863-763-6407
Serving Glades, Highlands and Okeechobee Counties.

West Palm Beach Local Office
750 S. Military Trail, Suite H
West Palm Beach, FL 33415
561-683-2285
Fax: 561-683-6249
Serving Broward, Dade, Indian River, Martin, Monroe, Palm Beach and St. Lucie Counties.

Georgia
USDA Rural Development State Office
Stephens Federal Building
335 East Hancock Avenue
Athens, GA 30601-2768
706-546-2162
Fax: 706-546-2152

Area I
Cartersville Area Office
Suite A, 12 Felton Place
Cartersville North Business Ctr.
Cartersville, GA 30120
770-386-3393
Fax: 770-387-0429
Serving Bartow, Butts, Carroll, Catoosa, Chatooga, Cherokee, Clayton, Cobb, Coweta, Dade, DeKalb, Douglas, Fannin, Fayette, Floyd, Fulton, Gilmer, Gordon, Haralson, Heard, Henry, Meriwether, Murray, Paulding, Pickens, Polk, Rockdale, Troup, Walker, and Whitfield Counties.

Area II
Athens Area Office
355 East Hancock Avenue
Stephens Federal Building
Room 259 Box 1
Athens, GA 30601
706-546-2471
Fax: 706-546-3273
Serving Banks, Barrow, Clarke, Dawson, Elbert, Forsyth, Franklin, Greene, Gwinnett, Habersham, Hall, Hart, Jackson, Lumpkin, Madison, Morgan, Newton, Oconee, Oglethorpe, Rabun, Stephens, Towns, Union, Walton, and White Counties.

Area III
Macon Area Office
915 Hill Park, Suite 100
Macon, GA 31201
912-752-8121
Fax: 912-752-3452
Serving Bibb, Bleckley, Chattahoochee, Clay, Crawford, Dodge, Harris, Houston, Jasper, Jones, Lamar, Laurens, Lee, Macon, Marion, Monroe, Muscogee, Peach, Pike, Pulaski, Quitman, Randolph, Schley, Spalding, Stewart, Sumter, Talbot, Taylor, Terrell, Twiggs, Upson, Webster, and Wilkinson Counties.

Area IV
Waynesboro Area Office
501 W. Sixth St.
P.O. Box 829
Waynesboro, GA 30830
706-554-7001
Fax: 706-554-4539
Serving Baldwin, Burke, Columbia, Emmanuel, Glascock, Hancock, Jefferson, Jenkins, Johnson, Lincoln, McDuffie, Putnam, Richmond, Screven, Taliaferro, Truetlen, Warren, Washington, and Wilkes Counties.

Area V
Tifton Area Office
Tift County Admin. Bldg.
114 West 12th St., Suite F
Tifton, GA 31794
912-382-0273
Fax: 912-382-2823
Serving Baker, Ben Hill, Berrien, Brooks, Calhoun, Clinch, Colquitt, Cook, Crisp, Decatur, Dooly, Dougherty, Early, Echols, Grady, Irwin, Lanier, Lowndes, Miller, Mitchell, Seminole, Thomas, Tift, Turner, Wilcox, and Worth Counties.

Area VI
Baxley Area Office
605 S. Main St. Building E
P.O. Box 30
Baxley, GA 31513
912-3657-3603
Fax: 912-367-0503
Serving Appling, Atkinson, Bacon, Brantley, Bryan, Camden, Candler, Charlton, Chatham, Clinch, Coffee, Effingham, Evans, Glynn, Jeff Davis, Liberty, Long, McIntosh, Montgomery, Pierce, Screven, Tatnall, Telfair, Toombs, Ware, Wayne, and Wheeler Counties.

Georgia Local Field Offices
Barnesville Local Field Office
118 Academy Drive
Barnesville, GA 30204
770-358-2280
Fax: 770-358-6788

Serving Lamar, Jasper, Jones, Monroe, Pike, Spalding, and Upson Counties.

Blackshear Local Field Office
707 Hendry Street
Blackshear, GA 31516
912-449-5577
Fax: 912-449-1024
Serving Appling, Bacon, Brantley, Camden, Charlton, Clinch, Glynn, Pierce, Ware, and Wayne Counties.

Byron Local Field Office
102 Church Street
P.O. Box 849
Byron, GA 31008-0849
912-956-6495
Fax: 912-956-6473
Serving Bibb, Chatahoochee, Crawford, Harris, Houston, Macon, Marion, Muscogee, Peach, Schley, Talbot, and Taylor Counties.

Camilla Local Field Office
30 W. Broad Street
P.O. Box 232
Camilla, GA 31730
912-336-0371
Fax: 912-336-1867
Serving Baker, Dougherty, Grady, Mitchell, and Thomas Counties.

Clarkesville Local Field Office
555 Monroe Street
P.O. Box 1240
Clarkesville, GA 30523
706-754-6239
Fax: 706-754-9821
Serving Banks, Habersham, Rabun, Stephens, Towns, Union, and White Counties.

Cochran Local Field Office
Professional Building
Peacock Street
P.O. Box 428
Cochran, GA 31014
912-934-6392
Fax: 912-934-9211
Serving Bleckley, Dodge, Laurens, Pulaski, Twiggs, and Wilkinson Counties.

Dawson Local Field Office
955 Forrester Drive
P.O. Box 311
Dawson, GA 31742
912-995-5819
Fax: 912-995-8414
Serving Clay, Lee, Quitman, Randolph, Stewart, Sumter, Terrell, and Webster Counties.

Douglas Local Field Office
711 E. Ward Street
P.O. Box 1344
Douglas, GA 31533
912-384-4811
Fax: 912-384-5446
Serving Atkinson, Coffee, Jeff Davis, Montgomery, Telfair, and Wheeler Counties.

Gainesville Local Field Office
734 E. Crescent Drive, Suite 100
Gainesville, GA 30501
770-536-0547
Fax: 770-536-6076
Serving Barrow, Dawson, Forsyth, Gwinnett, Hall, Jackson, Lumpkin, Union, and White Counties.

Hartwell Local Field Office
88 Market Street
P.O. Box 308
Hartwell, GA 30643
706-376-3954
Fax: 706-856-3350
Serving Clarke, Elbert, Franklin, Hart, Madison, and Oglethorpe Counties.

Jasper Local Field Office
35 West Church Street, Suite 119
Jasper, GA 30143
706-692-6417
Fax: 706-692-9344
Serving Cherokee, Cobb, Fannin, Gilmer, Gordon, Murray, and Pickens Counties.

LaFayette Local Field Office
208-A North Duke Street
LaFayette, GA 30728
706-638-2189
Fax: 760-638-2371
Serving Catoosa, Chattooga, Dade, Walker, and Whitfield Counties.

McDonough Local Field Office
333 Phillips Drive, Suite C
McDonough, GA 30253
770-957-1228
Fax: 770-957-3191
Serving Butts, Clayton, DeKalb, Henry, and Rockdale Counties.

Monroe Local Field Office
129 North Midland Avenue
Monroe, GA 30655
770-267-1413
Fax: 770-267-1341
Serving Greene, Morgan, Newton, Oconee, Walton Counties.

Newnan Local Field Office
580 Bullsboro Drive, Suite C
Newnan, GA 30263
770-253-2555
Fax: 770-253-7032
Serving Carroll, Coweta, Douglas, Fayette, Fulton, Heard, Meriwether, and Troup Counties.

Ocilla Local Field Office
Agricultural Building
1st Cherry Street
P.O. Box 86
Ocilla, GA 31774
912-468-9461
Fax: 912-468-9561
Serving Ben Hill, Crisp, Dooly, Irwin, Tift, Turner, Wilcox, and Worth Counties.

Rome Local Field Office
1401 Dean Street, Suite M
Rome, GA 30161
706-291-5705
Fax: 706-291-5623
Serving Bartow, Floyd, Haralson, Paulding, and Polk Counties.

Statesboro Local Field Office
52 North Main Street
Federal Building, Room 204
Statesboro, GA 30458
912-764-9841
Fax: 912-489-5947
Serving Bulloch, Bryan, Candler, Chatham, Effingham, Evans, Liberty, Long, McIntosh,

Screven, Tatnall, and
Toombs Counties.

Tennille Local Field Office
114 Smith Street
Tennille, GA 31089
912-552-0901
Fax: 912-553-0372
Serving Baldwin, Hancock,
Johnson, Putnam, and
Washington Counties.

Thomson Local Field Office
226 Bob Kirk Road, NW
Thomson, GA 30824
706-595-7643
Fax: 706-595-5025
Serving Columbia, Glascock,
Lincoln, McDuffie, Taliaferro,
Warren, and Wilkes Counties.

Valdosta Local Field Office
Federal Building, Room 108M
401 N. Patterson
Valdosta, GA 31601
912-244-9828
Fax: 912-249-9924
Serving Berrien, Brooks, Clinch,
Colquitt, Cook, Echols, Lanier,
and Lowndes Counties.

Waynesboro Local Field Office
Burke Co, Office Park
West 6th Street, Room 108
P.O. Box 689
Waynesboro, GA 30830
706-554-4486
Fax: 706-554-4408
Serving Burke, Emmanuel,
Jefferson, Jenkins, Richmond,
Screven, and Truetlen Counties.

Hawaii, American Samoa, Western Pacific

Rural Development Area Office
Room 311, Federal Building
154 Waianuenue Avenue
Hilo, HI 96720
808-933-8380
Fax: 808-933-8327

Area I - Hawaii/American Samoa
Hilo Local Office
USDA Rural Development
Room 327, Federal Building
154 Waianuenue Avenue

Hilo, HI 96720-2486
808-933-8330
Fax: 808-933-8336

Oahu Local Office
USDA Rural Development
99-193 Aiea Heights Dr.
Suite 156
Aiea, HI 96701-3911
808-483-8600/option 4
Fax: 808-483-8605

Kauai Local Office
USDA Rural Development
4334 Rice Street, Room 106
Lihue, HI 96766-1365
808-245-9014/option 4
Fax: 808-246-0277

Maui Local Office
USDA Rural Development
Millyard Plaza
210 Imi Kala St., Suite 206
Wailuku, HI 96793-1274
808-244-3100/option 4
Fax: 808-242-7005

Kealakekua (Kona) Local Office
USDA Rural Development
Ashikawa Building
P.O. Box 756
Kealakekua, HI 96750-0756
808-322-9351
Fax: 808-322-2565

Molokai Local Office
USDA Rural Development
Kahua Ctr, Unit 4
Kaunakakai Place
P.O. Box 527
Kaunakakai, HI 96748-0527
808-553-5321
Fax: 808-553-3739

American Samoa Local Office
USDA Rural Development
Pago Plaza, Suite 203
P.O. Box 2447
Pago Pago, AS 96799-2447
011-684-633-1131
Fax: 011-684-633-4329

Area II-Western Pacific
Rural Development Area Office
First Hawaiian Bank Bldg.
400 Route 8, Ste. 303

Hagatna, Guam 96910
671-472-7361
Fax: 671-472-7366

Barrigada Local Office
USDA Rural Development
494 West Route 8, Suite 103
Hagatna, GU 96910
671-735-2102
Fax: 671-735-2108

Palau Local Office
USDA Rural Development
Pierantozzi Bldg. II
Lebuu Rd, Dngeronger
P.O. Box 430
Koror, Palau, PW 96940
011-680-488-2499
Fax: 011-680-488-1373

Pohnpei Local Office
USDA Rural Development
Jem's Building
P.O. Box 396
Pohnpei, FM 96941
011-691-320-2581
Fax: 011-691-320-2662

Saipan Local Office
USDA Rural Development
D.Y. Building
P.O. Box 500370
Saipan, MP 96950
670-236-0875
Fax: 670-236-0876

Chuuk Local Office
USDA Rural Development
Inek Building
P.O. Box 430
Chuuk, FM 96942
011-691-330-2658
Fax: 011-691-330-4658

Yap Local Office
USDA Rural Development
Waab Commercial Center
P.O. Box 98
Yap, FM 96943
011-691-350-2191
Fax: 011-691-350-2250

Kosrae Local Office
USDA Rural Development
Skilling Building
P.O. Box 421

Tofol, Kosrae, FM 96944
011-691-370-3198
Fax: 011-691-370-2079

Majuro Local Office
USDA, Rural Development
Mako Building
P.O. Box 764
Majuro, MH 96960
011-692-625-3846
Fax: 011-692-625-3995

Idaho

Idaho State Office
USDA Rural Development
9173 West Barnes, Ste A 1
Boise, ID 83709
208-378-5600
Fax: 208-378-5643

Idaho Area Offices

Blackfoot Area Office
725 Jensen Grove Drive, Suite 1
Blackfoot, ID 83221
208-785-5840
Fax: 208-785-6561
Serving Bannock, Bear Lake,
Bingham, Bonneville, Butte,
Caribou, Clark, Custer, Franklin,
Fremont, Jefferson, Lemhi,
Madison, Oneida, Power, and
Teton Counties.

Caldwell Area Office
2208 East Chicago, Ste. C
Caldwell, ID 83605
208-459-0761
Fax: 208-459-0762
Serving Ada, Adams, Boise,
Canyon, Elmore, Gem, Owyhee,
Payette, Valley, and Washington
Counties.

Coeur d' Alene Area Office
7830 Meadowlark Way, Ste. C3
Coeur d'Alene, ID 83815
208-762-4939
Fax: 208-762-9799
Serving Benewah, Bonner,
Boundary, Clearwater, Idaho,
Kootenai, Latah, Lewis, Nez
Perce, and Shoshone Counties.

Twin Falls Area Office
1441 Fillmore, Suite C
Twin Falls, ID 83301

208-733-5380
Fax: 208-734-0428
Serving Blaine, Camas, Cassia,
Gooding, Jerome, Lincoln,
Minidoka, and Twin Falls
Counties.

Idaho Outreach Offices
Blackfoot Outreach Office
725 Jensen Grove Drive, Suite 1
Blackfoot, ID 83221
208-785-6600
Fax: 208-785-5847
Serving Bannock, Bingham,
Bonneville, Butte, Custer,
Oneida, and Power Counties.

Caldwell Outreach Office
2208 East Chicago, Suite C
Caldwell, ID 83605
208-454-8691
Fax: 208-454-8053
Serving Ada, Boise, Canyon,
Gem, and W. Owyhee Counties.

Coeur d' Alene Outreach Office
7830 Meadowlark Way, Suite C3
Coeur d'Alene, ID 83815
208-667-0833
Fax: 208-667-5693
Serving Benewah, Bonner,
Boundary Kootenai, and
Shoshone Counties.

Grangeville Outreach Office
Route 1, Box 2
(Highway 95 North)
Grangeville, ID 83530-1201
208-983-2330
Fax: 208-983-0519
Serving Idaho, and Lewis
Counties.

Lewistown Outreach Office
3113 E. Main St.
Lewiston, ID 83501
208-746-9621
Fax: 208-798-3164
Serving Clearwater, Latah, and
Nez Perce Counties.

Mountain Home Outreach Office
795 South Haskett
Mountain Home, ID 83647-3140
208-587-9791
Fax: 208-587-6630
Serving Elmore, and E. Owyhee
Counties.

Rexburg Outreach Office
265 East 4th North
Rexburg, ID 83440-0459
208-356-7248
Fax: 208-356-7240
Serving Clark, Fremont,
Jefferson, Lemhi, Madison, and
Teton Counties.

Rupert Outreach Office
98-B South 200 West
Rupert, ID 83350-9603
208-436-0116
Fax: 208-436-3098
Serving Cassia, and Minidoka
Counties.

Soda Springs Outreach Office
390 East Hooper, No. 3
Soda Springs, ID 83276
208-547-4926
Fax: 208-547-4801
Serving Bear Lake, Caribou,
Franklin, and SE Bonneville
Counties.

Twin Falls Outreach Office
1441 Fillmore, Suite C
Twin Falls, ID 83301
208-733-5380
Fax: 208-734-0428
Serving Blaine, Camas, Gooding,
Jerome, Lincoln, and Twin Falls
Counties.

Weiser Outreach Office
845 East 9th
Weiser, ID 83672-2356
208-549-4280
Fax: 208-549-4229
Serving Adams, Payette, Valley,
and Washington Counties.

Illinois

USDA Rural Development State
Office
2118 West Park Court, Suite A
Champaign, IL 61821
217-403-6202
Fax: 217-403-6243

Area Offices

Northeast Illinois
Morris Area Office
1802 N. Division, Suite 218
Morris, IL 60450

815-942-9390
Fax: 815-942-9394

Northwest Illinois
Princeton Area Office
312 E. Backbone Road, Ste B
Princeton, IL 61356
815-875-8732
Fax: 815-872-1175

East Central Illinois
Champaign Area Office
2118 West Park Court, Suite B
Champaign, IL 61821
217-403-6236
Fax: 217-403-6237

Southeast Central Illinois
Effingham Area Office
USDA Building
2301 Hoffman Drive
Effingham, IL 62401
217-347-7107
Fax: 217-342-9855

Southwest Central Illinois
Jacksonville Area Office
1904 West Lafayette
Jacksonville, IL 62650
217-243-1535
Fax: 217-245-4875

Southern Illinois
Harrisburg Area Office
230 W. Poplar
Harrisburg, IL 62946
618-252-8371
Fax: 618-252-8024

Southwest Illinois
Nashville Area Office
256 South Mill Street
Nashville, IL 62263
618-327-8822
Fax: 618-327-8774

Local Offices
Carthage Local Office
110 Buchanan Street
Route 136 West
Carthage, IL 62321
217-357-2188
Fax: 217-357-3412
Serving Hancock, and
McDonough Counties.

Champaign Local Office
2110 West Park Court, Suite B
Champaign, IL 61821
217-398-5201
Fax: 217-398-5200
Serving Champaign, Douglas,
Edgar, Iroquois, Macon, Piatt,
and Vermilion Counties.

Charleston Local Office
990A W. State Street
Charleston, IL 61920
217-345-3901
Fax: 217-345-9669
Serving Coles, Clark,
Cumberland, Montgomery,
Moultrie, and Shelby Counties.

Edwardsville Local Office
7205 Marine Road, Suite A
Edwardsville, IL 62025
618-656-7300
Fax: 618-656-9144
Serving Madison, Bond, Clinton,
Monroe, and St. Clair Counties.

Effingham Local Office
2301 Hoffman Drive
Effingham, IL 62401
217-347-7107
Fax: 217-342-9855
Serving Effingham, Crawford,
Fayette, and Jasper Counties.

Galesburg Local Office
233 South Soangetaha Road
Galesburg, IL 61401
309-342-5138
Fax: 309-342-2259
Serving Knox, Fulton,
Henderson, Peoria, and Warren
Counties.

Harrisburg Local Office
809 S. Commercial
Harrisburg, IL 62946
618-252-8621
Fax: 618-252-2295
Serving Saline, Gallatin,
Hamilton, Hardin, Pope, and
White Counties.

Jacksonville Local Office
1904 West Lafayette
Jacksonville, IL 62650
217-243-1535

Fax: 217-245-0371
Serving Morgan, Calhoun, Cass,
Christian, Greene, Jersey,
Macoupin, Sangamon, and Scott
Counties.

Lincoln Local Office
1650 Fifth Street
Lincoln, IL 62656
217-735-5508
Fax: 217-732-9916
Serving Logan, DeWitt,
Hancock, Mason, McDonough,
Menard, and Tazewell Counties.

Mt. Vernon Local Office
109 Shiloh Drive
Mt. Vernon, IL 62864
618-244-0773
Fax: 618-244-5942
Serving Jefferson, Marion, and
Washington Counties.

Murphysboro Local Office
1213 North 14th
Murphysboro, IL 62966
618-684-3471
Fax: 618-684-3980
Serving Jackson, Franklin, Perry,
and Randolph Counties.

Olney Local Office
821B South West Street
Olney, IL 62450
618-392-7141
Fax: 618-392-4325
Serving Richland, Clay,
Edwards, Lawrence, Wabash,
and Wayne Counties.

Ottawa Local Office
Rural Route 2
1691 N. 31st. Road
Ottawa, IL 61350
815-433-0551
Fax: 815-433-0665
Serving LaSalle, Boone, Cook,
DeKalb, DuPage, Grundy, Kane,
Kankakee, Kendall, Lake,
McHenry, and Will Counties.

Princeton Local Office
312 E. Backbone Rd. Suite B
Princeton, IL 61356
815-875-8732
Fax: 815-872-1175

Serving Bureau, Carroll, Henry, Jo Daviess, Lee, Marshall, Mercer, Ogle, Putnam, Rock

Pontiac Local Office
P.O. Box 80, Route 116 West
Pontiac, IL 61764
815-844-6127
Fax: 815-844-6344
Serving Livingston, Ford, McLean, and Woodford Counties.

Quincy Local Office
338 South 36th Street
Quincy, IL 62301
217-224-9307
Fax: 217-224-4969
Serving Adams, Brown, Pike, and Schuyler Counties.

Tamms Local Office
505 Front Street
R.R. #1. Box 19
Tamms, IL 62988
618-747-2305
Fax: 618-747-9210
Serving Alexander, Massac, Johnson, Pulaski, Union, and Williamson Counties.

Indiana

Indiana USDA Rural Development State Office
5975 Lakeside Boulevard
Indianapolis, IN 46278
317-290-3100 (ext. 400)
Fax: 317-290-3095

AREA 1

Columbia Rural Development Area Office
1919 East Business 30
P.O. Box 699
Columbia City, IN 46725
219-248-8924
Fax: 219-248-2778

Area I Local Offices - Albion, Decatur, Plymouth, LaPorte, Lafayette
Albion Rural Development Local Office
104 East Park Drive
Albion, IN 46701
219-636-7682

Fax: 219-636-2525
Serving DeKalb, LaGrange, Noble, Steuben, and Whitley Counties

Decatur Rural Development Local Office
210 E. Monroe
Decatur, IN 46733
219-724-4124
Fax: 219-728-2988
Serving Adams, Allen, Jay, Huntington, Wabash, and Wells Counties

Lafayette Rural Development Local Office
188 Professional Court
Lafayette, IN 47905
765-448-1805
Fax: 765-449-4451
Serving Benton, Cass, Carroll, Howard, Miami, Newton, Tippecanoe, and White Counties

Laporte Rural Development Local Office
100 Legacy Plaza W.
LaPorte, IN 46350
219-324-6303
Fax: 219-324-8317
Serving Jasper, Lake, LaPorte, Porter, and St. Joseph Counties

The Plymouth Rural Development Local Office
2903 Gary Drive
Plymouth, IN 46563
219-936-9872
Fax: 219-936-5715
Serving Elkhart, Fulton, Kosciusko, Marshall, Pulaski, and Starke Counties

AREA II

North Vernon Rural Development Area Office
Highway 7 North
P.O. Box 116
North Vernon, IN 47265
812-346-3411
Fax: 812-346-8154

Area II Offices - Anderson, Scottsburg, Shelbyville, Versailles, Winchester and Muncie
Muncie Sub-Office

2908 N. Granville Ave.
P.O. Box 1889
Muncie, IN 47308
317-747-5531
Fax: 317-747-5506

Anderson Rural Development Local Office
1917 E. University Blvd., Suite B
Anderson, IN 46011
765-644-4249
Fax: 765-640-9029
Serving Blackford, Delaware, Grant, Hancock, Madison, and Tipton Counties.

Scottsburg Rural Development Local Office
656 S. Boatman Rd., Suite 1
Scottsburg, IN 47170
812-752-2269
Fax: 812-752-7066
Serving Clark, Floyd, and Scott Counties.

Shelbyville Rural Development Local Office
1110 Amos Road, A
Shelbyville, IN 46176
317-392-1394
Fax: 317-392-0739
Serving Bartholomew, Decatur, Johnson, Rush and Shelby Counties

Versailles Rural Development Local Office
P.O. Box 716
1981 S. Industrial Park
Suite 4
Versailles, IN 47042
812-689-6410
Fax: 812-689-3141
Serving Dearborn, Franklin, Jefferson, Jennings, Ohio, Ripley, and Switzerland Counties.

Winchester Rural Development Local Office
975 E. Washington Street, Suite 3
Winchester, IN 47394
765-584-4505
Fax: 765-584-1939
Serving Fayette, Henry, Randolph, Union, and Wayne Counties.

AREA III
Bloomfield Rural Development
Area Office
30 W. Indiana Avenue
P.O. Box 191
Bloomfield, IN 47424
812-384-4634
Fax: 812-384-8131

Area III Offices - Bedford,
Bloomington, Boonville, Covington,
Jasper, Lebanon, Sullivan
Bedford Rural Development
Local Office
1919 Steven Avenue
Bedford, IN 47421
812-279-8117
Fax: 812-279-0472
Serving Harrison, Jackson,
Lawrence, and Washington
Counties.

Bloomington Rural
Development Local Office
1931 Liberty
Bloomington, IN 47403
812-334-4318
Fax: 812-334-4279
Serving Brown, Monroe,
Morgan, and Owen Counties.

Boonville Rural Development
Local Office
P.O. Box 442
1124 S. 8th Street
Boonville, IN 47601
812-897-2840
Fax: 812-897-2859
Serving Gibson, Perry, Posey,
Spencer, Vandenburgh, and
Warrick Counties.

Covington Rural Development
Local Office
P.O. Box 191
US 136 E. USDA Bldg.
Covington, IN 47932
765-793-3651
Fax: 765-793-7252
Serving Fountain, Montgomery,
Parke, Putnam, Vermillion, and
Warren Counties.

Jasper Rural Development Local
Office
1484 Executive Blvd.
Jasper IN 47547

812-482-1171
Fax: 812-482-9427
Serving Fountain, Montgomery,
Parke, Putnam, Vermillion, and
Warren Counties.

Lebanon Rural Development
Local Office
801 West Pearl Street
Lebanon, IN 46052
765-482-6355
Fax: 765-482-9478
Serving Boone, Clinton,
Hamilton, Hendricks, and
Marion Counties.

Sullivan Rural Development
Local Office
2326 N. Section St.
Sullivan, IN 47882
812-268-5157
Fax: 812-268-0232
Serving Clay, Greene, Knox,
Sullivan, and Vigo Counties.

Iowa

Iowa USDA Rural Development
State Office
210 Walnut Street, Room 873
Des Moines, IA 50309-2196
515-284-4663
Fax: 515-284-4821

Area 1
Storm Lake Area Office
1619 North Lake
P.O. Box 1107
Storm Lake, IA 50588-1107
712-732-1851
Fax: 712-732-6059
Serving Buena Vista, Cherokee,
Clay, Dickinson, Emmet, Ida,
Lyon, O'Brien, Osceola, Palo
Alto, Plymouth, Sac, Sioux and
Woodbury Counties.

Storm Lake Local Office
1619 North Lake
P.O. Box 1107
Storm Lake, IA 50588-1107
712-732-1851
Fax: 712-732-6059
Buena Vista, Ida and Sac
Counties.

LeMars Local Office

1100 B 12th Street SW
P.O. Box 809
LeMars, IA 51031-0809
712-546-5149
Fax: 712-546-5187
Serving Cherokee, Lyon,
O'Brien, Plymouth, Sioux and
Woodbury Counties.

Spencer Local Office
P.O. Box 1418
Spencer, IA 51301-1418
712-262-3173
Fax: 712-262-7127
Serving Clay and Palo Alto
Counties.

Spirit Lake Local Office
2414 17th Street
P.O. Box H
Spirit Lake, IA 51360-9407
712-336-3782
Fax: 712-336-4278
Serving Dickenson, Emmet and
Osceola Counties.

Area 2
Humboldt Area Office
1301 6th Ave. North, Suite 1
Humboldt, IA 50548-1150
515-332-4411
Fax: 515-332-4113
Serving Calhoun, Cerro Gordo,
Franklin, Hamilton, Hancock,
Hardin, Humboldt, Kossuth,
Pocahontas, Webster,
Winnebago, Worth and Wright
Counties.

Humboldt Local Office
1301 6th Ave. North, Suite 1
Humboldt, IA 50548-1150
515-332-4411
Fax: 515-332-4113
Serving Calhoun, Humboldt,
Kosuth, Pocahontas, Webster
and Wright Counties.

Garner Local Office
192 State Street
Garner, IA 50438-1227
641-923-2853
Fax: 641-923-3660
Serving Cerro Gordo, Hancock,
Winnebago and Worth Counties.

Iowa Falls Local Office
840 Brooks Road
Iowa Falls, IA 50126-8008
641-648-5181
Fax: 641-648-4630
Serving Franklin, Hamilton and
Hardin Counties.

Area 3
New Hampton Area Office
420 West Milwaukee
New Hampton, IA 50659-0430
641-394-3183
Fax: 641-394-3769
Serving Allamakee, Black Hawk,
Bremer, Buchanan, Butler,
Chickasaw, Clayton, Delaware,
Fayette, Floyd, Grundy,
Howard, Mitchell and
Winneshiek Counties.

New Hampton Local Office
420 West Milwaukee
New Hampton, IA 50659-0430
641-394-3183
Fax: 641-394-3769
Serving Chickasaw, Floyd,
Howard and Mitchell Counties.

Waverly Local Office
2504 East Bremer Avenue
Waverly, IA 50677-0179
319-352-1715
Fax: 319-352-5846
Serving Black Hawk, Bremer,
Buchanan, Butler and Grundy
Counties.

West Union Local Office
120 N. Industrial Parkway
West Union, IA 52175-1612
563-422-3839
Fax: 563-422-6018
Serving Alamakee, Clayton,
Delaware, Fayette and
Winneshiek Counties.

Area 4
Tipton Area Office
205 W. South Street
Tipton, IA 52772-0466
563-886-6006
Fax: 563-886-6023
Serving Benton, Cedar, Clinton,
Dubuque, Iowa, Jackson,
Johnson, Jones, Linn, Louisa,

Muscatine, Poweshiek, Scott,
Tama and Washington Counties.

Iowa City Local Office
238 Stevens Drive
Iowa City, IA 52240-4353
319-354-1074
Fax: 319-351-2997
Serving Benton, Cedar, Iowa,
Johnson, Linn, Louisa,
Muscatine, Poweshiek, Tama
and Washington Counties.

Maquoketa Local Office
603 E. Platt
Maquoketa, IA 52060-2416
563-652-3237
Fax: 563-652-4889
Serving Clinton, Dubuque,
Jackson, Jones and Scott
Counties.

Area 5
Albia Area Office
1709 South B Street
Albia, IA 52531
641-932-3031
Fax: 641-932-3370
Serving Appanoose, Davis, Des
Moines, Henry, Jefferson,
Keokuk, Lee, Lucas, Mahaska,
Monroe, Van Buren, Wapello
and Wayne Counties.

Albia Local Office
1709 South B Street
Albia, IA 52531
641-932-3031
Fax: 641-932-3370
Serving Appanoose, Lucas,
Monroe and Wayne Counties.

Fairfield Local Office
605 South 23rd Street
Fairfield, IA 52556-4212
641-472-6556
Fax: 641-472-1430
Serving Davis, Jefferson,
Mahaska, Keokuk, Van Buren
and Wapello Counties.

Fort Madison Local Office
1035 Avenue H
P.O. Box 401
Fort Madison, IA 52627-0401
319-372-4378

Fax: 319-372-9443
Serving Des Moines, Henry and
Lee Counties.

Area 6
Indianola Area Office
909 East 2nd Avenue, Suite C
Indianola, IA 50125-2812
515-961-5365
Fax: 515-961-3509
Serving Boone, Clarke, Dallas,
Decatur, Greene, Jasper,
Madison, Marion, Marshall,
Polk, Ringgold, Story, Union
and Warren Counties.

Indianola Local Office
909 East 2nd. Ave., Suite D
Indianola, IA 50125-2812
515-961-7473
Fax: 515-961-3509
Serving Clarke, Decatur,
Madison, Marion, Ringgold,
Union and Warren Counties.

Ankeny Local Office
1513 N. Ankeny Blvd
Ankeny, IA 50021-1793
515-964-4770
Fax: 515-964-8613
Serving Boone, Dallas, Greene,
Jasper, Marshall, Polk and Jasper
Counties.

Area 7
Atlantic Area Office
511 West 7th Street
P.O. Box 405
Atlantic, IA 50022-0405
712-243-2107
Fax: 712-243-1565
Serving Adair, Adams,
Audubon, Carroll, Cass,
Crawford, Fremont, Guthrie,
Harrison, Mills, Monona,
Montgomery, Page,
Pottawattamie, Shelby and
Taylor Counties.

Atlantic Local Office
511 West 7th Street
P.O. Box 405
Atlantic, IA 50022-0405
712-243-2107
Fax: 712-243-1565

Serving Adair, Adams, Audubon, Carroll, Cass, Guthrie, Montgomery, Page, and Taylor Counties.

Logan Local Office
721 North 2nd Avenue
Logan, IA 51546-1042
712-644-2993
Fax: 712-644-3247
Serving Crawford, Fremont, Harrison, Mills, Monona, Pottawattamie and Shelby Counties.

KANSAS

USDA - Rural Development State Office
1303 First American Pl., Ste 100
Topeka, KS 66604
785-271-2700
Fax: 785-271-2708

Altamonte Local Office
115 West 4th Street
Altamonte, KS 67330
620-784-5431
Fax: 620-784-5900
Serving Chautauqua, Cherokee, Crowford, Elk, Labette and Montgomery Counties.

Colby Local Office
915 East Walnut
Colby, KS 67701
785-462-7671
Fax: 785-462-9726
Serving Cheyenne, Rawlins, Decatur, Norton, Sherman, Thomas, Sheridan, Wallace, Logan, Gove, Greeley, Wichita, Scott and Lane Counties.

El Dorado Local Office
2503 Enterprise, Ste. C
El Dorado, KS 67042
316-321-5818
Fax: 316-321-4958
Serving Butler, Chase, Cowley, Greenwood, Harvey, Marion, Sedgwick and Sumner Counties.

Garden City Local Office
2106 East Spruce
Garden City, KS 67846
620-275-0211

Fax: 620-275-4903
Serving Clark, Finney, Ford, Grant, Gray, Hamilton, Haskell, Hodgeman, Kearney, Meade, Morton, Seward, Stanton and Stevens Counties.

Hays Local Office
2715 Canterbury Drive
Hays, KS 67601
785-628-3081
Fax: 785-625-6065
Serving Barton, Ellis, Graham, Jewell, Mitchell, Ness, Osborne, Pawnee, Phillips, Rooks, Rush, Russell, Smith and Trego Counties.

Iola Local Office
202 West Miller Road
Iola, KS 66749
620-365-2901
Fax: 620-365-5785
Serving Allen, Anderson, Bourbon, Coffey, Neosho, Wilson and Woodson Counties.

Lawrence Local Office
3010 Four Wheel Drive, Unit C
Lawrence, KS 66046
785-843-4260
Fax: 785-841-1087
Serving Atchison, Brown, Doniphan, Douglas, Franklin, Jackson, Jefferson, Leavenworth, Nemaha, Osage and Shawnee Counties.

Lyons Local Office
1480 Highway 56, Suite 103
Lyons, KS 67554
620-257-5184
Fax: 620-257-5653
Serving Barber, Comanche, Edwards, Ellsworth, Harper, Kingman, Kiowa, Lincoln, McPherson, Pratt, Reno, Rice, Saline, and Stafford Counties.

Manhattan Local Office
2615 Farm Bureau Road
Manhattan, KS 66502
785-776-7582
Fax: 785-539-2733
Serving Clay, Cloud, Dickinson, Geary, Lyon, Marshall, Morris,

Ottawa, Pottawatomie, Riley, Republic, Sabaunsee and Washington Counties.

Paola Local Office
100 North Angela
Paola, KS 66071
913-294-3751
Fax: 913-294-3386
Serving Johnson, Linn, Miami and Wyandotte Counties.

KENTUCKY

USDA Rural Development State Office
771 Corporate Drive, Suite 200
Lexington, KY 40503
859-224-7300
Fax: 859-224-7425

Area Offices
Western Kentucky Area Office
320B Traylor Street
Princeton, KY 42445
270-365-6530 Ext.5
Fax: 270-365-7842

South Central Kentucky Area Office
205 Burkesville Street
Columbia, KY 42728
270-384-4759-Ext.4
Fax: 270-384-6351

Central Kentucky Area Office
90 Howard Drive, #3
Shelbyville, KY 40065
502-633-0891-Ext 4
Fax: 502-633-0552

Northeastern Kentucky Area Office
220 West First Street
Morehead, KY 40351
606-784-6447-Ext.4
Fax: 606-784-2076

Southeastern Kentucky Area Office
95 South Laurel Road, Suite A
London, KY 40741
606-864-2172-Ext.5
Fax: 606-878-7717

Local Offices
Bardstown Local Office

974 Bloomfield Road
Bardstown, KY 40004
502-348-3024
Fax: 502-349-1136
Serving Nelson, Bullitt,
Jefferson, Spencer, Washington,
Marion, and Taylor Counties.

Bowling Green Local Office
975 Lovers Lane
Bowling Green, KY 42103
270-832-1111 Ext 4
Fax: 270-796-9228
Serving Warren, Simpson, Allen,
Edmonson, and Butler Counties.

Elizabethtown Local Office
587 Westport Road
Elizabethtown, KY 42701
270-769-1555
Fax: 270-765-2634
Serving Hardin, Grayson,
Breckinridge, Meade, and LaRue
Counties.

Elkton Local Office
101 Elk Fork Road
Elkton, KY 42220
270-265-5638 Ext.4
Fax: 270-265-2068
Serving Todd, Logan, Christian,
Hopkins, Caldwell, Lyon, and
Trigg Counties.

Flemingsburg Local Office
Flemming Agricultural Building
Highway 11 South
Route 2 Box 27A
Flemingsburg, KY 41041
606-845-2851 Ext.4
Fax: 606-845-0764
Serving Fleming, Bath, Rowan,
Lewis, Mason, Robertson,
Bracken, Pendleton, Campbell,
and Nicholas Counties.

Glasgow Local Office
108C Reynolds Road
Glasgow, KY 42141
270-678-2636
Fax: 270-678-1706
Serving Barren, Hart, Green,
Metcalfe, Adair, Cumberland,
Clinton, and Monroe Counties.

Grayson Local Office
526 East Main Street
Grayson, KY 41143
606-474-5185
Fax: 606-474-2047
Serving Carter, Greenup, Boyd,
Lawrence, and Elliott Counties.

Hazard Local Office
625 Memorial Drive
Hazard, KY 41701
606-439-1378
Fax: 606-436-6357
Serving Perry, Letcher, Harlan,
and Leslie Counties.

London Local Office
95 South Laurel Road, Suite B
London, KY 40741
606-864-2172-Ext.4
Fax: 606-878-7717
Serving Laurel, Clay, Knox, Bell,
and Whitley Counties.

New Castle Local Office
1125 Campbellsburg Road
New Castle, KY 40050
502-845-4700
Fax: 502-845-2005
Serving Henry, Franklin, Shelby,
Oldham, Trimble, and Carrol
Counties.

Nicholasville Local Office
800A South Main Street
Nicholasville, KY 40356
859-887-2461 Ext.4
Fax: 859-887-5517
Serving Jessamine, Woodford,
Anderson, Mercer, and Boyle
Counties.

Owensboro Local Office
3032 Alvery Park Drive West
Suite 3
Owensboro, KY 42303
270-683-0927
Fax: 270-926-7808
Serving Daviess, Hancock, Ohio,
McLean, Webster, Union,
Henderson, Muhlenburg, and
Crittenden Counties.

Paducah Local Office
2715 Olivet Church Road
Paducah, KY 42001

270-554-7265 Ext.4
Fax: 270-554-5702
Serving McCracken, Graves,
Fulton, Hickman, Carlisle,
Ballard, Calloway, Marshall, and
Livingston Counties.

Prestonburg Local Office
214 South Central Ave., Suite 103
Prestonburg, KY 41653
606-886-9545 Ext.4
Fax: 606-886-3971
Serving Floyd, Knott, Pike,
Johnson, and Martin Counties.

Richmond Local Office
2150 Lexington Road, Suite C
Richmond, KY 40475
859-624-1982 Ext.4
Fax: 859-624-5719
Serving Madison, Garrard, Estill,
Rockcastle, and Jackson
Counties.

Somerset Local Office
100 Parkway Drive
Somerset, KY 42503
606-678-4842 Ext.4
Fax: 606-677-9582
Serving Pulaski, Lincoln, Cassey,
Russell, Wayne, and McCreary
Counties.

West Liberty Local Office
955 Prestonburg Street, Suite 1
West Liberty, KY 41472
606-743-3193
Fax: 606-743-3174
Serving Morgan, Magoffin,
Breathitt, Owsley, Lee, Wolfe,
and Menifee Counties.

Williamstown Local Office
486 Helton Street
Williamstown, KY 41097
606-824-7171
Fax: 606-824-3172
Serving Grant, Boone, Kenton,
Owen, Gallatin, Scott, and
Harrison Counties.

Winchester Local Office
30 Taylor Avenue
Winchester, KY 40391
859-744-5561 Ext 4
Fax: 859-744-9714

Serving Clark, Fayette, Bourbon, Montgomery, and Powell Counties.

Louisiana

USDA, Rural Development
Louisiana State Office
3727 Government Street
Alexandria, LA 71302
318-473-7921
Fax: 318-473-7963

Area Offices
Monroe Area Office
2410 Old Sterlington Rd, Suite C
Monroe, LA 71203
318-343-4467 Ext. 4
Fax: 318-343-5776.
Serving Caldwell, Catahoula, Claiborne, Concordia, East Carroll, Franklin, Jackson, LaSalle, Lincoln, Madison, Morehouse, Ouachita, Richland, Tensas, Union, and West Carroll Parishes.

Natchitoches Area Office
6949 LA Hwy 1-Bypass
Suite 103
Natchitoches LA, 71457
318-352-7100 Ext. 4
Fax: 318-354-1682.
Serving Avoyelles, Bienville, Bossier, Caddo, DeSoto, Grant, Natchitoches, Rapides, Red River, Sabine, Vernon, Webster, and Winn Parishes.

Lafayette Area Office
Whitney National Bank
905 Jefferson Street, Suite 320
Lafayette LA 70501
337-262-6601, Ext. 4
Fax: 337-262-6823
Serving Acadia, Allen, Beauregard, Calcasieu, Cameron, Evangeline, Iberia, Jefferson Davis, Lafayette, St. Landry, St. Martin, St. Mary, and Vermilion Parishes.

Amite Area Office
805 West Oak Street, Room 3
Amite LA, 70422
985-748-8751 Ext. 4
Fax: 985-748-4940

Serving Ascension, Assumption, East Baton Rouge, East Feliciana, Iberville, Jefferson, Lafourche, Livingston, Orleans, Plaquemines, Pointe Coupee, St. John the Baptist, St. Bernard, St. Charles, St. Helena, St. James, St. Tammany, Tangipahoa, Terrebonne, Washington, West Baton Rouge, and West Feliciana Parishes.

Local Offices
Acadia Parish - Crowley Part-time Office
1708 N. Parkerson Avenue
Crowley LA, 70526
337-783-2061 Ext. 4
Serving Acadia Parish.

Avoyelles Parish - Marksville Part-time Office
313 North Monroe Street
Marksville LA 71351
318-253-9235 Ext. 4
Serving Avoyelles Parish.

Caddo Parish - Shreveport Sub Office
1402 Hawn Avenue
Shreveport, LA 71107
318-676-3461 Ext. 4
Fax: 318-676-3336
Serving Caddo, Bossier, and Desoto Parishes.

Catahoula Parish - Jonesville Sub Office
3545 Fourth Street
Jonesville, LA 71343
318-339-4239 Ext. 4
Fax: 318-339-4824
Serving Catahoula, Concordia, and LaSalle Parishes.

Concordia Parish - Ferriday Part-time Office
8331 Highway 84 West
Ferriday, LA 71334
318-757-4870 Ext. 4
Serving Concordia Parish.

Desoto Parish - Mansfield Part-time Office
R.C. Bridges Building
211 Washington

Mansfield, LA 71052
318-872-4814 Ext. 4
Serving Desoto Parish.

East Carroll Parish - Lake Providence Part-time Office
406 Lake Street, Suite B
Lake Providence, LA 71254
318-559-2188 Ext. 4
Serving East Carroll Parish.

Evangeline Parish - Ville Platte Part-time Office
205 Court Street
Ville Platte, LA 70586
337-363-6603 Ext. 4.
Serving Evangeline and Allen Parishes.

Franklin Parish - Winnsboro Part-time Office
616 Riser Road
Winnsboro, LA 71295
318-435-9424 Ext. 4
Serving Franklin Parish.

Jefferson Davis Parish - Jennings Part-time Office
2003 Port Drive
Jennings, LA 70546
318-824-0263 Ext. 4
Serving Jefferson Davis Parish.

Lafayette Parish - Lafayette Sub Office
Whitney National Bank
Suite 320, 905 Jefferson Street
Lafayette, LA 70501
337-262-6602 Ext. 4
Fax: 318-262-6823
Serving Lafayette and Vermillion Parishes.

Lafourche Parish - Thibodaux Sub Office
204 E. Bayou Road
Thibodaux, LA, 70301
985-447-6311, Ext. 4
Fax: 985-447-2793
Serving Lafourche, Assumption, St. James, and Terrebonne Parishes.

Lincoln Parish - Ruston Sub Office
1803 Trade Drive

P.O. Box 1990
Ruston, LA 71273-1990
318-255-2826 Ext. 4
Fax: 318-255-8063
Serving Lincoln, Claiborne, Jackson, and Union Parishes.

Livingston Parish - Denham Springs Sub Office
2191 Tower Street
Denham Springs, LA 70726
225-667-9528 Ext. 4
Fax: 225-791-8874
Serving Livingston, East Baton Rouge, East Feliciana, and West Feliciana Parishes

Madison Parish - Tallulah Local Office
1900 Crothers Drive
P.O. Box 1228
Tallulah, LA 71284
318-574-4158 Ext. 4
Fax: 318-574-5453
Serving Madison, Franklin, and Tensas Parishes.

Morehouse Parish - Bastrop Part-time Office
9602 Marlatt Street
Bastrop, LA 71220-9758
318-281-1561 Ext. 4
Serving Morehouse Parish.

Natchitoches Parish - Natchitoches Sub Office
6949 LA Hwy 1 Bypass
Suite 103
Natchitoches, LA 71457
318-352-7100 Ext. 4
Fax: 318-354-1682
Serving Natchitoches and Vernon Parishes.

Ouachita Parish - Monroe Sub Office
2410 Old Sterlington Rd, Suite C
Monroe, LA 71203
318-343-4467 Ext. 4
Fax: 318-343-5776
Serving Ouachita, Caldwell, and Richland Parishes.

Plaquemines Parish - Belle Chasse Part-time Office
805 West Oak Street, Room 3

Amite, LA 70422
985-748-8751 Ext. 4
Fax: 985-748-4940
Serving Plaquemines, Jefferson, Orleans, St. Bernard, St. Charles, and St. John Parishes.

Pointe Coupee Parish - New Roads Part-time Office
180 East Main Street
New Roads, LA 70760
225-618-8524 Ext. 4
Serving Point Coupee Parish.

Rapides Parish - Alexandria Local Office
3732 Government St, Building C
Alexandria, LA 71302
318-473-7710 Ext. 4
Fax: 318-473-7628
Serving Rapides and Avoyelles Parishes.

Red River Parish - Coushatta Part-time Office
1311 Ringgold Avenue
Coushatta, LA 71019
318-932-4231 Ext. 4
Serving Red River Parish.

Richland Parish - Rayville Part-time Office
141 Industrial Loop
Rayville, LA 71269
318-728-2081 Ext. 114
Serving Richland Parish.

St. Landry Parish - Opelousas Sub Office
111 N. Main Street, Suite A
Opelousas, LA 70570
337-948-3091 Ext. 4
Fax: 337-948-8241
Serving St. Landry, Evangeline, and Allen Parishes.

St. Martin Parish - St. Martin Part-time Office
Whitney National Bank
905 Jefferson Street, Suite 320
Lafayette, LA 70501
337-262-6602 Ext. 4
Fax: 337-262-6823
Serving St. Martin, St. Mary, and Iberia Parishes.

St. Mary Parish - Franklin Part-time Office
500 Main Street
Franklin, LA 70538-6144
337-828-4100 Ext. 104
Serving St. Mary Parish.

Tangipahoa Parish - Amite Sub Office
805 West Oak Street, Room 3
Amite, LA 70422
985-748-8751 Ext. 4
Serving Tangipahoa and St. Helena Parish.

Tensas Parish - St. Joseph Part-time Office
1301 Plank Road
St. Joseph, LA 71366
318-766-3502 Ext. 4
Serving Tensas Parish.

Vernon Parish - Leesville Part-time Office
1100 S. Third Street, Suite C
Leesville, LA 71449
337-239-0057 Ext. 4
Serving Vernon Parish.

Washington Parish - Franklinton Sub Office
1111 Washington Street
Franklinton, LA 70438
985-839-5686 Ext. 4
Fax: 985-839-9935
Serving Washington and St. Tammany Parishes.

Webster Parish - Minden Sub Office
216 B. Broadway
Minden, LA 71055
318-377-1871 Ext. 4
Fax: 318-377-2221
Serving Webster, Bienville, and Red River Parishes.

West Baton Rouge Parish - Addis Local Office
7747 Highway 1 South
Addis, LA 70710
225-687-2184 Ext. 4
Fax: 225-687-3412
Serving West Baton Rouge, Ascension, Iberville, and Point Coupee Parishes.

West Carroll Parish - Oak Grove
Sub Office
206 S. Constitution Avenue
P.O. Box 200
Oak Grove, LA 71263
318-428-9303 Ext. 4
Fax: 318-428-2822
Serving West Carroll, East
Carroll, and Morehouse
Parishes.

MAINE
USDA Rural Development State
Office
967 Illinois Avenue
P.O. Box 405
Bangor, ME 04402-0405
207-990-9100
Fax: 207-990-9165

Area Offices
Presque Isle Area Office
99 Fort Fairfield Road
Preque Isle, ME 04769-5015
207-764-4155/4157
Fax: 207-762-2246
Serving Aroostook, a Portion of
Northern Penobscot, and
Washington Counties

Bangor Area Office
28 Gilman Plaza, Suite 3
Bangor, ME 04401-3550
207-990-3676
Fax: 207-990-5092
Serving Hancock, Knox, Lincoln,
Penobscot, Piscataquis,
Somerset, and Waldo Counties

Lewistown Area Office
254 Goddard Road
P.O. Box 1938
Lewistown, ME 04241-1938
207-753-9400
Fax: 207-784-1335
Serving Androscoggin,
Cumberland, Franklin,
Kennebec, Oxford, Sagadahoc,
and York Counties

MARYLAND
Maryland USDA Rural
Development
4607 South DuPont Highway
Post Office Box 400
Camden, DE 19934

302-697-4300
Fax: 302-697-4390

Frederick Area Office
USDA Rural Development
92 Thomas Johnson Dr.
Suite 220
Frederick, MD 21702
301-694-7522, Ext 5
Fax: 301-694-5840

Mountain Lake Park Local Office
USDA/Rural Development
1916 Maryland Hwy, Suite D
Mt. Lake Park, MD 21550
301-334-6970
Fax: 301-334-6952
Serving Allegany and Garrett
Counties

Hagerstown Local Office
USDA/Rural Development
1260 Maryland Ave., Suite 105
Hagerstown, MD 21740
301-797-0500 Ext. 4
Fax: 301-739-4775
Serving Carroll, Frederick,
Howard, Montgomery,
Baltimore, and Washington
Counties

Prince Frederick Local Office
USDA/Rural Development
65 Duke Street, Suite 110
Prince Frederick, MD 20678
410-535-1521 Ext. 4
Fax: 410-535-0591
Serving Anne Arundel, Calvert,
Charles, District of Columbia,
Prince George's and St. Mary's
Counties

Elkton Local Office
USDA/Rural Development
Upper Chesapeake Corporate
Center
105 Chesapeake Blvd., Suite B4
Elkton, MD 21921
410-398-4411 Ext. 4
Fax: 410-392-6530
Serving Cecil, Harford and Kent
Counties

Denton Local Office
USDA/Rural Development
640 Legion Road, Suite 1
Denton, MD 21629
410-479-1202 Ext. 4

Fax: 410-479-2069
Serving Caroline, Dorchester,
Talbot and Queen Anne
Counties

Snow Hill Local Office
USDA/Rural Development
304 Commerce Street, Suite B
Snow Hill, MD 21863
410-632-0616 Ext. 4
Fax: 410-632-2732
Serving Worcester, Somerset and
Wicomico Counties:

MASSACHUSETTS
(*Southern New England*)
Rural Development State Office
451 West Street, Suite 2
Amherst MA 01002-2999
413-253-4300
Fax: 413-253-4347

Northampton Service Center
243 King Street, Room 24
Northampton, MA 01060
413-585-1000 Ext. 4
Fax: 413-586-8648
Serving Western Massachusetts
Berkshire, Franklin, Hampshire,
and Hampden Counties

Holden Service Center
52 Boyden Road
Holden, MA 01520
508-829-4477 Ext. 4
Fax: 508-829-3721
Serving Central Massachusetts
and North Shore
Worcester, Middlesex, Suffolk,
and Essex Counties

West Wareham Service Center
15 Cranberry Highway
West Wareham, MA 02576
508-295-5151 Ext. 3
Fax: 508-291-2368
Serving South Eastern
Massachusetts, Cape Cod and
the Islands, Bristol, Norfolk,
Plymouth, Dukes, Nantucket
and Barnstable Counties

MICHIGAN
East Lansing State Office
3001 Coolidge Road, Suite 200
East Lansing, MI 48823

517-324-5210
Fax: 517-324-5225

Gladstone Area Office
2003 Minneapolis
P.O. Box 231
Gladstone, MI 49837
906-428-1060, ext. 6
Fax: 906-428-1086

Caro Area Office
1975 Cleaver Road
P.O. Box 291
Caro, MI 48723
989-673-7588, ext. 6
Fax: 989-673-1848

Grand Rapids Area Office
3260 Eagle Park Drive, Suite 107
Grand Rapids, MI 49525
616-942-4111, ext. 6
Fax: 616-949-6042

Sault Ste. Marie Local Office
2769 Ashmum & M-129
Sault Ste. Marie, MI 49783
906-632-9611, ext. 4
Fax: 906-632-0341
Serving Alger, Baraga,
Chippewa, Delta, Dickinson,
Gogebic, Houghton, Iron,
Keweenaw, Luce, Mackinac,
Marquette, Menominee,
Ontonagon, and
Schoolcraft Counties.

Cadillac Local Office
7192 E. 34 Road
Cadillac, MI 49601
231-775-7681, ext. 4
Fax: 231-775-0938

Baldwin Local Office
1101 E. Washington
P.O. Box 220
Baldwin, MI 49304
231-745-8364
Fax: 231-745-8493
Serving Lake County.

West Branch Local Office
240 W. Wright Street
West Branch, MI 48661
517-345-5470, ext. 4
Fax: 517-345-4010

Serving Alcona, Alpena, Arenac,
Clare, Crawford, Gladwin, Iosco,
Montmorency, Ogemaw,
Oscoda, Ostego, Presque
Isle and Roscommon Counties.

Grand Rapids Local Office
3260 Eagle Park Dr, Suite 109
Grand Rapids, MI 49525
616-942-4111, ext. 4
Fax: 616-949-6042
Kent, Montcalm, Gratiot, Ionia,
Clinton, Mecosta, Muskegon,
Newago, Oceana,
Ottawa and Isabella.

Flint Local Office
1525 North Elms Rd.
Flint, MI 48532
810-230-8766, ext. 4
Fax: 810-230-2404
Serving Bay, Genesee, Huron,
Midland, Lapeer, Saginaw, St.
Clair, Sanilac, Shiawassee
and Tuscola Counties.

Howell Local Office
3469 E. Grand River
Howell, MI 48843
517-548-1550, ext. 4
Fax: 517-548-0533
Hillsdale Ingham Jackson
Lenawee Livingston, Macomb
Monroe, Oakland, Washtenaw
Wayne

Berrien Springs Local Office
3334 Edgewood Rd.
P.O. Box 129
Berrien Springs, MI 49103
616-471-9111, ext. 4
Fax: 616-471-3773
Allegan, Barry, Berrien, Branch,
Calhoun, Cass, Eaton,
Kalamazoo, St. Joseph and Van
Buren Counties

Howell Guaranteed Housing
Office
3469 East Grand River
Howell, MI 48843
517-548-1550, ext. 6
Fax: 517-548-0533

Traverse City Guaranteed
Housing Office

1501 Cass St., Suite A
Traverse City, MI 49684
231-941-0951, ext. 6
Fax: 231-929-7890

MINNESOTA

Rural Development State Office
410 Farm Credit Service Building
375 Jackson Street
St. Paul, MN 55101-1853
651-602-7800
Fax: 651-602-7824

Willmar Field Service Center
Willmar Service Center
1005 High Avenue
P.O. Box 1013
Willmar, MN 56201
320-235-5612 Option #4
Fax: 320-235-0984
Serving Becker, Beltrami, Blue
Earth, Big Stone, Brown, Cass,
Chippewa, Clay, Clearwater,
Cottonwood, Douglas, Faribault,
Grant, Hubbard, Jackson,
Kandiyohi, Kittson, LacQuiParle,
Lake of the Woods, Lincoln,
Lyon, Mahnomen, Marshall,
Martin, McLeod, Meeker,
Murray, Nicollet, Nobles,
Norman, Ottertail, Pennington,
Pipestone, Polk, Pope, Red Lake,
Redwood, Renville, Rock,
Roseau, Sibley, Stevens, Swift,
Todd, Traverse, Wadena,
Watonwan, Wilkin, and Yellow
Medicine Counties

North Branch Area Office
38694-12 Tanger Drive
North Branch, MN 55056
651-674-7051 Option #4
Fax: 651-674-8016
Serving Aitkin, Anoka, Benton,
Carlton, Carver, Cook, Chisago,
Crow Wing, Dakota, Dodge,
Fillmore, Freeborn, Goodhue,
Houston, Isanti, Itasca, Kanabec,
Lake, LeSeuer, Mille Lacs,
Morrison, Mower, Olmsted,
Pine, Rice, Scott, Sherburne, St.
Louis, Stearns, Steele, Wabasha,
Waseca, Winona, and Wright
Counties.

Northwest Region
Detroit Lakes Service Center
809 8th Street SE
Detroit Lakes, MN 56501
218-847-9392
Fax: 218-847-8910
Serving Becker, Mahnomen, Hubbard, Normal and Clay Counties.

Bemidji Service Center
3217 Bemidji Avenue
North Bemidji, MN 56601
218-751-1942
Fax: 218-751-9531
Serving Beltrami, Lake of the Woods, and Clearwater Counties

Thief River Falls Service Center
201 Sherwood Avenue South
P.O. Box 16
Thief River Falls, MN 56701
218-681-2843
Fax: 218-681-4732
Serving Pennington, Marshall, Red Lake, Roseau, Kittson, and Polk Counties.

Northeast Region
Brainerd Service Center
512 NE C. Street
Brainerd, MN 56401
218-829-5965
Fax: 218-829-8764
Serving Aitkin, Crow Wing, Morrison, and Cass Counties.

Duluth Service Center
4850 Miller Trunk Hwy, Suite 1B
Duluth, MN 55811
218-720-5330
Fax: 218-720-3129
Serving S. St. Louis, Carlton, Cook, Lake, Aitkin, and Pine Counties.

Virginia Field Service Center
230 1st Street South, Suite 104
Virginia, MN 55792
218-741-3929
Fax: 218-741-9407
Serving Itasca, N. St. Louis, and Koochiching Counties.

West Central Region
Willmar Field Service Center
1005 High Avenue
P.O. box 1013
Willmar, MN 56201
320-235-5612
Fax: 320-235-0984
Serving Kandiyohi, Meeker, Renville, Big Stone, Swift, and Chippewa Counties.

Alexandria Service Center
900 Robert Street NE, Suite 103
Alexandria, MN 56308
320-763-3191
Fax: 320-762-5502
Serving Douglas, Pope, Grant, Traverse, Stevens, Wilkin, Todd, Otter Trail, and Wadena Counties.

East Central Region
Cambridge Field Service Center
380 South Garfield Street
Cambridge, MN 55008
763-689-3354
Fax: 763-689-2309
Serving Anoka, Chisago, Isanti, Kanabec, and Washington Counties.

Buffalo Service Center
306 B. Brighton Avenue
Southeast Buffalo, MN 55313
763-682-1151
Fax: 763-682-2903
Serving Wright, Ramsey, Hennepin, Carver, Sibley, McLeod, and Nicollet Counties.

Waite Park Service Center
110 South 2nd Street, Suite 120
Waite Park, MN 56387
320-255-9111
Fax: 320-255-1455
Serving Stearns, Sherburne, Benton, Mille Lacs, and Morrison Counties.

Southwest Region
Worthington Service Center
1567 North McMillian
Worthington, MN 56187
507-372-7784
Fax: 507-372-7751
Serving Nobles, Jackson, Rock, Cottonwood, Murray, Pipestone,

Watonwan, and Martin Counties.

Marshall Service Center
1424 East College Dr, Suite 500
Marshall, MN 56258
507-532-3234
Fax: 507-532-7479
Serving Lyon, Brown, Lac qui Parle, Redwood, Lincoln, and Yellow Medicine Counties.

Southeast Region
Faribault Service Center
1810 30th Street, NW, #3
Faribault, MN 55021
507-332-7418, Option #4
Fax: 507-332-9892
Serving Rice, Goodhue, Scott, Dakota, Steele, LeSueur, Wabasha, and Waseca Counties.

Austin Service Center
101 21st Street SE
Austin, MN 55912
507-437-8247, Option #4
Fax: 507-437-8567
Serving Mower, Dodge, Winona, Blue Earth, Freeborn, Fillmore, Faribault, Houston, and Olmsted Counties.

Mississippi

USDA Rural Development State Office
100 West Capitol St., Suite 831
Federal Building
Jackson, MS 39269
601-965-4318
Fax: 601-965-5384

Area Offices
Brookhaven Area Office
1395 Johnny Johnson Drive.
Brookhaven, MS 39601
601-833-9321
Fax: 601-835-2437
Serving Adams, Amite, Claiborne, Copiah, Franklin, Hinds, Jefferson, Jefferson Davis, Lawrence, Lincoln, Pike, Warren and Wilkinson Counties.

Newton Area Office
100 North Main Street

Newton, MS 39345
601-683-6175
Fax: 601-683-7205
Serving Rankin, Simpson, Leake, Scott, Newton, Lauderdale, Jasper, Smith, Clarke, Jones, Wayne and Covington Counties.

Grenada Area Office
75 Kirk Avenue
Grenada, MS 38901
662-226-4724
Fax: 662-227-1018
Serving Attala, Carroll, Grenada, Leflore, Montgomery, Yalobusha, Calhoun, Chickasaw, Lafayette, Union and Pontotoc Counties.

Greenville Area Office
3038 East Reed Road
Greenville, MS 38704
662-335-4862
Fax: 662-378-9638
Serving Bolivar, Sunflower, Humphreys, Sharkey, Issaquena, Holmes, Yazoo, Madison and Washington Counties.

Batesville Area Office
103 Woodland Rd. Suite 1
Batesville, MS 38606
662-578-7008
Fax: 662-578-0670
Serving Desoto, Coahoma, Tunica, Quitman, Tallahatchie, Panola, and Tate Counties.

Booneville Area Office
109 North Road
Booneville, MS 38829
662-728-8104
Fax: 662-728-3120
Serving Marshall, Tippah, Benton, Alcorn, Tishomingo, Prentiss, Lee and Ittawamba Counties.

Hattiesburg Area Office
132 Mayfair Road, Suite C
Hattiesburg, MS 39402
601-261-3293
Fax: 601-261-3254
Serving Marion, Walthall, Lamar, Forrest, Perry, Stone, George, Greene, Jackson,

Hancock, Harrison and Pearl River Counties.

Starkville Area Office
505 Russell Street
Starkville, MS 39659
662-323-8031
Fax: 662-323-7648
Serving Monroe, Choctaw, Webster, Clay, Oktibbeha, Lowndes, Noxubee, Winston, Neshoba, and Kemper Counties.

Local Offices
Adams County Local Office
339-A Liberty Road
Natchez, MS 39120
601-442-1791
Fax: 601-446-6655
Serving Adams and Franklin Counties

Alcorn County Local Office
3301 Mullins Drive
Corinth, MS 38834
662-287-7223
Fax: 662-286-8068
Serving Alcorn and Tishomingo Counties

Amite County Local Office
442 Hwy 24
Centreville, MS 39631
601-645-5025
Fax: 601-645-6540
Serving Amite and Wilkinson counties

Attala County Local Office
502 Veterans Memorial Drive
Kosciusko, MS 39090
662-290-0702
Fax: 662-289-4241

Bolivar County Local Office
406 N. Martin Luther King
Cleveland, MS 38732
662-846-1448
Fax: 662-843-1688

Calhoun County Local Office
413 South Main Street
Calhoun City, MS 38916
662-628-8732
Fax: 662-628-8804

Serving Calhoun and Chickasaw Counties

Choctaw County Local Office
163 Highway 15 South
Ackerman, MS 39735
662-285-3238
Fax: 662-285-3166

Clarke County Local Office
109 East Donald Street
Quitman, MS 39355
601-776-9009
Fax: 601-776-5156

Clay County Local Office
515-A Highway 45 North
West Point, MS 39773
662-494-6344
Fax: 662-494-7480

Coahoma County Local Office
2655 North State Street
Clarksdale, MS 38614
662-776-9009
Fax: 662-627-5598
Serving Coahoma and Tunica Counties

Copiah County Local Office
1012 Carroll Drive
Hazlehurst, MS 39083
601-894-1118
Fax: 601-894-5588

Covington County Local Office
3193 Hwy 49
Collins, MS 39428
601-765-6311
Fax: 601-765-6497

Desoto County Local Office
Hwy 51 South 3260
Hernando, MS 39632
662-429-8687
Fax: 662-429-4882

Forrest County Local Office
701 North Main Street, Suite 311
Hattiesburg, MS 39401
601-583-4371
Fax: 601-583-3806
Serving Forrest, Perry and Stone Counties

George County Local Office
111 Ventura Drive
Lucedale, MS 39452
601-766-3962
Fax: 601-947-2911
Serving George, Greene and
Jackson Counties

Grenada County Local Office
782-B E. Govan
Grenada, MS 38901
662-226-4151
Fax: 662-226-7271
Serving Grenada, Montgomery
and Yalobusha Counties

Harrison County Local Office
2909 13th Street, Room 214
One Government Plaza
Gulfport, MS 39501
228-831-0881
Fax: 228-831-5578
Serving Harrison and Hancock
Counties

Hinds County Local Office
322 New Market Drive
Jackson, MS 39209
601-965-5682
Fax: 601-965-4199
Serving Hinds and Warren
Counties

Holmes County Local Office
Highway 12 West
Lexington, MS 39095
662-834-4688
Fax: 662-834-3196

Humphreys County Local Office
304 West Jackson Street
Belzoni, MS 39038
601-247-8732
Fax: 601-247-2368
Serving Humphreys, Issaquena
and Sharkey Counties

Jasper County Local Office
3rd & 8th Street
Bay Springs, MS 38422
601-764-2025
Fax: 601-764-2186
Serving Jasper and Smith
Counties

Jefferson County Local Office
415-B Gilcrest Street
Fayette, MS 39069
601-786-3412
Fax: 601-786-9955
Serving Jefferson and Claiborne
Counties

Jefferson Davis County Local
Office
2700 Highway 13
Prentiss, MS 39474
601-792-8601
Fax: 601-792-4595

Jones County Local Office
2011 Highway 15 North
Laurel, MS 39440
601-425-4622
Fax: 601-425-9289
Serving Jones and Wayne
Counties

Kemper County Local Office
101 Hooper Avenue
Dekalb, MS 39238
601-743-9588
Fax: 601-743-9070

Lafayette County Local Office
2606 West Oxford Loop
Oxford, MS 38655
662-234-8701
Fax: 662-234-6575
Serving Lafayette and Union
Counties

Lamar County Local Office
175 Shelby Speights
Purvis, MS 39475
601-794-5600
Fax: 601-794-8355

Lauderdale County Local Office
2412 7th Street
Meridian, MS 39302
601-483-4100
Fax: 601-693-5379

Lawrence County Local Office
214 Main Street
Monticello, MS 39654
601-587-0885
Fax: 601-587-0430

Leake County Local Office
407 Valley Street
Carthage, MS 39051
601-298-9101
Fax: 601-267-4571

Lee County Local Office
3098 Cliff Gookin Blvd.
Tupelo, MS 38803
662-680-9991
Fax: 662-844-6043
Serving Lee and Itawamba
Counties

Leflore County Local Office
517 Brentwood Ave.
Greenwood, MS 38930
662-455-1199
Fax: 662-455-5887
Serving Leflore and Carroll
Counties

Lincoln County Local Office
212 South First St.
Brookhaven, MS 39601
601-833-9322
Fax: 601-835-0930

Lowdnes County Local Office
1551 2nd Avenue North
Columbus, MS 39701
662-328-5921
Fax: 662-241-5944
Serving Lowndes and Noxubee
Counties

Madison County Local Office
175-B Commercial Parkway
Canton, MS 39046
601-859-4272
Fax: 601-859-7091

Marion County Local Office
1010 Main Street, Suite 6
Columbia, MS 39429
601-731-5400
Fax: 601-736-0784
Serving Marion and Walthall
Counties

Marshall County Local Office
250-C Whaley Drive
Holly Springs, MS 38635
662-252-1286
Fax: 662-252-7862

Monroe County Local Office
517 Hwy. 45 North
Aberdeen, MS 39730
662-369-0044
Fax: 662-369-3005

Neshoba County Local Office
511 East Lawn Drive
Philadelphia, MS 39350
601-656-8783
Fax: 601-656-3710

Oktibbeha County Local Office
706 Taylor Street
Starkville, MS 39759
662-320-4009,
Fax: 662-323-7146

Panola County Local Office
510 Hwy. 51 South,
Batesville, MS 38606
662-578-8045,
Fax: 662-563-3337
Serving Panola and Tate
Counties

Pearl River County Local Office
1222 South Main Street
Poplarville, MS 39470
601-795-4409
Fax: 601-795-6644

Pike County Local Office
101 North Cherry Street
Magnolia, MS 39652
601-783-2241
Fax: 601-783-6947

Pontotoc County Local Office
186 Hwy. 15 Bypass
Pontotoc, MS 38863
662-489-3563
Fax: 662-489-2802

Prentiss County Local Office
611 West Church Street
Booneville, MS 38829
662-728-9003
Fax: 662-728-9654

Rankin County Local Office
206-A East Government Street
Brandon, MS 39042
601-824–4601
Fax: 601-825-9662
Serving Rankin and Simpson
Counties

Scott County Local Office
1099 Hwy. 35 South
Forest, MS 39074
601-469-3464
Fax: 601-469-1713
Serving Scott and Newton
Counties

Sunflower County Local Office
214 North Martin Luther King
Indianola, MS 38751
662-887-9799
Fax: 662-887-5430

Tallahatchie County Local Office
309 West Cypress Street
Charleston, MS 38921
662-647-8857
Fax: 662-647-5673
Serving Tallahatchie and
Quitman Counties

Tippah County Local Office
733-A South Line Street
Ripley, MS 38663
662-837-4464
Fax: 662-837-8336
Serving Tippah and Benton
Counties

Washington County Local Office
3038 East Reed Road Suite 3
Greenville, MS 38701
662-332-5491
Fax: 662-335-6040

Winston County Local Office
218 South Columbus Avenue
Louisville, MS 39339
662-773-2207
Fax: 662-773-8731

Yazoo County Local Office
711 Jackson Avenue
Yazoo City, MS 39194
662-746-8358
Fax: 662-746-8496

Missouri

USDA Rural Development State
Office
601 Business Loop 70 West
Parkade Center, Suite 235
Columbia, MO 65203
573-876-0976
Fax: 573-876-0977

St. Joseph Area Office- Area 1
USDA Service Center
3915 Oakland Avenue
St. Joseph, MO 64506-4929
816-364-3767, ext. 5
Fax: 816-364-0562

Kirksville Area Office- Area 2
USDA Service Center
2410 South Franklin Street
Kirksville, MO 63501-6503
660-665-3274, ext. 4
Fax: 660-665-0266

Clinton Area Office- Area 3
USDA Service Center
1306 North Second Street
Clinton, MO 64735
660-885-5567 ext. 5
Fax: 660-885-6260

Farmington Area Office- Area 4
USDA Service Center
812 Progress Drive
Farmington, MO 63640
573-756-6413, ext. 4
Fax: 573-756-8037

Springfield Area Office- Area 5
USDA Service Center
688 State Highway B, Suite 400
Springfield, MO 65802
417-831-5246, ext. 5
Fax: 417-863-0256

Houston Area Office- Area 6
USDA Service Center
6726 South Highway 63, Suite B
Houston, MO 65483
417-967-4525
Fax: 417-967-4879

Dexter Area Office- Area 7
USDA Service Center
18450 Ridgeview Lane
Dexter, MO 63841
573-624-5939, ext. 4
Fax: 573-624-6964

Area 1 Local Offices
Chillicothe Local Office
1100 Morton Parkway
Chillicothe, MO 64601-3723
660-646-6222
Fax: 660-646-4894

Serving Daviess, Grundy,
Harrison, Linn, Livingston,
Mercer, Putnam and Sullivan
Counties

Marysville Local Office
206 E. South Hills Dr
Suite 103
Maryville, MO 64468-6504
660-582-7421
Fax: 660-582-8366
Serving Atchison, Gentry, Holt,
Nodaway and Worth Counties

Richmond Local Office
500 Wollard Blvd.
Richmond, MO 64085
816-776-2266
Fax: 816-776-6902
Serving Caldwell, Carroll, Clay
and Ray Counties

St. Joseph Local Office
3915 Oakland Avenue
St. Joseph, MO 64506-4929
816-364-2328
Fax: 816-364-0562
Serving Andrew, Buchanan,
Clinton, DeKalb and Platte
Counties

Area 2 Local Offices
Columbia Local Office
1715 W. Worley Street, Suite D
Columbia, MO 65203
573-446-9091
Fax: 573-446-0177
Serving Boone, Cooper and
Howard Counties

Kirksville Local Office
2410 South Franklin Street
Kirksville, MO 63501-6503
660-665-3274 ext. 4
Fax: 660-665-0266
Serving Adair, Knox, Macon,
Schuyler and Scotland Counties

Mexico Local Office
4617 South Clark
Mexico, MO 65265
573-581-4177
Fax: 573-581-7283
Serving Audrain, Callaway and
Montgomery Counties

Moberly Local Office
Route 3, Box 135
Moberly, MO 65270
660-263-7400
Fax: 660-263-3725
Serving Chariton, Monroe,
Randolph and Shelby Counties

London Local Office
17623 Highway 19
New London, MO 63459
573-985-7211
Fax: 573-985-3928
Serving Clark, Lewis, Marion
and Ralls Counties

Troy Local Office
114 Frenchman Bluff Road
Troy, MO 63379
636-528-7046
Fax: 636-528-9582
Serving Lincoln, Pike and
Warren Counties

Area 3 Local Offices
Butler Local Office
625 W. Nursery Box A
Butler, MO 64730
660-679-6114
Fax: 660-679-6207
Serving Bates, Cass and Vernon
Counties

Clinton Local Office
1306 North 2nd Street
Clinton, MO 64735
660-885-5567
Fax: 660-885-6812
Serving Cedar, Henry, Johnson
and St. Clair Counties

Eldon Local Office
405 W. 4th Street
Eldon, MO 65026
573-392-5667
Fax: 573-392-4052
Serving Camden, Miller and
Morgan Counties

Higginsville Local Office
120 West 19th Street
Higginsville, MO 64037
660-584-8732
Fax: 660-584-2191
Serving Jackson and Lafayette
Counties

Sedalia Local Office
1407 W. 32nd Street
Sedalia, MO 65301
660-826-3339
Fax: 660-826-7982
Serving Benton, Hickory, Pettis
and Saline Counties

Area 4 Local Offices
Farmington Local Office
812 Progress Drive
Farmington, MO 63640
573-756-6413
Fax: 573-756-8037
Serving Iron, Madison, St.
Francois and Ste Genevieve
Counties

Hillsboro Local Office
10820 State Route 21, Ste. 112
Hillsboro, MO 63050
636-789-3551
Fax: 636-789-2175
Serving Jefferson, St. Louis and
Washington Counties

Jackson Local Office
480 West Jackson Trails
Jackson, MO 63755-2665
573-243-1467
Fax: 573-243-8843
Serving Bollinger, Cape
Girardeau and Perry Counties

Area 5 Local Offices
Carthage Local Office
416 East Airport Drive
Carthage, MO 64836
417-358-8196
Fax: 417-358-5792
Serving Barton, Daade, Jasper
and Lawrence Counties

Neosho Local Office
1900 S Business Hwy 71
Neosho, MO 64850
417-451-1007, Ext. 4
Fax: 417-451-9244
Serving Barry, McDonald and
Newton Counties

Ozark Local Office
1786 S. 16th Avenue, Suite 103
Ozark, MO 65721
417-581-3905
Fax: 417-485-3863

Serving Christian, Stone and Taney Counties

Springfield Local Office
688 S. State Highway B
Suite 400
Springfield, MO 65802
417-831-5246
Fax: 417-863-0256
Serving Dallas, Greene and Polk Counties

Area 6 Local Offices
Houston Local Office
6726 S. Highway 63, Suite B
Houston, MO 65843
417-967-3321
Fax: 417-967-4059
Serving Dent, Shannon and Texas Counties

Jefferson City Local Office
1911 Boggs Creed Road
Jefferson City, MO 65101
573-893-8504
Fax: 573-893-7238
Serving Cole, Moniteau and Osage Counties

Lebanon Local Office
1242 Deadra Drive
Lebanon, MO 65536
417-532-5741
Fax: 417-533-3689
Serving Laclede, Webster and Wright Counties

Rolla Local Office
1050 Highway 72
Rolla, MO 65402
573-364-1479
Fax: 573-364-7936
Serving Crawford, Maries, Phelps and Pulaski Counties

Union Local Office
1004 Vondera, Suite 3
Union, MO 63084-3122
636-583-2121
Fax: 636-583-6936
Serving Franklin, Gasconade and St. Charles Counties

West Plains Local Office
111 Walnut Street
West Plains, MO 65775

417-256-7117
Fax: 417-256-5564
Serving Douglas, Howell, Oregon and Ozark Counties

Area 5 Local Offices
Charleston Local Office
831 South Hwy 105
Charleston, MO 63834
573-649-9947
Fax: 573-649-9950
Serving Mississippi and New Madrid Counties

Dexter Local Office
18450 Ridgeview Lane
Dexter, MO 63841
573-624-5939
Fax: 573-624-6964
Serving Scott and Stoddard Counties

Kennett Local Office
704 North Bypass
Kennett, MO 63857
573-888-6664
Fax: 573-888-6736
Serving Dunklin and Pemiscot Counties

Poplar Bluff Local Office
4327 Highway 67 N
Poplar Bluff, MO 63901
573-785-9679
Fax: 573-686-0187
Serving Butler, Carter, Reynolds, Ripley and Wayne Counties

MONTANA
USDA Rural Development State Office
P.O. Box 850
Bozeman, MT 59771
406-585-2580
Fax: 406-585-2565

Billings Local Office
1629 Avenue D
Billings, MT 59102
406-657-6297, ext. 4
Fax: 406-657-6294
Serving Big Horn, Carbon, Carter, Custer, Fallon, Golden Valley, Mussellshell, Powder River, Rosebud, Stillwater, Treasure, Yellowstone, Crow

and Northern Cheyenne Indian Reservations.

Bozeman Local Office
900 Technology Blvd, Suite B
Bozeman, MT 59718
406-585-2530
Fax: 406-585-2565
Serving Gallatin, Meagher, Park, Sweet Grass, and Wheatland

Choteau Local Office
1102 Main Avenue NW
P.O. Box 316
Choteau, MT 59422
406-466-5351, ext. 4
Fax: 406-466-5328
Serving Glacier, Lewis & Clark (No of Hwy 200), Pondera, Powell (No. of Hwy 200, including Helmville), Teton, Toole and Blackfeet Indian Reservation

Glasgow Local Office
54062 Highway 2 West
Glasgow, MT 59230
406-228-4321, ext. 4
Fax: 406-228-8101
Serving Blaine, Daniels, Dawson, Garfield, McCone, Phillips, Prairie, Richland, Roosevelt, Sheridan, Valley, Wibaux, Fort Belknap and Fort Peck Indian Reservations.

Great Falls Local Office
12 3rd Street, NW, 2nd Floor
Great Falls, MT 59404
406-761-4077, ext. 4
Fax: 406-452-3806
Serving Cascade, Chouteau, Fergus, Hill, Judith Basin, Liberty, Petroleum, and Rocky Boys Indian Reservation

Helena Local Office
790 Colleen Street
Helena, MT 59601
406-449-5000, ext. 4
Fax: 406-449-5039
Serving Beaverhead, Broadwater, Deer Lodge, Jefferson, Lewis and Clark (So. of Hwy 200), Madison, Powell (So. of Hwy 200 but not Helmville) and Silver Bow

Kalispell Local Office
30 Lower Valley Road
Kalispell, MT 59901
406-752-4242, ext. 4
Fax: 406-752-4879
Serving Flathead, Lake, Lincoln
and Flathead Indian Reservation

Missoula Local Office
5115 Hwy 93 South
Missoula, MT 59804
406-251-4826, ext. 4
Fax: 406-251-6268
Serving Granite, Mineral,
Missoula, Ravalli, and Sanders

Nebraska
USDA Rural Development State
Office
Federal Building Room 152
100 Centennial Mall North
Lincoln, NE 68508
402-437-5551
Fax: 402-437-5408

Area 1
West/West Central Nebraska
Kearney Area Office
4009 North 6th Avenue
P.O. Box 730
Kearney, NE 68848-0730
308-237-3118, Ext. 4
Fax: 308-236-6290

Hastings Branch Office of
Kearney Office
2727 West 2nd Street, Suite 108
Hastings, NE 68901-4608
402-463-6771, Ext. 4
Fax: 402-462-6771

Lexington Branch Office of
Kearney Office
721 E. Pacific Street
P.O. Box 0
Lexington, NE 68850
308-324-6314, Ext. 4
Fax: 308-324-7232
The Kearney Area Office, along
with the Hastings and Lexington
Branch Offices, services the
following Nebraska counties:
Adams, Blaine, Buffalo, Clay,
Custer, Dawson, Franklin,
Furnas, Garfield, Gosper, Hall,
Hamilton, Harlan, Howard,

Kearney, Loup, Merrick,
Nuckolls, Phelps, Sherman,
Valley, and Webster.

North Platte Field Office
1202 S. Cottonwood
P.O. Box 2009
North Platte, NE 69103
308-534-2360, Ext. 4
Fax: 308-534-8645

Mccook Branch Office of North
Platte Office
1400 W. 5th Street, Suite 4
McCook, NE 69001
308-345-4163, Ext. 4
Fax: 308-345-3642

Valentine Branch Office of North
Platte Office
518 W. Hwy 20, Suite 2
P.O. Box 607
Valentine, NE 69201
402-376-1712, Ext. 4
Fax: 402-376-3515
The North Platte Field Office,
along with the McCook and
Valentine Branch Offices,
services the following counties:
Arthur, Brown, Chase, Cherry,
Dundy, Frontier, Grant, Hayes,
Hitchcock, Hooker, Keith, Keya
Paha, Lincoln, Logan,
McPherson, Perkins, Red
Willow, Rock, and Thomas.

Scottsbluff Field Office
818 Ferdinand Plaza, Suite B
Scottsbluff, NE 69361-4401
308-632-2195, Ext. 4
Fax: 308-635-2787

Chadron Branch Office of
Scottsbluff Office
1020 West 6th
Chadron, NE 69337-2909
308-432-4616, Ext. 4
Fax: 308-432-5117

Sidney Branch Office of
Scottsbluff Office
2244 Jackson, Box 365
Sidney, NE 69162
308-254-4507, Ext. 4
Fax: 308-254-0545

The Scottsbluff Field Office,
along with the Chadron and
Sidney Branch Offices, services
the following counties: Banner,
Box Butte, Cheyenne, Dawes,
Deuel, Garden, Kimball, Morrill,
Scotts Bluff, Sheridan, and Sioux.

Area 2
Southeast Nebraska
Beatrice Area Office
201 N. 25th Street
Beatrice, NE 68310
402-223-3125, Ext. 4
Fax: 402-228-0535
The Beatrice Area Office services
the following counties: Gage,
Jefferson, Johnson, Nemaha,
Pawnee, Richardson, Saline, and
Thayer.

Lincoln Field Office
6030 S. 58th Street, Suite B
P.O. Box 6549
Lincoln, NE 68516
402-423-9683, Ext. 4
Fax: 402-423-7614
The Lincoln Field Office services
the following counties: Butler,
Cass, Fillmore, Lancaster, Otoe,
Polk, Saunders, Seward, and
York.

Area 3
Northeast Nebraska
Norfolk Area Office
1909 Vicki Lane, Suite 103
Norfolk, NE 68701
402-371-5350
Fax: 402-371-8930

Bloomfield Branch Office of
Norfolk Office
111 N. Washington St.
Bloomfield, NE 68718
402-373-4914, Ext. 4
Fax: 402-373-2621

O'Neill Branch Office of Norfolk
Office
107-B E. Hwy 20
P.O. Box 630
O'Neill, NE 68763
402-336-3796, Ext. 4
Fax: 402-336-1735

Wayne Branch Office of Norfolk Office
709 Providence Road
P.O. Box 200
Wayne, NE 68787
402-375-2453, Ext. 4
Fax: 402-375-4419
The Norfolk Area Office, along with the Bloomfield, O'Neill, and Wayne Branch Offices, services the following counties: Antelope, Boyd, Cedar, Dakota, Dixon, Holt, Knox, Madison, Pierce, Stanton, Thurston, Wayne, and Wheeler.

Columbus Field Office
3100 23rd Street
US 30 Center
Columbus, NE 68601
402-564-0506, Ext. 4
Fax: 402-564-6348
The Columbus Field Office services the following counties: Boone, Colfax, Greeley, Nance, and Platte

Omaha Field Office
8901 South 154th Street, Suite 2
Omaha, NE 68138-3621
402-891-0430
Fax: 402-891-0529

Fremont Branch Office of Omaha Office
1740 W. 23rd Street
Fremont, NE 68025-6607
402-721-8455, Ext. 4
Fax: 402-721-5268
The Omaha Field Office, along with the Fremont Branch Office, services the following counties: Burt, Cuming, Dodge, Douglas, Sarpy, and Washington.

Nevada

USDA Rural Development State Office
1390 S. Curry Street
Carson City, NV 89703
775-887-1222
Fax: 775-885-0841

Elko Field Office
2002 Idaho Street
Elko, NV 89801

775-738-8468
Fax: 775-738-7229

Fallon Field Office
111 Sheckler Road
Fallon, NV 89406
775-423-7541
Fax: 775-423-0784

Las Vegas Field Office
5820 S. Pecos Rd.
Bldg. A, Suite 400
Las Vegas, NV 89120
702-262-9047
Fax: 702-262-9969

Winnemucca Field Office
1200 Winnemucca Blvd E.
Winnemucca, NV 89445
775-623-4461
Fax: 775-623-0647

New Hampshire

USDA Rural Development State Office
Suite 218, Box 317
10 Ferry Street
Concord, NH 03301-5004
603-223-6035
Fax: 603-223-6061

Berlin Area Office
15 Mount Forist
Berlin, NH 03570
603-752-1328
Fax: 603-752-1354
Serving Coos and Carroll Counties

Concord Service Center
10 Ferry St.
Suite 212, Box 22
Concord, NH 03301-5081
603-223-6003
Fax: 603-223-6030
Serving Merrimack, Belknap & Hillsborough Counties

Epping Area Office
241 Calef Highway
Telly's Plaza
Epping, NH 03042
603-679-4650 ext 20
Fax: 603-679-4658
Serving Strafford, Rockingham Counties

Walpole Area Office
R1, Route 12, Box 315
Walpole, NH 03608-9744
603-756-3230 ext. 18
Fax: 603-756-2978
Serving Cheshire and Sullivan Counties

Woodsville Area Office
250 Swiftwater Road, Suite 4
Woodsville, NH 03785
603-747-2777
Fax: 603-747-3477
Serving Grafton County

New Jersey

Rural Development State Office
5th Floor North, Suite 500
8000 Midlantic Drive
Mt. Laurel, NJ 08054
856-787-7700
Fax: 856-787-7783

Hackettstown Local Office
Building 1, Hackettstown Commerce Park
101 Bilby Road
Hackettstown, NJ 07840
908-852-2576, Extension 4
Fax: 908-852-4666
Serving Bergen, Essex, Hudson, Hunterdon, Morris, Passaic, Somerset, Sussex, Union, and Warren Counties.

Hainesport Local Office
1289 Route 38, Suite 200
Hainesport, NJ 08036
609-267-1639, Extension 4
Fax: 609-261-3007
Serving Burlington, Mercer, and Middlesex Counties.

Toms River Local Office
776J Commons Way
Toms River, NJ 08755
732-349-1067
Fax: 732-505-8572
Serving Monmouth and Ocean Counties.

Vineland Local Office
1317 South Main Rd, Building 3
Vineland, NJ 08360
856-205-1225, Extension 4
Fax: 856-205-0691

Serving Atlantic, Cape May, and Cumberland Counties.

Woodstown Local Office
Suite 2, 51 Cheney Road
Woodstown, NJ 08098
856-769-1127, Ext 398
Fax: 856-769-0718
Serving Camden, Gloucester, and Salem Counties.

New Mexico
USDA Rural Housing State Office
6200 Jefferson NE, Room 255
Albuquerque, NM 87109
505-761-4944
Fax: 505-761-4976

Aztec Local Office
San Juan and McKinley
1427 West Aztec, Suite 1
Aztec, NM 87410-1977
505-334-3090
Fax: 505-334-8659
Serving San Juan and McKinley Counties

Carlsbad Local Office
114 South Halagueno, Room 108
Carlsbad, NM 88220-5738
505-887-6669 Ext. 202
Fax: 505-887-5700
Serving Eddy and Lea Counties

Deming Local Office
405 East Florida
Deming, NM 88030-5235
505-546-9692
Fax: 505-546-0038
Serving Luna & Hidalgo Counties

Espanola Local Office
424 Suite 1 South
Espanola, NM 87532
505-758-3701
Fax: 505-758-7650
Serving Taos, Rio Arriba, Northern Santa Fe & Northern Counties

Estancia Local Office
521 5th St
Estancia, NM 87016
505-384-2272

Fax: 505-384-3043
Serving Torrance & Southern Santa Fe Counties

Gallup Local Office
1658 South 2nd
Gallup, NM 87301
505-722-4357, Ext.4
Fax: 505-722-0847
Serving McKinley County

Las Cruces State Office
2507 N. Telshor, Suite 3
Las Cruces, NM 88011-8236
505-522-8775 Ext.4
Fax: 505-521-3905
Serving Dona Ana & Otero Counties

Los Lunas Local Office
267 Courthouse Rd
Los Lunas, NM 87031-6811
505-865-4643
Fax: 505-866-0662
Serving Valencia, Bernalillo, Cibola & Southern Sandoval Counties

Las Vegas Local Office
242 Mills Avenue
Las Vegas, NM 87701
505-425-3594
Fax: 505-425-1430
Serving San Miguel, Mora, Guadalupe, De Baca & Quay Counties

Raton Local Office
245 Park Avenue
Raton, NM 87740
505-445-9571
Fax: 505-445-4066
Serving Colfax, Harding and Union Counties

Roswell Local Office
1011 S Atkinson Ave
Roswell, NM 88203
505-622-8745
Fax: 505-623-0570
Serving Chaves, Curry, Lincoln, and Roosevelt Counties

Silver City Local Office
2610 N Silver Street
Silver City, NM 88061

505-546-9291
Fax: 505-546-0038
Serving Grant and Catron Counties.

Socorro Local Office
101 Elm Street
Socorro, NM 87777
505-835-5555
Fax: 505-835-5556
Serving Socorro and Sierra Counties

New York
Syracuse State Office
441 S Salina St
Syracuse, NY 13202-2405
315-477-6518
Fax: 315-477-6550

Batavia Service Center
29 Liberty St
Batavia, NY 14020-3247
585-343-9167
Fax: 585-344-4662
Serving Genesee, Monroe, Niagara, Orleans, and Wyoming Counties

Bath Service Center
415 W Morris St
Bath, NY 14810-1038
607-776-7398
Fax: 607-776-7487
Serving Allegany, Livingston, and Steuben Counties

Binghamton Service Center
1163 Upper Front St
Binghamton, NY 13905-1117
607-723-1384
Fax: 607-723-1015
Serving Broome, Chenango, Cortland, Delaware, and Tioga Counties

Canandaigua Service Center
3037 County Road 10
Canandaigua, NY 14424-8303
585-394-5970
Fax: 585-394-8224
Serving Ontario, Wayne, and Yates Counties

Canton Service Center
Route 2-3 Commerce Lane

Canton, NY 13617
315-386-2401
Fax: 315-386-1608
Serving St Lawrence County

Ellicottville Service Center
8 Martha St
Ellicottville, NY 14731-9714
716-699-2375
Fax: 716-699-5357
Serving Cattaraugus,
Chautauqua, and Erie Counties

Greenwich Service Center
2530 State Route 40
Greenwich, NY 12834-2300
518-692-9940
Fax: 518-692-2203
Serving Columbia, Hamilton,
Rensselaer, Saratoga, Warren,
and Washington Counties

Ithaca Service Center
903 Hanshaw Rd
Ithaca, NY 14850-1530
607-257-2737
Fax: 607-257-5592
Serving Chemung, Schuyler,
Seneca, and Tompkins Counties

Johnstown Service Center
113 Hales Mills Rd
Johnstown, NY 12095-3741
518-762-0077
Fax: 518-762-7020
Serving Albany, Fulton,
Montgomery, Otsego,
Schenectady, and Schoharie
Counties

Lafayette Service Center
2571 US Route 11
La Fayette, NY 13084-3353
315-677-3552
Fax: 315-677-0072
Serving Cayuga, and Oswego
Counties

Marcy Service Center
9025 State Route 49
Marcy, NY 13403-2301
315-736-3316
Fax: 315-768-2739
Serving Herkimer, Madison, and
Oneida Counties

Middletown Service Center
225 Dolson Ave
Middletown, NY 10940-6569
845-343-1872
Fax: 845-343-2630
Serving Bronx, Dutchess,
Greene, Kings, New York,
Orange, Putnam, Queens,
Richmond, Rockland, Sullivan
and Ulster Counties

Plattsburgh Service Center
6064 State Route 22
Plattsburgh, NY 12901-6263
518-561-4616
Fax: 518-563-4540
Serving Clinton, Essex, Franklin,
and Westchester Counties

Riverhead Service Center
209 E Main St
Riverhead, NY 11901-2456
631-727-5666
Fax: 631-727-4408
Serving Nassau, and Suffolk
Counties

Watertown Service Center
21168 State Route 232
Watertown, NY 13601-5377
315-782-7289
Fax: 315-788-2454
Serving Jefferson, and Lewis
Counties

North Carolina
USDA Rural Development State
Office
4405 Bland Road
Raleigh, NC 27609
919-873-2000
Fax: 919-873-2075

Waynesville Area Office
589 Racoon Road, Suite 202
Waynesville, NC 28786
828-452-0319
Fax: 828-452-1644
Serving Buncombe, Cherokee,
Clay, Cleveland, Gaston,
Graham, Haywood, Henderson,
Jackson, Lincoln, Macon,
Madison, McDowell, Mitchell,
Polk, Rutherford, Swain,
Transylvania and Yancey
Counties

Jefferson Area Office
134 Government Circle
Suite 201
Jefferson, NC 28640
336-246-2885
Fax: 336-246-9173
Serving Alleghany, Alexander,
Ashe, Avery, Burke, Caldwell,
Catawba, Forsyth, Iredell,
Stokes, Surry, Watauga, Wilkes,
and Yadkin Counties.

Elizabethtown Area Office
450 Smith Circle, Rm 137
Elizabethtown, NC 28337
910-862-3179
Fax: 910-862-4670
Serving Bladen, Brunswick,
Columbus, Hoke, New Hanover,
Pender, Robeson, and Scotland
Counties.

Albemarle Area Office
26032-F Newt Road, Box 10
Albemarle, NC 28001
704-982-5114
Fax: 704-983-7921
Serving Alamance, Anson,
Cabarrus, Caswell, Davidson,
Davie, Guilford, Mecklenburg,
Montgomery, Moore, Randolph,
Richmond, Rockingham, Rowan,
Stanley and Union Counties.

Henderson Area Office
945-B W. Andrews Avenue
Henderson, NC 27536
252-438-3141
Fax: 252-438-3647
Serving Durham, Edgecombe,
Franklin, Granville, Halifax,
Nash, Northampton, Orange,
Person, Vance, and Warren
Counties.

Williamston Area Office 104
Kehukee Park Road
Williamston, NC 27892
252-792-7603
Fax: 252-809-0561
Serving Beaufort, Bertie,
Camden, Chowan, Currituck,
Dare, Gates, Hertford, Hyde,
Martin, Northampton,
Pasquotank, Perquimans, Tyrell,
and Washington Counties.

Garner Area Office
Hartwell Plaza
1027 Hwy 70 East, Suite 219
Garner, NC 27529
919-779-7164
Fax: 919-779-9068
Serving Chatham, Cumberland,
Durham, Harnett, Johnston, Lee,
Pitt, Wake and Wilson Counties.

Kinston Area Office
1308 Hwy 258 North
PO Box 6189
Kinston, NC 28501
252-526-9799
Fax: 252-526-9607
Serving Carteret, Craven,
Duplin, Greene, Jones, Lenoir,
Onslow, Pamlico, Sampson and
Wayne Counties.

North Dakota

USDA Rural Development State
Office
Federal Building, Room 208
220 East Rosser Ave.
P.O. Box 1737
Bismarck, ND 58502
701-530-2037
Fax: 701-530-2108

Dickinson Area Office
2493 4th Ave West, Room B
Dickinson ND 58601-2623
701-225-9168
Toll Free in ND: 1-800-688-2251,
Ext. 4
Fax: 701-225-1353

Minot Area Office
2001 6th St SE
Minot ND 58701-6700
701-852-1754
Toll Free in ND: 1-800-765-9476,
Ext. 4
Fax: 701-839-8317

Devils Lake Area Office
502 Highway 2 West, Suite 5
Devils Lake ND 58301-0280
701-662-8634
Toll Free in ND: 1-800-688-2279,
Ext. 4
Fax: 701-662-1227

Valley City Area Office
575 10th St SW, #4
Valley City, ND 58072-3906
701-845-5150
Toll Free in ND: 1-800-688-2293,
Ext. 4
Fax: 701-845-5605

Bismarck Local Office - Single
Family Housing Serving Office
1511 East Interstate Ave
Bismarck, ND 58501-0560
701-250-4367
Toll free in ND: 1-800-688-2297,
Ext. 4
Fax: 701-250-4363

Park River Local Office - Single
Family Housing Serving Office
RR 1 Box 52, Suite 3
503 Park St West
Park River, ND 58270-9701
701-284-7118
Toll free in ND: 1-800-688-2307,
Ext. 4
Fax: 701-284-7238

Williston Local Office - Single
Family Housing Serving Office
1106 2nd St West
Williston, ND 58801-5804
701-572-4597
Toll Free in ND: 1-800-688-2308,
Ext. 4
Fax: 701-572-0482

Ohio

USDA Rural Development
Federal Building, Room 507
200 North High Street
Columbus, OH 43215
614-255-2500

Findlay Area Office
7868 C.R. 140, Suite D
Findlay, OH 45840
419-422-0242
Fax: 419-422-5423

Hillsboro Area Office
514 Harry Sauner Road
Suite 3
Hillsboro, OH 45133
937-393-1921
Fax: 937-393-1656

Wooster Area Office
5200 Cleveland Road, Suite A
Wooster, OH 44691
330-345-6791
Fax: 330-345-9206

Marietta Area Office
Route 9, Box 286A
Marietta, OH 45750
740-373-7113
Fax: 740-373-4838

Oklahoma

USDA Rural Development State
Office
100 USDA, Suite 108
Stillwater, OK 74074
405-742-1000
Fax: 405-742-1005

Atoka Area Office
Rt.4, Box 1118
Atoka, OK 74525
580-889-6668

Hobart Area Office
806 W. 11th St.
Hobart, OK 73651
580-726-5625

Stillwater Area Office
2600 S. Main, Ste. B
Stillwater, OK 74074
405-624-0144

Woodward Area Office
4900 Oklahoma Ave. Suite 310
Woodward, OK 73801
580-256-3375

*Area 1 Serving Northwest
Oklahoma*
Enid Local Office
1216 West Willow, Suite B
Enid, OK 73703
580-237-4323
Fax: 580-233-4608
Serving Canadian, Garfield,
Grant, Kay, Kingfisher, Logan
Noble and Oklahoma Counties.

Woodward Local Office
4900 Oklahoma Ave., Suite 110
Woodward, OK 73801-3713
580-256-6038
Fax: 580-254-5236

Serving Alfalfa, Blaine, Beaver, Cimarron, Dewey, Ellis, Harper, Major, Texas, Woods, and Woodward Counties.

Area 2 Serving Northeast Oklahoma
Chandler Local Office
210 North Sandy Lane, Suite B
Chandler, OK 74834-9003
405-258-1043
Fax: 405-258-1237
Serving Creek, Lincoln, Okfuskee, Pawnee, Payne, Pottawatomie, and Seminole Counties.

Muskogee Local Office
3001 Azalea Park Drive, Suite 3
Muskogee, OK 74401
918-686-0669
Fax: 918-686-0648
Serving Adair, Cherokee, Muskogee, Okmulgee, Sequoyah, Tulsa and Wagoner Counties

Vinita Local Office
P.O. Box 593
235 West Hope
Vinita, OK 74301
918-256-7863
Fax: 918-256-2407
Serving Craig, Delaware, Mayes, Nowata, Osage, Ottawa, Rogers, and Washington Counties

Area 3 Serving Southwest Oklahoma
Altus Local Office
3100 North Main, Suite B
Altus, OK 73521-1305
580-482-1714
Fax: 580-482-6243
Serving Comanche, Cotton, Greer, Harmon, Jackson, Kiowa, and Tillman Counties

Cordell Local Office
1505 N. Glenn English
Cordell, OK 73632
580-832-3393
Fax: 580-832-2434
Serving Beckham, Caddo, Custer, Grady, Roger Mills, and Washita Counties

Pauls Valley Local Office
P.O. Box 648
105 North Meridian
Pauls Valley, OK 73075
405-238-7561
Fax: 405-238-3279
Serving Carter, Cleveland, Garvin, Jefferson, Love, McClain, Stephens and Murray Counties

Area 4 Serving Southeast Oklahoma
Ada Local Office
1312 Cradduck Road
Ada, OK 74820
580-332-3070
Fax: 580-332-4256
Serving Bryan, Coal, Hughes, Johnston, Pontotoc and Marshall Counties

Antlers Local Office
P.O. Box 357
508 Highway 271 North
Antlers, OK 74523
580-298-3339
Fax: 580-298-3480
Serving Atoka, Choctaw, McCurtain and Pushmataha Counties

McAlester Local Office
P.O. Box 490
Federal Building, Room 303
McAlester, OK 74502
918-423-7602
Fax: 918-423-2745
Serving McIntosh, Haskell, LeFlore, Latimer and Pittsburg Counties

OREGON

USDA Rural Development State Office
101 SW Main, Suite 1410
Portland, OR 97204-3222
503-414-3300
Fax: 503-414-3392

Eugene Area Office
1600 Valley River Dr., Ste 230
Eugene, OR 97401-2129
541-465-6443, Ext. 4
Fax: 541-465-6483
Serving Benton, Lane, and Linn Counties

Medford Area Office
573 Parsons Drive Suite 103
Medford, OR 97501-1103
541-776-4270, Ext. 4
Fax: 541-776-4295
Serving Jackson, Josephine, Klamath, and Lake Counties

Pendleton Area Office
1229 SE 3rd St., Ste. A
Pendleton, OR 97801-4198
541-278-8049, Ext. 4
Fax: 541-278-8048
Serving Baker, Gilliam, Grant, Malheur, Morrow, Umatilla, Union, and Wallowa Counties

Redmond Area Office
625 S.E. Salmon Ave., Ste. 5
Redmond, OR 97756
541-923-4358 Ext. 4
Fax: 541-923-4713
Serving Crook, Deschutes, Harney, Hood River, Jefferson, Sherman, Wasco, and Wheeler Counties

Roseburg Area Office
251 NE Garden Valley Blvd., #M
Roseburg, OR 97470-1498
541-673-0136 Ext. 4
Fax: 541-672-3818
Serving Coos, Curry, Douglas, Lindie and Champ Counties

Salem Area Office
38l Development
67 Wolverine Way
Bldg. F, Ste. 19
Salem, OR 97305-1372
503-399-5741, Ext. 4
Fax: 503-399-5799
Serving Clackamas, Clatsop, Columbia, Lincoln, Marion, Multnomah, Polk, Tillamook, Washington, and Yamhill Counties

PENNSYLVANIA

USDA Rural Development State Office
Suite 330, One Credit Union Pl.
Harrisburg, PA 17110-2996
717-237-2186
Fax: 717-237-2193

Multi-Family Housing Area
Offices
Butler Area Office
602 Evans City Road, Suite 101
Butler, PA 16001-8701
724-482-4800, ext. 4
Fax: 724-482-4826
Serving Allegheny, Armstrong,
Beaver, Butler, Cambria, Fayette,
Greene, Indiana, Somerset,
Washington, Westmoreland
Counties

Crawford Area Office
14699 N. Main Street, Extension
Meadville, PA 16335-9441
814-336-6155
Fax: 814-337-0294
Serving Cameron, Clarion,
Clearfield, Crawford, Elk, Erie,
Forest, Jefferson, Lawrence,
McKean, Mercer, Potter,
Venango, Warren Counties

Juniata Area Office
R. D. #3, Box 301
Mifflintown, PA 17059-9621
717-436-8953, ext. 4
Fax: 717-436-9128
Serving Adams, Bedford, Blair,
Cumberland, Franklin, Fulton,
Huntingdon, Juniata, Mifflin,
Perry, York Counties

Lehigh Area Office
2211 Mack Blvd.
Allentown, PA 18103-5623
610-791-9810, ext. 4
Fax: 610-791-9820
Serving Berks, Bucks, Carbon,
Chester, Dauphin, Delaware (CF
only), Lackawanna, Lancaster,
Lebanon, Lehigh, Luzerne,
Monroe, Montgomery,
Northampton, Philadelphia,
Pike, Schuylkill, Wayne
Counties

Lycoming Area Office
542 County Farm Rd, Suite 205
Montoursville, PA 17754-9685
570-433-3008
Fax: 570-433-3013
Serving Bradford, Centre,
Clinton, Columbia, Lycoming,
Montour, Northumberland,

Snyder, Sullivan, Susquehanna,
Tioga, Union, Wyoming
Counties

Single Family Housing Area
Offices
Butler Area Office
602 Evans City Road, Suite 101
Butler, PA 16001-8701
724-482-4800, ext. 4
Fax: 724-482-4826
Serving Allegheny, Armstrong,
Beaver, Butler, Crawford, Erie,
Fayette, Forest, Greene, Indiana,
Lawrence, Mercer, Washington,
Westmoreland and Venango
Counties

Clinton Area Office
216 Spring Run Road, Room 103
Mill Hall, PA 17751-9543
570-726-3196, ext. 203
Fax: 570-726-0064
Serving Bradford, Cameron,
Centre, Clarion, Clearfield,
Clinton, Elk, Jefferson,
Lycoming, McKean, Montour,
Northumberland, Potter, Snyder,
Sullivan, Tioga, Union and
Warren Counties

Lehigh Area Office
2211 Mack Blvd.
Allentown, PA 18103-5623
610-791-9810, ext. 4
Fax: 610-791-9820
Serving Berks, Bucks, Carbon,
Chester, Columbia, Dauphin,
Delaware, Lackawanna,
Lancaster, Lebanon, Lehigh,
Luzerne, Monroe, Montgomery,
Northampton, Philadelphia,
Pike, Schuylkill, Susquehanna,
Wayne and Wyoming Counties

York Area Office
124 Pleasant Acres Road
York, PA 17402-9899
717-755-2966, ext. 4
Fax: 717-840-1302
Serving Adams, Bedford, Blair,
Cambria, Cumberland, Franklin,
Fulton, Huntingdon, Juniata,
Mifflin, Perry, Somerset and
York Counties

Puerto Rico

USDA Rural Development State
Office
IBM Building
654 Munoz Rivera Ave, Suite 601
San Juan, PR 00918
787-766-5095
Fax: 787-766-5844

Rhode Island

Southern New England
Rural Development State Office
451 West Street, Suite 2
Amherst MA 01002-2999
413-253-4300
Fax: 413-253-4347

Warwick Service Center
60 Quaker Lane, Suite 44
Warwick, RI 02886
Serving all of Rhode Island
Bristol, Kent, Newport,
Providence and Washington
Counties

South Carolina

USDA Rural Development State
Office
Strom Thurmond Federal Bldg.
1835 Assembly St., Room 1007
Columbia, SC, 29201
803-765-5163
Fax: 803-765-5633

Aiken Area Office
Aiken County Agriculture
Building
1555 E. Richland Ave, Room 100
Aiken, SC 29801
803-649-4221
Fax: 803-642-0732
Serving Aiken, Lexington and
Edgefield counties, plus offices
of Bamberg, Greenwood and
Orangeburg

Bamberg Local Office
3828 Main Highway
P.O. Box 503
Bamberg, SC 29003
803-245-4311
Fax: 803-245-0054
Serving Allendale, Bamberg, and
Barnwell Counties

Greenwood Local Office
115 Enterprise Court, Suite A
Greenwood, SC 29649
864-229-3004
Fax: 864-229-2845
Serving Abbeville, Greenwood,
and McCormick Counties

Orangeburg Office
1550 Henley Street, Room 100
Orangeburg, SC 29115
803-534-2409
Fax: 803-536-5827
Serving Orangeburg, Calhoun,
and Richland Counties

Colleton Area Office
531 Robertson Blvd., Suite D
Walterboro, SC 29488
401-826-0842
Fax: 401-828-6042
Serving Colleton, Beaufort,
Hampton, and Jasper counties,
plus offices of Charleston and
Williamsburg

Charleston Local Office
4045 Bridgeview Drive
Charleston, SC 29405
843-727-4160
Fax: 843-727-4541
Serving Charleston, Berkeley,
and Dorchester Counties

Williamsburg Local Office
502 Martin Luther King Hwy.
P.O. Box 769
Kingstree, SC 29556-0769
843-354-9613
Fax: 843-354-5463
Serving Williamsburg,
Clarendon, and Georgetown
Counties

Florence Area Office
McMillan Federal Building
401 West Evans St., Room 110-A
P.O. Drawer 2468
Florence, SC 29503-2468
843-669-9686
Fax: 843-669-2563
Serving Darlington, Florence,
and Marion counties, plus offices
of Horry, Marlboro and Sumter

Horry Local Office
1949 Industrial Park Road

Conway, SC 29526
843-365-8732
Fax: 843-365-6660
Serving Horry county

Marlboro Local Office
USDA Service Center
210 Throop Street
Bennettsville, SC 29512-4616
843-479-4341
Fax: 843-479-8386
Serving Marlboro, Dillon, and
Chesterfield Counties

Sumter Local Office
Federal Building
101 South Main Street, Suite 103
Sumter, SC 29150-5253
803-775-8732
Fax: 803-775-5712
Serving Sumter, Lee, and
Kershaw counties

Spartanburg Area Office
105 Corporate Drive, Suite G
Spartanburg, SC 29303
864-814-2471
Fax: 864-814-2904
Serving Spartanburg, Greenville,
Union and Cherokee Counties)

Anderson Local Office
1521 N. Pearman Dairy Road
Anderson, SC 29625
864-224-2126
Fax: 864-224-8914
Serving Anderson, Pickens, and
Oconee Counties

Chester Local Office
744 A Wilson Street
Chester, SC 29706
803-581-1906
Fax: 803-581-0852
Serving Chester, Fairfield,
Lancaster, and York Counties

Newberry Local Office
719 Kendall Road
P.O. Box 99
Newberry, SC 29108
803-276-1978
Fax: 803-276-7887
Serving Newberry, Laurens, and
Saluda Counties

South Dakota
USDA Rural Development State
Office
200 4th Street SW
Federal Building, Room 210
Huron, SD 57350
605-352-1100
Fax: 605-352-1146

Area I (Northeast) Office
810 10th Avenue SE, Suite 2
Watertown, SD 57201-5256
605-886-8202
Fax: 605-882-3268

Aberdeen Local Office
1707 4th Avenue, SE, Suite 100
Aberdeen, SD 57401
605-226-3360
Fax: 605-225-7829
Serving Brown, Campbell, Day,
Edmunds, Marshall, McPherson,
Roberts, and Walworth
Counties.

Huron Local Office
1386 Lincoln Ave, SW, Suite C
Huron, SD 57350
605-352-2998
Fax: 605-353-1476
ServingBeadle, Faulk, Hand, and
Spink Counties.

Watertown Local Office
810 10th Avenue, SE, Suite 2
Watertown, SD 57201-5256
605-886-8202
Fax: 605-882-3268
Serving Brookings, Clark,
Codington, Deuel, Grant,
Hamlin, and Kingsbury
Counties.

Area II (Southeast) Office
2408 Benson Road
Sioux Falls, SD 57104
605-330-4515
Fax: 605-330-4595

Mitchell Local Office
1820 North Kimball, Suite C
Mitchell, SD 57301-1114
605-996-1564
Fax: 605-996-0130
Serving Aurora, Brule, Buffalo,
Davison, Douglas, Hanson,

Hutchinson, Jerauld, and Sanborn Counties.

Sioux Falls Local Office
2408 Benson Road
Sioux Falls, SD 57104
605-330-4515
Fax: 605-330-4595
Serving Lake, Lincoln, McCook, Miner, Minnehaha, Moody and Turner Counties.

Vermillion Local Office
121 West Kidder Street
Suite 104
Vermillion, SD 57069-3033
605-624-7060
Fax: 605-624-4365
Serving Clay and Union.

Yankton Local Office
2914 Broadway
Yankton, SD 57078
605-665-2662
Fax: 605-668-9729
Serving Bon Homme, Charles Mix, and Yankton Counties.

Area III (West) Office
1530 Samco Road, Suite 2
Rapid City, SD 57702-8007
605-342-0301
Fax: 605-341-0583

Pierre Local Office
316 South Coteau, Suite 102
Pierre, SD 57501-3109
605-224-8870
Fax: 605-224-1803
Serving Corson, Dewey, Gregory, Hughes, Hyde, Jones, Lyman, Potter, Stanley, Sully, Tripp, and Ziebach Counties.

Rapid City Local Office
1530 Samco Road, Suite 2
Rapid City, SD 57702-8007
605-342-0301
Fax: 605-341-0583
Serving Bennett, Custer, Fall River, Haakon, Jackson, Mellette, Pennington, Shannon, and Todd Counties.

Sturgis Local Office
2202 West Main Street

Sturgis, SD 57785-0730
605-347-4952
Fax: 605-347-3016
Serving Butte, Harding, Lawrence, Meade, and Perkins Counties.

TENNESSEE
USDA Rural Development State Office
3322 West End Ave, Suite 300
Nashville, TN 37203
615-783-1300
Toll Free: 800-342-3149
Fax: 615-783-1301

Greeneville Area Office
214 N. College St., Suite 300
P.O. Box 307
Greeneville, TN 37744-0307
423-638-4771 ext. 4
Fax: 423-639-0956
Serving Carter, Greene, Hancock, Hawkins, Johnson, Sullivan, Unicoi, and Washington Counties.

Knoxville Area Office
4730 New Harvest Lane
Suite 300
Knoxville, TN 37918-7000
865-523-3338 ext. 4
Fax: 865-525-7622
Serving Anderson, Blount, Campbell, Claiborne, Cocke, Grainger, Hamble, Jefferson, Knox, Loudon, Monroe, Morgan, Roane, Scott, Sevier, and Union Counties

Chattanooga Area Office
25 Cherokee Blvd., Suite A
P.O. Box 4941
Chattanooga, TN 37405
423-756-2239 ext.100
Fax: 423-756-9278
Serving Bledsoe, Bradley, Grundy, Hamilton, McMinn, Marion, Meigs, Polk, Rhea, and Sequatchie Counties.

Cookeville Area Office
Fountain Court, Suite K
390 South Lowe Avenue
P.O. Box 555
Cookeville, TN 38503

931-528-6539
Fax: 931-528-1976
Serving Cannon, Clay, Cumberland, DeKalb, Fentress, Jackson, Macon, Overton, Pickett, Putnam, Smith, Van Buren, Warren, White Counties.

Nashville Area Office
3322 West End Ave, Suite 302
Nashville, TN 37203-6835
615-783-1359
Fax: 615-783-1340
Serving Cheatham, Davidson, Dickson, Houston, Humphries, Montgomery, Robertson, Rutherford, Stewart, Sumner, Trousdale, Williamson, and Wilson Counties.

Lawrenceburg Area Office
237 Waterloo Street
P.O. Box 1046
Lawrenceburg, TN 38464
931-762-6913 ext.4
Fax: 931-762-4193
Serving Bedford, Coffee, Franklin, Giles, Hickman, Lawrence, Lewis, Lincoln, Marshall, Maury, Moore, Perry and Wayne Counties.

Jackson Area Office
West Towne Commons
85G Stonebrook Place
Jackson, TN 38305
901-668-2091 ext. 100
Fax: 901-668-6911
Serving Chester, Decatur, Hardeman, Hardin, Haywood, Henderson, McNairy, and Madison Counties.

Covington Area Office
2043 Highway 51 South
Covington, TN 38019
901-475-3350 ext. 203
Fax: 901-475-3356
Serving Fayette, Lauderdale, Shelby, Tipton Counties.

Union City Area Office
1216 Stad Avenue, Suite 3
Union City, TN 38281
901-885-6480 ext. 203
Fax: 901-885-5487

Serving Benton, Carroll, Crockett, Dyer, Gibson, Henry, Lake, Obion, and Weakley Counties.

TEXAS

Texas USDA Rural Development
State Office
101 South Main Street, Suite 102
Temple, TX 76501
254-742-9700
Fax: 254-742-9709

Area #1 Rural Development Manager
6113 43rd Street, Suite B
Lubbock, TX 79407
806-785-5644
Fax: 806-785-5974
Serving Andrews, Armstrong, Bailey, Borden, Briscoe, Carson, Castro, Childress, Cochran, Collingsworth, Cottle, Crosby, Culberson, Dallam, Dawson, Deaf Smith, Dickens, Donley, El Paso, Floyd, Gaines, Garza, Gray, Hale, Hall, Hansford, Hartley, Hemphill, Hockley, Howard, Hudspeth, Hutchinson, King, Lamb, Lipscomb, Lubbock, Lynn, Martin, Moore, Motley, Ochiltree, Oldham, Parmer, Potter, Randall, Roberts, Sherman, Swisher, Terry, Wheeler, and Yoakum Counties

Amarillo Local Office Potter
County
6565 Amarillo Boulevard West
Suite C
Amarillo, TX 79106
806-468-8600
Fax: 806-468-7248
Serving Armstrong, Briscoe, Carson, Castro, Childress, Collingsworth, Dallam, Deaf Smith, Donley, Gray, Hall, Hansford, Hartley, Hemphill, Hutchinson, Lipscomb, Moore, Ochiltree, Oldham, Parmer, Potter, Randall, Roberts, Sherman, Swisher, and Wheeler Counties

El Paso Local Office El Paso
County

11930 Vista del Sol, Suite C
El Paso, TX 79936
915-855-1229
Fax: 915-857-3647
Serving Culberson, El Paso, and Hudspeth Counties

Lubbock Local Office (50-52)
Lubbock County
6113 - 43rd Street, Suite B
Lubbock, TX 79407
806-785-5644
Fax: 806-785-5974
Serving Andrews, Bailey, Borden, Cochran, Cottle, Crosby, Dawson, Dickens, Floyd, Gaines, Garza, Hale, Hockley, Howard, King, Lamb, Lubbock, Lynn, Martin, Motley, Terry, and Yoakum Counties

Area #2 Rural Development Manager
2608 Highway 377 South
Suite A
Brownwood, TX 76801
915-643-1585
Fax: 915-646-8630
Serving Archer, Baylor, Brewster, Brown, Callahan, Coke, Coleman, Comanche, Concho, Crane, Crockett, Eastland, Ector, Fisher, Foard, Glasscock, Hamilton, Hardeman, Haskell, Irion, Jeff Davis, Jones, Kent, Knox, Loving, McCulloch, Midland, Mills, Mitchell, Nolan, Pecos, Presidio, Reagan, Reeves, Runnels, San Saba, Scurry, Shackelford, Stephens, Sterling, Stonewall, Taylor, Terrell, Throckmorton, Tom Green, Upton, Ward, Wichita, Wilbarger, Winkler, and Young Counties

Abilene Local Office Taylor
County
4400 Buffalo Gap Rd, Suite 4150
Abilene, TX 79606
915-690-6162
Fax: 915-695-0528
Serving Archer, Baylor, Callahan, Fisher, Foard, Hardeman, Haskell, Jones, Kent,

Knox, Mitchell, Nolan, Scurry, Shackelford, Stephens, Stonewall, Taylor, Throckmorton, Wichita, Wilbarger, and Young Counties

Brownwood Local Office Brown
County
2608 Highway 377 South, Ste A
Brownwood, TX 76801
915-643-1585
Fax: 915-646-8630
Serving Brown, Coke, Coleman, Comanche, Concho, Eastland, Hamilton, Irion, McCulloch, Mills, Runnels, San Saba, Sterling, and Tom Green Counties

Fort Stockton Local Office Pecos
County
2306 West Dickinson Boulevard
Suite 2
Fort Stockton, TX 79735
915-336-7585
Fax: 915-336-9620
Serving Brewster, Crane, Crockett, Ector, Glasscock, Jeff Davis, Loving, Midland, Pecos, Presidio, Reagan, Reeves, Terrell, Upton, Ward, and Winkler Counties

Area #3 Rural Development Manager
1406-E North McDonald Road
McKinney, TX 75071
972-542-0081
Fax: 972-542-4028
Serving Clay, Collin, Cooke, Dallas, Denton, Ellis, Erath, Fannin, Grayson, Hood, Hunt, Jack, Johnson, Montague, Palo Pinto, Parker, Rockwall, Somervell, Tarrant, and Wise Counties

Cleburne Local Office Johnson
County
105-C Poindexter Street
Cleburne, TX 76033-4400
817-641-4481
Fax: 817-641-7629
Serving Ellis, Erath, Hood, Johnson, Somervell, and Tarrant Counties

Decatur Local Office Wise
County
1604 West Business 380, Suite A
Decatur, TX 76234
940-627-3531
Fax: 940-627-5228
Serving Clay, Cooke, Jack,
Montague, Palo Pinto, Parker,
and Wise Counties

McKinney Local Office Collin
County
1406-E North McDonald Road
McKinney, TX 75071
972-542-0081
Fax: 972-542-4028
Serving Collin, Dallas, Denton,
Fannin, Grayson, Hunt, and
Rockwall Counties

*Area #4 Rural Development
Manager*
1305 South Main, Suite 103
Henderson, TX 75654
903-657-8221
Fax: 903-657-2571
Serving Bowie, Camp, Cass,
Cherokee, Delta, Franklin,
Gregg, Harrison, Henderson,
Hopkins, Kaufman, Lamar,
Marion, Morris, Panola, Rains,
Red River, Rusk, Smith, Titus,
Upshur, Van Zandt, and Wood
Counties

Canton Local Office Van Zandt
County
700 Trade Days Blvd., Suite 3
Canton, TX 75103
903-567-6051
Fax: 903-567-4894
Serving Henderson, Kaufman,
Rains, Smith, and Van Zandt
Counties

Henderson Local Office Rusk
County
1305 South Main, Suite 103
Henderson, TX 75654
903-657-8221
Fax: 903-657-2571
Serving Cherokee, Gregg,
Harrison, Marion, Panola, Rusk,
Upshur, and Wood Counties

Mount Pleasant Local Office
Titus County
1809 Ferguson Road, Suite E
Mount Pleasant, TX 75456-1328
903-572-5411
Fax: 903-572-5411
Serving Bowie, Camp, Cass,
Delta, Franklin, Hopkins, Lamar,
Morris, Red River, and Titus
Counties

*Area #5 Rural Development
Manager*
1502 Highway 77 North
Hillsboro, TX 76645
254-582-7328
Fax: 254-582-7622
Serving Anderson, Bell, Bosque,
Brazos, Burnet, Coryell, Falls,
Freestone, Grimes, Hill,
Lampasas, Limestone,
McLennan, Milam, Navarro,
Robertson, Travis, Waller, and
Williamson Counties

Bryan Local Office Brazos
County
3833 South Texas Ave, Suite 117
Bryan, TX 77802
979-846-0548
Fax: 979-691-8967
Serving Brazos, Grimes,
Robertson, and Waller Counties

Georgetown Local Office
Williamson County
Post Office Box 58
505 West University Dr, Suite G
Georgetown, TX 78627-0058
512-863-6502
Fax: 512-869-0579
Serving Burnet, Milam, Travis,
and Williamson Counties

Groesbeck Local Office
Limestone County
Post Office Box 410
1213 East Yeagua
Groesbeck, TX 76642-0410
254-729-2310
Fax: 254-729-3459
Serving Anderson, Falls,
Freestone, Limestone, and
Navarro Counties

Hillsboro Local Office Hill
County
1502 Highway 77 North
Hillsboro, TX 76645
254-582-7328
Fax: 254-582-7622
Serving Bell, Bosque, Coryell,
Hill, Lampasas, and McLennan
Counties

*Area #6 Rural Development
Manager*
2 Financial Plaza, Suite 745
Huntsville, TX 77340
936-291-1901
Fax: 936-294-0533
Serving Angelina, Brazoria,
Chambers, Fort Bend, Galveston,
Hardin, Harris, Houston, Jasper,
Jefferson, Leon, Liberty,
Madison, Montgomery,
Nacogdoches, Newton, Orange,
Polk, Sabine, San Augustine, San
Jacinto, Shelby, Trinity, Tyler,
and Walker Counties

Angleton Local Office Brazoria
County
209 East Mulberry, Suite 500
Angleton, TX 77515-4650
979-849-5251
Fax: 979-849-7190
Serving Brazoria, Fort Bend, and
Galveston Counties

Huntsville Local Office Walker
County
2 Financial Plaza, Suite 745
Huntsville, TX 77340
936-291-1901
Fax: 936-294-0533
Serving Chambers, Harris, Leon,
Liberty, Madison, Montgomery,
San Jacinto, and Walker
Counties

Jasper Local Office Jasper
County
714 West Gibson, Suite 1
Jasper, TX 75951
409-384-5779
Fax: 409-384-7079
Serving Hardin, Jasper,
Jefferson, Newton, Orange, Polk,
and Tyler Counties

Lufkin Local Office Angelina County
1520 East Denman, Suite 104
Lufkin, TX 75901-5817
936-639-8661
Fax: 936-634-8140
Serving Angelina, Houston, Nacogdoches, Sabine, San Augustine, Shelby, and Trinity Counties

Area #7 Rural Development Manager
3251 North Highway 123 Bypass
Seguin, TX 78155-6115
830-372-1043
Fax: 830-372-0020
Serving Atascosa, Austin, Bandera, Bastrop, Bexar, Blanco, Burleson, Caldwell, Colorado, Comal, Fayette, Gillespie, Gonzales, Guadalupe, Hays, Karnes, Kendall, Kerr, Kimble, Lee, Llano, Mason, Medina, Menard, Schleicher, Sutton, Washington, and Wilson Counties

Bastrop Local Office Bastrop County
Post Office Box 576
208 Old Austin Hwy
Bastrop, TX 78602
512-321-3428
Fax: 512-321-4177
Serving Austin, Bastrop, Burleson, Colorado, Fayette, Lee, and Washington Counties

Fredericksburg Local Office Gillespie County
1906 North Llano, Room 102
Fredericksburg, TX 78624
830-997-8902
Fax: 830-997-0837
Serving Bandera, Blanco, Gillespie, Kendall, Kerr, Kimble, Llano, Mason, Medina, Menard, Schleicher, and Sutton Counties

Seguin Local Office Guadalupe County
3251 North Highway 123 Bypass
Seguin, TX 78155-6115
830-372-1043
Fax: 830-372-0020

Serving Atascosa, Bexar, Caldwell, Comal, Gonzales, Guadalupe, Hays, Karnes, and Wilson Counties

Area #8 Rural Development Manager
2287 North Texas Boulevard
Suite 1
Alice, TX 78332
361-668-0453
Fax: 361-668-3947
Serving Aransas, Bee, Brooks, Calhoun, DeWitt, Dimmit, Duval, Edwards, Frio, Goliad, Jackson, Jim Hogg, Jim Wells, Kenedy, Kinney, Kleberg, La Salle, Lavaca, Live Oak, Matagorda, Maverick, McMullen, Nueces, Real, Refugio, San Patricio, Uvalde, Val Verde, Victoria, Wharton, and Zavala Counties

Alice Local Office Jim Wells County
2287 North Texas Boulevard
Suite 1
Alice, TX 78332
361-668-0453
Fax: 361-668-3947
Serving Aransas, Bee, Duval, Frio, Jim Wells, Kenedy, Kleberg, La Salle, Live Oak, McMullen, Nueces, Refugio, and San Patricio Counties

Edna Local Office Jackson County
700 North Wells, Room 101
Edna, TX 77957
361-782-7151
Fax: 361-782-3680
Serving Calhoun, DeWitt, Goliad, Jackson, Lavaca, Matagorda, Victoria, and Wharton Counties

Hebbronville Local Office Jim Hogg County
1700 North Smith Street, Suite A
Hebbronville, TX 78361
361-527-3253
Fax: 361-527-5547
Serving Brooks and Jim Hogg Counties

Uvalde Local Office Uvalde County
101 Weeping Willow
Uvalde, TX 78801
830-278-9503
Fax: 830-278-9503
Serving Dimmit, Edwards, Kinney, Maverick, Real, Uvalde, Val Verde, and Zavala Counties

Area #9 Rural Development Manager
4400 East Highway 83
Rio Grande City, TX 78582
956-487-5576
Fax: 956-487-7882
Serving Cameron, Hidalgo, Starr, Webb, Willacy, and Zapata Counties

Edinburg Local Office Hidalgo County
2514 South I Road, Suite 4
Edinburg, TX 78539
956-383-4928
Fax: 956-383-6088
Serving Hidalgo County

Rio Grande City Local Office Starr County
4400 East Highway 83
Rio Grande City, TX 78582
956-487-5576
Fax: 956-487-7882
Serving Starr, Webb, and Zapata Counties

San Benito Local Office Cameron County
2315 West Expressway 83
Room 102
San Benito, TX 78586
956-399-1551
Fax: 956-399-9468
Serving Cameron and Willacy Counties

Utah

USDA Rural Development State Office
Wallace F. Bennett Federal Blvd.
Room 4311, 125 South State St
P.O. Box 11350
Salt Lake City, UT 84147-0350
801-524-4321
Fax: 801-524-4406

Richfield Area Office
340 North 600 East
Richfield, UT 84701-0218
435-896-8250 ext.22
Fax: 435-896-6566

Ogden Area Office
2871 South Commerce Way
Ogden, UT 84401-3277
801-629-0566 ext. 11
Fax: 801-629-0574

Richfield Area Office
340 North 600 East
Richfield, UT 84701-0218
435-896-8250 ext.23
Fax: 435-896-6566

Cedar City Local Office
2390 West Highway 56, Suite 13
Cedar City, UT 84720-4133
435-586-7274 ext. 27
Fax: 435-586-0649
Serving Iron, Beaver, Garfield

Manti Local Office
50 South Main St.
Manti, UT 84642-1349
435-835-4111 ext. 12
Fax: 435-835-4113
Serving Sanpete, Millard, Juab
Counties

Monticello Local Office
32 South 100 East
P.O. Box 10
Monticello, UT 84535-0010
435-587-2473 ext.10
Fax: 435-587-2104
Serving San Juan, Grand (East)
on a North-South line, West of
Townships 16 S - 26 S, Range
20E (52-10)

Price Local Office
350 North 4th East
Price, UT 84501-2571
435-637-4354 ext. 12
Fax: 435-637-1237
Serving Carbon, Emery, Grand
(West) on a North-South line,
East of Townships 16 S - 26 S,
Range 20E)

Provo Local Office
BOR Building

302 East 1860 South
Provo, UT 84606-7317
801-377-5580 ext. 12
Fax: 801-356-1237
Serving Utah, Salt Lake,
Wasatch, Summit, Tooele
Counties

Richfield Local Office
340 North 600 East
Richfield, UT 84701-0218
435-896-8258 ext. 19
Fax: 435-896-4819
Serving Sevier, Wayne, Piute
Counties

St. George Local Office
Federal Building, 196 East
Tabernacle, Room 34
St. George, UT 84770-3474
435-628-0461 ext.14
Fax: 435-673-0312
Serving Washington; Kane;
Coconino, Arizona; Mohave,
Arizona Counties

Tremonton Local Office
91 South 100 East
Tremonton, UT 84337-1605
435-257-5404 ext.25
Fax: 435-257-1930
Serving Box Elder, Cache, Rich,
Weber, Davis, Morgan Counties

Vernal Local Office
80 North 500 West
Vernal, UT 84078-2094
435-789-1338 ext. 19
Fax: 435-789-4160
Serving Daggett, Uintah,
Duchesne Counties

VERMONT
Montpelier Office Staff
3rd Floor, City Center
89 Main Street
Montpelier, VT 05602
802-828-6010
Fax: 802-828-6076

Brattleboro Area Office
28 Vernon Street, Suite 3
Brattleboro, VT 05301
802-257-7878 ext 102
Fax: 802-254-3307
Serving Windham & Windsor
Counties

Montpelier Area Office
3rd Floor, City Center
89 Main Street
Montpelier, VT 05602
802-828-6004
Fax: 802-828-6076
Serving Washington, Orange &
Lamoille Counties

Rutland Area Office
170 South Main Street at Trolley
Square
Rutland, VT 05701
802-775-8957 ext 4
Fax: 802-773-4177
Serving Addison, Rutland &
Bennington Counties

St. Johnsbury Area Office
1153 Main Street, Suite 3
St. Johnsbury, VT 05819
802-748-8646 ext 102
Fax: 802-748-1621
Serving Caledonia, Essex &
Orleans Counties

St. Albans Area Office
27 Fisher Pond Road, Suite 8
St. Albans, VT 05478
802-524-6503 ext 102
Fax: 802-524-4575
Serving Franklin, Chittenden &
Grand Isle Counties

VIRGINIA
USDA Rural Development State
Office
Culpeper Building, Suite 238
1606 Santa Rosa Road
Richmond, VA 23229
804-287-1552
Fax: 804-287-1718

Harrisonburg Area Office
1934 Deyerle Avenue, Suite D
Harrisonburg, VA 22801
540-433-9126
Fax: 540-432-1707
Serving Albemarle, Fluvanna,
Greene, Louisa, Nelson,
Culpeper, Fauquier, Orange,
Madison, Rappahannock,
Spotsylvania, Arlington,
Caroline, Falls Church,
Fairfax, Fredericksburg, King
George, Loudoun, Manassas,

Prince William, Stafford, Frederick, Clarke, Page, Shenandoah, Warren, Winchester, Augusta, Bath, Buena Vista, Harrisonburg, Highland, Lexington, Rockbridge, Rockingham, Staunton, and Waynesboro Counties

Lebanon Area Office
383 Highland Drive Suite 5
Lebanon, VA 24266
276-889-4650
Fax: 276-889-2105
Serving Russell, Tazewell, Dickenson, Buchanan, Lee, Scott, and Wise, and the City of Norton Counties.

Lynchburg Area Office
20311-A Timberlake Rd.
P.O. Box 4337
Lynchburg, VA 24502
434-239-3473
Fax: 434-239-3735
Serving Mecklenburg, Halifax, Brunswick, Prince Edward, Amelia, Cumberland, Nottoway, Lunenburg, Charlotte, Buckingham, Campbell, Amherst, Appomattox, Bedford, Lynchburg City, Franklin, Danville, Henry, Martinsville, Pittsylvania, Patrick and the cities of Lynchburg, Martinsville, Danville and Bedford Counties

Suffolk Area Office
1548 Holland Road
Suffolk, VA 23434
757-539-9265
Fax: 757-925-4750
Serving Accomack, Northampton, Dinwiddie, Charles City, Chesterfield, Colonial Heights, Emporia, Goochland, Greensville, Hanover, Henrico, Hopewell, New Kent, Petersburg, Prince George, Sussex, Surry, Powhatan, Isle of Wight, Chesapeake City, Franklin, Hampton, Suffolk, James City, Newport News Poquoson, Southampton, VA Beach City,

Williamsburg, York, Essex, Gloucester, King & Queen, Lancaster, Mathews, Richmond, Middlesex, King William, Northumberland, and Westmoreland Counties

Wytheville Area Office
100 USDA Drive
Wytheville, VA 24382
276-228-3513
Fax: 276-228-2049
Montgomery, Alleghany, Botetourt, Clifton Forge, Covington, Craig, Floyd, Giles, Pulaski, Radford, Roanoke, Salem, Wythe, Bland, Bristol, Carroll, Galax, Grayson, Smyth, and Washington Counties

Accomac Local Office
22545 Center Parkway
Accomac, VA 23301
757-787-3181
Fax: 757-787-8142
Serving Accomack and Northampton Counties

Boydton Local Office
1028 Madison Street
Boydton, VA 23917
434-738-0300
Fax: 434-738-0201
Serving Halifax, Mecklenburg and Brunswick Counties

Charlottesville Local Office
695 Berkmar Ct., Suite 3
Charlottesville, VA 22901
434-975-0047 Ext. 4
Fax: 434-975-0223
Serving Albemarle, Fluvanna, Greene, Louisa, and Nelson Counties

Christiansburg Local Office
75 Hampton Blvd
Christiansburg, VA 24073
540-382-0267
Fax: 540-381-5604
Serving Montgomery, Alleghany, Botetourt, Clifton Forge, Covington, Craig Floyd, Giles, Pulaski, Roanoke and Salem Counties

Culpeper Local Office
351 Lakeside Avenue
Culpeper, VA 22701
540-825-4200
Fax: 540-825-1655
Serving Culpeper, Fauquier, Orange, Madison, and Rappahannock Counties

Dinwiddie Local Office
P.O. Box 279
13915 Boydton Plank Rd.
Dinwiddie, VA 23841
804-469-3311
Fax: 804-469-5962
Serving Dinwiddie, Charles City, Chesterfield, Emporia, Goochland, Greensville, Hanover, Henrico, New Kent, Prince George, Sussex, Surry, and Powhatan Counties

Farmville Local Office
100 C. Dominion Drive
Farmville, VA 23901
434-392-4906
Fax: 434-392-4577
Serving Prince Edward, Amelia, Cumberland, Nottoway, and Lunenburg, Charlotte, Buckingham Counties

Fredericksburg Local Office
4805 Carr Drive
Jackson Sq. Office Park
Fredericksburg, VA 22408
540-899-9492
Fax: 540-889-2014
Serving Spotsylvania, Arlington, Caroline, Falls Church, Fairfax, Fredericksburg, King George, Loudoun, Manassas, Prince William, 55-12 Stafford Counties

Gate City Local Office
95 US Hwy 23 S., Suite 1
Gate City, VA 24251
540-386-3951
Fax: 540-386-9051
Serving Scott, Wise, Lee, and Norton Counties

Lebanon Local Office
383 Highland Drive, Suite 5
Lebanon, VA 24266
276-889-4650

Fax: 276-889-2105
Serving Russell, Buchanan, Dickenson, and Tazewell Counties

Lynchburg Local Office
20311-A Timberlake Rd.
P.O. Box 4337
Lynchburg, VA 24502
434-239-3473
Fax: 434-239-3735
Serving Campbell, Amherst, Appomattox, Bedford, and Lynchburg City Counties

Rocky Mount Local Office
1297 State Street
Rocky Mount, VA 24151
540-483-5341
Fax: 540-483-0006
Serving Franklin, Henry, Pittsylvania, Patrick and cities of Martinsville and Danville Counties

Smithfield Local Office
203 Wimbledon Lane
Smithfield, VA 23430-1853
757-357-7004
Fax: 757-357-7798
Serving Isle of Wight, Chesapeake City, Franklin, Hampton, Suffolk, James City, Newport News, Poquoson, Southampton, VA Beach City, Williamsburg, and York Counties

Stephens City Local Office
130 Carriebrook Drive
Stephens City, VA 22655
540-868-1130
Fax: 540-868-1135
Serving Frederick, Clarke, Page, Shenandoah, Warren, and Winchester Counties

Tappahannock Local Office
772 Richmond Beach Road
Rappahannock Office Bldg.
P.O. Box 700
Tappahannock, VA 22560
804-443-4304
Fax: 804-443-1375
Serving Essex, Gloucester, King & Queen, Lancaster, Mathews,

Richmond, Middlesex, King William, Northumberland, and Westmoreland Counties

Verona Local Office
PO Box 70
70 Dick Huff Lane
Verona, VA 24482
540-248-6218
Fax: 540-248-0691
Serving Augusta, Bath, Buena Vista, Harrisonburg, Highland, Lexington, Rockbridge, Rockingham, Staunton, and Waynesboro Counties

Wytheville Local Office
100 USDA Drive
Wytheville, VA 24383
276-228-3513
Fax: 276-228-2049
Serving Wythe, Bland, Bristol, Carroll, Galax, Grayson, Smyth, and Washington Counties

Washington

USDA Rural Development State Office
1835 Black Lake Blvd. SW
Suite B
Olympia, WA 98501-5715
360-704-7740
Fax: 360-704-7742

Multi-Family Housing Program Division
1011 East Main, Suite 306
Puyallup, WA 98372
253-845-9272
Fax: 253-845-9106
Serving Skagit, Snohomish, Whatcom Island, San Juan, Skagit, and King Counties

Olympia Area Office
1835 Black Lake Blvd. SW
Suite B
Olympia, WA 98512-5715
360-704-7768
Serving Clallam, Jefferson, Kitsap, Mason, Pierce Clark, Cowlitz, Grays Harbor, Lewis, Mason, Pacific, Pierce, Skamania, Thurston Counties

Yakima Area Office
1606 Perry Street, Suite E
Yakima, WA 98902-5769
509-454-5743 ext. 136
Serving Adams, Franklin, Kittitas, Whitman, Yakima, S. Grant Asotin, Benton, Columbia, Franklin, Klickitat, Walla Walla, Yakima Counties

Brush Prairie Local Office
11104 NE 149th St, Suite C-300
Brush Prairie, WA 98606-9558
360-883-1987 ext. 4
Fax: 360-885-2284
Serving Clark, Cowlitz, Lewis, Pacific, Skamania and Wahkiakum Counties

Mt. Vernon Local Office
2021 E. College Way, Suite 216
Mt. Vernon, WA 98273-3610
360-428-4322 ext. 4
Fax: 360-424-6172
Serving Island, San Juan, Skagit, Snohomish and Whatcom Counties

Port Angeles Local Office
111 E. Third Street, Suite 2C
Port Angeles, WA 98362-3020
360-452-8994 ext. 4
Fax: 360-452-5088
Serving Clallam, Grays Harbor, Jefferson, Kitsap and Mason Counties

Puyallup Local Office
1011 East Main, Suite 106
Puyallup, WA 98372-3796
253-845-0553 ext. 4
Fax: 253-770-2274
Serving King, Pierce and Thurston Counties

Spokane Local Office
1908 N. Dale Lane
Spokane, WA 99212
509-924-7350 ext. 4
Fax: 509-924-7787
Serving Asotin, Ferry, Lincoln, Pend O'reille, Stevens, Spokane and Whitman Counties

Wenatchee Local Office
Room 314, Federal Building

301 Yakima Street
Wenatchee, WA 98801-2998
509-664-0242
Fax: 509-664-0250
Serving Chelan, Douglas, N.
Grant and Okanogan Counties

Yakima Local Office
1606 Perry Street, Suite D
Yakima, WA 98902-5769
509-454-5740
Fax: 509-454-5682
Serving Adams, Benton,
Columbia, Franklin, S. Grant,
Garfield, Kittitas, Klickitat,
Walla Walla and Yakima
Counties

WEST VIRGINIA
USDA Rural Development State
Office
75 High Street, Room 320
Federal Building
Morgantown, WV 26505
304-284-4860
Fax: 304-284-4893

Parkersburg Area Office
425 Federal Building, Room 2052
Parkersburg, WV 26102
304-420-6664
Fax: 304-420-6876

Elkin Area Office
401 Davis Avenue
Elkins, WV 26241
304-636-2158
Fax: 304-636-5902

Beckley Area Office
481 Ragland Road
Beckley, WV 25801
304-252-8644
Fax: 304-252-5809

Beckley Community
Development Office
471 Ragland Road
Beckley WV 25801
304-252-4343
Fax: 304-252-5809

Cross Lanes Community
Development Office
418 Goff Mountain Road
Room 103

Cross Lanes, WV 25313
304-776-5298
Fax: 304-776-5326

Elkins Community Development
Office
Forest Svc. Bldg, Room 109
200 Sycamore St.
Elkins, WV 26241
304-636-6785
Fax: 304-636-1568

Fairmont Community
Development Office
7009 Mt. Park Dr.
Fairmont, WV 26554
304-366-2921
Fax: 304-363-7027

Huntington Community
Development Office
2631 Fifth St. Rd.
Huntington, WV 25701
304-697-6033
Fax: 304-697-4164

Lewisburg Community
Development Office
717 N. Jefferson St.
Lewisburg, WV 24901
304-645-7422
Fax: 304-647-9627

Logan Community
Development Office
513 Dingess St.
Logan, WV 25601
304-752-8427
Fax: 304-752-7657

Martinsburg Community
Development Office
1450-4 Edwin Miller Blvd.
Martinsburg, WV 25401
304-263-7547
Fax: 304-267-9172

Morgantown Community
Development Office
201 Scott Ave., Vista Del-Rio
Morgantown, WV 26505
304-291-4116
Fax: 304-291-4139

Mt. Clare Community
Development Office

Rt. 2, Box 204C
Stonewood, WV 26408
304-624-6453
Fax: 304-524-5976

Parkersburg Community
Development Office
Rt. 5 Box 1000
Mill Run Road
Parkersburg, WV 26102
304-422-9070
Fax: 304-422-9079

Pineville Community
Development Office
P.O. Bldg., Second Floor
Pineville, WV 24874
304-732-8855
Fax: 304-732-9140

Princeton Community
Development Office
114 Gott Road
Princeton, WV 24740
304-487-1402
Fax: 304-425-0695

Ripley Community
Development Office
530 Freedom Road
Ripley, WV 25271
304-372-3441
Fax: 304-372-6856

Romney Community
Development Office
500 East Main St.
Heritage Hill Complex
Romney, WV 26757
304-822-3891
Fax: 304-822-3728

Sistersville Community
Development Office
10 Pleasantview Lane
Sistersville, WV 26175
304-758-2351
Fax: 304-758-4303

Summersville Community
Development Office
Rt. 39 & Water St.
Federal Bldg.
Summersville, WV 26651
304-872-4966
Fax: 304-872-4715

Weston Community
Development Office
1 Gateway Center
Weston, WV 26452
304-269-8431
Fax: 304-269-7583

Wheeling Community
Development Office
RD #4 Box 297
Wheeling, WV 26003
304-242-0576
Fax: 304-242-7039

Wisconsin

Altoona Local Office
227 1st Street West
P.O. Box 158
Altoona, WI 54720-0158
715-839-5081
Fax: 715-839-1822
Serving Buffalo, Chippewa,
Dunn, Eau Claire, Pepin
Counties

Ashland Local Office
2014 3rd Street West
Ashland, WI 54806
715-682-9117
Fax: 715-682-0320
Serving Ashland, Bayfield, Iron,
Price, Walworth Counties

Barron Local Office
330 E LaSalle Avenue, Rm 100
Barron, WI 45812
715-537-5645
Fax: 715-537-6836
Serving Baron, Brown, Door,
Florence, Forest, Kewaunee,
Langglade, Marinette,
Menominee, Ononto, Oneida,
Outagamie, Polk, Shawano,
Vilas Counties

Black River Falls Local Office
311 County A
Black River Falls, WI 54615
715-284-4515
Fax: 715-284-9686
Serving Jackson, Juneau,
Monroe, Trempelaeau Counties

Dodgeville Local Office
138 S Iowa St
Dodgeville, WI 53533

608-935-2791 Ext. 4
Fax: 608-935-9713
Serving Dane, Grant, Green,
Iowa, Lafayette Counties

Elkhorn Local Office
225 O'Connor Dr.
Elkhorn, WI 53121
414-723-3216
Fax: 414-723-3292
Serving Kenosha, Racine, Rock,
Rusk Counties

Fond du Lac Local Office
485 S Military Rd
Fond du Lac, WI 54935
920-907-2976
Fax: 920-907-2983
Serving Calumet, Fon du Lac,
Manitowoc, Sheboygan,
Winnebago Counties

Medford Local Office
925 Donald St., Rm 104
Medford, WI 54451
715-748-3355
Fax: 715-748-9766
Serving Clark, Lincoln,
Marathon, Taylor Counties

Portage Local Office
2912 Red Fox Run
Portage, WI 53901
608-742-5361
Fax: 608-742-0194
Serving Adams, Columbia,
Green Lake, Marquette, Sauk
Counties

Spooner Local Office
206 Vine Street
Spooner, WI 54801
715-635-8228
Fax: 715-635-6816
Serving Burnett, Douglas, Pierce,
Sawyer, St Croix, Washburn
Counties

Stevens Point Local Office
1462 Strongs Ave
Stevens Point, WI 54481
715-346-1313
Fax: 715-343-6222
Serving Portage, Waupaca,
Waushara, Wood Counties

Viroqua Local Office
220 Airport Road
Viroqua, WI 54665
608-637-2183
Fax: 608-637-3146
Serving Crawford, La Crosse,
Richland, Vernon Counties

West Bend Local Office
333 E Washington St, Suite 3000
West Bend, WI 53095
262-335-6850
Fax: 262-335-6852
Serving Dodge, Jefferson,
Milwaukee, Ozaukee,
Washington, Waukesha
Counties

Wyoming

USDA Rural Development State
Office
100 E. B Street, Room 1005,
Casper, WY 82601
307-261-6300
Fax: 307-261-6327

Northwest Area Office
208 Shiloh Road
Worland, WY 82401-2914
307-347-2456 ext. 5
Fax: 307-347-2802
Serving Big Horn, Hot Springs,
Park, and Washakie Counties

Central Area Office
201 East Washington Avenue
P.O. Box 1607
Riverton, WY 82501-1607
307-856-5383
Fax: 307-856-4426
Serving Carbon, Fremont, and
Natrona Counties

Southwest Area Office
625 Washington St., Room B
P.O. Box 190
Afton, WY 83110-0190
307-886-9001
Fax: 307-886-3744
Serving Lincoln, Sublette,
Sweetwater, Teton, and Uinta
Counties

Northeast Area Office
1949 Sugarland Drive, Suite 118
Sheridan, WY 82801-5749

307-672-5820 ext. 4
Fax: 307-672-0052
Serving Campbell, Crook,
Johnson, Sheridan, and Weston
Counties

Southeast Area Office
1441 East "M" Street, Suite A
Torrington, WY 82240-3521
307-532-2125
Fax: 307-532-5783

Serving Albany, Converse,
Goshen, Laramie, Niobrara, and
Platte Counties

Other Agencies

In addition to the U.S. Department of Housing and Urban Development and the
Rural Housing Service of the U.S. Department of Agriculture, there are several other
agencies that offer special housing programs. The Bureau of Indian Affairs offer a
variety of grants and loan programs to Native Americans, Alaskan Indians, Aleuts,
Eskimos, and others to help fill a need for adequate housing. These programs
include block grants to communities to provide facilities and improve housing stock,
as well as guaranteed loan programs to help people purchase or rehabilitate their
homes. The U.S. Department of Veteran Affairs also offers loan guarantee programs
to veterans or surviving spouses, in addition to grants to help veterans adapt their
homes for a disability.

Many of the programs listed include a five-digit number in the description. The
number refers to the Catalog of Federal Domestic Assistance, which is a publication
that lists all the government money programs. You can search the catalog online at
{www.cfda.gov}, and it is also available in most public libraries.

For more information or to learn about different programs, you can contact:

Bureau of Indian Affairs
Office of Tribal Services
MS 4660 MIB
1849 C St., NW
Washington, DC 20240
202-308-3667
www.doi.gov/bureau-indian-affairs.html

U.S. Department of Veterans Affairs
Washington, DC 20420
202-273-7355
800-827-1000
www.va.gov

$55,000 To Help Build or Fix Up A Home For Native Americans

Now those much needed home improvements can be completed. Native American homeowners that are living in homes in need of major repairs can get assistance from the federal government. The resources of the Bureau of Indian Affairs' Housing Improvement Program (HIP) eliminates substantially substandard housing for very low income eligible Native Americans living in approved tribal service areas. Grants allow for renovations, repairs, or additions to existing homes. The program will even build an entire house when there is no other available program to meet the need in the immediate or near future. It is restricted to use within reservations and approved tribal service areas. Federally Recognized Indian Tribal Governments and tribal organizations administer the program with eligible applicants that have identified housing needs. Individual members of Federally recognized Indian tribes in need of housing assistance who are unable to obtain assistance from any other source, and who meet the eligibility criteria of the HIP regulations can apply.

The maximum funding for repairs and renovations is $35,000 and for interim improvements, the maximum is $2,500. $16,000,000 is available for this program. (15.141 Indian Housing Assistance)

For more information, the Office of Tribal Services, Human Services, Bureau of Indian Affairs, MS 4660 MIB, 1849 C St., NW, Washington, DC 20240; 202-208-3667; {www.doi.gov/bia/tservices/hip/housing.htm}; {www.doi.gov/bureau-indian-affairs.html}.

Grant To Native American Communities To Fix Up Homes

The federal government wants to assist Native American tribes and Alaska Native villages to develop viable communities. Block grants are available to improve the housing stock, provide community facilities, make infrastructure improvements, and expand job opportunities by supporting the economic development of communities. Funding may be used for housing rehabilitation programs, acquisition of land for housing, direct assistance to facilitate homeownership among low and moderate income persons, construction of tribal and other facilities for single or multi-use, streets and other public facilities, and economic development projects particularly those by nonprofit tribal organizations or local development corporations when the recipient determines that the provision of such assistance is appropriate to carry out an economic development project. The funds may not be used for government facilities and operations.

The average amount of funding is $600,000 with the primary beneficiary being low and moderate-income persons. Low and moderate income is generally defined as 80 percent of the median income. $70,000,000 has been budgeted for this program. Applicants may include any Native American tribe, band, group, nation, or tribal organization, including Alaska Indians, Aleuts, and Eskimos, and any Alaska Native village that is eligible for assistance under the Indian Self-Determination and Education Assistance Act or which had been eligible under the State and Local Fiscal Assistance Act of 1972. (14.862 Indian Community Development Block Grant Program).

For more information, contact your local HUD Office of Native American Programs (ONAP) Area Office, or the Denver Office of Native American Programs, U.S. Department of Housing and Urban Development, Suite 3990, 1999 Broadway, Denver, CO 80202; 800-561-5913; {www.hud.gov}.

$150,000 To Help Native Americans Buy A Home

Buying a home has just got easier for Native Americans! This program is a guarantee mortgage loan program made through private financial institutions to benefit Native Americans. Mortgage loans can be made for the purchase or rehabilitation of an existing home, construction of a new home, or refinance of a current mortgage. The applicant must be a Native American, or an Indian Housing Authority or Tribe, who may then rent the home to a Native American. The loan amount is calculated based on a percentage between 97.75 % and 98.75% of the appraised value of the property. The average loan amount is $90,602. $197,000,000 has been budgeted for this program. (14.865 Indian Housing Indian Loan Guarantee Program).

Check out the program at {www.codetalk.fed.us/loan184.html}; or for more information, contact Director, Office of Loan Guarantee, National Office of Native American Programs, 1999 Broadway, Suite 3390, Denver, CO 80202; 800-561-5913; {www.hud.gov}.

Money For Native Americans To Fix Up A Home

Grants are given to American Indian tribes in a way that recognizes their right to self-govern. Block grants are provided to the tribes with approved Indian Housing Programs, on an annual basis. The tribes and Alaska Native villages determine who will receive the grant. The funding serves the housing needs of low-income American Indians and Alaska Natives. The range of financial assistance is $25,000 to $92,530,695. Eligible affordable housing activities must include developing or supporting rental or ownership housing or providing housing services to benefit low-income Indian families on Indian reservations and other Indian areas. Affordable housing must cost no more than 30 percent of the family's adjusted income. Eligible activities include modernization or operating assistance for housing

previously developed using HUD resources; acquisition, new construction, or rehabilitation of additional units; housing-related services such as housing counseling, self-sufficiency services, energy auditing, and establishment of resident organizations; housing management services; crime prevention and safety activities; rental assistance; model activities; and administrative expenses. $650,000,000 has been budgeted for this program. (14.867 Indian Housing Block Grant).

For more information, contact the appropriate HUD Office of Native American Programs; or Office of Native American Programs, Denver Program Office, 1999 Broadway, Suite 3390, Denver, CO 80202; 800-561-5913; {www.hud.gov}.

Money For Native American Communities To Build Affordable Housing

Most of the native land of American Indians is held in trust by the federal government and must receive federal approval before a lien can placed on the property. Because of this, many lenders have not been willing to make home loans to individual Native Americans. This program offers a loan guarantee to private sector lenders who make home mortgage loans to eligible borrowers for homes located in Indian Country. The applicant must be a federally recognized Indian tribe or Tribally Designated Housing Entity that is either a beneficiary or recipient of Indian Housing Block Grants (IHBG) funds. However, Indian tribes and their members are the beneficiaries of the program. Basically, the individual leases the property from the tribe. The borrower's guaranteed obligations may not exceed an amount equal to the borrower's IHBG, less the amount needed to operate and maintain current assisted stock times five. $16,658,000 has been budgeted for this program. (14.869 Title VI Federal Guarantees for Financing Tribal Housing Activities).

For more information contact Director of the Office of Loan Guarantee, National Office of Native American Programs, 1999 Broadway, Denver, CO 80202; 800-561-5913; {www.hud.gov}.

$48,000 Grant For Veterans To Adapt Their Home For A Disability

Now disabled veterans will not have to struggle to get around in their own home. Severely disabled veterans can get help to purchase a home that is adapted to meet their special needs. The program uses grant money to provide 50% of the cost of the adapted house, land and allowable expenses. The money may be used to construct a suitable home, remodel an existing home, or to reduce the outstanding mortgage on an adapted home already owned by the veteran.

This program is for veterans with a permanent, total, and service-connected disability due to: (1) loss or loss of use of both lower extremities, (2) which includes (a) blindness in both eyes, having only light perception, plus (b) loss or loss of use of one lower extremity; or (3) loss or loss of use of one lower extremity, together with (a) residuals of organic disease or injury, or (b) the loss or loss of use of one upper extremity which so affect the functions of balance or propulsion as to preclude locomotion without the aid of braces, crutches, canes, or a wheelchair. It must be medically feasible for the veteran to reside in the particular home involved. Costs may include supplementary expenses such as connections to public facilities and customary fees for an attorney, architect, and others. The maximum grant amount is $48,000; the maximum amount for adaptation and/or equipment for the veterans home is $9,250. At least 600 veterans are expected to receive this grant. $22,000,000 has been budgeted for this program. (64.106 Specially Adapted Housing for Disabled Veterans).

For information, contact your nearest Regional VA Office or Department of Veterans Affairs, Washington, DC 20420; 202-273-7355; 800-827-1000; {www.va.gov}.

$150,000 To Help Veterans and Unmarried Spouses of Veterans to Buy or Fix Up A Home

Veterans can get more liberal financing terms to purchase their homes. This program is available to veterans, certain service personnel, and certain unmarried surviving spouses of veterans. Home loans may be guaranteed or secured by the VA for the purchase, refinance, construction, or improvement of homes. The guarantee is for up to 50% for loans of $45,000 or less; loans for more than $45,000 and up to $56,250 have a guaranteed of $22,500; loans between $56,250 and $144,000 have a guarantee of the lesser of $36,000 or 40%; loans of more than $144,000 that are made for the purchase or construction of a home, the guarantee is for the lesser of $60,00 or 25%. The guarantee for the refinance of an existing VA guaranteed home loan to a lower interest rate has a guarantee of 25% of the existing balance. Veterans must get a Certificate of Eligibility from their local Veterans Office. 250,000 people are expected to benefit from this program. $31,000,000,000 has been budgeted. (64.114 Veteran Housing Guaranteed and Insured Loan).

Contact your local Veterans Office or check out the program; or contact the Department of Veterans Affairs, Washington, DC 20420; 202-273-7390; 800-827-1000; {www.va.gov}.

$33,000 For Disabled Veterans To Fix Up A Home

If your home still needs more alterations after using the Specially Adapted Housing for Disabled Veterans grant, this program will help. Disabled Veterans who are eligible for the Specially Adapted Housing grant mentioned above may be eligible for a direct loan from the Veterans Administration. The funds are to be used for additional assistance in adapting the veteran's home to their special needs. To be considered for the loan, the veteran must meet the requirements for the grant, a loan must be necessary to supplement the grant, and home loans from a private lender cannot be available in the area where the property is located. The maximum amount of the loan is $33,000. When an existing housing unit is involved, the loan may be disbursed in one lump sum. When dealing with construction of a home is involved, the loan will be distributed in phases. (64.118 Veterans Housing Direct Loan for Certain Disabled Veterans).

For more information, contact your local Veterans Affairs field office; or contact the Department of Veterans Affairs, Washington, DC 20420; 202-273-7390; 800-827-1000; {www.va.gov}.

$20,000 For A Manufactured Home

Whether you have a lot for a manufactured home, or are looking for both, the VA can give you assistance to make that happen. Veterans, service persons, and certain unmarried surviving spouses of veterans can get help to obtain credit for the purchase of a manufactured home. The terms of the loan will be more liberal than those that are available to non-veterans. The guarantee is for the purchase of a new or used manufactured home and/or to purchase or improve a lot to place a manufactured home. The program also extends to the refinancing of an existing VA guaranteed or insured loan that was previously obtained. The property must be lived in as their home and it must be livable for all year round. The maximum term ranges from 25 years and 32 day to 20 years and 32 days, depending on the size of the home. The maximum term for a lot only is 15 years and 32 days. The loan amount may not exceed an amount equal to 95 percent of the purchase price of the property securing the loan. (64.119 Veterans Housing Manufactured Home Loans).

For more information, contact your local Veterans Benefits Administration field office; or the Department of Veterans Affairs, Washington, DC 20420; 202-273-7390; 800-827-1000; {www.va.gov}.

$541,000 To Help Homeless Vets

Are you looking for funding to help out homeless veterans? The creation of the Homeless Veterans Comprehensive Service Programs Act of 1992 provides funding to public and nonprofit entities so that they may deliver supportive services and housing for homeless veterans. The grant money may be used to acquire, renovate or alter facilities, and to provide per diem payment, or in-kind assistance, to those that provide these services. A veteran is considered one who has served in the active military, naval or air service, and who was discharged or released there from under conditions other than dishonorable. Applicants eligible for grants include public and nonprofit private entities with the capacity to effectively administer a grant; which demonstrate that adequate financial support will be available to carry out the project; and which agree to and demonstrate capacity to meet the applicable criteria and requirements of the grant program. The average range of financial assistance is $12,610 to $541,000. The funding has provided 2,500 new beds for veterans. The budget for this program is $31,653,000. (64.024 VA Homeless Providers Grant & Per Diem Program).

For information check out the program contact the Program Manager, VA Homeless Providers Grant and Per Diem Program, Mental Health Strategic Healthcare Group (116E), Department of Veterans Affairs, 810 Vermont Avenue, NW, Washington, DC 20420; 202-273-8966; 877-322-0334; {www.va.gov}.

State Housing Programs

The federal government may have many programs, but don't overlook your state. Every state has some type of Housing Finance Authority that offers a multitude of programs for renters, home buyers, and even developers. The range of options is astounding. Many states offer home ownership classes for free, which help home buyers learn about money management, credit, financing, and even home maintenance. Some states even offer closing cost assistance for those who attend classes. Other states offer assistance in either the form of grants, loans, or loan guarantees for down payments, closing costs, and other items for home buyers. Not surprisingly, there are many states that offer assistance for repair, renovation, or handicapped access improvements to homes. These programs may have income requirements, although these vary from city to city as the states recognize that the cost of living can be greater in some areas. Also remember that many programs are for first time home buyers, but if you have not owned a home in three years you may qualify for these programs. These programs may also be opened to divorced, separated, or widowed spouses, as well.

Developers can take advantage of tax credits for building or renovating affordable housing. Some areas offer lower than market interest rates for developers who promise to reserve some of their units for low income renters. Great financing is also available in some places for developers of senior housing, or for housing built in underdeveloped areas.

Some examples include:

- Rural Owner Occupied Loan Program in Alaska- low interest financing for home building in rural Alaska
- Down Payment Assistance in Arizona
- Home of Your Own Program: Fixed rate mortgages for disabled first time home
- buyer in Connecticut
- Senior Citizen Home Repair and Improvement Program in District of Columbia
- Mortgage Credit Certificate Program: tax credit for first time home buyers in Illinois
- Teachers' Home Buyers Program: 4% grant to cover closing costs for teachers in Louisiana
- Residential Energy Assistance Challenge Program: helping people reduce their energy costs in Maine

You can contact your state Housing Finance Agency listed in this section. If you are having trouble locating the correct resource, you can also go online at {www.govengine.com}. Another great website with a great deal of information for consumers is {www.consumer.gov}.

ALABAMA

Alabama Housing Finance Authority

Street Address
2000 Interstate Park Dr, Suite 408
Montgomery, AL 36109
334-244-9200
800-325-2432
Email: webmaster@ahfa.com
www.ahfa.com

Mailing Address
PO Box 230909
Montgomery, AL 36123-0909

HOMEOWNER PROGRAMS

Mortgage Revenue Bond Program: low rate loans for income eligible first-time homebuyers. Contact the Alabama Housing Finance Authority for application information.

Step Up Program: designed specifically for moderate-income home buyers: those whose incomes can sustain a market-rate mortgage but whose savings fall short of the amount needed for entry costs like a down payment, closing costs and prepaid items. The application can be found at the web site, {www.ahfa.com/StepUpmanuals.htm}

Habitat For Humanity Loan Purchase Program: loan purchasing program in which AHFA purchases loans from Alabama's 32 Habitat affiliates. The affiliate uses the up-front money to build more housing for low-income families.

Building Blocks To Homeownership: free seminar that educates Alabama's potential or current homebuyer in money management, credit, financing and home maintenance.

DEVELOPMENT PROGRAMS

Low Income Housing Tax Credit Program: federal tax credits for owners of low-income rental housing. The program increases the supply of affordable housing for economically disadvantaged families. {www.ahfa.com/LIHTCprgm.htm}.

HOME Program: provides additional opportunities for the production of affordable housing for low-income families. For an application, fill out the request form on the back of the HOME brochure booklet; {www.ahfa.com/HOMEprgm.htm}.

Multifamily Mortgage Revenue Bonds: lower than market interest rates for developers of multifamily housing that reserve some of their units for very-low income renters. Contact the Alabama Housing Finance Authority for application information.

Alabama Multifamily Loan Consortium: long-term financing for affordable multifamily housing development and rehabilitation. To view the Charter Members of the Consortium go to {www.ahfa.com/AMLCmembers.htm}.

RENTAL PROGRAMS

No programs at the time of this printing. Check with the organization for any updates.

ALASKA

Alaska Housing Finance Corporation

Street Address
4300 Boniface Parkway
Anchorage, AK 99504
907-338-6100
800-478-2432
www.ahfc.state.ak.us

Mailing Address
PO Box 101020
Anchorage, AK 99510-1020

HOMEOWNER PROGRAMS

Mobile Home Program: low down payment for affordable homes. To view a list of approved lenders, go to {www.ahfc.state.ak.us/Department_Files/Mortgage/approved-lenders.htm}.

Veteran Mortgage Program: low interest loans to qualified veterans. To view a list of approved lenders, go to {www.ahfc.state.ak.us/Department_Files/Mortgage/approved-lenders.htm}.

Refinance Program: reduce monthly payments on existing loans. To view a list of approved lenders, go to {www.ahfc.state.ak.us/Department_Files/Mortgage/approved-lenders.htm}.

Non-Conforming Program: financing for homes which cannot be financed through traditional financing. To view a list of approved lenders, go to {www.ahfc.state.ak.us/Department_Files/Mortgage/approved-lenders.htm}.

Senior Housing Plan: potential borrowers may apply for financing to purchase, construct, rehabilitate or improve various kinds of housing that would meet the needs of persons 60 or older. To obtain an application, call 800-478-AHFC, 907-330-8436, or email {jmccall@ahfc.state.ak.us}.

Energy Efficient Interest Rate Reduction Program: participants of an AHFC loan may qualify for an interest-rate reduction depending on the energy efficiency of their home. To view a list of approved lenders, go to {www.ahfc.state.ak.us/Department_Files/Mortgage/approved-lenders.htm}.

Low-Income Weatherization Program: eligible low-income Alaskans can lower the cost of heating their homes by providing energy-efficient improvements. To view a list of service providers, go to {www.ahfc.state.ak.us/Department_Files/RIC/Energy/weatherization-providers.htm}.

Affordable Housing Enhanced Loan Program: down payment assistance to moderate-income borrowers. To view a list of approved lenders, go to {www.ahfc.state.ak.us/Department_Files/Mortgage/approved-lenders.htm}.

Assistance Provider Interest Rate Reduction: subsidized interest rates for housing with a live-in care provider for physically or mentally disabled occupants. For a loan application, call 800-478-AHFC, 907-338-6100, or email {ehaveloc@ahfc.state.ak.us}.

Association Loan Program: funds to Homeowners' Associations for improvements to common-area that if not corrected could threaten the health and safety of the residents. For loan information, call 800-478-AHFC, 907-338-6100, or email {ehaveloc@ahfc.state.ak.us}.

Conventional Loan Program (Taxable Loan Program): loans for borrowers that do not meet the criteria of other special AHFC programs for eligible property. To view a list of approved lenders, go to {www.ahfc.state.ak.us/Department_Files/Mortgage/approved-lenders.htm}.

First Time Homebuyer Program: (Tax-Exempt Loan Program) loan program for income eligible first-time homebuyers. To view a list of approved lenders, go to {www.ahfc.state.ak.us/Department_Files/Mortgage/approved-lenders.htm}.

Interest Rate Reduction for Low Income Buyer: interest rate subsidy for low-income borrower. To view a list of approved lenders, go to {www.ahfc.state.ak.us/Department_Files/Mortgage/approved-lenders.htm}.

Rural Owner-Occupied Loan Program: low-interest financing for the construction or rehabilitation of a primary residence to qualified borrowers that live in "small communities" in rural Alaska. To view a list of approved lenders, go to {www.ahfc.state.ak.us/Department_Files/Mortgage/approved-lenders.htm}.

Second Mortgage Program: funds to qualified borrowers for home improvements or for the purchase of a home subject to an existing first mortgage. To view a list of approved lenders, go to {www.ahfc.state.ak.us/Department_Files/Mortgage/approved-lenders.htm}.

Second Mortgage for Health and Safety Repair: funding for health and safety repairs to a financed property of AHFC. To view a list of approved lenders, go to {www.ahfc.state.ak.us/Department_Files/Mortgage/approved-lenders.htm}.

Small Building Material Loan Program: financing for qualified borrowers to purchase materials to rehabilitate primary residences in areas that are defined as "small communities." Contact the Alaska Housing Finance Corporation for application information.

Streamline Refinance Program: applicants can get financing secured by property that is currently financed by AHFC without income, credit, or appraisal qualifications.

To view a list of approved lenders, go to {www.ahfc.state.ak.us/Department_Files/Mortgage/approved-lenders.htm}.

Rural Enhanced Loan Program (RELP): offers an interest rate reduction, reduced mortgage requirements, and one-step construction loans to low-moderate income borrowers in remote communities. To view a list of approved lenders, go to {www.ahfc.state.ak.us/Department_Files/Mortgage/approved-lenders.htm}.

Taxable First Time Home Buyer Program: reduced interest rate to eligible borrowers, without income limits. To view a list of approved lenders, go to {www.ahfc.state.ak.us/Department_Files/Mortgage/approved-lenders.htm}.

Rural Teacher Housing Loan Program: conventional loans to purchase or renovate housing occupied by educators in rural "small communities" of Alaska.

State Veterans Interest Rate Preference: a one percent rate reduction on the first $50,000 to low-to-moderate income qualified veterans.

Development Programs

Multifamily, Congregate and Special Needs Housing Loan: assists qualified nonprofit housing providers and for-profit companies in financing multifamily complexes for low- and moderate-income housing. Contact the Alaska Finance Corporation for information.

GOAL Program: provides grants, federal tax credits, and zero interest loans to for profit and non-profit developers who build affordable rental housing for low-to-moderate income families and seniors. This program is funded through three programs: For applications to this program, go to {www.ahfc.state.ak.us/Download/download-main-page.htm}.

   HOME Investment Partnership Program (HOME): funding for the development of affordable housing for low-to-moderate income families.

   Low-Income Housing Tax Credits (LIHTC): tax credits to owners of rental property where a number of units are set aside for low- to moderate-income families.

   Senior Citizens Housing Development Fund (SCHDF): grants to non-profit agencies.

Senior Housing Loan Program: potential borrowers may apply for financing to purchase, construct, rehabilitate or improve various kinds of housing that would meet the needs of persons 60 or older. To obtain an application, call 800-478-AHFC, 907-330-8436, or email {jmccall@ahfc.state.ak.us}.

Assistance Provider Interest Rate Reduction: subsidized interest rates for housing with a live-in care provider for physically or mentally disabled occupants. For a loan application, call 800-478-AHFC, 907-338-6100, or email {aliddelo@ahfc.state.ak.us}.

Multifamily Federally Insured Loan Program: up to 85% of financing for the acquisition, rehabilitation, or refinance of existing multifamily properties. To view a list of approved lenders, go to {www.ahfc.state.ak.us/Department_Files/Mortgage/approved-lenders.htm}.

Loans to Sponsors: funding to sponsors of affordable housing for low to moderate income people or those living in remote, underdeveloped, or blighted areas of the state. For a loan application, call 800-478-AHFC, 907-338-6100, or email {aliddelo@ahfc.state.ak.us}.

Multi Family Loan Purchase Program: loans for the acquisition, rehabilitation, and refinance of multifamily properties with at least 5 units. For an application, go to {www.ahfc.state.ak.us/Department_Files/mortgage/Loan-Programs/multi-family-loan-purchase-program.htm}.

Rental Programs

Public Housing Rental Program: safe, decent, and affordable rental housing to low-income Alaskans. To view a list of available rental housing locations, go to {www.ahfc.state.ak.us/Department_Files/Public_Housing/public-housing-program.htm}.

Arizona

Arizona Department of Commerce
Office of Housing Development
3800 North Central, Suite 1500
Phoenix, AZ 85012
602-280-1365
www.housingaz.com
Email: webmaster@azcommerce.com

Homeowner Programs

Low Interest Mortgages: affordable mortgages for first-time homebuyers that can include down payment assistance. Contact the Governor's Office of Housing Development for a list of participating lenders.

Down Payment Assistance: down payment and closing cost assistance offered in the area in which you live. The Homebuyer Counseling Agencies list is at {www.housingaz.com/homeownershipassistance/default.asp}.

Rural Home Purchase Program: assistance to qualified low-income families or individuals purchasing a home. Contact the Governor's Office of Housing Development for information on this program.

Weatherization Assistance Program: helps low-income families and individuals reduce their home energy costs. A list of agencies to apply to is located at {www.commerce.state.az.us/Etips/Weatherization.htm}.

HOME Program: provides help for low-income families with various housing needs from rehabilitation to rental assistance. Applications related to this program are available at {www.commerce.state.az.us/housing/ahtf1.shtml}.

DEVELOPMENT PROGRAMS

Special Needs Housing Program: grants to provide planning, technical assistance, and services to groups that serve low-income special needs groups. Contact the Governor's Office of Housing Development for application information.

State Housing Trust Fund: funding for the development of affordable housing for low-income families in Arizona. Applications related to this program are available at {www.commerce.state.az.us/housing/ahtf1.shtml}.

Low Income Housing Tax Credits: federal income tax credits for owners of low income housing units. The application is available at {www.housingaz.com/library/default.asp}.

RENTAL PROGRAMS

Tenant Based Rental Assistance Program: rental assistance to income eligible households. The application can be downloaded from {www.housingaz.com/library/default.asp}.

Project Based Rental Assistance: project based rent subsidies to income eligible households. Contact the Governor's Office of Housing Development for application information.

Publicly Assisted Affordable Rental Properties: affordable rental property available to income eligible households. Contact the Governor's Office of Housing Development for application information.

Low Income Housing Tax Credits: federal income tax credits for owners of low income housing units. The application is available at {www.housingaz.com/library/default.asp}.

ARKANSAS

Arkansas Development Finance Authority

423 Main Street, Suite 500
Little Rock, AR 72201
501-682-5900
Email: mdodson@adfa.state.ar.us
www.state.ar.us/adfa

HOMEOWNER PROGRAMS

Home To Own (Mortgage Revenue Bond Program): low interest rate loans to low and moderate income first time homebuyers. For a list of participating lenders, go to {www.acessarkansas.org/adfa/programs/H2OProgramGuide.htm}.

Down Payment Assistance Program: closing cost assistance for low to moderate-income first time homebuyers. The Homebuyer Counseling Agencies list can be viewed at {www.accessarkansas.org/adfa/programs/dpap.html}.

DEVELOPMENT PROGRAMS

Low Income Housing Tax Credit Program: federal tax credits for owners of low-income rental housing. The application can be found at {www.accessarkansas.org/adfa/programs/lihtcp.html}.

HOME Program: funds are used for a variety of activities to develop and support affordable housing for low-income households. Eligible activities include: Tenant Based Rental Assistance, Rental Rehabilitation, new construction, and assistance to homeowners and homebuyers. Download an application at {www.accessarkansas. org/adfa/home_program_2000.htm}.

Tax Exempt Multi Family Housing Bonds: below market rate loans for developers that agree to set affordable rental rates for low to moderate-income families. Contact the Arkansas Development Finance Authority for application information.

RENTAL PROGRAMS

No programs at the time of this printing. Check with the organization for any updates.

CALIFORNIA

California Housing Finance Agency
1121 L Street
Sacramento, CA 95814
916-322-3991
Email: homeownership@calhfa.ca.gov
www.calhfa.ca.gov

Visit {www.hcd.ca.gov/clearinghouse/} to find information on over 200 housing programs, government, private leaders and foundation grants. Each program listing identifies the goals, eligible activities and type of funding, as well as such critical and timely information as application deadlines and current funding availability.

HOMEOWNER PROGRAMS

100% Loan Program (CHAP): provides low interest financing along with CalHFA down payment assistance to qualified first-time homebuyers.

The Affordable Housing Partnership Program (AHPP): assists first-time homebuyers with closing cost and/or down payment. The Approved Subordinate Localities and Programs list can be viewed at {www.calhfa.ca.gov/homeownership/downpayment/ahpp-approved.pdf}.

Extra Credit Teacher Program: provides qualified teachers and principals down payment assistance to first-time homebuyers. The documents needed for this program are at {www.calhfa.ca.gov/homeownership/requirements/lender/index.htm}.

Oakland Teacher Program: provides affordable loans and down payment assistance to qualified teachers and principals on the purchase of their first home. For a list of approved lenders, go to {www.calhfa.ca.gov/quick/forms/homeownership/oakland_teacher_program/lenders.pdf}.

High Cost Area Home Purchase Assistance Pilot Program (HiCAP): designed to assist first-time homebuyers in the highest housing cost areas of the state. Eligible counties are: San Francisco, San Mateoa, Alameda, Contra Costa, Sonoma and Santa Clara counties. An application can be obtained from an approved lender. See the list at {www.calhfa.ca.gov/homeownership/requirements/lender/index.htm}.

Energy Efficient Mortgages: loans to finance energy-efficient improvements to new and existing homes.

California Housing Loan Insurance Fund: helps homeowners with the restrictions of conventional mortgage insurance by encouraging lenders to serve borrowers with limited funds for a down payment or closing costs.

DEVELOPMENT PROGRAMS

Builder Lock (BLOCK) Program: Builders/Developers may purchase forward commitments for permanent mortgage financing for CalHFA-eligible borrowers tied to their construction/marketing program at single-family new-home developments anywhere in the state. On any day, builders/developers may lock-in, through an approved CalHFA Lender, an interest rate for a pool of funds for terms of 6, 9, or 12 months (nonprofits up to 18 months) into the future for commitment fees of 0.5%, 1.5%, and 2% respectively. Contact the California Housing Finance Agency for application information.

Loan to Lender Financing: available to eligible sponsors to help reduce the cost of construction financing for affordable housing projects by providing low cost funds to eligible construction lenders. Contact the California Housing Finance Agency for application information. {www.calhfa.ca.gov/special/help/index.htm}.

Mulitfamily Housing Program: loans for new construction, rehabilitation preservation of permanent and transitional rental housing for lower income households. The application can be downloaded at {www.calhfa.ca.gov/rental/financing/mf_loanapp.doc}.

Self-Help Builder Assistance Program: permanent low interest loans for single family homes built by owner-builders through self-help construction. This gives families with limited down payments the opportunity to use their "sweat equity" to obtain homeownership. To view a list of nonprofit builders who have participated, go to {www.calhfa.ca.gov/homeownership/programs/sffdpap/builders.PDF}.

Rental Programs

No programs at the time of this printing. Check with the organization for any updates.

California Housing & Community Development

1800 Third Street
P.O. Box 952050
Sacramento, CA 94252
916-445-4782
www.hcd.ca.gov

Homeowner Programs

California Self-Help Housing Program: assists low- and moderate-income families to build and rehabilitate their homes with their own labor. The application can be downloaded at the following website, {www.hcd.ca.gov/ca/cshhp}.

Development Programs

HOME Program: assists communities and community housing development organization (CHDOs) in activities that create or retain affordable housing. The application can be found at {www.hcd.ca.gov/ca/home/nofa2001}.

Emergency Housing Assistance Program: grants to provide emergency shelters, transitional housing and services for the homeless. The forms for this program can be downloaded from the following website, {www.hcd.ca.gov/ca/ehap/ehapforms.html}.

California Indian Assistance Program: assists tribal organizations to obtain and administer housing, infrastructure. Call 916-445-4727 to check if funding is available and information on the application procedure.

Mobile Home Park Resident Ownership Program: loans to mobile home park resident organizations, nonprofit housing sponsors, or local public agencies that are purchasing the park. Go to {www.hcd.ca.gov/ca/mprop} for the necessary forms.

Federal Emergency Shelter Grant Program: grants to fund emergency shelters, services and transitional housing for the homeless. Applications and Request for Proposal (RFP) forms are available at {www.hcd.ca.gov/ca/fesg}.

Child Care Facilities Finance Program: loan guarantees and direct loans for the development and or expansion of child care facilities, child development facilities and family child care homes. Call 916-323-2180 for information on funding availability and the application process.

Rental Programs

Families Moving to Work Program: loans to Cal WORKS welfare reform program recipients for limited-term housing assistance, childcare, employment assistance and other services. The forms can be found at {www.hcd.ca.gov/ca/fmtw}.

Housing Assistance Program: rent assistance for extremely low and very-low income households in rural counties without housing authorities. For information on the application process, call 916-324-7696.

Office of Migrant Services: loans and grants to provide safe, decent and affordable seasonal rental housing and support services for migrant farm worker families during peak harvest season. Call 916-324-0695 for funding availability and application information.

Colorado

Colorado Housing and Finance Authority

1981 Blake Street
Denver, CO 80202-1272
303-297-2432
800-877-2432
www.colohfa.org

Homeowner Programs

HomeStart Program (tax-exempt bond program): first-mortgage financing program for eligible Colorado home buyers that offers a competitive interest rate loan and optional cash assistance to help pay down payment and closing expenses. For a list of participating lenders, go to {www.colohfa.org/hf_homestart_info.shtml}.

HomeStart Plus (taxable bond program): provides competitive interest rates and includes cash assistance. Eligibility income limits are higher than the CHFA HomeStart program but are still below market. For a list of participating lenders, go to {www.colohfa.org/hf_homestart_info.shtml}.

Home Access and Home Access Plus Program: CHFA can possibly make it easier for those with disabilities to purchase their first home with a low interest rate loan. CHFA also offers a second mortgage program for down payment and closing costs. Call 800-877-2432 ext. 376 or 303-297-7376 for application assistance.

Mortgage Credit Certificate Program: reduction of federal income tax for homebuyers to pay their monthly mortgage. Call 303-297-7376 for application information.

Down Payment Assistance: low interest second mortgage loan to help eligible homebuyers with down payment and closing costs; only available to those who get CHFA Forward Commitment Loans. Call 303-572-9445 for application information.

DEVELOPMENT PROGRAMS

Tax Exempt Private Activity Bonds: provides tax-exempt financing for construction loans and/or permanent mortgage loans. Call Colorado Housing and Finance Authority for a developer pack; 303-297-7351 or 800-877-2432.

Risk Sharing Program: provides long term, fully amortizing loans for new construction or acquisition with rehabilitation of rental housing for families or elderly. Contact the Colorado Housing and Finance Authority for application information.

Taxable Loans: combined with the Low Income Housing Tax Credit for new construction, acquisition, or rehabilitation of rental property to house families or the elderly. For an application, go to {www.colohfa.org/rf_forprof.shtml}.

Low Income Housing Tax Credit: federal tax credits for owners of low-income rental housing. For an application, you can email the tax credit staff; {Paulah@colohfa.org} or go to {www.colohfa.org/tc_lihtc.shtml}.

Small Affordable Rental Transaction (SMART): provides long term financing for small rental housing projects; also minimizes the paperwork, document costs and the time it takes to close the loan. The application is available at {www.colohfa.org/rf_forprof.shtml}.

RENTAL PROGRAMS

No programs at the time of this printing. Check with the organization for any updates.

CONNECTICUT

Connecticut Housing Finance Authority

999 West Street
Rocky Hill, CT 06067-4005
860-721-9501
Email: info@chfa.org
www.chfa.org

HOMEOWNER PROGRAMS

Home of Your Own Program (HOYO): offers a 30-year fixed rate mortgages to first time homebuyers with disabilities. Contact the Connecticut Housing Finance Authority for application information.

Urban Rehabilitation Home Ownership (UR Home) Program: a 2-year pilot program with hopes of revitalizing 16 targeted urban communities in Connecticut. This program offers a low interest rate, 30-year CHFA mortgage loan with low-cost down payment assistance. For a list of participating lenders, go to {www.chfa.org/FirstHome/UR%20Home.asp}.

Military Homeownership Program: a special, low-interest rate mortgage for full-time enlisted military personnel. If you are serving in the military full-time, whether it be U.S. Army, Navy, Air force, Marine Corps, Coast Guard, or National Guard, you may be eligible. Call 860-571-3502 for application information.

Teachers Mortgage Assistance Program: low interest rate mortgage available to Connecticut certified public school teachers. Call 860-571-3502 for application information.

Home Buyer Mortgages: below market interest rates for first time low or moderate income homebuyers that purchase moderate priced homes. Call 860-571-3502 for application information.

Rehabilitation Mortgage Loan Program: loans to income eligible home buyers that purchase a home that needs to be repaired, refinancing of a home in need of repair for income eligible homeowners. Call 860-571-3502 for application information.

Homeownership Program: mortgages for public housing tenants and certain public assisted housing residents that meet income requirements; a home buyer education seminar must be attended. Call 860-571-3502 for application information.

Police Homeownership Program: low interest rate mortgages to police officers that purchase a home in certain communities; must not have owned a home within the past 3 years unless they purchase in targeted areas. Call 860-571-3502 for application information.

Down Payment Assistance Program: down payment assistance to eligible homebuyers; closing costs assistance to low income buyers in the Homeownership Program. To download an application, go to {www.chfa.org/mainpages/dap_forms.htm}.

Apartment Conversion for the Elderly: funding for elderly homeowners so they can renovate or add an addition on their home to create an accessory apartment to provide rental income. Call 860-571-3502 for application information.

Reverse Annuity Mortgage Program: elderly low-income homeowners can use the equity in their homes as tax-free income which can be repaid after their death or when they no longer occupy the home. Call 860-571-3502 for application information.

Common Interest Community Common Element Repair Program: financing for repairs to common elements of condominiums and housing cooperatives where other financing is not available. Call 860-571-4216 for application information.

Employer Assisted Housing Tax credit Program: state tax credits to employers that create loan funds for low and moderate income employees so they can purchase or rent a home. For information on the application, go to {www.chfa.org/TaxCredits/application.pdf}.

DEVELOPMENT PROGRAMS

Community Development and Preservation Loan Fund: financing for developers to acquire, rehabilitate, and/or construct one to four family housing for income eligible buyers. Call 860-571-4374 for application information.

Multifamily Rental Housing Program: construction and permanent first mortgages to developers that build or rehabilitate affordable housing where some units are set aside for low income residents. Call 860-571-4216 for application information.

Mobile Manufactured Home Parks Pilot Program: financing for resident associations and certain non-profits to purchase mobile home park land to convert it to condominiums or cooperative ownership. Call 860-571-4216 for application information.

Low Income Housing Tax Credit: federal tax credits for developers of rental housing for low income tenants. Call 860-571-4216 for application information.

Housing Tax Credit Contribution Program: tax credits to non-profits that develop, sponsor or mange housing for very low, low, and moderate income individuals or families. Call 860-571-4216 for application information.

RENTAL PROGRAMS

No programs at the time of this printing. Check with the organization for any updates.

DELAWARE

Delaware State Housing Authority

18 The Green
Dover, DE 19901
302-739-4263
www2.state.de.us/dsha

HOMEOWNER PROGRAMS

Home Fix-Up Program: offered in Northeast Wilmington, this program provides housing rehabilitation loans to low- and moderate-income home owners and to landlords renting to low-income persons, to bring properties up to State Housing Code standards or to add handicapped-accessible modifications. Call the Delaware State Housing Authority for application information.

Housing Rehabilitation Loan Program: loans to low-to moderate-income homeowners or landlords who rent to low-income tenants. Loans can be for $35,000 for ten years at 3% for repairs or handicapped accessibility modifications. Call the Delaware State Housing Authority for application information.

Single-Family Mortgage Revenue Bond Program: low interest loans to first time homebuyers with low and moderate income. For a list of participating lenders, go to {www2.state.de.us/dsha/sfmrb_frame.htm}.

Second Mortgage Assistance Program: down payment and closing costs assistance to persons who have not owned a home in the past year. For a list of participating lenders, go to {www2.state.de.us/dsha/smal_frame.htm}.

Delaware Housing Partnership Program: second mortgages for settlement assistance to low to moderate-income families purchasing homes in targeted new construction subdivisions. For a list of participating lenders, go to {www2.state.de.us/dsha/home_buy_frame.htm}.

Acquisition/Rehabilitation Loan Program: loans for low- and moderate-income first time buyers to purchase homes that are in need of repair and then get a 3% interest loan to make the repairs all with one application. Call the Delaware State Housing Authority for application information.

DEVELOPMENT PROGRAMS

Multifamily Mortgage Revenue Bond Program: tax-exempt mortgage revenue bonds, for the acquisition, new construction or rehabilitation of an apartment, which will be rented to low-income individuals and families. Call the Delaware State Housing Authority for application information.

Home Fix-Up Program: offered in Northeast Wilmington, this program provides housing rehabilitation loans to low- and moderate-income homeowners and also to landlords renting to low-income persons, to bring properties up to State Housing Code standards or to add handicapped-accessible modifications. Call the Delaware State Housing Authority for application information.

Housing Development Funds: loans to developers of housing for low- and moderate-income persons and families. Call the Delaware State Housing Authority for application information.

Community Development Block Grant: funding to maintain or improve housing, in Kent and Sussex counties, of low/moderate income households. Call the Delaware State Housing Authority for application information.

Emergency Shelter Grant Program: federal funds for local communities in Kent and Sussex counties, to rehabilitate, expand and operate emergency shelters. Call the Delaware State Housing Authority for application information.

HOME Program: designed to expand affordable housing through tenant and homebuyer assistance, rehabilitation, and new construction. Call the Delaware State Housing Authority for application information.

Neighborhood Revitalization Fund: low-interest loans to help entire communities restore their homes to State Housing Code standards. To download the application, go to {www2.state.de.us/dsha/nrf_frame.htm}.

Low Income Housing Tax Credit: federal income tax credit to owners and investors of affordable rental housing that rent to low-income tenants. For an application, go to {www2.state.de.us/dsha/2002_QAP.htm}.

Housing Capacity Building Program: a range of assistance to providers of affordable housing to increase their capacity to build and maintain the housing. For an application, go to {www2.state.de.us/dsha/hcbp_frame.htm.}.

RENTAL PROGRAMS

Public Housing (PH): offers low-income persons in Kent and Sussex Counties who are in need of assistance to afford month-to-month rent payments. Call the Delaware State Housing Authority for application information.

Section 8 Vouchers (SEC8V): assistance for low-income households to meet costs of rental housing for DSHA-approved private rental residency. Call the Delaware State Housing Authority for application information.

Moving to Work Demonstration Program (MTW): Applicants on the two programs (MTW and SEC8V) are placed on a combined waiting list for assistance. They are given the first available subsidy location, whether it is at a public housing site, a DSHA-owned apartment complex, or it is in the form of a Section 8 Voucher for use in the private market. Most residents, with the exception of the elderly and disabled, are eligible to receive subsidy under these programs for a maximum of 5 years (with some one-year extensions) while they take part in a mandatory self-sufficiency program. Call the Delaware State Housing Authority for application information.

Resident Services (RS): this self-sufficiency program provides its residents with social workers, counseling and programs to assist them with becoming independent of government housing assistance. Call the Delaware State Housing Authority for application information.

Section 8 New Construction (SEC 8 NC): affordable housing to very low-income people at 30 different sites in the state where participants pay about 30% of their income for rent. Call the Delaware State Housing Authority for application information.

DISTRICT OF COLUMBIA

DC Department of Housing and Community Development

801 North Capitol Street, NE, Suite 8000
Washington, DC 20002
202-442-7200
http://dhcd.dc.gov

For application information on the following programs, please contact the Department of Housing and Community Development.

HOMEOWNER PROGRAMS

Home Purchase Assistance Program: low or no interest loans for low and moderate-income homebuyers.

First Right Purchase Assistance Program: low cost loans for low and moderate income individuals and tenant groups to exercise their right to purchase their rental housing that is being offered for sale.

Homestead Housing Preservation Program: repossessed properties are sold to eligible District residents at low cost and with deferred payment loans.

Handicapped Access Improvements Program: grants to remove barriers and improve accessibility; for homeowners or landlords on behalf of handicapped tenants.

D.C. Employer Assisted Housing Program: grants and deferred loans to first-time homebuyers that are employees of the District of Columbia government.

D.C. Metropolitan Police Housing Assistance Program: assistance to members of the Metropolitan Police Department for down payment and closing costs.

Senior Citizen Home Repair and Improvement Program: loans to senior citizens so that they can make emergency repairs to their home that would otherwise threaten their health and safety.

DEVELOPMENT PROGRAMS

Distressed Properties Improvement Program: tax incentives to encourage the repair of occupied or vacant rental housing and retain low-income residents.

Housing Finance for the Elderly, Dependent and Disabled: loans for the development of housing for special needs households.

Low Income Housing Tax Credit Program: tax credits for owners of low and moderate income rental housing.

Single-Family Housing Rehabilitation Program: low cost financing for the rehabilitation of one to four unit low-income housing in designated areas.

Handicapped Access Improvements Program: grants to remove barriers and improve accessibility; for homeowners or landlords on behalf of handicapped tenants.

Homeownership Developer Incentive Fund: grants to development entities to lower the development costs so that they are affordable to low and moderate-income residents.

Apartment Improvement Program: technical assistance to rental housing owners to make comprehensive property improvement plans that involve a cooperative effort between owners, renters and financial institutions.

Construction Assistance Program: assistance to nonprofit land trusts to develop acquired land and buildings to create low- and moderate-income housing.

Community Land Acquisition Program: assistance to nonprofits to acquire land and buildings to create low and moderate income housing.

Housing Production Trust Fund Program: financial assistance to developers for the planning and production of low- to moderate- income housing and related facilities; there are a wide range of housing initiatives concerning housing production and preservation.

RENTAL PROGRAMS

No programs at the time of this printing. Check with the organization for any updates.

FLORIDA

Florida Housing Finance Corporation
227 North Bronough Street, Suite 5000
Tallahassee, FL 32301-1329
850-488-4197
Fax: 850-488-9809
www.floridahousing.org

Homeowner Programs

First-Time Homebuyer Mortgage Revenue Bond Program: below market rate financing for first-time homebuyers with low/moderate income. Contact the Florida Housing Finance Corporation for application information.

Home Ownership Assistance Program: 0% interest, non-amortized second mortgage loans to low-income families; 3% interest rate loan for nonprofits to develop or substantially rehabilitate affordable housing. Contact the Florida Housing Finance Corporation for application information.

Development Programs

State Housing Initiative Program (SHIP): funds for the development and maintenance of affordable housing through public/private partnerships. Contact the Florida Housing Finance Corporation for application information.

State Apartment Incentive Loan Program (SAIL): low rate financing for developers who build or rehabilitate rental housing that is affordable to very low-income people. For an application, go to {www.floridahousing.org/sail/sail.html}.

HOME Program: provides states their opportunity to administer federally funded homeownership housing program. To download an application, go to {www.floridahousing.org/home-own/home.html}.

HOME Rental Program: mortgage loans to construct, rehabilitate, or acquire and rehabilitate affordable housing for low-income households. To obtain an application, go to {www.floridahousing.org/dpts/notice_universalapp.html}.

Housing Credit Program: federal tax reduction to acquire and rehabilitate or construct rental housing units for low- and very low-income renters. For an application, go to {www.floridahousing.org/combined-cycle/hc/housing_credits.html}.

Florida Affordable Housing Guarantee Program: issues guarantees on obligations of the financing of affordable housing in order to encourage lending activities. To download an application, go to {www.foridahousing.org/guarantee.html}.

Predevelopment Loan Program: financial assistance to non-profits with limited or no experience that develop affordable housing for very low- or low-income households. Download the Application Package Request Form at {www.floridahousing.org/plp.html}.

Multifamily Revenue Bonds: below market rate loans to developers who set aside 20% of the units to low-income or 40% of units to very low-income persons. For an application, go to {www.floridahousing.org/mrb.html}.

Home Ownership Assistance Program: 0% interest, non-amortized 2nd mortgage loans to low-income families; 3% interest rate loan for nonprofit to develop or substantially rehabilitate affordable housing.

RENTAL PROGRAMS

No programs at the time of this printing. Check with the organization for any updates.

GEORGIA

Georgia Department of Community Affairs

60 Executive Parkway South NE
Atlanta, GA 30329
404-679-4940
www.dca.state.ga.us

HOMEOWNER PROGRAMS

Own Home Down payment Program: loans to cover most of the down payment, closing costs and prepaid expenses to first time homebuyers. For a list of participating lenders, go to {www.dca.state.ga.us/housing/SFH/index.html}.

Home Buyer Program: low interest rate mortgages to qualified first-time homebuyers. For a list of participating lenders, go to {www.dca.state.ga.us/housing/SFH/index.html}.

DEVELOPMENT PROGRAMS

The Redevelopment Fund Program: provides flexible financial assistance to local governments to assist them in implementing challenging economic and community development projects that cannot be undertaken with existing public sector grant and loan programs. For an application, go to {www.dca.state.ga.us/economic/RedevFund.html}.

The CDBG Loan Guarantee Program (Section 108 Program): program is a method of assisting non-entitlement local governments with certain unique and large-scale economic development projects that cannot proceed without the loan guarantee. A pre-application manual can be downloaded from {www.dca.state.ga.us/economic/108manual.html}.

Bond Allocation Program: long-term low-interest financing to businesses and individuals for the construction or improvements of manufacturing facilities, single and multi-family housing projects and exempt facility bonds is available both at the state and local level. For an application, go to {www.dca.state.ga.us/economic/bond.html}.

The Community HOME Investment Program (CHIP): used for the production, acquisition, or rehabilitation of decent, safe, and sanitary housing units which will be occupied by income eligible homebuyers, homeowners, or tenants. For an application , use the "Small Cities" Program application at the website, {www.dca.state.ga.us/grants/grantprogram.html}.

Affordable Rental Housing Development Financing: DCA's rental housing finance programs work with for-profit, nonprofit and government partners to build or rehabilitate rental housing in Georgia. Download the application from the website, {www.dca.state.ga.us/housing/rentalfin.html}.

Appalachian Regional Commission: grants for site development and technical assistance for low- and moderate-income housing projects. For an application, go to {www.dca.state.ga.us/economic/arc.html}.

Emergency Shelter Grant Program: grants to shelter facilities for their operation and for the essential services for the homeless they service. To download an application, go to {www.dca.state.ga.us/housing/hopwamemo.html}.

Housing Opportunities for Persons with AIDS Program: direct subsidies of Federal funds to nonprofit groups that operate housing and provide supportive services to people with AIDS and related diseases. To download an application, go to {www.dca.state.ga.us/housing/hopwamemo.html}.

Community Development Block Grant Program: grant program including those for housing improvement projects, and economic development projects. For an application, go to {www.dca.state.ga.us/grants/grantprogram.html}.

Local Development Fund: matching grants to fund community improvement projects. {www.dca.state.ga.us/grants/developfund.html}.

Downtown Development Revolving Loan Fund: loans to eligible applicants to carry out downtown development projects. To download the application, go to {www.dca.state.ga.us/economic/ddrlf2.html}.

Rental Programs

Housing Opportunities for Persons with AIDS Program: direct subsidies of Federal funds to nonprofit groups that operate housing and provide supportive services to people with AIDS and related diseases. To download an application, go to {www.dca.state.ga.us/housing/hopwamemo.html}.

Hawaii

Housing and Community Development Corporation of Hawaii

677 Queen Street, Suite 300
Honolulu, HI 96813
800-587-0597
Email: hcdch@hcdch.state.hi.us
www.hcdch.state.hi.us

HOMEOWNER PROGRAMS

Lease to Fee Conversion: provides a method for lessee homeowners to acquire the fee simple title to their house lots. Contact the Housing and Community Development Corporation of Hawaii for application information.

Hula Mae Single Family Program: low interest loans to first-time homebuyers. For a list of participating lenders, go to {www.hcdch.state.hi.us/hulamae.htm}.

Mortgage Credit Certificate Program: direct federal tax credit to potential homebuyers so that they have more available income to qualify for a loan and to help make payments. For a list of participating lenders, go to {www.hcdch.state.hi.us/mortgagecredit.html}.

Housing Alteration Revolving Loan Fund Program: low interest loans to persons with physical disabilities to adapt their home or rental unit. For application information, call 808-587-0567.

Down Payment Loan Program: down payment loans for borrowers that meet certain criteria. For a list of participating lenders, go to {www.hcdch.state.hi.us/downpay_loan.html}.

DEVELOPMENT PROGRAMS

Interim Financing: a developer may receive interim construction financing from the Corporation at a reduced interest rate. Contact the Housing and Community Development Corporation of Hawaii for application information.

Rental Housing Trust Fund: provides "Equity Gap" low-interest loans or grants to qualified owners and developers constructing affordable housing units. Contact the Housing and Community Development Corporation of Hawaii for application information.

Rental Assistance Program: provides qualified owners monthly subsidies to assist eligible tenants who live in rental housing developments to make their rental payments. Also provides for interim construction financing for rental projects. Contact the Housing and Community Development Corporation of Hawaii for application information.

Low Income Housing Tax Credit: tax credit for developers that construct or rehabilitate affordable rental housing. Contact the Housing and Community Development Corporation of Hawaii for an application.

Seed Money Loan: loans or grants to help with the costs to initiate a low- to moderate-income housing project. Contact the Housing and Community Development Corporation of Hawaii for application information.

RENTAL PROGRAMS

Rental Assistance Program: provides qualified owners monthly subsidies to assist eligible tenants who live in rental housing developments to make their rental payments. Also provides for interim construction financing for rental projects. Contact the Housing and Community Development Corporation of Hawaii for application information.

Homeless Program: shelter and social services for homeless families and individuals. Contact the Housing and Community Development Corporation of Hawaii for application information.

State Rent Supplement Program: rent subsidies to tenants in approved projects. Contact the Housing and Community Development Corporation of Hawaii for an application.

Section 8 Housing Voucher Program: rental housing subsidies. Contact the Housing and Community Development Corporation of Hawaii for application information.

Housing Alteration Revolving Loan Fund Program: low interest loans to persons with physical disabilities to adapt their home or rental unit. Contact the Housing and Community Development Corporation of Hawaii for application information.

Lease Rent Renegotiation Program: arbitration of a lease renegotiation for one and two family residences leased by cooperative housing corporations. Contact the Housing and Community Development Corporation of Hawaii for application information.

IDAHO

Idaho Housing and Finance Association

565 West Myrtle
P.O. Box 7899
Boise, ID 83707-1899
208-331-4882
Email: about@ihfa.org
www.ihfa.org

HOMEOWNER PROGRAMS

First-Time Home Buyer Program: low interest rate loans for first-time low- to moderate-income homebuyers. Contact the Idaho Housing and Finance Association for application information.

Finally Home Program: after completing the education, program participants may be eligible for financial assistance to purchase a home. Contact the Idaho Housing and Finance Association for information.

DEVELOPMENT PROGRAMS

IHFA Housing Bonds: low-interest mortgage loans to first-time homebuyers, developers and nonprofit sponsors of affordable multifamily developments, for both families and seniors. Contact the Idaho Housing and Finance Association for application information.

501(c)(3) Nonprofit Facilities Bonds: provides loans for nonprofit facilities to be owned by qualified nonprofit organizations. Contact the Idaho Housing and Finance Association for application information.

HOME Program: funds used for the construction and rehabilitation of affordable rental housing for low-income families across the state. The application can be obtained from {www.ihfa.org/mulitfamily_taxcredit.html}.

Emergency Shelter Grant Program: grants to improve the quality of emergency homeless shelters. For an application go to {www.ihfa.org/grants_homeless.html}.

Homeless Program Assistance: provides technical assistance to participants in homeless care programs. For an application, go to {www.ihfa.org/grants_homeless.html}.

RENTAL PROGRAMS

Section 8 Rental Assistance Program: assistance for low-income households to meet costs of rental housing. Contact the Idaho Housing and Finance Association for application information.

Family Self-Sufficiency Program: recipients receive assistance to eventually free themselves of federal and state welfare assistance. Contact the Idaho Housing and Finance Association for application information.

Public Housing in Idaho: IHFA operated public housing in target areas where lower income renters pay 30% of their income towards rent. Contact the Idaho Housing and Finance Association for application information.

Housing Opportunities for Persons Living with HIV/AIDS: 45 units with rental assistance to people who have a family member with HIV/AIDS. To download the application, go to {www.ihfa.org/rental_housingopps.html}.

Supportive Housing Program: supportive housing services to help the homeless with the transition to independent living; long-term assisted housing for persons with disabilities; supportive services for hard-to-reach homeless person with severe mental illness. Contact the Idaho Housing and Finance Association for application information.

Shelter Plus Care Program: rental and supportive services for seriously mentally ill homeless people. Contact the Idaho Housing and Finance Association for application information.

ILLINOIS

Illinois Housing Development Authority

401 North Michigan Avenue, Suite 900
Chicago, IL 60611
312-836-5200
www.ihda.org

HOMEOWNER PROGRAMS

First-Time Home Buyer Program: low interest mortgages for first-time income eligible homebuyers. For a list of participating lenders, go to {www.ihda.org/sf_search_form.htm}.

Mortgage Credit Certificate Program: federal tax credit to first-time income eligible homebuyers. For a list of participating lenders, go to {www.ihda.org/sf_search_form.htm}.

DEVELOPMENT PROGRAMS

Affordable Housing Trust Fund: grants and loans to profit and nonprofit developers of low-income housing projects. For an application, go {www.ihda.org/cd2.htm}.

HOME Program: this program is designed to expand the availability of affordable housing for low and very low income persons. The application can be found at the following website; {www.ihda.org/home6.htm}.

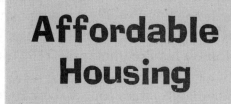

Low Income Housing Tax Credit: tax credit to investors for new construction and rehabilitation of rental housing for low-income families. For an application, go to {www.ihda.org/lihtc2.htm}.

Multifamily Program: low interest loans to build or rehabilitate low-income housing. The application can be downloaded at the following website, {www.ihda.org/mf2.htm}.

RENTAL PROGRAMS

No programs at the time of this printing. Check with the organization for any updates.

INDIANA

Indiana Housing Finance Authority

115 West Washington Street
Suite 1350, South Tower
Indianapolis, IN 46204
317-232-7777
800-872-0371
Fax: 317-232-7778
www.in.gov/ihfa

HOMEOWNER PROGRAMS

First Time Home Program: loans to first-time homebuyers below the market rate. For a list of participating lenders, go to {www.in.gov/ihfa/county/county.htm}.

Mortgage Credit Certificate Program: tax credit to low and moderate income families to purchase a single-family residence. For a list of participating lenders, go to {www.in.gov/ihfa/county/county.htm}.

First Home 100 Program: works with the First Home and Rural Development Direct Loan Programs for further financial assistance to eligible homebuyers. For a list of Rural Development Offices, go to {www.rurdev.usda.gov/in/}.

First Home/One Down Program: 0% interest forgivable loan to assist qualified first-time home buyers with a down payment. For a list of participating lenders, go to {www.in.gov/ihfa/county/county.htm}.

First Home/Plus Program: a 5% - 10% down payment assistance loan 0% in conjunction with a First Home Loan. For a list of participating lenders, go to {www.in.gov/ihfa/county/county.htm}.

The Housing Opportunities for People with AIDS (HOPWA) Program: provides housing assistance and related services for about 500 low-income persons with HIV/AIDS and their families.

First Home Community: enables teachers, fire fighters, law enforcement, state and municipal workers to purchase a home with as little as 1% of the purchase price or $500, whichever is less, of their own funds.

First Home Opportunity: enables qualified buyers the ability to purchase a home with as little as 1% of the purchase price or $500, whichever is less, of their own funds.

DEVELOPMENT PROGRAMS

Rental Housing Tax Credits: federal tax credit to owners of low-income rental housing. For information on how to request an application, go to {www.in.gov/ihfa/rental/tax/allo/programs/programs.htm}.

HOME Program: funds used for a number of different purposes to create affordable housing. For an application, go to {www.in.gov/ihfa/comdev/allo/apps/subrecipients/subrec.htm}.

Community Development Block Grant: funding to create affordable housing for low and very low income families. Contact the Indiana Housing Finance Authority for information.

Build-A-Home: grants to non-profit developers for construction or rehabilitation of single-family homes. Contact the Indiana Housing Finance Authority for application information.

The Low-Income Housing Trust Fund: uses various State funding sources to provide additional financing options and may be used by not-for-profit housing developers to obtain financing for various kinds of housing developments. Contact the Indiana Housing Finance Authority for application information.

RENTAL PROGRAMS

Market-to-Market: subsidies to bring rent down to market level. Contact the Indiana Housing Finance Authority for application information.

IOWA

Iowa Finance Authority
100 East Grand, Suite 250
Des Moines, IA 50309
515-242-4990
800-432-7230
Fax: 515-242-4957
Email: webmaster@ifahome.com
www.ifahome.com

HOMEOWNER PROGRAMS

First-Time Home Buyer Mortgage Loan Program: low interest rate mortgage loans for first-time homebuyers. For a list of participating lenders, go to {www.ifahome.com/docs/sf_lenders.pdf}.

First Home Plus Program: designed to help first-time homebuyers or individuals who have not owned a home in the last three years pay for closing costs, down payment and required repairs. For a list of participating lenders, go to {www.ifahome.com/docs/sf_lenders.pdf}.

Development Programs

Multifamily Preservation Loan Program: loans available to help preserve the existing supply of affordable rental units at risk of being lost – either from physical deterioration or the need for financial restructuring. Loans are made available to eligible nonprofit and for-profit sponsors. For information on the application, contact the Iowa Finance Authority.

Transitional Housing: grants for existing non-profit providers of transitional housing to increase the number of transitional housing units they provide or for domestic violence shelters/homeless shelters and other non-profits who wish to develop transitional housing units. To download an application, go to {www.ifahome.com/partner_2002_Strategic_Initiative.htm}.

Transitional Housing Technical Assistance: provide technical assistance for a variety of purposes. To download an application, go to {www.ifahome.com/partner_2002_Strategic_Initiative.htm}.

Capacity Building: grants for non-profit organizations producing affordable multi-family and/or single family housing units in Iowa. For an application, go to {www.ifahome.com/partner_2002_Strategic_Initiative.htm}.

LHAP (housing production): loans, grants or combination of loans and grants to focus on the creation of additional units that serve single-family and multi-family rental housing needs. The housing must be affordable to low and moderate income individuals and families. For an application, go to {www.ifahome.com/partner_2002_Strategic_Initiative.htm}.

Main Street Revitalization Loan Program: partnership between Main Street Iowa, the Iowa Finance Authority and the Federal Home Loan Bank of Des Moines created a program to make available funds for lending to Main Street communities in Iowa. The pre-application form can be downloaded from {www.ifahome.com/docs/MainStreet-PreeApp.doc}.

Housing Assistance Funds Program: a flexible program of financial assistance dedicated to a variety of housing projects, programs and activities which contribute to the goal of providing decent, safe and affordable housing for limited income persons. Contact the Iowa Finance Authority for application information.

Rental Programs

No programs at the time of this printing. Check with the organization for any updates.

KANSAS

Kansas Housing Resources Corporation

1000 SW Jackson Street, Suite 100
Topeka, KS 66612-1354
785-296-5865
Fax: 785-296-8985
Email: info@kshousingcorp.org
www.kshousingcorp.org

HOMEOWNER PROGRAMS

Kansas Accessibility Program: assists individuals with disabilities needing funds to make modification to their primary residence allowing them to better fulfill their abilities to use their home. The KAMP Service Providers list can be viewed at {www.kshousingcorp.org/programs.shtml}.

First Time Homebuyers Down Payment Assistance Program: loans for qualified homebuyers for down payment, closing costs, and legal fees associated with the purchase of a home. Forms for the program are available at the website, {www.kshousingcorp.org/programs.shtml}.

Homeowner Rehabilitation of Existing Property Program: funds to help homeowners to repair and rehabilitate their property. Priority is given to elderly homeowners and families with school-age children. Forms for this program are available at the website, {www.kshousingcorp.org/programs.shtml}.

Weatherization Assistance Program: a multi-funded program used to increase energy efficiency in low-income homes. A list of State providers and income limits is available at {www.kshousingcorp.org/programs.shtml}.

DEVELOPMENT PROGRAMS

State Housing Trust Fund: assists homeownership, rental housing, and housing with supportive services developments. The application can be found at {www.kshousingcorp.org/programs.shtml}.

Private Activity Bond Allocation: provides lower interest and longer term financing which reduces financing costs for multifamily housing. For an application, go to {www.kshousingcorp.org/programs.shtml}.

Low Income Housing Tax Credit: tax credits for developers who rent to low-income families. For an application, go to {www.kshousingcorp.org/programs.shtml}.

Emergency Shelter Grant Program: grants to local government agencies to provide emergency shelters for the homeless. To download the application, go to {www.kshousingcorp.org/programs.shtml}.

Interim Development Loan: financial assistance to aid difficult-to-develop rental housing projects. The application can be downloaded from the following website; {www.kshousingcorp.org/programs.shtml}.

Community Services Block Grant: funding for community action agencies to combat the causes and condition of poverty in the community.

First Home Community: enables teachers, fire fighters, law enforcement, state and municipal workers to purchase a home with as little as 1% of the purchase price or $500, whichever is less, of their own funds.

First Home Opportunity: enables qualified buyers the ability to purchase a home with as little as 1% of the purchase price or $500, whichever is less, of their own funds.

Rental Programs

Tenant Based Rental Assistance Program: grants to the owners of a rental unit to help renters with monthly rent payments. The application is available from the following website; {www.kshousingcorp.org/programs.shtml}.

KENTUCKY

Kentucky Housing Corporation

1231 Louisville Road
Frankfort, KY 40601
502-564-7630
800-633-8896
TTY: 800-648-6056
Email: webmaster@kyhousing.org
www.kyhousing.org

Homeowner Programs

Home Ownership Program: low interest loans to homebuyers who currently do not own property and meet income requirements. Contact the Kentucky Housing Corporation for application information.

Homeownership Trust Fund: low fixed interest rate for very low-income families with special needs. Contact the Kentucky Housing Corporation for application information.

Yes You Can...Own a Home Program: free homeownership education program. For the Qualified Counselor list, go to {www.kyhousing.org/programs/yesyoucan}.

Homeownership Counseling Program: homeownership counseling services to eligible potential homebuyers. Contact the Kentucky Housing Corporation for application information.

Repair Affair: assistance to homeowners that do not qualify for other existing programs to complete needed home repairs. Contact the Kentucky Housing Corporation for application information.

DEVELOPMENT PROGRAMS

Kentucky Appalachian Housing Program: site development grants and loans for housing development in 49 eastern KY counties. Contact the Kentucky Housing Corporation for application information.

New Construction/Substantial Rehabilitation Program: funds to create or substantially rehabilitate housing to make it affordable for very low-income residents. For a list of complexes to apply directly to, go to {www.kyhousing/programs/newconstruction}.

Risk Sharing Program: low interest, permanent rate financing to developers of new construction or substantial rehabilitation of apartment units. For an application, go to {www.kyhousing.org/programs/risksharing}.

Assisted Living Program: low interest rate financing to developers of housing/service units for the elderly. To download an application, go to {www.kyhousing.org/programs/assistedliving}.

Small Multi Family Affordable Loan Program: loans to be used for construction and/or permanent financing of rental housing development not exceeding 11 units for lower-income people. The application can be downloaded at the following website; {www.kyhousing.org/programs/smal}.

HOME Program: program to fund affordable housing production and rehabilitation. For an application, go to {www.kyhousing.org/programs/home}.

Nonprofit Housing Production and Repair Program: very low-interest loans for the production and repair of lower-income housing. To download an application, go to {www.kyhousing.org/programs/nonprofithousing}.

Housing Development Fund: flexible loan terms and low-interest rates to build affordable housing. Contact the Kentucky Housing Corporation for application information.

Affordable Housing Trust Fund: funds to acquire, rehabilitate, and/or build housing for very low-income residents. To download an application, go to {www.kyhousing.org/programs/affordablehtf}.

Housing Opportunities for Person with AIDS: funds to meet the housing needs of people with AIDS or related diseases. Download the application at {www.kyhousing.org/programs/hopwa}.

Renaissance Kentucky: assists communities to revitalize their downtown. Call the Kentucky Housing Corporation for application information.

RENTAL PROGRAMS

Housing Credit Program: offer eligible property owners a ten-year tax credit for each unit set aside for low-income families. Download the application at {www.kyhousing.org/programs/taxcredits}.

Rental Housing Deposits Program: assistance with utility and security deposits for low-income households. Contact the Kentucky Housing Corporation for application information.

Housing Choice Voucher Program: recipients can locate and rent a dwelling that meets the guideline on their own, provides rental assistance. For a list of housing contacts that will provide and application, go to {www.kyhousing.org/programs/housingvoucher}.

Family Self-Sufficiency Program: rental assistance and supportive services for very low-income people that are willing to commit to a goal of being free of government assistance. Contact the Kentucky Housing Corporation for application information.

Mark-to-Market: assistance to owners of properties with expiring Section 8 contracts to achieve market-rate rents and affordable rental units. Contact the Kentucky Housing Corporation for application information.

Continuum of Care Program: variety of programs that offer transitional housing, rental assistance, supportive services, and permanent housing for disabled homeless persons and operating funds for emergency shelters. Download the application at {www.kyhousing.org/programs/continuum}.

New Construction/Substantial Rehabilitation Program: offers rental units throughout the state. For a list of rental complexes, go to {www.kyhousing.org/programs/newconstruction/}.

LOUISIANA

Louisiana Housing Finance Agency

2415 Quail Drive
Baton Rouge, LA 70808
225-763-8700
Fax: 225-763-8710
www.lhfa.state.la.us

HOMEOWNER PROGRAMS

First-Time Homebuyer Program: low interest rate loans for first time low-to-moderate income homebuyers. For additional information, go to {www.lhfa.state.la.us/programs/programs.html}.

Teachers' Homebuyers Program: designed to help state classroom teachers buy single-family homes. Additional 4% grant to homebuyers to cover closing costs with no repayment. For additional information, go to {www.lhfa.state.la.us/programs/homeownership/teacher/teacherhome.html}.

Low Income Home Energy Assistance Program: assists low-income households meet their energy costs. For additional assistance, go to {www.lhfa.state.la.us/programs/energy/liheap.html}.

TANF Energy Assistance Program: energy assistance voucher program to prevent the loss of utility services for families participating in Family Independence Temporary Assistance Program (FITAP) and Kinship Subsidy Program (KSCP). For additional information, go to {www.lhfa.state.la.us/programs/energy/tanf.html}.

DEVELOPMENT PROGRAMS

Low Income Housing Tax Credit: federal tax credits to developer/owners of rental units for low-income families. The application can be downloaded from {www.lhfa.state.la.us/programs/rental/htc-dwnlds.html}.

HOME Programs

1. **Community Housing Development Organizations (CHDOs):** Section 231 of the Cranston-Gonzalez National Affordable Housing Act requires that 15% of HOME allocations are to be set-aside for CHDOs. The purpose of the set aside is to be used by CHDOs in housing activities to develop, sponsor or own. Contact the Lousiana Housing Finance Agency for information.

2. **Substandard Housing Assistance for Rural Economies (SHARE):** funds used for the purpose of rehabilitating owner occupied dwellings. Contact the Louisiana Housing Finance Agency for information.

3. **HOME/Mortgage Revenue Bond Program (MRB):** offers a lower interest rate to assists those homebuyers whose annual income does not exceed 80 percent of median income (adjusted for family size) in the parish in which the property being purchased is located. The application can be downloaded from {http://204.196.244.8/programs/homeownership/firsthome.html}.

4. **HOME Rental Program (5 or more units):** provided to non-profits and for profits to develop new construction or rehabilitate existing housing. The application can be downloaded from {www.lhfa.state.la.us/programs/rental/home-dwnlds.html}.

Weatherization Assistance Program: funds are distributed to nonprofit community agencies to assist low-income households through energy efficiency. For additional information, go to {www.lhfa.state.la.us/programs/energy/wap.html}.

RENTAL PROGRAMS

No programs at the time of this printing. Check with the organization for any updates.

MAINE

Maine State Housing Authority

353 Water Street
Augusta, ME 04330-4633
270-626-4600
800-452-4668
Fax: 207-626-4678
TTY: 800-452-4603
Email: myfirsthome@mainehousine.org
www.mainehousing.org

HOMEOWNER PROGRAMS

hoMEworks program: a network of homebuyer education that give potential homebuyers an opportunity to sort through the complex process of buying a home, including building good credit, shopping for a home, qualifying for a loan, and life as a homeowner.

> *Check the statewide schedule for available classes on the hoMEworks web site at:* {www.mainehomeworks.org}

Mortgage Insurance Program for Tribal Land: insures mortgage loans for individuals purchasing or refinancing homes on Passamaquoddy and Penobscot Tribal land where restrictions on ownership prevent lenders from ever taking possession of the property. For a list of participating lenders, go to {www.mainehousing.org/1stbuyer.html}.

Home Rehabilitation Program (Pilot): provides loans to income eligible households to perform necessary repairs. Currently offered in four counties (Cumberland, Knox, Hancock and Washington Counties). For a list of contacts to which you may apply, go to {www.mainehousing.org/homerepair.html}.

Low Income Assistance Plan (LIAP): bill payment assistance program to eligible low and very low-income households who receive residential electric service. For a list of CAP agencies that will have an application, go to {www.mainehousing.org/liap.html#CAP%20Agencies}.

Homeownership Program; low down payment and low rate financing for first-time income eligible homebuyers. For a list of participating lenders, go to {www.mainehousing.org/1stbuyer.html}.

Purchase Plus Improvement: home improvement loans for borrowers to make immediate repairs. For a list of participating lenders, go to {www.mainehousing.org/1stbuyer.html}.

Low Income Energy Assistance Program: offers assistance to fuel vendors to provide heating for low-income homeowners and renters. For a list of CAP agencies, go to {www.mainhousing.org/liheap.html#CAP%20Agencies}.

Closing Cost Assistance: a loan of 2% of the mortgage to eligible applicants to cover closing costs. For a list of participating lenders, go to {www.mainehousing.org/1stbuyer.html}.

Down Home Loan: allows a minimum cash contribution of $750 or $1,000 in out-of-pocket expenses for income eligible borrowers. For a list of participating lenders, go to {www.mainehousing.org/1stbuyer.html}.

New Neighbors Program: special financing to buy a home in inner city, low-income neighborhoods in specified areas. For a list of participating lenders, go to {www.mainehousing.org/1stbuyer.html}.

Great Rate Program: low interest rate for low-income applicants; a homebuyer education course must first be completed. For a list of participating lenders, go to {www.mainehousing.org/1stbuyer.html}.

Lead Hazard Control Program: grants and loans to low-income homeowners and renters with a child under 6 in the household to get rid of lead-based paint problems. For a list of CAP agencies to apply to, go to {www.mainehousing.org/leadpaint.html}.

Residential Energy Assistance Challenge Program (REACH): program to help low-income households reduce their energy costs. For a list of CAP agencies to apply to, go to {www.mainhousing.org/reach.html#CAP%20Agencies}.

Weatherization/Central Heating Improvement Program: delivers weatherization and central heating repair/replacement to low-income homeowners and renters. For a list of CAP agencies to apply to, got to {www.mainehousing.org/weather.html#CAP%20Agencies}.

Development Programs

Pre-development Loan Program: provides interest-free capital to cover mortgageable pre-development costs to nonprofit borrowers developing affordable housing projects. To download an application, go to {www.mainehousing.org/download/download.html#PDL}.

Subsequent Loan Program: provides funds to existing MSHA mortgagors to make capital improvements, including converting electrically heated projects to another energy source; to make major repairs or to create new affordable units within an existing project. Contact the Maine State Housing Authority for application information.

Preservation Financing Program: a program to preserve the future affordability of MSHA-financed Section 8 projects. Download an application from the following website, {www.mainehousing.org/download/download.html#Pres}.

Project-Based Rental Assistance: offered to housing developers, owners, and managers to maintain financial and physical viability of subsidized housing in order to continue providing affordable housing to very low and low income elderly, disabled and families. Contact the Maine State Housing Authority for application information.

Transitional Housing Request for Proposals Program: MSHA solicits proposals for the development of new transitional housing for youth, families and victims of domestic violence who are homeless. These funds may be used for acquisition, rehabilitation, and new construction. The application can be downloaded from {www.mainehousing.org/TransHousRFP.html}.

Rental Loan Program: below market rate loan for new or rehabilitated rental housing affordable to low- and very-low income households. Download an application at {www.mainehousing.org/download/download.html#RLP}.

Housing Program: funding to operate or improve shelters. For a list of CAP Agencies to apply to, go to {www.mainehousing.org/hhp.html#CAPAgencies}.

Low Income Energy Assistance Program: offers assistance to fuel vendors to provide heating for low-income homeowners and renters. For a list of CAP Agencies to apply to, go to {www.mainehousing.org/hhp.html#CAPAgencies}.

New Lease Program: reduced interest rate loans for the acquisition and rehabilitation of housing for low- and very low-income renters. To download an application, go to {www.mainehousing.org/download/download.html#NL}.

Supportive Housing Program: reduced interest rate mortgage financing and subsidy funding for nonprofits to create housing for persons who need supportive housing and services. For an application, go to {www.mainehousing.org/shp.html}.

RENTAL PROGRAMS

Low Income Assistance Plan (LIAP): bill payment assistance program to eligible low and very low-income households who receive residential electric service. For a list of CAP agencies to apply to, go to {www.mainehousing.org/liap.html#CAP%20Agencies}.

Preservation Financing Program: a program to preserve the future affordability of MSHA-financed Section 8 projects. Download an application from the following website, {www.mainehousing.org/download/download.html#Pres}.

Project-Based Rental Assistance: offered to housing developers, owners, and managers to maintain financial and physical viability of subsidized housing in order to continue providing affordable housing to very low and low income elderly, disabled and families. Contact the Maine State Housing Authority for application information.

The Continuum of Care Homeless Assistance Program: funds to assist homeless persons move to self-sufficiency and permanent housing. For an application, go to {www.mainehousing.org/download/download.html#CofC}.

Shelter Plus Care Program: provides housing and supportive services on a long-term basis for homeless people with disabilities, (primarily those with serious mental illness, chronic problems with alcohol or drugs, or acquired immunodeficiency (AIDS) or related diseases). The program provides rental vouchers that are matched with supportive services. Contact the Maine State Housing Authority for application information.

Section 8 Moderate Rehabilitation for Single Room Occupancy (SRO) Dwellings for Homeless Individuals: SRO housing contains units for occupancy for one person. The SRO program provides rental assistance on behalf of homeless individuals in connection with the moderate rehabilitation of SRO dwellings. Contact the Maine State Housing Authority for application information.

Low Income Energy Assistance Program: offers assistance to fuel vendors to provide heating for low-income homeowners and renters. For a list of CAP agencies to apply to, go to {www.mainehousing.org/liheap.html#CAP%20Agencies}.

Lead Hazard Control Program: grants and loans to low-income homeowners and renters with a child under 6 in the household to get rid of lead-based paint problems. For a list of CAP agencies to apply to, go to {www.mainehousing.org/leadpaint.html}.

Residential Energy Assistance Challenge Program (REACH): program to help low-income households reduce their energy costs. For a list of CAP agencies to apply to, go to {www.mainhousing.org/reach.html#CAP%20Agencies}.

Weatherization/Central Heating Improvement Program: delivers weatherization and central heating repair/replacement to low-income homeowners and renters. For a list of CAP agencies to apply to, go to {www.mainhousing.org/weather.html#CAP%20Agencies}.

Tenant Assistance Program: federal rent subsidies to very low- income elderly, disabled, or families. Contact the Maine State Housing Authority for application information.

MARYLAND

Department of Housing and Community Development
100 Community Place
Crownsville, MD 21032-2023
410-514-7000
800-756-0119
Email: customerservice@dhcd.state.md.us
www.dhcd.state.md.us

HOMEOWNER PROGRAMS

The Homeownership for Individuals with Disabilities Program: provides low-interest mortgage loans to eligible disabled homebuyers. Contact the Center for Community Development at 800-638-7781 to be referred to a housing counselor.

The HotSpot Homeownership Initiative: an initiative to promote homeownership in HotSpot neighborhoods. A HotSpot neighborhood is an at-risks high-crime neighborhood that has been targeted to receive additional federal and State funding for crime control and prevention efforts. Contact the Maryland Department of Housing and Community Development for application information.

Mortgage Program: below market interest rate mortgage financing for low- and moderate-income first time homebuyers. For a list of lenders, go to {www.dhcd.state.md.us/mmp.cfm}.

Housing Rehabilitation Program-Single Family: loans to limited income homeowners and owners of small nonresidential properties to preserve and improve the property. For a list of local housing offices to apply to, go to {www.dhcd.state.md.us/mhrp-sf/index.cfm#local}.

Downpayment and Settlement Expense Loan Program: borrowers through the *Mortgage Program* can get a 0% loan to help cover settlement expenses. Contact the Maryland Department of Housing and Community Development for application information.

Live Near Your Work Program: employees that purchase a home near their work in targeted areas receive a grant for costs associated with the purchase of a home. For an application, go to {www.dhcd.state.md.us/lnyw/index.cfm}.

Lead Hazard Reduction Grant and Loan Program: funds to homeowners and landlords to reduce or eliminate lead-based paint hazard.

Weatherization Assistance Program: low interest rate loans assist eligible low-income households to install energy conservation materials. For a list of local government or non-profit organizations to apply to, go to {www.dhcd.state.md.us/weather/index.cfm}.

Special Targeted Applicant Rehabilitated Program (STAR): funds to help single-family homeowners to bring their property up to code. Contact the Maryland Department of Housing and Community Development for application information.

DEVELOPMENT PROGRAMS

Community Housing Support Program (CHSP): for eligible non-profit organizations to renovate and resell properties to owner/occupants. Thus, reducing vacancies and encourages the health and vitality of those neighborhoods. For a list of available properties, go to {www.dhcd.state.md.us/chsp/index.cfm}.

Rental Housing Funds: provides loans to nonprofit and profit developers for new construction and rehabilitation projects for the development of affordable multifamily housing in priority funding areas. To download an application, go to {www.dhcd.state.md.us/rhfunds/index.cfm}.

The Self-Help Homeownership Technical Assistance Program: provides funds to non-profit organizations and local governments that operate self-help housing programs. To download an application, go to {www.dhcd.state.md.us/shhtag/index.cfm}.

Maryland Affordable Housing Trust (MAHT); a variety of opportunities that promote affordable housing for very low-income households earning less than 50% of area or Statewide median income. To download an application, go to {www.dhcd.state.md.us/maht/index.cfm}.

Operation Assistance Grant Program: consists of two types of grants -- production and capacity building. To download the applications, go to {www.dhcd.state.md.us/oagp/index.cfm}.

> **Production Grants:** for nonprofit organizations who are engaged in the production and/or rehabilitation of affordable housing.
>
> **Capacity Building Grants:** for inexperienced nonprofit organizations or existing nonprofit organizations that are undertaking new types of affordable housing activities, for the development of affordable housing.

Group Home Financing Program: low interest, no interest deferred payment loans to nonprofit organizations to purchase and modify housing for use as group homes and shelters. For information on the application process, call the Maryland Department of Housing and Community Development.

Multifamily Bond Program: below-market financing for low-income multifamily rental housing development. For information on the application process, call the Maryland Department of Housing and Community Development.

Accessory, Shared and Sheltered Housing Program: low rate loans to finance additions and improvement to create accessory, shared or sheltered housing for low-income households. For information on the application process, call the Maryland Department of Housing and Community Development.

Low Income Housing Tax Credit Program: federal tax credit to owners of low-income rental housing. To download an application, go to {www.dhcd.state.md.us/lihtc/index.cfm}.

Shelter and Transitional Housing Facilities Program: provides grants to improve or create transitional housing and emergency shelters. For information on the application process, call the Maryland Department of Housing and Community Development.

Lead Hazard Reduction Grant and Loan Program: funds to homeowners and landlords to reduce or eliminate lead-based paint hazard. For a listing of local housing offices to apply to, go to {www.dhcd.state.md.us/lead/index.cfm#local}.

HOME Program: funds for the construction, acquisition and rehabilitation of rental housing, owner occupied housing, and special needs housing. To download an application, go to {www.dhcd.state.md.us/home/index.cfm}.

Office and Commercial Space Conversion Initiative: financing to convert older offices and commercial space downtown into new affordable rental housing. To download an application, go to {www.dhcd.state.md.us/ocsci/index.cfm}.

Rental Programs

RAP to Work Program: subsidies to very low income individuals with emergency needs or that are homeless who are making the transition from welfare to work. To download the RAP Handbook, go to {www.dhcd.state.md.us/rap/index.cfm.}

Rental Allowance Program: subsidies to very low-income individuals with emergency needs or that are homeless. To download the RAP Handbook, go to {www.dhcd.state.md.us/rap/index.cfm}.

Section 8 Existing Certificate/Voucher Program: rent subsidies for low-income households. For application information, contact the Maryland Department of Housing and Community Development.

Lead Hazard Reduction Grant and Loan Program: funds to homeowners and landlords to reduce or eliminate lead-based paint hazard. For a listing of local housing offices to apply to, go to {www.dhcd.state.md.us/lead/index.cfm#local}.

MASSACHUSETTS

MassHousing
One Beacon Street
Boston, MA 02108
617-854-1000
Fax: 617-854-1029
TDD: 617-854-1025
Email: information@masshousing.com
www.mhfa.com

Homeowner Programs

Group Home Financing Program: low interest, no interest deferred payment loans to nonprofit organizations to purchase and modify housing for use as group homes and shelters. Contact the Massachusetts Housing Finance Agency for information.

Municipal Mortgage Program: financing available to police, firefighters, school teachers and other municipal employees that requires no down payment. For a list of participating banks, go to {http://mhfadata.com/municipal_results.asp}.

Home Improvement Loan Program: loans of up to $25,000 to eligible homeowners to make needed permanent general improvements to their homes. For a list of lenders, go to {www.mhfa.com/sf/sf_products.htm#1stTIMEHOMEBUYERS}.

General Lending: special loans for income eligible first time homebuyers. Contact the Massachusetts Housing Finance Agency for information.

Mortgage Insurance Fund: provides private mortgage insurance on mortgage loan down payments below 20%. Contact the Massachusetts Housing Finance Agency for information.

Get the Lead Out Program: provides low cost financing to owners of 1 to 4 family homes to remove lead paint. For a listing of local rehabilitation agencies, go to {www.mhfa.com/sf/sf_lra.htm}.

FreshRate Program: loan of 4% of the loan amount for down payment and closing cost assistance to qualified buyers. For a list of lenders, go to {www.mhfa.com/sf/sf_products.htm#FRESHRATE}.

Septic Repair Loan Program: financial assistance for income eligible homeowners to repair a failed septic system. For a list of lenders, go to {www.mhfa.com/sf/sf_septic_lenders.htm}.

MassAdvantage: below-market-rate mortgages or home improvement loans available to low-to-moderate income first-time homebuyers. For additional information, go to {www.mhfa.com}.

MassAdvantage100: 100% financing available to low-to-moderate first-time homebuyers. For additional information, go to {www.mhfa.com}.

Purchase and Rehabilitation Program: program covering purchase price plus necessary rehabilitation costs for first-time homebuyers. For additional information, go to {www.mhfa.com}.

RHS Loan Guarantee Loan: mortgage program for low-to-moderate income borrowers in identified rural areas. For additional information, go to {www.mhfa.com}.

Take the "T" Home Mortgage Program: provides 100% financing to qualified regular public transportation ("T") riders buying a home in close proximity to public transportation. For additional information, go to {www.mhfa.com}.

Development Programs

Elder 80/20: Supportive Housing for Seniors Program: for the development of housing that will serve elders who wish to live in independent rental apartments with on-site access to supportive services as needed. At least 20% of the units must be reserved for low-income occupancy. Contact the Massachusetts Housing Finance Agency for application information.

Elder Choice Program: fills the gap between independent living and a nursing home by providing a home-like setting coupled with on-site services that support the needs of frail elderly persons. To download the forms for this program, go to {www.mhfa.com/dev/dp_elderchguide.htm}.

Construction Loan Program: loans available to builders who agree to price 25% of their units at or below MHFA's acquisition cost limits. Thus, creating homeownership opportunities for low- and moderate-income persons and assist small-scale home builders who may not be able to access conventional sources of construction financing. Contact the Massachusetts Housing Finance Agency for application information.

Low Income Housing Tax Credit Program: federal tax credits for owners of low-income rental housing. Contact the Massachusetts Housing Finance Agency for application information.

Get the Lead Out Program: provides low cost financing to owners of 1 to 4 family homes to remove lead paint. For a listing of local rehabilitation agencies, go to {www.mhfa.com/sf/sf_lra.htm}.

The Massachusetts Affordable Housing Trust Fund: designed to provide resources to create or preserve affordable housing throughout the state for low-income households. To download an application, go to {www.mhfa.com/dev/da_1stpmnpg.htm}.

Expanding Rental Affordability Program (ERA): assistance for rental housing where at least 20% of the units are set aside for low-income renters. For information, contact the Massachusetts Housing Finance Agency.

Demonstration Disposition Program: funding to renovate development in specified areas. To download an application, go to {www.mhfa.com/dev/rfp_homepage.htm}.

Options for Independence Program: financing to community based residences for previously mentally institutionalized persons, homeless mentally ill, and other special needs persons. For information, contact the Massachusetts Housing Finance Agency.

Bridge Loan Financing: for developers of low-income rental housing in conjunction with construction/permanent financing. For information, contact the Massachusetts Housing Finance Agency.

504/ADA Technical Assistance: technical assistance for housing providers, residents, applicants, and service providers. For information, contact the Massachusetts Housing Finance Agency.

RENTAL PROGRAMS

Project TAP (Tenant Assistance Program): training for project residents and management for drug and alcohol-related problems. For information, contact the Massachusetts Housing Finance Agency.

Get the Lead Out Program: provides low cost financing to owners of 1 to 4 family homes to remove lead paint. For a listing of local rehabilitation agencies, go to {www.mhfa.com/sf/sf_lra.htm}.

Expanding Rental Affordability Program: assistance for rental housing where at least 20% of the units are set aside for low-income renters. For information, contact the Massachusetts Housing Finance Agency.

504/ADA Technical Assistance: technical assistance for housing providers, residents, applicants, and service providers. For information, contact the Massachusetts Housing Finance Agency.

Youth Resident Activities Program: programs and activities for youths that reside in MHFA properties in specified areas. For information, contact the Massachusetts Housing Finance Agency.

Massachusetts Department of Housing and Community Development

One Congress Street, 10th Floor
Boston, MA 02114
617-727-7765
Email: dhcdweb@hotmail.com
www.state.ma.us/dhcd/

The following websites provide location listings:
Local Housing Authorities;
www.state.ma.us/dhcd/publications/HOW_TO2K.HTM#LHAs
Department of Transitional Assistance (DTA);
www.state.ma.us/dhcd/publications/HOW_TO2K.HTM#DTAs
Neighborhood Housing Services Offices;
www.state.ma.us/dhcd/publications/HOW_TO2K.HTM#NHS
Community Development Corporations
www.state.ma.us/dhcd/publications/HOW_TO2K.HTM#CDCs
Community Action Agencies
www.state.ma.us/dhcd/publications/HOW_TO2K.HTM#CAAs
Area Agencies on Aging
www.state.ma.us/dhcd/publications/HOW_TO2K.HTM#AAonA
Independent Living Centers
www.state.ma.us/dhcd/publications/HOW_TO2K.HTM#ILC
Shelter Referral / Placement Services
www.state.ma.us/dhcd/publications/HOW_TO2K.HTM#SR/PS
Temporary Shelters
www.state.ma.us/dhcd/publications/HOW_TO2K.HTM#TSs

Other available resources:
For The Elderly:
Statewide Elder Hotline: 1-800-882-2003
Massachusetts Executive Office of Elder Affairs: 617-727-7550

For The Disabled
Independent Living Information Center: 1-800-462-5015

For Special Needs Housing:
Massachusetts Department of Mental Health: 617-626-8000
Massachusetts Department of Mental Retardation: 617-727-5608
www.dmr.state.ma.us/

HOMEOWNER PROGRAMS

The State Soft-Second Mortgage Program: a state funded program that will help first time homebuyers purchase a home. For more information contact the *Massachusetts Housing Partnership* at (617) 338-7868 or visit their website at {www.mhpfund.com}.

Homebuyer Counseling: educates first-time home buyers of the home buying process.
- Contact the *Massachusetts Homeownership Collaborative* for information on homebuyer counseling agencies across the state. Phone: 1-800-HOME-111 or visit the web site at {www.baystatehomebuyer.com}.
- The *City of Boston* operates the Boston Home Center. Phone (617) 635-4663 or visit the web site at {www.ci.boston.ma.us/dnd}.
- The *Massachusetts Housing Finance Agency* has a list of homebuyer counseling agencies. Phone 614-854-1000 or visit the web site at {www.mhfa.com}.

Home Rehabilitation Loans: loans made available to moderate and low income homeowners.

Low Income Home Energy Assistance Program (LIHEAP): helps low-income households to pay winter heating bills. Contact the Massachusetts Department o f Housing and Community Development for an application.

Weatherization Assistance Program: funds for full-scale energy conservation services in low-income households. Contact the Massachusetts Department o f Housing and Community Development for information.

Heating Emergency Assistance Retrofit Task Weatherization Assistance Program (HEARTWAP): provides heating system repair and replacement services to low-income households. Contact the Massachusetts Department of Housing and Community Development for information.

Low Income Sewer and Water Assistance Program: financial assistance to homeowners that have excessive water and sewer bills. Contact the Massachusetts Department of Housing and Community Development for information.

Homeownership Opportunity Program (HOP): reduced rate first mortgage loans to buyers of HOP units. Call 617-727-7824 for application information.

DEVELOPMENT PROGRAMS

Community Development Block Grant Program: variety of programs that fund housing and/or public facilities and infrastructure programs. Contact the Massachusetts Department of Housing and Community Development for application information.

Community Enterprise Economic Development Program: assistance for residents and their local community development corporation to revitalize their neighborhoods. Contact the Massachusetts Department of Housing and Community Development for application information.

HOME Program: funds available for rental housing production and rehabilitation, first time homebuyer assistance, rehabilitation assistance for homeowners, and tenant based rental assistance. Contact the Massachusetts Department of Housing and Community Development for application information.

Housing Innovations Fund: Deferred payment loans to non-profit developers who reserve at least 50% of the housing units to low-income families. Contact the Massachusetts Department of Housing and Community Development for application information.

Housing Stabilization Fund Program: funding for three specific programs: Neighborhood Restoration Initiative, Rehabilitation Initiative, and Soft-Second Loans. Contact the Massachusetts Department of Housing and Community Development for application information.

1. **Neighborhood Restoration Initiative (NRI):** funds used for neighborhood revitalization to support affordable rental housing and affordable homeownership.
2. **The Rehabilitation Initiative (RI):** funds to support the acquisition, rehabilitation, and reuse of distressed, reused, or abandoned properties as affordable housing.
3. **Soft-Second Loan Program:** creates homeownership opportunities by subsidizing mortgages, or providing closing cost assistance and down payments.

Local Initiative Program: technical assistance to communities and developers that are working together to create housing that sets aside 25% of its units for low and moderate income households.

Neighborhood Housing Services Program: support for agency or individual housing rehabilitation projects. Contact the Massachusetts Department of Housing and Community Development for application information.

RENTAL PROGRAMS

Contact the Massachusetts Department of Housing and Community Development for application information on these programs.

Rental Voucher Program (MRVP): subsidies for very low-income families.

Section 8 Certificate/Voucher Program: rent subsidies for very low-income families, the elderly and the disabled.

Section 8 Designated Housing Program: tenant based subsidies for non-elderly disabled individuals who are on waiting lists at MHFA developments.

Section 8 Family Self-Sufficiency Program: assists eligible families to achieve economic independence.

Section 8 Family Unification Program: eligible families are issued a Section 8 voucher. The family is then given up to 180 days to locate their own rental housing.

Section 8 Housing Choice Voucher Program: eligible families are issued a Section 8 voucher. The family is then given up to 180 days to locate their own rental housing.

Section 8 Housing Options Program: Section 8 vouchers for eligible low-income disabled individuals who are living in transitional housing.

Section 8 Mainstream Housing Program: available to eligible families where the head of household is disabled.

Section 8 Moderate Rehab Single Room Occupancy Program: available to very low-income homeless individuals that may or may not have a need for supportive services.

Section 8 Raising Next Generation Program: targeted for low-income families living independently in the community but need special support services for both the elderly and young children.

Section 8 Tenant Based Rental Assistance for Persons Living with HIV / AIDS: Section 8 vouchers, and supportive services for those eligible very low-income persons living with HIV / AIDS.

Section 8 Veterans Administration Supported Housing Program: provides Section 8 rental vouchers along with ongoing case management and clinical services administered by the Veterans Administration Supportive Housing (VASH) to homeless disabled veterans.

Alternative Housing Voucher Program (AHVP): provides rental assistance to people with disabilities under age 60 who either live in, or are eligible to live in elderly/disabled state-assisted public housing.

Low Income Home Energy Assistance Program (LIHEAP): helps low-income households to pay winter heating bills.

Weatherization Assistance Program: funds for full scale energy conservation services in low-income households.

Heating Emergency Assistance Retrofit Task Weatherization Assistance Program (HEARTWAP): provides heating system repair and replacement services to low-income households.

Homeless Intervention and Housing Services Program: supportive services that help people in a housing crisis situation, find housing.

McKinney Emergency Shelter Grant Program: provides emergency shelter and homelessness prevention to low-income families and individuals.

McKinney Local Housing Authority Transitional Housing Program: transitional housing and individual service plans that include job training, education, counseling, employment assistance, daycare, and life skills enhancements.

McKinney Shelter Plus Care Program: provides rental assistance and support services for homeless families or individuals with disabilities - primarily those with mental illness, chronic substance abuse, and/or HIV/AIDS.

Scattered Site Transitional Apartment Program (SSTAP): transitional housing provided to individuals, and their families, who are victims of domestic violence, and are homeless as a result of domestic violence.

MICHIGAN

Michigan State Housing Development Authority

735 E. Michigan Ave.
PO Box 30044
Lansing, MI 48912
517-373-8370
Fax: 517-335-4797
TTY: 800-382-4568
www.mshda.org

HOMEOWNER PROGRAMS

Property Improvement Loan: home improvement loans for owner and non-owner occupied homes over 20 years old at a low interest rate. Contact the Michigan State Housing Development Authority for application information.

Homeownership Counseling Network: free counseling for potential MSHDA borrowers. To use the counselor locator, go to the following website: {www.michigan.gov/mshda}.

Mortgage Credit Certificate: federal income tax credits that give homebuyers more income to qualify for a mortgage. To view the list of participating lenders, go to {www.michigan.gov/mshda}.

Single Family Mortgage Program: low interest loans for the purchase single family homes and condominiums. For a list of participating lenders to apply with, go to {www.michigan.gov/mshda}.

Acquisition Rehabilitation Mortgages: available to qualified homebuyers with repair costs or improvements of at least $5,000. Contact the Michigan State Housing Authority for application information.

DEVELOPMENT PROGRAMS

Housing Resource Fund: funds for nonprofit and local governments to create affordable housing projects. Contact the Michigan State Housing Development Authority for application information.

Community Development Block Grant: grants to small communities and counties so that lower income homeowners can upgrade their homes and carry out other housing activities. Contact the Michigan State Housing Development Authority for application information.

Habitat for Humanity Housing Grant Fund: grants to Habitat for Humanity to build or rehabilitate homes. Contact the Michigan State Housing Development Authority for information on this program.

Contractor's Assistance Program: provides working capital loans to small contractors who have been selected to work on rental housing projects. Contact the Michigan State Housing Development Authority for application information.

Low Income Housing Tax Credit Program: federal tax credit for owner/developers of low-income rental housing. Contact the Michigan State Housing Development Authority for application information.

More Independence Through HOME: funds used to finance nonprofit projects that provide rental units for disabled people. Contact the Michigan State Housing Development Authority for application information.

Rental Programs

Section 8 Existing Rental Allowance Program: rent subsidies for very low-income persons who find their own housing in private homes and apartment buildings. Contact the Michigan State Housing Development Authority for application information.

Tax Exempt Apartment for Michigan (TEAM): program for rental units where 20% of the units are for low income people and another 20% for very low income people. Contact the Michigan State Housing Development Authority for application information.

Family Self Sufficiency Program (FSS): help for families in assisted housing that contract to be off of government support. Contact the Michigan State Housing Development Authority for application information.

Taxable Bond Program: loans for rental housing where most tenants will have very low incomes. Contact the Michigan State Housing Development Authority for application information.

MINNESOTA

Minnesota Housing Finance Agency
400 Sibley Street, Suite 300
St. Paul, MN 55101-1998
651-296-7608
800-657-3769
TDD: 651-297-2361

Email: mhfa@state.mn.us
www.mhfa.state.mn.us

Homeowner Programs

Minnesota Mortgage Program (MMP): below market rate loans for low/moderate income first-time homebuyers. For a list of lenders, go to {www.mhfa.state.mn.us/homes/MMP.htm}.

Minnesota City Participation Program (MCPP): low interest mortgage loans for low to moderate income first-time homebuyers. For a list of communities and lenders, go to {www.mhfa.state.mn.us/homes/MCPP.htm}.

Urban Indian Housing Program: loans at below market interest rates for low to moderate income Indian families buying their first home in an urban area. Contact the Minnesota Housing Finance Agency for application information.

Home Equity Conversion Counseling (HECC): a Home Equity Conversion or Reverse Mortgage is designed to assist primarily senior homeowners (as defined by the participating lender), to be able to spend the equity in their home while still continuing to live there. In order to receive this type of mortgage, homeowners are required to receive counseling specifically designed to educate the homeowner on the options available under a reverse mortgage. Contact the Minnesota Housing Finance Agency for program information.

Home Ownership Assistance Fund (HAF): down payment and monthly payment assistance to low to moderate income MHFA mortgage recipients. Contact the Minnesota Housing Finance Agency for application information.

Entry Cost Homeownership Opportunity (ECHO): provides down payment and closing cost assistance to those purchasing a home through a community lending program. Contact the Minnesota Housing Finance Agency for application information.

Fix Up Fund Loans: loans offering below market interest rates to fix up your home. Contact the Minnesota Housing Finance Agency for application information.

Rehabilitation Loan Program: loans to low to moderate-income homeowners for home improvements directly affecting the safety, habitability, energy efficiency and accessibility of their home. Contact the Minnesota Housing Finance Agency for application information.

Community Fix-Up Fund: home improvement loans offered to low to moderate income homeowners who occupy the property to be improved, in participating communities. Eligible homeowners must also meet any additional targeting criteria established by the community. Contact the Minnesota Housing Finance Agency for application information.

Foreclosure Prevention Assistance Program: provides case management services and, if applicable, mortgage payment, or other financial assistance to homeowners facing foreclosure, due to a temporary financial crisis. For a list of FPAP Administrators, go to {www.mhfa.state.mn.us/homes/homes_foreclosure.htm}.

Accessibility Home Fund: provides loans to borrowers with a disabled family member to buy, remodel or refinance a home.

Development Programs

Urban Indian Housing Program: loans at below market interest rates for low to moderate income Indian families buying their first home in an urban area, and low interest rate loans for rental housing development for Indian families that have a low income. Contact the Minnesota Housing Finance Agency for application information.

Preservation Affordable Rental Investment Fund: a statewide program that will provide zero to one percent interest-deferred loans to help cover the costs of preserving permanent affordable rental housing with long term project-based federal subsidies that are in jeopardy of being lost. To download an application, go to {www.mhfa.state.mn.us/multifamily/multifamily-preserving.htm}.

Economic Development and Housing Challenge Program: supports economic development activities by providing loans and grants for construction, acquisition, rehabilitation, construction financing, permanent financing, interest rate reduction, refinancing, and gap financing of both single and multi-family homes. Contact the Minnesota Housing Finance Agency for application information.

Housing Trust Fund (HTF): zero interest deferred loans for acquisition, contraction or rehabilitation of a development of low-income rental and co-op housing. To download an application, go to {www.mhfa.state.mh.us/multifamily/RAFS.htm}.

Low to Moderate Income Rental Program: funds for the refinance or rehabilitation or acquisition/rehabilitation or new construction of existing properties for low income people; funds for the acquisition and rehabilitation or new construction/conversion of rental housing for low and moderate income people. To download an application, go to {www.mhfa.state.mn.us/managers/LMIRP%20Program%20Guide.pdf}.

Rental Programs

Rental Rehabilitation Loan Program: low interest loans to rental property owners to rehabilitate the property. For an application, go to {www.mhfa.state.mn.us/multifamily/RRLP.htm}.

HOME Rental Rehabilitation Program: grants to rental property owners to rehabilitate property so that it is safe and affordable for low-income people. To download an application, go to {www.mhfa.state.mn.us/multifamily/HomeRRG.htm}.

Family Homeless and Prevention Assistance Program: grants to support or establish support systems relating to homelessness. Funds can be used in an existing home, shelter, or with the transition to permanent affordable housing. To download an application, go to {www.mhfa.state.mn.us/multifamily/FHPAP.htm}.

Rental Assistance for Family Stabilization: rental assistance to families on public service enrolled in self-sufficiency programs that reside in specified counties. To download an application, go to {www.mhfa.state.mn.us/multifamily/RAFS.htm}.

Bridges: housing subsidy for low-income households that have at least one adult member with a serious and persistent mental illness. To download an application, go to {www.mhfa.state.mn.us/multifamily/bridges.htm}.

Section 8 New Construction: subsidized housing to assist low and moderate income families in need of housing. Contact the Minnesota Housing Finance Agency for application information.

Section 8 Existing Housing (Certificate Voucher Program): administered by local, county, or regional housing and redevelopment authorities (HRA) to help pay the rent on housing the applicant can find in the private market. For a list of local HRAs, go to {www.mhfa.state.mn.us/renters/section8.htm}.

Housing Opportunities for Persons with AIDS: grants for housing assistance and services to people with AIDS and/or related diseases and their families. Contact the Minnesota Housing Finance Agency for application information.

4dProperty Tax Classification: property tax reduction for owners of residential rental property that pledge to comply with 4d requirements for 5 years. To download an application, go to {www.mhfa.state.mn.us/managers/property_4d.htm}.

MISSISSIPPI

Mississippi Home Corporation

840 River Place, Suite 605
PO Box 23369
Jackson, MS 39225-3369
601-718-4642
Fax: 601-718-4643
Email: emailus@mshc.com
www.mshomecorp.com

HOMEOWNER PROGRAMS

Down Payment Assistance Program: for lower income buyers who can afford mortgage payments but not a down payment. Contact the Mississippi Home Corporation for application information.

Mortgage Revenue Bond Program: interest rate at or below market rate and 3% down payment assistance. For a list of participating lenders, go to {www.mshomecorp.com/news_pub.html}.

Mortgage Credit Certificate Program: reduction of the amount of Federal Income Tax paid by income eligible borrowers. For a list of participating lenders, go to {www.mshomecorp.com/news_pub.html}.

HomeRun: loan for down payment and closing costs to low to moderate income for first time homebuyers. For a list of participating lenders, go to {www.mshomecorp.com/news_pub.html}.

Housing Assistance for Teachers Program: down payment and closing cost assistance to licensed teachers that teach in a specified area. For a list of participating lenders, go to {www.mshomecorp.com/news_pub.html}.

Get on the Track Mortgage: provides prospective homebuyers with impaired credit a predetermined lease period to establish their credit reputation. For additional information contact the Mississippi Home Corporation.

Mississippi Home of Your Own Project (HOYO): assistance for persons with disabilities to locate financial counseling which may allow them to purchase a home. For additional information contact the Mississippi Home Corporation.

Development Programs

Mississippi Affordable Housing Development Fund: loans to owners for construction, mortgage, predevelopment costs and rehabilitation of housing for moderate income households. To download an application, go to {www.mshomecorp.com/mahdf.html}.

Rental Programs

Housing Tax Credit Program: tax credits for owners of low-income rental housing. For an application, go to {www.mshomecorp.com/htc%20program.htm}.

Mississippi Affordable Housing Development Fund: loans to owners for construction, mortgage, predevelopment costs and rehabilitation of housing for moderate income households. To download an application, go to {www.mshomecorp.com/mahdf.html}.

Missouri

Missouri Housing Development Commission

3435 Broadway
Kansas City, MO 64111-2415
816-759-6600
TDD: 816-758-6839
Email: info@mhdc.com
www.mhdc.com

HOMEOWNER PROGRAMS

Mortgage Revenue Bond Program: mortgage financing at interest rates below conventional market rates. For a list of participating lenders, go to {www.mhdc.com/lenders_list1.htm}.

More Help Program "Home Repair": assistance for low-to-moderate income families to make improvements and repairs to their homes. To download an application, go to {www.mhdc.com/rental_production/pdf/home%20repair%20app%20packet.pdf}.

Cash Assistance Payment: 4% cash assistance to eligible homebuyers of their loan amount that does not have to be repaid. The payment may be applied to down payment, closing costs, prepaid taxes or other loan expenses. For additional information, go to {www.mhdc.com/homebuyer_programs/MRB_guidelines.htm}.

DEVELOPMENT PROGRAMS

MHDC Rental Housing Production Program: funding to developers who acquire, rehabilitate, and/or construct rental housing for low- and moderate-income families. For an application, go to {www.mhdc.com/rental_production/forms/default.htm}.

HOME Rental Housing Program: provides financing for the acquisition and rehabilitation of housing for low- to very low-income families. For an application, go to {www.mhdc.com/rental_production/forms/default.htm}.

MISSOURI Housing Trust Fund: funds for eligible activities to meet the housing needs of very low income families; activities include rental housing production, housing and related services for the homeless, and rental subsidies. Contact the Missouri Housing Development Commission for an application package.

Affordable Housing Assistance Program (AHAP): tax credit for firms that donate cash, services, or property to a non-profit community organization that develops affordable housing. To download an application, go to {www.mhdc.com/rental_production/ahap/AHAPapplication.doc}.

RENTAL PROGRAMS

No programs at the time of this printing. Check with the organization for any updates.

MONTANA

Montana Board of Housing – Department of Commerce

Street Address
301 S. Park Ave.
Helena, MT 59601
406-841-2700
Fax: 406-841-2701
http://commerce.state.mt.us/Housing/Hous_Prog_BHB.html

Mailing Address
P.O. Box 200501
Helena, MT 59620-0501

HOMEOWNER PROGRAMS

Reverse Annuity Mortgage Loan: home equity loans for lower income seniors 68+ homeowners. Contact the Board of Housing for application information.

Single Family Bond Program: assists low and moderate income people in the purchase of a first home; in targeted areas. It does not need to be a first time purchase. Contact a participating lender in your area for application information.

Disabled Accessible Affordable Homeownership Program: assists people with disabilities to acquire affordable architecturally accessible homes enabling them to live independently. Contact the Board of Housing for application information.

Recycled Single Family Mortgage Program: below market rate funds are often coupled with federal grants or local funds to make purchasing a home more affordable for lower income families and individuals. Contact the Board of Housing for application information.

DEVELOPMENT PROGRAMS

HOME Program: funds to government and community housing organizations to create affordable housing and provide financial and technical assistance for low-income persons. To download an application, go to {http://commerce.state.mt.us/HOUSING/Hous_Prog_HOME.html}.

Risk Sharing Program: permanent mortgage financing for affordable rental housing to low income people. Contact the Board of Housing for application information.

RENTAL PROGRAMS

Section 8 Housing Program: subsidies for rent and utilities to very low-income families. Contact the Board of Housing for application information.

Low Income Housing Tax Credit Program: federal tax credits for owners of low-income housing. Contact the Board of Housing for application information.

Risk Sharing Program: permanent mortgage financing for affordable rental housing to low-income people. Contact the Board of Housing for application information.

NEBRASKA

Nebraska Investment Finance Authority

200 Commerce Court
1230 "O" Street
Lincoln, NE 68508-1402
402-434-3900

800-204-6432

A special telephone operator has a Telephone Device for the Deaf (TDD) and acts as an intermediary between the hearing impaired caller and the NIFA personnel.
Call 1-800-833-7352 and ask the operator to call 402-434-3900.
Email: webmaster@nifa.org
www.nifa.org

HOMEOWNER PROGRAMS

Agricultural Finance Programs: low interest rate loans to farmers and ranchers. Contact a local financial institution or a NIFA office for an application.

Single Family Home Ownership Program: loans for first time homebuyers that are income eligible. For a list of participating lenders, go to {www.nifa.org/programs/sfamily/sfamily.html#le}.

Affordable Housing Trust Fund: funds to help low and moderate income households obtain affordable housing. Contact the Nebraska Investment Finance Authority for application information.

Super-Targeted Mortgage Program: low interest loans for low-to-moderate income potential homeowners to purchase a home. Homebuyer education is required. For additional information contact the Nebraska Investment Finance Authority.

DEVELOPMENT PROGRAMS

Technical Assistance Review Process (TARP): provides technical assistance on financial resources, application, housing projects and more. Contact the Nebraska Investment Finance Authority for application information.

Community Empowerment Resource Funds (CERF): funds for the development of affordable housing development projects for low-to-moderate income individuals. Certain restrictions may apply. For additional information contact the Nebraska Investment Finance Authority.

RENTAL PROGRAMS

Low Income Housing Tax Credit Program: Federal tax credits for owners of low income housing. To download an application, go to {www.nifa.org/programs/lihtc/lihtc.html#download}.

Credits to Own (CROWN): provides qualified low-income individuals the resources to plan and save to buy a home. The 15-year rental period in affordable housing, allows time for the tenant to participate in homebuyer education, build equity and correct credit problems. For additional information contact the Nebraska Investment Finance Authority.

Nevada

Nevada Housing Division

1802 North Carson Street, Suite 154
Carson City, NV 89701
775-687-4258
800-227-4960
Fax: 775-687-4040
Email: nhd@govmail.state.nv.us
http://nvhousing.state.nv.us

Homeowner Programs

Single Family Mortgage Program: loans to moderate-income families with no previous home ownership interest in the past 3 years. For a list of participating lenders, go to {www.nvhousing.state.nv.us/single_family/participatinglenders.htm}.

Low Income Housing Trust Fund: funds available to homeowners for down payment assistance or rehabilitation of owner-occupied housing. Funds can also be used by developers to develop and support affordable rental housing through Acquisition, New Construction, Reconstruction, Moderate or Substantial Rehabilitation, Site Improvements, Conversion, Demolition and certain finance costs. Trust Funds may also be used for technical assistance. The application for developers can be found at {www.nvhousing.state.nv.us/low_income/developer%20information.htm}.

Low Income Weatherization Program: assist eligible low-income households with their utility bills by providing for various energy conservation measures. Contact the Nevada Housing Division for application information.

Down Payment and Closing Cost Loan Program: provides second mortgage loans to qualified buyers for down payment and closing cost assistance. For a list of participating lenders, go to {www.nvhousing.state.nv.us/single_family/participatinglenders.htm}.

Energy Efficient Mortgages (EEMs): loans to promote borrowers to purchase energy efficient homes or homes that can be made energy efficient through improvements. For additional information, go to {www.nvhousing.state.nv.us/single_family/energy%20efficient%20mortgages.htm}.

Development Programs

Emergency Shelter Grant Program: provides funding to help improve existing shelters, make available additional emergency shelters, as well as provide social and supportive services to homeless individuals. The forms for this program can be found at {www.nvhousing.state.nv.us/emer_shelter/Forms.htm}.

Low Income Housing Tax Credit Program: tax credits to developers of low and very low income housing. To download an application, go to {www.nvhousing.state.nv.us/tax_credit/tax%20credit%20index.htm}.

Multi-Family Project Bond Financing Program: funding to developers of affordable housing projects. For an application, go to {http://nvhousing.state.nv.us/bond_program/mfindex.htm}.

Low Income Housing Trust Fund: funds available to homeowners for down payment assistance or rehabilitation of owner-occupied housing. Funds can also be used by developers to develop and support affordable rental housing through Acquisition, New Construction, Reconstruction, Moderate or Substantial Rehabilitation, Site Improvements, Conversion, Demolition and certain finance costs. Trust Funds may also be used for technical assistance. The application for developers can be found at {www.nvhousing.state.nv.us/low_income/developer%20information.htm}.

HOME Program: federally funded programs to expand the number of rental housing and improve ownership opportunities for low income people. To download an application, go to {www.nvhousing.state.nv.us/fed_home/HOMEindex.htm}.

Rental Programs

No programs at the time of this printing. Check with the organization for any updates.

New Hampshire

New Hampshire Financing Authority
PO Box 5087
Manchester, NH 03108
603-472-8623
800-640-7239
Fax: 603-472-8501
TDD: 603-472-2089
www.nhhfa.org

Homeowner Programs

Single-Family Mortgage Program: low interest mortgage funds to qualifying individuals and households. For a list of participating lenders, go to {www.nhhfa.org/incpurln_lenders.htm}.

Cash Assistance Option: provides cash assistance grant to help defray down payment, closing, and prepaid escrow expenses. Contact the New Hampshire Financing Authority for application information.

First Time Homebuyers Seminar: free seminars on the process of buying a home. To view the seminar schedule, go to {www.nhhfa.org/homeown.htm#1sttime}.

HELP (Housing Expense Loan Program): closing cost funds to income eligible homebuyers. For a list of participating lenders, go to {www.nhhfa.org/incpurln_lenders.htm}.

Philip S. Rader Divorced Borrower Initiative: qualifying borrowers with minor children can refinance and retain their principal residence in connection with a divorce. Contact the New Hampshire Financing Authority for information.

Voucher Assisted Mortgage Option: uses *Housing Choice (Section 8 Vouchers)* as a portion of the monthly mortgage payment providing very-low income families the opportunity to purchase a home. For a list of participating lenders, go to {www.nhhfa.org/vamolenders.htm}.

Emergency Home Repair Loan (EHRL): affordable loans to borrows with existing mortgages through the Single-Family Mortgage program to cover costs of repairs when an emergency occurs in their home that is not covered by insurance and that affects the livability of the home. Contact the New Hampshire Financing Authority for application information

Purchase/Rehab Program: loans to eligible new homebuyers to make improvements to a home in need of repair. For a list of participating lenders, go to {www.nhhfa.org/incpurln_lenders.htm}.

Home of Your Own Program (HOYO): homeownership opportunities for developmentally disabled people that are income eligible. Contact the New Hampshire Financing Authority for application information.

HomeAccess Program: helps low and moderate-income borrowers acquire a home and/or make it accessible for a permanently disabled household member. For a list of participating lenders, go to {www.nhhfa.org/incpurln_lenders.htm}.

Manufactured Housing Program: financing to low-to-moderate-income borrowers to purchase new manufactured homes located in a NHHFA approved Housing Community. For a list of participating lenders, go to {www.nhhfa.org/incpurln_lenders.htm}.

DEVELOPMENT PROGRAMS

Low Income Housing Tax Credit Program: tax credits for owners of low income rental housing. To download an application, go to {www.nhhfa.org/mffinancingapp.htm}.

HOME Rental Housing Production Program: provides funds to support the development of rental housing opportunities for low- and very-low income households. To download an application, go to {www.nhhfa.org/mffinancingapp.htm}.

Special Needs Housing: permanent financing for the development of rental housing for low and very low income special needs people that also provide social services. An application can be downloaded from {www.nhhfa.org/multifam.htm#specneeds}.

Affordable Housing Fund: funds to support rental housing, group homes and manufactured housing co-ops for low income people. An application can be downloaded from {www.nhhfa.org/multifam.htm}.

Housing Finance Fund: funds for short-term construction and bridge financing for new or rehabilitated rental housing. An application can be downloaded from {www.nhhfa.org/multifam.htm}.

Multi-Family Housing

Tax Exempt Bond Financing: for multifamily housing that rents to moderate, low and very low income people. An application can be downloaded from {www.nhhfa.org/multifam.htm}.

Multi-Family Housing Production Initiative and the **Senior Housing Production Initiative:** in an effort to meet the demands for new affordable housing units, funding is available for the construction, or the adaptive reuse of non-residential structures An application can be downloaded from {www.nhhfa.org/multifam.htm}.

Rental Programs

Section 8 Existing Housing Program: rental assistance for low income households. For an application, go to {www.nhhfa.org/tenant.htmS8}.

Housing to Work Rental Assistance Program: rental assistance to families that either are eligible or are currently receiving *TANF (Temporary Assistance to Needy Families)* funds and sign an employment agreement. Request an application at {www.nhhfa.org/tenant.htm#htw}.

Family Self-Sufficiency Program: families receiving *Section 8* rental assistance that participate in a program to become economically self-sufficient. An application can be downloaded from {www.nhhfa.org/tenant.htm#FSS}.

Section 8 New Construction/Substantial Rehabilitation (Project-Based Rental Assistance): rental assistance to eligible persons that live in housing complexes financed by NHFA's tax exempt bonds or other public, private sources. Contact the New Hampshire Financing Authority for application information.

Supportive Services Program: technical assistance and training to managers of senior housing complexes so that they can provide quality supportive services for senior. The Service Directory can be viewed at {www.nhhfa.org/ssdirectory_temp.htm}.

Emergency Housing Program: short term rental assistance to eligible households when municipalities cannot help them. Contact the New Hampshire Financing Authority for application information.

NEW JERSEY

New Jersey Housing and Mortgage Finance Agency
637 South Clinton Avenue
P.O. Box 18550
Trenton, NJ 08650-2085
609-278-7400
800-NJ-HOUSE
Email: webmaster@jnhmfa.state.nj.us
www.state.nj.us/dca/hmfa

HOMEOWNER PROGRAMS

Home Buyer Mortgage Program: low interest loans to urban area, income eligible, first-time buyers with a 3% down payment. For a list of lenders, , go to {www.state.nj.us/dca/hmfa/singfam/lenderlist07201.htm}.

Home Ownership for Performing Employees (HOPE): employer guaranteed below market, fixed rate loans to eligible employees. Contact the New Jersey Housing and Mortgage Finance Agency for application information.

Home Plus Program: low rate financing for income-eligible first time homebuyers in urban areas that need immediate home improvements. For a list of approved lenders, go to {www.state.nj.us/dca/hmfa/singfam/homeplus.htm}.

One Hundred Percent Mortgage Program: no down payment, no mortgage insurance, mortgage loans for qualified first time and urban area buyers at pre-approved single family housing developments. For a list of approved lenders, go to {www.state.nj.us/dca/hmfa/sinfgam/ndpfact.htm}.

Police and Firemen's Retirement System Mortgage Program: loans for active members of the New Jersey Police and Fireman's Retirement System with at least 1 year of active duty for purchase or refinancing of a home. For a list of approved lenders, go to {www.state.nj.us/dca/hmfa/singfam/pfrsfact.htm}.

Potable Water Loan Program: loans available to owners of single family residences to pay for an alternative water supply or adequate treatment of drinking water that comes from a private well that violates the State's Primary Drinking Water standards or the standards for sodium, chloride, lead, mercury, iron or manganese. Contact the New Jersey Housing and Mortgage Finance Agency for application information.

Purchase/Rehabilitation Mortgage Program: below market rate financing to qualified first time buyers and urban target area buyers that purchase and rehabilitate a home or rehabilitate a presently owned home. For a list of approved lenders, go to {www.state.nj.us/dca/hmfa/singfam/buy&fix.htm}.

Reverse Mortgage Program: allows seniors to access the equity in their home without a monthly repayment schedule. Counseling is required. To view the list of lenders, go to {www.state.nj.us/dca/hmfa/singfam/lenderlist070201.htm}.

Upstairs-Downtown Mortgages: below market rate funds to acquire and rehabilitate, or refinance and rehabilitate residential structures with a storefront commercial component. To view the list of lenders, go to {www.state.nj.us/dca/hmfa/singfam/lenderlist070201.htm}.

Development Programs

Urban Home Ownership Recovery Program: construction financing for developers of urban for sale housing. For information on the application process, contact the New JerseyHousing and Mortgage Finance Agency.

Rental Programs

No programs at the time of this printing. Check with the organization for any updates.

New Mexico

New Mexico Mortgage Finance Authority
344 4th Street SW
Albuquerque, NM 87102
505-843-6880
800-444-6880
TTY: 800-659-8331
www.nmmfa.org

Homeowner Programs

Help Program: loans to first-time, income eligible homebuyers who participate in the Mortgage Saver Home Program for down payment and closing costs. To view the list of lenders, go to {www.nmmfa.org/consumer/lender.asp}.

Helping Hand Program: down payment and closing cost assistance to low income families where a member has a disability. Contact the New Mexico Mortgage Finance Authority for application information.

Mortgage Saver Program: loans to first time homebuyers at two interest rates; one below market value and one about even with conventional market rate. To view the list of lenders, go to {www.nmmfa.org/consumer/lender.asp}.

Mortgage Saver Plus: buyers that choose the higher rate in the *Mortgage Saver Program*, get credit towards closing costs up to 3.5% of the principal. To view the list of lenders, go to {www.nmmfa.org/consumer/lender.asp}.

Payment Saver Program: first time, income eligible, buyers get a below market interest rate and a 2nd zero percent interest loan to pay for up-front costs. To view the list of lenders, go to {www.nmmfa.org/consumer/lender.asp}.

"Take 5" Program: down payment assistance to low-income first-time homebuyers. To download the forms for this program, go to {www.nmmfa.org/forms/formsLenTake5.htm}.

Weatherization Assistance Program: assistance to low-income homeowners to improve the energy efficiency of their homes. The forms for this program can be downloaded at {www.nmmfa.org/consumer/consWAP.htm}.

Low Income Energy Assistance Program: assistance for low-income households to pay their energy bills. Call 800-285-4465 for information on this program.

Building Trust: assistance for Native Americans interested in buying, building or repairing a home on trust land. For additional information, go to {www.nmmfa.org/consumer/consBuildingTrust.asp}.

DEVELOPMENT PROGRAMS

Housing Opportunities for Persons with AIDS: provides housing and supportive services to persons with AIDS/HIV; funding to enhance and expand housing opportunities for people with AIDS/HIV. The application can be downloaded at {www.nmmfa.org/AllPrograms;Hopwa/HOPWA_ProgSheets.htm}.

Section 8 Assisted Housing Program: permanent financing for 5 multi-family housing projects in specified areas. Call the New Mexico Mortgage Finance Authority for application information.

501(c) (3) Bond Program: funds for the acquisition, new construction, rehabilitation, or refinance of residential rental projects of nonprofit corporations. Call the New Mexico Mortgage Finance Authority for application information.

Build It: guaranties of conventional interim loans to nonprofit organizations, tribal, or public agencies to develop affordable housing. Call the New Mexico Mortgage Finance Authority for application information.

Primero Investment Fund: seed money to nonprofit, tribal, and public agencies to develop multifamily rental or special needs housing projects. Call the New Mexico Mortgage Finance Authority for application information.

Rental HOME: gap financing for projects that create low income housing and special needs projects. The application for this program can be downloaded at {www.nmmfa.org/multifamily/rentalHomeProgram.htm}.

Emergency Shelter Grants Program: assistance to improve the quality of emergency shelters, help with operational costs, and of providing essential services to the homeless. Contact the New Mexico Mortgage Finance Authority for application information.

State Homeless Assistance Program: assistance to shelters that provide emergency shelter or short-term services to homeless people and their families. The application can be downloaded at {www.nmmfa.org/consumer/consHomelessAssit.htm}.

RENTAL PROGRAMS

Housing Opportunities for Persons with AIDS: provides housing and supportive services to persons with AIDS/HIV; funding to enhance and expand housing opportunities for people with AIDS/HIV. The application can be downloaded at {www.nmmfa.org/forms/documents/frmCommHOPWA_Application.pdf}.

State Homeless Assistance Program: assistance to shelters that provide emergency shelter or short-term services to homeless people and their families. The application can be downloaded at {www.nmmfa.org/consumer/consHomelessAssit.htm}.

Housing Tax Credits: federal tax credits for owners of low-income rental housing. The application can be downloaded from {www.nmmfa.org/multifamily/HTC/HTC_Allocations.htm}.

Emergency Shelter Grants Program: assistance to improve the quality of emergency shelters; help with operational costs, and of providing essential services to the homeless. Contact the New Mexico Mortgage Finance Authority for application information.

Low Income Energy Assistance Program: assistance for low-income households to pay their energy bills. Call 800-285-4465 for information on this program.

Shelter Plus Care Program (S+C): funding to service providers to help disabled homeless persons through supportive services. Contact the New Mexico Mortgage Finance Authority for application information.

Supportive Housing: funding for transitional housing with supportive services enabling the homeless to live more independently. Contact the New Mexico Mortgage Finance Authority for application information.

Tenant Based Rental Assistance Program: one time cash assistance for security deposits, utility deposits, and/or first month's rent, and up to 6 months of rent subsidy to low income tenants in order to obtain permanent or transitional housing.

Special Needs Rental Program: below market rate loans to develop affordable rental housing projects with a maximum of 20 units where half are set aside for special needs people.

NEW YORK

New York State Division of Housing and Community Renewal

Hampton Plaza
38-40 State Street
Albany, NY 12207
518-473-2517
www.dhcr.state.ny.us

HOMEOWNER PROGRAMS

Weatherization Assistance Program: services to low-income households including life-saving health and safety tests and fuel consumption analysis to identify the potential to save energy.

Residential Emergency Services to Offer Repairs to the Elderly Program (RESTORE): funds to make emergency repairs in order to eliminate hazardous conditions in elderly owned homes when the homeowner cannot afford to make the repairs.

DEVELOPMENT PROGRAMS

Rural Preservation Program: funds to local not-for-profit organizations engaging in a variety of activities for the benefit of low and moderate income persons in rural areas.

Neighborhood Preservation Program: funding to defray administrative costs of nonprofit agencies performing neighborhood preservation activities.

HOME Program: provides funds for a variety of housing needs for low-income families.

Disaster Recovery Initiative Grant: grants to help cities, counties, and States recover from declared disasters, especially in low income areas.

Farmworker Housing Program: low-cost loans for the improvement of existing housing or construction of new housing for seasonal farmworkers.

Homes for Working Families Initiative: substantial rehabilitation or new construction of affordable rental housing.

Senior Housing Initiative: funding for projects that substantially rehabilitate or construct rental housing for seniors.

Housing Development Fund: loans to nonprofits for development of low-income housing projects

Low-Income Housing Credit Program: reduction in federal income tax liability for project owners that develop, rehabilitate, and acquire rental housing for low-income families.

Residential Emergency Services to Offer Repairs to the Elderly Program (RESTORE): funds to make emergency repairs in order to eliminate hazardous conditions in elderly owned homes when the homeowner cannot afford to make the repairs.

Low Income Housing Trust Fund: funds to nonprofit sponsors to rehabilitate existing properties into affordable low income housing..

Rural Rental Assistance Program: rent subsidies for multifamily project development of rental housing for elderly, and family, low-income tenants.

Mitchell-Lama Housing Program: low-interest mortgage loans to build affordable housing for middle-income people.

RENTAL PROGRAMS

Rural Rental Assistance Program: rent subsidies for multifamily project development of rental housing for elderly, and family, low-income tenants.

Section 8 Statewide Program: rent subsidies for low income households.

New York Housing Finance Agency

641 Lexington Avenue
New York, NY 10022
212-688-4000
www.nyhomes.org

HOMEOWNER PROGRAMS

No programs at the time of this printing. Check with the organization for any updates.

DEVELOPMENT PROGRAMS

80/20 Program: loans for projects that will rent 80% of the units to individuals or families at market-rate rents, while the other 20% must be rented to low income households. Contact the New York Housing Finance Agency for application information.

The All Affordable Program: for production of new construction or rehabilitation of multi-family rental housing where all the units are affordable to low-income families. Contact the New York Housing Finance Agency for application information.

The Senior Housing Financing Program: financing for new construction or acquisition/rehabilitation of senior housing; assisted living, rental or state licensed housing. Contact the New York Housing Finance Agency for application information.

501(c) (3) Bond Program: funds to nonprofit organizations for new construction, or rehabilitation of existing multi-family rental housing projects. Contact the New York Housing Finance Agency for application information.

Manufactured Homes Cooperative Fund Program: technical and financial assistance to encourage and facilitate cooperative ownership of mobile home parks. Contact the New York Housing Finance Agency for application information.

Low Income Housing Tax Credit Program: federal tax credits for owners of low-income housing. Contact the New York Housing Finance Agency for application information.

Empire Housing Fund Program: low interest or no-interest loans made to developers to subsidize costs for the construction or rehabilitation of low-income housing. Contact the New York Housing Finance Agency for application information.

RENTAL PROGRAMS

No programs at the time of this printing. Check with the organization for any updates.

NORTH CAROLINA

North Carolina Housing Finance Agency
3508 Bush Street
Raleigh, NC 27609-7509
919-877-5700
800-393-0988
Email: webmaster@nchfa.com
www.nchfa.com

HOMEOWNER PROGRAMS

Low Interest Home Loans: below market, fixed rate loans for first-time homebuyers with low/moderate income. For a list of participating lending institutions, go to {www.nchfa.com/lib/html/Homeownership%20Programs/For20Individuals/mortgage%20participating_lenders.htm}.

Mortgage Credit Certificate: federal tax-credit for first-time income eligible homebuyers. {www.nchfa.com/lib/html/Homeownership%20Programs/For%20Individuals/mortgage%20participating_lenders.htm}.

Urgent Repair Program: grants to fix housing conditions that pose a threat to health and safety in low-income homes. The application can be downloaded from {www.nchfa.com/lib/html/Urgent%20Repair%20&%20Rehab/URP2003_Application_Guidelines.doc}.

Mortgage Revenue Bond (MRB) Program: reduced rate loans to low and moderate-income first-time homebuyers. Contact the North Carolina Housing Finance Agency for application information.

DEVELOPMENT PROGRAMS

Self-Help Housing Program: funding for nonprofit organizations building 1-5 homes a year. Homebuyer sweat equity and volunteer labor must be used to reduce the construction costs by at least 30% from the cost of conventional construction. The

application can be downloaded at
{www.nchfa.com/lib/html/Homeownership%20Programs/For%20Govts%20&%20
Nonprofits/Self-Help%20Housing%20Program.htm}.

Supportive Housing Development Program: loans for the production of transitional
and permanent housing and for the rehabilitation of emergency housing for people
with special needs. An application can be downloaded at
{www.nchfa.com/lib/html/Special%20Needs%20Housing/Supportive%20Housing
%20Page.htm}.

Multifamily Rental Development Program: federal and state tax credits for developers
of low-income housing and below market rate loans to develop the housing. The
application can downloaded at {www.nchfa.com/lib/html/rental/
Rental%20Development%20Home%20Page.htm}.

Low Income Housing Tax Credit Program: federal tax credit for owners of low-income
housing. The application can be downloaded at {www.nchfa.com/lib/html/rental
/Tax%20Credit/Application%20Forms%20Page.htm}.

Affordable Homeownership Program: loans for the purchase of newly constructed,
rehabilitated, or existing homes for income-eligible homebuyers. Contact the North
Carolina Housing Finance Agency for information.

Rental Production Program: financing for the construction of rental housing for low
income households. The application can be downloaded at
{www.nchfa.com/lib/html/rental/Tax%20Credit/Application%20Forms%20Page.h
tm}.

Rental Programs

Low Income Housing Tax Credit Program: federal tax credit for owners of low income
housing. The application can be downloaded at
{www.nchfa.com/lib/html/rental/Tax%20Credit/Application%20Forms%20Page.h
tm}.

North Dakota

North Dakota Housing Finance Agency

1500 E. Capital Ave.
PO Box 1535
Bismarck, ND 58502-1535
701-328-8080
800-292-8621
Fax: 701-328-8090
TTY: 800-366-6888
www.ndhfa.org

HOMEOWNER PROGRAMS

HomeSmart Homebuyer Education Incentive Program: after completion of the course to help first-time homebuyers prepare for home ownership, borrowers may receive a $100 grant to be used towards closing costs. A listing of the homebuyer education providers is available at {www.ndhfa.org/HMFP/HMFP.Asp?FileName=Programs/homesmart.htm}.

Home Mortgage Finance Program: low interest rate mortgages for first-time income eligible homebuyers. Contact the North Dakota Housing Finance Agency for application information.

Rural Real Estate Mortgage Program: creates a secondary market for residential real estate mortgages for purchases of a single-family, owner occupied, non-farm, principal residences. Contact the North Dakota Housing Finance Agency for application information.

Start Program: a low interest second mortgage for first-time homebuyers for down payment assistance. Contact the North Dakota Housing Finance Agency for application information.

Down Payment and Closing Cost Assistance Program: zero percent interest loans to participants of a single-family mortgage loan from NDHFA for down payment and closing costs.

HomeWork: down payment and closing cost assistance to employees of those employers have partnered with the North Dakota Housing Finance Agency (NDHFA). Contact the North Dakota Housing Finance Agency for application information.

Major Home Improvement Program: low interest rate loans to income eligible borrowers to buy and rehabilitate single-family homes or to rehabilitate their existing homes. Contact the North Dakota Housing Finance Agency for application information.

Homeownership Acquisition and Rehabilitation Program: low-income households receive home owner education, assistance in finding an affordable home, rehabilitation funds to make the property safe and sanitary and if necessary, help in acquiring the home. For a list of Community Action Agencies to contact, go to {www.ndcaa.org/index.htm}.

HomeKey Program: one-percent interest rate reduction for the first three years of a Home Mortgage Finance Program loan. Borrowers must meet income-eligible guidelines.

DEVELOPMENT PROGRAMS

Rental Rehab Assistance Program: funds for property improvement to rental units that address the needs of physically disabled people. The application can be downloaded at {www.ndhfa.org/Grants/Grants.asp?cFileName=../Rental/RRAP.htm}.

Helping Housing Across North Dakota (Helping Hand): funds to Habitat for Humanities Affiliates, Native American Reservations, and North Dakota Community Action Agencies to support new or existing single family or multi-family housing rehabilitation programs for low-income housing. The application can be downloaded from {www.ndhfa.org/Grants/Grants.asp?cFileName=helping_hand.htm}.

Rental Programs.

Moderate Rehabilitation Program: provides low-income households the ability to acquire affordable, safe and decent housing through the use of rent subsidies available to qualified individuals in specified locations. Contact the North Dakota Housing Finance Agency for application information.

Low Income Housing Tax Credit Program: federal tax credits for owners of low-income rental housing. The application can be downloaded from {www.ndhfa.org/Rental/Rental.asp?cFileName=LIHTC.htm.&Detail=59}.

Rental Rehab Assistance Program: funds for property improvement to rental units that address the needs of physically disabled people. The application can be downloaded at {www.ndhfa.org/Grants/Grants.asp?cFileName=../Rental/RRAP.htm}.

OHIO

Ohio Housing Finance Agency
57 E. Main St.
Columbus, OH 43215-5135
614-466-7970
Fax: 614-644-5393
TDD: 614-466-1940
www.odod.state.oh.us/ohfa

Homeowner Programs

First-Time Homebuyer Program: below market financing for first-time, low- to moderate-income homebuyers. A listing of participating lenders is available at {www.odod.state.oh.us/ohfa/Owner/1stBUYER/Default.htm}.

Development Programs

Housing Credit Program: federal tax credits for owners of low-income rental housing. The application can be downloaded at {www.odod.state.oh.us/ohfa/RENTAL/LIHTC/default.htm}.

Affordable Housing Loan Program: loans to developers of low- to moderate-income residents. The application can be downloaded at {www.odod.state.oh.us/ohfa/RENTAL/AHL/downld2.htm}.

Housing Development Assistance Program: financing available for eligible housing projects to expand housing for very low-income individuals and households. The application can be downloaded at {www.odod.state.oh.us/ohfa/RENTAL/HDAP/downld4.htm}.

Multifamily Bond Program: financial assistance with the acquisition, construction, and substantial rehabilitation of multifamily dwelling units and single-family housing. The application can be downloaded at {www.odod.state.oh.us/ohfa/RENTAL/MRDBP/downld3.htm}.

Loan Guaranteed Program: the OHFA may guarantee the repayment of all or part of a loan for costs of development housing for low- and moderate-income families and the elderly. The application is located in Appendix B of the Affordable Housing Loan application. To download that form, go to {www.odod.state.oh.us/ohfa/RENTAL/LOANGUAR/Default.htm}.

CHDO Competitive Operating Grant Program: funding to develop self-sufficient organizations with the capacity to create affordable housing. For additional information, go to {www.odod.state.oh.us/ohfa/RENTAL/CHDO/default.htm}.

Rental Programs

Housing Credit Program: federal tax credits for owners of low-income rental housing. The application can be downloaded at {www.odod.state.oh.us/ohfa/RENTAL/LIHTC/default.htm}.

Section 8 Rental Assistance Program: rent subsidies on behalf of low-income people and families including the elderly and handicapped. Contact the Ohio Housing Finance Agency for application information.

Oklahoma

Oklahoma Housing Finance Agency
100 N 63rd Street, Suite 200
PO Box 26720
Oklahoma City, OK 73126-0720
405-848-1144
800-256-1489
TDD: 405-848-7471
www.ohfa.org

Homeowner Programs

Mortgage Revenue Bond Program: low rate loans to first-time home buyers. For a list of participating lenders, go to {www.ohfa.org/HDT/Bondl/lendermap.html}.

1st Four: statewide down payment and closing cost assistance for first-time homebuyers and non-first time homebuyers in Targeted areas. For additional information, go to {www.ohfa.org/HDT/Bond1/Types/1stfour.html}.

Market Best: statewide low interest rate assistance for first-time homebuyers and non-first time homebuyers in Targets areas. For additional information, go to {www.ohfa.org/HDT/Bond1/Types/Market.html}.

Future Foundation: statewide low interest rate assistance for first-time homebuyers and non-first time homebuyers in Targets areas that want to build a new home. For additional information, go to {www.ohfa.org/HDT/Bond1/Types/Future.html}.

HOME Plus: low interest rate loans for homebuyers with limited or fixed income. Loans not available in Norman, Lawton, Tulsa or Oklahoma City. For additional information, go to {www.ohfa.org/HDT/Bond1/Types/HOMEPlus.html}.

Development Programs

Housing Tax Credit Program: tax credits for new construction and rehabilitation of existing rental properties. The application can be downloaded from {www.ohfa.org/HDT/Tcredits1/ohfalihp.html}.

HOME Program: funding for programs that increase the supply of housing and single family new construction. The application can be downloaded from {www.ohfa.org/HDT/HOME1/homepage.html}.

Rental Programs

Section 8 Rental Assistance Program: rent subsidies for low-income households who locate their own housing. The application can be downloaded at {www.ohfa.org/Rental/Preapp/works.html}.

Transitional Housing Pilot Program: pays maintenance and utility bills at transitional homes. Contact the Oklahoma Housing Finance Agency for application information.

Housing Opportunities for People with AIDS (HOPWA): provides assistance that can help a family find a place to rent, provide utility or rental assistance, or provide housing counseling to people with AIDS that are homeless or at risk of becoming homeless. Contact the Oklahoma Housing Finance Agency for application information.

Family Self-Sufficiency Program: helps families work towards economic independence. The application can be downloaded from {www.ohfa.org/Rental/FSS/ohfafsspsk.html}.

Moderate Rehabilitation "Mod Rehab": section project based rental assistance. For additional information, go to {www.ohfa.org/Rental/Modrehab/contact.htm}.

OREGON

Oregon Housing Agency
PO Box 14508
Salem, OR 97309-0409
503-986-2000
Fax: 503-986-2020
TTY: 503-986-2100
www.hcs.state.or.us/

HOMEOWNER PROGRAMS

Residential Energy Assistance Challenge Program (REACH): provides low-income households assistance with utility payments, energy education, weatherization assistance, and family services related to budget management. A list of participating lenders, go to {www.hcs.state.or.us/community_resources/energy_wx/reach-agencies.htm}.

Low-Income Energy Assistance Program: helps low-income households pay heating bills. A listing of local Community Action Agencies is at {www.hcs.state.or.us/community_resources/energy_wx/lieap.html}.

Low-Income Weatherization Assistance Program: free weatherization and energy conservation services to income eligible households. A listing of local Community Action Agencies is at {www.hcs.state.or.us/community_resources/energy-wx/liwap.html}.

Energy Rated Home of Oregon (ERHO): provides Oregon home-builders and home-buyers with Home Energy Ratings which can be used to qualify for certain mortgages and programs. Contact the Oregon Housing Agency for application information.

Homebuyer Training: classes offered to help the first-time homebuyer understand the home buying process. Contact the Oregon Housing Agency for program information.

Downpayment and Closing Cost Assistance Program: assistance to low-income, first-time homebuyers with down payment and closing costs. A list of participating lenders is at {www.hcs.state.or.us/housing/homebuying/downpayment.htm}.

Residential Loan Program: below market interest rate loans to low and moderate-income homebuyers. Contact the Oregon Housing Agency for application information.

Manufactured Dwelling Park Ombudsman Program: assists park owners and residents to resolve conflicts and provides technical assistance. Contact the Oregon Housing Agency for application information.

DEVELOPMENT PROGRAMS

Multi-Family Housing Finance Program: financing for multi-unit rental housing for moderate, low, and very low-income families. Contact the Oregon Housing Agency for application information.

Elderly and Disabled Loan Program: offers below market rate permanent mortgages to profit and non-profit developers for the development of newly constructed properties or the acquisition / rehabilitation of existing properties for elderly and/or disabled residents. The application can be downloaded at {www.hcs.state.or.us/housing/multi_family_finance/elderly_disabled.html}.

Loan Guarantee Program: provides partial loan repayment guarantees to assist the financing of new housing construction or the acquisition and/or rehabilitation of existing housing for low- and very low-income families. A list of Regional Advisors to the Director can be found at {www.hcs.state.or.us/rads/rads.html}.

Oregon Rural Rehabilitation Loan Program: funding specifically for the construction or rehabilitation of farm worker housing. A list of Regional Advisors to the Director can be found at {www.hcs.state.or.us/rads/rads.html}.

Seed Money Advance Loan: loans to help cover predevelopment costs for the production of housing for low-income individuals and families. A list of Regional Advisors to the Director can be found at {www.hcs.state.or.us/rads/rads.html}.

Risk Sharing Program: below market financing for the development of affordable housing for low- and very low-income individuals or families. The application can be downloaded from {www.hcs.state.or.us/housing/multi_family_finance/risk_sharing.html}.

HELP Program: assistance for the development of housing for very-low income families. The Consolidated Funding Cycle form can be downloaded from {www.hcs.state.or.us/housing/help}.

HOME Investment Partnership: provides funding for the development of affordable housing for low and very low-income families and individuals. The Consolidated Funding Cycle form can be downloaded from {www.hcs.state.or.us/housing/home}.

Housing Development Grant Program: funding for the acquisition, construction, and/or rehabilitation of housing for low and very low-income families. The Consolidated Funding Cycle form can be downloaded from {www.hcs.state.or.us/housing/hsgdevgrant}.

Low Income Housing Tax Credit: federal income tax credit to developers who construct, rehabilitate, or acquire qualified low-income rental housing. The application can be downloaded at {ww.hcs.state.or.us/housing/lihtc}.

Oregon Affordable Housing Tax Credits: tax credits for housing projects or community rehabilitation projects for low-income people. Savings must be passed on to the tenants by reduced rents. The application can be downloaded at {www.hcs.state.or.us/housing/oahtc}.

Rental Programs

Residential Energy Assistance Challenge Program (REACH): provides low-income households assistance with utility payments, energy education, weatherization assistance, and family services related to budget management. A list of participating lenders to apply with is at {www.hcs.state.or.us/community_resources/energy_wx/reach-agencies.htm}.

Low-Income Energy Assistance Program: helps low-income households pay heating bills. A listing of local Community Action Agencies is at {www.hcs.state.or.us/community_resources/energy_wx/lieap.html}.

Low-Income Weatherization Assistance Program: free weatherization and energy conservation services to income eligible households. A listing of local Community Action Agencies is at {www.hcs.state.or.us/community_resources/energy-wx/liwap.html}.

Emergency Housing Account: assistance to homeless people or those at risk of becoming homeless to pay for emergency shelter, services and housing assistance. A list of participating agencies is available at {www.hcs.state.or.us/community_resources/housing_shelter/index.html}.

Emergency Shelter Grant: money to increase the number of beds in emergency shelters. A list of participating agencies is available at {www.hcs.state.or.us/community_resources/housing_shelter/index.html}.

HOME Tenant Based Assistance (TBA): rental assistance to very low-income tenants for housing costs and security deposits. A list of service agencies can be viewed at {www.hcs.state.or.us/community_resources/housing_shelter/hometba.html}.

Housing Stabilization Program: assistance to households with children that are at risk of becoming homeless or are homeless. Contact the Oregon Housing Agency for application information.

Low Income Rental Housing Fund: rental assistance to very low-income families. A list of local service providers is available at {www.hcs.state.or.us/community_resources/housing_shelter/lirhf.html}.

State Homeless Assistance Program: funding to emergency shelters and services directly related to them. Contact the Oregon Housing Authority for application information.

Low Income Housing Tax Credit: federal income tax credit to developers who construct, rehabilitate, or acquire qualified low-income rental housing. The application can be downloaded from {www.hcs.state.or.us/housing/lihtc}.

Manufactured Dwelling Park Ombudsman Program: assists park owners and residents to resolve conflicts and provides technical assistance. Contact the Oregon Housing Agency for application information.

PENNSYLVANIA

Pennsylvania Housing Finance Agency

2101 North Front Street
PO Box 8029
Harrisburg, PA 17105-8029
717-780-3800
TDD: 717-780-1869
www.phfa.org

HOMEOWNER PROGRAMS

Future Home Buyer Program: teaches high school students the importance of budgeting, the use of credit and the ramifications of credit abuse and some of the everyday legal issues they may face in the near future. Contact the Pennsylvania Housing and Finance Agency for information on this program.

Homeowners Emergency Assistance Program; loans to keep delinquent homeowners from losing their homes to foreclosure. A list of counseling agencies is available at {www.phfa.org/programs/hemap/index.htm}.

PennVest Individual On-Lot Sewage System Loans: very low interest rate loans up to $25,000 for homeowners to repair or upgrade malfunctioning on-lot sewer systems in rural areas. The Participating Lending Institutions list can be viewed at {www.phfa.org/programs/singlefamily/pennvest.htm}.

Access Down Payment and Closing Cost Assistance Loan Program: loans for down payment and closing cost assistance for those persons with disabilities or who have a family member(s) living in the household with disabilities who are purchasing a home. Contact the Pennsylvania Housing and Finance Agency for application information.

Access Home Modification Program: no-interest accessibility improvement loans ranging from $1,000 to $10,000 in conjunction with PHFA first mortgage financing. Contact the Pennsylvania Housing and Finance Agency for application information.

Closing Cost Assistance Program: pays up to $2,000 toward closing costs for homes that are bought by participants in the Lower Income Home Ownership Program. Qualified participants must have dependent children or be disabled. Contact the Pennsylvania Housing and Finance Agency for application information.

FHA 203(k) Program: loans to acquire property in need of repair and to finance the improvements. Contact the Pennsylvania Housing and Finance Agency for application information.

Homestead Second Mortgage Program: non-interest loans from $1,000 to $10,000 to income eligible families with at least one child or a member with a disability, for down payment and closing costs. Contact the Pennsylvania Housing and Finance Agency for application information.

Joint Financing Program: below-market interest rate loans to first-time buyers in specified areas of the Commonwealth. Contact the Pennsylvania Housing and Finance Agency for application information.

Low Income Homeownership Program: provides mortgage loans to low income first time homebuyers that have children or a member with a disability and meet income and home purchase price guidelines. Contact the Pennsylvania Housing and Finance Agency for application information.

PHFA/Fannie Mae Disability Access Modification Loan Program: provides mortgage assistance to those with disabilities or who have a family member(s) with a disability to retrofit the home to meet accessibility needs of the household member with the disability. To view a list of lenders, go to {www.phfa.org/programs/singlefamily/lenders/index.htm}.

Purchasing-Improvement Program: allows up to $15,000 in improvements in conjunction with an Agency first mortgage loan. Contact the Pennsylvania Housing and Finance Agency for application information.

Statewide Homeownership Program: low interest financing for first-time qualified home buyers or buyers of property in targeted areas. To view a list of lenders, go to {www.phfa.org/programs/singlefamily/lenders/index.htm}.

Development Programs

Construction Loan Program: construction loans to sponsors of low-income rental housing who have permanent take-out financing from other lenders. To view a list of lenders, go to {www.phfa.org/programs/singlefamily/lenders/index.htm}.

Low Income Housing Tax Credit Program: tax credits to owners and investors of affordable rental housing. To download an application, go to {www.phfa.org/programs/multifamily/taxcredit.htm}.

PennHOMES Program: provides interim and permanent mortgage financing to developers of low income rental housing. An application can be downloaded at {www.phfa.org/mfapg/index.htm}.

Taxable and Tax Exempt Bond Financing: below market loans for the development of or rehabilitation of affordable rental units. To view a list of lenders, go to {www.phfa.org/programs/singlefamily/lenders/index.htm}.

RENTAL PROGRAMS

Low Income Housing Tax Credit Program: tax credits to owners and investors of affordable rental housing. To download an application, go to {www.phfa.org/programs/multifamily/taxcredit.htm}.

Supportive Services Program: provides on-site supportive housing services for residents of PHFA-financed rental developments. Contact the Pennsylvania Housing and Finance Agency for application information.

RHODE ISLAND

Rhode Island Housing and Mortgage Finance Corporation

44 Washington Street
Providence, RI 02903-1721
401-751-5566
TDD: 401-427-9799
www.rihousing.com

Contact the Rhode Island Housing and Mortgage Finance Corporation for application information for the following programs.

HOMEOWNER PROGRAMS

First HOMES: low interest rates with low down payment requirements for first time home buyers, assistance with down payment costs for lower income first time homebuyers.

Jump Start Program: low interest rate loans with up to $5,000 in down payment and closing cost assistance.

Opening Doors Program: first mortgages from other banks with down payment and closing cost assistance from RIHMFC for minority purchases; employment and credit history requirements are relaxed.

Purchase Plus Program: loans for income-eligible, first time homebuyers to purchase a home and make up to $10,000 worth of repairs or improvements.

Buy It/Fix It Program: low-interest mortgage with construction financing to first time income eligible purchasers; current income eligible homeowners can refinance their mortgage providing they make at least $5,000 worth of needed repairs.

Zero Down Program: low-interest loans with federal loan guarantees that allow you to borrow up to 100% of the purchase price for down payment assistance to first-time, income-eligible buyers.

Equity Rebate: a grant to income eligible homebuyers that equals 2% of the purchase price of the home you buy or $1,000, whichever is less, to be used to pay closing costs.

Silent Second Mortgage: a deferred payment second mortgage that must be repaid when you sell your home.

Closing Costs Assistance Loan: income eligible homebuyers can borrow up to 5% of the purchase price, or $5,000, whichever is less, to pay closing costs.

Home Repair: fixed rate loans to make needed repairs to owner occupied homes and on one to four unit dwellings that meet income requirements.

Lead Hazard Reduction: loans to income eligible homeowners and landlords who rent to income eligible tenants to make eligible repairs so their homes/units are lead safe.

EquiSense Program: low interest rate, second mortgage based on home equity that has no points or application, title, credit report or appraisal fees.

Reverse Mortgages Program: elderly income eligible home owners can use their home equity to provide them with tax-free income; no monthly payments and no repayment as long as they own the home.

Access Independence Program: low-interest loans and grants for qualified low- and moderate-income owner-occupied single family homes so they can remodel for persons with functional disabilities.

DEVELOPMENT PROGRAMS

HOME: grants and low interest loans to encourage the construction or rehabilitation of affordable housing.

Low Income Housing Tax Credit Program: tax credits for owners of rental housing for low income households.

Predevelopment Loan: qualified nonprofit developers can get short-term loans to cover pre-closing costs incurred in determining development feasibility.

Preservation Loan Program: below market rate loans to preserve affordability of existing subsidized rental housing.

Rental Housing Production Program: a combination of financing programs to construct or rehabilitate affordable housing where portions of the units are rented to low income people.

Targeted Loans Program: loans for the construction or rehabilitation of affordable apartments; generally available only with first mortgage financing.

Technical Assistance Program: technical help and short-term loans to individuals, municipalities, and nonprofit groups to help preserve affordable housing.

Thresholds Program: grants for the development of housing that introduces persons with long-term mental illness into the community.

RENTAL PROGRAMS

Home Repair: fixed rate loans to make needed repairs to owner occupied homes and on one to four unit dwellings that meet income requirements.

Lead Hazard Reduction: loans to income eligible homeowners and landlords who rent to income eligible tenants to make eligible repairs so their homes/units are lead safe.

Low Income Housing Tax Credit Program: tax credits for owners of rental housing for low income households.

Next Step Program: loans to nonprofit social service agencies for the development of transitional apartments for people in crisis.

Family Self Sufficiency Program: education and training available to Section 8 certificate and voucher holders to help them move from welfare into a job that will give them financial independence.

Foundation for Senior Health Program: funding for homemaker services to frail elderly and disabled residents of specified Section 8 apartments.

Youth RAP: funding for tutoring, employment and self-esteem building activities for disadvantaged children living in RIHMFC financed apartments.

SOUTH CAROLINA

South Carolina State Housing Finance and Development Authority

919 Bluff Road
Columbia, SC 29201
803-734-2000
Email: webmaster@sha.state.sc.us
www.sha.state.sc.us

HOMEOWNER PROGRAMS:

Homeownership Mortgage Purchase Program: below market rate financing for income eligible homebuyers funded through the sale of bonds. A list of participating lenders is available at {www.sha.state.sc.us/Programs/HomeOwnership/lenders/lenders.html}.

Mortgage Assistance Loan Program: loans for down payment and for up-front closing costs not in excess of $2,000 for qualified home buyers that participate in one of the Homeownership Programs. The list of participating lenders is located at {www.sha.state.sc.us/Programs/HomeOwnership/Lenders/lenders.html}.

DEVELOPMENT PROGRAMS:

MultiFamily Tax-Exempt Bond Financing Program: permanent financing for property being developed for low- to moderate-income multifamily rental projects. The application can be downloaded at {www.sha.state.sc.us/Programs/Rental/Multifamily/multifamily.html}.

Low Income Housing Tax Credit Program: tax credits for developers of low-income rental housing. An application can be downloaded at {www.sha.state.sc.us/Programs/Rental/Tax_Credit/tax_credit.html}.

HOME Program: affords state and local government the flexibility to fund a wide range of low income housing activities. An application can be downloaded from {www.sha.state.sc.us/Programs/Other/HomeInvest/homeinvest.html}.

RENTAL PROGRAMS:

Section 8 Certificates and Vouchers: rental subsidies for low-income households. The application is available at {www.sha.state.sc.us/Programs/Rental/Section-8/section-8.html}.

SOUTH DAKOTA

South Dakota Housing Development Authority

221 South Central Ave
Pierre, SD 57501-1237
605-773-3181
Fax: 605-773-5154
TTY: 605-773-6107
www.sdhda.org

HOMEOWNER PROGRAMS:

First-Time Homebuyer Program: below market rates to income qualified first-time homebuyers. For a list of participating lenders, go to {www.sdhds.org/hofthb.htm}.

Mortgage Assistance Program: provides down payment and closing costs assistance up to $2,000 to qualified first-time homebuyers. For a list of participating lenders, go to {www.sdhds.org/homap.htm}.

Employer Mortgage Assistance Program (EMAP): provides down payment and closing cost assistance to income eligible employees with a participating employer. For a list of current participating employers, go to {www.sdhda.org/hoemap.htm}. For a list of participating lenders, go to {www.sdhds.org/hofthb.htm}.

Cooperative Home Improvement Program: low interest loans for up to seven years for the improvement, repair, or addition to the borrower's home. For a list of participating banks, go to {www.sdhda.org/hochip.htm}.

DEVELOPMENT PROGRAMS:

Housing Tax Credit: tax credits for the construction and rehabilitation of rental housing for low-income households. The application can be downloaded from {www.sdhda.org/planapp.htm#htc}.

HOME Program: designed to expand the supply of affordable housing for very low- and low-income families. The application is available at {www.sdhda.org/planapp.htm#home}.

Multifamily Bond Financing Program: mortgage loans to finance the construction of multifamily housing. The application can be downloaded from {www.sdhda.org/planapp.htm#bond}.

Emergency Shelter Grant Program: financing of shelters for homeless people. The application can be downloaded from {www.sdhda.org/planapp.htm#esg}.

Rural Site Development Program: funding for the development of new affordable housing in rural areas. Contact the South Dakota Housing Development Authority for a pre-application meeting.

The Governor's House: provides reasonably sized, affordable, energy efficient homes to income eligible families. Contact the South Dakota Housing Development Authority for information on this program.

RENTAL PROGRAMS:

Services to the Aging Residents Program: owners of SDHDA financed housing developments targeted for the elderly can provide supportive services to their residents. Housekeeping, transportation, meals, service coordination, and other services are available. Contact the South Dakota Housing Development Authority for information.

TENNESSEE

Tennessee Housing Development Agency

404 James Robertson Parkway, Suite 1114
Nashville, TN 37243-0900
615-741-2400
www.state.tn.us/thda

HOMEOWNER PROGRAMS:

Great Rate Mortgage Program: loans for low- and moderate-income first-time homebuyers for homes that meet certain requirements. Contact the Tennessee Housing Development Authority for application information.

Great Start Mortgage Program: loans for low and moderate-income first-time homebuyers at a slightly higher interest rate, but offers down payment and closing cost assistance. Contact the Tennessee Housing Development Authority for application information.

DEVELOPMENT PROGRAMS:

New Start 0% Mortgage Loan Program: loans for nonprofit organizations for the construction of new single-family homes for very low-income families. An application can be downloaded from {www.state.tn.us/thda/Programs/Mortgage/0startmemo.htm}.

HOME Programs: federal funding to create affordable housing programs for income eligible people. An application can be downloaded from {www.state.tn.us/thda/Programs/grants00/grants.htm}.

Low Income Housing Tax Credit: tax credits for 10 years to owners of low-income housing. An application can be downloaded from {www.state.tn.us/thda/Programs/lihtc/lihtccvr.html}.

Tax Exempt Multi Family Bond Authority: loans for development of multifamily housing that sets aside units for certain income households. An application can be downloaded from {www.state.tn.us/thda/Programs/temfba/mfcvr.html}.

RENTAL PROGRAMS:

Family Self-Sufficiency Program: provides access to the supportive services families need to become free of public assistance within five years. Contact the Tennessee Housing Development Authority for application information.

Housing Choice Voucher Program: subsidy funds to low-income households that find their own dwelling. An application can be downloaded from {www.state.tn.us/thda/Programs/section8/sec8cvr.html}.

Self-Sufficiency Program

TEXAS

Texas Department of Housing and Community Affairs

Street Address
507 Sabine Street
Austin, TX 78701
512-475-3800
Email: info@tdhca.state.tx.us
www.tdhca.state.tx.us

Mailing Address
PO Box 13941
Austin, TX 78711-3941

HOMEOWNER PROGRAMS:

Comprehensive Energy Assistance Program (CEAP): case management, education, and financial assistance to very low- and extremely low-income families to help reduce utility bills to comfortable levels. Services include utility payment assistance, energy education and budget counseling. A list of service providers is available at {www.tdhca.state.tx.us/ea.htm#consumer CEAP}.

Emergency Nutrition/Emergency Relief Program (ENERP): provides Texans with emergency and energy related assistance to low-income households. Services include, utility assistance, housing, clothes, food, medical assistance and transportation. Contact the Texas Department of Housing and Community Affairs for application information.

Weatherization Assistance Program: provides energy related improvements to homes, and also provides education about energy conservation. Priority is given to those families with children, the elderly and/or disabled, and those households with the highest energy costs, and the lowest income. The Service Provider list is at {www.tdhca.state.tx.us/ea.htm#consumersWAP}.

Down Payment Assistance Program: assists low and very low-income families with an interest fee loan to be used for down payment and certain closing costs on a home purchased through the First Time Homebuyer Program. Contact the Texas Department of Housing and Community Affairs for application information.

First time Homebuyer Program: low interest revenue bonds channeled through certain Texas lenders to eligible families purchasing their first home. For a list of participating lenders, go to {www.tdhca.state.tx.us/hf_sfbp.htm}.

HOME Program:
To download the application for this program, go to {www.tdhca.state.tx.us/HOMEApps2003.htm}.

> **Owner Occupied Housing Assistance Program:** funds to rehabilitate single family, owner occupied, homes where the owner meets income requirements.
> **Homebuyer Assistance Program:** loans up to $10,000 to income eligible borrowers for down payment, closing costs and gap financing.

Housing Trust Fund Program: funds to nonprofit, local government, public housing authorities, community housing developments and income eligible families to acquire, rehabilitate, or construct affordable housing for low and very low income people. The application can be downloaded at {www.tdhca.state.tx.us/htf.htm}.

"Bootstrap" Homebuilder Loan Program: loans to low-income families who agree to help build their house. An application is available at {www.tdhca.state.tx.us/bootstrap.htm}.

Contract for Deed Consumer Education Program: classes to teach consumers about contract for deed sales. Contact the Texas Department of Housing and Community Affairs for information on this program.

Contract for Deed Conversion Initiative: available to residents who are currently purchasing residential property within 150 miles of the Texas-Mexico border and reside in a colonia identified by the Texas Water Development Board or meet the Department's definition of a colonia. Residents interested in converting their contract for deed into a traditional note and deed of trust may apply. Contact the Texas Department of Housing and Community Affairs for information on this program.

Development Programs:

Mortgage Revenue Bond Program: finances below market loans to nonprofit and for profit developers of apartment projects that agree to set aside units for rental to low income families and special needs people. The application can be downloaded from {www.tdhca.state.tx.us/hf_mfbp.htm}.

HOME Program:

> **Rental Housing Development Program:** funds to build, acquire, and/or rehabilitate rental property for mixed income, mixed use, single room occupancy, or transitional housing. The application is available at {www.tdhca.state.tx.us/HOMEApps2003.htm}.

Housing Trust Fund Program: funds to nonprofit, local government, public housing authorities, community housing developments and income eligible families to acquire, rehabilitate, or construct affordable housing for low and very low income people. The application can be downloaded from {www.tdhca.state.tx.us/htf.htm}.

Low Income Housing Tax Credit Program: tax credit to developers of low-income rental housing used to offset a portion of their federal tax liability in exchange for the production of affordable rental housing. The application can be downloaded from {www.tdhca.state.tx.us/lihtc.htm}.

Rental Programs:

Emergency Nutrition/Emergency Relief Program (ENERP): provides Texans with emergency and energy related assistance to low-income households. Services include; utility assistance, housing, clothes, food, medical assistance and transportation. Contact the Texas Department of Housing and Community Affairs for application information.

Emergency Shelter Grants Program: provides grants to entities that provide shelter and related services for the homeless. Also provides grants to assist those at risk of becoming homeless. An application can be downloaded from {www.tdhca.state.tx.us/pubs.htmHCS}.

HOME Program:

>   **Tenant Based Rental Assistance Program:** rent subsidies and security deposit payments to tenants that participate in a self-sufficiency program. The application is available at {www.tdhca.state.tx.us/HOMEApps2003.htm}.

Section 8 Housing Assistance Program: rental assistance via subsidies for low income households, elderly, disabled and handicapped people. Contact the Texas Department of Housing and Community Affairs for application information.

UTAH

Utah Housing Finance Agency
554 South 300 East
Salt Lake City, UT 84111
801-521-6950
800-284-6950 (Utah only)
800-344-0452 (outside Utah)
Fax: 801-359-1701
Email: info@utahhousingcorp.org
www.utahhousingcorp.org

HOMEOWNER PROGRAMS:

First Home Program: below market rate mortgage loans to qualifying first time home buyers; purchases made in targeted areas do not need to meet the first time homebuyer requirements. The list of participating mortgage lenders is located at {www.utahhousingcorp.org/homebuyer_firsthome.html}.

Low Income Housing Tax Credit Program: tax credits for developers/owners of rental housing for income eligible people. The application can be downloaded at {www.utahhouingcorp.org/multifamily_lowincome.html}.

DEVELOPMENT PROGRAMS:

Tax Exempt Bond Financing: financing for the development of multifamily housing for low to moderate income persons. The application is available at {www.utahhousingcorp.org/multifamily_taxexempt.html}.

Low Income Housing Tax Credit Program: tax credits for developers/owners of rental housing for income eligible people. The application can be downloaded at {www.utahhouingcorp.org/multifamily_lowincome.html}.

Rental Programs:

Low Income Housing tax Credit Program: tax credits for developers/owners of rental housing for income eligible people. The application can be downloaded at {www.utahhouingcorp.org/multifamily_lowincome.html}.

VERMONT

Vermont Housing Finance Agency
One Burlington Square
P.O. Box 408
Burlington, VT 05402-0408
802-864-5743
Fax: 802-864-5746
Email: home@vhfa.org
www.vhfa.org

Homeowner Programs:

Mortgages for Vermonters (MOVE): offers several interest rate and point options with flexible down payment requirements. A list of participating lenders is at {www.vhfa.org/partners/index.htm}.

Cash Assistance Rate Option: provides up to 3% of the loan amount to be used towards down payment and closing costs associated with a VHFA loan. Contact the Vermont Housing Finance Authority for application information.

Homeownership Opportunities Using Shared Equity: loans with stepped interest rates to nonprofit housing organizations that work together to reduce the purchase price and related costs; they agree to keep the property affordable to future home buyers by sharing any profit when it is sold. A list of participating lenders is at {www.vhfa.org/partners/index.htm}.

Limited Refinance: provides qualified homeowners the opportunity to replace high interest rate mobile home loans and all other property types can replace shared appreciation financing. Borrowers can also finance the cost of property improvements, and all associated closing costs. A list of participating lenders is at {www.vhfa.org/partners/index.htm}.

DEVELOPMENT PROGRAMS:

Construction and Permanent Loan Financing Program: financing for the development and preservation of affordable rental housing where at least 51% of the units are rented to low and moderate income people. The application can be downloaded at {www.vhfa.org/development/loan-programs.htm#cplfp}.

Nonprofit Housing Predevelopment and Bridge Loan Program: low cost financing to eligible nonprofit housing developers for projects such as transitional housing, nursing homes, co-op housing, single family homes and more. Call the Vermont Housing Finance Agency for an application.

Low Income Housing Tax Credit Program: tax credits for developers/owners of rental housing for low-income households. The application is available at {www.vhfa.org/development/lihtc.htm}.

RENTAL PROGRAMS:

No programs at the time of this printing. Check with the organization for any updates.

Vermont State Housing Authority

One Prospect Street
Montpelier, VT 05602
802-828-3295
Fax: 802-828-3248
www.vsha.org

HOMEOWNER PROGRAMS:

Section 8 HomeOwnership Program: allows some people to convert Section 8 Rental vouchers into HomeOwnership vouchers. This can provide those eligible, assistance meeting monthly costs associated with owning a home. The Questionnaire and Mutual Release can be downloaded from {www.vsha.org/homeown.htm}.

DEVELOPMENT PROGRAMS:

Development Program: assistance for the development and preservation of affordable multi-unit complexes and mobile home parks. Contact the Vermont State Housing Authority for application information.

New Construction/Substantial Rehabilitation Program: creates new and rehabilitated housing in communities without safe and sanitary housing for low-income families and the elderly. Contact the Vermont State Housing Authority for application information.

Rental Programs:

Section 8 Rental Assistance Program: rental assistance to eligible persons who choose their own housing. An application can be downloaded at {www.vsha.org/ra.htm}.

Shelter Plus Care Program: rental assistance to disabled homeless people. Contact the Vermont State Housing Authority for application information.

Project Based Certificates and Moderate Rehabilitation Program: a rent subsidy that is attached to the unit and not the tenant. The application can be downloaded from {www.vsha.org/ra.htm}.

Family Unification Program: promotes family unification by providing rental assistance to families for whom the lack of adequate housing is a primary factor in the separation, or threat of imminent separation, of children from their families. The Department of Social and Rehabilitative Services refer eligible households to VSHA. Contact the Vermont State Housing Authority for application information.

Mainstream Housing: rental assistance for disabled families. Contact the Vermont State Housing Authority for application information.

VIRGINIA

Virginia Housing Development Authority
601 South Belvidere Street
Richmond, VA 23220
804-782-1986
800-968-7837
www.vhda.com

Homeowner Programs:

Home Ownership Education: helps prepare first-time homebuyers with the purchase of their first home. A list of class schedules is located at {www.vhda.com/sf/singlefam.asp}.

Fresh Start Loan Program: offers low rate interest loans to qualified first-time homebuyers that have had difficulty purchasing a home due to past credit issues. The list of housing counseling agencies to apply with is at {www.vhda.com/sf/freshstart.asp}.

FHA Plus Loan Program: assists qualified borrowers who need down payment assistance. Contact a local VHDA originating lender (www.vhda.com/sf/singlefam.asp) for information.

Flexible Alternative Program: optioning for a slightly higher interest rate, allows up to 100% loan-to-value financing without mortgage insurance to eligible buyers. The application can be downloaded at {www.vhda.com/sf/SF_Flex_Apply_right.asp}.

Flexible Alternative Step Rate Program: couples the flexible features of the *Flexible Alternative Program* with the lower interest rate loan of the Step Rate program; lower interest rate for the first two years of the loan. Contact the Virginia Housing Development Authority for application information.

Flexible Alternative Home Enhancer Program: offers qualified borrowers the same features as the *Flexible Alternative Program*, but also offers financing for modest home improvements. Contact the Virginia Housing Development Authority for application information.

Flexible Alternative Home Access Program: a variation of the *Flexible Alternative Program* offering up to 100% of the sale price, but also offers an additional 10% more to be used for home modifications for accessibility. Contact the Virginia Housing Development Authority for application information.

Fixed Rate Loan: lower interest fixed rate loans for eligible homebuyers. Contact the Virginia Housing Development Authority for application information.

Step Rate Loan Program: lower interest rate for the first two years of the loan creating lower mortgage payments for those years. Contact the Virginia Housing Development Authority for application information.

Home Improvement Loan: loans for home improvement with a lower interest rate, low closing costs, and no points for low and moderate income homeowners. Contact the Virginia Housing Development Authority for application information.

Development Programs:

Low Income Housing Tax Credit Program: federal tax credits for owners of low-income rental housing. The application can be downloaded at {www.vhda.com/multifam/taxcredframes.htm}.

Virginia Housing Fund: low interest rate funds for multi-family projects available to for-profits and non-profits for minority, and rural area developers. The application can be downloaded from {www.vhda.com/multifam/mfvhf.htm}.

Bond-Funded Program: funding for multi-family projects that rent to low and very low-income tenants. An application is available at {www.vhda.com/multifam/mfbond.htm}.

Rental Programs:

Low Income Housing Tax Credit Program: federal tax credits for owners of low-income rental housing. The application can be downloaded at {www.vhda.com/multifam/taxcredframes.htm.}

State Credit Rent Reduction Program: tax credit to property owners who fill vacant units and/or reduce rent amounts for elderly, disabled, and homeless persons. Contact the Virginia Housing Development Authority for application information.

WASHINGTON

Washington State Housing Finance Commission

1000 Second Avenue, Suite 2700
Seattle, WA 98104-1046
206-464-7139
800-767-4663
www.wshfc.org

HOMEOWNER PROGRAMS:

Home Choice Program: down payment assistance and lower interest rates for low and moderate income people with a disability, or that have a family member with a disability that are first time buyers or are buying in a targeted area; must complete an education counseling course. For the Service Provider list, go to {www.wshfc.org/buyers/homechoice.htm}.

House Key Program: below market rate loans for income eligible first time home buyers and buyers of residences in target areas. The list of participating lenders is at {www.wshfc.org/buyers/key.htm}.

House Key Plus Program: loans to income eligible buyers to help pay down payment and closing costs in conjunction with the *House Key Program*. The list of participating lenders is at {www.wshfc.org/buyers/keyplus.htm}.

House Key Teacher Program: offers lower down payment requirements to eligible full-time employed teacher, administrator, principal, vice-principal, librarian, or health care professional (such as nurse or counselor) who is a first-time homebuyer or buying in a targeted area. For a list of House Key Loan originaters, go to {www.wshfc.org/buyers/key.htm#lenders}.

House Key Extra: mortgage loan for income eligible first time home buyers with a disability, or a family member with a disability in a rural area and the home is within the specified price range. Contact the Washington State Housing Finance Commission for application information.

House Key Rural (Pilot Program): down payment and closing cost assistance available to first time homebuyers buying in a rural area. If buying in a rural targeted area, you do not need to be a first time homebuyer. The list of participating lenders is at {www.wshfc.org/buyers/krural.htm}.

Open Door Second Mortgage Loan Program: down payment and closing cost assistance to eligible first time homebuyers in the city of Tacoma. The list of participating lenders is at {www.wshfc.org/buyers/open.htm}.

DEVELOPMENT PROGRAMS:

Low Income Housing Tax Credit Program: federal tax credits to developers/owners of low-income rental housing. The application can be downloaded at {www.wshfc.org/tax-credits/index.htm}.

For Profit Multifamily Developer Program: financing for developers of rental projects or new construction, acquisition and/or rehabilitation, and predevelopment costs. The application can be downloaded from {www.wshfc.org/bonds/fp-bond.htm}.

Bonds for Nonprofit Capital Projects: funding to nonprofits for a range of real estate and capital equipment projects. {www.wshfc.org/bonds/np-capital.htm}.

Bonds for Nonprofit Housing: funding to nonprofits for housing projects such as transitional housing, group homes, independent living apartments and more. The application is available at {www.wshfc.org/bonds/np-housing.htm}.

RENTAL PROGRAMS:

Low Income Housing Tax Credit Program: federal tax credits to developers/owners of low-income rental housing. The application can be downloaded at {www.wshfc.org/tax-credits/index.htm}.

WEST VIRGINIA

West Virginia Housing Development Fund

814 Virginia Street East
Charleston, WV 25301
304-345-6475
800-933-9843
Email: wvhdf@wvhdf.com
www.wvhdf.com

HOMEOWNER PROGRAMS:

Teacher and Education Employee Loan Assistance Program: designed for employees of the West Virginia school system who have sufficient income to support a monthly payment, but have limited funds to cover down payment and closing cost expenses. Contact a local banking or financial institution for application information.

Single Family Bond Program: low interest rate financing for low- and moderate-income families to buy a home in a specified price range. For a list of participating lenders, go to {www.wvhdf.com/home_ownership/limitsandlenders/index.cfm}.

Secondary Market Program: below market rate loans or refinancing for eligible homebuyers. For a list of participating lenders, go to {www.wvhdf.com/home_ownership/limitsandlenders/index.cfm}.

Closing Cost Assistance Program: assistance with closing costs for participants of the *Single Family Bond Program*. For a list of participating lenders, go to {www.wvhdf.com/home_ownership/limitsandlenders/index.cfm}.

Closing Cost and Down Payment Assistance Loan: loan to be used towards down payment and closing costs available to income eligible participants in the *Secondary Market Program*. For a list of participating lenders, go to {www.wvhdf.com/home_ownership/limitsandlenders/index.cfm}.

HOME Program: a mortgage program providing funding for low-income families. The application is available when funding is available. It can be downloaded at {www.wvhdf.com/home_ownership/home/index.cfm}.

Housing Emergency Loan Program (HELP): funding for structural or construction problems that threaten the health and safety of low-income homeowners. For a list of participating lenders, go to {www.wvhdf.com/home_ownership/limitsandlenders/index.cfm}.

Mini-Mod Rehabilitation Program (MMRP): offers landlords affordable financing for upgrading rental units for low-income households. The Area Manager list is available at {www.wvhdf.com/area_managers/index.cfm}.

Development Programs:

Constructing Affordable Sensible Homes (CASH) Program: provides a guaranteed sales program for single-family homebuilders. This program is only offered in counties affected by the 2001 flood. Contact the West Virginia Housing Development Fund for application information.

Construction Loan Incentive Program (CLIP): construction loans for low- and moderate-income multifamily or elderly housing in designated rural areas. Contact the West Virginia Housing Development Fund for application information.

Low Income Housing Tax Credit Program: federal tax credits for developers/owners of low-income multifamily housing. Contact the West Virginia Housing Development Fund for application information.

Rental Programs:

Low Income Housing Tax Credit Program: federal tax credits for developers/owners of low-income multifamily housing. Contact the West Virginia Housing Development Fund for application information.

WISCONSIN

Wisconsin Housing and Economic Development Authority

201 West Washington, Suite 700
P.O. Box 1728
Madison, WI 53701-1728
608-266-7884
800-334-6873
Fax: 608-267-1099
Email: info@wheda.com
www.wheda.com

This website also offers links to several related websites by selecting Related Links from the main menu on the Home page. Links are categorized by; Homeownership, Multifamily, and Agricultural

HOMEOWNER PROGRAMS:

HOME Loan: mortgage loans with low interest rates for low- and moderate-income people for first time home buyers. The list of lenders to apply with is at {www.wheda.com/programs/singlefamily/sfbuyers/lenderlist/lenderlist.stm}.

CROP Program: loan guarantees for agricultural production loans. The list of lenders to apply with is at {www.wheda.com/programs/agricultural/lenderlist/lenderlist.stm}.

FARM Program: guarantees for agricultural expansion and modernization loans. The list of lenders to apply with is at {www.wheda.com/programs/agricultural/lenderlist/lenderlist.stm}.

Beginning Farmer Bond Program: low interest rate funding for the first time purchase of a farm, including land, equipment, livestock, or buildings. The list of lenders to apply with is at {www.wheda.com/programs/agricultural/lenderlist/lenderlist.stm}.

Home Improvement Loans: home improvement loans of up to $17,500 to low-to-moderate-income Wisconsin homeowners. For additional information, go to {www.wheda.com/programs/singlefamily/sfbuyers/hilp.stm}.

DEVELOPMENT PROGRAMS:

Tax-Exempt Bond Financing: below-market-rate loans for development of multifamily rental housing. Loans can be used for new construction, acquisition and rehabilitation of one-to-three story apartment buildings. For additional information, go to {www.wheda.com/programs/multifamily/bmrfinan.stm}.

Affordable Housing Tax Credit: federal tax incentive to encourage the creation of affordable rental housing. For additional information, go to {www.wheda.com/programs/multifamily/ahtc/taxcred.stm}.

RENTAL PROGRAMS:

Section 8 Preservation Options: offer mortgage-restructuring options that provide incentive for owners to maintain affordable Section 8 housing for low-income tenants. Contact the Wisconsin Housing and Economic Development Authority for application information.

WYOMING

Wyoming Community Development Authority
155 North Beech
Casper, WY 82602
307-265-0603
Fax: 307-266-5414
Email: curry@wyomingcda.com
www.wyomingcda.com

HOMEOWNER PROGRAMS:

Qualified Rehabilitation Loan: low interest rate loans for rehabilitation projects from extensive major structural repair to major disrepairs. Contact the Wyoming Community Development Authority for application information.

Mortgage Revenue Bond (MRB): low interest rate mortgages for first-time Wyoming homebuyers with low and moderate incomes. For additional information, go to {www.wyomingcda.com/firsthome.html}.

DEVELOPMENT PROGRAMS:

HOME Investment Partnership Program: funds for the development of affordable housing for low and very low income households. The application can be downloaded at {www.wyomingcda.com/hs-prog1.htm}.

Low Income Housing Tax Credit Program: tax credits for owners of rental housing affordable to low income households. The application can be downloaded at {www.wyomingcda.com/hs-prog2.htm}.

Housing Trust Fund: financing of non-traditional affordable housing. Contact the Wyoming Community Development Authority for application information.

Community Development Block Grant (CDBG): loans for housing-related programs that benefit low-income households of Wyoming. For additional information, go to {www.wyomingcda.com/hs-prog3.html}.

RENTAL PROGRAMS:

Low Rent Public Housing: rental program of single family detached units for very-low income large families. Contact the Wyoming Community Development Authority for application information.

Section 8 Rental Assistance Program: certificates and vouchers to assist low-income rental households. Contact the Wyoming Community Development Authority for application information.

County Housing Programs

Like the housing programs cities offer, counties also provide an impressive list of assistance to home owners and home buyers. You can take classes on homeownership before you even start the buying process. Some counties offer repair programs for seniors, and others offer grants and loans to anyone needing to fix their home. Los Angeles County offers federal income tax deductions to those that live in certain areas, and also provides deferred loans to qualified home buyers. Orange County has a Mortgage Assistance Program that will help with the purchase of a home valued at up to $392,000! Obviously these people want you to own a home! Weatherization and energy assistance, down payment assistance, and even rental help are just a phone call away. Most of the county programs are offered through the county housing, community development departments, or planning commissions. Some are provided through the county housing agency. Programs do vary from place to place, so contact your county to see what is offered in your area. You can find your county on the web at {www.govengine.com }

Described below is a representative sample of the kinds of money programs that are available at the county level. Make sure you contact every county in your area and get a complete listing of available programs

Alabama
Jefferson County Office of Planning and Development
805 North 22nd Street
Birmingham, AL 35203
205-325-5092
Fax: 205-325-5095
http://www.jeffcointouch.com/
- Housing Rehabilitation Program-1% to 3% loans available for low to moderate income homeowners
- Housing Accessibility Program-up to $3,000 grants
- Deferred Loan Program
- Housing Counseling Program Housing Ownership Counseling Program

Alaska
North Slope Borough
Housing and Property Management Department
P.O. Box 69
Barrow, AK 99723
907-852-0290
Fax: 907-852-0373
http://www.north-slope.org/nsb/default.htm
- Down Payment Assistance-up to $12,500
- Technical Assistance Program

- Rental Stock Sales Program-renters may purchase home after 3 years of renting

Arizona

Yuma County Housing Department
8450 West Highway 95, Suite 88
Somerton, AZ 85350
928-627-8828
Fax: 928-627-8715
http://www.co.yuma.az.us/housing/housing_servic
es.htm
- Affordable Rental Housing
- Self-Sufficiency Program

California

Almeda County Housing Authority
22941 Atherton Street
Hayward, CA 94541
510-538-8876
http://www.haca.net/
- Affordable Housing
- Family Self-Sufficiency
- Home Buyers Education Classes

Calaveras County
891 Mountain Ranch Road
San Andreas, CA 95249
209-754-6303
http://www.co.calaveras.ca.us/departments/admin
/housing.html
- Housing Repair Loan Program-0% to 5% loans for low-income owners or landlords of low-income renters
- Deferred Housing Repair Loan Program-no payments on loans for up to 15 years for elderly, disabled and very low-income families

Fresno County Housing
1331 Fulton Mall
Fresno, CA 93721
559-443-8400
http://www.hafresno.org/agency/about.htm
- Homeownership Opportunities Program
- Homeownership Training Programs

Kings County Housing
1400 W Lacey Blvd.
Hanford, CA 93230
559-582-3211
http://www.countyofkings.com/
- Housing Rehabilitation Loan Program-up to $55,000 to bring homes to code and can provide new carpet, paint or other fixtures. Low interest 3% loans or deferred loans

Los Angeles County Community Development
Commission
2 Coral Circle
Monterey Park, CA 91755
323-890-7001
Fax: 323-838-1079
http://www.lacdc.org/home.shtm
- Mortgage Credit Certificate Program-reduces federal income taxes. A family of three may earn up to $76,300 to qualify for homes in the designated area.
- Homeownership Ownership Program-deferred loans up to $40,000 for qualified homebuyers in the targeted areas
- Consumer Affairs Counseling-information on maintenance, warranties, budgeting and more
- Willowbrook Grant Program-home improvement grants up to $20,000 for painting, Fencing, roofing, windows and driveway repairs
- Single Family Grant Program-emergency grants up to $5,000 for eligible homeowners
- Single Family Rehabilitation Loan Program-3% loan up to $25,000. One 10-year deferred loan with no monthly payment and one 15-year loan with monthly payments.
- Residential Sound Insulation Program-grants to eligible homeowners to reduce noise caused by the Los Angeles World Airport

Montgomery County Housing and Redevelopment
29 Bishop Street, Suite 203
Pajaro, CA 95076
831-786-1350
Fax: 831-786-1342
http://www.co.monterey.ca.us/housing/
- Inclusion Homes-homes sold throughout the community at a lower price than market homes in the area to low and moderate-income families
- Housing Rehabilitation Program
- Redevelopment Programs

Nevada County Housing and Community Services
950 Maidu Avenue
Nevada City, CA 95959
530-265-1218
- Down Payment Loan Assistance-3% loans up to $40,000 to income qualified, first time homebuyers
- Self-Help Housing Program
- Affordable Rental Housing
- Rehabilitation Loan Program-3% loans from $5,000 to $30,000 for income qualifying home owners to repair roofing, plumbing, heating, windows or foundation repairs

Orange County Housing and Community
Development Department
1770 North Broadway
Santa Ana, CA 92706
714-480-2900
Fax: 714-480-2803
http://www.ochousing.org/index.htm
- H.I.R.E. Program-designed for people to live and
  work in Orange County. Low interest loans and
  down payment assistance for homebuyers who
  attend the Homebuyers Workshop and earn less
  than $105,850.
- Mortgage Assistance Program-up to $20,000 for
  first-time homebuyers with deferred payments,
  maximum purchase price $392,413. Income limits
  apply and Homebuyer Education Class is
  required.
- Affordable Rental Housing
- Mobile Home Exterior Grant Program-up to
  $9,000 to repair or replace roofs,
  porches,windows, entry doors, undercarriages,
  exterior paint and termite work.
- Rehabilitation Loan Program-low interest loans
  to repair or replace roofs, windows, entry doors,
  garage door, driveway, fencing, exterior paint
  and termite work.

Sacramento Housing & Redevelopment Agency
320 Commerce Circle
Sacramento, CA 95815
916-444-9210
http://www.shra.org/Content/Housing/Housing.ht
m
- Affordable Housing
- Home Repair Program-grants and loans for low-
  income homeowners

County of San Bernardino Housing Development
Division
290 North D Street, 6th Floor
San Bernardino, CA 92415
909-388-0900
Fax: 909-388-0920
http://www.co.san-bernardino.ca.us/ecd/housing/
- Single Family Home Mortgage Revenue Bond
  Program-providing low interest rate loans and
  down payment assistance

County of San Diego Housing and Community
Development Building
3989 Ruffin Road
San Diego, CA 92123
858-694-4814
http://www.sdcounty.ca.gov/sdhcd/index_homeow
ner.html

- Down Payment Assistance-low interest loans up
  to $10,000 for first-time homebuyers
- Mortgage Credit Certificate Program-reduces
  federal income taxes. A family of three may earn
  up to $81,760 to qualify for homes in the
  designated area.
- Minor Rehabilitation and Home Security
  Program
- Residential Rehabilitation Assistance Program-
  low interest and deferred loans for income
  eligible homeowners

San Mateo County Housing and Community
Development
262 Harbor Blvd., Building A
Belmont, CA 94002
605-802-5033
Fax: 650-802-5049
http://www.co.sanmateo.ca.us/hsa.dir/hoowner.ht
m#mcc
- Mortgage Credit Certificate Program-reduces
  federal income taxes. A family of three may earn
  up to $66,240 to qualify
- Family Self-Sufficiency Home Buyer Club

Santa Barbara County Comprehensive Planning
Department
123 East Anapamu Street
Santa Barbara, CA 93101
805-568-2000
http://www.countyofsb.org/plandev/comp/progra
ms/housing/default.html
- Affordable Housing Program

County of Tulare
5140 W. Cypress Avenue
P.O. Box 791
Visalia, CA 93279
559-627-3700
Fax: 559-733-0169
http://www.hatc.net/
- Mortgage Credit Certificate Program-reduces
  federal income taxes. A family of three may earn
  up to $70,000 to qualify for homes in the
  designated area.

Colorado
Adams County Housing Programs
450 South Fourth Avenue
Brighton, CO 80601
303-659-2120
800-824-7842
http://www.co.adams.co.us/services/department/c
ommunity_outreach/housing.html
- Home Buyer Training Classes

Apapahoe County Community Services Division
2009 West Littleton Boulevard
Littleton, CO 80120-2024
303-738-8060
http://www.co.arapahoe.co.us/CS/
- Down Payment Assistance-up to $20,000 with no payments for the first five years then 3% interest starting in the sixth year
- Home Buyer Workshop
- Rehabilitation Program-up to $800 for emergency grants. $800.01-$3,000 deferred loan

Eagle County Government
500 Broadway
Eagle, CO 81631
970-328-8600
http://www.eagle-county.com/housing.cfm
- Down Payment Assistance-up to $10,000 loan for homebuyers with incomes of $68,195 for a family of three
- Affordable Housing
- Mortgage Credit Certificate Program-reduces federal income taxes. A family of three may earn up to $68,195 to qualify for homes in the designated area.

Florida

Alachua County Department of Growth Management
Housing Division
10 SW 2nd Avenue
Gainesville, FL 32601
352-374-5249
Fax: 352-338-3224
http://growth-management.alachua.fl.us/housing/housing_index.php
- Down Payment Assistance-first-time homebuyers
- Affordable Rental Housing

Broward County Office of Housing Finance
110 NE 3rd Street, Suite 300
Fort Lauderdale, FL 33301
954-765-5311
Fax: 954-765-5340
http://www.broward.org/hfi00300.htm
- Home Buyer Workshop
- Home Buyer Counseling Program
- Home Owner Workshop
- Affordable Home Purchase Loans-below market financing
- SHIP Second Mortgage Program-below-market second mortgages for qualifying families
- SHIP Purchase Assistance-funds to reduce eligible homebuyers mortgages and assist in closing costs

- Water/Sewer Connection Program-deferred loan to help with connecting to water/sewage system

Orange County Housing and Community Development
525 South Street
Orlando, FL 32801
407-836-5150
http://www.orangecountyfl.net/dept/growth/housing/programs.htm
- Down Payment Assistance-"soft" second mortgage up to $7,500 that is forgivable
- Homebuyer Counseling Program
- Homeowners Rehabilitation Program-deferred loans up to $7,500 for emergency repairs and $28,000 for substantial repairs to income qualifying
- Minor Repair Grant-grants for emergency repairs for income eligible homeowners
- Total Rehabilitation Program-assistance for major projects to income eligible homeowners
- Mobile Home Repair Program-assistance to income eligible mobile home owners
- Paint the Town Program

Georgia

Athens-Clarke County Unified Government
Department of Human and Economic Development
375 Satula Avenue
Athens, GA 30601
706-613-3155
http://www.athensclarkecounty.com/~hed/HEDhome.htm
- Emergency Home Repair Program-assistance to seniors and handicapped individuals
- Housing Counseling Service
- Neighborhood Revitalization

Decatur/DeKalb County Housing Authority
325 Swanton Way
P.O. Box 1627
Decatur, GA 30031
404-377-0425
Fax: 404-378-7249
http://www.ddhainfo.org/
- Down Payment Assistance-grants up to $2,525
- Affordable Rental Housing
- Affordable Housing
- Housing Rehab Grants-deferred forgivable grants up to $20,000 for very low-income families
- Housing Rehab Low-Interest Loans-assists low-to-moderate income homeowners

Fulton County Housing Authority
10 Park Place South, SE
Suite 550

Atlanta, GA 30303-2913
404-730-5841
Fax: 40735847
http://www.hafc.org/
- Elderly and Special Needs Housing
  Developments
- Home Buyer Education Counseling
- Home Ownership Programs

Augusta-Richmond County Housing & Development
One 10th Street, Suite 430
Augusta, GA 30901
706-821-1797
Fax: 706-821-1784
http://www.co.richmond.ga.us/departments/housing_dev/home_pro.htm
- Down Payment Assistance-deferred loan up to
  $2,500 to income eligible first-time home buyers
- Housing Rehabilitation Program
- Paint Improvement Program-paint materials
  provided to eligible homeowners

Hawaii

County of Kauai Housing Agency
4193 Hardy Street
Lihue, HI 96766
808-241-6444
http://www.kauaigov.org/housing.htm
- Home Loan Programs
- Rehabilitation Loan Program
- Self-Help Housing Program

Maui County Department of Housing and Human
Concerns
200 South High Street
Wailuku, HI 96793
http://countyofmaui.maui.net/departments/Housing/
- Affordable Housing
- Affordable Rental Housing

Idaho

Ada County Housing
1276 W. River St., Suite 300
Boise, ID 83702
208-345-4907
Fax: 208-345-4909
http://www.bcacha.org/
- Affordable Rental Housing
- Down Payment Assistance

Illinois

Lake County Planning, Building and Development
18 N County Street
Waukegan, IL 60085-4355
847-377-2875

Fax: 847-360-6734
http://www.co.lake.il.us/planning/conplan.htm
- First Time Homebuyers Program
- Housing Rehabilitation Program

The County of Madison
157 North Main Street
Edwardsville, IL 62025
618-692-6200
http://www.co.madison.il.us/
- Weatherization Program
- Energy Assistance

Will County Community Development
100 Manhattan Road
Joliet, IL 60433
815-727-2332
http://www.willcountycommunitydevelopment.com/
- First Time Homebuyer Program

Iowa

Buchanan County Community Services
210 5th Avenue, N.E.
Independence, IA 50644
319-334-4290
http://www.buchanancounty.com/comminfo.htm
- Rental Assistance

Cerro Gordo County
220 North Washington Avenue
Mason City, IA 50401
641-421-3083
Fax: 641-421-3092
http://www.co.cerro-gordo.ia.us/GenA_Overview.cfm
- Rental Assistance-emergency assistance
- Utility Assistance-emergency assistance

Story County Affordable Housing Program
515 Clark Avenue, Room 214
P.O. Box 811
Ames, IA 50010
515-239-5400
Fax: 515-239-5133
http://www.city.ames.ia.us/housingweb/AffordableHousing/housing.htm
Applicants do not have to be first-time homebuyers to
qualify for these programs.
- Down Payment Assistance-low interest loans up
  to $15,000
- Closing Cost Assistance-grants up to $2,000
- Home Repair Program-very low interest loans up
  to $5,000

Win-Worth Betco
203A North First Avenue West

Lake Mills, IA 50450
641-592-0800
Fax: 641-592-0801
http://www.win-
worthbetco.com/html/housing.html
- Down Payment Assistance-up to $7,000 for
  income eligible homebuyers
- County Housing Trust-$5,00 for new single-
  family homes and up to $5,000 per unit for multi-
  family housing

Wright County Economic Development
115 North Main
P.O. Box 214
Clarion, IA 50525
515-532-6422
Fax: 515-532-2348
http://www.wrightcounty.org/fthop.htm
- First Time Home Owners Program-down
  payment matching loans up to $3,000 for income
  eligible
- Supplementary Homeowners Program-down
  payment matching loans up to $5,500 with no
  income minimums

Kansas
Wyandotte County Community Development
701 North 7th Street
Kansas City, KS 66101
913-573-5100
http://www.wycokck.org/departments/commdevel
opment.html
- Housing Enhancement Loan Program-to upgrade
  major systems in the home

Louisiana
Calcasieu Parish Housing Department
130 West Kirby Street
Lake Charles, LA 337-437-3577
Fax: 337-437-3376
http://www.cppj.net/dept/housing/default.asp
- Housing Choice Voucher System
- Home Ownership Program

Maryland
Allegany County Government Housing Services
Division
701 Kelly Road
Cumberland, MD 21502
301-777-2372
Fax: 301-777-2126
http://www.gov.allconet.org/housing/housing_wel
come.htm
- Subsidized Housing Inventory
- Rental Assistance Program
- Rehabilitation Program

Charles County Department of Community Services
8190 Port Tobacco Road
Port Tobacco, MD 20677
301-934-9305
http://www.govt.co.charles.md.us/cs/housing/
- First Time Homebuyer Programs
- Special Homebuyer Loan Programs
- Affordable Rental Housing

Harford County Housing Agency
15 South Main Street, Suite 106
Bel Air, MD 21014-8725
410-638-3045 or 410-879-3136
Fax 410-893-9816
http://www.co.ha.md.us/housing/
- Police and Teacher Homeownership Program-
  grants up to $20,000 to live in targeted areas
- Homeownership Counseling
- Rental Counseling
- Housing Assistance for Families with Disabilities
- Rehabilitation Program

Howard County Northern District
3410 Courthouse Drive
Ellicott City, MD 21043
410-313-6320
http://www.co.ho.md.us/servicesresidents_financial
assistance.htm#anch25202
- Homeownership Program
- First Time Home Buyer Loan Program-loans up
  to $6,000
- Rental Assistance

Housing Opportunities Commission of Montgomery
County
10400 Detrick Avenue
Kensington, MD 20895
301-929-6700
Fax: 301-929-6755
http://www.hocweb.org/
- Mortgage Purchase Program-below-market rate
  mortgages for first-time homebuyers
- Closing Cost Grant Program-down payment
  assistance for first-time homebuyers

Department of Housing and Community Affairs
100 Maryland Avenue, 4th Floor
Rockville, MD 20850
240-777-3600
http://hca.emontgomery.org/index.html
- Moderately Priced Dwelling Units Program-
  moderate income first-time homebuyers
- Weatherization Program
- Home Improvement Loan Program-low to
  moderate-income homebuyers
- Affordable Housing

Prince George's County Department of Housing and
Development
9400 Peppercorn Place
Largo, MD 20774
301-883-5501
Fax: 301-883-5427
http://www.co.pg.md.us/
- Down Payment and Closing Assistance Program
- Single Family Housing Rehabilitation Assistance
  Program
- Lead Reduction Program
- Weatherization Assistance Program

Queen Anne's County Department of Housing and
Community Services
107 North Liberty Street (Lower Level)
Centreville, MD 21617
410-758-3977
Fax: 410-758-4499
http://www.qac.org/
- Affordable Housing

Massachusetts
Barnstable County
Cape Cod Housing Commission
3225 Main St., P.O. Box 226
Barnstable, MA 02630-0226
508-362-3828
Fax: 508-362-3136
http://www.capecodcommission.org/housing/
- Affordable Housing
- Soft Second Mortgage Loan Program-first-time
  low and moderate homebuyers

Michigan
Antrim County Housing Committee
230 E Cayuga
P.O. Box 206
Bellaire, MI 49615
231-533-8727
Fax: 231-533-5848
http://www.antrimcounty.org/webpages/housing.h
tml
- Trailer Replacement Program-replacement of
  trailers with new doublewide homes
- Home Rehabilitation Program

Alpena County Home Improvement Program
719 W. Chisholm Street, Suite 5
Alpena, MI 49707
989-354-9663
Fax 989-354-9783
http://www.alpenacounty.org/alpcnty/home%20im
provement.htm
- Home Improvement Program-0 to 3% loans up to
  $25,000 for qualifying homeowners

Bay County Housing Department
515 Center Avenue, Suite 502
Bay City, MI 48708-5126
989-895-4138
Fax: 989-895-4068
http://www.co.bay.mi.us/bay/home.nsf/Public/Ho
using_Rehabilitation_Program.htm
- Housing Rehabilitation Loan Program

Kalamazoo County Human Services
3299 Gull Road
Kalamazoo, MI 49048
269-373-5200
http://www.kalcounty.com/hsd/index.htm
- Housing Rehabilitation Loan Program-no-
  interest loans for low-income homeowners to
  upgrade essential home systems
- Affordable Rental Housing
- Weatherization Assistance Program

Shiawassee County Housing Rehabilitation Program
201 North Shiawassee Street
Third Floor, Surbeck Building
Corunna, MI 48817
517-743-2270
Fax: 517-743-5453
http://www.shiawassee.net/Housing/index.html
- Rehabilitation Program-loans to very low to
  moderate income families

Minnesota
Hennepin Housing Development Division
417 N. 5th Street, Suite 320
Minneapolis, MN 55401-1362
612-348-9260
Fax: 612-348-2920
http://www.co.hennepin.mn.us/tcw/housing/welc
ome.html
- Affordable Housing
- First-Time Homebuyers Program

Ramsey County Housing and Redevelopment
250 Courthouse
15 West Kellogg Blvd.
St. Paul, MN 55102
651-266-8006
http://www.co.ramsey.mn.us/cm/ced/index.asp
- First-Time Homebuyer Program
- Rehabilitation Program-deferred loan program
  for income eligible homeowners
- Weatherization Program-deferred loan program
  for income eligible homeowners

Stevens County Housing
P.O. Box 530
400 Colorado Avenue

Morris, MN 56267
320-589-7416
http://www.co.stevens.mn.us/docs/departments/hra/default.html
- Affordable Rental Housing
- Revolving Loan Fund

Missouri
Saint Louis County Office of Community Development
121 S. Meramec, Suite 444
Clayton, MO 63105
314-615-4405
Fax: 314-615-8674
http://www.co.st-louis.mo.us/plan/ocd.html
- Home Improvement Program-up to $5,000, 5-year forgivable home improvement loans for low to moderate-income families
- Lead Hazard Control Program-grants to low to moderate-income homeowners

Nebraska
Adams County
500 West 4th Street
Hastings, NE 68901
402-461-7155
http://www.adamscounty.org/assessors/homestead/
- Homestead Exemption Program-property tax relief for seniors over 65 or certain disabled

New Jersey
Bergen County Community Development
25 East Salem Street, Room 601
Hackensack, NJ 07601
201-646-2204
Fax: 201-487-0945
http://www.co.bergen.nj.us/dcd/Services.html
- American Dream Program-up to $42,000 soft second mortgage due when the property is sold. Matching funds of up to $15,000 for a soft third mortgage which becomes a grant after 10 years. An additional $2,500 for down payment assistance and depending on need, a $5,000 grant.
- Home Buyer Education

Camden County Community Development
A-5 Collier Drive
Lakeland Complex
Blackwood, NJ 08012
856-374-6637
www.camdencounty.com
- Home Maintenance and Repair Loans

Camden County Division of Senior Services
Parkview Terrace
700 Browning Road, Suite 11
West Collingswood, NJ 08107
877-222-3737
- Mr. Fix-it Program-minor carpentry, electrical, plumbing, concrete, windows and lock repair or replacement for seniors

Mercer County Administration Building
Mercer County Affordable Housing Program
640 South Broad Street
P.O. Box 8068
Trenton, NJ 08650-0068
609-989-6544
Fax: 609-989-0306
http://www.mercercounty.org/_private/affordable%20housing.htm
- Down Payment Assistance-first-time homebuyer
- Helping Hands-assistance to elderly for home maintenance repair and modification
- Project Access-assist homeowners with installation of ramps and interior modifications
- Residential Energy Conservation Assistance-grants and technical help to income eligible families requiring energy improvements

Middlesex County
Housing and Community Development
P.O. Box 871, Second Floor
New Brunswick, NJ 08901
732-745-4336
http://co.middlesex.nj.us/housing/index.asp
- Housing Preservation Loan Program-up to $25,000 for essential repairs. Loan is due when property is sold.

New Mexico
Bernalillo County Housing
One Civic Plaza NW
Albuquerque, NM 87102
505-768-4000
http://www.bernco.gov/departments/housing/index.html
- Home Ownership Program
- Elderly and Disabled Housing Programs

Los Alamos County Housing
P.O. Box 30
Los Alamos, NM 87544
505-662-8197
http://www.lac-nm.us/
- Affordable Rental Housing
- Home Purchase Payment Saver Program-down payment assistance for first-time homebuyers

New York

Dutchess County Planning and Development
Department
27 High Street
Poughkeepsie, NY 12601
845-486-3600
Fax: 845-486-3610
http://www.dutchessny.gov/planning.htm
- Senior Citizen Owner-Occupied Property
  Rehabilitation Program-0% loans or deferred
  loans up to $15,000 for approved home repairs

Genesee County Planning Department
Housing Council
3837 West Main Street
Batavia, NY 14020
585-344-2580, Ext. 5470
http://www.co.genesee.ny.us/
- Housing Assistance and Directory
- Educational Housing Programs

Livingston County Planning Department
Office of Housing Assistance
6 Court Street
Geneseo, NY 14454
585-243-7555
http://www.co.livingston.state.ny.us/housing.htm
- Housing Assistance-help with rental payments
- Weatherization Program-energy audits in
  addition to repairs for income eligible
  homeowners and renters

Monroe County Planning and Development
Department
50 West Main Street, Suite 8100
Rochester, NY 14614
585-428-2970
http://www.monroecounty.gov/
- Home Improvement Program

Onondaga County Housing
11th Floor John H. Mulroy Civic Center
421 Montgomery Street
Syracuse, NY 13202
315-435-3558
Fax: 315-435-3794
http://www.ongov.net/C_Development/
- Housing Programs
- Housing Rehabilitation Program

Orleans County Department of Housing Assistance
14016 Route 31 West
Albion, NY 14411
585-589-7000 ext 3207
Fax: 585-589-6571
http://www.orleansny.com/housing.htm

- Housing Assistance
- Home Rehabilitation Program

St. Lawrence County Planning Department
48 Court Street
Canton, NY 13617
315-379-2292
Fax: 315-379-2252
http://www.co.st-lawrence.ny.us/Planning/SLCPl.htm
- Housing Workshops
- Housing Rehabilitation

Westchester County Affordable Housing
148 Martine Avenue, Room 414
White Plains, NY 10601
914-995-2427
Fax: 914-995-9093
http://www.westchestergov.com/planning/housing/
- Affordable Housing
- Lead Based Paint removal Program
- Homebuyer Counseling

North Carolina

Orange County Housing and Community
Development
200 South Cameron Street
P.O. Box 8181
Hillsborough, NC 27278
919-732-8181
http://www.co.orange.nc.us/
- Affordable Housing

Wake County Homes and Housing
Resource Center
418 S. McDowell St.
Raleigh, NC 27601
919-856-5689
http://www.wakegov.com/county/housing/
- Affordable Housing
- Home Buyer Workshops
- Affordable Rental Housing
- Housing Fair-rental and home buyer information

Ohio

Clermont County Department of Community
Planning and Development
2379 Clermont Center Dr.
Batavia, OH 45103
513-732-7230
http://www.co.clermont.oh.us/planning/default.htm
- Home Rehabilitation-for income eligible
  homeowners
- Weatherization Program
- Home Counseling and Education Program

Cuyahoga County Department of Development
112 Hamilton Avenue, 4th Floor
Cleveland, OH 44114
216-443-7535
- Exterior Maintenance Program-grants and loans for exterior home improvement
- Housing Rehabilitation Loan Program-low interest loans up to $25,000
- Down Payment Assistance-deferred loans up to $7,500 to income eligible first-time homebuyers
- Weatherization Program-free assistance for income eligible homeowners

Erie County Housing and Community Development
2900 Columbus Avenue
Sandusky, OH 44870
419-627-7792
Fax: 419-627-6670
http://www.erie-county-ohio.net/planning/houscommdev.htm
- Home Rehabilitation-up to $25,000 for income eligible homeowners
- Emergency Home Repair-grants up to $5,000 to income eligible homeowners
- First-Time Homebuyers Program-up to $5,000 down payment assistance and $10,000 home renovations for income eligible families

Franklin County
The Columbus Housing Partnership
562 East Main Street
Columbus, OH 43215
614-221-8889
Fax: 614-221-8904
http://www.co.franklin.oh.us/Commissioners/ced/comm_dev_programs.htm
- Down Payment Assistance-up to $5,000 forgivable loans to moderate-income first-time homebuyers

Franklin County Community Economic Development Department
373 South High Street
Columbus, OH 43215
614-462-5631
Fax: 614-462-5549
http://www.co.franklin.oh.us/commissioners/ced/
- Rehabilitation Loan-deferred or forgivable loans up to $25,000 available for low to moderate-income
- Urgent Needs Grants-up to $4,500 to repair or replace major home systems for low income homeowners. $7,500 for failed septic systems
- Accessibility Grants-up to $6,500 to remove barriers from homes

Franklin County
Mid-Ohio Regional Planning Commission
285 East Main Street
Columbus, OH 43215
614-228-2663
Fax: 614-228-1904
http://www.morpc.org/MORPC.htm
- Hazardous Lead Paint Mitigation-up to $15,000 to remove lead-based paint

Greene County Department of Development
61 Greene Street
Xenia, OH 45385
937-562-5007
Fax: 937-562-5645
http://www.co.greene.oh.us/dod/default.htm
- Home Buyer Education Classes-free educational classes
- Emergency Home Repair Loan-up to $5,000 to income eligible homeowners

OREGON

Lane County Housing and Community Services Agency
Eugene Office:
177 Day Island Rd
Eugene, OR 97401
541-682-3755
Fax: 541-682-3411

Springfield Office:
300 W Fairview Dr.
Springfield, OR 97477
541-682-4090
Fax: 541-682-3875
http://www.hacsa.org/
- Affordable Rental Housing
- Moderate Rehabilitation Program
- Weatherization Program

Marion County Office of Housing
555 court St. NE
P.O. Box 14500
Salem, OR 97309
503-373-4448
Fax: 503-373-4439
http://Housing.co.marion.or.us
- Affordable Rental Housing

Washington County Housing Services
111 NE Lincoln Street, Suite 200-L. MS 63
Hillsboro, OR 97124-3072
503-846-4794
Fax: 503-846-4795
http://www.co.washington.or.us/deptmts/hse_serv/housmain.htm

- Affordable Rental Housing
- Affordable Housing
- First-Time Home Buyer Education Classes

PENNSYLVANIA

Bucks County Housing Development
55 E. Court Street
Doylestown, PA 18901
215-348-6000
http://www.buckscounty.org/departments/housing
_development/index.html
- Affordable Rental Housing
- Senior Housing

Cambria County Redevelopment Authority
P.O. Box 93
Ebensburg, PA 15931
814-472-6711
Fax: 814-472-4233
http://www.co.cambria.pa.us/
- Redevelopment Program

Chester County Department of Community
Development
601 Westtown Rd., Suite 365
P.O. Box 2747
West Chester, PA 19380-0990
610-344-6900
800-692-1100
http://www.chesco.org/ccdcd/about.html
- Affordable Housing
- Affordable Rental Housing
- Housing Rehabilitation-up to $3,000 for safety
  repairs
- Home Maintenance Program-up to $3,000 for
  repairs
- First-Time Home Buyers Program-down
  payment assistance
- Weatherization Program
- Senior Rental Housing

Dauphin County Department of Community and
Economic Development
P.O. Box 1295
2 South 2nd Street
Harrisburg, PA 17108-1295
717-780-6250
Fax: 717-257-1513
http://www.dcoed.org/
- Down Payment Assistance-grants up to $3,500
  for first-time homebuyer
- HomeBuyers Workshop
- Weatherization Program

Delaware County Office of Housing and Community
Development

600 North Jackson St., Room 101
Media, PA 19063-2561
610-891-5425
Fax: 610-566-0532
http://www.co.delaware.pa.us/hcd/
- Homeowners Emergency Mortgage assistance
  Program-up to 24 months of mortgage payments
  on emergency basis
- Down Payment Assistance-first-time
  homebuyers
- PA Access Program-up to $25,000 for home
  modifications for disabled
- Home Improvement Grant Program-forgivable
  loan up to $15,000 for income eligible
  homeowners
- Home Improvement Loan Program-up to $25,000
  with graduates interest rates based on income
- Housing Rehabilitation Program-up to $25,000,
  0$ deferred loan

Monroe County Planning Commission
1 Quaker Plaza, Room 106
Stroudsburg, PA 18360-2169
570-517-3100
Fax: 570-420-3564
http://www.co.monroe.pa.us/home_buyers/index.h
tm
- Down Payment Assistance-first-time
  homebuyers deferred/forgivable loans up to
  $5,000, additional $5,000 for repairs

Montgomery County Human Services Center
Housing, Economic and Community Development
1430 DeKalb Street; P.O. Box 311
Norristown, PA 19404-0311
610-278-3540
Fax: 610-278-3636
http://www.montcopa.org/mcdhs/programs.htm
- Down Payment Assistance-first-time
  homebuyers 0% grant program
- Housing Rehabilitation Loan and Grant
  Program-income eligible families

Union County Affordable Housing Trust
103 S. 2nd Street
Lewisburg, PA 17837
570-524-8600
http://dsf.seda-cog.org/union/
- Down Payment Assistance-up to $10,000

SOUTH CAROLINA

Richland County
2020 Hampton St
Columbia, SC 29204-1002
803-576-2050
http://www.richlandonline.com/home.htm#Top

- Home Ownership Assistance Program-up to $5,000 forgivable loan to income eligible first-time homebuyers

TENNESSEE
Shelby County Housing Department
1075 Mullins Station Rd.
Memphis, TN 38134
901-387-5700
http://www.co.shelby.tn.us/county_gov/divisions/comm_serv/housing/index.htm
- Affordable Housing
- Homebuyers Revolving Loan Fund

TEXAS
El Paso Community Development
500 E. San Antonio, Suite 313
El Paso, TX 79901
915-543-3845
Fax: 915-543-3846
http://www.co.el-paso.tx.us/communitydev/
- Housing Programs

Harris County Office of Housing and Economic Development
8410 Lantern Point
Houston, TX 77054
713-741-1452
http://www.cda.co.harris.tx.us/
- Housing Programs

Tarrant County Community Development and Housing Division
100 E. Weatherford
Fort Worth, TX 76196
817-884-1111
http://www.tarrantcounty.com/comm_devepmt/site/default.asp
- First-Time Home Buyer Assistance
- Home Rehabilitation

Travis County Housing Finance Corporation
314 West 11th Street, Suite 540
Austin, TX 78701
512-854-4743
Fax: 512-854-4210
http://www.co.travis.tx.us/housing_finance/default.asp
- Down Payment Assistance-4% loans to qualified first-time homebuyers

UTAH
Utah County Housing
240 East Center Street
Provo, UT 84606
801-373-8333

Fax: 801-373-2270
http://www.co.utah.ut.us/Dept/Hauc/index.asp
- Affordable Rental Housing
- Weatherization Program
- Home Improvement Program-very low interest loans to qualified homeowners

VIRGINIA
Albemarle County Housing
401 McIntire Road
Charlottesville, VA 22902-4596
434-296-5639
Fax: 434-293-0281
http://www.albemarle.org/housing/index.html
- Housing Counseling
- HOMEBUYER'S CLUB-monthly meetings for first-time home buyers
- Home Maintenance and Repair Seminars

Arlington County Office of Housing & Community Development
#1 Courthouse Plaza
2100 Clarendon Boulevard, Suite 701
Arlington, VA 22201
703-228-3760
http://www.co.arlington.va.us/cphd/housing/index.htm
- Affordable Rental Housing
- Employer Assisted Home Ownership Program
- Home Improvement Program
- First-Time Home Buyer Assistance Program

Fairfax County Housing and Community Development
3700 Pender Drive, Suite 100
Fairfax, VA 22030-7442
703-246-5170
http://www.fairfaxcounty.gov/gov/rha/Homepage.htm
- Affordable Rental Housing
- Affordable Dwelling Unity Program-for income eligible first-time homebuyers
- Homebuyer Education Classes
- Down Payment and Closing Cost Assistance Program-up to $5,000
- Home Repair for the Elderly Program
- Senior Housing Programs

James City County Housing and Community Development
5248 Olde Towne Rd.
Williamsburg, VA 23188
757-220-1272
Fax: 757-220-0640
http://www.james-city.va.us/resources/communityserv/div_cs_hcd.html

- Affordable Housing
- Down Payment Assistance-first-time homebuyers
- Indoor Plumbing/Housing Rehabilitation-income eligible families
- Emergency Home Repair Grant Program
- Home Buyer Seminars

Loudoun County Office of Housing Services
102 Heritage Way, N.E., Suite 103
Leesburg, VA 20176
703-777-0389
http://www.loudoun.gov/services/housing.htm
- Down Payment Assistance-first-time homebuyers
- Affordable Housing

Prince William County Office of Housing and Community Development
15941 Donald Curtis Drive
Woodbridge, VA 22191
703-792-7530
Fax: 703-792-4978
http://www.pwcgov.org/housing/default.asp
- Homeownership Assistance Program-providing down payment assistance, education, and counseling for income eligible homebuyers
- Housing Rehabilitation

York County Housing and Neighborhood Rehabilitation Division
224 Ballard St.
P.O. Box 532
Yorktown, VA 23690
757-890-3885
http://www.yorkcounty.gov/comser/housing/house.htm
- Information and Referral-questions regarding low to moderate assisted housing
- Housing Counseling
- Housing Rehabilitation
- Individual Development Accounts-2 for 1 matching up to $4,000 savings
- Utility Connection Fee Assistance-assistance for water and sewer connections for low to moderate income homeowners

Washington

Pierce County Community Services
8815 South Tacoma Way, Suite 211
Lakewood, WA 98499-4588
253-798-7038
Fax: 253-798-3999
http://www.co.pierce.wa.us/
- Emergency/Minor Home Repair Program-up to $1,000 available for income eligible homeowners

- Barrier Removal for Disabled Persons Program-grants and loans for low-income homeowners to make their homes fully accessible
- Warm and Dry Program-up to $10,000 loans available for income eligible homeowners to make repairs
- Down Payment Assistance Program-up to $5,000 deferred low interest loan

Spokane County Housing & Community Development
721 N. Jefferson, Suite 200
Spokane, WA 99260-0190
509-477-2521
Fax: 509-477-2561
http://spokanecounty.org/communitydev/default.asp
- Community Aquifer Protection Assistance-grants and zero interest loans to eligible homeowners to connect their homes to the sewer system

Wisconsin

Chippewa County Housing
711 North Bridge St., Room 014
Chippewa Falls, WI 54729
715-726-7933
http://www.co.chippewa.wi.us/
- Home Buyer Programs
- VISION-assists homeowners with minor repairs

Milwaukee County Housing and Community Development Division
2711 W. Wells Street
City Campus, Room 102
Milwaukee, WI 53208
414-278-4894
Fax: 414-233-8196
http://204.194.250.11/Service/OrganizationDetail.asp?org=1190&audience=
- Home Repair Loan Program
- Affordable Housing

Pepin County Housing
510 Lee Street
Durand, WI 54736
715-672-4498
http://www.co.pepin.wi.us/
- Senior Housing-income eligible seniors

Portage County Housing
1100 Center Point Drive, Suite 201B
Stevens Point, WI 54481
715-346-1392
Fax: 715-343-6259
http://www.co.portage.wi.us/Housing%20Authority/housing_authority.htm
- Affordable Housing

Wyoming

Sheridan County Planning and Zoning Office
224 South Main, Suite B-1
Sheridan, WY 82801
307-674-2920
Fax: 307-674-2927
http://www.sheridancounty.com/planning/index.ht
ml
- Housing Programs

Teton County Housing
180 Center Street, #7
P.O. Box 714
Jackson, WY 83001
307-732-0867
Fax: 307-732-2897
http://tetonwyo.org/housing/
- Affordable Housing
- New Homebuyer Education Courses

City Housing Programs

This is the town you call — or want to call — home. Maybe you need help sprucing up your house, or maybe you are searching for a place but money is tight. Cities across America are trying to entice people to come to their town. It helps their economy, and keeps the community vital. How are cities helping homeowners? Programs vary from place to place, but city leaders know that good housing stock will bring in more dollars to fund the budget. Many towns have developed programs designed to provide emergency assistance for housing repairs. Grants and loans are sometimes available to help the physically disabled make their homes more accessible. Others offer low interest loans to first time home buyers. Remember, if you haven't owned a home in three years or are divorced, you are considered a first time home owner. Phoenix, Arizona offers a Home Ownership Training Program, as do other cities. Some programs include:

➡ Anniston, AL: Emergency Home Repair
➡ Anchorage, AK: Disabled Access Grant Program
➡ Phoenix, AZ: Down Payment and Closing Costs Assistance
➡ Bakersfield, CA: Home Improvement Loans
➡ Gainesville, FL: Roof Repair Program
➡ Champaign, IL: Caulk and Paint Assistance
➡ Bloomington, IN: Historic Preservation Programs
➡ Lowell, MA: Lead Paint Abatement Program

Don't for a minute think that the listing that follows is complete. We just wanted to give you a flavor of what is available and some ideas of who to call in your current or future home town. You can also search for your town online at {www.govengine.com }.

Alabama

City of Anniston
Planning Department, Community Development
1128 Gurnee Avenue
P.O. Box 2168
Anniston, AL 36202
256-231-7660

Fax: 256- 231-7748
http://www.ci.anniston.al.us/
-    Emergency Home Repair Program- up to $7,500

City of Decatur
Community Development
402 Lee Street NE

Decatur, AL 35601
256-341-4960
Fax: 256-341-4969
http://www.digitaldecatur.com/
- Housing Rehabilitation Programs
- Redevelopment Housing Projects

City of Gadsden
Community and Economic Development, Housing
Assistance Programs
90 Broad Street
P.O. Box 267
Gadsden, AL 35902
256-549-4532
Fax: 256-549-4689
http://www.ci.gadsden.al.us/
- Housing Rehabilitation Assistance Loan Program
- Affordable Housing Loan Program-below market
  rate loans
- Optional Housing Replacement Loan Program-
  voluntary program, existing home must be
  beyond repair
- Emergency Housing Repairs Loan Program- up
  to $5,000

City of Tuscaloosa
Community Planning and Development
2201 University Boulevard
P.O. Box 2089
Tuscaloosa, AL 35403-2089
205-349-0160
Fax: 205-349-0135
http://www.ci.tuscaloosa.al.us/
- Housing Rehabilitation Loans and Grants

Alaska

City of Anchorage
Planning, Development & Public Works, Housing
Department
4700 South Bragaw Street
P.O. Box 196650
Anchorage, AK 99519
907-343-7900
Fax: 907-343-7927
http://www.ci.anchorage.ak.us/homepage/index.cf
m
- Emergency Repair Program-grants from $1,000 to
  $15,000
- Mobile Home Dislocation Assistance Program
- Disabled Access Program- grants up to $15,000 to
  qualified applicants

Arizona

City of Douglas
Public Housing Department, Housing Programs
425 Tenth Street

Douglas, AZ 85607
520-364-8458
http://housing.ci.douglas.az.us/Programs/programs
.asp
- Housing Rehabilitation Programs-owner
  occupied
- Rental Rehabilitation Loans-$7,500 to $25,000

City of Mesa
Housing Services Division
415 North Pasadena
Mesa, AZ 85201
480-644-3535
Fax: 480-644-2923
http://www.ci.mesa.az.us/cityhome/default.asp
- Affordable Rental Housing
- Housing Rehabilitation Programs

City of Phoenix
Housing Department
200 West Washington Street
Phoenix, AZ 85003
602-262-6794
http://phoenix.gov/HOUSING/index.html
- Affordable Rental Housing
- First Time Home Buyer Mortgage Assistance
- Scattered Sites Housing Program-lease with
  option to purchase program
- Home Ownership Training
- Down Payment and Closing Costs Assistance

City of Scottsdale
Neighborhood Services and Preservation
7447 East Indian School Road
Scottsdale, AZ 85251
480-312-3111
Fax: 480-312-2455
http://www.scottsdaleaz.gov/Departments/Default.
asp
- Housing Rehabilitation Programs-interest free,
  deferred payment loans
- Emergency Repair Program-grants up to $8,000

City of Tucson
Community Services Department
310 North Commerce Park Loop
P.O. Box 27210
Tucson, AZ 85726-7210
520-791-4171
Fax: 520-791-5407
http://www.ci.tucson.az.us
- Affordable Home Ownership Opportunities
- First Time Home Buyers/ Infill Housing
- Homeowner Rehabilitation Deferred Loan
  Program
- Housing Rehabilitation Collaboration
- Affordable Rental Housing

Arkansas

City of Fort Smith
Community Development
623 Garrison Avenue
Fort Smith, AR 72902
479-784-2209
http://www.fsark.com/CommunityDevelopment/index.html
- Housing Rehabilitation Assistance-grants up to $15,000, loans up to $10,000

City of Little Rock
Department of Housing and Neighborhood Programs
City Hall Room #120W
500 West Markham
Little Rock, AR 72201
501-371-4748
Fax: 501-399-3461
http://www.accesslittlerock.org/departments/housing_p1.html
- Home Buyer Assistance Grants-down payment and closing costs assistance, matching funds up to $2,000
- Sewer Service Grants-up to $2,500 for installation or replacement of sewer service lines
- Redevelopment Housing Programs-save-a-home, affordable new homes, and model block program
- Limited Home Repair Loans-deferred loans up to $6,000 for low income seniors
- Leveraged Home Rehabilitation Loans

City of Pine Bluff
Economic and Community Development
200 East Eighth Avenue
Pine Bluff, AR 71601
870-543-1820
http://www.pbecd.org/
- First Time Home Buyer Program-down payment and closing costs assistance
- Emergency Rehabilitation Program-up to $4,500 for minor repairs
- Homeowner Rehabilitation Programs
- Housing Reconstruction Program
- New Construction Program
- Housing Counseling Services
- Rental rehabilitation Program-matching assistance up to $7,500

California

City of Alhambra
Development Services
Housing Assistance
111 South First Street
Alhambra, CA 91801
626-570-5034
Fax: 626-576-4201
http://www.cityofalhambra.org/government/development_services/housing_assistance/property_rehab.html
- First Time Home Buyer Loan Assistance Program
- Housing Rehabilitation loan and Grant Programs

City of Anaheim
Community Development, Housing Assistance
200 South Anaheim Boulevard
Anaheim, CA 92805
714-765-5162
http://www.anaheim.net/com_dev/housing.html
- Second Mortgage Assistance Program (SMAP)-up to $25,000
- Home Improvement Loans-low interest, up to $60,000

City of Bakersfield
Community Development
1501 Truxton Avenue
Bakersfield, CA 93301
661-326-3765
http://www.ci.bakersfield.ca.us/edcd/commdev/index.htm
- Rental Rehabilitation Loans
- Home Improvement Loans
- Home Accessibility Program-pays for housing modifications to provide access for disabled home owners and renters
- First Time Home Buyers Assistance-up to $3,500 to help with down payment and closing costs

City of Chico
Community Development, Housing Division
411 Main Street
P.O. Box 3420
Chico, CA 95927
530-895-4845
Fax: 530-895-4726
http://www.ci.chico.ca.us/commdev/Home_Page.asp
- First Time Home Buyers Mortgage Subsidy Program
- Housing Rehabilitation Program-home repair loans
- Housing Counseling

City of Chula Vista
Community Development, Housing Division
439 Davidson Street
Chula Vista, CA 91910
619-585-5722
Fax: 619-585-5698
http://www.ci.chula-vista.ca.us/City_Services/Development_Services/Community_Development/Housing/Programs/default.asp

- Redevelopment Housing Programs
- Community Housing Improvement Program (CHIP) Grants-must be used for health and safety related repairs and improvements
- Community Housing Improvement Program (CHIP) Loans-deferred payment, up to $24,000

City of Commerce
Community Development, Housing and Resource Assistance
2535 Commerce Way
Commerce, CA 90040
http://www.ci.commerce.ca.us/housingresources.htm
- Home Improvement Loans- up to $15,000, 3% interest, deferred payments
- Home Improvement Rebates- up to $15,000 for materials and/or labor costs
- First Time Home Buyer Programs-mortgage credit certificates, reduced fees, low interest, down payment assistance loans, Fresh Rate Program

City of Fresno
Department of Housing, Economic and Community Development
2600 Fresno Street, 3rd Floor
Fresno, CA 93721
559-621-8300
Fax: 559-488-1076
http://www.fresno.gov/hnr/
- Down Payment Assistance-up to $4,000 for First Time Home Buyers
- Low Income Homebuyer Program-up to $19,400 in financing

City of Fullerton
Development Services, Housing Programs
303 West Commonwealth
Fullerton, CA 92832
714-738-6317
http://www.ci.fullerton.ca.us/dev_serv/housing.html
- Down Payment Assistance Program-for First Time Home Buyers, deferred loans, no interest
- Housing Rehabilitation Programs-deferred loans, and below market interest rate loans
- Mobile Home Rehabilitation Assistance-deferred, no interest, up to $10,000
- Housing Rehabilitation Grants-several programs are available to very low income households

City of Los Banos
Redevelopment Agency, Housing Programs
520 J Street
Los Banos, CA 93635

209-827-7000
Fax: 209-827-7006
http://www.losbanos.org/web/d/rda/housing.html
- Home Repair Loans-low interest, deferred payment, up to $40,000
- First Time Home Buyer No Interest Loan Program

City of Merced
Housing Department
678 West 18th Street
Merced, CA 95340
209-385-6863
Fax: 209-384-5805
http://www.ci.merced.ca.us/housing/housing.htm
- First Time Home Buyer Assistance
- Housing Rehabilitation Program

City of Modesto
Housing Element
1010 Tenth Street, Suite 3300
Modesto, CA 95354
209-571-5566
http://www.ci.modesto.ca.us/cdd/housing/programs/default.asp
- Down Payment Assistance-maximum of $25,000
- Emergency Home Repair Program-maximum of $15,000 for qualified repairs
- Housing Rehabilitation Programs
- Property Enhancement Program-rebates on exterior improvements
- Lease-to-Own Program

City of Monterey
Community Services, Housing Programs
669 Van Buren Street
Monterey, CA 93940
831-646-5615
Fax: 831-646-5616
http://www.monterey.org/housing
- Home Repair Loans-low interest, deferred payment
- Affordable Rental Housing
- Down Payment Assistance for First Time Home Buyers
- Purchase and Resale Ownership Program

City of Morgan Hill
Community Services, Housing
17555 Peak Avenue
Morgan Hill, CA 95037-4128
408-776-7373
Fax: 408-779-3117
http://www.morgan-hill.ca.gov/html/citysvc/comm/house.asp

- Housing Rehabilitation Loans-owner occupied, rental, and mobile home programs
- Minor Home Repair Grants-up to $5,000

City of National City
Community Development Commission
140 East 12th Street, suite B
National City, CA 91950
619-336-4250
Fax: 619-336-4286
http://www.ci.national-city.ca.us/
- First Time Home Buyer Loan Program
- Rehabilitation Loan Program-low interest
- Rental Rehabilitation Loan Program
- Housing Redevelopment Projects

City of Palmdale
Business Programs, Housing Section
38300 Sierra Highway
Palmdale, CA 93550
661-267-5100
Fax: 661-267-5122
http://www.cityofpalmdale.org/business/housing.html
- Mortgage Assistance Program for First Time Home Buyers-down payment assistance of up to $20,000 through a deferred payment second mortgage
- Neighborhood Improvement Program
- Emergency Repair Grants- up to $3,000
- Housing Rehabilitation Programs

City of Pico Rivera
Housing Services Department
6615 Passons Boulevard
Pico Rivera, CA 90660-1016
562-801-4347
http://www.ci.pico-rivera.ca.us/ourcommunity/housingprograms.html
- Home Improvement Rebates-50% reimbursement up to $2,000 per project
- Home Improvement Grants-up to $3,000 for emergency repairs
- Home Repair and Improvement Loans-3% interest, deferred payment
- Affordable New Housing
- Lease-Purchase Home Ownership Assistance Program
- Housing Replacement-the Redevelopment Agency may assist in paying for the rebuilding of the entire structure if it is beyond repair

City of Pleasanton
Affordable Housing and Community Development
Housing Division
P.O. Box 520

123 Main Street
Pleasanton, CA 94566-0802
925-931-5007
Fax: 925-931-5483
http://www.ci.pleasanton.ca.us/housing_toc1.html
- Affordable Rental Housing-for seniors
- First Time Home Buyer Program- mortgage credit certificates, down payment assistance, and Pleasanton Home Ownership Assistance Program
- Community Assisted Shared Appreciation (CASA) Home Loan Program-small down payment, low monthly payments
- CaHLIF Home Loan Program
- Home Rehabilitation Loans-low interest, deferred loan up to $20,000 to low income home owners
- Emergency Home Repair Grants-up to $500 for labor and materials
- Seismic Loans-up to $5,000 to increase the safety of homes in the event of an earthquake
- Mobile Home Repair Grants- up to $2,000 for labor and materials
- Mobile Home Seismic Grants-up to $2,000
- Rental Rehabilitation Loans
- Paint Grants-up to $5,000 for exterior painting

City of Redding
Housing and Community Development
777 Cypress Avenue
Redding, CA 96001
530-225-4048
Fax: 530-225-4126
http://www.ci.redding.ca.us/housing/hcd.htm
- Rental Rehabilitation Loans-long term, low interest
- Homeowner Rehabilitation Program-low interest loans to low income homeowners
- Emergency Repair Program-3% interest, loans up to $2,500 for both mobile and conventional homes
- Down Payment Assistance Program

City of Redwood City
Housing Office
P.O. Box 391
1017 Middlefield Road
Redwood City, CA 94064
650-780-7290
Fax: 650-780-0128
TDD: 650-780-0129
http://www.redwoodcityhousing.org/index_programs.htm
- Home Improvement Loans-3% interest
- Emergency Home Improvement Grants-up to $2,000
- Redevelopment Housing Programs
- First Time Home Buyer Programs

City of Rohnert Park
Community Development Commission, Housing
Programs
6750 Commerce Boulevard
Rohnert Park, CA 94928
707-588-2200
Fax: 707-588-2274
http://www.rpcity.org/services/housing.cfm
- Home Improvement Loans-deferred payment,
  forgivable loans of up to $50,000 to qualifying
  residents
- First Time Home Buyer Program-down payment
  assistance
- Affordable Rental Housing

City of Sacramento
Sacramento Housing and Redevelopment Agency
630 I Street
Sacramento, CA 95814
916-444-9210
http://www.shra.org/Content/Housing/Housing.htm
- Housing Redevelopment Programs
- Affordable Rental Housing
- Mortgage Credit Certificate Program
- Down Payment Assistance Programs
- Home Repair/Improvement Grants and Loans

City of San Francisco
Mayor's Office of Housing
25 Van Ness Avenue, Suite 600
San Francisco, CA 94102
415-252-3177
Fax: 415-252-3140
http://www.ci.sf.ca.us/moh/
- First Time Home Buyer Program-mortgage
  assistance
- Mortgage Credit Certificate Program
- Housing Rehabilitation Programs
- Code enforcement Rehabilitation Fund-loans
  from $250 to $15,000 to correct code violations

City of San Jose
Department of Housing
4 North Second Street, Suite 1350
San Jose, CA 95113
407-277-4747
http://www.sjhousing.org/program/hpp_e.html
- Home Owner Grant Program-up to $15,000 for
  emergency repairs
- Housing Preservation Program-up to $100,000,
  low interest, deferred loans for improvements
  and/or repairs
- Mobile Home Repair Loan and Grant Programs-
  up to $20,000 low interest loans for
  improvements, or up to $12,000 grants for
  emergency repairs

- Rental Housing Rehabilitation Program-low
  interest loans
- Home Owner Exterior Paint Program- maximum
  of $5,000 grant
- Rental Exterior Paint Program- grants of up to
  $5,000
- First Time Home Buyer-Quick Reference Guide

City of San Mateo
Neighborhood Improvement and Housing
330 West 20th Avenue
San Mateo, CA 94403
650-522-7220
Fax: 650-522-7221
http://www.ci.sanmateo.ca.us/dept/housing/assist
ance_rental.html
- Affordable Housing Listings- both rental and to
  own
- First Time Home Buyer Program-reduced
  interest rates and deferred payments
- Housing Rehabilitation Loan Program-up to
  $85,000 ($100,000 for historic homes)

City of Santa Rosa
Housing and Redevelopment
90 Santa Rosa Avenue
Santa Rosa, CA 95404
707-543-3300
Fax: 707-543-3317
http://ci.santa-rosa.ca.us/hr/
- Owner-Occupant Rehabilitation Loans
- Affordable Housing Loans
- Mobile Home Rehabilitation Loans
- Housing Redevelopment Projects

City of Santee
Department of Economic Development and Housing
10601 Magnolia, Building 3
El Cajon, CA 92019
619-258-4100 ext. 133
http://www.ci.santee.ca.us/dhr/
- First Time Home Buyer Program-down payment
  and closing costs loans, up to $20,000
- Home Improvement Loans-low interest, up to
  $25,000
- Mobile Home Improvement loans-no interest, up
  to $8,500
- Mortgage Credit Assistance Program

City of Stockton
Housing and Redevelopment
22 East Weber Avenue, Room 350
Stockton, CA 95202
209-937-8539
Fax: 209-937-8822
http://www.stocktongov.com/HRD/index.htm

- Single Family Housing Loan Program-home repair loans
- Home Buyers Assistance Program-financing for purchase and/or rehabilitation of existing housing
- Rental Rehabilitation Loan Program
- Emergency Home Repair Program-one time only, loans up to $5,000
- Housing Redevelopment Programs

City of Vallejo
Housing and Community Development
200 Georgia Street
Vallejo, CA 94590
707-648-4507
Fax: 707-648-5249
http://www.ci.vallejo.ca.us/housing/hprog.htm
- Affordable housing Projects
- Home Buyer Assistance- down payment assistance loans
- Housing Rehabilitation Loans- owner occupied and rental rehabilitation loans

City of Vista
Redevelopment and Housing
600 Eucalyptus Avenue
P.O. Box 1988
Vista, CA 92085
760-726-1340
Fax: 760-639-6132
http://www.ci.vista.ca.us/gov/redev/default.htm
- Redevelopment Housing Programs
- Mortgage Credit Certification Program
- Down Payment and Closing Costs Assistance-up to $10,000, deferred loan, no interest
- Housing Rehabilitation Loan Program-maximum of $25,000
- Mobile Home Rehabilitation Program- deferred loan, no interest, up to $10,000
- Mobile Home Rehabilitation Grant Program
- Exterior Enhancement Grant Program-up to $5,000 loans, forgivable, no interest, no payments

Colorado

City of Arvada
Housing and Neighborhood Revitalization
8101 Ralston Road
Arvada, CO 80002
720-898-7494
http://www.ci.arvada.co.us/
- Rental Improvement Loan Program
- Essential Home Repair Program-grants and loans

City of Aurora
Community Development Division
9801 East Colfax Avenue

Aurora, CO 80010
303-739-7900
http://www.ci.aurora.co.us/index.cfm
- Home Ownership Assistance Program
- Home Ownership Counseling
- Down Payment and Closing Costs Assistance-up to $3,000
- Emergency Repair Grants-up to $2,500
- Paint up/Fix up Grants -up to $1,500
- Housing Rehabilitation Loans

City of Boulder
Department of Housing and Human Services,
Division of Housing
1101 Arapahoe Avenue, 2nd floor
P.O. Box 791
Boulder, CO 80306
303-441-3157
Fax: 303-441-4368
http://www.ci.boulder.co.us/hshhs/homeownership/index.htm
- Homeownership Orientation Program
- Home Buyer Classes
- Homeworks Affordable Homes
- Down Payment Assistance- First Home Grants and H2O deferred loans

City of Colorado Springs
30 South Nevada, Suite 601
Colorado Springs, CO 80903
719-385-5912
Fax: 719-385-5367
http://www.springsgov.com/SectionIndex.asp?SectionID=2
- Housing Redevelopment Programs
- Housing Development Programs

City of Commerce City
Commerce City Housing Authority
5291 East 60th Avenue
Commerce City, CO 80022
303-289-3600
Fax: 303-289-3688
http://www.ci.commerce-city.co.us/departments/housing.html
- Housing Rehabilitation Loan Program
- Home Buyers Program

City of Denver
Housing and Neighborhood Development Services
201 West Colfax, Dept 204
Denver, CO 80202
720-913-1555
http://www.denvergov.org/dephome.asp?depid=1467
- Emergency Home Repair

- Housing Rehabilitation Programs-low or no interest loans
- Homeownership Assistance- home ownership counseling, down payment assistance

City of Fort Collins
Advance Planning, Affordable Housing Department
P.O. Box 580
Fort Collins, CO 80522
970-221-6376
http://www.ci.fort-collins.co.us/affordablehousing/
- Housing Counseling Assistance
- Home Buyer Assistance Program-down payment and closing costs loans up to $9,000

City of Longmont
Community Development, Housing Programs
350 Kimbark Street
Longmont, CO 80501
303-651-8736
Fax: 303-651-8590
http://www.ci.longmont.co.us/cdbg/housing/index.htm
- Community Housing Program-affordable housing
- Down Payment Assistance Program- loans up to $9,000 for first time home buyers
- Housing Rehabilitation Programs-several programs including general repair loans, emergency repair grants, accessibility loans, and rental rehabilitation loans

City of Pueblo
Department of Housing and Citizen Services
2631 East 4th Street
Pueblo, CO 81001
719-583-4477
http://www.pueblogov.com
- Home Down Payment Assistance Program
- Buy-It/Fix-It Program-up to $15,000 to purchase and rehabilitate homes in need of repair
- Housing Rehabilitation Loans-low interest, from $2,500 to $13,000

City of Thornton
Policy Planning Division, Housing Department
9500 Civic Center Drive
Thornton, CO 80229
303-538-7605
http://www.ci.thornton.co.us/comd/policyplanning.asp
- Home Ownership Classes and Counseling
- Down Payment and Closing Costs Assistance
- Mortgage Assistance- to First Time Home Buyers
- Home Owner Housing Rehabilitation

- Help for Homes-matching funds grants up to $2,000, volunteer program
- Home Maintenance-seasonal and topical guides

City of Westminster
Department of Community Development
Housing Assistance Programs
4800 West 92nd Avenue
Westminster, CO 80031
303-430-2400 ext. 2111
http://www.ci.westminster.co.us/gov/depts/cd/admin.htm
- Down Payment Assistance
- Housing Rehabilitation Loans

CONNECTICUT
City of Hartford
Housing and Community Development
250 Constitution Plaza
Hartford, CT 06103
860-757-9005
http://www.hartford.gov/housing/
- Housing Preservation Loan Fund-home improvement loans for approved repairs
- Housing Redevelopment Program
- Housing Counseling Services
- Relocation Services

City of Manchester
Planning and Economic Development
41 Center Street
P.O. Box 191
Manchester, CT 06045-0191
860-647-3044
http://www.ci.manchester.ct.us/Planning/homeownership_Programs.htm
- Down Payment and Closing Costs Assistance Program
- Home Ownership Program for First Time Home Buyers
- Home Ownership Incentive Program

City of New London
Community Development Division
Stanton Building, 2nd Floor
111 Union Street
New London, CT 06320
860-437-6392
Fax: 860-437-4467
http://www.ci.new-london.ct.us/
- Housing Rehabilitation Programs

City of Stamford
Community Development Department
Government Center 10th Floor
888 Washington Boulevard

Stamford, CT 06901
203-977-4155
http://www.ci.stamford.ct.us/CommunityDevelopm
entAndGrants/CommDevMain.htm
-   Housing Rehabilitation Programs-partial
    financing, low interest

Delaware
City of Dover
Planning & Inspections, Community Development
Department
15 East Loockerman Street
P.O. Box 475
Dover, DE 19903-0475
302-736-7010
Fax: 302-736-4217
www.cityofdover.com
-   Housing Rehabilitation Assistance

City of Wilmington
Department of Real Estate and Housing
Louis L. Redding City/County Building
800 North French Street, 7th Floor
Wilmington, DE 19801
302-576-3000
Fax: 302-573-5588
http://www.ci.wilmington.de.us/departments/hous
ing.htm
-   Home Improvement Loans
-   Housing Rehabilitation Loan Program- low
    interest
-   Down Payment and Settlement Assistance
    Program

Florida
City of Bradenton
Housing Programs
912 7th Avenue
Bradenton, FL 34208
941-708-6200
Fax: 941-708-6226
http://www.cityofbradenton.com
-   Home Repair Loans-up to $15,000, low interest
-   Housing Rehabilitation Grant Program-up to
    $22,000
-   Down Payment Assistance Program-first time
    home buyers, up to $3,500
-   Emergency Repair Grants

City of Clearwater
Economic Development and Housing Department
112 North Osceola Avenue
Clearwater, FL 33756
727-562-4030
Fax: 727-562-4037

http://www.clearwater-
fl.com/City_Departments/econdev/housing.html
-   Housing Rehabilitation Program
-   Homebuyer Assistance-down payment and
    closing costs loans up to $15,000

City of Fort Pierce
Community Development Department
100 North US 1
P.O. Box 1480
Fort Pierce, FL 34950
772-460-2200
http://www.cityoffortpierce.com/
-   Housing Rehabilitation Program
-   Emergency Repair Program
-   U-Paint It Program

City of Gainesville
Community Development Department
P.O. Box 490
200 East University Avenue
Gainesville, FL 32601
352-334-5029
http://comdev.cityofgainesville.org/
-   Housing Redevelopment Program
-   Owner Occupied Rehabilitation Program
-   Rental Rehabilitation Program
-   Emergency Repair Program
-   Roof Repair Program
-   Down Payment Assistance
-   Mortgage Foreclosure Intervention

City of Lakeland
Community Development, Housing Division
228 South Massachusetts Avenue
Lakeland, FL 33801
863-834-6011
http://www.lakelandgov.net/commdev/home.html
-   Affordable Housing Programs
-   Housing Rehabilitation

City of Melbourne
Housing and Community Development Department
695 East University Boulevard
Melbourne, FL 32901
321-674-5734
Fax: 321-953-6224
http://www.melbourneflorida.org/housing/
-   Purchase Assistance Program-down payment
    and closing costs assistance
-   Housing Rehabilitation Program-up to $35,000
-   Housing Replacement Program - maximum of
    $45,000
-   Rental Rehabilitation Program -matching funds,
    up to $5,000

City of Miami
Community Development
444 S.W. 2nd Avenue
Miami, FL 33130
305-416-2080
Fax: 305-416-2090
http://www.ci.miami.fl.us/community.asp
- Housing Development Programs
- Housing Redevelopment Programs
- Single Family Housing Rehabilitation Program

City of Ocala
Community Programs Department
City Hall Annex
405 S.E. Osceola Avenue
P.O. Box 1270
Ocala, FL 34478
352-629-8231
Fax: 352-867-1781
http://www.ocalafl.org/CommPrograms/
- Housing Rehabilitation Programs
- Down Payment and Closing Costs Assistance

City of Orlando
Housing and Community Development
One City Commons, 6th floor
400 South Orange Avenue
P.O. Box 4990
Orlando, FL 32802-4990
407-246-2708
Fax: 407-246-3055
http://www.cityoforlando.net/planning/housingan
dcommunitydev/default.htm
- Down Payment Assistance Program
- Rental Rehabilitation Assistance
- Housing Rehabilitation Programs
- Housing Code Assistance-up to $5,000 grants to
  repair exterior code violations
- Emergency Repair Program- grants up to $5,000
  to repair health and safety conditions

City of Panama City
Community Development Department
9 Harrison Avenue
Panama City, FL 32401
850-872-7230
http://www.cityofpanamacity.com/Community/co
mmunity_dev.aspx
- New Housing Assistance Program-up to $2,250
  for closing costs, and up to $7,500 for down
  payment
- Housing Rehabilitation Program-loans up to
  $25,000

City of Pensacola
Housing Department

Third Floor, City Hall
180 Government Center
222 West Main Street
Pensacola, FL 32501
850-435-1665
http://www.ci.pensacola.fl.us/services/index.html
- Owner Occupied Housing Rehabilitation-up to
  $33,000 in low interest loans and supplemental
  grants
- Down Payment and Closing Costs Assistance-to
  first time home buyers
- Housing Development Program

City of Plant City
Community Development Department
P.O. Box C
302 West Reynolds Street
Plant City, FL 33564
813-659-4200
Fax: 813-659-4206
http://www.lakelandgov.net/commdev/home.html
- Affordable Housing Program-down payment
  and closing costs assistance
- Façade and Interior Improvement Matching
  Grant Program-up to $15,000 in matching funds
  for eligible improvements

City of Sarasota
Housing and Community Development
1565 First Street
Sarasota, FL 34236
941-316-1070
http://www.sarasotagov.com/LivingInSarasota/Co
ntents/Housing/Programs.html
- Down Payment Assistance Program
- Purchase/Rehabilitation Program-no interest,
  deferred payment
- Homebuyer Education
- Home Improvement Programs-rehabilitation,
  barrier removal, water/sewer connection

City of St. Petersburg
Housing and Community Development Department
440 2nd Avenue North
St. Petersburg, FL 33701
727-893-4159
http://www.stpete.org/house.htm
- Housing Rehabilitation Assistance
- Housing Replacement Program

City of Tallahassee
Department of Neighborhood and Community
Services
208 West Carolina Street
Tallahassee, FL 32301
850-891-6500

http://talgov.com/citytlh/dncs/index.html
- Affordable Housing Strategies
- Housing Rehabilitation and Relocation

City of Tampa
Housing and Community Development
2105 North Nebraska Avenue
Tampa, FL 33602
813-274-7954
Fax: 813-274-7927
http://www.stpete.org/house.htm
- Housing Redevelopment Programs
- Mayor's Challenge Fund
- Down Payment and Closing Costs Assistance
- Home Rehabilitation Assistance

City of Titusville
Housing and Community Development Department
555 South Washington Avenue
Titusville, FL 32780
321-383-5779
Fax: 321-383-5614
http://www.titusville.com/depts/hcd/index.htm
- Emergency Repair Loans-up to $5,000
- Housing Rehabilitation Programs

Georgia
City of Albany
Community and Economic Development, Housing
Programs
230 South Jackson Street, Suite 315
Albany, GA 31701
229-430-5283
Fax: 229-430-2737
http://www.albany.ga.us/
- Emergency Repair Loans-up to $5,000
- Home Owner's Rehabilitation Program-low
  interest, up to $25,000
- Affordable Home Ownership Program

City of Athens
Human and Economic Development
375 Satula Avenue
Athens, GA 30601
706-613-3155
http://www.athensclarkecounty.com/~hed/Progra
ms.htm
- Emergency Home Repair Program
- Housing Counseling Service

City of Atlanta
Department of Planning, Development, and
Neighborhood Conservation
55 Trinity Avenue
Atlanta, GA 30303
404-330-6390

Fax: 404-658-7384
http://www.ci.atlanta.ga.us/citydir/dpdnc/index.htm
- Housing Development Programs
- Housing Rehabilitation Programs

City of Augusta
Housing and Neighborhood Development
One 10th Street, Suite 430
Augusta, GA 30901
706-821-1797
Fax: 706-821-1784
http://augusta.co.richmond.ga.us/departments/hou
sing_dev/default.htm
- Demolition/Rebuild Program
- Home Ownership Assistance-up to $2,500 in
  down payment assistance loans
- Rental Rehabilitation Program
- Owner Occupied Housing Rehabilitation
  Program
- Paint Improvement Program

City of Macon
Economic and Community Development
439 Cotton Avenue
Macon, GA 31201
478-751-7190
Fax: 478-751-7390
http://www.cityofmacon.net/CityDept/ecdd.htm
- Home Improvement Programs
- Rental Rehabilitation Program
- Home Purchase Program
- Affordable Housing Program

City of Rome
Community Development Department
607 Broad Street
P.O. Box 1433
Rome, GA 30162-1433
706-236-4477
Fax: 706-235-4448
http://www.romegacitygov.org/commdev.htm
- Down Payment Assistance Program-up to $2,100,
  no interest, deferred loans
- First Time Home Buyer Projects

City of Savannah
Housing Department
P.O. Box 1027
10 East Bay Street
Savannah, GA 31402
912-651-6927
http://www.ci.savannah.ga.us/cityweb/webdatabas
e.nsf
- Rental Rehabilitation Program
- Home Rehabilitation Loans
- Relocation Assistance

Hawaii

City of Honolulu
Community Services Department
715 South King Street
Honolulu, HI 96813
808-527-6269
Fax: 808-527-5498
http://www.co.honolulu.hi.us/
- Rehabilitation Loan Program
- Down Payment Assistance
- Sewer Connection Loans

Idaho

City of Boise
Housing and Community Development Division
1025 South Capitol Boulevard
Boise, ID 83706-3000
208-384-4158
Fax: 208-384-4195
www.boise-airport.com/pds/housing
- Affordable Housing Loans
- Affordable Rental Housing
- Home Repair Loans-up to $45,000, low interest, and deferred payment
- Emergency Home Repair Loans-low interest, up to $5,000
- Handicapped Accessibility Loans

City of Pocatello
Neighborhood and Community Services Division
911 North 7th Avenue
Pocatello, ID 83201
208-234-6188
http://www.ci.pocatello.id.us/departments/pokydrct.html
- Emergency Home Repair Loans-for low to moderate income home owners
- Housing Rehabilitation Programs
- Redevelopment Housing Programs

Illinois

Village of Arlington Heights
Property Development and Improvement
33 South Arlington Heights Road
Arlington Heights, IL 60005
847-368-5200
http://www.vah.com/property/prop.html
- Single Family Rehabilitation Program-0% interest, deferred loans
- Multi-Family Rehabilitation Program-low interest loans/grants for rental rehabilitation

City of Aurora
Neighborhood Redevelopment Division
501 College Avenue, Suite 320
Aurora, IL 60507

630-264-8280
http://www.ci.aurora.il.us/NeighborhoodRedevelopment/index.html
- First Time Home Buyer Programs
- Emergency Housing Rehabilitation Program-up to $5,000
- Tenant Relocation Assistance Program

City of Bloomington
Community Development Division
109 East Olive Street
P.O. Box 3157
Bloomington, IL 61702-3157
309-434-2244
http://www.cityhall.ci.bloomington.il.us/cityhall/html/community_development.html
- Home Rehabilitation Loans-several types of assistance offered including city direct loans, grants, forgivable loans, and deferred loans

City of Champaign
Neighborhood Services, Housing Assistance
102 North Neil Street
Champaign, IL 61820
217-351-4427
http://www.city.champaign.il.us/neighborhood/index.html
- Caulk and Paint Assistance
- Emergency Repair Grants
- First Time Home Buyers Assistance
- Full Home Rehabilitation-grants and low interest loans
- Handicap Accessibility Retrofit Program-grants and loans

City of Danville
Community Development/Housing Rehabilitation Division
17 West Main Street
Danville, IL 61832
217-431-2320
http://www.cityofdanville.org/DDS_files/DDS.htm
- Home Rehabilitation Program-grants up to $15,000 to repair code violations

City of East Moline
Community Development
912 16th Avenue
East Moline, IL 61244
309-752-1599
http://www.eastmoline.com/planning/economic/housing/
- Single Family Owner Occupied Housing Rehabilitation
- Multi-Family Rental Housing Rehabilitation

City of Evanston
Community Development
2100 Ridge Avenue, Room 3105
Evanston, IL 60201
847-448-8022
http://www.cityofevanston.org/Departments/Com
munityDev/index.html
-    Housing Rehabilitation Loans-low interest loans
     for low to moderate income home owners

City of Joliet
Community and Economic Development
150 West Jefferson Street
Joliet, IL 60432
815-724-4090
Fax: 815-724-4118
http://www.ci.joliet.il.us/econdev.htm
-    Housing Rehabilitation Assistance

City of Normal
Community Development
101 North Street
Normal, IL 61761
309-454-9557
Fax: 309-454-9723
http://www.normal.org/Departments/Community
Development/CDOverview.htm
-    Down Payment and Closing Costs Assistance-
     maximum of $3,000 in matching funds
-    Rehabilitation Grant/Loan Program-up to
     $10,000

City of North Chicago
Community Development and Planning Department
1850 Lewis Avenue
North Chicago, IL 60064
847-596-8670
Fax: 847-596-8679
http://www.northchicago.org/planning/plan.htm
-    Housing Rehabilitation Programs

City of Rock Island
Community and Economic Development
Planning and Development Division
1528 Third Avenue
Rock Island, IL 61201
309-732-2900
Fax: 309-732-2930
http://www.rigov.org/citydepartments/ced/housin
grehab.html
-    Project Facelift- up to $5,000 for exterior repairs if
     you live on a major thoroughfare
-    Rental Rehabilitation Program-five year
     forgivable loans

City of Rockford
Neighborhood Development Division
425 East State Street

Rockford, IL 61104-1068
815-987-5690
http://www.ci.joliet.il.us/econdev.htm
-    First Time Home Buyer Programs
-    Owner Occupied Rehabilitation Programs
-    Rental Rehabilitation Programs

City of Springfield
Office of Planning and Economic Development
231 South Sixth Street
Springfield, IL 62701
217-789-2317
800-357-2379
http://www.springfield.il.us/Oped/Default.htm
-    Emergency Home Repair-grants of up to $6,000
-    Home Repair Loans-deferred payment loans up
     to $20,000 to remedy code violations
-    Home Ownership Assistance Program-down
     payment and closing costs assistance
-    Rental Rehabilitation Loan Program

City of Waukegan
Community Development
410 Robert V. Sabonjian Place
Waukegan, IL 60085
847-599-2530
http://www.waukeganweb.net/cdbg.html
-    Emergency Rehabilitation/Repair Program
-    Substantial Housing Rehabilitation Program-
     waiting list

Indiana

City of Anderson
Office of Community Development
120 East 8th Street
Anderson, IN 46016
765-645-6097
http://www.cityofanderson.com/commdev.asp
-    Emergency Rehabilitation Program
-    Urban Homesteading
-    Housing Rehabilitation-low interest rate loans
-    Demolition-Operation Upgrade

City of Columbus
Community Development
123 Washington Street
Columbus, IN 47201
812-376-2520
Fax: 812-376-2565
http://www.columbus.in.gov/community-
index.html
-    Housing Rehabilitation Programs

City of Bloomington
Housing and Neighborhood Development
401 North Morton Street
Bloomington, IN 47404

812-349-3401
Fax: 812-349-3582
http://www.city.bloomington.in.us/hand/housing/index.html
- Owner Occupied Rehabilitation-interest free loans to eligible home owners
- Purchase/Rehabilitation Program- interest free loans to buy and rehabilitate existing housing
- Historic Preservation Programs
- Rental Rehabilitation- interest free loans
- Housing Redevelopment Programs- Land Acquisition Program
- Home Buyer Education and Counseling Classes

City of South Bend
Division of Community Development
224 West Jefferson, Suite 100
South Bend, IN 46601
219-235-9660
Fax: 219-235-9697
http://www.ci.south-bend.in.us/Redevelopment/CommDevelop.htm
- Affordable Rental Housing
- Lease Purchase Programs
- Mortgage Loans-80/20 Loan Program
- Affordable Loan Program-partial grant and low interest loan to make home repairs, up to $25,000
- Christmas in April-free repairs by volunteer workers
- Repair Grant Program-maximum of $7,500

Iowa
City of Ames
Department of Planning and Housing
515 Clark Avenue, Room 214
P.O. Box 811
Ames, IA 50010
515-239-5400
Fax: 515-239-5404
http://www.city.ames.ia.us/housingweb/AffordableHousing/housing.htm
- Down Payment and Closing Costs Assistance Program- loans up to $15,000 towards down payment, grants up to $2,000 for closing costs, and loans up to $5,000 for minor repairs

City of Cedar Falls
Community Services Division
217 Washington Street
Cedar Falls, IA 50613
319-273-8606
Fax: 319-273-8610
http://www.ci.cedar-falls.ia.us/developmental/index.htm
- Housing Rehabilitation Program

City of Cedar Rapids
Housing Services
1211 6th Street SW
Cedar Rapids, IA 52404
319-286-5187
http://www.cedar-rapids.org/housing/index.asp
- Owner Occupied Housing Rehabilitation-comprehensive rehabilitation, up to $23,000
- Emergency housing Repair Grants-up to $4,500
- First Time Home Buyer Down Payment and Closing Costs Assistance-maximum of $6,000

City of Davenport
Community and Economic Development
226 West 4th Street
Davenport, IA 52801
563-326-7766
http://www.ci.davenport.ia.us/ced/index.htm
- Housing Redevelopment Program-Urban Homestead Program
- Relocation Assistance
- Housing Rehabilitation Program-low interest loans

City of Des Moines
Community Development Department
602 East First Street
Des Moines, IA 50309-1881
515-283-4182
http://www.ci.des-moines.ia.us/departments/CD/index.htm
- Weatherization Program
- Furnace Repair and Replacement Program
- Technical Assistance Program-Housing Counseling
- Affordable Housing Development
- Rental Rehabilitation Loan Program
- Owner Occupied Rehabilitation Loan Program
- Home Ownership Program
- Affordable Rental Housing

City of Dubuque
Housing Department
1805 Central Avenue
Dubuque, IA 52001
563-589-4230
Fax: 563-589-4244
http://www.cityofdubuque.org/index.cfm?pageid=485
- First Time Home Buyer Loan Program-long term, no interest loans up to $5,000
- Homeowner Rehabilitation Program-loans up to $25,000, or up to $35,000 when addressing lead paint
- New Sewer Program-loans up to $3,500 for new connections

- Operation Paintbrush-free exterior paint for homeowners
- Operation Up-Keep-grants and loans to make exterior improvements
- Sewer Line Replacement Program-deferred payment loans
- Water Line Replacement-loans up to $4,500, deferred payment, no interest
- Historic Preservation Grants and Loans
- Rental Rehabilitation Programs

City of Lake Mills
Economic Development, Housing Incentive Programs
105 West Main Street
Lake Mills, IA 50450-1403
641-592-0881
http://www.lkmills.com/econ/housing_incentive.html
- Lake Mills Tax Abatement-taxes are abated on the first $80,000 for five years

City of Sioux City
Housing Assistance Center
405 6th Street
Suite 107, City Hall
Sioux City, IA 51101
712-279-6348
http://www.sioux-city.org/Housing%20Assistance/SCHousingAssistance.htm
- Condemned Housing Rehabilitation Program
- Affordable Home Ownership Program-down payment and closing costs assistance

City of West Des Moines
Community Development, Housing Department
4200 Mills Civic Parkway
West Des Moines, IA 50265
515-222-3630
Fax: 515-222-0602
http://www.wdm-ia.com/asp/commdev/default.asp?deptid=2
- Emergency Home Repair Loans-forgivable loans from $500 to $12,500

KANSAS

City of Kansas City
Community Development
701 North 7th Street
Kansas City, KS 66101
913-573-5100
http://www.wycokck.org/departments/commdevelopment.html
- Home Buyers Education Classes
- Mortgage Assistance -CHIP loans

- Home Rehabilitation Program-HELP loans, up to $25,000

City of Lawrence
Department of Neighborhood resources
One Riverfront Plaza, Suite 110
P.O. Box 708
Lawrence, KS 66044
785-832-3122
http://www.lawrenceneighres.org/
- Voluntary Demolition Program-funding for clearance of outbuildings and trees
- Weatherization Program
- Furnace Loan Program- up to $5,000 ($1,500 for mobile homes) for replacement of existing furnaces
- Emergency Home Repair Loans-up to $5,000 ($1,500 for mobile homes), no interest, deferred payment
- Comprehensive Home Rehabilitation Program- up to $25,000

City of Overland Park
Planning and Development Services Department; Neighborhood Preservation
6300 West 87th Street, Room 207
Overland Park, KS
913-895-6370
http://www.opkansas.org/_Res/Neighborhoods/Assistance_&_Resources/index.cfm
- Home Improvement Loans-low interest
- Minor Home Repair Program- coordinates financing and labor

City of Salina
Department of Planning and Community Development
300 West Ash
Salina, KS 67401
785-359-5720
http://www.ci.salina.ks.us/Overviews/PL.htm
- Housing Rehabilitation Programs-grants and loans

City Of Topeka
Department of Housing and Neighborhood Development
707 Quincy, 3rd Floor
Topeka, KS 66603-3914
785-368-3711
Fax: 785-368-2546
http://www.topeka.org/departmt/hap.htm#SUBLINK7
- Home Rehabilitation Loans- deferred payment, no interest
- Home Ownership Counseling and Training

- Acquisition/Relocation/Demolition Program- a voluntary program in which the city acquires property not suitable for habitation, relocates the owner, and then demolishes the property.

City of Wichita
Department of Housing Services
332 Riverview
Wichita, KS 67203
316-268-4688
Fax: 316-268-4219
http://www.wichitagov.org/housing/index.asp
- Neighborhood Improvement Services-free paint
- Emergency Home Repair Assistance Program-0% interest, deferred payment
- Home Improvement Loan Programs
- Rental Housing Rehabilitation Loans

KENTUCKY

City of Ashland
Planning and Community Development Department
1700 Greenup Avenue, Room 208
P.O. Box 1839
Ashland, KY 41105-1839
606-327-2030
Fax: 606-325-8412
http://www.ashlandky.org/Planning/index.htm
- Housing Rehabilitation Program

City of Covington
Housing Department
638 Madison Avenue
Covington, KY 41011
859-292-2188
Fax: 859-292-2139
http://www.covingtonky.com/housing_department.asp?id=2008
- Owner Occupied Rehabilitation Program
- Investor Loan Program
- Home Buyer Assistance Program
- Home Repair and Emergency Repair Program

City of Lexington
Division of Community Development
200 East Main Street
Lexington, KY 40507
859-258-3000
http://www.lfucg.com/AdminSvcs/CommDev/Index.asp
- Housing Rehabilitation Program-up to $18,000 to correct safety and code violations

City of Louisville
Department of Housing
745 West Main Street
Louisville, KY 40202

502-574-3107
Fax: 502-574-4199
http://www.louky.org/directory/housing.htm
- Rental Rehabilitation Program
- Rehabilitation Incentive Program
- Weatherization Assistance Program
- Winter Emergency Repair Program-energy systems only
- Home Repair Program
- New Construction Home Ownership Program

LOUISANA

City of Baton Rouge
Office of Community Development
300 Louisiana Avenue
P.O. Box 1471
Baton Rouge, LA 70802
225-389-3039
Fax: 225-389-3939
http://www.ci.baton-rouge.la.us/Dept/OCD/default.htm
- Home Buyers Assistance Program-mortgage assistance, no interest second mortgage for down payment and/or closing costs
- Homebuyer Education Seminars
- Housing Rehabilitation Grant Program-maximum grant award of $22,000
- Weatherization Assistance Program
- Sewer Line Assistance Program
- Rental Housing Assistance Program
- New Housing Developments
- Housing Rehabilitation Loan Program

City of Bossier City
620 Benton Road
Bossier City, LA 71111
318-741-8560
http://www.bossiercity.org/dept/affairs/commdev/default.htm
- Home Buyers Assistance Program-grants for down payment or closing costs
- Housing Rehabilitation-deferred forgivable, or low cost loans to meet current building codes
- Self Help Paint Program
- Fix-It Loan Program-forgivable loans to be used for energy conservation and roof systems

City of New Orleans
Central City Housing Development Corporation
2020 Jackson Avenue
New Orleans, LA 70113
504-522-4273
Fax: 504-522-7948
http://www.centralcityhousing.org/programs.htm
- Affordable Rental Housing
- Housing Redevelopment Programs
- First Time Home Buyer Training

City of Shreveport
Department of Community Development
City Hall Annex, Room 210
1237 Murphy Street
Shreveport, LA 71101
318-673-7555
http://www.ci.shreveport.la.us/dept/cd/neighrev.h
tm
- First Time Home Buyer-down payment,
  buydown, and closing costs assistance
- Emergency Repair Program- maximum of $7,000
- Limited Housing Repairs-up to $12,000 for health
  and safety rehabilitation

Maine

City of Bangor
Department of Community and Economic
Development
73 Harlow Street
Bangor, ME 04401
207-945-4400 ext 211
Fax: 207-945-4447
http://www.bgrme.org/index.php3?c1=business_de
velopment&c2=community_and_economic_develop
ment
- Housing Redevelopment Program
- Housing Rehabilitation Loan Programs

City of Lewiston
Community Development, Housing, Rehabilitation
Programs
City Building
Lewiston, ME 04240
207-784-2951
Fax: 207-795-5071
http://ci.lewiston.me.us/development/rehabhousin
g.htm
- Housing Rehabilitation Loan Program-up to
  $50,000, matching funds, low interest
- Emergency Home Repair Loan-up to $5,000,
  1%interest rate
- Home Ownership Loan Assistance-up to $3,000
  for down payment and closing costs to First Time
  Homebuyers

City of Portland
Housing and Neighborhood Services Division
Portland City Hall
389 Congress Street
Portland, ME 04101
207-874-8711
http://www.ci.portland.me.us/planning/housingfin
ancial.htm
- Multi Family Rehabilitation and Acquisition
  Loan Program-maximum of $100,000 or 50% of
  total project costs

- Owner Occupied Rehabilitation Program-up to
  $15,000 per home
- First Time Home Buyer Program

Maryland

City of Annapolis
Department of Planning and Zoning
160 Duke of Gloucester Street
Annapolis, MD 21401
410-263-7961
http://www.annapolis.gov/citizens/depts/pl_zon/
CDBG.html
- Housing Redevelopment Projects
- Housing Rehabilitation Assistance
- Affordable Housing Development

City of Frederick
Department of Community Development
4 West 7th Street, Suite 100
Frederick, MD 21701
301-228-2840
http://www.cityoffrederick.com/departments/Com
munityDevelopment/communityD.html
- Housing Rehabilitation Program-single family,
  owner occupied
- Home Ownership Assistance-second mortgages
- Housing Redevelopment Program

City of Hagerstown
Community Development Department
City Hall
4th Floor, Room 401
One East Franklin Street
Hagerstown, MD 21740
301-739-8577 ext 136
TDD 301-797-6617
http://www.cityoffrederick.com/departments/Com
munityDevelopment/communityD.html
- Homebuyer Education-Hagerstown Home Store
- Home Ownership Assistance-low down payment
  program
- Housing Rehabilitation/Home Improvement
  Loans
- Emergency Home Repair Grants-up to $1500
- Self-Help Housing Programs
- Housing Redevelopment Programs

City of Rockville
Community Planning and Development
111 Maryland Avenue
Rockville, MD 20850
240-314-8208
http://www.ci.rockville.md.us/DEPT/COMMDEV.
HTM
- Home Improvement Program-low interest or
  deferred loans

- Affordable Housing Program-moderately priced dwelling units (MPDU)

MASSACHUSETTS
City of Boston
Department of Neighborhood Development
26 Court Street
Boston, MA 02201
617-635-3880
Fax: 617-635-10561
http://www.cityofboston.gov/DND/D_Housing_Programs.asp
- Housing Development Program
- Housing Counseling Services

City of Brookline
Planning and Community Development
2nd Floor, Town Hall
333 Washington Street
Brookline, MA 02445
617-730-2130
Fax: 617-730-2442
http://www.town.brookline.ma.us/Planning/#Housing
- Affordable Housing Development Program
- Housing Rehabilitation and Purchase Program

City of Cambridge
Community Development Department, Housing Division
238 Broadway
Cambridge MA 02139
617-349-4600
TTY: 617-349-4621
Fax: 617-349-4669
http://www.ci.cambridge.ma.us/~CDD/housing/
- Home Buyer Classes and Counseling
- Middle Income Homebuyer Assistance- must be a first time home buyer
- Home Improvement Programs

City of Fall River
Community Development Agency
66 Troy Street
Fall River, MA 02720
508-679-0131
http://www.fallriverma.org/community/community_main.asp
- Home Rehabilitation Program
- Rental Rehabilitation Program
- Affordable New Housing Construction Program
- Rental Housing Acquisition Program

City of Fitchburg
Office of the Planning Coordinator
718 Main Street

Fitchburg, MA 01420
978-345-1518
http://www.ci.worcester.ma.us/
- Home Owner Occupied Rehabilitation Program- counseling and financial Assistance
- Housing Ownership Assistance- counseling and financial assistance
- Rental Housing Assistance

City of Lowell
Division of Planning and Development
375 Merrimack Street
Lowell, MA 01852
978-970-4252
http://web.ci.lowell.ma.us/cityhall/depart/dpd/housingpages/housing.html
- Lead Paint Abatement Program
- Painting Pride Program- up to $400 for any exterior painting
- First Time Home Buyer Program
- Home Repair Assistance-low interest, deferred loans

City of Medford
Office of Community Development
85 George P. Hassett Drive
Medford, MA 02155
781-393-2480
Fax: 781-393-2342
http://www.medford.org/fGoverment.htm
- Housing Rehabilitation Program-low interest loans/grants

City of New Bedford
Office of Housing and Community Development
608 Pleasant Street
New Bedford, MA 02740
508-979-1581
Fax: 308-979-1575
http://www.ci.new-bedford.ma.us/Nav3.htm
- Home Rehabilitation Program-financial and technical assistance to correct code violations
- Handicap Accessibility Program-grants up to $4,000
- Rental Housing Rehabilitation Program-low interest loans up to $20,000
- Home Improvement Loan Program-low interest loans up to $15,000
- Lead Paint Reimbursement Program-50% of cost up to $2,500
- Home Mortgage Assistance

City of Pittsfield
Department of Community Development
Room 205, City Hall
70 Allen Street

Pittsfield, MA 01201
413-499-9368
Fax: 413-442-5661
http://www.pittsfield-
ma.org/departments/community.html
- Housing Rehabilitation Program-grants and/or
  low interest loans

City of Quincy
Planning and Community Development
1305 Hancock Street
Quincy, MA 02169
617-376-1362
http://www.scstest.com/quincy/pcdhousing.asp
- Home Rehabilitation Program
- Handicapped Home Adaptation Program
- Rental Rehabilitation Program

City of Somerville
Office of Housing and Community Development
City Hall
93 Highland Avenue
Somerville, MA 02143
617-625-6600 ext 2500
http://www.ci.somerville.ma.us/
- Homebuyer Training Classes
- Affordable Homeownership Opportunities
- Heating System Replacement Program-
  forgivable loans to help homeowners replace
  their heating systems
- Down Payment Assistance Program
- Lead Paint Abatement Program
- Housing Rehabilitation Program-financial and
  technical assistance

City of Springfield
Office of Housing and Neighborhood Services
36 Court Street
Springfield, MA 01103
413-787-6000
http://www.cityofspringfieldma.com/housing/inde
x.htm
- Homebuyer Education Classes
- Housing Rehabilitation Program
- First Time Home Buyer-down payment and
  closing costs assistance

City of Weymouth
Department of Planning and Community
Development
Weymouth Town Hall
75 Middle Street
East Weymouth, MA 02189
781-340-5015
Fax: 781-335-3283
http://www.weymouth.ma.us/plan/programs.html

- Housing Rehabilitation Loan Program-low
  interest financing and technical assistance
- First Time Home Buyer Assistance

City of Worcester
Neighborhood Services
418 Main Street, Suite 400
Worcester, MA 01608
508-799-1400
http://www.ci.worcester.ma.us/
- Affordable New Construction
- Affordable Rental Housing
- Down Payment and Closing Costs Assistance
- Emergency Home Repair Program-financial and
  technical assistance

Michigan

City of Ann Arbor
Community Development Department
City Center Building
220 East Huron
Ann Arbor, MI 48104
734-994-2912
http://www.ci.ann-
arbor.mi.us/CommunityDevelopment/index.html
- Housing Rehabilitation Program
- Affordable Home Ownership Program

City of Battle Creek
Code Compliance/Housing Assistance
10 North Division Street, Suite 311
Battle Creek, MI 49016
269-966-3387
Fax: 269-966-3659
http://ci.battle-creek.mi.us/Services/
CodeCompliance/High/HousingAssistance.htm
- Home Weatherization Assistance
- Housing Rehabilitation Assistance
- Emergency Home Repair Assistance
- Down Payment Assistance-grants up to $7,000,
  deferred loans above $7,000

City of East Lansing
Community and Economic Development Department
410 Abbott Road, Room 205
East Lansing, MI 48823
517-319-6930
Fax: 517-337-1607
http://www.cityofeastlansing.com/
- Housing Rehabilitation Program-0% interest,
  loans up to $20,000
- Homeownership Opportunity Assistance
  Program

City of Farmington Hills
Planning and Community Development Office

31555 West Eleven Mile Road
Farmington Hills, MI 48336-1165
248-473-9541
Fax: 248-426-4423
http://www.ci.farmington-hills.mi.us/
- Housing Rehabilitation Program-low interest,
  deferred payment loans

City of Ferndale
Community Development Services Department
300 East Nine Mile Road
Ferndale, MI 48220
248-546-2367
http://www.ferndale-
mi.com/Services/CommunityDevelopmentServices/
CDSOverview.htm
- Minor Home Repair Assistance-maximum of
  $2,000
- Housing Rehabilitation Assistance

City of Grand Rapids
Community Development Department
City Hall, 4th Floor
300 Monroe Avenue, NW
Grand Rapids, MI 49503
616-456-3677
Fax: 616-456-4619
http://www.grand-
rapids.mi.us/departments/community/indexmain.as
p?menu=main
- First Time Homebuyer Informational Assistance
- Housing Rehabilitation Program-low interest
  loans

City of Jackson
Community Development Department
161 West Michigan Avenue
Jackson, MI 49201-1324
517-788-4070
http://www.cityofjackson.org/departments/commu
nitydevelopment/communitydevelopment.asp
- Housing Rehabilitation Loans-deferred loans up
  to $20,000 to repair code violations
- Emergency Hazard Loans-maximum loan of
  $10,000 for emergency repairs
- Exterior Only Code Enforcement Loans-up to
  $20,000

City of Kalamazoo
Community Development Division
241 West South Street
Kalamazoo, MI 49007
269-337-8225
Fax: 269-337-8513
http://www.ci.kalamazoo.mi.us/
- Home Rehabilitation Program

- Emergency Home Repair Program
- Rental Rehabilitation Program

City of Lansing
Department of Planning and Development
316 North Capitol Ave, Suite D-2
Lansing, MI 48933-1234
http://plandevelopment.cityoflansingmi.com/develo
pment/index.html
- Rental Rehabilitation Program-matching funds,
  0% interest
- Single Family Rehabilitation Program-0%
  interest, deferred payment loans
- Weatherization Assistance-grants up to $2,000 to
  weatherize your home
- Down Payment Assistance-up to $3,000 for down
  payment or closing costs
- Rehabilitation/Purchase Program

City of Livonia
Housing Department
33000 Civic Center Drive
Livonia, MI 48154
734-466-2200
http://ci.livonia.mi.us/Services/ServicesFrame.htm
- Homebuyer Assistance Program-up to $10,000 in
  down payment assistance, up to $20,000 for home
  improvements
- Home Improvement Loan Program-deferred
  payment, low interest loans

City of Madison Heights
Community Improvement Division (Housing)
300 West Thirteen Mile Road
Madison Heights, MI 48071-1853
248-583-0842
http://www.ci.madison-
heights.mi.us/bin/site/wrappers/default.asp?pane_
1=cdd-housingleft&pane_2=cdd-
commimp&pane_3=0
- Home Improvement Repair Loans-low interest
  and/or deferred payment loans, up to $18,000

City of Mount Pleasant
Planning and Community Development
401 North Main Street
Mount Pleasant, MI 48858
989-779-5347
Fax: 989-779-6791
http://www.mt-pleasant.org/
- Rental Rehabilitation Program-75% of the cost,
  up to $15,000

City of Muskegon
Community and Neighborhood Services
933 Terrace

Muskegon, MI 49440
231-724-6717
Fax: 231-726-2501
http://www.ci.muskegon.mi.us/cityservices/depart
ments/department.asp?ID=10
- Emergency Housing Repair Assistance
- Rental Rehabilitation Assistance
- Affordable New Housing Construction
- Exterior Paint and Vinyl Siding Assistance

City of Port Huron
Community Development Department
100 McMorran Boulevard
Port Huron, MI 48060
810-984-9736
http://www.porthuron.org/residents/dept-
community.asp
- Clearance/Demolition Program-assists residents
  in the demolition of unsafe garages and/or
  outbuildings
- Affordable Housing Program
- Down Payment Assistance-up to $5,000
- Property Improvement Program-combination
  grant/loan package up to $10,000
- Housing Rehabilitation Program-matching funds
  grant up to $10,000
- Home Rental Rehabilitation Program

City of Saginaw
Community Development/Housing
City Hall, Second Floor
1315 South Washington Avenue
Saginaw, MI 48601
989-759-1530
http://www.saginaw-mi.com/
- Home Maintenance Classes
- Minor Home Repair Program
- Affordable New Housing Construction

City of Southfield
Housing Department
26000 Evergreen Road
Southfield, MI 48076
248-354-4968
http://www.cityofsouthfield.com/departments/hou
sing/index.php
- Home Improvement Program
- Low interest loans up to $18,000
- Manufactured Home Improvement Program-
  emergency grants
- Sewer Loan Program-grants up to $5,000 to cover
  the cost of connection from street to house

MINNESOTA
City of Brooklyn Park
Community Development Department

5200 85th Avenue, North
Brooklyn Park, MN 55443
763-493-8056
http://www.brooklynpark.org/government/commd
ev/housing.html
- Housing Redevelopment Program
- Home Improvement Loan Program
- Rental Rehabilitation Program
- Home Energy Loans-loans from $1,000 to $8,000
  to make improvements that lower energy use.

City of Mankato
Housing Services Office
Intergovernmental Center
10 Civic Center Plaza
Mankato, MN 56001
507-387-8622
Fax: 507-387-6845
http://www.ci.mankato.mn.us/cityh/housing/index
.php3
- Neighborhood Improvement Projects
- Home Rehabilitation Loans
- Home Stretch Workshops
- Affordable Rental Housing

City of Minnetonka
Community Development Department
14600 Minnetonka Boulevard
Minnetonka, MN 55345
952-939-8282
Fax: 952-939-8244
http://www.eminnetonka.com
- Home Improvement Loans-no interest, deferred
  payment, up to $20,000

City of Moorhead
Community and Economic Development, Housing
Programs
500 Center Avenue
Box 779
Moorhead, MN 56561-0779
877-833-6667
218-299-5370
Fax: 218-299-5399
http://www.ci.moorhead.mn.us/housing/programs.
php3
- First Time Home Buyer Programs
- Home Improvement Loans- no interest, deferred
  payment
- Mortgage Financing

City of New Hope
Community Development/Housing
4401 Xylon Avenue North
New Hope, MN 55428
763-531-5110

http://www.ci.new-hope.mn.us/Departments/
commudev/housing/housing.html
- Redevelopment Housing
- Housing Rehabilitation Program-up to $20,000,
  but there is a waiting list
- Homeownership and Tenant Services-home
  buyer education and counseling, home
  maintenance, repair and rehabilitation program
- Multi Family Rehabilitation Loan Program

City of St. Paul
Housing Department
15 West Kellogg Boulevard
St. Paul, MN 55102
651-266-6621
Fax: 651-266-8513
http://www.stpaul.gov/housing/
- Rehabilitation Assistance-maximum of $10,000
- Closing Costs Assistance-loans up to $5,000
- Cityliving Mortgage Program
- Home Buyer Education and Counseling
- Rental Rehabilitation Loan Program
- Home Improvement Loan Program-4% interest,
  up to $35,000

Mississippi

City of Pascagoula
Community Development
1206 Communy
Pascagoula, MS 39567
2280938-6639
http://www.cityofpascagoula.com/communitydev.htm
- First Time Homeowners Assistance

City of Vicksburg
Planning and Community Development
819 South Street
Vicksburg, MS 39181-0150
601-631-2988
Fax: 601-638-4229
http://www.vicksburg.org/pages/planning/homeb
uyers.htm
- Homebuyer Education Classes
- Homebuyer Assistance Program-up to $5,000 for
  down payment or closing costs

Missouri

City of Cape Girardeau
Planning Services Division
City Hall-Second Floor
401 Independence Avenue
Cape Girardeau, MO 63702
573-334-8326
Fax: 573-651-0860
http://www.cityofcapegirardeau.org/depts/plannin
g/housing.htm
- Housing Rehabilitation Grants

City of Columbia
Department of Planning and Development
701 East Broadway
Columbia, MO 65205
573-874-7239
Fax: 573-874-7546
http://www.ci.columbia.mo.us/Planning/Housing_
Programs/
- Homeownership Assistance Program-grants up
  to $2,300 for down payment and closing costs
- Owner Occupied Housing Rehabilitation
  Program-$1,000 to $25,000 in low interest loans
- Code Deficiency Abatement Program-to correct
  exterior code violations, $500 in grants, up to
  $4,500 in low interest loans
- Emergency Repair Program-maximum assistance
  is $5,000, $500 as a grant and the remainder as a
  low interest loan

City of Independence
Community Planning and Development
111 East Maple Avenue
Independence, MO 64050
816-325-7000
http://www.ci.independence.mo.us/comdev/comSe
rvices.stm
- Owner Occupied Rehabilitation Program
- Rental Rehabilitation Program
- First Time Home Buyers Assistance

City of Kansas City
Housing and Community Development
414 East 12th Street
Kansas City, MO 64106
816-513-3000
Fax: 816-513-3011
http://www.kcmo.org/housing.nsf/web/rehab?ope
ndocument
- Minor Home Repair Grants
- Home Rehabilitation Rebate Program-grants of
  up to 1/3 the cost of home repairs, maximum of
  $4,800
- Home Weatherization Program
- Home Rehabilitation Loans-low interest

City of St. Joseph
Community Development Department
1100 Frederick Avenue
St. Joseph, MO 64501
816-271-5361
http://www.ci.st-joseph.mo.us/commdev.html
- Emergency Home Repair Program
- Rental Rehabilitation Program
- Home Rehabilitation Program-low interest loans

City of St. Louis
Housing Authority
1200 Market Street

St. Louis, MO 63103
314-622-4000
http://stlouis.missouri.org/housing/houseprog.html
- Home Buyer Programs-down payment and
  closing costs assistance
- Home Repair Programs
- Home Buyers' Guide

Montana
City of Billings
Community Development Division
P.O. Box 1178
Billings, MT 59103
406-657-8281
Fax: 406-657-8252
http://ci.billings.mt.us/government/cs/
- Housing Rehabilitation Loan Program-low
  interest deferred loans up to $20,000
- Rental Rehabilitation Program-matching grants
  for repairs up to $5,000
- Minor Home Repair Program-grants for minor
  repairs including repairs to mobile homes and
  emergency repairs

City of Great Falls
Community Development Department
Civic Center, Room 112
P.O. Box 5021
Great Falls, MT 59403
406-455-8404
http://www.ci.great-
falls.mt.us/people_offices/cdev/cdbg/housprogaps/
index.htm
- Housing Rehabilitation Program-deferred
  payment loans
- Rental Improvement Loan Program

Nebraska
City of Grand Island
Community Development Division
100 East 1st Street
Grand Island, NE 68801
308-385-5444 ext 140
http://www.grand-
island.com/departments/Community_Projects/com
munity_projects_index.htm
- Down Payment Assistance
- Owner Occupied Housing Rehabilitation
  Program
- Rental Housing Rehabilitation Program
- Home Ownership Opportunity Program

City of Lincoln
Housing Rehabilitation and Real Estate Division
808 P Street, Suite 400
Lincoln, NE 68508

402-441-7864
http://www.ci.lincoln.ne.us/city/urban/real/home.
htm
- Home Improvement Loan Program-0% interest
  loans for up to 10 years
- Emergency Repair Loan Program-0% interest
  deferred payment
- First Home Program
- Rental Rehabilitation Loan Program

City of Norfolk
Housing Division
127 North 1st Street
Norfolk, NE 68701
402-844-2080
http://www.ci.norfolk.ne.us/housing/housingprogr
ams.htm
- Homeowner Rehabilitation Program-maximum
  grant/loan amount is $20,000
- New Construction Homeownership Program

Nevada
City of Henderson
Community Development Department
240 Water Street
Henderson, NV 89012
702-565-2474
http://www.cityofhenderson.com/planning/plannin
g.html
- Housing Redevelopment Program
- First Time Homebuyer Assistance
- Home Improvement Program-low interest loans

City of Las Vegas
Neighborhood Development Division
City Hall, Second Floor
400 Stewart Avenue
Las Vegas, NV 89101
702-229-2555
Fax: 702-382-3045
http://www.ci.las-vegas.nv.us/2297.htm
- Housing Rehabilitation Program

City of North Las Vegas
Neighborhood Services Division
2266 Civic Center drive
North Las Vegas, NV 89030
702-633-1532
Fax: 702-642-1511
http://www.cityofnorthlasvegas.com/Departments/Co
mmunityDevelopment/NeighborhoodServices.cfm
- Housing Rehabilitation Assistance Program-
  grants of up to $25,000
- Emergency Repair Grant Program-grants of up to
  $5,000
- Down Payment Assistance Program

NEW HAMPSHIRE

City of Dover
Department of Planning and Community
Development
288 Central Avenue
Dover, NH 03820
603-743-6008
http://www.ci.dover.nh.us/
- Housing rehabilitation Program-up to $10,000 in financial assistance for the repair and upgrade of housing units

City of Laconia
Planning and Community Development Department
45 Beacon Street East
Laconia, NH 03246
603-527-1264
Fax: 603-524-2167
http://www.cityoflaconianh.org/
- Housing Assistance Programs-energy efficiency improvements, code compliance, housing preservation grants

City of Portsmouth
Community Development, Housing Programs
One Junkins Avenue
Portsmouth, NH 03801
603-431-2006
http://www.cityofportsmouth.com/community/cdbghouse.htm
- First Time Home Buyers Program-Down payment assistance, mortgage loans
- Housing Rehabilitation Programs-loans and/or grants to repair code deficiencies

City of Rochester
Department of Planning and Development
Second Floor, City Hall
31 Wakefield Street
Rochester, NH 03867-1917
603-335-1338
Fax: 603-335-7585
http://www.rochesternh.net/Public_Documents/RochesterNH_Planning/index#CDBG
- Housing Rehabilitation Program
- Emergency Repair Program
- Weatherization Grants

NEW JERSEY

City of Bridgeton
Office of Economic Development
181 East Commerce Street
Bridgeton, NJ 08302
856-455-3230 ext 1216
Fax: 856-455-7421

- Home Buyers Program-grants of up to $5,000 for down payment and closing costs

City of Elizabeth
Planning and Community Development
50 Winfield Scott Plaza
Elizabeth, NJ 07201
908-820-4000
http://www.elizabethnj.org/CityRoster/policy.htm
- Housing Redevelopment Program
- Home Improvement Program

City of Long Branch
Office of Community and Economic Development
344 Broadway
Long Branch, NJ 07740
732-923-2040
http://www.longbranch.org/OCED/oced.htm
- Home Repair Program for Single Family Homes-up to $20,000 to correct code violations
- Home Repair Program for Multi Family Homes-up to $14,000 to correct code violations
- Weatherization/Special Housing Assistance
- First Time Home Buyer Assistance
- Housing Redevelopment Projects

City of Montclair
Planning and Community Development Department
205 Claremont Avenue
Montclair, NJ 07042
973-509-4954
http://www.to.montclair.nj.us/planningdept/index.cfm
- Housing Rehabilitation Program
- Affordable Rental Housing

City of New Brunswick
Department of Planning, Community and Economic Development
25 Kirkpatrick Street
Civic Square
P.O. Box 269
New Brunswick, NJ 08903-0269
732-745-5050
Fax: 732-565-7532
http://www.cityofnewbrunswick.org/depts/economicdev/preserving.asp
- Emergency Rehabilitation Program-maximum of $6,000 per unit
- Housing Rehabilitation Program-moderate rehabilitation, up to $20,000/unit
- Buy It and Fix It Program-buy and rehabilitate vacant houses, up to $20,000 per unit
- Rental Rehabilitation Program
- Lead Based Paint Abatement Program-up to $15,000 in financial assistance

City of Orange
Neighborhood Preservation Program Office
29 North Day Street
Orange, NJ 07050
973-266-4201
http://www.ci.orange.nj.us/CITY_SERVICES_NPP.h
tm
- Direct Housing Rehabilitation Grant Program-
  grants up to $10,000
- Partial Housing Rehabilitation Grant Program-
  60/40 partial grants up to $10,000
- Materials Grants-up to $1,000

New Mexico

City of Albuquerque
Albuquerque Housing Services
1840 University Boulevard, SE
Albuquerque, NM 87106
505-764-3920
Fax: 505-764-3981
http://www.cabq.gov/housing/ahs_programs.html
- Affordable Housing Development
- Affordable Rental Housing
- Home Rehabilitation Program-deferred and low
  interest loans
- Rental Rehabilitation Program-low interest loans

City of Las Cruces
Community Development Department
575 South Alameda Boulevard
Las Cruces, NM 88001
505-528-3222
http://www.las-cruces.org/community.htm
- Home Rehabilitation Programs
- Affordable Housing Development Program

City of Santa Fe
Division of Community Development
P.O. Box 909
120 S. Federal Place, 3rd Floor
Santa Fe, NM 87504-0909
505-955-6568
http://sfweb.ci.santa-fe.nm.us/community-
services/community-development/index.html
- Affordable Housing Programs
- Housing Rehabilitation Programs

New York

City of Albany
Division of Housing and Community Development
200 Henry Johnson Boulevard
Albany, NY 12210
518-434-5240
http://www.albanyny.org/government/department
s/d_develop3.asp

- Down Payment Assistance Program-0% interest,
  maximum loan of $12,000
- Albany HomeStore-counseling, training, and
  financial assistance
- Home Acquisition Program
- Homeowner Rehabilitation Assistance Program
- Rental Rehabilitation Assistance
- Emergency Repair Assistance

City of Auburn
Housing and Community Development
24 South Street, 2nd Floor
Auburn, NY 13021
315-255-4115
Fax: 315-253-0282
http://auburnny.virtualtownhall.net/public_docume
nts/auburnny_planning/home
- Housing Repair Assistance Program-low interest
  loans up to $20,000 to address major code
  violations and lead based paint hazards

City of Binghamton
Department of Planning, Housing and Community
Development
City Hall, 4th Floor
38 Hawley Street
Binghamton, NY 13901
607-772-7028
http://www.bingnyphcd.com/housing.htm
- Home Rehabilitation Program
- Rental Housing Rehabilitation Program-exterior
  and interior improvements
- Handicapped Accessibility Grant
- Affordable Housing Program-deferred loans, up
  to $5,000 for closing costs, up to $10,000 for
  rehabilitation
- Paint Program
- Emergency Repair Program-limited to repairs of
  broken water or sewer lines to a house and
  furnace or water heater breakage

City of Corning
Planning and Economic Development Department
7 Civic Center Plaza
Corning, NY 14830
607-962-8589
http://www.corningny.com/Content/Business.asp#
Economic+Development
- Rental Rehabilitation Program
- Housing Rehabilitation Program-low interest
  loans

City of Elmira
Department of Business and Housing Development
317 East Church Street
Elmira, NY 14901

607-737-5691
http://www.ci.elmira.ny.us/offices/business_and_housing.html#general
- Paint Fix-Up Program-$1,000 grants to paint home exteriors, $100 vouchers for paint
- Owner Occupied Home Rehabilitation Program-deferred, forgivable grants up to $15,000; low interest loans up to $10,000
- Rental Rehabilitation Program-up to 50% of the cost of Rehabilitation, maximum grant of $10,000

City of Glens Falls
Community Development Office
42 Ridge Street
Glens Falls, NY 12801
518-761-3833
Fax: 518-798-5029
http://www.cityofglensfalls.com/Cityoffices/comm_dev/comm_dev.htm
- Rental Housing Rehabilitation Financial Assistance
- Owner Occupied Housing Rehabilitation Financial Assistance
- First Time Homebuyer Program
- Housing Rehabilitation Programs
- Repaint Program
- Housing Rehabilitation and Resale Program

City of Middletown
Office of Economic and Community Development
16 James Street
Middletown, NY 10940
845-346-4170
http://www.ci.middletown.ny.us/cityhall/cityhall.htm#phone
- Housing Rehabilitation Programs
- Homebuyer Assistance Programs

City of Mount Vernon
Department of Planning and Community Development
One Roosevelt Square, Room 211
Mount Vernon, NY 10550
914-699-7230
http://www.ci.mount-vernon.ny.us/mv/Departments/PCD.htm
- Housing Redevelopment Program
- Multi Family Rehabilitation Program-low interest loans
- Residential Rehabilitation Program-low interest loans

City of New York City
Department of Housing Preservation and Development
100 Gold Street

New York, NY 10038
212-863-8000
http://home.nyc.gov/html/hpd/home.html
- Housing Redevelopment Programs-HomeWorks, New Foundations, etc
- Home Improvement Program-low interest loans
- Code Compliance Loan Program
- Affordable Housing Programs

City of Oswego
Community Development Office Department
20 West Oneida Street, 3rd Floor
Oswego, NY 13126
315-343-3795
http://www.oswegony.org/
- Home Ownership Program-grants for $10,000 to $17,000
- Housing Rehabilitation Program-maximum grant/loan combination is $20,000

City of Rochester
Department of Community Development
Bureau of Housing and Project Development
30 Church Street
Rochester, NY 14614-1265
585-325-4663
http://www.ci.rochester.ny.us/dcd/srvguide/housingprojdev.htm
- Rehabilitated Housing Program-HOME Rochester
- Home Purchase Assistance Program-$3,000 to $5,000 in Down Payment/Closing Costs Assistance
- Home Improvement Grants-$500 to $3,500 for emergency repairs, security improvements, or exterior repairs
- Homesteading Lottery

City of Rome
Planning Department
City Hall Suite 3B
198 North Washington Street
Rome, NY 13440-5815
315-339-7643
Fax: 315-339-7788
http://www.romenewyork.com/planning.html
- Homebuyer Assistance Program
- Neighborhood Improvement Program

City of Schenectady
Department of Development
105 Jay Street
Schenectady, NY 12305
518-382-5147
Fax: 518-382-5275
http://www.schenectadydnr.com/development.htm

- Schenectady Neighborhood Assistance Program
  (S.N.A.P.)

City of Troy
Planning Department
City Hall
One Monument Square
Troy, NY 12180
518-270-4618
http://www.troyny.org/index.html
- Paint Program-grants up to $1,000 to cover the
  cost of paint and supplies for exterior painting

City of White Plains
Planning Department
255 Main Street-Annex
White Plains, NY 10601
914-422-1252
http://www.ci.white-
plains.ny.us/planning/planning.htm
- Neighborhood Rehabilitation Program-low
  interest loans

North Carolina

City of Asheville
Department of Planning and Development
29 Haywood Street
P.O. Box 7148
Asheville, NC 28802
828-259-5721
http://www.ci.asheville.nc.us/planning/main.htm
- Housing Rehabilitation Loan Program

City of Burlington
Planning and Community Development Department
425 South Lexington Avenue
P.O. Box 1358
Burlington, NC 27216
336-222-507-
Fax: 336-222-5410
http://www.ci.burlington.nc.us/planning/home.ht
m
- Housing Rehabilitation programs-deferred and
  regular loans

City of Chapel Hill
Planning Department
306 North Columbia Street
Chapel Hill, NC 27516
919-968-2728
http://townhall.townofchapelhill.org/planning/HC
D/index.htm
- Affordable Housing Development
- Housing Loan Trust Fund
- Housing Rehabilitation Program

City of Concord
Community Development Division
66 Union Street, South
Concord, NC 28025
704-920-5133
http://www.ci.concord.nc.us/pcd/cd_0.asp
- Housing Rehabilitation Loans-low interest
- Affordable Housing- New Construction and
  Purchase for Resale Programs
- Emergency Repair Program-maximum assistance
  is $3,500 in low interest loans or deferred grants

City of Durham
Housing and Community Development
401 East Lakewood Avenue
Durham, NC 27701
919-560-4570
Fax: 919-560-4090
http://www.ci.durham.nc.us/departments/housing
/programs.asp
- Housing Redevelopment Programs
- Housing Rehabilitation Programs
- Homeownership Assistance

City of Fayetteville
Community Development Department
433 Hay Street
Fayetteville, NC 28301
910-433-1601
Fax: 910-433-1592
http://www.cityoffayetteville.org/dept_commdev.ht
m
- Owner Occupied Housing Rehabilitation Loan
  Program
- Rental Housing Rehabilitation Loan Program

City of Gastonia
Community Improvement Department
P.O. Box 1748
Gastonia, NC 28053
704-866-6752
http://www.cityofgastonia.com/citydepts/communi
tyimprovement/commimp.htm
- New Construction/Affordable Housing Program
- Acquisition/Rehabilitate/Resale Program
- Down Payment and Closing Costs Assistance
- Homebuyer Education
- Water/Sewer Connection Assistance
- Emergency Repair Program
- Housing Rehabilitation Program-low interest and
  principle only loans
- Housing Redevelopment Program

City of Goldsboro
Planning and Community Development
222 North Center Street

City Hall Annex
Goldsboro, NC 27530
919-580-4333
http://www.ci.goldsboro.nc.us/planning.html
- Housing Rehabilitation Program
- Down Payment Assistance

City of Greensboro
Department of Housing and Community
Development
Room 315 Melvin Municipal Office Building
300 West Washington Street
P.O. Box 3136
Greensboro, NC 27402-3136
336-373-2349
Fax: 336-412-6315
http://www.ci.greensboro.nc.us/HCD/Housing%20
Programs/housing.htm
- Homeowner Housing Rehabilitation-low interest
  loans and grants
- Rental Housing Improvement Program
- Affordable Home Loan Initiative

City of Greenville
Planning and Community Development Department
201 Martin Luther King Jr. Drive
P.O. Box 7207
Greenville, NC 27835
252-329-4504
http://ci.greenville.nc.us/
- Affordable Housing Programs
- Down Payment Assistance
- Housing Rehabilitation Program

City of Hickory
Community Development
76 North Center Street
Hickory, NC 28601
828-323-7414
http://www.ci.hickory.nc.us/planning/communityd
ev
- Emergency Repair Program-up to $3,500
- Home Energy Loan Program (HELP) - up to
  $1,000
- First Time Home Buyer's Assistance Program
- Hickory Home Ownership Program

City of High Point
Community Development and Housing Department
211 South Hamilton Street, Room 312
P.O. Box 230
High Point, NC 27261
336-883-3349
Fax: 336-883-3355
http://www.high-point.net/cd/
- Purchase-Rehabilitate-Resell Program

- Redevelopment Housing Program
- Homeowner Rehabilitation Program-low interest
  loans
- Rental Rehabilitation Program-Low interest loans
- Emergency and Limited Home Repair Program-
  loans up to $5,000

City of Jacksonville
Community Development Department
P.O. Box 128
Jacksonville, NC 28541
910-938-5286
Fax: 910-938-5366
http://www.ci.jacksonville.nc.us/cd/cd.htm
- Housing Rehabilitation Program-low interest
  loans for improvements and code corrections
- Demolition and Clearance Program
- CREATE Program-student built houses
- Home Ownership Assistance-interest free loans
  for down payment and closing costs

City of Kannapolis
Department of Planning and Zoning
P.O. Box 1199
209 Centergrove Road
Kannapolis, NC 28082-1199
704-933-5999
Fax: 704-933-6160
http://www.ci.kannapolis.nc.us/plan_0.asp#block
- Housing Rehabilitation Program
- Urgent Repair Program

City of Raleigh
Community Development Department
310 West Martin Street, Suite 101
P.O. Box 590
Raleigh, NC 27602
919-857-4330
http://www.raleigh-
nc.org/communitydevelopment/index.htm
- Affordable Rental Housing
- Housing Redevelopment Programs
- Homeownership Purchase and Rehabilitation
  Program-low interest loans
- Homebuyer Counseling Classes
- City-Wide Homeownership Loan Program
- Down Town Homeownership Program
- Emergency Rehabilitation Program

City of Rocky Mount
Community Development Department
One Government Plaza
P.O. Box 1180
Rocky Mount, NC 27802-1180
252-972-1100
http://www.ci.rocky-mount.nc.us/commdev.html

- Housing Rehabilitation Program-low interest loans up to $30,000
- Emergency Assistance Grants-up to $5,000 towards approved emergency repairs
- Urgent Repair Program-grants up to $3,500
- Acquisition/Demolition Program

City of Winston-Salem
Housing and Neighborhood Services Department
225 West 5th Street
Winston-Salem, NC 27101-2848
336-727-8595
Fax: 336-727-2878
http://www.cityofws.org/Departments/Housing_an
d_Neighborhood_Servi/housing_and_neighborhood
_servi.html
- Housing Rehabilitation Program-direct and deferred payment loans
- Rental Rehabilitation Program
- Emergency Repair Program
- Operation Paintbrush-grants for exterior painting
- Purchase/Tandem Loan Program-financial assistance for the purchase and rehabilitation of substandard structures

North Dakota
City of Bismarck
Planning and Development Department
221 North 5th street
Bismarck, ND 58506
701-222-6447
Fax: 701-222-6450
http://www.bismarck.org/city_departments/depart
ment/default.asp?dID=16
- Housing Rehabilitation Program

City of Fargo
Department of Planning and Development
City Hall
200 3rd Street, North
Fargo, ND 58102
701-241-1474
Fax: 701-241-1526
http://www.cityoffargo.com/Planning/default.htm
- Housing Rehabilitation Program, Owner Occupied-loans up to $15,000
- Rental Housing Rehabilitation Program-0% interest, deferred payment loans up to $10,000

Ohio
City of Akron
Housing and Community Services Division
161 South High Street, Suite 201A
Akron, OH 44308
330-375-2050
http://www.ci.akron.oh.us/planning/hcs/index.htm

- Housing Inspection/Rehabilitation Program
- Rental Rehabilitation Program-matching funds grants and technical assistance

City of Alliance
Planning and Development Department
504 East Main Street
Alliance, OH 44601
330-829-2235
Fax: 330-821-9362
http://www.cityofalliance.com/planning/
- Owner Occupied Housing Rehabilitation Program

City of Ashtabula
Housing and Community Development
4717 Main Avenue
Ashtabula, OH 44004
440-992-7127
http://ci.ashtabula.oh.us/housing.htm
- Owner Occupied Housing Rehabilitation Program
- Rental Housing Rehabilitation Program

City of Bowling Green
Grants Administration Department, Housing
Programs
304 North Church Street
Bowling Green, OH 43402-2399
419-354-6204
Fax: 419-352-1262
http://www.bgohio.org/grants-administration-
housing-programs.htm
- Rental Rehabilitation-deferred payment, forgivable loans
- Down Payment Assistance-loans from $1,000 to $6,600, no interest, deferred payment
- Owner Occupied Rehabilitation Loans-$3,000 to $25,000, zero interest, deferred payment
- Mobile Home Repair Loans-up to $2,500
- Emergency Home Repair Grants- to eligible senior citizens

City of Canton
Community/Economic Development and Planning
218 Cleveland Avenue, SW
5th Floor
Canton, OH 44702
330-489-3040
http://www.cityofcanton.com/citygov/ecdevdept/i
ndex.html
- Emergency Home Repair Grants-grants up to $6,000
- General Home Repair-grants up to $4,000
- Homeowner Rehabilitation Program-grants up to 90% of the total cost of rehabilitation, maximum of $20,000

City of Cincinnati
Community Development and Planning Department
805 Central Avenue, Suite 700
Cincinnati, OH 45202
513-352-6146
Fax: 513-352-6113
http://www.cincinnati-oh.gov/pages/-536-/
- Home Buyer Training Classes
- Housing Counseling
- Rental Rehabilitation Program-up to 50% of the total Rehabilitation Cost as a forgivable, deferred loan
- Homeowner Rehabilitation Loan Program
- Emergency Repair Assistance Program

City of Cleveland
Division of Neighborhood Services
601 Lakeside Avenue, Room 302
Cleveland, OH 44102
216-664-4074
Fax: 216-420-7964
http://www.city.cleveland.oh.us/government/departments/commdev/cdneigserv/cdneigservind.html
- Mortgage Assistance Program-Afford-A-Home, maximum assistance is $10,000
- Repair-A-Home Program-low interest loans
- Home Weatherization Assistance Program-grants up to $3,250
- Paint Refund Program-refunds up to $300 to cover the cost of paint and materials for exterior painting

City of Columbus
Department of Development
Housing Division
90 West Broad Street
Columbus, OH 43085
614-645-8526
http://td.ci.columbus.oh.us/Housing/index.htm#cip
- Emergency Repair Program-grants up to $7,500
- Home Modification Program-grants up to $15,000 for physical home alterations that promote accessibility
- Lead-Safe Columbus-grants up to $15,000 for lead paint abatement, interior and exterior
- Homeownership Development Program-$15,000 forgivable loans for rehabilitation or new construction of affordable housing
- Homeowner Assistance Program-grants up to $7,500, loans up to $15,000 for rehabilitation
- Down Payment Assistance-up to $3,000 for first time home buyers
- Mobile Tool Library-tools that can be borrowed for home maintenance and repair projects
- Sewer Tie-In Program-low interest or deferred loans

City of Dayton
Division of Housing and Neighborhood Development
101 West Third Street
Dayton, OH 45402
937-333-3670
http://www.ci.dayton.oh.us/planning/housing_assistance.asp
- Down Payment Assistance-up to 3%, $3,000 maximum through the Neighborhood Lending Program

City of Lancaster
Community Development Department
111 South Broad Street, Suite 217
Lancaster, OH 43130
740-687-6663
Fax: 740-681-5011
http://www.ci.lancaster.oh.us/dept/commdev/default.asp
- Homeowner Housing Rehabilitation Assistance Program-deferred loans up to $24,000
- Homebuyer Acquisition Assistance Program-deferred loans of $5,000 for a mortgage buy down

City of Lima
Department of Community Development
50 Town Square
Lima, OH 45801
419-221-5146
http://www.cityhall.lima.oh.us/
- Home Rehabilitation Program-Home ReNew low interest home repair loans up to $25,000
- Emergency Repair Program-grants up to $5,000

City of Mansfield
Community Development Department
30 North Diamond Street
Mansfield, OH 44902
419-755-9795
http://www.ci.mansfield.oh.us/community_development.htm
- Housing Rehabilitation Loan/Grant Program

City of Mentor
Community Development Department
8500 Civic Center Boulevard
Mentor, OH 44060
440-974-5740
http://www.cityofmentor.com/living/rehab.shtml
- Housing Rehabilitation Grant Program-maximum grant amount is $10,000
- Emergency Home Repair Grants

City of Middletown
Planning Department

One Donham Plaza
Middletown, OH 45042
513-425-7766
http://www.ci.middletown.oh.us/c07x00.html#Com
munity
- Housing Rehabilitation Program-revolving,
  deferred, and combination loans
- Emergency Home Repair Program

City of Sandusky
Community Development, Division of Housing,
Housing Rehabilitation Programs
222 Meigs Street
Sandusky, OH 44870
419-627-5844
Fax: 419-627-5825
http://www.ci.sandusky.oh.us/San2-
HousingRehab.htm
- Home Owner Rehabilitation
- Emergency Home Repair
- Down Payment Assistance

City of Springfield
Department of Human Relations, Housing and
Neighborhood Services
76 East High Street, 2nd Floor
Springfield, OH 45502
937-324-7368
http://www.ci.springfield.oh.us/depts/hr/housing.
htm
- Housing Comprehensive Rehabilitation
  Program-ten year, low interest loan, or home
  deferred loan
- Windows and Siding Program-low interest loans
  to install replacement windows and/or vinyl
  siding
- Emergency Repair Program-installment and
  deferred loans

City of Steubenville
Community Development and Planning Department
308 Market Street
Steubenville, OH 43952
740-283-6076
http://www.ci.steubenville.oh.us/
- Home Repair Program

City of Zanesville
Community Development Department
401 Market Street
City Hall, 2nd Floor, Room 207
Zanesville, OH 43701
740-455-0666
Fax: 740-452-2596
http://www.coz.org/communitydev.cfm
- Housing Rehabilitation Program

Oklahoma

City of Edmund
Department of Planning and Zoning
100 East First
Edmund, OK 73034
405-359-4789
http://www.ci.edmond.ok.us/city_services/comm_s
rvc/planning/plan_cdbg.html
- Housing Rehabilitation Program

City of Lawton
Community Development Department
103 SW 4th Street
Lawton, OK 73501
580-581-3347
http://www.cityof.lawton.ok.us/comdevelop.htm
- Owner Occupant Housing Rehabilitation
  Program
- Rental Housing Rehabilitation Program
- Emergency Home Repair Program

City of Oklahoma City
Neighborhood Services Department
420 West Main Street, 10th Floor
Oklahoma City, OK 73102
405-297-2972
Fax: 405-297-3374
http://www.okc.gov/
- Housing Rehabilitation Program-loans and
  grants

Oregon

City of Corvallis
Department of Community Development
501 SW Madison Avenue
Corvallis, OR 97333
541-766-6981
Fax: 541-766-6936
http://www.ci.corvallis.or.us/
- Housing Rehabilitation Loans-low interest loans
  for critical repairs
- Emergency Repair Loans-no interest, deferred
  payment loans for critical repairs
- Rental Rehabilitation Program-low interest loans
- Home Ownership Education Program

City of Eugene
Neighborhood, Housing and Community
Development
Planning and Development Department
99 West 10th Avenue
Eugene, OR 97401
541-682-5443
Fax: 541-682-5572
http://www.ci.eugene.or.us/
- Emergency Home Repair Program- up to $3,500

- Home Owner Rehabilitation Loan Program-low interest and interest free loans for eligible repairs
- Rental Rehabilitation Loan Program- $10,000 to $25,000, low interest
- Historic Rehabilitation Loan Program
- Home Buyer Assistance Program-up to $4,000 in down payment or closing costs loans to first time home buyers

City of Springfield
Housing Programs
225 Fifth Street
Springfield, OR 97477
541-726-2358
http://www.ci.springfield.or.us/dsd/Housing/
- Emergency Home Repair Program-up to $2,000 for repairs to enhance health, safety, or accessibility
- Down Payment or Closing Costs Assistance-up to $4,000 for eligible first time home buyers
- Home Improvement Program- low interest, deferred payment loans
- The Chore Program-up to $250/year for home and yard maintenance for qualified homeowners

Pennsylvania
City of Allentown
Housing, Home Ownership Programs
435 Hamilton Street
Allentown, PA 18101
610-437-7604
http://www.allentownpa.org/about_housing.htm
- Housing Rehabilitation Program-deferred payment loans for the correction of code violations, up to $20,000
- Emergency Home Repair Loans
- Rental Rehabilitation Program-low interest loans up to $8,500

City of Harrisburg
Department of Building and Housing Development
City Government Center
10 North Second Street, Suite 206
Harrisburg, PA 17101
717-255-6480
Fax: 717-255-6421
http://www.harrisburgcity.com/bhDevelopment/
- Home Improvement Program-loans and grants for housing rehabilitation

City of Lancaster
Neighborhood Assistance Unit
120 North Duke Street, 1st Floor
Lancaster, PA 17603
717-291-4731
http://www.cityoflancasterpa.com/

- Housing Redevelopment Program
- Homeowner Loan and Grant Programs for Housing Rehabilitation
- Critical Repair Program-low interest loans, maximum amount of $5,000

City of New Castle
Department of Community and Economic Development
230 North Jefferson Street
New Castle, PA 16101-2220
724-656-3510
http://www.newcastlepa.org/Government/Community_Develop_/community_develop_.htm
- Owner Occupied Housing Rehabilitation-low interest loans to correct code deficiencies

City of Norristown
Department of Planning and Municipal Development
235 East Airy Street
Norristown, PA 19401
610-272-8080
http://www.norristown.org/department5.htm
- Down Payment Assistance for First Time Home Buyers
- Owner Occupied Housing Rehabilitation
- Home Ownership Counseling

City of Philadelphia
Office of Housing and Community Development
1234 Market Street, 17th Floor
Philadelphia, PA 19107
215-686-9727
Fax: 215-686-9801
http://www.phila.gov/ohcd/index.html
- Home Weatherization Assistance Program-Home Ownership Opportunities
- Philadelphia Home Improvement Program
- Basic Systems Repair Program

City of Pittsburgh
Urban Development Authority, Housing Department
200 Ross Street
Pittsburgh, PA 15219-2016
412-255-6666
http://www.ura.org/housing.htm
- Housing Redevelopment Programs
- Housing Recovery Programs-mortgage loans for purchase/repair or refinance/repair
- Home Ownership Program-low interest mortgage program
- Home Improvement and Repair Loans
- Emergency Home Repair Loans

City of Williamsport
Economic and Community Development Department

245 West Fourth Street
Williamsport, PA 17701
570-327-7511
http://www.cityofwilliamsport.org/lyc-
williamsport/site/default.asp
- Owner Occupied Housing Rehabilitation-grants
  and low interest loans
- Rental Housing Rehabilitation-low interest loans
  or 50% matching funds grants
- Accessibility Improvements Grants
- Historic Property Rehabilitation-low interest
  loans

Rhode Island

City of Central Falls
Department of Planning
580 Broad Street, 2nd Floor
Central Falls, RI 02863
401-727-7480
Fax: 401-727-7410
http://www.centralfallsri.us/default2.htm
- Home Buyer Assistance Loans
- Housing Rehabilitation Programs

City of Cranston
Community Development Office
The Hamilton Building
1090 Cranston Street
Cranston, RI 02920
401-461-1000 ext. 7226
http://www.cranstonri.com/
- Home Repair Loans-low interest, up to $15,000
- Rental Rehabilitation Loans
- Lead Paint Removal Grants
- Closing Costs Assistance

City of Pawtucket
Department of Planning and Redevelopment
Benjamin Chester Building, 3rd Floor
175 Main Street
Pawtucket, RI
401-724-5200
Fax: 401-726-6237
http://www.pawtucketri.com/
- Housing Rehabilitation Program

City of Providence
Department of Planning and Development
25 Dorrance Street
Providence, RI 02903-3215
401-421-7740
http://www.providenceri.com/government/plannin
g/planning-index.html
- Housing Rehabilitation Programs

South Carolina

City of Anderson
Housing and Community Services Division
401 South Main Street
Anderson, SC 29621
864-231-2200
http://www.cityofandersonsc.com/divisions_housin
g.htm
- Housing Rehabilitation Programs

City of Charleston
Department of Housing and Community
Development
701 East Bay Street
Charleston, SC 29403
843-724-3766
http://www.ci.charleston.sc.us/hud.html
- Charleston Housing Trust-redevelopment
  program
- Home Rehabilitation Programs

City of Greenville
Economic and Community Development Department
P.O. Box 2207
206 South Main Street
Greenville, SC 29602-2207
864-467-4570
Fax: 864-467-5735
http://www.greatergreenville.com/neighborhoods/
comm_development.asp
- The Key Program for Home Ownership-free
  home ownership counseling and education
  program
- Emergency Rehabilitation Program
- Paint the Neighborhood Program
- Physically Challenged Housing Rehabilitation
- Community Improvement Program

City of Sumter
Community Development Department
21 North Main Street
3rd Floor, Opera House
P.O. Box 1449
Sumter, SC 29150
803-436-2685
http://www.sumter-sc.com/commundev.html
- Home Ownership Program-homeownership
  training, low interest financing, closing costs and
  down payment assistance
- Emergency Repair Program-low interest loans up
  to $13,000
- Housing Rehabilitation Programs

South Dakota

City of Rapid City
Community Development Department

300 Sixth Street
Rapid City, SD 57701
605-394-4136
Fax: 605-394-2232
http://www.rcgov.org/commdev/cdhome.htm
- Housing Rehabilitation Program-grants up to
  $7,000, 3% loans

City of Sioux Falls
Community Development Department
235 West 10th Street
Sioux Falls, SD 57104
605-367-7125
http://www.siouxfalls.org/comdev/index.asp
- Housing Rehabilitation Loan Program
- Emergency Mobile Home Repair Program-
  maximum of $2,000

TENNESSEE
City of Bristol
Community Development Office
Easley Municipal Annex Building
104 Eight Street
Bristol, TN 37621
423-989-5514
Fax: 423-989-5717
http://www.bristoltn.org/planning/page5.htm
- Owner Occupied Housing Rehabilitation
  Program-grants/loans to improve housing
  conditions and meet code requirements
- Homeownership Program-principal reduction
  grants

City of Johnson City
Community and Economic Development
601 East Main Street
Johnson City, TN 37601
423-434-6000
http://www.johnsoncitytn.org/CED/?BISKIT=40118
81946
- Housing Rehabilitation Programs
- Home Ownership Programs
- Housing Development Programs

City of Knoxville
Community Development department
City County Building, Room 503
Knoxville, TN 37902
865-215-2120
Fax: 865-215-2962
http://www.ci.knoxville.tn.us/development/
- Housing Rehabilitation programs-rental and
  owner occupied
- Preservation Rehabilitation Program
- Housing Redevelopment Programs

City of Memphis
Division of Housing and Community Development
701- North Main Street
B2, Suite 100
Memphis, TN 38107
901-576-7300
Fax: 901-576-7318
http://www.cityofmemphis.org/
- Home Owner Down Payment Assistance
- Single and Multi-Family Housing Rehabilitation
  and Development
- Affordable Housing Development Programs
- Housing Rehabilitation Program-assistance for
  minor and major repairs

City of Nashville
Office of the Mayor
Division of Affordable Housing
100 Metro Courthouse
Nashville, TN 37201
615-880-1891
Fax: 615-880-1893
http://www.nashville.gov/afford_housing/index.htm
- Affordable Housing Programs
- Home Ownership Preservation Effort (HOPE) -
  up to $5,000 in rehabilitation assistance

TEXAS
City of Abilene
Community Development
555 Walnut Street
P.O. Box 60
Abilene, TX 79604
915-676-6200
Fax: 915-676-6229
http://www.abilenetx.com/community_dev/community_dev.htm
- Rental Rehabilitation
- First Time Home Buyers Assistance
- Emergency Repair Assistance

City of Amarillo
Community Development Department
509 East 7th Avenue
Amarillo, TX 79105-1971
806-378-3098
Fax: 806-378-9389
http://www.ci.amarillo.tx.us/departments/commdev/commdev.htm
- Emergency Repair Grants-maximum grant
  amount is $3,500
- Housing Rehabilitation Grant Program

City of Arlington
Housing Division

Grants Management
201 East Abram Street, 7th Floor
Mail Stop 63-0700
P.O. Box 90231
Arlington, TX 76004-3231
817-459-6237
Fax: 817-459-6772
http://www.ci.arlington.tx.us/housing/index.html
- Owner Occupied Housing Rehabilitation Program-grants and loan subsidies up to $24,500
- Rental Rehabilitation Loan Program-low interest loans
- Affordable Housing Development

City of Austin
Neighborhood Housing and Community Development Office
505 Barton Springs Road, Suite 600
P.O. Box 1088
Austin, TX 78767
512-974-3100
http://www.ci.austin.tx.us/housing/
- First Time Home Buyer Assistance-down payment assistance, mortgage credit certificate
- Housing Rehabilitation Challenge Fund
- Home Owner Rehabilitation Loan Program-low interest loans
- Emergency Home Repair Program

City of Beaumont
Housing Services Division
P.O. Box 3827
801 Main Street, Room 225
Beaumont, TX 77704-3827
409-880-3763
Fax: 409-880-3125
http://www.ci.beaumont.tx.us/ecodev.htm#cdbg
- Housing Rehabilitation Program
- Affordable New Housing Developments
- Home Buyers Assistance Programs

City of Dallas
Housing Department
1500 Marilla Street
Room 6D, North
Dallas, TX 75201
214-670-4028
Fax: 214-670-0156
http://www.dallascityhall.com/dallas/eng/html/housing.html
- Mortgage Assistance Program
- Rental Housing Rehabilitation Program-low interest loans up to $35,000
- People Helping People Program-provides minor home repairs through volunteer services

- Home Improvement Program-up to $30,000 for substantial rehabilitation
- Minor Home Repair Program-up to $8,000 for emergency repairs

City of Edinburg
Community Development Department
409 West McIntyre
Edinburg, TX 78539-3229
956-383-0104
http://www.ci.edinburg.tx.us/CommunityDevelopment/index.htm
- Housing Rehabilitation/Reconstruction Program-low interest loans and partial deferred grants

City of Fort Worth
Housing Department
1000 Throckmorton Street
Fort Worth, TX 76102
817-392-7540
Fax: 817-392-7328
http://www.fortworthgov.org/housing/index.asp
- Homeownership Training
- Down Payment and Closing Costs Assistance
- Housing Redevelopment Programs-DreamHome
- Weatherization Program
- Emergency Repair Program-up to $5,000

City of Galveston
Grants and Housing Department
902-25th Street
Galveston, TX 77550-4401
409-766-2101
http://www.cityofgalveston.org/cityorg/purchasing/grants/index.shtml
- Emergency Home Repair Program
- First Time Homebuyers/Small Repair Assistance Program
- Home Improvement Loan Program-deferred payment loans

City of Houston
Housing and Community Development Department
Housing Assistance
900 Bagby
Houston, TX 77002
713-868-8300
http://www.ci.houston.tx.us/citydesk/housingassist.html
- Affordable Rental Housing
- Mortgage Assistance Programs
- Home Improvement and Repair Programs
- Redevelopment Housing Programs

City of Irving
Community Development Department
825 West Irving Boulevard
Irving, TX 75060
972-721-2424
Fax: 972-721-2422
http://www.ci.irving.tx.us/CommDev/blockgrants/
housing.htm
- Housing Rehabilitation Program
- Minor Home Repair Program-grants up to $3,000
- Homebuyer Assistance Program

City of Laredo
Department of Community Development
P.O. Box 1276
Transit Center East Wing, 3rd Floor
1301 Farragut Street
Laredo, TX 78042
956-795-2675
http://www.ci.laredo.tx.us/CommDev/develop.htm
- Housing Rehabilitation Program-loans up to
  $30,000 to correct code deficiencies
- Emergency Repair Grants-up to $8,000
- Fire Rehabilitation Grants-up to $30,000 to repair
  fire damaged homes
- Sewer Connection Grants-up to $8,000 to
  eliminate pit privies, cess pools, and septic tanks
- Paint Grants-up to $2,500 to paint home exteriors

City of Lubbock
Community Development
P.O. Box 2000
1625 13th Street
Lubbock, TX 79457-2000
806-775-2301
http://housing.ci.lubbock.tx.us/
- Residential Rehabilitation Program-home
  improvement loans
- Emergency Repair Program
- Barrier Free Living Program
- Water and Sewer Assistance Program

City of Midland
Community Development Department
P.O. Box 1152
300 North Loraine
Midland, TX 79701
915-685-7100
Fax: 915-685-0523
http://www.ci.midland.tx.us/Engineering/cdbg.htm
#housing
- Housing Rehabilitation Loan Program
- Housing emergency Repairs Program
- Homebuyer Assistance Program-loans for down
  payment and closing costs

City of Mission
Community Development Department
1201 East 8th Street
Mission, TX 78572
956-580-8670
http://www.missiontexas.us/commdevelopment.ht
ml
- Housing Rehabilitation/Replacement Deferred
  Loan Program-first come first served basis

City of Odessa
Community Development Department
Municipal Plaza, 1st Floor
119 West 4th Street
Odessa, TX 79761
915-335-4820
http://www.ci.odessa.tx.us/departments/commdev
/index.htm
- Housing Rehabilitation Program-deferred
  payment loans and/or grants
- Emergency Repair Rehabilitation Program-grants
  to make eligible repairs

City of San Antonio
Neighborhood Action Department
1400 South Flores Street
San Antonio, TX 78204
210-207-7881
Fax: 210-208-7914
http://www.sanantonio.gov/nad/
- Home Owner Rehabilitation Program
- Rental Rehabilitation Program-low interest
  financing
- Lead-Based Paint Hazard Reduction Program
- Homebuyer Education Program
- Down Payment Assistance Program

City of Sherman
Neighborhood Services
1000 North East Street
Sherman, TX 75090
903-892-7227
Fax: 903-870-4045
http://www.ci.sherman.tx.us/neighbor_serv_dept.ht
m
- Owner Occupied Housing Rehabilitation
  Program
- First Time Home Ownership Closing Costs
  Program

City of Waco
Housing and Community Development Services
300 Austin Avenue
P.O. Box 2570
Waco, TX 76702
254-750-5656

Fax: 254-750-5604
http://www.waco-texas.com/city_depts/housingservices/housing.htm
- New/Acquisition Housing Loan Program
- Emergency Repair Grants
- Rehabilitation Loan Program

City of Wichita Falls
Housing Division
1300 7th Street
P.O. Box 1431
Wichita Falls, TX 76301
940-761-7454
http://www.cwftx.net/HOUSING.htm
- Christmas in April Program-the city provides funds for materials, and the work is done by volunteers
- Rental Rehabilitation Program-up to 1/2 the costs of rehabilitation
- Emergency Repair Program

Utah

City of Ogden
Neighborhood Development
2549 Washington Boulevard
Ogden, UT 84401
801-629-8940
http://www.ogdencity.com/index.cfm/neighborhood.main
- Rental Rehabilitation Program-low interest loans
- Emergency Home Repair Program
- Home Owner Loan Program-low interest loans to rehabilitate your home
- Urban Homesteading Program-takes vacant homes, rehabilitates them and sells them to First Time Home Buyers
- Own-In-Ogden Program-up to $3,000 in closing costs and down payment assistance

City of Orem
Community and Neighborhood Services
56 North State, Room 222
Orem, UT 84057
801-229-7025
Fax: 801-229-7301
http://www.orem.org/html/community___n_hood_svcs.cfm
- Housing Rehabilitation Loans-up to $15,000 at 3% interest
- Emergency Repair Grants-up to $3,000
- Accessibility Grants- up to $3,000
- Tool Lending Library-for income qualified home owners for use in maintaining their homes and yards

City of Salt Lake City
Housing and Neighborhood Development
City and County Building, Room 406
Salt Lake City, UT 84070-4148
801-535-7902
http://www.slcgov.com/CED/hand/
- Mortgage Assistance-loans with low or no interest to qualified home buyers
- Housing Rehabilitation Program
- Free Housing Inspections

City of Sandy
Community Development Department
10000 Centennial Parkway
Sandy City, UT 84070-4148
801-568-7100
http://www.sandy-city.net/city_depts/commdev/index2.htm
- Emergency Home Repair Program
- Housing Rehabilitation Program

Vermont

City of Burlington
Community and Economic Development Office
City Hall, Room 32
149 Church Street
Burlington, VT 05401
802-865-7144
Fax: 802-865-7024
http://www.cedoburlington.org/
- Affordable Housing Development
- Homeownership Program
- Employer Assisted Housing Program
- Down Payment Assistance for Duplex Buyers-up to $30,000
- Homeowner Rehabilitation Loans-low interest
- Emergency Repair Loans-$3,000 to $5,000 in low interest loans
- Exterior Paint Grants-covers the cost of paint only
- RePAIR Program-Rehabilitation Program Assisting Investment Rentals
- Access Modification grants-up to $5,000

City of Montpelier
Community and Economic Development
39 Main Street
Montpelier, VT 05602-2950
802-223-9506
Fax: 802-223-9524
http://www.montpelier-vt.org/cda/index.cfm
- Handicapped Accessibility Loan Fund
- Homeownership Opportunity Program
- Home Weatherization Program

Virginia

City of Alexandria
Office of Housing
301 King Street
Alexandria, VA 22314
703-838-4990
Fax: 703-706-3904
http://ci.alexandria.va.us/city/housing/
- Housing Counseling-information for persons seeking rental housing in the city
- Home Ownership Assistance-down payment and closing costs assistance, below market interest rates
- Home Rehabilitation Loans-up to $90,000
- Housing Redevelopment Programs-Blighting Influences

City of Danville
Housing and Development Division
Room 207, Municipal Building
P.O. Box 3300
Danville, VA 24543
434-799-5260
Fax: 434-797-8919
http://www.ci.danville.va.us/com_dev/hddiv.html
- Housing Rehabilitation Assistance-loans, grants, and technical assistance
- Rental Housing Rehabilitation Assistance
- First Time Home Buyer Program-financial and technical assistance in the purchase and rehabilitation of a home

City of Richmond
Department of Community Development
City Hall, Room 501
900 East Broad Street
Richmond, VA 23219
804-646-6304
Fax: 804-646-5789
http://www.ci.richmond.va.us/services_guide.asp#N5
- Housing and Neighborhood Improvement Programs
- Homeownership Programs

City of Roanoke
Housing and Neighborhood Services
215 Church Avenue, SW
Noel C. Taylor Municipal Building, Room 162
Roanoke, VA 24011
540-853-1689
Fax: 540-853-6597
http://www.roanokegov.com/
- Mortgage Assistance Program for First Time Home Buyers
- Home Buyer Workshops and Training

- Housing Redevelopment Programs
- Neighborhood Revitalization Programs

City of Virginia Beach
Housing and Neighborhood Preservation
Municipal Center Building 18A
2424 Courthouse Drive
Virginia Beach, VA 23456
757-426-5750
Fax: 757-426-5794
http://www.vbgov.com/dept/housing/homeless.asp
- First Time Home Buyer Program-provides info on down payment and closing costs assistance, home buyer classes, and various loans
- Home Improvement Programs-low interest loans and grants

Washington

City of Bellingham
Office of Neighborhood and Community Development
114 West Magnolia Street, Suite 501
Bellingham, WA 98225
360-676-6880
http://www.cob.org/oncd/source/htm/housing.htm
- Owner Occupied Home Repair Loans-no interest loans up to $20,000
- Rental Rehabilitation Program-50% matching grants up to $7,500 per unit
- Housing Development Programs

City of Bremerton
Community Development Department
286 4th Street
Bremerton, WA 98337
360-473-5375
http://www.ci.bremerton.wa.us/communitydev/housinginfo.html
- Down Payment Assistance-low interest second loans up to $5,000
- Owner Occupied Rehabilitation -loans from $5,000 to $25,000

City of Everett
Department of Planning and Community Development
3200 Cedar Street
Everett, WA 98201
425-257-8856
http://www.everettwa.org/cityhall/default.asp?sectionid=4&parentid=14
- Community Housing Improvement Program (CHIP)-housing rehabilitation loans, 3% interest, deferred payments

City of Kent
Housing and Human Services
400 West Gowe
4th floor, Centennial Center
Kent, WA 98032
253-856-5065
Fax: 253-856-6070
www.ci.kent.wa.us
- Home Repair Program-minor repairs are free, major repairs are funded by grants and/or loan combinations up to $10,000

City of Lakewood
General Services Department
6000 Main Street, SW
Lakewood, WA 98499-5027
253-589-2489
Fax: 253-589-3774
http://www.ci.lakewood.wa.us/
- Housing Rehabilitation Program-up to $50,000, 80% loan, 20% grant
- Major Home Repair Program-up to $7,500, 80% loan, 20% grant
- Emergency Minor Home Repair Program-grants up to $1,000
- Down Payment Assistance-zero interest loans up to $5,000

City of Olympia
Housing and Community Development Division
P.O. Box 1967
Olympia, WA 98507-1967
360-753-8554
http://www.ci.olympia.wa.us/CPD/housing/
- Housing Rehabilitation Program-zero interest, deferred loans
- Investor-Owned (Rental) Rehabilitation Program
- Land Acquisition Program-assistance for the purchase of property for new affordable housing development

City of Richland
Housing Redevelopment Division
505 Swift Boulevard
P.O. Box 190
Richland, WA 99352
509-942-7580
Fax: 509-942-5665
http://www.ci.richland.wa.us/ed/index.html
- Down Payment Assistance Program-50/50 matching funds, loans from $1,000 to $5,000
- Owner Occupied Rehabilitation Program-maximum loan amount $20,000, flexible repayment terms
- Rental Rehabilitation Loans-maximum loan is 50% of the total cost of rehabilitation up to $8,500
- In-fill Homeownership Program

City of Seattle
Office of Housing
Key Tower
700 Fifth Avenue, 57th floor
Seattle, WA 98104-5032
206-684-0721
Fax: 206-233-7117
http://www.cityofseattle.net/housing/default.htm
- Home Repair Loans
- Weatherization Grants
- Home Buyer and Renters Guides
- Hometown Home Loan Program

City of Spokane
Community Development Department, Housing
801 West Spokane Falls Boulevard, room 650
Spokane, WA 99201
509-625-6325
http://www.spokanecitycd.org/housing/index.htm
- Affordable Rental Housing
- Housing Rehabilitation Loans
- Minor Home Repair Program
- Home Buyer Education Classes
- Down Payment Assistance Loans
- Emergency Housing Repair Program

City of Tacoma
Housing Development
747 Market Street, 9th Floor
Tacoma, WA 98402
253-591-5238
Fax: 253-591-5232
http://www.cityoftacoma.org/default.asp?main=/34
housing/default.asp
- Home Repair Loans-no interest, no payments until home is sold, loans for major repairs
- Minor Home Repair Program-loans up to $400
- Neighborhood Preservation Program-loans up to $50,000 for code related repairs
- Down Payment Assistance Program-loans up to $5,000 to help with down payment and closing costs

City of Vancouver
Community Services Department
610 Esther Street
P.O. Box 1995
Vancouver, WA 98668-1995
360-619-1139
Fax: 360-966-8009
http://www.ci.vancouver.wa.us/chservices/cdbg/index.htm
- Housing Rehabilitation Program-deferred and low interest loans for rehabilitation and emergency repairs

- First Home Loan Program-interest free loans for down payment assistance or interest buy downs
- Homeownership Education and Counseling

City of Yakima
Office of Neighborhood Development Services
112 South 8th Street
Yakima, WA 98901
509-575-6101
Fax: 509-575-6176
http://www.ci.yakima.wa.us/services/onds/
Down Payment Assistance Program-up to $4,000 for First Time Home Buyers
- Housing Rehabilitation Program-low interest loans for owner occupied rehabilitation
- First Time Home Buyers Program

West Virginia

City of Buckhannon Housing Authority
70 East Main Street
Buckhannon, WV 26201
304-472-1305
http://ci.buckhannon.wv.us/

City of Clarksburg Housing Authority
Clarksburg Municipal Building
Clarksburg, WV 26301
304-624-1673
www.clarksburg.com

Fairmont Housing Authority
103 12th Street
Fairmont, WV 26554
304-363-0860
Fax: 304-363-0469
www.fmhousing.com
- Affordable Rental
- Lease to Own Homeownership Program
- Homebuyer Financing

Wheeling Economic & Community Development Office
City-County Building, Room 305
1500 Chapline Street
Wheeling, WV 26003
304-234-3701
Fax: 304-234-3899
www.cityofwheelingwv.gov
- First Time Homebuyer Program
- Down Payment Assistance

Wisconsin

City of Appleton
Economic Development department
100 North Appleton Street
Appleton, WI 54911

920-832-6007
Fax: 920-832-5994
http://www.appleton.org/departments/development/housing/
- Rental Rehabilitation Loan Program
- Housing Rehabilitation Loan Program

City of Eau Claire
Housing Division
City Hall, Ground Floor
203 South Farwell Street
Eau Claire, WI 54703
715-839-4943
Fax: 715-839-4939
http://www.ci.eau-claire.wi.us/Departments/Default.htm
- Housing Rehabilitation Loans

City of Green Bay
Planning and Development, Neighborhood Division
100 North Jefferson, Street
Green Bay, WI 54301
920-448-3400
Fax: 920-448-3426
http://www.ci.green-bay.wi.us/
- Down Payment and Closing Costs Assistance-$3,000 to $5,000
- Home Improvement Loan Program-deferred payment, zero interest

City of Greenfield
Planning and Economic Development Department
City Hall, Room 202
7325 West Forest Home Avenue
Greenfield, WI 53220
414-329-5342
http://www.ci.greenfield.wi.us/planning/index.htm
- Home Repair Loan Program

City of Janesville
Housing, Building and Neighborhood Services
200 West Milwaukee Street
Janesville, WI 53545
608-755-3065
Fax: 608-755-3207
http://www.ci.janesville.wi.us/DeptHome.asp?Dept=Housing
- Home Buyer's Workshops
- Down Payment and Closing Costs Assistance
- Rental Rehabilitation Program-low to no interest loans
- Home Improvement Program-low to no interest loans for repairs to recently purchased homes

City of Madison
Department of Planning and Development

Room LL-100, Municipal Building
201 Martin Luther King Jr. Boulevard
Madison, WI 53703-3348
608-266-4254
http://www.ci.madison.wi.us/planning/plandept.ht
ml
- Affordable Rental Housing
- Housing Rehabilitation Program-deferred
  payment loans
- Affordable Housing Development
- Housing Counseling

City of Manitowoc
City Planning Commission
900 Quay Street
Manitowoc, WI 54220-4543
920-686-6930
Fax: 920-686-6939
http://www.manitowoc.org/housing_loan_program.
html
- Housing Loan Program-up to $10,000, zero
  interest, deferred payment
- Housing Rehabilitation Loans-no interest,
  deferred payment, up to $8,500

City of Milwaukee
Department of Neighborhood Services
841 North Broadway, 10th Floor
Milwaukee, WI 53202
414-286-8212
http://www.ci.mil.wi.us/citygov/dns/home.htm
- Direct Service Program-helps eligible
  homeowners with home maintenance
- Home Rehabilitation Loan Program-low interest
  loans and technical assistance
- Rental Rehabilitation Loan Program-forgivable
  loans up to 50% of the cost of eligible
  improvements, maximum of $8,500 per unit
- Mixed Use Rehabilitation Loan Program-
  forgivable loans up to $10,000 in matching funds
- Community Homes Development Program-
  buy/rehabilitate/resell program
- Affordable Housing Development
- In-Fill Housing Program

City of Racine
Housing Department
Room 114, City Hall Annex
800 Center Street
Racine, WI 53403
414-636-9197
http://www.cityofracine.org/housing/Housing.sht
ml
- Free Exterior Paint Program
- Mixed Use Rehabilitation Loans

- Rental Assistance Rehabilitation Program-up to
  75% of the cost of rehabilitation
- Homeowner Fixed Interest Rehabilitation Loan
  Program
- Homeowner Deferred Rehabilitation Loan
  Program

City of Sheboygan
Department of City Development
807 Center Avenue
Sheboygan, WI 53081
920-459-3377
Fax: 920-459-3919
http://www.ci.sheboygan.wi.us/planning.html
- Owner Occupied Home Rehabilitation Loan
  Program-up to $16,000
- Rental Rehabilitation Loan Program-75% of the
  cost of rehabilitation up to $16,000

City of Superior
City Planning Department
1409 Hammond Avenue
Superior, WI 54880-1674
715-394-0278
Fax: 715-394-7247
http://www.ci.superior.wi.us/planning/index.htm
- Weatherization Program
- Housing Rehabilitation Program-home
  improvement loans
- Home Ownership Opportunities Program-down
  payment and closing costs assistance
- Purchase/Rehabilitation/Resale Program

City of Wausau
Community Development
407 Grant Street
Wausau, WI 54403
715-261-6680
http://www.wausaudevelopment.com/community_
dev.htm
- Rental Rehabilitation program
- Housing Rehabilitation Program
- Home Buyer Down Payment Program
- Employer Assisted Down Payment Program

Wyoming
City of Casper
Housing Programs
200 North David
Casper, WY 82601
307-235-82601
http://www.cityofcasperwy.com/housing/housing.
html
- Owner Occupied Rehabilitation-up to $17,500
- Emergency Repair Assistance-up to $7,500

- Exterior Repair Grants-World Changers Program, up to $2,500 for materials
- Mobile Home Repair Assistance-up to $2,500

City of Cheyenne
Housing and Community Development Office
2102 O'Neil Avenue, Room 309
Cheyenne, WY 82001
307-637-6252
http://www.cheyennecity.org/communit.htm

- HAND Program-grants/loans for emergency repairs
- Homeowner Rehabilitation Program

City of Rawlins
Community Development Department
521 West Cedar Street
Rawlins, WY 82301
307-328-4540
http://www.rawlins-wyoming.com/
- Self Help Housing Program

More Nonprofit Housing Programs

Local and national nonprofit organizations provide a significant opportunity for individuals seeking help with housing and real estate. They can provide help for:

* ★ renters who have trouble making their monthly payments
* ★ new homeowners who need help with down payments and closing costs
* ★ home buyers who are seeking big discounts on properties
* ★ renters and homeowners who need help paying their housing bills
* ★ investors looking for bargains and opportunities
* ★ homeowners who need cash to fix up their home
* ★ seniors and people with disabilities who need help buying, renting for fixing up property

Many of these organizations receive their funding from government agencies, individual solicitations or other nonprofit organizations.

Because so many of these groups only serve people in specific geographic areas, it is extremely difficult to be able to list all nonprofits in this book. There are literally thousands of nonprofits that help with housing issues. We have described a few below in order to give you a feel of the types of help available from such groups.

Help Finding Local Money

The following organizations can help you find local nonprofit organizations that offer financial assistance with housing in your area:

* *National Association of Housing and Redevelopment Officials*, 630 Eye St., NW, Washington, DC 20001; 202-289-3500, 877-866-2476, Fax: 202-289-8181; {www.nahro.org}.
* *Information Center*, Office of Community Planning and Development, P.O. Box 7189, Gaithersburg, MD 20898; 800-998-9999; Fax: 301-519-5027; {www.comcon.org}.
* *Association of Community Organizations for Reform Now (ACORN)*, 88 3rd Avenue, Brooklyn, NY 11217, 1-877-55ACORN; Fax: 718-246-7939; {www.acorn.org}.
* *The National Community Action Foundation*, 810 First St., Suite 530, Washington, DC 20002; 202-842-2092; Fax: 202-842-2095: {www.ncaf.org/linkcaas.htm}.

- *All your elected representatives*. Your U.S. Congressman and Senator, your State Representative or Senator, your mayor or city councilman. Most of these people have a staff member whose job it is to assist the people they represent, that is, their constituents with issues such as housing. This person should know the local community and how you can best go about finding the services you need. If you cannot find their phone number, your local library can help.
- *Your local library*. See your reference librarian.

Nonprofits That Help People With Disabilities Find Housing

In addition to the resources listed above, people with disabilities should also contact the following:

- *The U.S. Department of Housing and Urban Development* maintains a listing of programs and groups that are helpful for people with disabilities: {www.hud.gov/groups/disabilities.cfm}.
- *National Organization on Disability*, 910 16th Street, NW, Suite 600, Washington, DC 20006; 202-293-5960; Fax: 202-293-7999; {www.nod.org}.

Free Home Repair

Families and seniors living in New York can get free home repair if they do not have the funds to pay for the repairs themselves. New plumbing, walls, floors, appliances and even a new roof are the kinds of repairs that can be provided. Contact: Bishop Sheen Ecumenical Housing Foundation, 935 East Avenue, Suite 300, Rochester, NY 14607; 585-461-4263; Fax: 585-461-5177; {www.sheenhousing.org/}.

Down Payments and Sweat Equity In Florida

Grants and low interest rate loans are available for down payments. For new home construction and rehab homes, this program allows a person to use work (sweat equity) as a down payment. Contact: Affordable Housing Concepts, Inc. 809 E. Bloomingdale Ave., Suite 395, Brandon, FL 33511; {www.affordablehousing.com}; {affordahouse@mindspring.com}.

Grants and Low Interest Loans For Housing

Communities can get access to grants, short term loans and long term loans to provide affordable housing, day care and other facilities. They also provide a clearing house for other sources of housing income for groups who want to provide affordable housing. Contact: The Enterprise Foundation, 10227 Wincopin Circle, Suite 500, Columbia, MD 21044; 410-964-1230; {www.enterprisefoundation.org}.

Volunteers Will Fix Up Your Home For Free

Many service organizations have begun to organize community service days, where the town is beautified along with certain homes in need of repair. *Christmas in April* is a national organization with over 185 affiliates that gather together volunteers to help rehabilitate the homes of low-income homeowners. The work is done for free with the goal being to provide a safe and secure home for those in need. An example of a program in the Dallas area is the Volunteer Home Repair and Weatherization Program. This program provides home repairs that improve the health, safety, and energy efficiency of a home for low-income homeowners.

Contact your city government, your county government and your local community development office to learn about local programs. In the Dallas area, contact Volunteer Home Repair and Weatherization Program, Center for Housing Resources, 3103 Greenwood, Dallas, TX 75204; 214-828-4390; Fax: 214-828-4412; {www.chrdallas.org}.

Free Money For Your Downpayment

Here is a program that will give you 5% of the downpayment costs for your new home. This program is open to everyone, not just first time home buyers, and the homes can be valued at up to $300,700! Funds for this program do not need to be repaid and come from funds raised through the AmeriDream Charity. You must purchase a home from a builder or seller who has enrolled their home in the program. Over 4,500 people become homeowners each month through the AmeriDream Downpayment Gift Program.

To learn more contact AmeriDream Charity, 18310 Montgomery Village Ave., Suite 300, Gaithersburg, MD 20879; 301-977-9133; toll-free 866-263-7437; {www.ameridream.org}.

Make Up To $50,000 and Get Your Rent and Fuels Bills Paid For

If you are within a certain income and need help paying your heating bills, need money to make your house more energy efficient, or need funds for urgent repairs, call your local Community Action Agency. There are about 1,000 of them around the country to help neighborhoods. They will also come out and check if your home or apartment needs to be more energy efficient.

To find an agency near you, contact Community Action Partnership, 1100 17th St., NW, Suite 500, Washington, DC 20036; 202-265-7546; Fax: 202-265-8850; {www.communitypartnership.com}. Also, your local utility can provide you with information or refer you to other programs in your area to analyze your energy usage, recommend energy saving measures, provide fuel and utility assistance to retain or restore service, establish payment discounts based on income and usage, or establish affordable payment plans if you are in arrears. Contact your local utility company to take advantage of these services.

Get a $2,000 Grant To Fix Up Your Home

A family of four can be making close to $30,000 year and still be eligible for a 2% interest loan from local Community Action Agency. Some agencies also offer grants or are aware of other local organizations that provide grants. There are about 1,000 of them around the country to help neighborhoods.

To find an agency near you, contact Community Action Partnership, 1100 17th St., NW, Suite 500, Washington, DC 20036; 202-265-7546; Fax: 202-265-8850; {www.communitypartnership.com}.

Cheap and Free Money For Home Fix Up

The Housing Preservation Grant program in Mississippi covers part or all of the cost of providing repair/rehabilitation assistance to rural homeowners for loans, grants, and interest reduction payments, or other assistance that will reduce the cost of repair and rehabilitation. Contact: Pearl River Valley Opportunity, Inc., 756 Highway 98 Bypass, Columbia, MS 39429; 601-736-9564; {www.prvoinc.org/index.html}.

No Money Down and 0% Interest Mortgage

Over 150,000 have receive this offer through this national organization that works with volunteer labor and donations for money and materials. They build and rehabilitate simple, decent housing with the help of homeowner (partner) families. The houses are sold to the partner families at no profit, financed with affordable, no-interest loans. Contact: Habitat for Humanity International, 121 Habitat Street, Americus, GA 31708; 229-924-6935; {www.habitat.org}.

Money To Buy a House, Pay Your Rent or Fix Up Your Home

There are over 1,000 Community Action Agencies around the country that help who cannot afford the housing that they need. Some of their sweat equity allow home buyers to pay only 50% of the property's value. Other programs pay for rent and repairs. To find as program near you contact: Community Action Partnership. 1100 17th Street, NW, Suite 500, Washington, DC 20036, 202-265-7546, fax: 202-265-8850, {www.communityactionpartnership.com}.

$1,000 Moves You In

That's is all you need to come up with if you want to live in certain counties in Illinois. It's for people who are close to the median income level and it can't be for investment real estate. You have to live there.

Contact C.E.F.S. Economic Opportunity Corporation, 1805 S. Banker, P O Box 928, Effingham, IL 62401-0928; 217-342-2193; Fax: 217-342-4701; {www.advant.com/cefs/}.

Money To Pay Your Utility Bills Plus Free Storm Windows

Homeowners and even renters in certain areas of Massachusetts can qualify for grants to pay these utility bills. Homeowners and renters can also receive free insulation, air sealing and storm windows. You can even receive grants to make house repairs or replace a heating system. Contact: Citizens for Citizens, 264 Griffin St., Fall River, MA 02724; 508-679-0041; Fax: 508-821-9254; {www.cfcinc.org}.

Save $1 For a House and Get $8 More FREE

The program is called Individual Development Accounts (IDA) and it allows those that would otherwise not be able to save, the chance to save faster by having the government and nonprofit organizations give you $8 for every $1 you put into a saving program. There are over 150 such programs around the country now. The money has to be used for housing, starting a business or education. Find a program near you at {www.acf.hhs.gov/programs/ocs/demo/ida/}.

Emergency Home Repair

A nonprofit in Illinois provides emergency home repair services to homes that require rehabilitation. This includes: Roofing, Plumbing, Foundation, Electrical Wiring, and Flooring They also provide pay for the installation of furnaces, bathroom plumbing, and repairs to rotted floors.

Contact: Community Action of Greater Indianapolis, Inc.
2445 North Meridian Street Indianapolis, IN 46208; 317-396-1800; Fax: 317-396-1530; {www.cagi-in.org/}.

Money For Seniors To Fix Up Their Home

Grants are available to those over 60 to enhance the health, safety and well being of a home. Contact: NORWESCAP, 350 Marshall Street, Phillpsburg, NJ 08865; 908-454-7999; Fax: 908-859-0729; {www.norwescap.org/index.asp}.

10,000 Families Get Money To Pay Housing Bills

In Fort Wayne Indiana:
- 9,303 families received an average of $311 to pay utility bills,
- 1,569 homes kept cool by getting free money to pay their utility bills, free fans or free air conditioners,
- 181 homes received free weatherization to reduce their energy bills by 29%, and
- 146 families received an average of $348 a month to pay their rent

Contact: Community Action of Northeast Indiana, 2260 Lake Avenue, Fort Wayne, IN 46853; 260-4323-3546; Fax: 260-422-4041; {www.canihelp.org}.

$1,200 For Seniors

The Emergency Repairs for the Elderly provides for emergency repairs to elderly homeowners with total household income of 50% or median or less. Contact: Accord Corporation, 84 Schuyler Street, Belmont, NY 14813; 585-268-7605; Fax: 585-268-7241; {www.accordcorp.org/index2.html}.

Get A Home No Matter What Your Income

A program in Kentucky assists low and moderate-income households through homebuyer education classes and one-on-one homeownership counseling that enables many families who never believed they could own their own home to become homeowners. The program uses grant funds to provide assistance and the family secures a very low interest loan to cover the remaining cost.

Contact: Kentucky River Foothills Development Council, Inc., P.O. Box 743, Richmond, KY 40476; 859-624-2046; Fax: 859-624-2049; {www.kyriverfoothills.org}.

$2,500 To Fix Up Your Heating System

Plus you can also get emergency fuel delivery or an electrical disconnect emergency. Or extra money so you don't pay more than 30% of your income on rent. Or 1 free 10-hour course to teach you about the best way to buy a home. Or money to fix up a home you want to buy. Or a free inspection to see if lead paint is in your home. Or even grants to fix up your home. Contact: Aroostock County Action Program, 771 Main Street, Presque Isle, ME 04769; 207-764-3721; {www.acap-me.org}.

More Free Money And Help For Homeowners and Renters

Free Money For Closing Costs And A Down Payment

Houston has a program that offers $4,000 in down-payment and closing costs through their First-Time Homebuyers Program. Iowa offers up to $2,750 in grants for a down-

payment. You can be earning up to $65,000 a year and still be eligible for the money in their Down Payment/Closing Cost Grant Program. Many cities, like Minneapolis, will offer interest free loans, called Equity Participation Loans, for up to 10% of the cost of the home. You pay back the money when you sell the house.

Programs vary from state to state and city to city. Contact your city government, your county government, and your local community development office to learn about local programs. If you have trouble locating your local community development office, the following organizations may be able to help:

- National Association of Housing and Redevelopment Officials, 630 Eye St, NW, Washington, DC 20001; 202-289-3500; 877-866-2476, Fax: 202-289-8181; {www.nahro.org}
- Information Center, Office of Community Planning and Development, P.O. Box 7189, Gaithersburg, MD 20898; 800-998-9999, Fax: 301-519-5027; {www.comcon.org}
- Also be sure to check the State Housing Programs beginning on page 163.

"WOW!...The Government Will Pay My Mortgage"

You'd never have thought to ask, would you?

There are now programs that will make your mortgage payments for you when you get into financial trouble. For example, Pennsylvania law, 35 P.S. § 1680.401 et seq., states it will provide "*mortgage assistance payments to homeowners who are in danger of losing their homes through foreclosure and through no fault of their own and who have a reasonable prospect of resuming mortgage payments within the prescribed time frame.*" Pennsylvania calls it the *"Homeowners' Emergency Mortgage Assistance Program."*

One of the best ways to find out if there are programs like this in your area is to contact the local HUD approved Housing Counseling agencies. To find your closest agency, contact your state housing office (see the State Housing Programs beginning on page 163), the Housing Counseling Center locator at 1-888-466-3487; {www.hud.gov/hsgcoun.html}, or Housing Counseling Clearinghouse, P.O. Box 9057, Gaithersburg, MD 20898; 800-217-6970; Fax: 301-519-6655.

> **Who Qualifies As A First Time Homebuyer?**
>
> Most government programs define a first time homebuyer as someone who has not owned a home during the past 3 years or who is legally separated or divorced.

If your local agency doesn't have money to pay your mortgage, they will certainly help you work out other arrangements with your mortgage company.

Make Money Going To Housing Classes

A HUD-approved housing counseling agency in Philadelphia offers $1,000 in settlement costs to certain people who attend pre-purchase house counseling sessions. A counseling agency in Boston offers new home buyers access to special low down-payment mortgages if they attend pre-housing classes.

There are over 350 HUD-approved counseling agencies that offer free classes and help in housing related issues including:

- "The Best Way To Buy And Finance A Home"
- "Is A Reverse Mortgage For You?"
- "Foreclosure and Eviction Options"
- "The Best Way To Finance A Home Fix-Up"

These nonprofit agencies are trained and approved by the U.S. Department of Housing and Urban Development (HUD). To find your closest agency, see the State Housing Programs beginning on page 163, the Housing Counseling Center locator at 1-888-466-3487; {www.hud.gov/hsgcoun.html}, or Housing Counseling Clearinghouse, P.O. Box 9057, Gaithersburg, MD 20898; 800-217-6970, Fax: 301-519-6655.

Home Repair Programs

Here are a few *HOME REPAIR* programs we found that were available at the time we were doing research. Things change, but make sure to contact local agencies to see what may be available to you!

City of Sunnyvale
Housing Division
P.O. Box 3707
Sunnyvale, CA 94088
408-730-7250
www.ci.sunnyvale.ca.us/comm
unity-dev/housing/index.htm

Tacoma Community
Redevelopment Authority
747 Market St., Room 1036
Tacoma, WA 98402
253-591-5238
www.cityoftacoma.org

Community Development
City of Canton
218 Cleveland Ave., SW
Canton, OH 44702
330-489-3040
www.canton-
ohio.com/canton/homerep.html

Minneapolis Community
Development Agency

Crown Roller Mill
105 Fifth Ave. S, Suite 200
Minneapolis, MN 55401
612-673-5095
www.mcda.org

Los Angeles Housing
Department
111 N. Hope St., Lobby Level
Los Angeles, CA 90012
213-369-9175; 800-994-4444
www.cityofla.org/LAHD

Department of Housing and
Community Development
300 W. Washington St.
P.O. Box 3136
Greensboro, NC 27402
336-373-2349
www.ci.greensboro.nc.us/HCD/

Metropolitan Development and
Housing Agency
701 S. 6th St.
Nashville, TN 37202

615-252-8590
www.nashville.org/mdha

Department of Community
Development
Neighborhood Conservation
Services Division
602 E. 1st St.
Des Moines, IA 50309
515-283-4787
www.ci.des-
moines.ia.us/departments/cd/

Low-Income Weatherization
Program
Housing Authority and
Community Services Agency
177 Day Island Rd.
Eugene, OR 97401
541-682-3755
www.hacsa.org

"Get The Lead Out"
And Get Your House Or Apartment Painted For Free

If you are living in a house or apartment that was built before 1978, you, or even your landlord, may be eligible for grant money and other assistance to make sure that you do not suffer the effects of lead poisoning from lead-based paint. Chips or dust from this type of paint can be highly dangerous to humans, especially children.

The U.S. Department of Housing and Urban Development spends over $60 million a year helping home owners and apartment owners eliminate the problems that may be caused by lead paint. Contact your state department of housing (see the State Housing Programs beginning on page 163) to see if your state has money for lead paint removal.

How Lead Paint Can Affect Your Kids

Houses and apartments built before 1978 may contain lead contaminated surface dust and paint chips, which, if consumed by children, can result in reduced intelligence, behavioral problems, learning disabilities, and even permanent brain damage. Government sponsored programs can help you inspect your home for lead paint and even get a blood test for your children for potential problems. To find out more about these programs or the effects of lead-based paint, contact the following:

♦ **National Lead Information Center**, EPA, 1200 Pennsylvania Ave., NW, Mail Code: 7404, Washington, DC 20460; 800-424-LEAD; {www.epa.gov/lead/nlic.htm}.

♦ **Office of Lead Hazard Control**, U.S. Department of Housing and Urban Development, 451 7th Street, SW, Room B-133, Washington, DC 20410; 202-708-1112; Fax: 202-708-1455; {www.hud.gov/offices/lead}.

Free Money To Fix Up Your Home

States, cities, and counties, as well as local community development agencies are providing grants, loans, and even supplies and technical assistance for homeowners who want to fix up the inside or outside of their homes. Many of these have income requirements you must meet. Others offer forgivable loans if you stay in the house a certain number of years. Here are some examples of what communities are offering to their residents:

☞ *Sunnyvale, CA*: $2,000 grant for disabled homeowners to fix up anything through the Home Access Grant Program.

☞ *Houston, TX*: loans and grants for major repairs through their Housing Assistance Program for the Elderly and Disabled.

☞ *Tacoma, WA*: Up to $3,500 loan at 0% interest with no monthly payments through the Major Home Repair Program.

☞ *Minneapolis, MN*: $15,000, no interest, and no payments until you sell in their Deferred Rehabilitation Loans.

☞ *Baton Rouge, LA*: $20,000 grant to fix up your home through the Housing Rehabilitation Grant Program.

☞ *Los Angeles, CA*: Free help with roofing, plumbing, electrical and heating work, painting, deadbolt locks, smoke alarms, screens, windows, and yard maintenance for seniors or disabled persons through the Handy Worker Program.

☞ *Michigan*: $1,000 to $10,000 at zero interest, to be paid back when you sell your home through the Rehabilitation Assistance Program.

☞ *Nashville, TN*: $18,000 at 3% to fix up your home.

☞ *Lane County, OR*: offers grants for weatherization assistance for weatherstripping, storm doors and windows, and insulation.

☞ *Des Moines, IA*: offers emergency repair loans.

☞ *Greensboro, NC*: has low interest loans for people with incomes over $30,000 and $8,500 grants for people with incomes up to $20,000.

Programs vary from state to state and city to city. Contact your city government, your county government, and your local community development office to learn about local programs. If you have trouble locating your local community development office, the following organizations may be able to help:

- National Association of Housing and Redevelopment Officials, 630 Eye St., NW, Washington, DC 20001; 202-289-3500, 877-866-2476, Fax: 202-289-8181; {www.nahro.org}
- Information Center, Office of Community Planning and Development, P.O. Box 7189, Gaithersburg, MD 20898; 800-998-9999, Fax: 301-519-5027; {www.comcon.org}
- Also be sure to check the State Housing Programs beginning on page 163.

Your Rich Uncle Will Cosign A Loan To Buy or Fix Up a Home

Both the U.S. Department of Housing and Urban Development (HUD) and the Rural Housing Service of the U.S. Department of Agriculture offer loan guarantees to lending agencies around the county. A loan-guarantee assures the lending agency that the government will pay for the loan if you can't.

In addition, the Rural Housing Service has a direct loan program that provides loans to lower income families to buy, build, repair, renovate, or relocate their home. This is called the Section 502 Program.

To investigate the programs available in your area, contact your local HUD office listed in the blue pages of your telephone book, or U.S. Department of Housing and Urban Development (HUD), 451 7th Street, SW, Washington, DC 20410; 202-708-1112, 800-245-2691; {www.hud.gov}. To find your local Rural Housing Service, look in the blue pages of your telephone book, or contact Single Family Housing Programs, USDA Rural Housing Service, Room 5037, South Building, 14th St. and Independence Ave., SW, Washington, DC 20250; 202-720-4323; {www.rurdev.usda.gov/}. You may also check the State Housing Programs beginning on page 163.

$4,000 Grant To Paint Your Home

That's what Canton, Ohio offers to very low-income residents — grants to paint their house or put on new siding. They feel that an investment like this improves the value of all the properties in the area. Sunnyvale, California offers some of their residents $400 in grant money to paint their homes. And if you're over 60 or have a disability, you can get a $1,200 grant. See if your city or state offers a program like this.

Money For Seniors And Those With A Disability To Buy or Fix Up A Home

The city of Houston offers $5,000 fix up money for the disabled and elderly in their Emergency Repair Program. Minneapolis offers home repair grants of $10,000 to people with disabilities who have incomes under $18,000. Nebraska has a special low interest loan program to help people with disabilities buy a home.

The Rural Housing Service of the U.S. Department of Agriculture offers special grants through their Section 504 program of up to $7,500 if you're over 62, and need to fix up your home. Programs vary from state to state and city to city, and obviously, many have eligibility requirements.

Contact your city government, your county government and your local community development office to learn about local programs. If you have trouble locating your local community development office, contact *National Association of Housing and Redevelopment Officials*, 630 Eye St., NW, Washington, DC 20001; 202-289-3500, 877-866-2476, Fax: 202-289-8181; {www. nahro.org}, or *Information Center, Office of Community Planning and Development*, P.O. Box 7189, Gaithersburg, MD 20898; 800-998-9999, Fax: 301-519-5027; {www. comcon.org}.

To find your local *Rural Housing Service*, look in the blue pages of your telephone book, or contact Single Family Housing Programs, USDA Rural Housing Service, Room 5037, South Building, 14th St. and Independence Ave., SW, Washington, DC 20250; 202-720-4323; {www.rurdev.usda.gov/}. In addition, you may check the State Housing Programs beginning on page 163.

Money To Buy Or Fix Up A Mobile Home

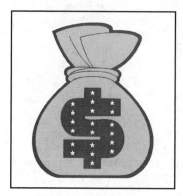

The city of Sunnyvale, Ca will lend you up to $7,500 at 0-5% interest for a mobile home. New York State offers loans to help you buy a mobile home park or the land your mobile home sits on through their *Manufactured Home Cooperative Fund Program.* And the U.S. Department of Agriculture has what is called *Section 504 funds* that allow loans of up to $20,000 to fix a mobile home or to move it from one site to another. Here is how to contact the major programs for manufactured (mobile) homes.

VA-Guaranteed Manufactured Home Loan

Contact your local office of the Department of Veterans Affairs, or U.S. Department of Veterans Affairs, 1120 Vermont Avenue, Washington, DC 20420; 800-827-1000; {www.va.gov/about_va/programs.htm}.

FHA Insured Title 9 Manufactured Home Loan

Contact your local office of Housing and Urban Development listed in the blue pages of your telephone book, or your state housing office (see the State Housing Programs beginning on page 163), or the Housing Counseling Clearinghouse, P.O. Box 10423, McLean, VA 22102; 800-217-6970; {www.hud.gov}

Section 504 Rural Housing Loans and Grants

To find your local Rural Housing Service, look in the blue pages of your telephone book, or contact Single Family Housing Programs, USDA Rural Housing Service, Room 5037, South Building, 14th St. and Independence Ave., SW, Washington, DC 20250; 202-720-4323; {www.rurdev.usda.gov/}.

HUD-man Goes After The Mobile Home Salesman

If your mobile home is not all that was promised, call HUD. The U.S. Department of Housing and Urban Development regulates the construction of mobile homes and investigates complaints about their performance.

Contact: Manufactured Housing and Standards, Office of Consumer and Regulatory Affairs, U.S. Department of Housing and Urban Development, 451 7th St., SW, Room

9152, Washington, DC 20410; 800-927-2891, 202-708-1112, Fax: 202-708-4231; E-mail: {jerrold_h_mayer@ hud.gov};
{www.hud.gov/offices/hsg/sfh/mhs/mhshome.cfs}.

Lead Poisoning and Your Children

This publication is free along with three fact sheets, and a list of state and local contacts for additional information. Specific lead questions can be answered by an information specialist at 800-424-LEAD.

For more information, contact National Lead Information Center, EPA, 1200 Pennsylvania Ave., NW, Washington, DC 20460; 800-424-LEAD; {www.epa.gov/lead/nlic.htm}.

Free Houses

Well, maybe they're not free, but they can cost you as little as a few hundred dollars a month. And maybe they're not in good shape, but many of the programs will also offer you a low interest loan to fix up the house. Some states refer to the program as an *Urban Homesteading Act*. The idea of the program is that the government gets you a home for next to nothing and you agree to live there for a certain number of years.

Minnesota has a program. Baltimore had a very active program for many years. Davenport, Iowa purchases homes, completely rehabs them, and then offers the houses in a lottery each May. You must get a mortgage, but your monthly payments are under $400 a month for a completely rebuilt house!

There are some states, like Alaska, that still offer wilderness land for homesteading. Because the houses are so cheap, there is usually a lottery for eligible buyers. Contact your city government, your county government and your local community development office to learn about local programs. If you have trouble finding your local community development agency, the following organizations may be able to help:

◆ National Association of Housing and Redevelopment Officials, 630 Eye St., NW, Washington, DC 20001; 202-289-3500, 877-866-2476, Fax: 202-289-8181; {www.nahro.org}

◆ Information Center, Office of Community Planning and Development, P.O. Box 7189, Gaithersburg, MD 20898; 800-998-9999; Fax: 301-519-5027; {www.comcon.org}

◆ You can also check the State Housing Programs beginning on page 163.

Free Legal Help For Renters and Home Buyers

It's illegal for landlords, realtors, bankers and others to discriminate against you because of your race, religion, sex, family status, or handicap. Landlords also have rules to follow in dealing with you as a tenant. With the proper free help you can find out how to:

- ★ Stop paying the rent if your toilet doesn't work.
- ★ Get the government to sue your landlord for discriminating against your child.
- ★ Break a lease and not pay a penalty.
- ★ Get your eviction stopped.
- ★ Force a bank to give you a loan for a new home.
- ★ Get your landlord to widen your doorways to fit your wheelchair.
- ★ Get a third party to fight your landlord for you.

To file a complaint or to learn more about your rights in dealing with landlords and people in the housing industry, contact any of the following:

Your state housing office

Your state Attorney General's office

Fair Housing and Equal Opportunity, U.S. Department of Housing and Urban Development, Room 5204, 451 Seventh St, SW, Washington, DC 20410; 800-669-9777; {www.hud.gov/complaints/housediscrim.cfm}

National Fair Housing Advocate Online, Tennessee Fair Housing Council, 719 Thompson Lane, Suite 324, Nashville, TN 37206; {www.fairhousing.com}.

Get Money For Down Payments And Closing Costs Here

The following are examples of financial assistance programs offered by states, cities and counties at the time we were doing our initial research for this book. Be aware that these programs are constantly changing and all have some form of eligibility requirements, but don't let that stop you! New ones are added and old ones may be discarded.

To be sure that you are aware of all the programs available in your area, contact your state office on housing (see the State Housing Programs beginning on page 163), your city housing office, your county housing office, as well as any local community development offices that may be in your area. If you need help locating your community development office, the following may be of assistance: National Association of Housing and Redevelopment Officials, 630 Eye St., NW, Washington, DC 20001; 202-289-3500, 877-866-2476; Fax: 202-289-8181: {www.nahro.org}.

* *Houston*: $3,500 to help with a down payment and closing costs in the First-Time Homebuyers Program.

* *Iowa*: 5% of your mortgage in grant money for a down payment and closing costs through Down Payment/ Closing Cost Grant Program.

* *Minneapolis, MN*: $3,000 at 0% interest due when you sell the home

* *Michigan*: $5,000 at 0% interest and no monthly payments

* *Baton Rouge, LA*: $10,000 at 0% interest and no payments for 20 years through Home Buyers Assistance Program.

* *Georgia*: $5,000 for a down payment at 0% interest through Own HOME Program.

* *Hawaii*: $15,000 loans at 3% for down payments, but you only pay interest for the first 5 years in the Down Payment Loan Program.

* *Kansas*: You only need $500 and Kansas will assist with down payment, closing costs, and legal fees in First Time Homebuyers Downpayment Assistance Program.

* *Maine*: Buy a house with only $750, and finance your down payment at 0% through Down Home Program.

* *La Miranda, CA*: 10% loan for down payment for first time homebuyers in the Down Payment Assistance Program.

* *Tacoma, WA*: A $5,000 loan for your down payment and settlement costs in Down Payment Assistance Program.

* *Indianapolis, IN*: Put 1% down and your closing costs go into a 2nd mortgage in Good Neighbor II Loan Program.

* *Los Angeles, CA*: 2% forgivable loan for closing costs money, plus $35,000 loan for repairs with no payments for 30 years or until the house is sold through Home WORKS! Program.

* *New York State*: 0% down payment in Low Down Payment, Conventional Rate Program.

* *Walnut Creek, CA*: Get a second mortgage for half of the closing costs and 2% of down payment with nothing due until you sell or refinance.

* *Washington County, OR*: $19,300 loan with no interest and no payment for the first 5 years in First-Time Home Buyer Program.

* *Michigan*: Move into a $60,000 home with only $600 in your pocket in the Down Payment Assistance Program.

* *New Hampshire*: $5,000 low interest loan for closing costs through HELP Program.

- *Nashville, TN*: Nashville Housing Fund provides down payments, closing costs and low interest loans for first time home buyers.
- *Tucson, AZ*: $3,000 loan for down payment and they will pay all closing costs with the Tucson Metropolitan Ministry.
- *Oregon*: $500 to $6,000 grant for closing costs, down payment, or minor repairs in their First-Time Homebuyer Program.
- *Missouri*: Move into a home with only $750 through Down Payment Assistance for Homebuyers.
- *Canton, OH*: Renters can apply for $5,000 loan for first time home buyers that's forgiven after 5 years through the Down Payment Assistance Program.
- *South Carolina*: Loans for SINGLE PARENTS for a down payment and closing costs in their Single Parent Program.

Use Your Sweat as a Down Payment and Get a No-Interest Loan

One of the biggest providers of this type of program is the nonprofit organization called Habitat for Humanity. You've probably seen them in the news with Ex-President Jimmy Carter helping them build houses. They have even received government money to help support their program.

The typical arrangement is for people with incomes between $9,000 and $30,000. You and your family work an average of 300 to 500 hours building your home or other people's homes, and in return you get a home with no down-payment and a very low mortgage payment. Because people provide free labor to build the home, you only pay about $60,000 for a $100,000 home, and you get the money interest free. A typical bank loan can cost you over $700 per month, but through this program you pay only about $200 a month.

Other local or national organizations may run similar programs in your area, with or without government financing. To find programs in your area, you can contact:

- Habitat for Humanity International, 121 Habitat Street, Americus, GA 31709; 229-924-6935; {www.habitat. org}. To find a local affiliate, call 229-924-6935, ext. 2551 or ext. 2552
- Information Center, Office of Community Planning and Development, P.O. Box 7189, Gaithersburg, MD 20898; 800-998-9999, Fax: 301-519-5027; {www.comcon.org}.

Free Housing Books

★ *A Consumer's Guide to Mortgage Settlement Costs*

★ *Home Mortgages: Understanding the Process*

★ *A Consumer's Guide to Mortgage Refinancings*

★ *Consumer Handbook on Adjustable Rate Mortgages*

For your copies, contact Board of Governors of the Federal Reserve System, Publications Services, MS-127, Washington, DC 20551; 202-452-3245; {www.federalreserve.gov/}.

Staying Clear Of Deadly Radon Gases

Nowadays when you buy a home, you often have a radon level reading taken, but what do the numbers mean? The **National Radon Information Hotline** has a free brochure that explains what radon is, how to test for it, and more.

There is also a Radon FIX-IT Program operated by the Consumer Research Council, a nonprofit consumer organization that provides free guidance and encouragement to consumers who are trying to fix their homes that have elevated radon levels. The Program operates from noon to 8 p.m. EST and has information on reducing elevated radon levels, referrals to experts, and names of contractors who are qualified to help.

For more information, contact National Radon Information Hotline at 800-767-7236 (SOS-RADON) and the Radon Fix-It Program at 800-644-6999; or Indoor Air Quality Information Clearinghouse, IAQ Info, P.O. Box 37133, Washington, DC 20013; 800-438-4318; {www.epa.gov/iaq/iaqinfo.html}.

Is Your Drinking Water Safe?

According to the National Consumer Water Survey, 75% of those surveyed have concerns about the quality of the water they drink. Many people are purchasing bottled water or water purification devices for drinking water, but is it a wise use of your money?

The *Safe Drinking Water Hotline* can answer any question or concern you may have regarding drinking water, and can provide you with publications such as: *Is Your Drinking Water Safe?*, *Home Water Testing*, *Home Water Treatment Units*, *Bottled Water* fact sheet, and more.

Contact Safe Drinking Water Hotline, U.S. Environmental Protection Agency, 401 M St., SW, Washington, DC 20460; 800-426-4791; {www.epa.gov/OGWDW}.

How To Save Up To $650/Year On Fuel Bills

The average family spends close to $1300 a year on their home's utility bills, and a large portion of that energy is wasted. By using a few inexpensive energy efficient measures, you can reduce your energy bills by 10% to 50%.

With the publication, *Energy Savers: Tips on Saving Energy and Money at Home*, you can go step by step through your home to learn energy saving tips. Topics covered include insulation/weatherization, water heating, lighting, appliances, and more. There is even a major appliance shopping guide that explains the energy labels on appliances and shows you how to choose the best one for you.

The Energy Efficiency and Renewable Energy Clearinghouse can answer your questions on all these topics and has publications and easy to understand fact sheets. Contact the Energy Efficiency and Renewable and Energy Clearinghouse, Mail Stop EE-1, Washington, DC 20585; 800-363-3732, 202-586-9220; {www.eren.doe.gov}.

Volunteers Will Fix Up Your (Or Your Mom's) Home For Free

Many service organizations have begun to organize community service days, where the town is beautified along with certain homes in need of repair. *Christmas in April* is a national organization with over 185 affiliates that gather together volunteers to help rehabilitate the homes of low-income homeowners. The work is done for free with the goal being to provide a safe and secure home for those in need.

An example of a program in the Dallas area is the Volunteer Home Repair and Weatherization Program. This program provides home repairs that improve the health, safety, and energy efficiency of a home for low-income homeowners.

Contact your city government, your county government and your local community development office to learn about local programs.

✖ In the Dallas area, contact Volunteer Home Repair and Weatherization Program, Center for Housing Resources, 3103 Greenwood, Dallas, TX 75204; 214-828-4390, Fax: 214-828-4412; {www.chrdallas.org}

Free Housing Experts

The HUD website includes text of over 20 helpful guides, such as: *How To Buy a Home*, *How to Get A Mortgage*, and *Hud-approved Lenders*, as well as listings of government homes for sale. These are not just HUD homes, but also those from the Department of Veteran Affairs, General Services Administration, and more. Although the houses are not steals, you can find some great deals. For housing information, call HUD USER, P.O. Box 6091, Rockville, MD 20850; 800-245-2691; {www.huduser.org}.

Money To Pay Your Heating Bill

Storm windows, insulation, and even weatherstripping, can help reduce your fuel bill. Families can receive assistance to weatherize their homes and apartments at no charge if you meet certain income guidelines.

States allocate dollars to nonprofit agencies for purchasing and installing energy-related repairs, with the average grant being $2,000 per year. The elderly and families with children get first dibs.

Contact your State Energy Office or the Weatherization Assistance Programs Branch, EE44, U.S. Department of Energy, 1000 Independence Ave., SW, Washington, DC 20585; 800-DIAL-DOE, 202-586-4074; {www.eren.doe.gov/EE/buildings-state.html}.

How To Keep Your Air Clean Of Asbestos, Carbon Monoxide, and Second Hand Smoke

You don't need to hire some high priced consultants to find how to keep the air in your home clean of pollution and other toxic substances. The Indoor Air Quality Information Clearinghouse is the expert on all forms of indoor air pollution. They have publications and information on second hand smoke, asbestos, carbon monoxide, air cleaners, and more. You can contact them at Indoor Air Quality Information Clearinghouse, IAQ Info, P.O. Box 37133, Washington, DC 20013; 800-438-4318; {www.epa.gov/iaq/iaqinfo.html}.

$2,000 Grants or 2% Interest Loan To Fix Up Your Home

A family of 4 can be making close to $30,000 year and still be eligible for a 2% interest loan from local Community Action Agency. Some agencies also offer grants or are aware of other local organizations that provide grants. There are about 1,000 of them around the country to help neighborhoods.

To find an agency near you, contact Community Action Partnership, 1100 17th Street, NW, Suite 500, Washington, DC 20036, 202-265-7546; Fax: 202-265-8850; {www.communitypartnership.org}.

Free Nutrition Counseling and Classes

Nutrition counseling, menu planning, cooking instruction and comparison shopping is available from your local County Cooperative Extension Service. Group instruction is free of charge, but persons requesting individual lessons are asked to pay for the lesson materials.

They also help neighborhoods establish and maintain community gardens, which provide fresh vegetables to area residents. To find an office near you, look in the blue pages of your local telephone book under county government for County Cooperative Extension Service.

Free Weatherization, Fuel Bills, and Rent for Incomes Up to $50,000

If you are within a certain income and need help paying your heating bills, need money to make your house more energy efficient, or need funds for urgent repairs, call your local Community Action Agency. There are about 1,000 of them around the country to help neighborhoods. They will also come out and check if your home or apartment needs to be more energy efficient.

To find an agency near you, contact
Community Action Partnership, 1100
17th St., NW, Suite 500, Washington,
DC 20036; 202-265-7546; Fax: 202-265-
8850;
{www.communitypartnership.org}.

Also, your local utility can provide you
with or refer you to other programs in
your area to analyze your energy usage,
recommend energy saving measures,
provide fuel and utility assistance to
retain or restore service, establish

> **$83,000 / YR INCOME AND THE GOVERNMENT CONSIDERS YOU NEEDY?**
>
> Many of the government housing programs, especially the grant and low interest programs, may have income requirements. But don't let a good salary stop you from investigating the opportunities. The first time home buyer program in Illinois has income requirements that go up to $83,000.

payment discounts based on income and usage, or establish affordable payment plans if
you are in arrears. Contact your local utility company to take advantage of these
services.

50% Discount On a New Heating System

The California Energy Commission offers residences and small businesses up to 50% of
the cost of a new heating or air conditioning system if it meets their standards for
"emerging renewable technologies," like solar heating, but more. Their program is
called Emerging Renewables Buy-Down Program.

To learn more, contact California Energy Commission, Energy Call Center, 1516 Ninth
St., MS-29, Sacramento, CA 95814; 800-555-7794; {www.consumerenergy center.org}.
Check with your state utility commission to see if your state offers similar programs.

Free Furniture

The Community Action Agency in Albany, New York offers free furniture for those
with a need because of fire or other hardship reasons. Other agencies offer free furniture
if you are moving into a Community Action Agency's affordable housing or housing
units operated by the agency. See if your local agency offers free furniture. There are
about 1,000 of them around the country to help neighborhoods.

To find an agency near you, contact Community Action Partnership, 1100 17th St., NW,
Suite 500, Washington, DC 20036; 202-265-7546; Fax: 202-265-8850;
{www.communitypartnership.org}.

Free Legal Help With Land Developers

Sometimes when you are buying land in another state, you may be susceptible to fraud. The government provides some consumer protection by requiring full disclosure of conditions surrounding the purchase of subdivided land where the land is to be divided into 100 or more lots, and an effort is made to sell the land to interstate buyers. The developers must provide all purchasers with a copy of a Property Report which sets forth important facts about the development and the developer. Failure to provide a Property Report prior to the purchaser signing a purchase agreement subjects the developer to statutory and regulatory penalties.

Anti-fraud provisions of the Act are applicable to subdivisions of 25 lots or more. Failure to comply with the anti-fraud provisions subjects developers to civil and criminal penalties. Other consumer protection provisions include a seven-day cooling-off period and required contractual provisions. The Act and regulations provide exemption from full disclosure where a subdivision meets certain requirements. (14.168 Land Sales-Certain Subdivided Land (Interstate Land Sales Registration Program)).

For more information contact Office of RESPA and Interstate Land Sales, Department of Housing and Urban Development, 451 7th Street, SW., Room 9146, Washington, DC 20410; 202-708-0502; {www.hud.gov/offices/hsg/sfh/ils/ilshome.cfm}.

Fannie Mae/Freddie Mac

You often hear those terms when housing is being discussed, but what do they really mean? Neither of these companies lend money directly to home buyers. Both of these are private companies that purchase mortgages from lenders, thereby replenishing the lender's supply of available funds. Mortgage lenders use the proceeds from selling loans to fund new mortgages.

As a secondary market for mortgage loans, both Freddie Mac and Fannie Mae purchase mortgages from lenders across the country and package them into securities that can be sold to investors. The ultimate goal is to provide homeowners and renters with lower costs and better access to home financing. The competition between Freddie Mac and

Fannie Mae helps to ensure that the benefits from the secondary market are passed onto the homeowners. Both companies work directly with lenders to create mortgage products designed to make homeownership more affordable to lower and middle-income people.

Fannie Mae created {www.homepath.com}, which takes you through the home buying process, as well as helping you find Fannie Mae-approved lenders and mortgages. Under the Community heading on the toolbar, Freddie Mac {www.freddiemac.com} offers step-by-step instructions regarding credit, homebuyer education, and homebuyer resources. Fannie Mae was started in 1938 to help the housing industry during the Great Depression and became a private company in 1968. Freddie Mac was chartered in 1970. Publications and other helpful tools are available on the websites.

For more information contact:

Freddie Mac
8200 Jones Branch Dr.
McLean, VA 22102
703-2000
800-373-3343 (publications)
www.freddiemac.com

Fannie Mae
3900 Wisconsin Ave., NW
Washington, DC 20016
202-752-7000
www.fanniemae.com

Free Money For Your Downpayment

Here is a program that will give you 5% of the downpayment costs for your new home. This program is open to everyone, not just first time home buyers, and the homes can be valued at up to $300,700!

Funds for this program do not need to be repaid and come from funds raised through the AmeriDream Charity. You must purchase a home from a builder or seller who has enrolled their home in the program. Over 4,500 people become homeowners each month through the AmeriDream Downpayment Gift Program.

To learn more contact AmeriDream Charity, 18310 Montgomery Village Ave., Suite 300, Gaithersburg, MD 20879; 301-977-9133; toll-free 866-263-7437; {www.ameridream.org}.

What Is Your Home Worth?

In order to best determine your current or prospective new home's value, you need to know the going price in the neighborhood. There are many different ways to do this. You can search public records and compare house sizes. You can also access several internet sites which provide information on square footage, home sales, and more. Check out the following sites:

> http://list.realestate.yahoo.com/re/homevalues/
> http://www.homegain.com/h/index_html
> http://www.aimrelocation.com/relo_tools/
> http://www.ehome.com/ehome/sellers/home_valuation.asp
> http://www.housevalues.com/HomePage.aspx

New Home Help

Here's a listing of programs we found that were available at the time we were doing research. Don't forget to contact state and local housing agencies to see what may be available for you.

Nashville Housing Fund
P.O. Box 846
Nashville, TN 37202
615-252-8400
www.nashville.gov/mdha/
index.htm

Washington County
Department of Housing Services
111 NE Lincoln St.
Suite 200-L
Hillsboro, OR 97124
503-846-4794
www.co.washington.or.us/
deptmts/hse_serv/housmain.htm

Indianapolis Neighborhood
Housing Partnership
3550 N. Washington Blvd.
Indianapolis, IN 46205
317-925-1400
www.inhp.org

Department of Community
Affairs
60 Executive Parks
Atlanta, GA 30329
800-651-0597

404-679-4940
www.dca.state.ga.us

State of New York Mortgage
Agency
641 Lexington Ave.
New York, NY 10022
800-382-HOME
212-688-4000
www.nyhomes.org/sony/
sonyma.html

Housing Hotline
Division of Housing
Kansas Department of
Commerce and Housing
1000 SW Jackson St.
Suite 100
Topeka, KS 66612-1354
785-296-3481
www.kansascommerce.com

Homes For Houston
P.O. Box 1562
Houston, TX 77251
713-868-8300
www.ci.houston.tx.us/departme
/housing/

Iowa Finance Authority
100 E. Grand Ave., Suite 250
Des Moines, IA 50309
515-242-4990
800-432-7230
www.ifahome.com/
home_buyer.htm

MN Housing Finance Agency
400 Sibley St., Suite 300
St. Paul, MN 55101
800-657-3769
651-296-7608
www.mhfa.state.mn.us

Missouri Housing Development
Commission
3435 Broadway
Kansas City, MO 64111
816-759-6600
www.mhdc.com

Office of Community
Development
P.O. Box 1471
Baton Rouge, LA 70802
225-389-3039

www.ci.baton-rouge.
la.us/dept/ocd/
Housing/housing.htm

New Hampshire Housing
Finance Authority
32 Constitution Dr.
P.O. Box 5087
Bedford, NH 03110
800-640-7239
www.nhhfa.org

Oregon Housing and
Community Services Dept.
1600 State St.
Salem, OR 97301

503-986-2000
www.hcs.state.or.us

Maine State Housing Authority
353 Water St.
Augusta, ME 04330
207-626-4600
800-452-4668
www.mainehousing.org

Community Development Dept.
1666 N. Main St.
Walnut Creek, CA 94596
925-943-5800
www.ci.walnut-creek.ca.us

South Carolina State Housing
Finance and Development
Authority
919 Bluff Rd.
Columbia, SC 29201
803-734-2207
www.sha.state.sc.us

Housing and Community
Development
677 Queen St., Suite 300
Honolulu, HI 96813
808-587-0567
www.hcdch.state.hi.us/

$2,500 To Insulate Your Home

Storm windows, insulation, and even weatherstripping can help reduce your heating and cooling bills. The U.S. Department of Energy offers the Weatherization Assistance program.

As many as 20-30 million people are eligible for this program; everyone from homeowners to renters, from those who live in single or multi-family housing to those who lie in mobile homes. Each state varies on who is eligible for these services, but typically a family of four can make $24,000 and still qualify. Preference is given to persons over 60, those with disabilities and families with children. If you receive Supplemental Security Income to Temporary Assistance to Needy Families, you are automatically eligible.

You must apply through your state weatherization agency. States allocate dollars to nonprofit agencies for purchasing and installing energy-related repairs, with an energy audit being the first step to determine what is necessary. The average grant is $2,500. For more information on eligibility and where to apply in your state, contact Weatherization Assistance Programs Branch, EE44, U.S. Department of Energy, 1000 Independence Ave., SW, Washington, DC 20585; 800-DOE-3732; {www.eren.doe.gov/buildings/home_weatherizing.html}.

State Weatherization Agencies

Alabama
Program Manager
Alabama Dept. of Economic and
Community Affairs
401 Adams Avenue
P.O. Box 5690
Montgomery, AL 36103-5690
334-242-5365
Fax: 334-353-4311
http://www.adeca.state.al.us/

Alaska
Weatherization Program
Manager
Alaska Housing Finance
Corporation
P.O. Box 101020
Anchorage, AK 99510-1020
907-330-8192
Fax: 907-338-1747
http://www.ahfc.state.ak.us/

Arizona
Arizona Department of
Commerce
3800 N. Central Ave., Suite 1500
Phoenix, AZ 85012
602-280-8115
Fax: 602-280-1445
http://www.commerce.state.az.
us/

Arkansas
Division of County Operations
Office of Community Services
P.O. Box 1437, Slot #1330
Little Rock, AR 72203-1437
501-682-8722
Fax: 501-682-6736

California
Department of Community
Services and Development
700 North 10th Street
Sacramento, CA 95814-0338
916-341-4376
Fax: 916-319-5129
http://www.csd.ca.gov/

Colorado
Governor's Office of Energy
Management and Conservation
225 E. 16th Avenue, Suite 650

Denver, CO 80203
303-894-2383
Fax: 303-894-2388
http://www.state.co.us/oemc/

Connecticut
Energy Services Program
Supervisor
Department of Social Services
25 Sigourney Street, 10th Floor
Hartford, CT 06106-5033
860-424-5889
Fax: 860-424-4952
http://www.dss.state.ct.us/svcs
/energy.htm

Delaware
Division of State Service Centers
Delaware Office of Community
Service
1401 North Dupont Highway
New Castle, DE 19720
302-577-4965, ext. 232
Fax: 302-577-4973
http://www.state.de.us/dhss/d
ssc/dsschome.htm

District of Columbia
District of Columbia Energy
Office
2000 14th St., NW, Suite 300 East
Washington, DC 20009
202-673-6700
Fax: 202-673-6725
http://www.dcenergy.org

Florida
Florida Energy Office
Dept. of Community Affairs
2555 Shumard Oak Boulevard
Tallahassee, FL 32399-2100
850-488-7541
Fax: 850-488-2488
http://dlis.dos.state.fl.us/fgils/
agencies/energy.html

Georgia
Division of Energy Resources
Georgia Environmental Facilities
Authority
100 Peachtree St, NW, Suite 2090
Atlanta, GA 30303
404-656-3826

Fax: 404-656-7970
http://www.gefa.org/energy_p
rogram.html

Hawaii
Office of Community Services
Department of Labor and
Industrial Relations
830 Punchbowl Street, Room 420
Honolulu, HI 96813
808-586-8675
Fax: 808-586-8685
http://dlir.state.hi.us/

Idaho
Bureau of Benefit Program
Operations
Dept. of Health and Welfare
P.O. Box 83720
Boise, ID 83720-0036
208-334-5753
Fax: 208-332-7343
http://www2.state.id.us/dhw/

Illinois
Division of Economic
Opportunity
Department of Commerce and
Community Affairs
620 East Adams Street, 4th Floor
Springfield, IL 62701
217-785-6135
Fax: 217-524-5904
http://www.commerce.state.il.us/

Indiana
Division of Family and Children
Housing and Community
Services Section
P.O. Box 6116
Indianapolis, IN 46206-6116
317-232-1997
Fax: 317-232-7079
http://www.state.in.us/fssa/fa
milies/

Iowa
Division of Community Action
Agencies
Department of Human Rights
Lucas State Office Building
Des Moines, IA 50319
515-242-6314

Fax: 515-242-6119
http://www.state.ia.us/govern
ment/dhr/

KANSAS

Department of Commerce and
Housing
700 Southwest Harrison Street
Suite 1300
Topeka, KS 66603-3712
785-296-2262
Fax: 785-296-8985
http://kdoch.state.ks.us/Progra
mApp/index.jsp

KENTUCKY

Cabinet for Families and
Children
Department of Community
Based Services
275 East Main Street, 3W-B
Frankfort, KY 40621
502-564-3703
Fax: 502-564-6907
http://cfc.state.ky.us/

LOUISIANA

Louisiana Housing Finance
Agency
Energy Assistance Section
200 Lafayette, Suite 102
Baton Rouge, LA 70801
225-342-1320 ext. 304
Fax: 225-342-1310
http://www.lhfa.state.la.us/

MAINE

Energy and Housing Services
Maine State Housing Authority
353 Water Street
Augusta, ME 04339-4633
207-626-4601
Fax: 207-624-5780
http://www.mainehousing.org

MARYLAND

Maryland Department of
Housing and Community
Development
100 Community Place
Crownsville, MD 21032-2023
410-514-7244
Fax: 410-514-7291
http://www.dhcd.state.md.us/

MASSACHUSETTS

Bureau of Energy Programs
Department of Housing and
Community Development
One Congress Street, 10th Floor
Boston, MA 02114
617-727-7004 ext. 533
Fax: 617-727-4259
http://www.state.ma.us/dhcd/
addrbook/default.htm

MICHIGAN

Family Independence Agency
P.O. Box 30037
Grand Tower, Suite 1313
Lansing, MI 48909
517-335-5857
Fax: 517-335-5042
http://www.mfia.state.mi.us/

MINNESOTA

Energy Division Department of
Commerce
85 7th Place East, Suite 500
St. Paul, MN 55101-2198
651-284-3265
Fax: 651-297-7891
http://www.commerce.state.mn
.us/

MISSISSIPPI

Weatherization Program
Manager
Mississippi Department of
Human Services
750 North State Street
Jackson, MS 39202
601-359-4772
Fax: 601-359-4370
http://www.mdhs.state.ms.us/

MISSOURI

Division of Energy
Department of Natural
Resources
P.O. Box 176
Jefferson City, MO 65102-0176
573-751-7657
Fax: 573-751-6860
http://www.dnr.state.mo.us

MONTANA

Department of Public Health
and Human Services
P.O. Box 4210

Helena, MT 59601
406-447-4267
Fax: 406-447-4287
http://www.dphhs.state.mt.us/

NEBRASKA

Nebraska Energy Office
P.O. Box 95085
Lincoln, NE 68509-5085
402-471-3347
Fax: 402-471-3064
http://www.nol.org/home/NE
O/

NEVADA

Housing Division
1802 North Carson St., Suite 154
Carson City, NV 89701
775-687-4258 x226
Fax: 775-687-4040
http://nvhousing.state.nv.us/

NEW HAMPSHIRE

Governor's Office of Energy and
Community Services
57 Regional Drive
Concord, NH 03301
603-271-6813
Fax: 603-271-2615
http://www.state.nh.us/govern
or/energycomm/

NEW JERSEY

New Jersey Department of
Community Affairs
P.O. Box 806
101 South Broad Street
Trenton, NJ 08625-0806
609-984-3301
Fax: 609-292-9798
http://www.state.nj.us/dca/

NEW MEXICO

New Mexico Mortgage Finance
Authority
344 Fourth Street, SW
Albuquerque, NM 87102
505-843-6880
Fax: 505-243-3289
http://www.nmmfa.org/

NEW YORK

Energy Services Bureau
New York State Division of
Housing and Community
Renewal

38-40 State Street
Albany, NY 12207
518-473-3845
Fax: 518-474-9907
http://www.dhcr.state.ny.us

North Carolina

North Carolina Department of
Health and Human Services
1110 Navaho Drive, Suite 106
Raleigh, NC 27609
919-981-5270
Fax: 919-981-5296
http://www.dhhs.state.nc.us/

North Dakota

ND Department of Commerce
Division of Community Services
400 East Broadway, Suite 50
P.O. Box 2057
Bismarck, ND 58502-2057
701-328-4140
Fax: 701-328-2308
http://www.state.nd.us/dcs/

Ohio

Office of Energy Efficiency
Ohio Dept. of Development
77 South High Street, Floor 26
Columbus, OH 43215-6108
614-466-8434
Fax: 614-466-1864
http://www.odod.state.oh.us/c
dd/oee/default.htm

Oklahoma

Division of Community Affairs
and Development
Oklahoma Dept. of Commerce
P.O. Box 26980
Oklahoma City, OK 73126-0980
405-815-5339
Fax: 405-815-5344
http://www.odoc.state.ok.us

Oregon

Oregon Housing and
Community Services
123 Northeast 3rd St, Suite 470
Portland, OR 97232
503-963-2283
Fax: 503-230-8863
http://www.hcs.state.or.us/

Pennsylvania

Pennsylvania Department of
Community and Economic
Development
Forum Building, Room 352
Harrisburg, PA 17120
717-720-7439
http://www.inventpa.com

Rhode Island

Central Services Division
Rhode Island State Energy Office
One Capitol Hill
Providence, RI 02908-5890
401-222-3370
Fax: 401-222-1260
http://www.doa.state.ri.us

South Carolina

Office of the Governor
1205 Pendleton Street
Columbia, SC 29201
803-734-9861
Fax: 803-734-0356
http://www.state.sc.us/energy/

South Dakota

Office of Energy Assistance
Department of Social Services
206 West Missouri Avenue
Pierre, SD 57501-4517
605-773-4131
Fax: 605-773-6657
http://www.state.sd.us/social/
ENERGY/

Tennessee

Tennessee Department of
Human Services
Citizens Plaza Building
400 Deaderick Street, 14th Floor
Nashville, TN 37248-9500
615-313-4764
Fax: 615-532-9956
http://www.state.tn.us/human
serv/

Texas

Community Affairs Division
Texas Department of Housing
and Community Affairs
P.O. Box 13941

Austin, TX 78711-3941
512-475-3864
Fax: 512-475-3935
http://www.tdhca.state.tx.us/

Utah

Division of Community
Development
Utah Office of Energy Services
324 South State Street, Suite 500
Salt Lake City, UT 84111
801-538-8657
Fax: 801-538-8888
http://www.nr.utah.gov/energ
y/home.htm

Vermont

Vermont Office of Economic
Opportunity Agency of Human
Services
103 South Main Street
Waterbury, VT 05671-1801
802-241-2452
Fax: 802-241-2325
http://www.ahs.state.vt.us/oeo/

Virginia

Virginia Department of Housing
and Community Development
501 North Second Street
Richmond, VA 23219-1321
804-371-7112
Fax: 804-371-7091
http://www.dhcd.state.va.us/

Washington

Office of Community
Development
P.O. Box 48350
Olympia, WA 98504-8350
360-725-2948
Fax: 360-586-5880
http://www.cted.wa.gov/

West Virginia

Office of Economic Opportunity
950 Kanawha Boulevard, East
Charleston, WV 25301
304-558-8660
Fax: 304-558-4210
http://www.wvdo.org/

Wisconsin
Residential Efficiency Bureau
Department of Administration
Division of Energy
P.O. Box 8944
Madison, WI 53708-8944
608-266-7601

Fax: 608-264-6688
http://www.doa.state.wi.us/de
pb/weatherization/index.asp

Wyoming
Wyoming Department of Family
Services

2300 Capitol Avenue, 3rd Floor
Cheyenne, WY 82002-0490
307-777-6346
Fax: 307-777-7747
http://dfsweb.state.wy.us/

Short-Term Rent Money

Many city and states offer short-term rent assistance for those in danger of losing their homes or who need help with the security deposit. This is usually only for assistance lasting one to six months. Often an unexpected car repair or hospitalization, can send a family into a financial crisis situation, so rental assistance programs were begun to help address this need, hoping to stabilize a family. Who qualifies for these programs varies from place to place and where this money is located can also be a challenge.

The first place you should check is with your local Social Services Department, local housing programs, or with the welfare office. Although the following list is not by all means comprehensive, it is designed to give you some ideas of the programs that do exist. Contact your local authorities to see what may be available to you in your area.

STATE CONTACTS

Arizona
Arizona Department of Housing
1700 West Washington, Suite 210
Phoenix, AZ 85007
602-771-10100
www.housingaz.com

California
California Department of Mental Health
1600 9th St., Room 151
Sacramento, CA 95814
916-653-0261
www.dmh.cahwnet.gov

Connecticut
Connecticut Department of
Social Services
Family Services Division
25 Sigourney St.

Hartford, CT 06106
860-424-5031
www.dss.state.ct.us/divs/famsv
c.htm

Delaware
West End Neighborhood House
710 N. Lincoln St.
Wilmington, DE 19805
302-658-4171
www.state.de.us/dhss/main/m
aps/other/wstendnh.htm

Lutheran Community Services
1304 N. Rodney St.
Wilmington, DE 19806
302-654-8886
www.lcsde.org/index.html

District of Columbia
Community Partnership for
Prevention of Homelessness
801 Pennsylvania Ave., SE
Suite 360
Washington, DC 20003
202-543-5298
www.community-
partnership.org/index.html

Florida
Department of Community
Development
695 E. University Blvd.,
Melbourne, FL 32901
321-674-5734
(for Melbourne only)
www.melbourneflorida.org/hou
sing/

Department of Community
Development
4401 Emerson St., Suite 1
Jacksonville, FL 32207
904-398-4424
(for Jacksonville only)
www.jaxhousing.com/

Georgia
Georgia Department of
Community Affairs
60 Executive Park South, NE
Atlanta, GA 30329
404-327-6870
www.dca.state.ga.us

Illinois
Department of Human Services
100 S. Grand Ave.
Springfield, IL 62762
217-782-1317
www.dhs.state.il.us/ts/ccfs/

Department of Housing
Chicago Low Income Housing
Trust Fund
318 S. Michigan Ave.
Chicago, IL 60604
312-747-6172
www.ci.chi.il.us/Housing/

Louisiana
Department of Social Services
Office of Community Services
755 3rd St.
Baton Rouge, LA 70802
225-342-2763
www.dss.state.la.us/offocs

Maine
Department of Human Services
221 State St.
Augusta, ME 04333
207-287-1921
www.state.me.us/dhs/

Maryland
Department of Housing and
Community Development
100 Community Place

Crownsville, MD 21032
410-514-7494
www.dhcd.state.md.us/rental.cf
m

Minnesota
Minnesota Office of Economic
Opportunity
Department of Children,
Families and Learning
1500 Highway 36 West
Roseville, MN 55113
651-582-8399
www.dhs.state.mn.us/CFS/OE
O/

Missouri
Missouri Housing Development
Commission
Housing Trust Fund
3435 Broadway
Kansas City, MO 64111
816-759-6600
www.mhdc.com

Nevada
Nevada Department of Business
and Industry
Housing Trust Fund
1802 North Carson St., Suite 154
Carson City, NV 89701
775-687-4258
www.state.nv.us/bi/hd

New Hampshire
Department of Health and
Human Services
129 Pleasant St.
Concord, NH 03301
603-271-5043
www.dhhs.state.nh.us

New Jersey
Department of Human Services
P.O. Box 700
Trenton, NJ 08625
800-792-9773
www.state.nj.us/humanservices
/index.html

North Carolina
Department of Health and
Human Services
325 North Salisbury Ave.
Raleigh, NC 2703
919-733-7831
www.dhhs.state.nc.us/

Ohio
Department of Development
Housing Trust Fund
77 South High St.
P.O. Box 1001
Columbus, OH 43215
614-752-8096
www.odod.state.oh.us

Oregon
Department of Housing and
Community Services
1600 State St.
Salem, OR 97301
503-986-2101
www.hcs.state.or.us

Rhode Island
Rhode Island Housing and
Mortgage Finance Corporation
44 Washington St.
Providence, RI 02903
401-457-1285
www.rihousing.com/

Virginia
Department of Housing and
Community Development
501 North Second St.
Richmond, VA 23219
804-371-7113
www.dhcd.vipnet.org

Washington
Department of Community
Development
906 Columbia St. SW
P.O. Box 48350
Olympia, WA 98504
360-725-2800
www.ocd.wa.gov/index.htm

Emergency Rent Money

Need rent money in a hurry or you could lose your house or apartment? Close to half the states offer some type of emergency assistance to help prevent homelessness. These programs sometimes focus on exclusively on families or those of very low-income. Who operates these programs also varies from place to place.

The first place you should check is with your local Social Services Department, local housing programs, or with the welfare office. Although the following list is not by all means comprehensive, it is designed to give you some ideas of the programs that do exist. Contact your local authorities to see what may be available to you in your area.

STATE CONTACTS

Arizona
Arizona Department of Housing
1700 West Washington, Suite 210
Phoenix, AZ 85007
602-771-10100
www.housingaz.com

California
California Department of
Housing and Community
Development
1800 3rd St., Room 390-A
Sacramento, CA 95814
916-323-3176
www.hcd.ca.gov/

Connecticut
Connecticut Department of
Social Services
Family Services Division
25 Sigourney St.
Hartford, CT 06106
860-424-5031
www.dss.state.ct.us/divs/famsv
c.htm

Department of Economic and
Community Development
505 Hudson St.
Hartford, CT 06106

860-270-8171
www.ct.state.us/ecd

Delaware
West End Neighborhood House
710 N. Lincoln St.
Wilmington, DE 19805
302-658-4171
www.state.de.us/dhss/main/m
aps/other/wstendnh.htm

District of Columbia
Community Partnership for
Prevention of Homelessness
801 Pennsylvania Ave., SE
Suite 360
Washington, DC 20003
202-543-5298
www.community-
partnership.org

Georgia
Georgia Department of
Community Affairs
60 Executive Park
Atlanta, GA 30329
404-327-6870
www.dca.state.ga.us

Illinois
Department of Human Services

100 S. Grand Ave.
Springfield, IL 62762
217-782-1317
www.dhs.state.il.us/ts/ccfs/

Iowa
Iowa Finance Authority
100 E. Grand Ave., Suite 250
Des Moines, IA 50309
515-242-4990
www.ifahome.com/

Maine
Department of Human Services
221 State St.
Augusta, ME 04333
207-287-1921
www.state.me.us/dhs/

Michigan
Family Independence Agency
235 South Grand
P.O. Box 30037
Lansing, MI 48909
517-335-6158
www.michigan.gov/fia

Minnesota
Minnesota Office of Economic
Opportunity

Department of Children,
Families and Learning
1500 Highway 36 West
Roseville, MN 55113
651-582-8399
www.dhs.state.mn.us/CFS/OEO/

Missouri
Missouri Housing Development
Commission
Housing Trust Fund
3435 Broadway
Kansas City, MO 64111
816-759-6600
www.mhdc.com/

Nevada
Nevada Department of Business
and Industry
Housing Trust Fund
1802 North Carson St., Suite 154

Carson City, NV 89701
775-687-4258
www.state.nv.us/bi/hd

New Hampshire
Housing Finance Authority
P.O. Box 5087
Manchester, NH 03108
603-472-8623 ext. 235
www.nhhfa.org

North Dakota
North Dakota Housing Finance
Agency
P.O. Box 1535
Bismarck, ND 58502
701-328-8056
www.ndhfa.state.nd.us

Rhode Island
Rhode Island Housing and
Mortgage Finance Corp.

44 Washington St.
Providence, RI 02903
401-457-1285
www.rihousing.com/

Virginia
Department of Housing and
Community Development
501 North Second St.
Richmond, VA 23219
804-371-7113
www.dhcd.vipnet.org

Washington
Department of Community
Development
906 Columbia St. SW
P.O. Box 48350
Olympia, WA 98504
360-725-2800
www.ocd.wa.gov/index.htm

Money To Pay Your Heating Bill

Even if you are not approved for the U.S. Department of Energy's Weatherization Assistance Program, you might still be eligible for short-term assistance on your utility bill for the Low-Income Home Energy Assistance Program (LIHEAP). Funded by the U.S. Department of Health and Human Services, LIHEAP serves low-income families by offering heating and cooling subsidies, energy crisis intervention to assist in weather-related and fuel supply shortages and household energy-related emergencies, such as utility shutoffs.

The amount of money and eligibility for this program varies from state to state, so you need to contact your state LIHEAP coordinator to learn how to apply. Contact Office of Community Services, Division of Energy Assistance, Administration for Children and Families, U.S. Department of Health and Human Services, 370 L'Enfant Promenade, SW, 5th Floor West, Washington, DC 20447; 202-401-9351; toll-free 888-674-6327; {www.acf.dhhs.gov/programs/liheap/liheap.htm}.

STATE CONTACTS

Alabama
Energy Section Supervisor
Alabama Department of
Economic and Community
Affairs
Community Services Division
P.O. Box 5690
Montgomery, AL 36103-5690
334-242-5365
Fax: 334-353-4311
http://www.adeca.state.al.us/

Alaska
Energy Assistance Coordinator
Department of Health and Social
Services
Division of Public Assistance
400 W. Willoughby Ave.
Room 301
Juneau, AK 99801-1700
907-465-3066
Fax: 907-465-3319
www.hss.state.ak.us/dpa/progr
ams/hap.html
Public Inquiries: 1-800-470-3058

Arizona
Project Specialist
Community Services
Administration
Arizona Department of
Economic Security
1789 W. Jefferson, site code 086z
P.O. Box 6123
Phoenix, AZ 85007
602-542-6600
Fax: 602-364-1756
www.de.state.az.us/links/csa_
web/index.asp
Public Inquiries: 1-800-582-5706

Arkansas
Manager, Home Energy
Assistance Program
Office of Community Services
Department of Human Services
P.O. Box 1437/Slot 1330
Little Rock, AR 72203-1437
501-682-8726
Fax: 501-682-6736
www.state.ar.us/dhs/dco/ocs/i
ndex.htm#haap
Public Inquiries: 1-800-432-0043

California
Chief Deputy Director
Department of Community
Services and Development
700 North 10th Street, Room 258
Sacramento, CA 95814
916-323-8694
Fax: 916-327-3153
www.csd.ca.gov/LIHEAP.htm
Public Inquiries: 1-800-433-4327

Colorado
Director, LIHEAP
Office of Self Sufficiency
Department of Human Services
1575 Sherman Street, 3rd Floor
Denver, CO 80203
303-866-5968
Fax: 303-866-5488
www.cdhs.state.co.us/oss/FAP/L
EAP/LEAP.htm
Public Inquiries: 1-800-782-0721
or 303-866-5970

Connecticut
Program Supervisor
Energy Services Unit
Dept. Of Social Services
25 Sigourney Street, 10th Floor
Hartford, CT 06106
860-424-5889
Fax: 860-424-4952
www.dss.state.ct.us/svcs/energ
y.htm
Public Inquiries: 1-800-842-1132

Delaware
Management Analyst
Department of Health and Social
Services
Division of State Service Centers
1901 N. Dupont Hwy.
New Castle, DE 19720
302-577-4965, ext. 231
Fax: 302-577-4973
1-800-464-HELP (4357)
New Castle County: 654-9295
Kent County: 674-1782
Sussex County: 856-6310
Public Inquiries: 1-800-464-HELP
(4357)

District of Columbia
LIHEAP Director
Citizens Energy Resources
Division
District of Columbia Energy
Office
2000 14th St. N.W.
Washington, D.C. 20001
202-673-6727
Fax: 202-673-6725
www.dcenergy.org/programs/fue
l.htm#LIHEAP
Public Inquiries: 202-673-6750 or
6700

Florida
Planning Manager
Community Assistance Section
Bureau of Community
Assistance
Division of Housing and
Community Development
Department of Community
Affairs
2555 Shumard Oak Boulevard
Tallahassee, FL 32399-2100
850-922-1834
Fax: 850-488-2488
www.dca.state.fl.us/fhcd/progr
ams/liheap
Public Inquiries: 850-488-7541

Georgia
Unit Chief
Community Services Section
Division of Family and Children
Services
4 Department of Human
Resources
Two Peachtree Street, N.W.
Suite 19-268
Atlanta, GA 30303-3180
404-463-2016
Fax: 404-657-4480
www.state.ga.us/departments/d
hr/energy.html
Public Inquiries: 1-800-869-1150

Hawaii
LIHEAP Coordinator
Department of Human Services
Benefit, Employment and
Support Division (LIHEAP)

820 Mililani Street, Suite 606
Honolulu, HI 96813
808-586-5734
Fax: 808-586-5744
Public Inquiries: 1-808-586-5740

Idaho

Grants Unit Manager
Bureau of Benefit Program
Operations
Idaho Department of Health and
Welfare
P.O. Box 83720
Boise, ID 83720-0036
208-334-5753
Fax: 208-332-7343
Public Inquiries: 208-334-5730
www.idhw.state.id.us

Illinois

Chief
Office of Human Services
Department of Commerce &
Community Affairs
620 East Adams Street - CIPS-4
Springfield, IL 62701
www.commerce.state.il.us/reso
urce_efficiency/Energy/LIHEA
P.htm
Public Inquiries: 1-800-252-8643
or 217-785-6135

Indiana

Programs Specialist
Division of Children & Families
Indiana Family and Social
Services Administration
P.O. Box 6116
Indianapolis, IN 46206-6116
317-232-7015
Fax: 317-232-7079
http://www.IN.gov/fssa/famili
es/housing/eas.html
Public Inquiries: 1-800-622-4973

Iowa

Chief
Bureau of Energy Assistance
Division of Community Action
Agencies
Department of Human Rights
Lucas State Office Building
Des Moines, IA 50319
515-281-0859
Fax: 515-242-6119

www.state.ia.us/government/d
hr/caa/LIHEAP.html
Public Inquiries: 515-281-4204

Kansas

Energy Assistance Program
Administrator
Economic Employment Support
Services, DSRS
Docking State Office Building,
6th Floor
915 S.W. Harrison St.
Topeka, KS 66612-1505
785-296-3340
Fax: 785-296-0146
http://www.srskansas.org/ees/
lieap.htm
Public Inquiries: 1-800-432-0043

Kentucky

Manager
Energy Assistance Branch, DMD
Cabinet for Families and
Children
275 East Main Street, 2nd Floor
Frankfort, KY 40621
502-564-7536
Fax: 502-564-0328
http://cfc.state.ky.us/help/lihe
ap.asp
Public Inquiries: 1-800-456-3452

Louisiana

Ms. Lawand Johnson, Program
Manager
Louisiana Housing Finance
Agency
Energy Assistance Section
200 Lafayette Street, Suite 102
Baton Rouge, LA 70801
225-342-1320, Ext. 304
Fax: 225-342-1339
www.lhfa.state.la.us/
Public Inquiries: 225-342-2288

Maine

LIHEAP Coordinator
Energy and Housing Services
Maine State Housing Authority
353 Water Street
Augusta, ME 04330
207-624-5708
Fax: 207-624-5780
www.bundlemeup.org/grants.htm
Public Inquiries: 1-800-452-4668

Maryland

Director, Home Energy
Programs
Department of Human
Resources
311 West Saratoga Street
Baltimore, MD 21202
410-767-7062
Fax: 410-333-0079
www.dhr.state.md.us/meap
Public Inquiries: 1-800-352-1446

Massachusetts

Director, Bureau of Energy
Programs
Department of Housing and
Community Development
One Congress Street, Suite 1001
Boston, MA 02114
617-727-7004, Ext. 533
Fax: 617-727-4259
www.state.ma.us/dhcd/compo
nents/dns/htoha.htm
Winter Heating Helpline Web
Site:
www.state.ma.us/winterheating/
Public Inquiries: 1-800-632-8175

Michigan

Director
Family Support Services
Michigan Family Independence
Agency
235 S. Grand Avenue
Lansing, MI 48909
Fax: 517-241-8053
http://www.mfia.state.mi.us/19
97fact.htm#a6-6
Public Inquiries: 1-800-292-5650

Minnesota

Energy Assistance Programs
Energy Division
Minnesota Department of
Commerce
85 7th Place East, Suite 500
St. Paul, MN 55101-2198
651- 284-3275
Fax: 651-284-3277
www.commerce.state.mn.us/pa
ges/Energy/mainassistance.htm

Mississippi

Branch Director
Division of Community Services

Mississippi Department of
Human Services
750 N. State Street
Jackson, MS 39202-4772
601 359-4766
Fax: 601-359-4370
www.mdhs.state.ms.us/cs_info.
html

Missouri

SS Manager, Energy Assistance
Division of Family Services
Department of Social Services
P.O. Box 88
Jefferson City, MO 65103
573-751-0472
Fax: 573-526-5592
http://www.dss.state.mo.us/df
s/liheap.htm
Public Inquiries: 1-800-392-1261

Montana

Intergovernmental Human
Services Bureau
Department of Public Health
and Human Services
1400 Carter Drive
Helena, MT 59620
406-447-4260
Fax: 406-447-4287
Public Inquiries: 1-800-332-2272

Nebraska

Program and Planning Specialist
Program Assistance Unit
Department of Health and
Human Services
301 Centennial Mall South
4th Floor
P.O. Box 95026
Lincoln, NE 68509
402-471-9262
Fax: 402-471-9597
www.hhs.state.ne.us/fia/energy
.htm
Public Inquiries: 1-800-430-3244

Nevada

Acting LIHEA Program
Manager
Nevada Department of Human
Resources
State Welfare Division
559 S. Saliman Rd., #101
Carson City, NV 89701-5040

775-687-6919
Fax: 775-687-1272
http://welfare.state.nv.us/benef
it/lihea.htm
Public Inquiries: 1-800-992-0900
(ext. 4420]

New Hampshire

Fuel Assistance Program
Manager
Governor's Office of Energy and
Community Services
57 Regional Drive
Concord, NH 03301-8519
603-271-8317
Fax: 603-271-2615
www.state.nh.us/governor/ene
rgycomm/assist.html

New Jersey

Coordinator
Home Energy Assistance
Program
DHS, Division of Family
Development
6 Quakerbridge Plaza, CN 716
Trenton, NJ 08625
609-588-2478
Fax: 609-588-3369
www.state.nj.us/humanservices/
dfd/liheap.html
Public Inquiries: 1-800-510-3102

New Mexico

LIHEAP Program Manager
Income Support Division
Community Development &
Commodities Bureau
New Mexico Human Services
Department
5301 Central NE, Suite 1520
Albuquerque, NM 87108
505-841-6535 (Albuquerque
Area)
1-800-283-4465 (Statewide)
Fax: 505-841-6522
http://www.state.nm.us/hsd/is
d.html

New York

LIHEAP Coordinator
Division of Temporary
Assistance
Office of Temporary and
Disability Assistance

New York State Department of
Family Assistance
40 North Pearl Street
Albany, NY 12243-0001
518-473-0332
Fax: 518-474-9347
www.otda.state.ny.us/otda/hea
p/default.htm
Public Inquiries: 1-800-342-3009

North Carolina

LIHEAP Coordinator
Division of Social Services
Department of Health and
Human Services
325 North Salisbury Street
Raleigh, NC 27603-5905
919-733-7831
Fax: 919-733-0645
www.dhhs.state.nc.us/dss
Public Inquiries: 1-800-662-7030
(CARE LINE)

North Dakota

Assistant Director of Energy &
Nutrition
Department of Human Services
State Capitol Bldg, Judicial Wing
600 E. Boulevard, Dept. 325
Bismarck, ND 58505-0250
701-328-4882
Fax: 701-328-1060
http://lnotes.state.nd.us/dhs/d
hsweb.nsf/
Public Inquiries: 701-328-2065

Ohio

Chief, OCS/HEAP
Ohio Department of
Development
77 South High, 25th Floor
Columbus, OH 43216
614-644-6858
Fax: 614-728-6832
www.odod.state.oh.us/cdd/ocs
/heap.htm
Public Inquiries: 1-800-282-0880
(TDD: 1-800-686-1557)

Oklahoma

Program Supervisor
Division of Family Support
Services
Department of Human Services
P.O. Box 25352

Oklahoma City, OK 73125
405-521-4488
Fax: 405-521-4158
Email:
Melvin.Phillips@okdhs.org
http://www.okdhs.org/fssd/Pr
ogramInformation.htm#Low-
Income

OREGON
LIHEAP Program Manager
Oregon Department of Housing
and Community Services
1600 State Street
Salem, OR 97310
503-986-2094
Fax: 503-986-2006
www.hcs.state.or.us/communit
y_resources/energy_wx/index.h
tml
Public Inquiries: 1-800-453-5511

PENNSYLVANIA
Director
Division of Federal Programs
Department of Public Welfare
P.O. Box 2675
Harrisburg, PA 17105
717-772-7906
Fax: 717-772-6451
www.dpw.state.pa.us/oim/oim
liheap.asp
Public Inquiries: 1-800-692-7462

Rhode Island
Program Manager
Dept. of Administration
Division of Central Services
State Energy Office
One Capitol Hill
Providence, RI 02908-5850
401-222-6920, ext. 112
Fax: 401-222-1260
Public Inquiries: 1-800-253-4328
or 401-222-6920

South Carolina
Program Manager for Energy
Division of Economic
Opportunity
Suite 342, 1205 Pendleton Street
Columbia, SC 29201
803-734-9861

South Dakota
Administrator
Office of Energy Assistance
Department of Social Services
206 W. Missouri Avenue
Pierre, SD 57501-4517
605-773-4131/3668
Fax: 605-773-6657
www.state.sd.us/social/ENERGY/
Public Inquiries: 1-800-233-8503

Tennessee
Program Specialist
Department of Human Services
Citizens Plaza Building
400 Deaderick Street
Nashville, TN 37248
615-313-4764
http://www.state.tn.us/human
serv/commsrv.htm#home

Texas
Program Manager
Energy Assistance Section
Texas Department of Housing
and Community Affairs
P.O. Box 13941
Austin, TX 78711-3941
512-475-3864
Fax: 512-475-3935
www.tdhca.state.tx.us/ea.htm
Public Inquiries: 1-877-399-8939

Utah
Program Manager
HEAT & SNAPS
Department of Community &
Economic Development
324 South State, Suite 500
Salt Lake City, UT 84111
801-538-8644
Fax: 801-538-8888
www.dced.state.ut.us/communi
ty/heat.html
Public Inquiries: 1-877-488-3233

Vermont
Fuel Assistance Program Chief
Office of Home Heating Fuel
Assistance
Department of Prevention,
Assistance, Transition, and
Health Access
103 South Main Street
Waterbury, VT 05676

802-241-2994
Fax: 802-241-1394
www.dsw.state.vt.us/districts/f
uel/index.htm
Public Inquiries: 1-800-479-6151
or 1-802-241-1165

Virginia
Energy & Emergency Assistance
Unit
Division of Benefit Programs
Virginia Department of Social
Services
Theater Row Building
730 E. Broad Street, 7th Floor
Richmond, VA 23219-1849
804-692-1751
Fax: 804-225-2196
www.dss.state.va.us/benefit/en
ergyasst.html
Public Inquiries: 1-800-552-3431
or 1-800-230-6977

Washington
LIHEAP (EPA/ECIP)
Coordinator
Washington Department of
Community,
Trade and Economic
Development
906 Columbia Street, S.W.
P.O. Box 48300
Olympia, WA 98504-8300
360-725-2854
Fax: 360-586-0489
www.liheapwa.org
Public Inquiries: 360-725-2854

West Virginia
LIHEAP Coordinator
Office of Family Support
West Virginia Department of
Health and Human Resources
350 Capitol Street, Room B-18
Charleston, WV 25301-3704
304-558-8290
Fax: 304-558-2059
Public Inquiries: 304-558-8290

Wisconsin
Director, Energy Services
Wisconsin Department of
Administration
P.O. Box 8944
Madison, WI 53708-8944

608-267-7601
Fax: 608-264-6688
www.doa.state.wi.us/depb/boe
/index.asp
Public Inquiries: 608-267-3680

Wyoming
Program Manager
Department Of Family Services
Room #388 Hathaway Building
2300 Capitol Avenue
Cheyenne, WY 82002-0490

307-777-6346
Fax: 307-777-7747
http://dfsweb.state.wy.us/fieldop/
briefing5a.htm
Public Inquiries: 1-800-246-4221

Don't Pay Your Property Tax

Or pay a reduced amount. Almost all states have some type of property or homestead tax exemption for the elderly and disabled, and often those with low incomes or veterans. How the program operates varies from state to state, with some states offering a reduced tax rate off of a percentage of the home's value. Other states offer a property tax deferral program for the elderly, where the state would pay the homeowner's property taxes. This would be considered a loan, and the equity would be the value of the home. The loan would be repaid when the home was sold or the homeowner dies. Contact your state or county tax office to see what your area offers.

State Tax Agencies

Alabama
Alabama Department of Revenue
50 N. Ripley
Montgomery, AL 36132-7123
334-242-1170
http://www.ador.state.al.us/advalorem/index.html
Alabama Homestead Exemption provides property tax exemption for citizens over 65 years of age on homes on less than 160 acres of land. Permanent & totally disabled citizens may also apply for the homestead exemption. Certain income levels also apply.

Alaska
Alaska State Office Building
333 Willoughby Ave., 11th Floor
P.O. Box 110400
Juneau, AK 99811-0400
907-465-2300
Fax: 907-465-2389
http://www.revenue.state.ak.us/
Alaska has a Permanent Fund Dividend Program. You must meet certain requirements such as

residency to apply. Contact the state office for more information.

Arizona
Arizona Department of Revenue
1600 W. Monroe
Phoenix, AZ 85007
602-542 3572
Fax: 602-542-3867
http://www.revenue.state.az.us/

Arkansas
Office of Excise Tax Administration
P. O. Box 8054
Room 234, Ledbetter Bldg.
Little Rock, AR 72203
501-682-7106
Fax: 501-682-7900
http://www.state.ar.us/dfa/
Arkansas provides for a reduction in the amount of real property taxes assessed on the homestead of each taxpayer beginning with the 2000 assessment year. To claim this credit you must contact your local County Collector.

California

California Franchise Tax Board
P.O. Box 942840
Sacramento, CA 94240-0040
800-852-5711
http://www.ftb.ca.gov/geninfo/hra/index.html
California provides a Homeowner Assistance
Program that allows a once-a-year payment from the
State of California to qualified individuals based on
part of the property taxes assessed and paid on their
homes. You may be eligible if you were 62 years of
age or older, blind, or disabled, owned and lived in
your own home, and had a limited income. There is
also a Renter Assistance Program.

Colorado

Colorado Division of Property Taxation
222 S. 6th, #410
Grand Junction, CO 81501
303-866-2371
http://www.dola.state.co.us/PropertyTax/
The Colorado Department of Local Affairs, Division
of Property Taxation Department administers the
Senior Homestead Exemption Program. To qualify
residents must be 65 years of age or older, a 10 year
owner of the residence and they must currently
occupy the residence. Fifty percent of the first
$200,000 value of the property is exempt from taxes.
The state will pay the exempted property tax.

Connecticut

Department of Policy and Management
450 Capitol Avenue
Hartford, CT 06106-1308
860-418-6200
Fax: 860-418-6487
http://www.drs.state.ct.us/pubs/IP's/2001/ip01-
12.html
There are property tax and rental exemptions for the
elderly and disabled.

Delaware

Delaware Division of Revenue
820 N. French Street
Wilmington, DE 19801
302-323-2600
Fax: 302-577-8202
http://www.state.de.us/revenue/index.htm
Delaware provide property tax and school tax
exemption to the disabled and elderly residents 65
years and older with certain income limitations.

District of Columbia

Office of Tax and Revenue
Real Property Tax Administration
941 North Capitol Street, NE, 4th Floor

Washington, DC 20002
202-727-4TAX
http://cfo.dc.gov/services/tax/property/credits.shtm
The District of Columbia provides for a variety of
property tax relief including: homestead deductions,
property tax deferral, senior citizen and low-income
exemptions.

Florida

Tax Information Services
Florida Department Of Revenue
1379 Blountstown Hwy.
Tallahassee, FL 32304-2716
800-352-3671
850-488-6800
http://www.state.fl.us/dor/property/exemptions.html
Every person who has legal or equitable title to real
property in the State of Florida and who resides on
the property may be eligible for a homestead
exemption. Check to see if you qualify to reduce your
property taxes. There are additional exemptions for
elderly and disabled homeowners.

Georgia

Georgia Department of Revenue
Property Tax Division offices
4245 International Parkway, Suite A
Hapeville, GA 30354-3918
404-968-0707
Fax: 404-968-0778
http://www2.state.ga.us/departments/dor/ptd/ad
m/taxguide/exempt/homestead2.html
There are several types of homeowner tax relief. The
homestead exemption exempts a portion of the value
of the home from property tax. The basic homestead
exemption is not age or income dependent and varies
from county to county. Other larger exemptions are
age and income dependent. Contact the office or web
site for your specific situation.

Hawaii

Hawaii Department of Taxation
P.O. Box 259
Honolulu, HI 96809-0259
808-587-4242
Fax: 808-587-1488
http://www.state.hi.us/tax/tax.html

Idaho

Idaho State Tax Commission
PO Box 36
Boise, ID 83722-0410
208-334-7500
800-972-7660
http://www2.state.id.us/tax/index.html

Idaho provides a "Circuit Breaker" program that gives property tax relief to the elderly, disabled, and veterans with a qualifying income. This program is administered at a local level.

Illinois

Illinois Department of Revenue
Willard Ice Building
101 West Jefferson Street
Springfield, IL 62702
217-782-3336
http://www.revenue.state.il.us/LocalGovernment/PropertyTax/general.htm
Illinois provides for a number of tax relief provisions. Homeowners 65 year and older with total household income of less than $25,000 may qualify for tax relief. Veteran also may be eligible for property tax exemption up to $58,000 of the value of the assessed value.

Indiana

Indiana Department of Revenue
Department of Local Government Finance
100 N. Senate Ave, N-1058
Indianapolis, IN 46204
317-233-8285
http://www.in.gov/dlgf/
Indiana has property tax deductions for the elderly and the disabled; each has different requirements. Indiana also has a homestead credit and standard deduction, which all homeowners are eligible to receive. All of these are filed in the office of the county auditor where the property is located.

Iowa

Iowa Department of Revenue and Finance
Taxpayer Services
P.O. Box 10457
Des Moines, IA 50306-0457
515-281-4040
http://www.state.ia.us/tax/index.html
To be eligible for property tax reduction Iowa residents must meet certain income levels and be 65 years old or totally disabled and 18 years of age or older.

Kansas

Kansas Department of Revenue
Docking State Office Building
915 SW Harrison St.
Topeka, KS 66625-0001
785-368-8222
Fax: 785-291-3614
http://www.ksrevenue.org/pvd/main.html
There are currently no homestead property exemptions in Kansas.

Kentucky

Kentucky Revenue Cabinet
200 Fair Oaks Lane
Frankfort, KY 40620
502-564-4581
http://revenue.state.ky.us/property_info.htm
The homestead exemption in Kentucky is for homeowners who are at least 65 years of age.

Louisiana

Louisiana Tax Commission
P. O. Box 66788
Baton Rouge, LA 70896-6788
504-925-7830
Fax: 504-925-7827
http://leap.ulm.edu/LaGin/rtdepar/ltaxcomm.htm
Louisiana's homestead program provides property tax exemptions for homeowners 65 years and older.

Maine

Maine Property Tax Division
14 Edison Drive
Augusta, ME 04332
207-287-2011
Fax: 207-287-6396
http://www.state.me.us/revenue/propertytax/homepage.html
Maine provides a property tax or rent refund if you meet residency and income qualifications. They also provide a program for the disabled and elderly.

Maryland

Maryland State Department of Assessments and Taxation
301 W. Preston St.
Baltimore, MD 21201
410-767-1184
http://www.dat.state.md.us/sdatweb/homestead.html
The State of Maryland has developed a program that allows credits against the homeowner's or renter's property tax bill if the property taxes exceed a fixed percentage of the person's gross income. In other words, it sets a limit on the amount of property taxes any homeowner must pay based upon his or her income. There are many tax exemptions for the disabled, veterans, elderly, and charitable property. Check with the Maryland State Department of Assessments and Taxation for details on your specific situation.

Massachusetts

Massachusetts Department of Revenue
51 Sleeper Street
Boston, MA 02205
617-626-2201

http://www.dor.state.ma.us/help/taxtalk/105.htm
The credit for real estate taxes paid for persons Age 65
and Older, also known as the "Circuit Breaker" allows
certain senior citizens in Massachusetts to claim a
credit on their state income tax returns for the real
estate taxes paid on their Massachusetts residential
property.

Michigan

Michigan Department of Treasury
Lansing, MI 48922
517-373-3200
800-487-7000
http://www.michigan.gov/treasury/
Michigan has several options for homestead tax
reduction. Contact your state and local agencies to
determine your level of savings.

Minnesota

Minnesota Department of Revenue
Mail Station 5510
St. Paul, MN 55146-5510
651-296-3781
http://www.taxes.state.mn.us/proptax/factshts/pro
p.html
Minnesota has a Senior Citizens Property Tax
Deferral program which is a low interest loan from
the state, not a tax forgiveness program. The deferred
tax is paid by the state to your county. Interest will be
charged on this loan. Michigan also has a Special
Agricultural Homestead program for qualifying
farms.

Mississippi

Mississippi State Tax Commission
P.O. Box 1033
Jackson, MS 39215-1033
601-923-7000
http://www.mstc.state.ms.us/taxareas/property/rul
es/homeruls.htm
Mississippi has two kinds of homestead exemptions:
regular and special. Each program has its own criteria
for qualification.

Missouri

Missouri Department of Revenue
Harry S Truman State Office Building
301 West High Street
Jefferson City, MO 65101
573-751-5337
http://dor.state.mo.us/tax/ptcinfo.htm
Missouri has a property tax exemption that is
determined by income. Check with your tax office or
the web site to see if you qualify.

Montana

Montana Department of Revenue
P.O. Box 5805
Helena, MT. 59604-5805
406-444-6900
Montana has property exemption programs for
veterans, disabled persons, the elderly and low-
income families.

Nebraska

Nebraska Department of Revenue
301 Centennial Mall South
P.O. Box 94818
Lincoln, NE 68509-4818
402-471-5729
http://www.revenue.state.ne.us/
Nebraska has property exemption for persons over
65, certain disabled individuals and certain disabled
veterans and their widows.

Nevada

Nevada Department of Taxation
1550 E. College Parkway, Suite 115
Carson City NV 89706
775-687-4892
Fax: 775-687-5981
http://tax.state.nv.us/
Homesteads are handled on a county level and apply
to all taxpayers. Contact Nevada Department on
Aging for Senior Citizens Property Tax Assistance
Act.

New Hampshire

Department of Revenue Administration
45 Chenell Drive
P.O. Box 457
Concord, NH 03302-0457
603-271-2191
Fax: 603-271-6121
http://www.state.nh.us/revenue/property_tax/inde
x.htm
New Hampshire has a Property Tax Hardship Relief
Program to help families pay their property taxes.

New Jersey

New Jersey Division of Taxation
Office of Information and Publications
PO Box 281
Trenton, NJ 08695-0281
609-292-6400
http://www.state.nj.us/treasury/taxation/
New Jersey has property exemption programs for the
disabled, the elderly and low- income families.

New Mexico

New Mexico Taxation and Revenue Department:
1100 S. St. Francis Dr.
P.O. Box 630
Santa Fe, NM 87504-0630
505-827-0870
Fax: 505-827-0782
http://www.state.nm.us/tax/
New Mexico provides a Property Tax Rebate for citizens age 65 and older.

New York

New York State Tax Department
Taxpayer Assistance Bureau
W. A. Harriman Campus
Albany, NY 12227
800-225-5829
http://www.tax.state.ny.us/
New York States Real Property Tax Credit is available to low-income families and residents 65 years old and older. Most taxpayers receive relief through exemptions to their property assessments for school tax purposes. The exemptions vary depending on the age of the taxpayer, income, and the county where the property is located.

North Carolina

North Carolina Property Tax Division
P.O. Box 871
Raleigh, NC 27602
919-733-7711
Fax: 919-733-1821
http://www.dor.state.nc.us/practitioner/property/index.html
North Carolina has property tax exemptions for elderly and disability persons and disabled veterans.

North Dakota

Office of State Tax Commissioner
State Capitol
600 E. Boulevard Avenue
Bismarck, ND 58505-0599
http://www.state.nd.us/taxdpt/forms/property.html
North Dakota provides property tax credits for homeowners and renters who are disabled or 65 years old or older.

Ohio

Ohio Department of Taxation
30 E. Broad Street, 22nd Floor
Columbus, OH 43215
888-644-6778
Fax: 614-466-6401
http://www.state.oh.us/tax/
Ohio's Homestead tax relief is granted to qualified elderly and disabled homeowners.

Oklahoma

Oklahoma Tax Commission
Post Office Box 26850
Oklahoma City, OK 73126-0850
405-521-3178
http://www.oktax.state.ok.us/
Oklahoma offers a homestead exemption for homeowners. A taxpayer who is at least 65 years old, or who is totally disabled, and whose gross household income from all sources does not exceed the current income levels may apply for a homestead exemption that reduces the assessed value of a taxpayer's actual residence.

Oregon

Oregon Department of Revenue
955 Center Street NE
Salem, OR 97301-2555
503-378-4988
http://www.dor.state.or.us/
Oregon offers property tax deferral programs for disabled and senior citizens age 62 and older. There is also a tax exemption for veterans.

Pennsylvania

Pennsylvania Dept of Revenue
Property Tax or Rent Rebate Program
Dept 280503
Harrisburg, PA 17128-0503
717-787-8201
http://www.revenue.state.pa.us/revenue/cwp/browse.asp
The Property Tax or Rent Rebate Program provides residents 65 years of age or older, widows or widowers 50 years of age or older and the permanently disabled 18 years of age or older meeting income eligibility requirements, rebates of paid property tax or rent.

Rhode Island

One Capitol Hill
Providence, RI 02908
401-222-2909
401-274-3676
http://www.tax.state.ri.us/
Rhode Island provides Property assistance for low-income families. This program is administered through the local government agencies.

South Carolina

South Carolina Department of Revenue
Post Office Box 125
Columbia, SC 29214
803-898-5480
http://www.sctax.org/

South Carolina provides a homestead exemption to residents who are 65 years of age, who are totally disabled or who are totally blind.

South Dakota

South Dakota Department of Revenue
445 East Capitol Avenue
Pierre, SD 57501
800-TAX-9188
605-773-3311
Fax: 605-773-5129
http://www.state.sd.us/revenue/spcltax.htm
To receive a property tax refund on your home, you must meet the residence, age or disability and income requirements.

Tennessee

Tennessee Comptroller of the Treasury
Property Tax Relief Program
1600 James K. Polk Building
505 Deaderick Street
Nashville, TN 37243-0278
615-747-8858
http://www.comptroller.state.tn.us/pa/patxr.htm
Tennessee provides tax relief for residence 65 years and older, totally disabled residence and veterans.

Texas

Comptroller of Public Accounts
111 E. 17th Street
Austin, TX 78774
512-305-9999
http://www.cpa.state.tx.us/taxinfo/proptax/propta
x.html
Texas provides for several types of exemptions. All residence may receive a homestead exemption for their home's value for school taxes. Additional exemptions are available for disabled, veterans and homeowners 65 and older.

Utah

Utah Tax Commission
210 North 1950 West
Salt Lake City, UT 84134
801-297-3600
801-297-3699
http://www.tax.ex.state.ut.us/property/index.html
Utah provides abatement and deferral programs for veterans, disabled and low-income residence age 65 or older.

Vermont

Vermont Department of Taxes

109 State Street
Montpelier, VT 05609-1401
http://www.state.vt.us/tax/index.htm
Vermont provides a School Property Tax adjustment that is based on family income.

Virginia

Virginia Department of Taxation
Office of Customer Services
Post Office Box 1115
Richmond, VA 23218-1115
804-367-8031
http://www.tax.state.va.us/

Washington

Washington Department of Revenue
2101 4th Ave, Suite 1400
Seattle, WA 98121-2300
206-956-3002
Fax: 206-956-3037
http://dor.wa.gov/
Any homeowner or mobile home owner is eligible if they use their home as their principal residence, have a limited income, and will be age 61 by December 31st or is a disabled person of any age.

West Virginia

West Virginia Property Tax Division
P.O. Box 2389
Charleston, WV 25328-2389
304-558-3940
http://www.state.wv.us/taxdiv/
West Virginia provides a Homestead program for veterans, disabled homeowners and elderly 65 years and older.

Wisconsin

Wisconsin Department of Revenue
P.O. Box 34
Madison, WI 53786-0001
608-266-1657
Fax: 608-267-8964
http://www.dor.state.wi.us/

Wyoming

Wyoming Department of Revenue
Herschler Bldg, 2nd Floor West
122 West 25th Street
Cheyenne, WY 82002-0110
307-777-7961
http://revenue.state.wy.us/revframe.htm
Wyoming provides for property tax relief for veterans and other residence.

Federal Law May Save You Hundreds of Dollars Each Year

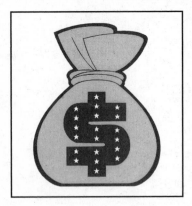 Private Mortgage Insurance (PMI) is a monthly premium you must pay when you put less than a 20%downpayment on a home. It protects the lender if you default on the loan. The Homeowners Protection Act of 1998 establishes rules for automatic termination and borrowers cancellation of PMI on home mortgages. PMI can end up costing you thousands of dollars during a loan. Check your annual escrow account statement or call your lender to find out exactly what it costs you each year. This act is applicable for certain mortgages signed on or after July 29, 1999 for the purchase, initial construction, or refinance of a single-family home. It does not apply to government-insured FHA or VA loans or to loans with lender-paid PMI.

With a few exceptions, for those mortgages meeting the date feature, the PMI must be terminated automatically when you reach 22% equity in your home. Your PMI can also be canceled, with a few exceptions, when you request its removal when you reach 20% equity in your home.

The exceptions are as follows:

⇨ if your loan is high risk,
⇨ if you have not been current in your payments within the year prior to the time for termination or cancellation, and
⇨ if you have other liens on your property.
⇨ If any of those are present, your PMI may continue.
⇨ Other provisions in the Homeowners Protection Act are:
⇨ New borrowers must be informed at closing and once a year about PMI terminations and cancellation.
⇨ Mortgage servicers must provide a telephone number to call for information about termination and cancellation of PMI.
⇨ Even those with loans signed before July 29, 1999, or loans with lender paid PMI, must be notified of termination or cancellation rights they may otherwise have under those loans.

If your mortgage was signed before July 29, 1999, you can still request the removal of the PMI once you exceed 20% equity in your home. However, federal law does not require the lender or mortgage servicer to cancel the insurance in that situation.

Some states may also have laws concerning the removal or cancellation of PMI even if the mortgage was signed before the July 29, 1999 date. Be sure to check with your lender or mortgage servicer or call Fannie Mae or Freddie Mac for information.

To receive information from the Federal Trade Commission on the removal of PMI, contact Federal Trade Commission, Public Reference, Washington, DC 20580; 877-FTC-HELP (382-4357); {www.ftc.gov}.

$800 For Your Security Deposit

Several states and more and more local organizations and nonprofits provide money for renters with grants or loans that can be used for security deposits. Programs constantly come and go, but the state of Delaware has provided grants to nonprofit agencies to administer 2 security deposit programs. Two counties in Florida provide grants to cover deposits for people at certain incomes, and New Hampshire guarantees landlords the full amount so the renter can make payments on a security deposit.

This information was collected from the National Low Income Housing Coalition, 1012 Fourteenth Street NW, Suite 610, Washington, DC 20005; 202-662-1530; {www.nlihc.org}. This organization does not provide assistance to those looking for housing. To locate available programs in your area, contact your state housing office, social services office, or your local reference librarian who can assist you in finding other organizations who might provide this assistance.

6 Months Free Rent

There are a number of state and local programs that will pay your rent for a limited period of time. These programs are usually referred to as "Transitional Rental Assistance Programs" and are usually available to certain populations or income groups. Programs constantly come and go but Minnesota provides rent for up to 6 months for at-risk youths from 15 to 21. Idaho gives 6 months of rental assistance to parolees. Oregon provides 6 months rents for people with incomes close to $30,000.

This information was collected from the National Low Income Housing Coalition, 1012 Fourteenth Street NW, Suite 610, Washington, DC 20005; 202-662-

1530; {www.nlihc.org}. This organization does not provide assistance to those looking for housing. To locate available programs in your area contact your state housing office, social services office, or your local reference librarian who can assist you in finding other organizations who might provide this assistance.

Make $82,000 And Get A 20% Rental Discount

Some 26 states have something referred to as "Circuitbreaker Programs" which provide refunds through the state tax system for a portion of rent paid by certain populations. The programs and requirements vary widely by state, but its purpose is to refund the portion of a person's yearly rental costs that pay the owner's property tax. Typically this can be between 15 to 20 percent of annual rent.

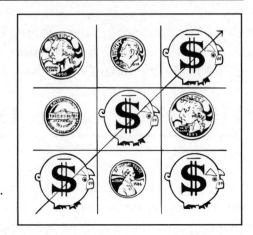

This information was collected from the National Low Income Housing Coalition, 1012 Fourteenth Street NW, Suite 610, Washington, DC 20005; 202-662-1530; {www.nlihc.org}. This organization does not provide assistance to those looking for housing. For more information see the report "State Funded Rental Assistance." To locate available programs in your area contact your state housing office, social services office, or your local reference librarian who can assist you in finding other organizations who might provide this assistance.

Rent FREE For Special Populations

About half of the states have programs that pay rental assistance for certain populations like, elderly, those with mental or physical disabilities, or people who have recently lost their jobs. Some programs even have no income restrictions. They may give you $3,000 to help you pay rent, or subsidize your rent for 2 years, or give you a voucher that can pay part of your rent forever.

This information was collected from the National Low Income Housing Coalition, 1012 Fourteenth Street NW, Suite 610, Washington, DC 20005; 202-662-1530; {www.nlihc.org}. This organization does not provide assistance to those looking for housing. For more information see the report "State Funded Rental Assistance." To locate available programs in your area contact your state housing office, social services office, or your local reference librarian who can assist you in finding other organizations who might provide this assistance.

Get $400/Mo Towards Rent From Your State

A number of states have programs similar to the federal Section 8 Program that provides vouchers and other forms of rental assistance to people with certain incomes and the assistance can last forever. This information was collected from the National Low Income Housing Coalition, 1012 Fourteenth Street NW, Suite 610, Washington, DC 20005; 202-662-1530; {www.nlihc.org}. This organization does not provide assistance to those looking for housing. For more information see the report "State Funded Rental Assistance." To locate available programs in your area contact your state housing office, social services office, or your local reference librarian who can assist you in finding other organizations who might provide this assistance.

Emergency Rent Money

About half the states provide money for people who are in an emergency situation to pay their rent, like being close to eviction. There are different requirements for almost every program and the income requirement can go up to $50,000. This information was collected from the National Low Income Housing Coalition, 1012 Fourteenth Street NW, Suite 610, Washington, DC 20005; 202-662-1530; {www.nlihc.org}. This organization does not provide assistance to those looking for housing. For more information see the report "State Funded Rental Assistance." To locate available programs in your area contact your state housing office, social services office, or your local reference librarian who can assist you in finding other organizations who might provide this assistance.

House Rich, But Cash Poor

A Reverse Mortgage is a type of home equity loan that allows you to convert some of the equity in your home into cash while you retain ownership. This works like a traditional mortgage, but in reverse. So, instead of making a house payment each month, you receive a payment from your lender. Depending on the type of Reverse Mortgage and the lender, you can take the money in a lump sum, in monthly advances, through a line-of-credit, or a combination of the three. Most Reverse Mortgages do not require any repayment of principal, interest, or servicing fees, for as long as you live in your home. These loans are called rising-debt loans for that reason. The money you get from this type of loan can normally be used for any reason, including paying housing expenses like taxes, insurance, fuel, and maintenance costs.

You do not need income to qualify, but you must own your home. The value of your home, your age and life expectancy, the loan's interest rate, and the lenders policy determines the maximum loan amount limit. That can range from 50% to 75% of your home's fair market value. Generally, the older you are, the more money you can get; and the more your house is worth, the more money you can get. However, you must be at least 62 years old to apply for a Reverse Mortgage. You will keep the title to your home and you are still responsible for the taxes, repairs, and maintenance. Depending on the plan you choose, the Reverse Mortgage becomes due with interest either when you permanently move, sell your home, die, or reach the end of the loan term. After your death, your heirs must pay off the loan. The debt is usually repaid by refinancing the loan into a forward mortgage (if the heirs are eligible) or by using the proceeds of the sale of the home.

Eligible properties are single family one-unit dwellings. Some lenders will allow 2 to 4 unit owner-occupied dwellings, condominiums, planned unit developments, and manufactured homes. However, mobile homes and cooperative are not normally eligible properties. A Reverse Mortgage generally must be first mortgages which means there cannot be any other debt against your house. If there is, you can either pay off that debt first, or pay it off with the Reverse Mortgage money.

Major Types Of Reverse Mortgages

These types of loans differ in where they are available; who can get them; what types of loan advances they provide; how much cash they will likely provide; how much they will likely cost; who offers them; and who backs them.

A) The FHA-insured plan has several payment options.
  1) You can receive monthly loan advances for a fixed term or for as long as you live in the home,
  2) a line of credit, or
  3) monthly loan advances plus a line of credit.
  4) The loan is not due as long as you live in your home.

Some of the costs associated with this loan are, closing costs, a mortgage insurance premium, and sometimes a monthly servicing fee. Interest is charged at an adjustable rate on your loan balance. The change in interest rates does not affect the monthly payment, but the rate at which the loan balance grows.

This type of Reverse Mortgage allows changes in payment options at a small cost. It also protects you by ensuring that the payments continue even if your lender defaults.

The balance of the credit line grows larger every month until all of the funds are withdrawn. This is because the unused portion of the credit line grows at the same rate that you are charged on your loan balance.

The down side is that FHA-insured Reverse Mortgages may provide smaller loan advances than other lender-insured plans. This type of loan is offered by banks, mortgage companies, and other private sector lenders.

B) Lender-insured Reverse Mortgages offer two types of payment options:
    1) monthly loan advances, or
    2) monthly loan advances plus a line of credit.
These are available to you as long as you live in your home at either a fixed or adjustable interest rate.

This type of Reverse Mortgage may have a larger loan advance than those with an FHA-insured plan. They may also allow you to mortgage less than the full value of your home, which will preserve some equity for you or your heirs. But they may involve greater costs than FHA-insured loans or uninsured loans.

Additional loan costs can include a mortgage premium, at a fixed or variable rate, and other fees. Those higher costs mean that your loan balance will grow more quickly, leaving you with less equity over time.

Some lender-insured plans include an annuity that continues to make monthly payments even if you sell your home. The security of those payments are dependent upon the company's financial strength, so it is important to check their financial rating. Annuity payments may be taxable and affect eligibility for Supplemental Security Income and Medicaid. Reverse annuity mortgages can also include additional charges based on any increase in the value of your home during the term of the loan. These loans are offered by banks, mortgage companies, and other private sector lenders.

It may be to your benefit to choose a lender that offers both of these types of Reverse Mortgages. That way you could get a side-by-side comparison of the costs of each, how much money you could get from each, and what would be the equity that is left in your home at the end of the loan.

C) Single-purpose reverse mortgages are usually offered by state and local governments. The lump sum advances can only be used for a specific purpose. Some can be only for home improvements or repairs; others for the payment of property taxes or special assessments. Connecticut has a program that can only be used to pay for long term care services. This is the least expensive type of Reverse Mortgage. Because of the restrictions, they do not offer as much money as other types Reverse Mortgages. It is not available in all areas and may not be available to homeowners with high income.

D) Uninsured Reverse Mortgages are only available now in parts of Arizona, California, Massachusetts, and Minnesota. It differs greatly from the previous programs. It offers monthly advances for a fixed term that you determine when you take out the loan. The balance is due at the end of that term. Interest is normally set at a fixed rate and a mortgage insurance premium is not needed.

There are some important factors to consider before choosing this type of Reverse Mortgage. You should think about the amount of money you need monthly; how many years you may need it; how you will repay the loan when it is due; and how much remaining equity you will need after paying off the loan.

If you need a substantial amount of money for just a short time, this type of Reverse Mortgage can offer greater monthly payments than other plans. It is important though to have a source of repayment when the loan comes due. If not, you may have to sell your home.

While the value of your home is part of the equation in a Reverse Mortgage, each home is subject to a maximum mortgage limit. If your home's worth exceeds the county's median home value, the amount of your loan will be limited by that value. The ranges for 2002 are $144,336 in most non-metro areas to $261,609 in a majority of urban areas. These values change yearly and there is currently discussion on a single national limit. You can look up your county limit at {https://entp.hud.gov/idapp/html/hicostlook.cfm}.

The following are common features of all Reverse Mortgages

♦ Reverse Mortgages are rising-debt loans. The interest is added to the principal loan balance each month, because it is not paid on a current basis.

Because of this, the total amount of interest you owe, increases significantly with time.

♦ All 3 plans charge origination fees and closing costs. Insured plans also charge insurance premiums and some will add mortgage servicing charges. Your lender may allow you to finance those costs instead of paying cash. However, doing so will add more to your loan amount.

♦ Reverse Mortgages use up all or some of the equity in your home.

♦ Generally, you can request a loan advance at closing that is substantially larger than the rest of your payments.

♦ Your legal obligation to pay back the loan is limited by the value of your home at the time the loan is repaid. This cap, called a "non-recourse" limit, means you can never owe more than your home is worth at the end of the loan term.

♦ Reverse Mortgage loan advances are not taxable. They do not affect your Social Security or Medicare benefits. If you get Supplemental Security Income, it is not affected by your Reverse Mortgage payments as long as you spend the SSI benefits within the month it is received. This also applies to Medicaid benefits in most states. To be sure, check with a benefit specialist.

♦ Loans can be for a fixed rate or adjustable rate.

♦ Interest on the loan is not deductible on your income taxes until you pay off all or part of your Reverse Mortgage debt.

There are some safeguards with a Reverse Mortgage. The Federal Truth in Lending Act is one of the best protections to have. It requires lenders to inform you about the plan's terms and costs. Make sure you understand those before signing the loan papers. Among other information, the Annual Percentage Rate (APR) and payment terms must be disclosed. On plans with adjustable rates, they must inform you of specific information on the variable rate feature. For those plans with credit lines, you must be made aware of any charges to open and use the account, such as appraisal, credit report or attorney's fees. Also, the non-recourse limit mentioned above, means that the lender cannot come after yours or you heirs income or other assets in order to pay back a loan with that cap.

Lenders can require repayment at any time if you:
• fail to pay property taxes;
• fail to maintain and repair your home; or
• fail to keep your home insured.
• you declare bankruptcy;
• you donate or abandon your home;

Because of the costs and complexity of a Reverse Mortgage, other options should be considered before taking the step to obtain a loan. You should check to see if you could be eligible for Supplemental Security Income, Medicaid, or Qualified Medical Benefits; or consider selling your home and moving; or check out state or local plans that could help you pay taxes and make repairs as alternatives first.

If you would like a current list of lenders that participate in the FHA-insured program, sponsored by the Department of Housing and Urban Development (HUD), or additional information on reverse mortgages, write to:

> AARP Home Equity Information Center
> 601 E Street, NW
> Washington, DC 20049

or visit their web site at {www.aarp.com}.

For additional information, send a self-addressed stamped envelope to :

> National Center for Home Equity Conversion
> 7373-147 Street West, Suite 115
> Apple Valley, MN 55124

You can also contact the Federal Trade Commission (FTC) for information about Reverse Mortgages. Contact Federal Trade Commission, Public Reference, Washington, DC 20580; 877-FTC-HELP (382-4357); {www.ftc.gov}.

Having Trouble Getting the House or Apartment You Want?

Federal law prohibits housing discrimination based on your race, color, national origin, religion, sex, family status, or disability. If you have been trying to buy or rent a home or apartment and you believe your rights have been violated, you can file a fair housing complaint. There are several ways to file a complaint; you can file a complaint on line at {http://www.hud.gov/complaints/housedis crim.cfm}, you can call 1-800-669-9777 toll free, or you can print out a form on line, complete it, and drop it off at your local HUD office or mail it to the Office of Fair Housing and Equal Opportunity.

Office of Fair Housing and Equal Opportunity
U.S. Department of Housing and Urban Development- HUD)
Room 5204
451 Seventh St. SW
Washington, DC 20410-2000

You can also file a complaint in your own letter, which includes the following information:

★ Your name and address
★ The name and address of the person your complaint is about
★ The address of the house or apartment you were trying to rent or buy
★ The date when this incident occurred
★ A short description of what happened

Then mail it to the Fair Housing Hub closest to you.

What Happens When You File A Complaint?

You should be notified that your complaint has been received, and then HUD will

notify the alleged violator and ask them to respond to your complaint. They will then investigate to determine if there is reasonable cause to believe the Fair Housing Act has been violated. HUD will try to reach an agreement with the person your complaint is against. HUD may determine that your State or local agency has the same fair housing powers as HUD, so HUD will refer your complaint to that agency for investigation. That agency must begin work on your complaint within 30 days.

If you need immediate help to stop a serious problem, HUD may be able to assist you as soon as you file a complaint. HUD may authorize the United States Attorney General to go to court to seek temporary or preliminary relief pending the outcome of your complaint. For example if a builder agrees to sell a house, but then fails to keep the agreement once he realizes the buyer is black, the Attorney General can go to court to prevent a sale to another buyer.

If HUD finds that there is reasonable cause that your were discriminated against, your case will be heard in an administrative hearing. HUD attorneys will litigate the case for free on your behalf. You can be compensated for actual damages, including humiliation, pain, and suffering, as well as other equitable relief such as making the housing available to you.

Fair Housing Hubs

Alabama

Fair Housing Hub
U.S. Department of Housing and
Urban Development
Five Points Marietta Plaza
40 Marietta Street, 16th floor
Atlanta, GA 30303-2806
404-331-5140
1-800-440-8091
TTY 404-730-2654

Alaska

Fair Housing Hub
U.S. Department of Housing and
Urban Development
Seattle Federal Office Building
909 First Avenue, Room 205
Seattle, WA 98104-1000
206-220-5170
1-800-877-0246
TTY 206-220-5185

Arizona

Fair Housing Hub
U.S. Department of Housing and
Urban Development
Phillip Burton Federal Building
and U.S. Courthouse
450 Golden Gate Ave, 9th Floor

P.O. Box 36003
San Francisco, CA 94102-3448
415-436-8400
1-800-347-3739
TTY 415-436-6594

Arkansas

Fair Housing Hub
U.S. Department of Housing and
Urban Development
801 Cherry Street, 27th Floor
P.O. Box 2905
Fort Worth, TX 76113-2905
817-978-5900
1-800-669-9777
TTY 817-978-5595

California

Fair Housing Hub
U.S. Department of Housing and
Urban Development
Phillip Burton Federal Building
and U.S. Courthouse
450 Golden Gate Ave, 9th Floor
P.O. Box 36003
San Francisco, CA 94102-3448
415-436-8400
1-800-347-3739
TTY 415-436-6594

Caribbean

Fair Housing Hub
U.S. Department of Housing and
Urban Development
Five Points Marietta Plaza
40 Marietta Street, 16th floor
Atlanta, GA 30303-2806
404-331-5140
1-800-440-8091
TTY 404-730-2654

Colorado

Fair Housing Hub
U.S. Department of Housing and
Urban Development
633 17th Street, 13th Floor
Denver, CO 80202-3690
303-672-5437
1-800-877-7353
TTY 303-672-5248

Connecticut

Fair Housing Hub
U.S. Department of Housing and
Urban Development
Thomas P. O'Neill, Jr.
Federal Building
10 Causeway Street, Room 321
Boston, MA 02222-1092
617-994-8300

Free Home Owner Calculators at
{www.fanniemae.com/homebuyers/homepath}
Look under Resources

- How Much Is Your Monthly Payment?

- How Much House Can You Afford?

- What Monthly Payment Is Needed for a House with a Specific Sales Price?

- How Much House Can You Afford with a Specific Monthly Payment?

- Is Now A Good Time To Refinance?

1-800-827-5005
TTY 617-565-5453

Delaware
Fair Housing Hub
U.S. Department of Housing and
Urban Development
The Wanamaker Building
100 Penn Square East, 12th Floor
Philadelphia, PA 19107-3380
215-656-0663 ext.3260
1-888-799-2085
TTY 215-656-3450

District of Columbia
Fair Housing Hub
U.S. Department of Housing and
Urban Development
The Wanamaker Building
100 Penn Square East, 12th Floor
Philadelphia, PA 19107-3380
215-656-0663 ext.3260
1-888-799-2085
TTY 215-656-3450

Florida
Fair Housing Hub
U.S. Department of Housing and
Urban Development
Five Points Marietta Plaza
40 Marietta Street, 16th floor
Atlanta, GA 30303-2806
404-331-5140
1-800-440-8091
TTY 404-730-2654

Georgia
Fair Housing Hub
U.S. Department of Housing and
Urban Development
Five Points Marietta Plaza
40 Marietta Street, 16th floor
Atlanta, GA 30303-2806
404-331-5140
1-800-440-8091
TTY 404-730-2654

Hawaii
Fair Housing Hub
U.S. Department of Housing and
Urban Development
Phillip Burton Federal Building
and U.S. Courthouse
450 Golden Gate Ave, 9th Floor
P.O. Box 36003

San Francisco, CA 94102-3448
415-436-8400
1-800-347-3739
TTY 415-436-6594

Idaho
Fair Housing Hub
U.S. Department of Housing and
Urban Development
Seattle Federal Office Building
909 First Avenue, Room 205
Seattle, WA 98104-1000
206-220-5170
1-800-877-0246
TTY 206-220-5185

Illinois
Fair Housing Hub
U.S. Department of Housing and
Urban Development
Ralph H. Metcalfe Federal Bldg.
77 West Jackson Boulevard
Room 2101
Chicago, IL 60604-3507
312-353-7776 ext. 2453
1-800-765-9372
TTY 312-353-7143

Indiana
Fair Housing Hub
U.S. Department of Housing and
Urban Development
Ralph H. Metcalfe Federal Bldg.
77 West Jackson Boulevard
Room 2101
Chicago, IL 60604-3507
312-353-7776 ext. 2453
1-800-765-9372
TTY 312-353-7143

Iowa
Fair Housing Hub
U.S. Department of Housing and
Urban Development
Gateway Tower II
400 State Avenue, Room 200
Kansas City, KS 66101-2406
913-551-6958
1-800-743-5323
TTY 913-551-6972

Kansas
Fair Housing Hub
U.S. Department of Housing and
Urban Development
Gateway Tower II

400 State Avenue, Room 200
Kansas City, KS 66101-2406
913-551-6958
1-800-743-5323
TTY 913-551-6972

Kentucky
Fair Housing Hub
U.S. Department of Housing and
Urban Development
Five Points Marietta Plaza
40 Marietta Street, 16th floor
Atlanta, GA 30303-2806
404-331-5140
1-800-440-8091
TTY 404-730-2654

Louisiana
Fair Housing Hub
U.S. Department of Housing and
Urban Development
801 Cherry Street, 27th Floor
P.O. Box 2905
Fort Worth, TX 76113-2905
817-978-5900
1-800-669-9777
TTY 817-978-5595

Maine
Fair Housing Hub
U.S. Department of Housing and
Urban Development
Thomas P. O'Neill, Jr.
Federal Building
10 Causeway Street, Room 321
Boston, MA 02222-1092
617-994-8300
1-800-827-5005
TTY 617-565-5453

Maryland
Fair Housing Hub
U.S. Department of Housing and
Urban Development
The Wanamaker Building
100 Penn Square East, 12th Floor
Philadelphia, PA 19107-3380
215-656-0663 ext.3260
1-888-799-2085
TTY 215-656-3450

Massachusetts
Fair Housing Hub
U.S. Department of Housing and
Urban Development
Thomas P. O'Neill, Jr.

Federal Building
10 Causeway Street, Room 321
Boston, MA 02222-1092
617-994-8300
1-800-827-5005
TTY 617-565-5453

Michigan

Fair Housing Hub
U.S. Department of Housing and
Urban Development
Ralph H. Metcalfe Federal Bldg.
77 West Jackson Boulevard
Room 2101
Chicago, IL 60604-3507
312-353-7776 ext. 2453
1-800-765-9372
TTY 312-353-7143

Minnesota

Fair Housing Hub
U.S. Department of Housing and
Urban Development
Ralph H. Metcalfe Federal Bldg.
77 West Jackson Boulevard
Room 2101
Chicago, IL 60604-3507
312-353-7776 ext. 2453
1-800-765-9372
TTY 312-353-7143

Mississippi

Fair Housing Hub
U.S. Department of Housing and
Urban Development
Five Points Marietta Plaza
40 Marietta Street, 16th floor
Atlanta, GA 30303-2806
404-331-5140
1-800-440-8091
TTY 404-730-2654

Missouri

Fair Housing Hub
U.S. Department of Housing and
Urban Development
Gateway Tower II
400 State Avenue, Room 200
Kansas City, KS 66101-2406
913-551-6958
1-800-743-5323
TTY 913-551-6972

Montana

Fair Housing Hub
U.S. Department of Housing and
Urban Development

633 17th Street, 13th Floor
Denver, CO 80202-3690
303-672-5437
1-800-877-7353
TTY 303-672-5248

Nebraska

Fair Housing Hub
U.S. Department of Housing and
Urban Development
Gateway Tower II
400 State Avenue, Room 200
Kansas City, KS 66101-2406
913-551-6958
1-800-743-5323
TTY 913-551-6972

Nevada

Fair Housing Hub
U.S. Department of Housing and
Urban Development
Phillip Burton Federal Building
and U.S. Courthouse
450 Golden Gate Ave, 9th Floor
P.O. Box 36003
San Francisco, CA 94102-3448
415-436-8400
1-800-347-3739
TTY 415-436-6594

New Hampshire

Fair Housing Hub
U.S. Department of Housing and
Urban Development
Thomas P. O'Neill, Jr.
Federal Building
10 Causeway Street, Room 321
Boston, MA 02222-1092
617-994-8300
1-800-827-5005
TTY 617-565-5453

New Jersey

Fair Housing Hub
U.S. Department of Housing and
Urban Development
26 Federal Plaza, Room 3532
New York, NY 10278-0068
212-264-9610
1-800-496-4294
TTY 212-264-0927

New Mexico

Fair Housing Hub
U.S. Department of Housing and
Urban Development

801 Cherry Street, 27th Floor
P.O. Box 2905
Fort Worth, TX 76113-2905
817-978-5900
1-800-669-9777
TTY 817-978-5595

New York

Fair Housing Hub
U.S. Department of Housing and
Urban Development
26 Federal Plaza, Room 3532
New York, NY 10278-0068
212-264-9610
1-800-496-4294
TTY 212-264-0927

North Carolina

Fair Housing Hub
U.S. Department of Housing and
Urban Development
Five Points Marietta Plaza
40 Marietta Street, 16th floor
Atlanta, GA 30303-2806
404-331-5140
1-800-440-8091
TTY 404-730-2654

North Dakota

Fair Housing Hub
U.S. Department of Housing and
Urban Development
633 17th Street, 13th Floor
Denver, CO 80202-3690
303-672-5437
1-800-877-7353
TTY 303-672-5248

Ohio

Fair Housing Hub
U.S. Department of Housing and
Urban Development
Ralph H. Metcalfe Federal Bldg.
77 West Jackson Boulevard
Room 2101
Chicago, IL 60604-3507
312-353-7776 ext. 2453
1-800-765-9372
TTY 312-353-7143

Oklahoma

Fair Housing Hub
U.S. Department of Housing and
Urban Development
801 Cherry Street, 27th Floor

P.O. Box 2905
Fort Worth, TX 76113-2905
817-978-5900
1-800-669-9777
TTY 817-978-5595

Oregon
Fair Housing Hub
U.S. Department of Housing and
Urban Development
Seattle Federal Office Building
909 First Avenue, Room 205
Seattle, WA 98104-1000
206-220-5170
1-800-877-0246
TTY 206-220-5185

Pennsylvania
Fair Housing Hub
U.S. Department of Housing and
Urban Development
The Wanamaker Building
100 Penn Square East, 12th Floor
Philadelphia, PA 19107-3380
215-656-0663 ext.3260
1-888-799-2085
TTY 215-656-3450

Rhode Island
Fair Housing Hub
U.S. Department of Housing and
Urban Development
Thomas P. O'Neill, Jr.
Federal Building
10 Causeway Street, Room 321
Boston, MA 02222-1092
617-994-8300
1-800-827-5005
TTY 617-565-5453

South Carolina
Fair Housing Hub
U.S. Department of Housing and
Urban Development
Five Points Marietta Plaza
40 Marietta Street, 16th floor
Atlanta, GA 30303-2806
404-331-5140
1-800-440-8091
TTY 404-730-2654

South Dakota
Fair Housing Hub

U.S. Department of Housing and
Urban Development
633 17th Street, 13th Floor
Denver, CO 80202-3690
303-672-5437
1-800-877-7353
TTY 303-672-5248

Tennessee
Fair Housing Hub
U.S. Department of Housing and
Urban Development
Five Points Marietta Plaza
40 Marietta Street, 16th floor
Atlanta, GA 30303-2806
404-331-5140
1-800-440-8091
TTY 404-730-2654

Texas
Fair Housing Hub
U.S. Department of Housing and
Urban Development
801 Cherry Street, 27th Floor
P.O. Box 2905
Fort Worth, TX 76113-2905
817-978-5900
1-800-669-9777
TTY 817-978-5595

Utah
Fair Housing Hub
U.S. Department of Housing and
Urban Development
633 17th Street, 13th Floor
Denver, CO 80202-3690
303-672-5437
1-800-877-7353
TTY 303-672-5248

Vermont
Fair Housing Hub
U.S. Department of Housing and
Urban Development
Thomas P. O'Neill, Jr.
Federal Building
10 Causeway Street, Room 321
Boston, MA 02222-1092
617-994-8300
1-800-827-5005
TTY 617-565-5453

Virginia
Fair Housing Hub

U.S. Department of Housing and
Urban Development
The Wanamaker Building
100 Penn Square East, 12th Floor
Philadelphia, PA 19107-3380
215-656-0663 ext.3260
1-888-799-2085
TTY 215-656-3450

Washington
Fair Housing Hub
U.S. Department of Housing and
Urban Development
Seattle Federal Office Building
909 First Avenue, Room 205
Seattle, WA 98104-1000
206-220-5170
1-800-877-0246
TTY 206-220-5185

West Virginia
Fair Housing Hub
U.S. Department of Housing and
Urban Development
The Wanamaker Building
100 Penn Square East, 12th Floor
Philadelphia, PA 19107-3380
215-656-0663 ext.3260
1-888-799-2085
TTY 215-656-3450

Wisconsin
Fair Housing Hub
U.S. Department of Housing and
Urban Development
Ralph H. Metcalfe Federal Bldg.
77 West Jackson Boulevard
Room 2101
Chicago, Illinois 60604-3507
312-353-7776 ext. 2453
1-800-765-9372
TTY 312-353-7143

Wyoming
Fair Housing Hub
U.S. Department of Housing and
Urban Development
633 17th Street, 13th Floor
Denver, CO 80202-3690
303-672-5437
1-800-877-7353
TTY 303-672-5248

Save $328 Per Month On Rent

This is not the only rental assistance program available. You should also see the following chapters for additional programs that can help renters.

In some parts of the country, a family of four can make up to $61,700 and still qualify for this program! The U.S. Department of Housing and Urban Development (HUD) offers a variety of rental assistance under the Section 8 Program. Public housing was established to provide decent and safe rental housing for eligible low-income families, the elderly, and persons with disabilities. Public housing comes in all sizes and types, from scattered single family houses to high-rise apartments for elderly families. There are approximately 1.3 million households living in public housing units, managed by some 3,300 housing agencies.

In addition to public housing, there are many different voucher programs designed to assist very low-income families, the elderly, and the disabled to afford decent, safe, and sanitary housing in the private market. Participants are often able to find their own housing, including single-family homes, townhouses and apartments. The Vouchers are administered locally by public housing agencies (PHAs). A family that is issued a housing voucher is responsible for finding a suitable housing unit of the family's choice where the owner agrees to rent under the program. A housing subsidy is paid to the landlord directly by the PHA on behalf of the participating family. The family then pays the difference between the actual rent charged by the landlord and the amount subsidized by the program. Under certain circumstances, if authorized by the PHA, a family may use its voucher to purchase a modest home. A voucher holder must pay 30% of its monthly adjusted gross income for rent and utilities.

Some voucher options include:

- Housing Choice Vouchers—allows very low-income families to choose and lease or purchase safe, decent, and affordable privately-owned rental housing.
- Conversion Vouchers—assists PHAs with the relocation or replacement housing needs that result from the demolition, disposition, or mandatory conversion of public housing units.

- Family Unification Vouchers—made available to families for whom the lack of adequate housing is a primary factor in the separation, or threat of imminent separation of children from their families or in the prevention of reunifying the children with their families.
- Homeownership Vouchers—assist first-time homeowners with their monthly homeownership expenses. The home must pass an initial housing quality standards conducted by the PHA and an independent home inspection before the PHA may approve the purchase by the family.
- Mainstream Program Vouchers—enable families having a person with disabilities to lease affordable private housing of their choice. Vouchers also assist persons with disabilities who often face difficulties in locating suitable and accessible housing on the private market.
- Welfare to Work Vouchers—extra housing choice vouchers were awarded for this program to help families who have a critical need for housing in order to obtain or retain viable employment. Housing authorities are to work with others to ensure assistance is combined with job training, childcare, and other services families need.

Who Is Eligible?

Public housing is usually limited to families who make up to 80% of the median income for the area. This could be as much as $38,000. Be sure to check what the limits are in your area. A housing agency determines your eligibility based on: 1) annual gross income; 2) whether you qualify as elderly, a person with a disability, or as a family; and 3) U.S. citizenship or eligible immigration status. If you are eligible, the housing agency will check your references to make sure you and your family will be good tenants. Housing agencies will deny admission to any applicant whose habits and practices may be expected to have a detrimental effect on other tenants or on the project's environment.

Housing Agencies use income limits developed by the U.S. Department of Housing and Urban Development (HUD). HUD sets the lower income limits at 80% and very low income limits at 50% of the median income for the county or metropolitan area in which you choose to live. Income limits vary from area to area so you may be eligible at one housing agency but not at another. The Housing Agency serving your community can provide you with the income levels for your area and family size, or you can also find the income limits on the internet at {www.hud.gov}.

How Do I Apply?

If you are interested in applying for public housing or the voucher programs, contact your housing agency. Not all Public Housing Agencies offer all vouchers, and there is often a waiting list. Once you get a voucher, you are frequently allowed to use the voucher outside the jurisdiction of the Public Housing Agency. If you are interested in applying for rental assistance, contact the local public housing agency or HUD office near you; {www.hud.gov}. If you have trouble contacting the Housing Authority, contact the local HUD Field office.

Contact the resource center through their toll-free number at 1-800-955-2232 from 9:00 a.m. to 6:00 p.m., Eastern Standard Time (EST) daily Monday through Friday.

> U.S. Department of Housing and Urban Development
> 451 7th Street S.W.
> Washington, DC 20410
> Telephone: (202) 708-1112
> TTY: (202) 708-1455
> www.hud.gov

A list of public housing agencies follows the HUD list.

HUD State Offices

U.S. Department of Housing and Urban Development
451 7th Street, S.W.
Washington, DC 20410
202-708-1112
http://www.hud.gov

Alabama
HUD - Birmingham office
950 22nd St N, Suite 900
Birmingham, AL 35203-2617
205-731-2630
Fax: 205-731-2592
www.hud.gov/local/index.cfm?
state=al

Alaska
HUD Anchorage office
949 East 36th Avenue, Suite 401
Anchorage, AK 99508-4399
907-271-4663
Fax: 907-271-3667
www.hud.gov/local/index.cfm?
state=ak

Arizona
HUD Phoenix office
One N. Central Ave., Suite 600
Phoenix, AZ 85004-2361
602-379-7100

Fax: 602-379-3985
www.hud.gov/local/index.cfm?
state=az

Tucson Area office
HUD Tucson office
160 North Stone Ave., Suite 100
Tucson, AZ 85701-1467
520-670-6000
Fax: 520-670-6207
www.hud.gov/local/index.cfm?
state=az

Arkansas
HUD Little Rock office
425 West Capitol Avenue #900
Little Rock, AR 72201-3488
501-324-5931
Fax: 501-324-6142
www.hud.gov/local/index.cfm?
state=ar

California
HUD - San Francisco office
450 Golden Gate Avenue
San Francisco, CA 94102-3448
415-436-6532
Fax: 415-436-6446
www.hud.gov/local/index.cfm?
state=ca

Fresno Area office
HUD - Fresno office
2135 Fresno Street, Suite 100
Fresno, CA 93721-1718
559-487-5033
Fax: 559-487-5191
www.hud.gov/local/index.cfm?
state=ca

Los Angeles Area office
HUD Los Angeles office
611 W. Sixth Street, Suite 800
Los Angeles, CA 90017
213-894-8007
Fax: 213-894-8110
www.hud.gov/local/index.cfm?
state=ca

Sacramento Area office
HUD Sacramento office
925 L Street
Sacramento, CA 95814
916-498-5220
Fax: 916-498-5262
www.hud.gov/local/index.cfm?
state=ca

San Diego Area office
HUD San Diego office
Symphony Towers
750 B Street, Suite 1600

San Diego, CA 92101-8131
619-557-5310
Fax: 619-557-5312
www.hud.gov/local/index.cfm?
state=ca

Santa Ana Area office
HUD Santa Ana office
1600 N. Broadway, Suite 100
Santa Ana, CA 92706-3927
714-796-5577
Fax: 714-796-1285
www.hud.gov/local/index.cfm?
state=ca

Caribbean office

HUD Caribbean office
171 Carlos E. Chardon Avenue
San Juan, PR 00918-0903
787-766-5201
Fax: 787-766-5995

Colorado

HUD Denver office
633 17th Street, 14th Floor
Denver, CO 80202-3607
303-672-5440
Fax: 303-672-5004
www.hud.gov/local/index.cfm?
state=co

Connecticut

HUD - Hartford office
One Corporate Center
Hartford, CT 06103-3220
860-240-4800, ext. 3100
Fax: 860-240-4850
www.hud.gov/local/index.cfm?
state=ct

Delaware

HUD - Wilmington office
920 King Street, Suite 404
Wilmington, DE 19801-3016
302-573-6300
Fax: 302-573-6259
www.hud.gov/local/index.cfm?
state=de

District of Columbia

HUD Washington, DC office
820 First Street NE Suite 300
Washington, DC 20002-4205
202-275-9200
Fax: 202-275-9212

www.hud.gov/local/index.cfm?
state=dc

Florida

HUD Florida State office
909 SE First Avenue
Miami, FL 33131
305-536-4456
Fax: 305-536-5765
www.hud.gov/local/index.cfm?
state=fl

Jacksonville Area office
HUD - Jacksonville office
301 West Bay Street, Suite 2200
Jacksonville, FL 32202-5121
904-232-2627
Fax: 904-232-3759
www.hud.gov/local/index.cfm?
state=fl

Orlando Area office
HUD - Orlando office
3751 Maguire Blvd., Room 270
Orlando, FL 32803-3032
407-648-6441
Fax: 407-648-6310
www.hud.gov/local/index.cfm?
state=fl

Tampa Area office
HUD Tampa office
500 Zack Street, Suite 402
Tampa, FL 33602
813-228-2026
Fax: 813-228-2431
www.hud.gov/local/index.cfm?
state=fl

Georgia

Five Points Plaza
40 Marietta Street
Atlanta, GA 30303-2806
404-331-4111
Fax: 404-730-2392
www.hud.gov/local/index.cfm?
state=ga

Hawaii

HUD Honolulu office
500 Ala Moana Blvd. Suite3A
Honolulu, HI 96813-4918
808-522-8175
Fax: 808-522-8194
www.hud.gov/local/index.cfm?
state=hi

Idaho

HUD Boise office
Plaza IV, Suite 220
800 Park Boulevard
Boise, ID 83712-7743
208-334-1990
Fax: 208-334-9648
www.hud.gov/local/index.cfm?
state=id

Illinois

Ralph Metcalfe Federal Building
77 West Jackson Boulevard
Chicago, IL 60604-3507
312-353-5680
Fax: 312-886-2729
www.hud.gov/local/index.cfm?
state=il

Springfield Area office
HUD - Springfield office
320 West Washington 7th Floor
Springfield, IL 62701
217-492-4120
Fax: 217-492-4154
www.hud.gov/local/index.cfm?
state=il

Indiana

HUD Indianapolis office
151 North Delaware Street
Suite 1200
Indianapolis, IN 46204-2526
317-226-6303
Fax: 317-226-6317
www.hud.gov/local/index.cfm?
state=in

Iowa

HUD Des Moines office
210 Walnut Street, Room 239
Des Moines, IA 50309-2155
515-284-4512
Fax: 515-284-4743
www.hud.gov/local/index.cfm?
state=ia

Kansas

HUD Kansas City office
400 State Avenue, Room 200
Kansas City, KS 66101-2406
913-551-5462
Fax: 913-551-5469
www.hud.gov/local/index.cfm?
state=ks

Kentucky
HUD - Louisville office
601 West Broadway
Louisville, KY 40202
502-582-5251
Fax: 502-582-6074
www.hud.gov/local/index.cfm?
state=ky

Louisiana
HUD New Orleans office
Hale Boggs Bldg.
501 Magazine Street, 9th Floor
New Orleans, LA 70130-3099
504-589-7201
Fax: 504-589-6619
www.hud.gov/local/index.cfm?
state=la

Shreveport Area office
HUD Shreveport office
401 Edwards Street, Room. 1510
Shreveport, LA 71101-5513
318-676-3440
Fax: 318-676-3407
www.hud.gov/local/index.cfm?
state=la

Maine
HUD - Bangor office
202 Harlow Street
Chase Bldg., Suite 101
Bangor, ME 04402-1384
207-945-0467
Fax: 207-945-0533
www.hud.gov/local/index.cfm?
state=me

Maryland
HUD Baltimore office, 5th Floor
10 South Howard Street
Baltimore, MD 21201-2505
410-962-2520
Fax: 410-962-1849
www.hud.gov/local/index.cfm?
state=md

Massachusetts
HUD - Boston office
10 Causeway Street, Room 301
Boston, MA 02222-1092
617-994-8200
Fax: 617-565-5257
www.hud.gov/local/index.cfm?
state=ma

Michigan
HUD Detroit office
477 Michigan Avenue
Detroit, MI 48226-2592
313-226-7900
Fax: 313-226-5611
www.hud.gov/local/index.cfm?
state=mi

Flint Area office
HUD Flint office
1101 S. Saginaw St.
Flint, MI 48502-1953
810-766-5112
Fax: 810-766-5122
www.hud.gov/local/index.cfm?
state=mi

Grand Rapids Area office
HUD Grand Rapids office
Trade Center Building
50 Louis Street, N.W.
Grand Rapids, MI 49503-2633
616-456-2100
Fax: 616-456-2114
www.hud.gov/local/index.cfm?
state=mi

Minnesota
HUD Minneapolis office
920 Second Avenue, South
Minneapolis, MN 55402
612-370-3000
Fax: 612-370-3220
www.hud.gov/local/index.cfm?
state=mn

Mississippi
HUD Jackson office
McCoy Federal Building
100 W. Capitol Street, Room 910
Jackson, MS 39269-1096
601-965-4757
Fax: 601-965-4773
www.hud.gov/local/index.cfm?
state=ms

Missouri
HUD St. Louis office
1222 Spruce Street #3207
St. Louis, MO 63103-2836
314-539-6583
Fax: 314-539-6384
www.hud.gov/local/index.cfm?
state=mo

Montana
HUD Helena office
7 W 6th Ave
Helena, MT 59601
406-449-5050
Fax: 406-449-5052
www.hud.gov/local/index.cfm?
state=mt

Nebraska
HUD Omaha office
10909 Mill Valley Rd, Suite 100
Omaha, NE 68154-3955
402-492-3103
Fax: 402-492-3150
www.hud.gov/local/index.cfm?
state=ne

Nevada
HUD Las Vegas office
333 N. Rancho Drive
Atrium Bldg. Suite 700
Las Vegas, NV 89106-3714
702-388-6500, ext. 6500
Fax: 702-388-6244
www.hud.gov/local/index.cfm?
state=nv

Reno Area office
HUD Reno office
3702 S. Virginia Street
Reno, NV 89502-6581
775-784-5383
Fax: 775-784-5005
www.hud.gov/local/index.cfm?
state=nv

New Hampshire
HUD - Manchester office
Norris Cotton Federal Bldg.
275 Chestnut Street
Manchester, NH 03101-2487
603-666-7510
Fax: 603-666-7667
www.hud.gov/local/index.cfm?
state=nh

New Jersey
HUD - Newark office
13th Floor, One Newark Center
Newark, NJ 07102-5260
973-622-7900
Fax: 973-645-2323
www.hud.gov/local/index.cfm?
state=nj

Camden Area office
HUD - Camden office
Hudson Bldg. 2nd Floor
800 Hudson Square
Camden, NJ 08102-1156
856-757-5081
Fax: 856-757-5373
www.hud.gov/local/index.cfm?
state=nj

New Mexico

HUD Albuquerque office
625 Silver Avenue SW, Suite 100
Albuquerque, NM 87102
505-346-7320
Fax: 505-346-6704
www.hud.gov/local/index.cfm?
state=nm

New York

HUD - New York office
26 Federal Plaza, Suite 3541
New York, NY 10278-0068
212-264-8000
Fax: 212-264-3068
www.hud.gov/local/index.cfm?
state=ny

Albany Area office
HUD - Albany office
52 Corporate Circle
Albany, NY 12203-5121
518-464-4200
Fax: 518-464-4300
www.hud.gov/local/index.cfm?
state=ny

Buffalo Area office
HUD - Buffalo office
Lafayette Court, 5th Floor
465 Main Street
Buffalo, NY 14203-1780
716-551-5755
Fax: 716-551-5752
www.hud.gov/local/index.cfm?
state=ny

Syracuse, Storefront office
128 Jefferson Street
Syracuse, NY 13202
315-477-0616
Fax: 315-477-0196
www.hud.gov/local/index.cfm?
state=ny

North Carolina

HUD Greensboro office
Koger Building
2306 West Meadowview Road
Greensboro, NC 27401-3707
336-547-4001
Fax: 336-547-4138
www.hud.gov/local/index.cfm?
state=nc

North Dakota

HUD - Fargo office
657 2nd Avenue North
Room 366
Fargo, ND 58108
701-239-5136
Fax: 701-239-5249
www.hud.gov/local/index.cfm?
state=nd

Ohio

HUD Columbus office
200 North High Street
Columbus, OH 43215-2463
614-469-2540
Fax: 614-469-2432
www.hud.gov/local/index.cfm?
state=oh

Cincinnati Area office
HUD Cincinnati office
15 E. Seventh Street
Cincinnati, OH 45202-2401
513-684-3451
Fax: 513-684-6224
www.hud.gov/local/index.cfm?
state=oh

Cleveland Area office
HUD Cleveland office
1350 Euclid Avenue, Suite 500
Cleveland, OH 44115-1815
216-522-4058
Fax: 216-522-4067
www.hud.gov/local/index.cfm?
state=oh

Oklahoma

HUD Oklahoma City office
500 W. Main Street, Suite 400
Oklahoma City, OK 73102-2233
405-553-7509
Fax: 405-553-7588
www.hud.gov/local/index.cfm?
state=ok

Tulsa Area office
HUD Tulsa office
1516 South Boston Avenue
Suite 100
Tulsa, OK 74119-4030
918-581-7434
Fax: 918-581-7440
www.hud.gov/local/index.cfm?
state=ok

Oregon

HUD Portland office
400 SW 6th Avenue #700
Portland, OR 97204-1632
503-326-2561
Fax: 503-326-2568
www.hud.gov/local/index.cfm?
state=or

Pennsylvania

HUD Philadelphia office
The Wanamaker Building
100 Penn Square, East
Philadelphia, PA 19107-3380
215-656-0500
Fax: 215-656-3445
www.hud.gov/local/index.cfm?
state=pa

Pittsburgh Area office
HUD Pittsburgh office
339 Sixth Avenue, Sixth Floor
Pittsburgh, PA 15222-2515
412-644-6436
Fax: 412-644-4240
www.hud.gov/local/index.cfm?
state=pa

Puerto Rico

San Juan/ US Virgin Islands
171 Carlos Chardon Ave.
Suite 301
San Juan, Puerto Rico 00918-0903
787-766-5201
Fax: 787-766-5995
www.hud.gov/local/index.cfm

Rhode Island

HUD - Providence office
10 Weybosset Street Sixth Floor
Providence, RI 02903-2818
401-528-5230
Fax: 401-528-5312
www.hud.gov/local/index.cfm?
state=ri

South Carolina
HUD Columbia office
1835 Assembly Street
Columbia, SC 29201-2480
803-765-5592
Fax: 803-253-3043
www.hud.gov/local/index.cfm?
state=sc

South Dakota
HUD - Sioux Falls office
2400 West 49th St, Room. I-201
Sioux Falls, SD 57105-6558
605-330-4223
Fax: 605-330-4428
www.hud.gov/local/index.cfm?
state=sd

Tennessee
HUD - Nashville office
235 Cumberland Bend, Suite 200
Nashville, TN 37228-1803
615-736-5213
Fax: 615-736-7848
www.hud.gov/local/index.cfm?
state=tn

Knoxville Area office
HUD - Knoxville office
710 Locust Street, SW, Suite 300
Knoxville, TN 37902-2526
865-545-4384
Fax: 865-545-4569
www.hud.gov/local/index.cfm?
state=tn

Memphis Area office
HUD - Memphis office
200 Jefferson Avenue, Suite 1200
Memphis, TN 38103-2335
901-544-3367
Fax: 901-544-3697
www.hud.gov/local/index.cfm?
state=tn

Texas
HUD Ft. Worth office
801 Cherry Street
PO Box 2905
Ft. Worth, TX 76113-2905
817-978-5980
Fax: 817-978-5567
www.hud.gov/local/index.cfm?
state=tx

Dallas Area office
HUD Dallas office
525 Griffin Street, Room 860
Dallas, TX 75202-5007
214-767-8300
Fax: 214-767-8973
www.hud.gov/local/index.cfm?
state=tx

Houston Area office
HUD Houston office
2211 Norfolk #200
Houston, TX 77098-4096
713-313-2274
Fax: 713-313-2319
www.hud.gov/local/index.cfm?
state=tx

Lubbock Area office
HUD Lubbock office
1205 Texas Avenue, Room. 5111
Lubbock, TX 79401-4093
806-472-7265
Fax: 806-472-7275
www.hud.gov/local/index.cfm?
state=tx

San Antonio Area office
HUD San Antonio office
One Alamo Center
106 South Street
San Antonio, TX 78205
210-475-6806
Fax: 210-472-6804
www.hud.gov/local/index.cfm?
state=tx

Utah
HUD Salt Lake City office
125 South State St., Suite 3001
Salt Lake City, UT 84138
801-524-6070
Fax: 801-524-3439
www.hud.gov/local/index.cfm?
state=ut

Vermont
HUD - Burlington office
159 Bank Street, 2nd Floor
Burlington, VT 05401
802-951-6290
Fax: 802-951-6298
www.hud.gov/local/index.cfm?
state=vt

Virginia
HUD Richmond office
600 East Broad Street
Richmond, VA 23219-4920
804-771-2100
Fax: 804-771-2090
www.hud.gov/local/index.cfm?
state=va

Washington
HUD Seattle office
909 First Avenue, Suite 200
Seattle, WA 98104-1000
206-220-5101
Fax: 206-220-5108
www.hud.gov/local/index.cfm?
state=wa

Spokane Area office
HUD Spokane office
US Courthouse Bldg.
920 W. Riverside, Suite 588
Spokane, WA 99201-1010
509-353-0674
Fax: 509-353-0682
www.hud.gov/local/index.cfm?
state=wa

West Virginia
HUD - Charleston office
405 Capitol Street, Suite 708
Charleston, WV 25301-1795
304-347-7000
Fax: 304-347-7050
www.hud.gov/local/index.cfm?
state=wv

Wisconsin
HUD Milwaukee office
310 West Wisconsin Avenue
Room 1380
Milwaukee, WI 53203-2289
414-297-3214
Fax: 414-297-3947
www.hud.gov/local/index.cfm?
state=wi

Wyoming
HUD - Wyoming office
150 East B Street, Room 1010
Casper, WY 82601-1969
307-261-6250
Fax: 307-261-6245
www.hud.gov/local/index.cfm?
state=wy

Public Housing Agencies

Alabama

Abbeville
Abbeville Housing
Authority
PO Box 515
Abbeville, AL 36310-0515
334-585-2165

Albertville
Albertville Housing
Authority
711 S Broad Street
Albertville, AL 35950-2674
256-878-2641

Alexander City
Housing Authority of The
City of Alexander City
2110 County Road
Alexander City, AL 35010-
3800
256-329-2201, ext. 201

Aliceville
Housing Authority of The
City of Aliceville
851 Franconia Road NE
Aliceville, AL 35442-1108
205-373-8333

Altoona
Altoona Housing Authority
6762 Samuel Circle
Altoona, AL 35952-8673
256-593-9164

Anniston
Housing Authority
Anniston
PO Box 2225
Anniston, AL 36202-2225
256-236-1575

Anniston
Housing Authority of The
Town of Hobson City
800 Armstrong Street
Anniston, AL 36201-7304
256-831-1651

Arab
Housing Authority Arab
720 Cullman Road
Arab, AL 35016-1885
256-586-5904

Ashford
Housing Authority Ashford

100 Bruner Street
Ashford, AL 36312-4488
334-899-5463

Ashland
Housing Authority of the
Town of Ashland
128 1st Street N
Ashland, AL 36251-4100
256-354-2661

Athens
Housing Authority of The
City of Athens, Al
700 5th Avenue, Building J
Athens, AL 35611-1565
256-232-5300

Atmore
Housing Authority Atmore
415 Bragg Street
Atmore, AL 36502-2113
334-368-8442

Attalla
Housing Authority of the
City of Attalla
904 9th Street SW
Attalla, AL 35954-2315
256-538-9365

Auburn
Housing Authority Auburn
931 Booker Street
Auburn, AL 36832-2902
334-821-2262

Bay Minette
Housing Authority Bay
Minette
400 South Street
Bay Minette, AL 36507-2963
334-937-2211

Bear Creek
Bear Creek Housing
Authority
227 County Highway 79
Bear Creek, AL 35543-4724
205-935-5214

Berry
Housing Authority of The
Town of Berry
11 Hud Drive
Berry, AL 35546-2231
205-689-4564

Bessemer
Housing Authority
Bessemer

1515 Fairfax Avenue
Bessemer, AL 35020-6648
205-481-4420, ext. 205

Birmingham
Housing Authority
Jefferson County
3700 Industrial Parkway
Birmingham, AL 35217-5316
205-849-0123

Birmingham
Housing Authority of The
Birmingham District
1826 3rd Avenue S
Birmingham, AL 35233-1905
205-324-0641

Blountsville
Housing Authority of The
Town of Blountsville, Al
134 Solar Drive
Blountsville, AL 35031-3313
205-582-2123

Boaz
Boaz Housing Authority
400 Woodley Terrace
Boaz, AL 35957-1361
256-593-5824

Collinsville Housing
Authority
PO Box 733
Boaz, AL 35957-0733
256-593-9164

Top of Alabama Regional
Housing Authority
PO Box 733
Boaz, AL 35957-0733
256-593-9164

Brantley
Housing Authority of the
City of Brantley
81 Maple Street
Brantley, Al 36009-2424
334-527-3454

Brewton
Housing Authority of the
City of Brewton
201 Washington Circle
Brewton, AL 36426-1253
334-867-5247

Brundidge
Brundidge Housing
Authority

PO Box 595
Brundidge, AL 36010-0595
334-735-2657

Calera
Housing Authority of The
Town of Calera
PO Box 136
Calera, AL 35040-0136
205-668-0783

Carbon Hill
Housing Authority of The
City of Carbon Hill
PO Box 70
Carbon Hill, AL 35549-0070
205-924-4171

Centre
Housing Authority of The
City of Centre, Al
905 Louise Street
Centre, AL 35960-1043
256-593-9164

Chickasaw
Housing Authority of The
City of Chickasaw
604 Dumont Street
Chickasaw, AL 36611-1504
334-457-6841

Childersburg
Childersburg Housing
Authority
250 6th Avenue SW
Childersburg, AL35044-
1621
256-378-6008

Citronelle
Mobile County Housing
Authority
16545 Highway 45
Citronelle, AL 36522-2633
334-866-9696

Clanton
Housing Authority of The
City of Clanton
512 Ollie Avenue
Clanton, AL 35045-2239
205-755-1801

Clayton
Housing Authority of The
Town of Clayton
2 Holly Street
Clayton, AL 36016-4600
334-775-8881

Cordova
Housing Authority
Cordova
205 Stewart Street
Cordova, AL 35550-5815
205-483-7454

Cottonwood
Cottonwood Housing
Authority
29 Willow Lane
Cottonwood, AL 36320-4209
334-691-2451

Crossville
Crossville Housing
Authority
128 George Street
Crossville, AL 35962-3423
256-593-5824

Cullman
Housing Authority Cullman
408 Cleveland Avenue SW
Cullman, Al 35055-3929
256-734-6171

Dadeville
Housing Authority of The
City of Dadeville
845 Freeman Drive
Dadeville, AL 36853-2120
205-825-6004

Daleville
Housing Authority of the
City of Daleville
101 Donnell Circle
Daleville, AL 36322-5704
334-598-8841

Decatur
Housing Authority of the
City of Decatur
100 Wilson Street NE
Decatur, AL 35601-1763
256-353-4691

Demopolis
Housing Authority of the
City of Demopolis, AL
808 E Pettus Street
Demopolis, AL 36732-3043
334-289-1347

Dothan
Housing Authority of the
City of Dothan
602 S Lena Street
Dothan, AL 36301-2485
334-794-6713

Elba
Housing Authority Elba
1130 Deal Street

Elba, AL36323-1418
334-897-2737

Housing Authority Elba
1130 Deal Street
Elba, AL 36323-1418
334-897-2737

Enterprise
Enterprise Housing
Authority
300 Mildred Street
Enterprise, AL 36330-3999
334-347-0080

Enterprise Housing
Authority
300 Mildred Street
Enterprise, AL 36330-3999
334-347-0080

Eufaula
Eufaula Housing Authority
737 S Orange Avenue
Eufaula, AL 36027-2493
334-687-2451

Eutaw
Housing Authority of
Greene County, Al
PO Box 389
Eutaw, AL 35462-0389
205-372-3342

Housing Authority of the
City of Eutaw
100 Carver Circle
Eutaw, AL35462-1610
205-372-3926

Evergreen
Evergreen Housing
Authority
130 Rabb Drive
Evergreen, AL 36401-3342
334-578-1488

Fairfield
Fairfield Housing Authority
6704 Avenue D
Fairfield, AL 35064-2526
205-923-8017

Fayette
Housing Authority of The
City of Fayette
405 6th Street SW
Fayette, AL 35555-2879
205-932-6250

Florala
Housing Authority of The
City of Florala
1900 W 6th Avenue

Florala, AL 36442-1700
334-858-6421

Florence
Florence H/A
303 N Pine Street
Florence, AL 35630-5418
256-764-3030

Foley
Housing Authority Foley
302 W 4th Avenue
Foley, AL 36535-1777
205-943-5370

Fort Payne
Housing Authority of The
City of Fort Payne
203 13th Street NW
Fort Payne, AL 35967-3129
256-845-0424

Housing Authority of The
Town of Valley Head, Al
203 13th Street NW
Fort Payne, AL 35967-3129
256-845-0424

Gadsden
Greater Gadsden
422 Chestnut Street
Gadsden, AL 35901-4238
256-547-2501

Georgiana
Housing Authority of the
City of Georgiana
PO Box 279
Georgiana, AL36033-0279
334-376-9131

Greensboro
Housing Authority of the
City of Greensboro
101 Centerville Circle
Greensboro, AL 36744-1000
334-624-7728

Greenville
Housing Authority
Greenville
601 Beeland Street
Greenville, AL 36037-1605
334-382-6581

Guntersville
The Guntersville Housing
Authority
1205 Wyeth Drive
Guntersville, AL 35976-2353
256-582-4331

Hackleburg
Hackleburg Housing
Authority

443 Ray Road
Hackleburg, AL 35564-4165
205-935-5214

Haleyville
Haleyville Housing
Authority
2601 Newburg Road
Haleyville, AL 35565-1834
205-486-3571

Hamilton
Housing Authority of The
City of Hamilton
690 Bexar Avenue E
Hamilton, AL 35570-4029
205-921-3155

Hanceville
Housing Authority of The
Town of Hanceville
P.O. Box 330
819 Kiki Drive
Hanceville, AL 35077
256-352-6600

Hartford
Housing Authority of The
City of Hartford
207 Newton Street
Hartford, AL 36344-1423
334-588-3303

Hartselle
Housing Authority of The
City of Hartselle
616 Adelle Street SW
Hartselle, AL 35640-2909
256-773-5481

Regional Housing
Authority of Lawrence,
Cullman & Morgan
Counties
206 Puckett Road SW
Hartselle, AL 35640-2662
205-773-4835

Housing Authority of the
City of Headland, Al
225 Boynton Street
Headland, AL 36345-2305
334-693-2525

Huntsville
The Housing Authority of
the City of Huntsville
200 Washington Street NE
Huntsville, AL 35801-4843
256-539-0774

Jasper
Housing Authority of the
City of Jasper

1005 Highway 69 S
Jasper, AL 35501-6429
205-384-4864

Kennedy
Housing Authority of The
Town of Kennedy
PO Box 38
Kennedy, AL 35574-0038
205-596-3705

Lanett
Housing Authority of The
City of Lanett, Al
1431 S 14th Street
Lanett, AL 3686- 2729
334-644-5330

Linden
Housing Authority of The
City of Linden
403 Martin Luther King
Drive
Linden, AL 36748-2125
334-295-5544

Livingston
Livingston Housing
Authority
PO Box 397
Livingston, AL 35470-0397
205-652-2721

Luverne
Housing Authority of The
City of Luverne, Al
66 Mitchell Drive
Luverne, AL 36049-2025
334-335-5164

Madison
Triana Housing Authority
250 Zierdt Road
Madison, AL 35756-8208
205-772-0524

Marion
Housing Authority of The
City of Marion, Al
102 Cahaba Heights
Marion, AL 36756-2706
334-683-6658

Midland City
Housing Authority Midland
City
100 Headland Highway
Midland City, AL 36350-
9438
334-983-3581

Mobile
Mobile Housing Board
151 S Claiborne Street

Mobile, AL 36602-2323
334-434-2202

Montevallo
Housing Authority of The
Town of Montevallo
1204 Island Street
Montevallo, AL 35115-3823
205-665-7250

Montgomery
Housing Authority of The
City of Montgomery
1020 Bell Street
Montgomery, AL 36104-
3006
334-206-7200

Moulton
Housing Authority of The
City of Moulton, Al
200 Burch Boulevard
Moulton, AL 35650-1504
256-974-1196

New Brockton
Housing Authority of The
Town of New Brockton
329 King Street
New Brockton, AL 36351-
6625
334-894-5505

Newton
Housing Authority of The
City of Newton
2 Spring Street
Newton, AL 36352-9514
334-299-3114

Newton
Housing Authority of The
City of Newton
2 Spring Street
Newton AL 36352-9514
334-299-3114

Northport
Housing Authority
Northport
PO Box 349
Northport AL 35476-0349
205-752-8171

Oneonta
H A Oneonta
1 Hillcrest Circle
Oneonta, AL 35121-1803
205-625-5955

Opelika
Housing Authority Opelika
1706 Toomer Street

Opelika, AL 36801-6544
334-745-4171

Opp
Housing Authority Opp
800 Barnes Street
Opp, AL36467-3258
334-493-9741

Ozark
Ozark Housing Authority
309 Ed Lisenby Drive
Ozark, AL 36360-1473
334-774-8210

Parrish
Housing Authority of The
Town of Parrish
PO Box 9
Parrish, AL 35580-0009
205-686-7621

Pell City
Pell City Housing Authority
110 32nd Street N
Pell City, AL 35125-1935
205-338-7012

Phenix City
Phenix City Housing
Authority
200 16th Street
Phenix City, AL 36867-1401
334-298-7803

Phil Campbell
Phil Campbell Housing
Authority
19 Stalcup Circle
Phil Campbell, AL 35581-
3550
205-935-5214

Piedmont
Housing Authority
Piedmont
154 Craig Avenue
Piedmont, AL 36272-1412
256-447-6734

Prattville
Housing Authority of The
City of Prattville, Al
318 Water Street
Prattville, AL 36067-3922
334-365-7580

Prichard
The Housing Authority of
The City of Prichard
800 Hinson Avenue
Prichard, AL 36610-2716
334-456-3324

Ragland
Ragland Housing Authority
406 8th Street
Ragland, AL 35131-3134
205-472-2522

Rainsville
Rainsville Housing
Authority
118 Northside Drive
Rainsville, AL 35986-6455
256-593-9164

Reform
Housing Authority of
Reform
510 5th Court Nw
Reform, AL 35481-2328
205-375-6360

Roanoke
Housing Authority of The
City of Roanoke, Al
231 Avenue A
Roanoke, AL36274-1604
334-863-4513

Samson
Housing Authority Samson
10b N Wise Street
Samson, AL36477-1148
334-898-7152

Scottsboro
Housing Authority
Scottsboro
102 Worthington Street
Scottsboro, AL 35768-2430
256-259-5600

Selma
Selma Housing Authority
444 Washington Street
Selma, AL 36703-4456
334-874-6271

Sheffield
Sheffield Housing
Authority
2120 W 17th Street
Sheffield, AL 35660-8508
256-383-4773

Stevenson
Stevenson Housing
Authority
52 Old Mount Carmel Road
Stevenson, AL 35772-3718
256-437-3009

Sulligent
Housing Authority of The
City of Sulligent, Al
211 Project Street

Sulligent, AL 35586-3739
205-698-9482

Sylacauga
Sylacauga Housing
Authority
415 W 8th Street
Sylacauga, AL 35150-1442
205-249-0381

Talladega
Housing Authority of The
City of Talladega, Al
151 Curry Court
Talladega, AL35160-1583
255-362-5010 ext. 13

Tallassee
Housing Authority
Tallassee
904 Hickory Street
Tallassee, AL 36078-1719
334-283-2801

Tarrant
Tarrant Housing Authority
624 Bell Avenue
Tarrant, AL 35217-3628
205-841-2270

Troy
Housing Authority So
Central Alabama Regional
100 Spring Road
Troy, AL 36079-9206
334-566-4495

Troy
Housing Authority Troy
201 Segars Street
Troy, AL 36081-1700
334-566-1271

Tuscaloosa
Housing Authority
Tuscaloosa
PO Box 2281
Tuscaloosa, AL 35403-2281
205-758-6619

Tuscumbia
Housing Authority of The
City of Tuscumbia
106 S Main Street
Tuscumbia, AL 35674-2429
256-381-0915

Valley
Housing Authority of The
City of Valley
1 Boyd Circle
Valley, AL36854-4609
334-745-4171

Vernon
Housing Authority of The
City of Vernon, AL
230 Strickland Circle
Vernon, AL 35592-5413
205-695-7122

Winfield
Winfield Housing
Authority
826 Tahoe Road
Winfield, AL 35594-5019
205-487-2400

Alaska

Anchorage
Alaska Housing Finance
Corporation
4300 Boniface Parkway
Anchorage, AK 99504-4387
907-338-6100

Arizona

Casa Grande
Pinal County Housing
Authority
970 N Eleven Mile Corner
Road
Casa Grande, AZ 85222-7242
520-868-7203

Chandler
Chandler Housing &
Redevelopment Division
265 E Buffalo Street
Chandler, AZ 85225-5593
480-782-3207

Eloy
Eloy Housing Authority
100 W Phoenix Avenue
Eloy, AZ 85231-1935
520-466-7162

Flagstaff
Flagstaff Housing Authority
3481 N Fanning Drive
Flagstaff, AZ 86004-4051
520-526-0002

Glendale
City of Glendale Housing
Authority
6842 N 61st Avenue
Glendale, AZ 85301 -3111
602-930-3700

Nogales
Nogales Housing Authority
951 N Kitchen Street
Nogales, AZ 85621-1632
520-287-4183

Peoria
Peoria Housing Authority
8401 W Monroe Street
Room 190
Peoria, AZ 85345-6560
623-773-7140

Phoenix
City of Phoenix Housing
Department
251 W Washington Street
Floor 4
Phoenix, AZ 85003-2201
602-262-6974

Phoenix
Maricopa County Housing
Department
2024 N 7th Street, Suite 101
Phoenix, AZ 85006-2155
602-257-1113

Somerton
Yuma County Housing
Department
8450 W. Highway 95, Suite
88
Somerton, AZ 85350
520-627-9596 ext. 112

South Tucson
South Tucson Housing
Authority
1713 S 3rd Avenue
South Tucson, AZ 85713-2912
520-623-8481

Tucson
Community Services
Department of Tucson
PO Box 27210
Tucson, AZ 85726 -7210
520-791-4739

Williams
Williams Housing
Authority
620 W Sheridan Avenue
Williams, AZ 86046-2366
520-635-4717

Winslow
Winslow Public Housing
Authority
900 Henderson Street
Winslow, AZ 86047-2318
520-289-4617

Yuma
Yuma City Housing
Authority
1350 W Colorado Street
Yuma, AZ 85364-1372
520-782-3823

Arkansas

Alma
Housing Authority of The
City of Alma
9 W Main Street
Alma, AR 72921-3617
501-632-2043

Amity
Housing Authority of The
City of Amity
232 N Biggs Street
Amity, AR 71921-9539
870-342-5750

Arkadelphia
Arkadelphia Housing
Authority
670 S 6th Street
Arkadelphia, AR 71923-6232
870-246-4632

Atkins
Housing Authority of The
City of Atkins
301 Avenue 5 Nw
Atkins, AR 72823-4037
501-641-2268

Augusta
Housing Authority of The
City of Augusta
100 Riverdale Street
Augusta, AR 72006-2733
870-347-5551

Bald Knob
Housing Authority of The
City of Bald Knob
2007 Highway 367 N
Bald Knob, AR 72010-9428
501-724-5930

Beebe
Housing Authority of The
City of Beebe
836 S Apple Street
Beebe, AR 72012-3322
501-882-5151

Benton
Benton Housing Authority
1200 W Pine Street

Benton, AR 72015-4088
501-778-7302

Blytheville
Blytheville Housing
Authority
31 Arkansas St.
Blytheville, AR 7231- 0387
870-763-0704

Booneville
Housing Authority of The
City of Booneville
272 S Sharpe Avenue
Booneville, AR 72927-4333
501-675-2130

Brinkley
Housing Authority of The
City of Brinkley
501 W Cedar Street
Brinkley, AR 72021-2713
870-734-3165

Camden
Camden Housing Authority
800 Monroe Avenue
Camden, AR 71701-2939
870-836-9309

Caraway
Housing Authority of The
City of Caraway
PO Box 489
Caraway, AR 72419-0489
870-482-3736

Clarendon
Clarendon Housing
Authority
601 Jefferson Street
Clarendon, AR 72029-2455
870-747-3366

Clarksville
Housing Authority of The
City of Clarksville
605 W Lucas Street
Clarksville, AR 72830 -4109
501-754-3564

Coal Hill
Housing Authority of The
City of Coal Hill
605 Buster Street
Coal Hill, AR 72832-8707
501-497-1666

Conway
Conway Housing Authority
335 S Mitchell Street
Conway AR 72032-6861
501-327-0156

Cotton Plant
Housing Authority of The
City of Cotton Plant
102 Conley Drive
Cotton Plant, AR 72036-
9736
501-459-2531

Crossett
Housing Authority of The
City of Crossett
700 N Arkansas Street
Crossett, AR 71635-3300
870-364-5095

Dardanelle
Housing Authority of The
City of Dardanelle
402 S 5th Street
Dardanelle, AR 72834-3919
501-229-3666

DE Queen
Housing Authority of The
County of Sevier
PO Box 807
DE Queen, AR 71832-0807
501-642-2960

DE Witt
Housing Authority of The
City of Dewitt
101 W 4th Street
DE Witt, AR 72042-2631
870-946-2622

Decatur
Housing Authority of The
City of Decatur
578 N Main Street
Decatur, AR 72722-9763
501-752-3258

Des Arc
Housing Authority of The
City of Des Arc
PO Box 309
Des Arc, AR 72040-0309
870-256-4577

Dover
Housing Authority of The
City of Dover
200 Davis Street
Dover, AR 72837-8865
501-331-2670

Dumas
Housing Authority of The
City of Dumas
224 W Bowles Street
Dumas, AR 71639-2114
870-382-5457

Earle
Housing Authority of The
City of Earle
531 2nd Street
Earle, AR 72331-1509
870-792-8733

England
Housing Authority of The
City of England
102 Benafield Drive
England, AR 72046-2301
501-842-2591

Fayetteville
Housing Authority of The
City of Fayetteville
1 N School Avenue
Fayetteville, AR 72701-5110
501-521-3850

Forrest City
Housing Authority of The
City of Forrest City
805 Mann Street
Forrest City, AR 72335-3054
870-633-7929

Fort Smith
Fort Smith
2100 N 31st Street
Fort Smith, AR 72904-6102
501-782-4991

Greenwood
Housing Authority of The
City of Greenwood
319 W Cedar Street
Apartment 1
Greenwood, AR 72936-5455
501-996-4661

Gurdon
Housing Authority of The
City of Gurdon
401 S 2nd Street
Gurdon, AR 71743-1909
870-353-2507

Harrison
NW Regional Housing
Authority
114 Sisco Avenue
Harrison, AR 72601-2130
870-741-5405

Heber Springs
Housing Authority of The
City of Heber Springs
400 E Spring Street
Heber Springs, AR 72543-
3246
501-362-6108

Helena
Housing Authority of The
City of Helena
1000 Holly
Helena, AR 72342-2618
870-338-3407

Hickory Ridge
Housing Authority of The
City of Hickory Ridge
121 W Larry Street
Hickory Ridge, AR 72347-
9114
870-697-2202

Hope
Hope Housing Authority
720 Texas Street
Hope, AR 71801-6327
870-777-5742

Hot Springs
Hot Springs Housing
Authority
110 Highrise Circle
Hot Springs, AR 71901-4315
501-624-4420

Hoxie
Housing Authority of The
City of Hoxie
400 Maple Street
Hoxie, AR 72433-1749
870-886-3145

Hughes
Housing Authority of The
City of Hughes
116 Tucker Road
Hughes, AR 72348-9131
870-339-2896

Jacksonville
Jacksonville Housing
Authority
3600 Max Howell Drive
Jacksonville, AR 72076-1845
501-982-3088

Jonesboro
Jonesboro Urban Renewal
Housing Authority
330 Union Street
Jonesboro, AR 72401-2815
870-935-9800

Judsonia
Housing Authority of The
City of Judsonia
1301 Wade Avenue
Judsonia, AR 72081-8912
501-729-4091

Kensett
Housing Authority of The
City of Kensett
PO Box 665
Kensett, AR 72082-0665
501-742-3842

Lake City
Housing Authority of The
City of Lake City
701 Carter Street
Lake City, AR 72437-9003
870-237-8815

Leachville
Housing Authority of The
City of Leachville
410 E 5th Street
Leachville, AR 72438-8906
870-539-2212

Luxora
Housing Authority of The
City of Luxora
316 S Cedar Street
Luxora, AR 72358-2406
870-658-2270

Magnolia
Housing Authority of The
City of Magnolia
100 Meadowbrook Lane
Magnolia, AR 71753-3735
870-234-5540

Mammoth Spring
Housing Authority of The
City of Mammoth Spring
110 N 14th Street
Apartment 23
Mammoth Spring, AR
72554-9414
870-625-3911

Marianna
Housing Authority of The
City of Marianna
327 Ward Drive
Marianna, AR 72360-2911
870-295-2691

Marked Tree
Housing Authority of The
County of Poinsett
1104 Elm Street
Marked Tree, AR 72365-
1914
870-358-2990

Marmaduke
Housing Authority of The
City of Marmaduke
957 W Lillian Boulevard

Marmaduke, AR 72443-9692
870-597-4352

Mc Rae
Housing Authority of The
City of Mcrae
106 3rd Street
Mc Rae, AR 72102-9640
501-726-3652

Mcgehee
Housing Authority of The
City of Mcgehee
300 Shady Lane
Mcgehee, AR 71654
870-222-3732

Melbourne
Housing Authority of The
City of Melbourne
206 College Drive
Melbourne, AR 72556-8708
870-368-4374

Mena
Housing Authority of The
City of Mena
509 Morrow Street S
Mena, AR 71953-2520
501-394-1565

Mena
Polk County Housing
Authority
509 Morrow Street S
Mena, AR 71953-2520
501-394-1565

Monette
Housing Authority of The
City of Monette
429 S Williams Street
Monette, AR 72447 -9771
870-486-5487

Morrilton
Housing Authority of The
City of Morrilton
123 Cherokee Court
Morrilton, AR 72110-3805
501-354-2330

Mount Ida
Housing Authority of The
City of Mount Ida
19 Graham Court
Mount Ida, AR 71957-9422
870-867-2332

Nashville
Housing Authority of The
County of Howard
1010 S Pope Street

Nashville, AR 71852-2901
870-845-1080

Newark
Housing Authority of The
City of Newark
530 Akron Circle
Newark, AR 72562-9696
870-799-3339

Newport
Housing Authority of The
City of Newport
945 Hout Circle
Newport, AR 72112-2274
870-523-2195

Osceola
Housing Authority of The
City of Osceola
501 Coston Avenue
Osceola, AR 72370-3119
870-563-6662

Ozark
Housing Authority of The
City of Ozark
310 N 6th Street
Ozark, AR 72949-2747
501-667-3632

Paragould
Paragould Housing
Authority
612 Canal Street
Paragould, AR 7245- 2350
870-239-8084

Paris
Housing Authority of The
City of Paris
109 Logan Drive
Paris, AR 72855-2121
501-963-2130

Pine Bluff
Pine Bluff Housing
Authority
2503 Belle Meade Drive
Pine Bluff, AR 71601-6815
870-536-2074

Pocahontas
Housing Authority of The
City of Pocahontas
1320 Dalton Street
Pocahontas, AR 72455-2277
870-892-9278

Pocahontas
Pocahontas Public Housing
Agency
1403 Hospital Drive

Pocahontas, AR 72455
870-892-4547 ext. 241

Prescott
Housing Authority of The
City of Prescott
401 Hale Avenue
Prescott, AR 71857-3334
870-887-3718

Rector
Housing Authority of The
City of Rector
137 N Stewart Street
Rector, AR 72461-1427
870-595-2182

Rison
Housing Authority of The
City of Rison
500 Rice Street
Rison, AR 71665-9444
870-325-7420

Russellville
Russellville Housing
Authority City
318 S Glenwood Avenue
Russellville, AR 72801-5971
501-968-5440

Searcy
Searcy Housing Authority
501 S Fir Street
Searcy, AR 72143-6614
501-268-9250

Springdale
Springdale Housing
Authority
5 Applegate Drive
Springdale, AR 72764-5630
501-751-0560

Star City
Star City (City of)
201 E Joslyn Avenue
Star City, AR 71667-4825
870-628-4500

Trumann
Trumann Housing
Authority (City)
109 Spruce Drive
Trumann, AR 72472-3826
870-483-5223

Van Buren
Housing Authority of The
City of Van Buren
1701 Chestnut Street
Van Buren, AR 72956-5311
501-474-6901

Waldron
Housing Authority of The
City of Waldron
420 Shipley Circle Drive
Waldron, AR 72958-9650
501-637-3864

Warren
Warren Housing Authority
801 W Central Street
Warren, AR 71671-2425
870-226-2600

West Helena
Housing Authority of The
City of West Helena
115 N 3rd
West Helena, AR 72390-
2404
870-572-6702

West Memphis
West Memphis Housing
Authority
2820 E Harrison Avenue
West Memphis, AR 72301-
6013
870-735-3520 ext. 11

Wilson
Housing Authority of The
City of Wilson
10 S Jefferson Street
Wilson, AR 72395-1423
870-655-8620

Wynne
Wynne Housing Authority
200 Fisher Place
Wynne, AR 72396-2783
870-238-7671

Yellville
Housing Authority of The
City of Yellville
415 W Old Main Street
Yellville, AR 72687-7949
870-449-4120

CAliForNiA

Alameda
City of Alameda Housing
Authority
701 Atlantic Avenue
Alameda, CA 94501-2161
510-522-8422

Bakersfield
Housing Authority of The
County of Kern
525 Roberts Lane

Bakersfield, CA 93308-4799
661-393-2150

Baldwin Park
Housing Authority of The
City of Baldwin Park
14403 Pacific Avenue
Baldwin Park, CA 91706-
4226
626-960-4011 ext. 102

Belmont
County of San Mateo
Housing Authority
264 Harbor Boulevard
Building A
Belmont, CA 94002-4017
650-802-3300

Benicia
City of Benicia Housing
Auth
28 Riverhill Drive
Benicia, CA 94510-2725
707-745-2071

Berkeley
City of Berkeley Housing
Authority
1901 Fairview Street
Berkeley, CA 94703-2718
510-644-4840

Brawley
Imperial Valley Housing
Authority
1401 D Street
Brawley, CA 92227-2117
619-351-7000

Calexico
Housing Authority of The
City of Calexico
1006 E 5th Street
Calexico, CA 92231-2970
619-357-3013

Capitola
Santa Cruz County Housing
Auth
2160 41st Avenue
Capitola, CA 95010-2009
831-464-0170

Carlsbad
Carlsbad Housing And
Redevelopment Dept.
2965 Roosevelt St Ste B
Carlsbad, CA 92008
760-434-2810

Chico
County of Butte Housing
Auth

580 Vallombrosa Avenue
Chico, CA 95926 -4038
530-895-4474

Dublin
Dublin Housing Authority
6700 Dougherty Road
Apartment 151
Dublin, CA 94568-3158
510-727-8513

Eureka
City of Eureka Housing
Authority
735 W Everding Street
Eureka, CA 95503 -5007
707-443-4584

Fresno
City of Fresno Housing
Authority
1331 Fulton Mall
Fresno, CA 93721-1630
559-443-8400

County of Fresno Housing
Auth
1331 Fulton Mall
Fresno, CA 93721-1630
559-443-8400

Hanford
Kings County Housing
Auth
680 N Douty Street
Hanford, CA 93230-3913
559-582-2806

Hawthorne
Department of Housing &
Community Development
Dept of Housing &
Community Development
4455 West 126th Street
Hawthorne, CA 90250
310-970-7912

Hayward
Alameda County Housing
Auth
22941 Atherton Street
Hayward, CA 94541-6633
510-538-8876

Livermore
Housing Auth of The City
of Livermore
3203 Leahy Way
Livermore, CA 94550-3668
925-447-3600

Lomita
Housing Authority of The
City of Lomita

24925 Walnut Street
Lomita, CA 90717 -1977
310-325-7110

Lompoc
Housing Authority of The
County of Santa Barbara
815 W Ocean Avenue
Lompoc, CA 93436-6526
805-736-3423

Los Angeles
Housing Authority of The
City of Los Angeles
PO Box 17157
Los Angeles, CA 90017-0157
213-252-2500

Madera
The Housing Authority of
The City of Madera
205 N G Street
Madera, CA 93637-3512
559-674-5695 ext. 223

The Housing Authority of
The City of Madera
205 N G Street
Madera, CA 93637-3512
559-674-5695 ext. 223

Martinez
County of Contra Costa
Housing Auth
3133 Estudillo Street
Martinez, CA 94553-3258
510-372-0791

Housing Authority of The
City of San Pablo
PO Box 2759
Martinez, CA 94553-7759
510-215-3081

Merced
County of Merced Housing
Authority
405 U Street
Merced, CA 95340-6548
209-722-3501

Modesto
County of Stanislaus
Housing Auth
PO Box 581918
Modesto, CA 95358-0033
209-523-0705

Monterey Park
Housing Authority of The
County of Los Angeles
2 S Coral Circle
Monterey Park, CA 91755-
7404
213-260-3300

Needles
Housing Authority of The
City of Needles
908 Sycamore Drive
Needles, CA 92363-3131
619-326-3222

Newbury Park
Housing Authority of The
County of Ventura
1400 W Hillcrest Drive
Newbury Park, CA 91320-2721
805-480-9991

Oceanside
Housing Authority of The
City of Oceanside
321 North Nevada Street
Oceanside, CA 92054
760-966-4585

Oxnard
Oxnard Housing Authority
1470 E Colonia Road
Oxnard, CA 93030-3714
805-385-8096

Paso Robles
Housing Authority of The
City of Paso Robles
3201 Pine Street
Paso Robles, CA 93446-1047
805-238-4015

Pleasanton
Housing Authority of The
City of Pleasanton
123 Main Street
Pleasanton, CA 94566-7320
925-484-8008

Port Hueneme
Housing Authority of The
City of Port Hueneme
250 N Ventura Road
Port Hueneme, CA 93041-3094
805-986-6527

Quincy
County of Plumas Housing
Authority
183 W Main Street
Quincy, CA 95971-9372
530-283-2466

Redding
County of Shasta Housing
Auth
1670 Market Street
Suite 300
Redding, CA 96001
530-225-5169

Richmond
City of Richmond Housing
Auth
330 24th Street
Richmond, CA 94804-1725
510-237-3271

Riverbank
Housing Authority of The
City of Riverbank
3309 Stanislaus Street
Riverbank, CA 95367-2458
209-869-4501

Riverside
Housing Authority of The
County of Riverside
5555 Arlington Avenue
Riverside, CA 92504-2506
909-351-0700

Sacramento
City of Sacramento Housing
Authority
630 I Street
Floor 3
Sacramento, CA 95814-2404
916-440-1351

County of Sacramento
Housing Authority
630 I Street
Floor 3
Sacramento, CA 95814-2404
916-440-1351

Salinas
County of Monterey
Housing Auth
123 Rico Street
Salinas, CA 93907-2157
831-424-2892

San Bernardino
Housing Authority of The
County of San Bernardino
715 E. Brier Dr
San Bernardino, CA 92408-2841
909-890-0644

San Diego
Housing Authority of The
County of San Diego
3989 Ruffin Road
San Diego, CA 92123-1815
619-694-4831

San Diego Housing
Commission
1625 Newton Avenue
San Diego, CA 92113-1012
619-231-9400

San Francisco
San Francisco Housing
Auth
440 Turk Street
San Francisc,o CA 94102-3330
415-554-1200

San Jose
County of Santa Clara
Housing Auth.
505 W Julian Street
San Jose, CA 95110-2338
408-993-2900

San Luis Obispo
Housing Authority of The
City of San Luis Obispo
487 Leff Street
San Luis Obispo, CA 93401
805-543-4478

San Rafael
County of Marin Housing
Authority
4020 Civic Center Drive
San Rafael, CA 94903-4173
415-491-2533

Santa Barbara
Housing Authority of The
City of Santa Barbara
808 Laguna Street
Santa Barbara, CA 93101-1510
805-965-1071

Soledad
Housing Authority of The
City of Soledad
121 Alder Street
Soledad, CA 93960-3023
831-678-3686

South San Francisco
City of South San Francisco
Housing Authority
350 C Street
South San Francisco, CA
94080-4429
650-583-7631

Stockton
County of San Joaquin
Housing Auth.
448 S Center Street
Stockton, CA 95203-3426
209-466-1487

Ukiah
Mendocino County
1076 N State Street
Ukiah, CA 95482-3414
707-463-5466

Upland
Housing Authority of The
City of Upland
1226 N Campus Avenue
Upland, CA 91786-3337
909-982-2649

Ventura
Housing Authority of The
City of San Buenaventura
995 Riverside Street
Ventura, CA 93001-1636
805-648-5008

Visalia
Tulare County Housing
Auth
5140 W Cypress Avenue
Visalia, CA 93277-8303
559-627-3700

Wasco
City of Wasco Housing
Authority
750 H Street
Wasco, CA 93280-2065
661-758-6406

Woodland
Yolo County Housing
Authority
1224 Lemen Avenue
Woodland, CA 95776-3312
530-662-5428

Yuba City
County of Sutter Housing
Authority
448 Garden Highway
Yuba City, CA 95991-6310
530-671-0220

Colorado

Alamosa
Housing Authority of The
City of Alamosa
213 Murphy Drive
Alamosa, CO 81101-2348
719-589-6694

Aurora
Aurora Housing Authority
10745 E Kentucky Avenue
Aurora, CO 80012-3123
303-340-1900

Boulder
Boulder City Housing
Authority
3120 Broadway Street

Boulder, CO 80304-2644
303-441-3150

Boulder
Boulder County Housing
Authority
2040 14th Street
Boulder, CO 80302-5303
303-441-3929

Brighton
Housing Authority of The
City of Brighton
22 S 4th Avenue
Brighton, CO 80601-2030
303-655-2160

Brush
Housing Authority of The
City of Brush
418 Edison Street
Brush CO 80723-2100
970-842-5046

Burlington
Burlington Housing
Authority
944 Lowell Avenue
Burlington, CO 80807-1831
719-346-5464

Cheyenne Wells
Housing Authority For The
Town of Cheyenne Wells
1245 N 1st Street W
Lot 36
Cheyenne Wells, CO 80810-
9610
719-767-5964

Colorado Springs
El Paso County Housing
Authority
105 East Vermijo
Colorado Springs, CO 80903
719-520-6480

Housing Authority of The
City of Colorado Springs
831 S. Nevada Avenue
Colorado Springs, CO 80901
719-385-5902

Commerce City
Adams County Housing
Authority
7190 Colorado Blvd.
Floor 6
Commerce City, CO 80022-
1812
303-227-2075

Cortez
Housing Authority of The
County of Montezuma

37 N Madison Street
Cortez, CO 81321-3301
970-565-3831

Delta
Delta Housing Authority
511 E 10th Street
Delta, CO 81416-2484
970-874-7266

Denver
Colorado Department of
Human Services
4131 South Julian Way
Denver, CO 80236
303-866-7350

Colorado Division of
Housing
1313 Sherman St., Room 518
Denver, CO 80203
303-866-2033

Colorado Housing Finance
Authority
1981 Blake Street
Denver, CO 80202
303-297-7302

Housing Authority of The
City And County of Denver
1100 W Colfax Avenue
Denver, CO 80204-2027
720-932-3000

Englewood
Englewood Housing
Authority
3460 S Sherman Street
Suite 101
Englewood, CO 80110-2664
303-761-6200

Fort Collins
Fort Collins Housing
Authority
1715 W Mountain Avenue
Fort Collins, CO 80521-2359
970-221-5484

Fort Lupton
Housing Authority of Fort
Lupton
400 2nd Street
Fort Lupton, CO 80621-1959
303-857-4400

Fort Morgan
Fort Morgan Housing
Authority
1100 Linda Street
Fort Morgan, CO 80701-
3588
970-867-2734

Fountain
Housing Authority of
Fountain
501 E Iowa Avenue
Fountain, CO 80817-2252
719-382-5639

Ft. Collins
Larimer County Housing
Authority
1715 W. Mountain Ave.
Ft. Collins, CO 80521
970-221-5484

Grand Junction
Grand Junction Housing
Authority
805 Main Street
Grand Junction, CO 81501-
3572
970-245-0388

Greeley
Housing Authority of The
City of Greeley
315 N 11th Avenue
Building B
Greeley, CO 80631-2014
970-352-1551 ext. 6541

Housing Authority of Weld
County
315 N. 11th Avenue
Greeley, CO 80631
970-352-1551 ext. 6541

Haxtun
Housing Authority of The
Town of Haxtun
136 S Miller Avenue
Haxtun, CO 80731-2776
970-774-7251

Holly
Housing Authority of The
Town of Holly
PO Box 486
Holly, CO 81047-0486
719-537-6050

Holyoke
Holyoke Housing Authority
330 W Kellogg Street
Holyoke, CO 80734-1324
970-854-2289

Julesburg
Julesburg Housing
Authority
520 W 9th Street
Julesburg, CO 80737-1009
970-474-3675

Keenesburg
Housing Authority of The
Town of Keenesburg
250 Woodward Street
Keenesburg, CO 80643-9011
303-732-4221

LA Jara
Conejos County Housing
Authority
510 Richfield Road
LA Jara, CO 81140-9769
719-274-5417

LA Junta
LA Junta Housing
Authority
315 E 5th Street
LA Junta, CO 81050-1751
719-384-9055

Lakewood
Lakewood Housing
Authority
445 S Allison Parkway
Lakewood, CO 80226-3106
303-987-7599

Lamar
Housing Authority of The
City of Lamar
206 E Cedar Street
Lamar, CO 81052-3400
719-336-9575

Las Animas
Las Animas Housing
Authority
332 Prowers CT.
Las Animas, CO 81054
719-456-2748

Limon
Housing Authority of The
Town of Limon
1880 Circle Lane
Limon, CO 80828-9103
719-775-9309

Littleton
Littleton Housing Authority
5844 S Datura Street
Littleton, CO 80120-2153
303-794-9608

Longmont
Longmont Housing
Authority
900 Coffman Street, Suite C
Longmont, CO 80501-4543
303-651-8581

Loveland
Loveland Housing
Authority
375 W 37th Street

Loveland, CO 80538-2261
970-667-3232

Pueblo
Housing Authority of The
City of Pueblo
1414 N Santa Fe Avenue
Pueblo, CO 81003-3732
719-544-6230

Rifle
Garfield County Housing
Authority
2128 Railroad Avenue
Rifle, CO 81650
970-945-0779

Salida
Housing Authority of The
City of Salida
525 W 16th Street
Salida, CO 81201-2260
719-539-6243

Sterling
Housing Authority of The
City of Sterling
441 Macgregor Road
Sterling, CO 80751-2765
970-522-0869

Trinidad
Trinidad Housing
Authority
128 W 1st Street
Trinidad, CO 81082-2957
719-846-7204

Walsenburg
Housing Authority of The
City of Walsenburg
220 Russell Avenue
Walsenburg, CO 81089-1858
719-738-2720

Wheat Ridge
Jefferson County Housing
Authority
6025 W 38th Avenue
Wheat Ridge, CO 80033-
5139
303-422-8600

Wray
Housing Authority of The
City of Wray
722 Hale Street
Wray, CO 80758-2125
970-332-4238

Yuma
Housing Authority of The
Town of Yuma
700 W 3rd Avenue

Yuma, CO 80759-1851
970-848-5590

CONNECTICUT

Ansonia
Ansonia Housing Authority
36 Main Street
Ansonia, CT 06401-1807
203-736-8888

Bloomfield
Bloomfield Housing
Authority
1190 Blue Hills Avenue
Bloomfield, CT 06002-1902
860-769-3520

Bridgeport
Bridgeport Housing
Authority
150 Highland Avenue
Bridgeport, CT 06604-3503
203-337-8900

Bristol
Bristol Housing Authority
31 Quaker Lane
Bristol, CT 06010-3715
860-582-6313

Danbury
Danbury Housing
Authority
2 Mill Ridge Road
Danbury, CT 06811-5231
203-744-2500

East Hartford
East Hartford Housing
Authority
546 Burnside Avenue
East Hartford, CT 06108-
3511
860-290-8301

Glastonbury
Glastonbury Housing
Authority
25 Risley Road
Glastonbury, CT 06033-1111
860-652-7568

Greenwich
Greenwich Housing
Authority
249 Milbank Avenue
Greenwich, CT 06830
203-869-1138

Hartford
Hartford Housing
Authority

475 Flatbush Avenue
Hartford, CT 06106-3728
860-275-8400

Manchester
Manchester Housing
Authority
24 Bluefield Drive
Manchester, CT 06040-4702
860-643-2163

Meriden
Meriden Housing Authority
22 Church Street
Meriden, CT 06451-3209
203-235-0157

Middletown
Middletown Housing
Authority
40 Broad Street
Middletown, CT 06457-3249
860-346-8671

Milford
Milford Housing Authority
75 Demaio Drive
Milford, CT 06460-4356
203-877-3223

Milford
Milford Housing Authority
75 Demaio Drive
Milford, CT 06460-4356
203-877-3223

Naugatuck
Naugatuck Housing
Authority
16 Ida Street
Naugatuck, CT 06770-4422
203-729-8214

New Britain
New Britain Housing
Authority
34 Marimac Road
New Britain, CT 06053-2602
860-225-3534

New Haven
New Haven Housing
Authority
360 Orange Street
New Haven, CT 0651- 6403
203-498-8800

New London
New London Housing
Authority
78 Walden Avenue
New London, CT 06320-
2723
860-443-2851

Norwalk
Norwalk Housing
Authority
PO Box 508
Norwalk, CT 06856-0508
203-838-8471

Norwich
Norwich Housing
Authority
10 Westwood Park
Norwich, CT 06360-6620
860-887-1605

Portland
Portland Housing Authority
11 Riverside Street
Portland, CT 06480-1958
860-342-1688

Putnam
Putnam Housing Authority
123 Laconia Avenue
Putnam, CT 06260-1753
860-963-6829

Seymour
Housing Authority of The
Town of Seymour
32 Smith Street
Seymour, CT 06483-3738
203-888-4579

Stamford
Stamford Housing
Authority
PO Box 1376
Stamford, CT 06904-1376
203-977-1400

Stratford
Stratford Housing
Authority
295 Everett Street
Stratford, CT 06615-6846
203-375-4483

Torrington
Torrington Housing
Authority
110 Prospect Street
Torrington, CT 06790-6330
860-482-3581

Vernon
Vernon Housing Authority
21 Court Street
Vernon, CT 06066-3650
860-871-0886

Waterbury
Waterbury Housing
Authority
2 Lakewood Road

Waterbury, CT 06704-2477
203-596-2640

West Hartford
West Hartford Housing
Authority
759 Farmington Avenue
West Hartford, CT 06119-
1646
860-236-2921

Willimantic
Willimantic Housing
Authority
49 West Avenue
Willimantic, CT 06226-1918
860-456-1413

Windsor Locks
Windsor Locks Housing
Authority
41 Oak Street
Windsor Locks, CT 06096-
1822
860-627-1455

Winsted
Winchester Housing
Authority
80 Chestnut Street
Winsted, CT 06098-1601
860-379-4573 ext. 10

Delaware

Dover
Delaware State Housing
Authority
18 The Green
Dover, DE 19901-3612
302-739-4263

Dover Housing Authority
76 Stevenson Drive
Dover, DE 19901-4021
302-678-1965

Newark
Newark Housing Authority
313 E Main Street
Newark, DE 19711-7152
302-366-0826

District of Columbia

Washington
D.C. Housing Authority
1133 N Capitol Street NE
Washington, DC 20002-7561
202-535-1500

Florida

Apalachicola
Housing Authority of The
City of Apalachicola
141 15th Street
Apalachicola, FL 32320-2146
850-653-9304

Arcadia
Housing Authority of The
City of Arcadia
11 Booker T Washington
Road
Arcadia, FL 34266-3017
941-494-4343

Avon Park
Housing Authority of Avon
Park
406 Tulane Drive
Avon Park, FL 33825-5417
941-452-4432

Bartow
Housing Authority of
Bartow
1060 S Woodlawn Avenue
Bartow, FL 33830-5540
941-533-6311

Boca Raton
Housing Authority Boca
Raton
1350 N Dixie Highway
Boca Raton, FL 33432-1849
407-393-7756

Bradenton
Housing Authority of The
City of Bradenton
1300 5th Street W
Bradenton, FL 34205-8450
941-748-5568

Manatee County Housing
Authority
5631 11th Street E
Bradenton, FL 34203-5978
941-756-3974

Branford
Suwanee County Housing
Authority
202 Houston Avenue Se
Branford, FL 32008-2834
904-935-2779

Bronson
Gilchrist County Housing
Authority
611 S Pine Street

Bronson, FL 32621-6731
352-486-5420

Levy County Housing
Authority
611 S Pine Street
Bronson, FL 32621-6731
352-486-5420

Brooksville
Brooksville Housing
Authority
800 Continental Drive
Brooksvill, FL 34601-3500
352-796-6547

Chipley
Chipley Housing Authority
1370 Old Bonifay Road
Chipley, FL 32428-1302
850-638-0134

Clearwater
Clearwater Housing
Authority
210 Ewing Avenue
Clearwater, FL 33756-5704
727-461-5777

Cocoa
Housing Authority of The
City of Cocoa
828 Stone Street
Cocoa, FL 32922-7157
321-452-5331 ext. 16

Crestview
Crestview Housing
Authority
371 W Hickory Avenue
Crestview, FL 32536-3305
850-682-2413

Dade City
Pasco County Housing
Authority
14517 7th Street
Dade City, FL 33523-3102
352-567-0848 ext. 109

Dania
Housing Authority of The
City of Dania
715 W Dania Beach
Boulevard
Dania, FL 33004-3227
954-920-9662

Daytona Beach
Housing Authority of The
City of Daytona Bea
118 Cedar Street
Daytona Beach, FL 32114-
4904
904-253-5653

Deerfield Beach
Housing Authority of The
City of Deerfield Be
425 Nw 1st Terrace
Deerfield Beach, FL 33441-
1992
954-428-0678

Defuniak Springs
Defuniak Springs Housing
Authority
120 Oerting Drive
Defuniak Springs, FL 32433-
2722
850-892-2823

Deland
Deland Housing Authority
300 Sunflower Circle
Deland, FL 32724-5939
904-736-1696

Delray Beach
Delray Beach Housing
Authority
770 SW 12th Terrace
Delray Beach, FL 33444-
1367
407-272-6766

Fernandina Beach
Housing Authority of The
City of Fernandina
1300 Hickory Street
Fernandina Beach, FL
32034-2954
904-261-5051

Fort Lauderdale
Housing Authority of The
City of Fort Lauder
437 SW 4th Avenue
Fort Lauderdale, FL 33315-
1007
954-525-6444

Fort Pierce
Housing Authority of The
City of Fort Pierce
707 N 7th Street
Fort Pierce, FL 34950-3131
407-461-7281

Fort Walton Beach
Fort Walton Beach Housing
Authority
27 Robinwood Drive SW
Fort Walton Beach, FL
32548-5347
850-243-3224

Gainesville
Alachua County Housing
Authority

703 NE First Street
Gainesville, FL 32601
352-372-2549

Gainesville
Gainesville Housing
Authority
1900 SE 4th Street
Gainesville, FL 32641-8791
352-334-4000

Graceville
Northwest Florida Regional
Housing Authority
5302 Brown Street
Graceville, FL 32440-2236
850-263-4442

Hialeah
Hialeah Housing Authority
70 E 7th Street
Hialeah, FL 33010-4492
305-888-9744

Hollywood
Housing Authority
Hollywood
7350 N Davie Road
Extension
Hollywood, FL 33024
954-989-4691

Jacksonville
Jacksonville Housing
Authority
1300 Broad Street
Jacksonville, FL 32202-3938
904-630-3810

Key West
Housing Authority of The
City of Key West
1400 Kennedy Drive
Key West, FL 33040-4079
305-296-5621

Monroe CO Housing
Authority
1400 Kennedy Drive
Key West, FL 33040-4079
305-453-9200

Lake Butler
Union County Housing
Authority
715 W Main Street
Lake Butler, FL 32054-1034
904-496-2047

Lake Wales
Lake Wales Housing
Authority
10 W Sessoms Avenue

Lake Wales, FL 33853-3632
813-676-7414

Lakeland
Housing Authority of The
City of Lakeland
430 Hartsell Avenue
Lakeland, FL 33815-4502
941-687-2911

Largo
Dunedin Housing
Authority
11479 Ulmerton Road
Largo, FL 33778-5421
813-443-7684

Largo
Pinellas County Housing
Authority
11479 Ulmerton Road
Largo, FL 33778-5421
813-443-7684

Lauderhill
Broward County Housing
Authority
1773 N State Road 7
Lauderhill, FL 33313-5005
954-739-1114

Live Oak
The Housing Authority of
The City of Live Oak
406 Webb Drive NE
Live Oak, FL 32060-2532
904-362-2123

Macclenny
Macclenny Housing
Authority
402 E Stansell Avenue
Macclenny, FL 32063-2230
904-259-6881

Marianna
Marianna Housing
Authority
2912 Albert Street
Marianna, FL 32448-7709
850-482-3512

Melbourne
Melbourne Housing
Authority
1686 Marywood Road
Melbourne, FL 32934-7134
407-452-5331

Miami
Miami-Dade Housing
Authority
1401 NW 7th Street

Miami, FL 33125-3601
305-644-5100

Miami Beach
Housing Authority of The
City of Miami Beach
200 Alton Road
Miami Beach, FL 33139-6742
305-532-6401

Milton
Milton Housing Authority
1498 Byrom Street
Milton, FL 32570-3827
850-623-8216

Miami
Miami Housing
Conservation
444 SW 2nd Avenue
2nd Floor
Miami, FL 33130
305-416-2138

Mulberry
Housing Authority of The
City of Mulberry
200 NW 3rd Avenue
Mulberry, FL 33860-2314
941-425-1433

New Smyrna Beach
Housing Authority of New
Smyrna Beach
1101 S Dixie Freeway
New Smyrna Beach, FL
32168-7405
904-428-8171

Niceville
Niceville Housing
Authority
500 Boyd Circle
Niceville, FL 32578-2639
850-678-7816

North Fort Myers
Housing Authority Lee
County
14170 Warner Circle
North Fort Myers, FL 33903-
3528
813-997-6688

Orlando
Housing Authority of The
City of Orlando
300 Reeves Court
Orlando, FL 32801-3103
407-894-1500

Ormond Beach
Ormond Beach Housing
Authority

100 New Britain Avenue
Ormond Beach, FL 32174-
5662
904-677-2069

Oviedo
Seminole County Housing
Authority
662 Academy Place
Oviedo, FL 32765-9310
407-365-3621

Pahokee
Pahokee Housing Authority
465 Friend Terrace
Pahokee, FL 33476-1941
305-924-5565

Palatka
Palatka Housing Authority
400 N 15th Street
Palatka, FL 32177-3104
904-329-0132

Panama City
Housing Authority of
Springfield
3806 E 8th Street
Panama City, FL 32401-5389
850-796-1596

Panama City Housing
Authority
804 E 15th Street
Panama City, FL 32405-6102
850-769-2358

Pensacola
Area Housing Commission
1920 W Garden Street
Pensacola, FL 32501-4420
850-438-8561

Plant City
Plant City Housing
Authority
1306 Larrick Lane
Plant City, FL 33566-6642
813-752-0569

Pompano Beach
Housing Authority of
Pompano Beach
321 W Atlantic Boulevard
Pompano Beach, FL 33060-
6048
954-785-7200

Punta Gorda
Punta Gorda Housing
Authority
PO Box 511146
Punta Gorda, FL 33951-1146
941-639-4344

Riviera Beach
Riviera Beach Housing
Authority
2014 W 17th Court
Riviera Beach, FL 33404-5002
407-845-7450

Saint Petersburg
Housing Authority of The
City of St. Petersburg
3250 5th Avenue N
Saint Petersburg, FL 33713-7612
813-323-3171, ext. 334

Sanford
The Housing Authority of
The City of Sanford
94 Castle Brewer Court
Sanford, FL 32771-2349
407-323-3150 ext. 21

Sarasota
Housing Authority of The
City of Sarasota
1300 6th Street
Sarasota, FL 34236-4967
941-361-6210

Stuart
Housing Authority of The
City of Stuart
611 E Church Street
Stuart, FL 34994-3135
561-287-0496

Tallahassee
Tallahassee Housing
Authority
2940 Grady Road
Tallahassee, FL 32312-2210
850-385-6126

Tampa
Tampa Housing Authority
1514 W Union Street
Tampa, FL 33607-4426
813-253-0551, ext. 233

Tarpon Springs
Tarpon Springs Housing
Authority
500 S Walton Avenue
Tarpon Springs, FL 34689-4714
727-937-4411

Titusville
Housing Authority of The
City of Titusville
1108 South Street
Titusville, FL 32780-4052
407-267-4204

Venice
Venice Housing Authority
201 Grove Street N
Venice, FL 34292-2650
941-488-3526

West Palm Beach
Palm Beach County
Housing Authority
3432 45th Street
West Palm Beach, FL 33407-1844
561-684-2160

West Palm Beach
West Palm Beach Housing
Authority
3801 Georgia Avenue
West Palm Beach, FL 33405-2126
561-655-8530

Winter Haven
Winter Haven Housing
Authority
2670 Avenue C SW
Winter Haven, FL 33880-2566
941-294-7369

Winter Park
Housing Authority of The
City of Winter Park
718 Margaret Square
Winter Park, FL 32789-1932
407-645-2869

Georgia

Abbeville
Housing Authority of The
City of Abbeville
248 Barnes Street
Abbeville, GA 31001-1401
912-467-3202

Albany
Housing Authority of The
City of Albany
521 Pine Avenue
Albany, GA 31702-4918
912-434-4500

Alma
Housing Authority of The
City of Alma
401 E 12th Street
Alma, GA 31510-2620
912-632-4298, ext. 12

Americus
Housing Authority of The
City of Americus

825 N Mayo Street
Americus, GA 31709-2627
229-924-3386

Ashburn
Housing Authority of The
City of Ashburn
200 Perry Drive, Office 412
Ashburn, GA 31714-5420
912-567-4668

Athens
Housing Authority of The
City of Athens
259 Waddell Street
Athens, GA 30605-1135
706-548-4446

Atlanta
Housing Authority of
Fulton County
10 Park Place South SE
Suite 550
Atlanta, GA 30303-2920
404-730-5842

Housing Authority of The
City of Atlanta Georgia
230 John Wesley Dobbs Ave
N.E.
Atlanta, GA 30303-2429
404-817-7463

Augusta
Housing Authority of The
City of Augusta
1425 Walton Way
Augusta, GA 30901-2644
706-724-5466

Barnesville
Housing Authority of The
City of Barnesville
285 Indian Trail
Barnesville, GA 30204-1175
770-358-3935

Baxley
Housing Authority of The
City of Baxley
88 Highland Drive
Baxley, GA 31513-0339
912-367-2572

Blackshear
Housing Authority of The
City of Blackshear
525 Mcduffie Street
Blackshear, GA 31516-1738
912-287-2440

Blakely
Housing Authority of The
City of Blakely

411 Damascus Road
Blakely, GA 31723-1688
912-723-3446

Bremen
Housing Authority of The
City of Bremen
PO Box 776
Bremen, GA 30110-0776
770-537-4020

Buchanan
Housing Authority of The
City of Buchanan
106 Griffith Street
Buchanan, GA 30113-5202
770-646-3775

Buena Vista
Housing Authority of The
City of Buena Vista
125 Church Street
Buena Vista, GA 31803-9117
706-571-2800

Buford
Housing Authority of The
City of Buford
2050 Hutchins Street
Buford, GA 30518-3354
770-945-5212

Byron
Housing Authority of The
City of Byron
503 Boy Scout Road
Byron, GA 31008-7137
912-956-3135

Cairo
Housing Authority of The
City of Cairo
224 6th Avenue NE
Cairo, GA 31728-2146
912-377-2065

Calhoun
Housing Authority of The
City of Calhoun
111 S Fair Street F
Calhoun, GA 30701-5308
706-629-9183

Camilla
Housing Authority of The
City of Camilla
51 Hilliard Street
Camilla, GA 31730-2370
912-336-8543

Canton
Housing Authority of The
City of Canton
1400 Oakside Drive

Apartment 76
Canton, GA 30114 -2445
770-479-4969

Carrollton
Housing Authority of The
City of Carrollton
1 Roop Street
Carrollton, GA 30117-4448
770-834-2046

Cartersville
Cartersville; Adairsville
Housing Authority
240 Stonewall Street
Cartersville, GA 30120-3658
770-382-1414

Cedartown
Housing Authority of The
City of Cedartown
344 West Avenue
Cedartown, GA 30125-3435
770-748-1650

Chatsworth
Housing Authority of The
City of Chatsworth
1311 Old Dalton Ellijay
Road
Chatsworth, GA 30705-5898
706-695-3353

Claxton
Housing Authority of The
City of Claxton
PO Box 849
Claxton, GA 30417-0849
912-739-4474

Colquitt
Housing Authority of The
City of Colquitt
208 W Pine Street
Colquitt, GA 31737-3532
912-758-3348

Columbus
Housing Authority of The
City of Columbus
1000 Wynnton Road
Columbus, GA 31906-2801
706-571-2800

Comer
Housing Authority of The
City of Comer
55 Ivy Street
Comer, GA 30629-3310
706-783-4463

Commerce
Housing Authority of The
City of Commerce

100 Willoughby Homes
Commerce, GA 30529-3054
706-335-3611

Conyers
Housing Authority of The
City of Conyers
1258 Irvin Bridge Road Nw
Conyers, GA 30012-4327
770-483-9301

Cordele
Housing Authority of The
City of Cordele
401 S 10th Street
Cordele, GA 31015-2301
912-273-3938

Covington
Housing Authority of The
City of Covington
5160 Alcovy Road NE
Covington, GA 30014-1358
770-786-7739

Crawfordville
Housing Authority of The
City of Crawfordville
301 Thompson Street Se
Crawfordville, GA 30631-
3233
706-465-3479

Cumming
Housing Authority of The
City of Cumming
102 Social Circle
Cumming, GA 30040-2331
770-887-5331

Dahlonega
Housing Authority of The
City of Dahlonega
90 Thompson Circle
Dahlonega GA 30533-1501
706-864-3758

Dallas
Housing Authority of The
City of Dallas
434 Paulding Lane
Dallas, GA 30132-4814
770-445-3758

Dalton
Housing Authority of The
City of Dalton
405 Sequoyah Place
Dalton, GA 30721-2928
706-278-6622

Dawson
Housing Authority of The
City of Dawson

553 Lemon Street NE
Dawson, GA 31742-1171
912-995-2675

Decatur
Housing Authority of The
City of Decatur
325 Swanton Way
Decatur, GA 30030-3001
404-377-0425

Douglas
Housing Authority of The
City of Douglas
312 Bryan Street E
Douglas, GA 31533-5316
912-384-5812

Douglasville
Housing Authority of The
County of Douglas
8474 Pounds Circle
Douglasville, GA 30134-
7010
770-942-3121

Dublin
Housing Authority of The
City of Dublin
PO Box 36
Dublin, GA 31040-0036
912-272-2450

East Point
Housing Authority of The
City of East Point
1600 Connally Drive
East Point, GA 30344-2528
404-762-6664

Eastman
Housing Authority of The
City of Eastman
704 Griffin Avenue SW
Eastman, GA 31023-2222
912-374-5414

Eatonton
Housing Authority of The
City of Eatonton
208 Lawson Drive
Eatonton, GA 31024- 2078
706-485-5361

Edison
Housing Authority of The
City of Edison
156 Tower Drive Se
Edison, GA 31746-9303
912-835-2307

Elberton
Housing Authority of The
City of Elberton

324 Elbert Street
Elberton, GA 30635-2306
706-283-5801

Ellaville
Housing Authority of The
City of Ellaville
134 W Buena Vista Street
Ellaville, GA 31806-3048
706-571-2800

Ellijay
Housing Authority of The
City of Ellijay
PO Box 426
Ellijay, GA 30540-0006
706-635-4644

Fort Gaines
Housing Authority of The
City of Fort Gaines
James Avenue
Fort Gaines, GA 31751
912-768-2356

Fort Oglethorpe
Housing Authority of The
City of Fort Oglethorpe
1 Patterson Place
Fort Oglethorpe, GA 30742-
3382
706-866-3303

Fort Valley
Housing Authority of The
City of Fort Valley
201 W Church St,, Suite B
Fort Valley, GA 31030-3754
912-825-5056

Franklin
Housing Authority of The
City of Franklin
900 S River Road
Franklin, GA 30217-6526
706-675-6060

Gainesville
Housing Authority of The
City of Gainesville
854 Davis Street
Gainesville, GA 30501-6769
770-536-1294

Gibson
Housing Authority of The
City of Gibson
347 Project Street
Gibson GA 30810 4005
706-598-3840

Grantville
Housing Authority of The
City of Grantville

Glanton Street
Grantville, GA 30220
706-637-8153

Greensboro
Housing Authority of The
City of Greensboro
PO Box 217
Greensboro, GA 30642-0217
706-453-7371

Greenville
Housing Authority of The
City of Greenville
3041 Highway 100
Greenville, GA 30222-3195
706-672-1353

Griffin
Housing Authority of The
City of Griffin
518 Nine Oaks Drive
Griffin, GA 30224-4169
770-227-7657

Hamilton
Housing Authority of The
County of Harris
420 Copeland Road
Hamilton, GA 31811-5319
706-571-2800

Hampton
Housing Authority of The
City of Hampton
20 College Street
Hampton, GA 30228-2166
770-946-4039

Harlem
Housing Authority of The
City of Harlem
140 E Milledgeville Road
Harlem, GA 30814-3627
706-556-3025

Hartwell
Housing Authority of The
City of Hartwell
116 W Franklin Place
Hartwell, GA 30643-1158
706-376-3153

Hawkinsville
Housing Authority of The
City of Hawkinsville
314 Progress Avenue
Hawkinsville, GA 31036-
1115
478-892-3364

Hazlehurst
Housing Authority of The
City of Hazlehurst

29 Wildwood Drive
Apartment 59
Hazlehurst, GA 31539-6062
912-375-7299

Hinesville
Housing Authority of The
City of Hinesville
301 Olive Street
Hinesville, GA 31313-2910
912-876-6561

Hogansville
Housing Authority of The
City of Hogansville
200 Boyd Road
Hogansville, GA 30230-1708
706-637-8153

Homerville
Housing Authority of The
City of Homerville
110 Crescent Drive
Homerville, GA 31634-1213
912-487-5486

Jackson
Housing Authority of The
City of Jackson
160 Carter Avenue
Jackson, GA 30233-1568
770-358-3935

Jasper
Housing Authority of The
City of Jasper
164 Landrum Circle 147
Jasper, GA 30143-1212
706-692-5514

Jesup
Housing Authority of The
City of Jesup
327 Bay Acres Road
Jesup, GA 31545-7816
912-427-2535

Jonesboro
Housing Authority of The
City of Jonesboro
203 Hightower Street
Jonesboro, GA 30236-3647
770-478-7282

Lagrange
Housing Authority of The
City of Lagrange
201 Chatham Street
Lagrange, GA 30240-5313
706-882-6416

Lavonia
Housing Authority of The
City of Lavonia

13032 Jones Street
Lavonia, GA 30553-1140
706-356-8224

Lawrenceville
Housing Authority of The
City of Lawrenceville
502 Glen Edge Drive
Lawrenceville, GA 30045-
8872
770-963-4900

Lincolnton
Housing Authority of The
City of Lincolnton
311 Moss Street
Lincolnton, GA 30817-2814
706-359-3243

Lithonia
Housing Authority of The
City of Lithonia
6878 Max Cleland
Boulevard
Lithonia, GA 30058- 4467
770-482-6563

Loganville
Housing Authority of The
City of Loganville
117 Winston Byrd Lane
Loganville, GA 30052-2677
770-267-6591

Louisville
Housing Authority of The
City of Louisville
710 W Nelms Street
Louisville, GA 30434-1464
706-554-2233

Lumber City
Housing Authority of The
City of Lumber City
PO Box 668
Lumber City GA 31549-0668
912-363-4246

Lumpkin
Housing Authority of The
County of Stewart
PO Box 327
Lumpkin, GA 31815-0327
912-838-4493

Lyons
Housing Authority of The
City of Lyons
208 N Lanier Street
Lyons, GA 30436-7223
912-526-8504

Macon
Housing Authority of The
City of Macon

2015 Felton Avenue
Macon, GA 31201-2404
912-752-5000

Madison
Housing Authority of The
City of Madison
509 Madison Avenue
Madison, GA 30650-1705
770-267-6591

Marietta
Housing Authority of The
City of Marietta
95 Cole Street NE
Marietta, GA 30060-2090
770-419-3200

Mc Caysville
Housing Authority of The
City of McCaysville
160 Briggs Street
Mc Caysville, GA 30555-
2532
706-492-4936

Mc Rae
Housing Authority of The
City of Mcrae
109 W Willow Creek Lane
Mc Rae, GA 31055-2422
912-868-6634

Mcdonough
Housing Authority of The
City of Mcdonough
345 Simpson Street
Mcdonough, GA 30253-3417
770-957-4494

Menlo
Housing Authority of The
City of Menlo
77 Ralph Chamblee Drive
Menlo, GA 30731-6417
706-862-2240

Metter
Housing Authority of The
City of Metter
PO Box 207
Metter, GA 30439-0207
912-685-5377

Milledgeville
Housing Authority of The
City of Milledgeville
545 Martin Luther King
Milledgeville, GA 31061-
2740
912-445-2875

Sparta
Housing Authority of The
City of Sparta

545 Martin Luther King
Milledgeville, GA 31061-
2740
706-444-7360

Millen
Housing Authority of The
City of Millen
824 Hart Avenue
Millen, GA 30442-1722
706-554-2233

Monroe
Housing Authority of The
City of Monroe
808 Marable Street
Monroe, GA 30656-1579
770-267-6591

Montezuma
Butler; Marshallville;
Montezuma; Oglethorp
542 Richardson Street
Montezuma, GA 31063-1768
912-472-8209

Monticello
Housing Authority of The
City of Monticello
405 Funderburg Drive
Monticello, GA 31064-1440
706-468-6201

Moultrie
Housing Authority of The
City of Doerun
800 4th Avenue SE
Moultrie, GA 31768-4959
912-985-4162

Housing Authority of The
City of Moultrie
800 4th Avenue SE
Moultrie, GA 31768-4959
912-985-4162

Nahunta
Housing Authority of The
City of Nahunta
101 Burton Terrace
Nahunta GA 31553-9773
912-462-5680

Nashville
Housing Authority of The
City of Nashville
409 Hull Avenue
Nashville, GA 31639-1159
229-686-9321

Newnan
Housing Authority of The
City of Newnan
2 Hannah Street

Newnan, GA 30263-1479
770-253-6461

Newnan
Housing Authority of The
City of Senoia
72 Main Street
Newnan, GA 30263-5806
770-599-6442

Norcross
Housing Authority of The
City of Norcross
19 Garner Street
Norcross, GA 30071-4203
770-448-3668

Ocilla
Housing Authority of The
City of Ocilla
534 N Alder Street
Ocilla, GA 31774-1257
912-468-5400

Pelham
Housing Authority of The
City of Pelham
548 Palmer Street SW
Pelham, GA 31779-1856
912-294-8444

Perry
Housing Authority of The
City of Perry
822 Perimeter Road
Perry, GA 31069-2134
912-987-5097

Quitman
Housing Authority of The
City of Quitman
609 N Highland Circle
Quitman, GA 31643-1747
912-263-4631

Reidsville
Housing Authority of The
City of Reidsville
PO Box 608
Reidsville, GA 30453-0608
912-557-4259

Ringgold
Housing Authority of The
City of Ringgold
137 Circle Drive
Ringgold, GA 30736-2529
706-935-3028

Roberta
Housing Authority of The
City of Roberta
PO Box 445

Roberta, GA 31078-0445
912-836-3530

Rockmart
Housing Authority of The
City of Rockmart
811 Forrest Avenue
Rockmart, GA 30153-1969
770-684-6571

Rome
Housing Authority of The
City of Rome
800 N 5th Avenue NE
Rome, GA 30165-2737
706-291-0780

Roswell
Housing Authority of The
City of Roswell
766 Myrtle Street
Roswell, GA 30075-4558
770-993-6226

Royston
Housing Authority of The
City of Royston
216 Hartwell Street
Royston, GA 30662-4208
706-245-7277

Sandersville
Housing Authority of The
City of Sandersville
419 Morningside Drive
Sandersville, GA 31082-7605
478-552-6955

Savannah
Housing Authority of
Savannah
200 E Broad Street
Savannah, GA 31401-4149
912-235-5800

Social Circle
Housing Authority of The
City of Social Circle
742 Walton Court
Social Circle, GA 30025-3036
770-267-6591

Soperton
Housing Authority of The
City of Soperton
700 Eastman Road
Soperton, GA 30457-1431
912-529-4596

Summerville
Housing Authority of The
City of Summerville
56 Ross Street

Summerville, GA 30747-
1404
706-857-3016

Swainsboro
Housing Authority of the
City of Swainsboro
420 N Racetrack Street
Swainsboro GA 3040- 3305
912-237-7381

Sylvester
Housing Authority of the
City of Sylvester
411 N Jefferson Street
Sylvester, GA 31791-1617
912-776-7621

Tallapoosa
Housing Authority of the
City of Tallapoosa
304 Arbacoochee Road
Tallapoosa, GA 30176-1100
770-574-2207

Tennille
Housing Authority of the
City of Tennille
300 E Church Street
Tennille, GA 31089-1178
912-552-0026

Thomaston
Housing Authority of the
City of Thomaston
574 Triune Avenue
Thomaston, GA 30286-5911
706-647-7420

Thomasville
Housing Authority of The
City of Boston
216 S College Street
Thomasville, GA 31792-6432
912-226-4065

Housing Authority of The
City of Thomasville
216 S College Street
Thomasville, GA 31792-6432
912-226-4065

Thomson
Housing Authority of The
City of Thomson
219 Pecan Avenue
Thomson, GA 30824-1736
706-595-4878

Toccoa
Housing Authority of The
City of Clarkesville
605 Pond Street S

Toccoa, GA 30577-2905
706-886-9455toccoa

Housing Authority of The
City of Cleveland
605 Pond Street S
Toccoa, GA 30577-2905
706-886-9455

Housing Authority of the
City of Cornelia
605 Pond Street S
Toccoa, GA 30577-2905
706-886-9455

Housing Authority of the
City of Homer
605 Pond Street S
Toccoa, GA 30577-2905
706-886-9455

Housing Authority of the
City of Toccoa
605 Pond Street S
Toccoa, GA 30577-2905
706-886-9455

Unadilla
Housing Authority of the
City of Unadilla
PO Box 447
Unadilla, GA 31091-0447
912-627-3572

Valdosta
Housing Authority of the
City of Valdosta
610 E Ann Street
Valdosta, GA 31601-4090
912-242-4130

Vidalia
Housing Authority of The
City of Vidalia
907 Morris Street
Vidalia, GA 30474-3951
912-537-4885

Vienna
Housing Authority of The
City of Vienna
700 Fitzpatrick Place
Vienna, GA 31092-1474
912-268-4458

Villa Rica
Housing Authority of The
City of Villa Rica
35 Walnut Drive
Villa Rica, GA 30180-1229
770-459-3112

Warner Robins
Housing Authority of The
City of Warner Robins
112 Memorial Terrace
Warner Robins, GA 31093-
2072
912-929-0229

Housing Authority of the
County of Houston
112 Memorial Terrace
Warner Robins, GA 31093-
2072
912-929-0229

Warrenton
Housing Authority of the
City of Warrenton
101 Phelps Drive
Warrenton, GA 30828-3410
706-465-3479

Washington
Housing Authority of the
City of Washington
311 Mcguire Street
Washington, GA 30673-1635
706-678-3261

Waycross
Housing Authority of the
City of Waycross
1130 Tebeau Street
Waycross, GA 31501-5438
912-287-2440

West Point
Housing Authority of the
City of West Point
PO Box 545
West Point, GA 31833-0545
706-645-1216

Winder
Housing Authority of The
City of Winder
11 Horton Street
Winder, GA 30680-2078
770-867-7495

Woodbury
Housing Authority of The
City of Woodbury
125 Tulip
Woodbury, GA 30293
706-553-5480

Woodland
Talbot Co.;Talbotton;
Woodland
P. O. Box 220
Woodland, GA 31836-0220
706-674-2316

GUAM

Sinajana
Guam Housing And Urban
Renewal Authority
117 Bien Venida Avenue
Sinajana, GU 96926-4643
671-477-9851

HAWAII

Honolulu
State of Hawaii Housing
Authority
677 Queen Street
Suite 300
Honolulu, HI 96813-5112
808-587-0680

IDAHO

American Falls
Housing Authority of The
City of American Falls
290 Tyhee Avenue
American Falls, ID 83211-
1176
208-226-5262

Boise
Ada County Housing
Authority
1276 River St.
Suite 300
Boise, ID 83702
208-345-4907

Boise
Boise City Housing
Authority
1276 River St.
Suite 300
Boise, ID 83702
208-345-4907

Boise
Idaho Housing And Finance
Association
565 W Myrtle Street
Boise, ID 83702-7606
208-331-4882

Buhl
Housing Authority of The
City of Buhl
1310 Main Street
Buhl, ID 83316-1711
208-543-6171

Jerome
Housing Authority of The
City Jerome
100 N Fillmore Street
Jerome, ID 83338-2447
208-733-5765

Nampa
Nampa Housing Authority
1703 3rd Street N
Nampa, ID 83687-4447
208-466-2601

Nampa
Southwestern Idaho
Cooperative Housing
Authority
1108 W Finch Drive
Nampa, ID 83651-1732
208-467-7461

Pocatello
Housing Authority of The
City of Pocatello
711 N 6th Avenue
Pocatello, ID 83201-6233
208-233-6276

Twin Falls
Twin Falls Housing
Authority
200 Elm Street N
Twin Falls, ID 83301-5246
208-733-5765

ILLINOIS

Albion
Edwards County Housing
Authority
125 W Cherry Street
Albion, IL 62806-1104
618-445-2715

Aledo
Mercer County Housing
Authority
609 Nw 4th Avenue
Aledo, IL 61231-1085
309-582-5410

Alton
Housing Authority - City of
Alton
2406 Crawford Street
Alton, IL 62002-4612
618-465-4260

Anna
Housing Authority of The
County of Union
131 Hillside Terrace

Anna, IL 62906-1015
618-833-5129

Aurora
Aurora Housing Authority
1630 Plum Street
Aurora, IL 60506-3462
630-859-7210

Beardstown
The Housing Authority of
The County of Cass IL.
12 Frank Wessel Drive
Beardstown, IL 62618-8093
217-323-2303

Belleville
St. Clair County Housing
Authority
100 N 48th Street
Belleville, IL 62226-4707
618-277-3290

Bloomington
Housing Authority of The
City of Bloomington, IL
104 E Wood Street
Bloomington, IL 61701-6791
309-829-3360

Cairo
Alexander County Housing
Authority
PO Box 191
Cairo, IL 62914-0191
618-734-1910

Canton
Fulton County Housing
Authority
250 S Main Street
Canton, IL 61520-2632
309-647-4120

Carlinville
Macoupin County Housing
Authority
760 Anderson Street
Carlinville, IL 62626-1003
217-854-8606

Centralia
Housing Authority of
Marion County
PO Box 689
Centralia, IL 62801-0689
618-533-7100

Champaign
Housing Authority of
Champaign County
205 W Park Avenue
Champaign, IL 61820-3928
217-378-7100

Chester
Randolph County Housing
Authority
916 George Street
Chester, IL 62233-1707
618-826-4314

Chicago
Chicago Housing Authority
626 W Jackson Boulevard
Chicago, IL 60661-5601
312-791-8500

Habitat Property
Management Corp
350 W Hubbard
Chicago, IL 60610
312-527-5700

Housing Authority of The
County of Cook
310 S Michigan Avenue
Floor 15
Chicago, IL 60604-4207
312-939-0742

Cicero
Housing Authority of The
Town of Cicero
5933 W. 35th St.
Cicero, IL 60804
708-652-0386

Clayton
Housing Authority of
Adams County
PO Box 207
Clayton, IL 62324-0207
217-894-7022

Clinton
Dewitt County Housing
Authority
100 S Railroad Street
Clinton, IL 61727-2053
217-935-8804

Collinsville
Madison County Housing
Authority
1609 Olive Street
Collinsville, IL 62234-4909
618-345-5142

Dallas City
Hancock County Housing
Authority
PO Box 472
Dallas City, IL 62330-0472
217-852-3482

Danville
The Housing Authority of
The City of Danville, IL

1607 Clyman Lane
Danville, IL 61832-3682
217-443-0621 ext. 101

Decatur
Decatur Housing Authority
1808 E Locust Street
Decatur, IL 62521-1565
217-423-7711

Dekalb
Housing Authority of The
County of Dekalb
310 N 6th Street
Dekalb, IL 60115-3404
815-758-2692

Dixon
Lee County Housing
Authority
1000 Washington Avenue
Dixon, IL 61021-1266
815-284-2759

Du Quoin
Perry County Housing
Authority
120 S Walnut Street
Du Quoin, IL 62832-1885
618-542-5409

East Saint Louis
The Housing Authority of
City of East St. Louis
700 N 20th Street
East Saint Louis, IL 62205-1814
618-271-0498

Effingham
Effingham County Housing
Authority
215 N Banker Street
Effingham IL 62401-2351
217-342-3520

Elgin
Housing Authority of Elgin
120 S State Street
Elgin, IL 60123-6403
847-742-3853

Eureka
Woodford County Housing
Authority
410 E Eureka Avenue
Eureka, IL 61530-1263
309-467-4623

Fairfield
Housing Authority of The
County of Wayne, Illinois
303 N 1st Street
Fairfield, IL 62837-2549
618-842-9008

Flora
Clay County Housing
Authority
201 S Locust Street
Flora, IL 62839-2117
618-662-5311

Freeport
Housing Authority of The
City of Freeport
1052 W Galena Avenue
Suite A
Freeport, IL 61032-3820
815-232-4171

Galena
Housing Authority of The
County of Jodaviess
341 Franklin Street
Galena, IL 61036-1843
815-777-0782

Galesburg
Knox County Housing
Authority
216 W Simmons Street
Galesburg, IL 61401-4407
309-342-8129

Gibson City
Housing Authority of The
County of Ford
214 E 7th Street
Gibson City, IL 60936-1547
217-784-5488

Granite City
Granite City Housing
Authority
1800 Kirkpatrick Homes
Granite City, IL 62040-5749
618-876-0975

Grayslake
Housing Authority of The
County of Lake, IL.
33928 N Route 45
Grayslake, IL 60030-1700
847-223-1170

Greenville
Housing Authority of The
County of Bond
220 E Winter Avenue
Greenville, IL 62246-1831
618-664-2321

Hammond
Housing Authority of Piatt
County
PO Box 200
Hammond, IL 61929-0200
217-262-3231

Hardin
Housing Authority of
Calhoun County
PO Box 426
Hardin, IL 62047-0426
618-576-2236

Havana
Mason County Housing
Authority
201 E Hurst Street
Havana, IL 62644-1071
309-543-4515

Hillsboro
Montgomery County
Housing Authority
216 Shelbyville Road
Hillsboro, IL 62049-2351
217-532-3672

Jacksonville
Morgan County Housing
Authority
301 W Beecher Avenue
Jacksonville, IL 62650-2478
217-243-3338

Jerseyville
Housing Authority of The
County of Jersey
505 Horn Drive
Jerseyville, IL 62052-2644
618-498-9516

Joliet
Housing Authority of Joliet
6 S Broadway Street
Joliet, IL 60436-1753
815-727-0611

Kankakee
Kankakee County Housing
Authority
185 N Saint Joseph Avenue
Kankakee, IL 60901-2737
815-939-7125

Kewanee
The Housing Authority of
Henry County
100 Fairview Junction
Kewanee, IL 61443-3950
309-852-2801

Lawrenceville
Housing Authority of The
County of Lawrence, IL.
1109 12th Street
Lawrenceville, IL 62439-
2542
618-943-4762

Lincoln
Logan County Housing
Authority
1028 N College Street
Lincoln, IL 62656-1181
217-732-7776

Macomb
Housing Authority of
Mcdonough County
322 W Piper Street
Macomb, IL 61455-2881
309-837-2363

Marion
Housing Authority of The
City of Marion, Illinois
501 N Market Street
Marion, IL 62959-2365
618-997-1258

Marshall
Housing Authority of The
County of Clark, IL.
208 Maple Street
Marshall, IL 62441-1166
217-826-5541

Mattoon
Housing Authority of The
County of Coles
109 Prairie Avenue
Mattoon, IL 61938-4532
217-235-4175

Mc Leansboro
Hamilton County Housing
Authority
500 S Marshall Avenue
Mc Leansboro, IL 62859-
1208
618-643-3265

Moline
Moline Housing Authority
4141 11th Avenue A
Moline, IL 61265-2592
309-764-1819

Monmouth
Warren County Housing
Authority
200 E Harlem Avenue
Monmouth, IL 61462-1273
309-734-2080

Morris
Grundy County Housing
Authority
1700 Newton Place
Morris, IL 60450-1113
815-942-6198

Mounds
Housing Authority of
Pulaski County
130 Richland Terrace
Mounds, IL 6296- 1233
618-745-6330

Mount Sterling
Housing Authority of The
County of Brown
400 N Maple Street
Mount Sterling, IL 62353-
1127
217-773-2731

Mount Vernon
Housing Authority of
Jefferson County
1000 S 9th Street
Mount Vernon, IL 62864 -
5409
618-244-5910

Mt Carmell
Housing Authority of The
County of Wabash, IL.
330 W 10th Street
Mt Carmell, IL 62863-1372
618-262-5518

Murphysboro
Housing Authority of The
County of Jackson, IL.
300 N 7th Street
Murphysboro, IL 62966-
2101
618-684-3183

North Chicago
Housing Authority of The
City of North Chicago, IL
1440 Jackson Street
North Chicago, IL 60064-
1840
847-785-4300

Oak Park
Oak Park Housing
Authority
1025 Pleasant Place
Oak Park, IL 60302 -3172
708-386-9322

Olney
Housing Authority of The
County of Richland
129 E Scott Street
Olney, IL 62450 -2014
618-395-2571

Ottawa
Housing Authority For
Lasalle County
526 E Norris Drive

Ottawa, IL 61350 -2352
815-434-0380

Pana
Housing Authority of
Christian County, Illinois
202 S Poplar Street
Pana, IL 62557-1681
217-562-3742

Paris
Housing Authority of Edgar
County
602 E Highland Drive
Paris, IL 61944-2277
217-465-8458

Park Forest
Housing Authority of Park
Forest
350 Victory Drive
Park Forest, IL 60466
708-748-1112

Pekin
Housing Authority of The
City of Pekin
1901 Broadway Street
Pekin, IL 61554-3823
309-346-7996

Peoria
Peoria Housing Authority
100 S Sheridan Road
Peoria, IL 61605-3905
309-676-8736

Petersburg
Menard County Housing
Authority
101 W Sheridan Road
Petersburg, IL 62675-1349
217-632-7723

Polo
Ogle County Housing
Authority
407 N Union Avenue
Polo, IL 61064-1240
815-946-2922

Pontiac
Livingston County Housing
Authority
903 W North Street
Pontiac, IL 61764-1062
815-844-6013

Princeton
Bureau County Housing
Authority
444 S Church Street
Princeton, IL 61356-2188
815-879-8106

Quincy
Quincy Housing Authority
540 Harrison Street
Quincy, IL 62301-7236
217-222-0720

Rock Falls
Whiteside County Housing
Authority
401 W 18th Street
Rock Falls, IL 61071-2917
815-625-0581

Rock Island
Housing Authority of The
City of Rock Island
111 20th Street
Rock Island, IL 61201-8822
309-788-0825

Rockford
Rockford Housing
Authority
223 S Winnebago Street
Rockford IL 61102-2259
815-987-3895

Winnebago County
Housing Authority
2901 Searles Avenue
Rockford IL 61101-2781
815-963-2133, ext. 11

Rossville
Housing Authority of The
County of Vermilion, Ill.
601 S Chicago Street
Rossville, IL 60963-1213
217-748-6812

Savanna
Carroll County Housing
Authority
525 3rd Street
Savanna, IL 61074-1584
815-273-7081

Shawneetown
Housing Authority of
Gallatin County
117 W Wilson Avenue
Shawneetown, IL 62984-
3015
618-269-3080

Shelbyville
Housing Authority of The
County of Shelby, IL.
PO Box 252
Shelbyville, IL 62565-0252
217-774-2167

Silvis
Grtr Metro. Area Housing
Auth of Rock Island County
325 2nd Street
Silvis, IL 61282-2128
309-755-4527

Springfield
Springfield Housing
Authority
200 N 11th Street
Springfield, IL 62703-1004
217-753-5757

Toledo
Housing Authority of The
County of Cumberland, IL.
206 E Washington Street
Toledo, IL 62468-1325
217-849-2071

Vienna
Housing Authority of
Johnson County
501 N 4th Street
Vienna, IL 62995-1638
618-658-5811

Waukegan
Housing Authority of The
City of Waukegan
215 S Utica Street
Waukegan, IL 60085-5522
847-244-8500

West Frankfort
Housing Authority of The
County of Franklin
302 E Elm Street
West Frankfort, IL 62896-
2737
618-932-2124

White Hall
Housing Authority of
Greene County
PO Box 336
White Hall, IL 62092-0336
217-374-2128

Winchester
Scott County Housing
Authority
143 S Walnut Street
Winchester, IL 62694-1230
217-742-3174

Woodstock
Mchenry County Housing
Authority
1108 N Seminary Avenue
Woodstock, IL 60098-2959
815-338-7752

Indiana

Anderson
Housing Authority of The
City of Anderson
528 W 11th Street
Anderson, IN 46016-1228
765-641-2620

Angola
Angola Housing Authority
617 Williams Street
Angola, IN 46703-1173
219-665-9741

Bedford
Housing Authority of The
City of Bedford
1305 K Street
Bedford, IN 47421-3245
812-279-2356

Bloomfield
Bloomfield Housing
Authority
100 W Main Street
Bloomfield, IN 47424-1345
812-384-8866

Bloomington
Housing Authority of The
City of Bloomington
1007 N Summitt Street
Bloomington, IN 47404-3172
812-339-3491

Brazil
Brazil Housing Authority
122 W Jackson Street
Brazil, IN 47834-2565
812-446-2517

Charlestown
Housing Authority of The
City of Charlestown
214 McCampbell Street
Charlestown, IN 47111-1024
812-256-6311

Columbus
Columbus Housing
Authority
799 Mcclure Road
Columbus, IN 47201-6610
812-378-0005

Elkhart
Housing Authority of The
City of Elkhart
1396 Benham Avenue
Elkhart, IN 46516-3341
219-295-8392

Evansville
Housing Authority of The
City of Evansville
500 Court Street
Evansville, IN 47708-1340
812-428-8500

Fort Wayne
Fort Wayne Housing
Authority
2013 South Anthony
Boulevard
Fort Wayne, IN 46803-3609
219-449-7800

Fremont
Fremont Housing Authority
PO Box 189
Fremont, IN 46737-0189
219-495-2422

Gary
Housing Authority of The
City of Gary
578 Broadway
Gary, IN 46402-1900
219-883-0387

Greendale
Greendale Housing
Authority
489 Ludlow Street
Greendale, IN 47025-1579
812-537-0164

Hammond
Housing Authority of The
City of Hammond
7329 W Columbia Circle
Hammond, IN 46324-2831
219-989-3265

Huntingburg
Housing Authority of The
City of Huntingburg
1102 Friendship Village
Huntingburg, IN 47542-
1266
812-683-2513

Indianapolis
Indianapolis Housing
Agency
1919 North Meridian Street
Indianapolis, IN 46202
317-261-7200

Jeffersonville
Housing Authority of The
City of Jeffersonville
206 Eastern Boulevard
Jeffersonville, IN 47130-2802
812-283-7984

Kendallville
Housing Authority of The
City of Kendallville
240 Angling Road
Kendallville, IN 46755-1002
219-347-1091

Kokomo
Kokomo Housing Authority
210 E Taylor Street
Kokomo, IN 46901-4790
765-459-3162

Linton
Linton Housing Authority
Rural Route 2, Box 680
Linton, IN 47441
812-847-8254

Marion
Marion Housing Authority
601 S Adams Street
Marion, IN 46953-2042
765-664-5194

Michigan City
Housing Authority of The
City of Michigan City
621 E Michigan Boulevard
Michigan City, IN 46360-
3224
219-872-7287

Mishawaka
Housing Authority of The
City of Mishawaka
Post office Box 1347
Mishawaka, IN 46546-1347
219-258-1656

Mt Vernon
Mount Vernon Housing
Authority
1500 Jefferson Street
Mt Vernon, IN 47620-1282
812-838-6356

Muncie
Delaware County Housing
Authority
2401 S Haddix Avenue
Muncie, IN 47302-7547
765-284-3801

Muncie
Muncie Housing Authority
409 E 1st Street
Muncie, IN 47302-2483
765-288-9242

New Albany
Housing Authority of The
City of New Albany
500 Scribner Drive

New Albany, IN 47150-3644
812-948-2319

New Castle
New Castle Housing
Authority
274 S 14th Street
New Castle, IN 47362-3373
765-529-1517

Peru
Housing Authority of The
City of Peru
701 E Main Street
Peru, IN 46970-2640
765-473-6601

Richmond
Housing Authority of The
City of Richmond
58 S 15th Street
Richmond, IN 47374-5606
765-966-2687

Rockport
Rockport Housing
Authority
601 Washington Street
Rockport, IN 47635-1272
812-649-4533

Rome City
Housing Authority of The
City of Rome City
PO Box 415
Rome City, IN 46784-0415
219-854-4122

South Bend
South Bend Housing
Authority
501 S Scott Street
South Bend, IN 46601-2766
219-235-9346

Sullivan
Sullivan Housing Authority
200 N Court Street
Sullivan, IN 47882-1215
812-268-4600

Tell City
Housing Authority of The
City of Tell City
1648 10th Street
Tell City, IN 47586-1342
812-547-8581

Terre Haute
Housing Authority of The
City of Terre Haute
1 Dreiser Square
Terre Haute, IN 47807-4617
812-232-1381

Vincennes
Vincennes Housing
Authority
501 Hart Street
Vincennes, IN 47591-2141
812-882-5494

Washington
Washington Housing
Authority
520 S.E. Second Street
Washington, IN 47501
812-254-1596

Iowa

Afton
Afton Housing Commission
611 E Polk Street
Afton, IA 50830-2044
515-347-8826

Agency
Area Xv Multi-County
Housing Agency
417 N College Street
Agency, IA 52530-9733
515-937-5222

Bancroft
Low Rent Housing Agency
of Bancroft
539 E Ramsey Street
Bancroft, IA 50517-8138
515-573-7751

Burlington
Low Rent Housing Agency
of Burlington
2830 Winegard Drive
Burlington, IA 52601-2056
319-753-2142

Centerville
Centerville Municipal
Housing Agency
317 E Oak Street
Centerville, IA 52544-1537
641-856-8742

Chariton
Housing Board of Chariton
429 S Main Street
Chariton, IA 50049-2556
515-774-2725

Charles City
Charles City Housing And
Redev Authority
1000 S Grand Avenue
Charles City, IA 50616-3751
641-228-6661

Clarinda
Clarinda Low Rent Housing
Agency
402 W Willow Street
Clarinda, IA 51632-2500
712-542-2912

Clinton
Low Rent Housing Agency
of Clinton
215 6th Avenue S
Suite 33
Clinton, IA 52732-4339
319-243-1280

Corning
Corning Housing
Commission
1125 Westgate Drive
Corning, IA 50841-1200
641-322-4098

Council Bluffs
Municipal Housing Agency
of Council Bluffs
505 S 6th Street
Council Bluffs, IA 51501-
6402
712-322-1491

Creston
Southern Iowa Regional
Housing Authority
219 N Pine Street
Creston, IA 50801-2413
641-782-8585

Davenport
Davenport Housing
Commission
501 W 3rd Street
Davenport, IA 52801-1125
319-326-7899

Des Moines
Des Moines Municipal
Housing Authority
Park Fair Mall, Suite 101
100 East Euclid
Des Moines, IA 50313
515-288-2201

Dubuque
Eastern Iowa Regional
Housing Authority
799 Main Street
Suite 330
Dubuque, IA 52001-6825
319-556-4166

Emmetsburg
Low Rent Housing Agency
of Emmetsburg
2111 11th Street

Emmetsburg, IA 50536
712-852-4169

Essex
Essex Low Rent Housing
Agency
604 South Avenue
Essex, IA 51638-3001
712-379-3510

Evansdale
Evansdale Municipal
Housing Authority
119 Morrell Court
Evansdale, IA 50707-1146
319-234-0385

Farragut
Low Rent Housing Agency
of Farragut
804 Jackson Avenue
Farragut, IA 51639-2000
712-385-8113

Fort Dodge
Fort Dodge Municipal
Housing Agency
700 S 17th Street
Fort Dodge, IA 50501-5300
515-573-7751

Fort Madison
Fort Madison Housing
Authority
1102 48th Street
Fort Madison, IA 52627-
4624
319-372-6083

Hamburg
Low Rent Housing Agency
of Hamburg
407 H Street
Hamburg, IA 51640-1324
712-382-1557

Indianola
Warren County Housing
Authority
301 N. Buxton, #210
Indianola, IA 50125
515-961-1073

Iowa City
Iowa City Housing
Authority
410 E Washington Street
Iowa City, IA 52240-1825
319-356-5400

Keokuk
Keokuk Housing Authority
111 S 2nd Street

Keokuk, IA 52632-5840
319-524-4386

Knoxville
Low Rent Housing Agency
of Knoxville
305 S 3rd Street
Knoxville, IA 50138-2255
641-828-7371

Lenox
Lenox Low Rent Housing
Agency
401 E Ohio Street
Lenox, IA 50851-1169
515-333-4415

Leon
Low Rent Housing Agency
of Leon
401 Se Q Street
Leon, IA 50144-1747
641-446-4163

Lone Tree
Lone Tree Housing
Commission
401 E Linn Street
Lone Tree, IA 52755-9765
319-629-4689

Malvern
Malvern Low Rent Housing
Agency
306 Lincoln Avenue
Malvern, IA 51551-9627
712-624-8561

Manning
Municipal Housing Agency
of Manning
421 Center Street
Manning, IA 51455-1057
712-653-2155

Mason City
North Iowa Regional
Housing Authority
217 2nd Street SW
Mason City, IA 50401-3715
641-423-0897

Missouri Valley
Low Rent Housing Agency
of Missouri Valley
505 E Huron Street
Missouri Valley, IA 51555-
1606
712-642-2458

Mount Ayr
Low Rent Housing Agency
of Mount Ayr
306 E Monroe Street

Mount Ayr, IA 50854-1755
515-464-3832

Muscatine
Muscatine Municipal
Housing Agency
215 Sycamore Street
Muscatine, IA 52761-3839
319-264-1554

Onawa
Low Rent Housing Agency
of Onawa
1017 11th Street
Onawa, IA 51040-1555
712-423-1736

Ottumwa
Ottumwa Housing
Authority
102 W Finley Avenue
Ottumwa, IA 52501-4659
515-682-8369

Red Oak
Low Rent Housing Agency
of Red Oak
1805 N 8th Street
Red Oak, IA 51566-1184
712-623-4558

Rock Rapids
Rock Rapids Municipal
Housing Agency
206 1st Avenue
Rock Rapids, IA 51246-1504
712-472-3896

Shenandoah
Shenandoah Low Rent
Housing Agency
707 W Summit Avenue
Shenandoah, IA 51601-2238
712-246-3213

Sidney
Low Rent Housing Agency
of Sidney
901 Clay Street
Sidney, IA 51652-2007
712-374-2644

Sioux Center
Low Rent Housing Agency
of Sioux Center
510 N Meadow Drive
Sioux Center, IA 51250-1665
712-722-2237

Sioux City
Sioux City Housing Services
Division
405 6th Street

Sioux City, IA 51101-1211
712-279-6980

Spencer
Northwest Iowa Regional
Housing Authority
919 2nd Ave. SW
P.O. Box 446
Spencer, IA 51301
712-262-7460

Tabor
Tabor Low Rent Housing
Agency
204 W Orange Street
Tabor, IA 51653-4058
712-629-1645

Villisca
Villisca Low Rent Housing
Agency
600 E 3rd Street
Villisca, IA 50864-1169
712-826-7602

Waterloo
Waterloo Housing
Authority
620 Mulberry Street
Waterloo, IA 50703-5713
319-233-0201

Waverly
Low Rent Housing Agency
of Waverly
320 15th Street Nw
Waverly, IA 50677-2123
319-352-3394

West Des Moines
Central Iowa Regional
Housing Authority
950 office Park Road
Suite 321
West Des Moines, IA 50265
515-453-2323 ext. 207

Winterset
Low Rent Housing Agency
of Winterset
415 N 2nd Street
Winterset, IA 50273-1270
515-462-4340

KANSAS

Anthony
Anthony Housing
Authority
924 E Spring Street
Anthony, KS 67003-2120
316-842-5331

Atchison
Atchison Housing
Authority
103 S 7th Street
Atchison, KS 66002-2842
913-367-3323

Atwood
Atwood Housing Authority
801 S 3rd Street
Atwood, KS 67730-2149
785-626-9572

Beloit
Beloit Housing Authority
200 Cedar Avenue
Beloit, KS 67420-3429
785-738-5210

Blue Rapids
Blue Rapids Housing
Authority
504 E 5th Street
Blue Rapids, KS 66411-1538
785-363-7711

Bonner Springs
Bonner Springs Housing
Authority
420 N Park Avenue
Bonner Springs, KS 66012-
1498
913-441-3816

Burrton
Burrton Housing Authority
460 E Adams Street
Burrton, KS 67020-9210
316-463-5077

Cawker City
Cawker City Housing
Authority
125 Sunrise Drive
Cawker City, KS 67430-9791
785-781-4443

Chanute
Chanute Housing Authority
110 Ronda Lane
Chanute, KS 66720-1954
316-431-7320

Chapman
Chapman Housing
Authority
829 Sheeran
Chapman, KS 67431-8946
785-922-6229

Cherryvale
Cherryvale Housing
Authority
621 W 4th Street

Cherryvale, KS 67335-1718
316-336-3939

Clay Center
Clay Center Housing
Authority
330 W Court Street
Clay Center, KS 67432-2316
785-632-2100

Colby
Colby Housing Authority
600 S Mission Ridge
Avenue
Colby, KS 67701-3201
785-462-6763

Columbus
Columbus Housing
Authority
910 S Florida Avenue
Columbus, KS 66725-9150
620-429-1050

Dodge City
Dodge City Housing
Authority
407 E Bend Street
Dodge City, KS 67801-2178
316-225-1965

Downs
Downs Housing Authority
1109 Delay Street
Downs, KS 67437-1425
785-454-3914

Florence
Florence Housing Authority
124 E 9th Street
Florence, KS 66851-1138
316-878-4371

Fort Scott
Fort Scott Housing
Authority
315 Scott Avenue
Fort Scott, KS 66701-2064
316-223-4570

Frontenac
Frontenac Housing
Authority
508 S Linn Street
Frontenac, KS 66763-2451
316-232-1042

Galena
Galena Housing Authority
1301 Elm Street
Galena, KS 66739-1435
620-783-5525

Garden City
Garden City Housing
Authority
606 Pershing Avenue
Garden City, KS 67846-4568
316-276-1240

Gaylord
Gaylord Housing Authority
PO Box 540
Gaylord, KS 67638-0540
785-697-2690

Girard
Girard Housing Authority
100 N Water Street
Girard, KS 66743-1400
316-724-8668

Sek-Cap, Inc.
401 North Sinnet
Girard, KS 66743
316-724-8204

Goodland
Goodland Housing
Authority
515 E 5th Street
Goodland, KS 67735-2053
785-899-5591

Great Bend
Great Bend Housing
Authority
1101 Kansas Avenue
Great Bend, KS 67530-4460
316-793-7761

Greenleaf
Greenleaf Housing
Authority
300 Hillcrest Lane
Greenleaf, KS 66943-9481
785-747-2865

Halstead
Halstead Housing
Authority
815 W 6th Street
Halstead, KS 67056-2157
316-835-2026

Hanover
Hanover Housing
Authority
100 N Hollenberg Avenue
Hanover, KS 66945-9000
785-337-2692

Hays
Hays Housing Authority
1709 Sunset Trail
Hays, KS 67601-2657
785-625-1188

Herington
Herington Housing
Authority
201 E Helen Street
Herington, KS 67449-1660
785-258-2510

Hill City
Hill City Housing Authority
905 N 3rd Avenue
Hill City, KS 67642-1439
785-421-2348

Hillsboro
Hillsboro Housing
Authority
506 W Grand Avenue
Hillsboro, KS 67063-1347
316-947-2235

Horton
Horton Housing Authority
1701 Euclid Avenue
Horton, KS 66439-1241
785-486-3615

Howard
Howard Housing Authority
134 E Washington Street A
Howard, KS 67349-9405
620-374-2386

Humboldt
Humboldt Housing
Authority
410 S 9th Street
Humboldt, KS 66748-1920
316-473-2391

Iola
Iola Housing Authority
217 N Washington Avenue
Iola, KS 66749-2849
620-365-5143

Jetmore
Jetmore Housing Authority
412 E Bramley Street
Jetmore, KS 67854-9027
316-357-8535

Junction City
Junction City Housing
Authority
1202 Country Club Lane
Junction City, KS 66441-
3205
785-238-5882

Kansas City
Kansas City Housing
Authority
1124 N 9th Street

Kansas City, KS 66101-2120
913-281-3300

Kinsley
Kinsley Housing Authority
210 W 9th Street
Kinsley, KS 67547-2224
316-659-2602

Lawrence
Lawrence/Douglas County
Housing Authority
1600 Haskell Avenue
Lawrence, KS 66044 -4361
785-842-8110

Leavenworth
Leavenworth Housing
Authority
200 Shawnee Street
Leavenworth, KS 66048-
2075
913-682-9201

Liberal
Liberal Housing Authority
1401 N New York Avenue
Liberal, KS 67901-2787
316-624-5501

Lincoln
Lincoln Housing Authority
107 E Court Street
Lincoln, KS 67455-2329
785-524-4887

Lindsborg
Lindsborg Housing
Authority
421 E Saline Street
Lindsborg, KS 67456-2020
785-227-3597

Linn
Linn Housing Authority
305 Cedar Street
Linn, KS 66953-9558
785-348-5774

Luray
Luray Housing Authority
PO Box 302
Luray, KS 67649-0302
785-698-2455

Lyons
Lyons Housing Authority
215 S Bell Avenue
Lyons, KS 67554-2845
316-257-5241

Manhattan
Manhattan Housing
Authority

300 N 5th Street
Manhattan, KS 66502-5937
785-776-8588

Mankato
Mankato Housing
Authority
525 N Clinton Street
Mankato, KS 66956-1805
785-378-3017

Marion
Marion Housing Authority
1501 E Lawrence Street
Marion, KS 66861-1154
316-382-2218

Medicine Lodge
Medicine Lodge Housing
Authority
200 S Cherry Street
Medicine Lodge, KS 67104-
1445
316-886-5801

Merriam
Johnson County Housing
Authority
9305 W. 74th Street
Merriam, KS 66204
913-432-2174, ext. 3321

Minneapolis
Minneapolis Housing
Authority
PO Box 227
Minneapolis, KS 67467-0227
785-392-3272

Moundridge
Moundridge Housing
Authority
612 S Christian Avenue
Moundridge, KS 67107-7107
316-345-2644

Neodesha
Neodesha Housing
Authority
118 S 6th Street
Neodesha, KS 66757-1726
316-325-2440

Newton
Newton Housing Authority
115 W 9th Street
Newton, KS 67114-1970
316-283-8500

North Newton
North Newton Housing
Authority
307 W 24th Street

North Newton, KS 67117-
8080
316-283-8731

Norton
Norton Housing Authority
213 Horace Greeley Avenue
Norton, KS 67654-2223
785-877-2714

Oakley
Oakley Housing Authority
700 W 5th Street
Oakley, KS 67748-1355
785-672-4414

Oberlin
Oberlin Housing Authority
202 N Elk Avenue
Oberlin, KS 67749-1863
785-475-3010

Olathe
Olathe Housing Authority
300 N Chestnut Street
Olathe, KS 66061-3304
913-393-6260

Osborne
Osborne Housing Authority
200 E Vermont Street
Osborne, KS 6747- 2551
785-346-2727

Paola
Paola Housing Authority
310 S Iron Street
Paola, KS 66071-1615
913-294-4731

Parsons
Parsons Housing Authority
1900 Belmont Avenue
Parsons, KS 67357-4263
316-421-7040

Phillipsburg
Phillipsburg Housing
Authority
302 W F Street
Phillipsburg, KS 67661-1826
785-543-5921

Pleasanton
Pleasanton Housing
Authority
PO Box 425
Pleasanton, KS 66075-0425
913-352-6289

Russell
Russell Housing Authority
330 W 4th Street

Russell, KS 67665-2648
785-483-3400

Sabetha
Sabetha Housing Authority
1011 Oregon Street
Sabetha, KS 66534-2072
785-284-3075

Salina
Salina Housing Authority
PO Box 1202
Salina, KS 67402-1202
785-827-0441

Sedgwick
Sedgwick Housing
Authority
111 Hymer Drive
Sedgwick, KS 67135-8702
316-772-5354

Seneca
Seneca Housing Authority
504 Edward Street
Seneca, KS 66538-2251
785-336-2144

Solomon
Solomon Housing
Authority
105 W 6th Street
Solomon, KS 67480-8204
785-655-9422

St Francis
St. Francis Housing
Authority
200 N Ash Street
St Francis, KS 67756-9145
785-332-3934

Stafford
Stafford Housing Authority
615 E Broadway Street
Stafford, KS 67578-1812
316-234-6929

Sterling
Sterling Housing Authority
220 N 3rd Street
Sterling, KS 67579-1900
316-278-2640

Topeka
Topeka Housing Authority
2010 Se California Avenue
Topeka, KS 66607-1444
785-357-8842

Ulysses
Ulysses Housing Authority
PO Box 613

Ulysses, KS 67880-0613
316-356-3972

Valley Falls
Valley Falls Housing
Authority
940 Frazier Street
Valley Falls, KS 66088-1153
785-945-3245

Victoria
Victoria Housing Authority
612 Grant Street Terrace
Victoria, KS 67671-9505
785-735-2620

Wamego
Wamego Housing
Authority
1201 Chrysler Drive
Wamego, KS 66547-1267
785-456-7675

Washington
Washington Housing
Authority
350 Washington Street
Washington, KS 66968-1610
785-325-2416

Waterville
Waterville Housing
Authority
500 E Walnut Street
Waterville, KS 66548-9779
785-363-2239

Wellington
Wellington Housing
Authority
400 S C Street
Wellington, KS 67152 -2754
620-326-5821

Wichita
Sedgwick County Housing
Authority
604 North Main #E
Wichita, KS 67203
316-383-7433

Wichita Housing Authority
332 Riverview Street
Wichita, KS 67203-4245
316-268-4688

Winfield
Winfield Housing
Authority
1417 Pine Terrace
Winfield, KS 67156-1428
316-221-4936

KENTUCKY

Albany
Housing Authority of
Albany
200 Harvest Street
Albany, KY 42602-1313
606-387-7708

Ashland
Housing Authority of
Ashland
3131 Winchester Avenue
Ashland, KY 41101-2057
606-325-7112

Barbourville
Housing Authority of
Barbourville
640 Manchester Street
Barbourville, KY 40906-1720
606-546-3567

Bardstown
Housing Authority of
Bardstown
513 W Broadway Street
Bardstown, KY 40004-1302
502-348-3525

Beattyville
Housing Authority of
Beattyville
227 Boone Avenue
Apartment 31
Beattyville, KY 41311-8819
606-464-8471

Beaver Dam
Housing Authority of
Beaver Dam
3030 James Court
Beaver Dam, KY 42320-1942
270-274-7504

Benton
Housing Authority of
Benton
101 Walnut Court
Benton, KY 42025-1650
270-527-3626

Berea
Housing Authority of Berea
110 Orchard Street
Berea, KY 40403-1416
859-986-4436

Bowling Green
Housing Authority of
Bowling Green
PO Box 116

Bowling Green, KY 42102-
0116
270-843-6074

Burkesville
Housing Authority of
Burkesville
401 Sunset Drive
Burkesville, KY 42717-9643
270-864-5111

Cadiz
Housing Authority of Cadiz
117 Lincoln Avenue
Apartment 51
Cadiz, KY 42211-6122
270-522-3916

Campbellsville
Campbellsville Housing
and Redevelopment
Authority
400 Ingram Avenue
Campbellsville, KY 42718-
1627
270-465-3576

Carrollton
Housing Authority of
Carrollton
1201 9th Street
Carrollton, KY 41008-1402
502-732-4330

Catlettsburg
Housing Authority of
Catlettsburg
210 24th Street
Catlettsburg, KY 41129-1266
606-739-6851

Central City
Housing Authority of
Central City
509 S 9th Street
Central City, KY 42330-1615
270-754-2521

Columbia
Housing Authority of
Columbia
922 Carrie Bolin Drive
Columbia, KY 42728-1001
270-384-2271

Corbin
Housing Authority of
Corbin
1336 Madison Avenue
Corbin, KY 40701-1945
606-528-5104

Covington
Housing Authority of
Covington

2940 Madison Avenue
Covington, KY 41015-1068
859-491-5311

Cumberland
Housing Authority of
Cumberland
178 Russell Drive
Cumberland, KY 40823-1647
606-589-4600

Cynthiana
Housing Authority of
Cynthiana
149 Federal Drive
Cynthiana, KY 41031-1421
859-234-5388

Danville
Housing Authority of
Danville
102 Mcintyre Circle
Danville, KY 40422-1267
859-236-6116

Dawson Springs
Housing Authority of
Dawson Springs
100 Clarkdale Court
Dawson Springs, KY 42408-
1405
270-797-2512

Dayton
Housing Authority of
Dayton
201 Clay Street
Dayton, KY 41074-1249
859-491-7749

Dry Ridge
Housing Authority Dry
Ridge
300 Meadowview Circle
Dry Ridge, KY 4103- 8889
859-824-4432

Eddyville
Housing Authority of Lyon
County
425 Linden Avenue
Eddyville, KY 42038-8212
270-388-7108

Elizabethtown
Housing Authority of
Elizabethtown
63 Public Square
Elizabethtown, KY 42701-
1459
270-765-2092

Eminence
Housing Authority of
Eminence

791 Cannon Court
Eminence, KY 40019-1078
502-845-4769

Falmouth
Housing Authority of
Falmouth
412 Beech Street
Falmouth, KY 41040-1215
859-654-8492

Flemingsburg
Housing Authority of
Flemingsburg
142 Circle Drive
Flemingsburg, KY 41041-
1442
606-845-1651

Frankfort
Housing Authority of
Frankfort
590 Walter Todd Drive
Frankfort, KY 40601-2026
502-223-2148

Franklin
Housing Authority of
Franklin
1301 Crestmore Drive
Franklin, KY 42134-2524
270-586-8500

Fulton
Housing Authority of
Fulton
200 N Highland Drive
Fulton, KY 42041-1462
270-472-1115

Georgetown
Housing Authority
Georgetown
139 Scroggins Park
Georgetown, KY 40324-2039
502-863-3773

Glasgow
Housing Authority of
Glasgow
106 Bunche Avenue
Glasgow, KY 42141-2321
270-651-3859

Greensburg
Housing Authority
Greensburg
200 Nancy Street
Greensburg, KY 42743-1375
270-932-4296

Greenville
Housing Authority of
Greenville

613 Reynolds Drive
Greenville, KY 42345-1151
270-338-5900

Guthrie
Housing Authority of Todd
County
150 Pennyrile Court
Guthrie, KY 42234-9241
270-483-9750

Harlan
Housing Authority of
Harlan
509 Poplar Street
Harlan, KY 40831-1653
606-573-5800

Harrodsburg
Housing Authority of
Harrodsburg
502 W Office Street
Harrodsburg, KY 40330-
1430
859-734-4447

Hazard
Housing Authority of
Hazard
100 Campbell St., Room A
Hazard, KY 41701-1353
606-436-5741

Henderson
Housing Authority of
Henderson
111 S Adams Street
Henderson, KY 42420-3611
270-827-1294

Hickman
Housing Authority of
Hickman
50 Holly Court
Hickman, KY 42050
270-236-2888

Hindman
Housing Authority of Knott
County
997 Highway 160 S
Hindman, KY 41822-8961
606-785-3451

Hodgenville
Housing Authority of
Hodgenville
501 Miami Court
Hodgenville, KY 42748-1213
270-358-4705

Hopkinsville
Housing Authority of
Hopkinsville

400 N Elm Street
Hopkinsville, KY 42240-
2255
270-887-4275

Horse Cave
Housing Authority of Horse
Cave
990 N Dixie Street
Horse Cave, KY 42749-1863
270-786-2481

Irvine
Housing Authority of Irvine
200 Wallace Circle
Irvine, KY 40336-1044
606-723-3116

Irvington
Housing Authority of
Irvington
PO Box 399
Irvington, KY 40146-9746
270-547-7648

Jackson
Housing Authority of
Jackson
400 Railroad Street
Jackson, KY 41339-9253
606-666-2859

Lancaster
Housing Authority of
Lancaster
109 Kinnaird Avenue
Lancaster, KY 40444-1229
859-792-3813

Lebanon
Housing Authority of
Lebanon
100 Sunset Terrace
Lebanon, KY 40033-1329
270-692-3481

Lexington
Housing Authority of
Lexington
300 W New Circle Road
Lexington, KY 40505-1428
859-281-5062

Liberty
Housing Authority of
Liberty
75 Riverdale Drive
Liberty, KY 42539-3200
606-787-7821

London
Housing Authority of
London
100 Scott Street

London, KY 40741-1424
606-864-5474

Louisa
Housing Authority of
Lawrence County
200 Gene Wilson Boulevard
Louisa, KY 41230-9645
606-638-9414

Louisville
City of Louisville, Dept. of
Hud
617 West Jefferson Street
Louisville, KY 40202
502-574-3107 ext. 401

Louisville
Housing Auth of Jefferson
County
801 Vine Street
Louisville, KY 40204-2020
502-574-1000

Louisville
Housing Authority of
Louisville
420 S 8th Street
Louisville, KY 40203-1906
502-574-3400

Madisonville
Housing Authority of
Madisonville
211 Pride Avenue
Madisonville, KY 42431-
1889
270-821-5517

Manchester
Housing Authority of
Manchester
306 Town Branch Road
Manchester, KY 40962-1335
606-598-3884

Mayfield
Housing Authority
Mayfield
312 Brookside Drive
Mayfield, KY 42066-1724
270-247-6391

Maysville
Housing Authority of
Maysville
600 Clark Street
Maysville, KY 41056-1710
606-564-4409

Mc Kee
Housing Authority of
Mckee
1405 Roberts Court

Mc Kee, KY 40447-9402
606-287-8777

Monticello
Housing Authority of
Monticello
712 Homestead Heights
Monticello, KY 42633-1721
606-348-6286

Morehead
Housing Authority of
Morehead
200 Heritage Place
Morehead, KY 40351-1000
606-784-4314

Morganfield
Housing Authority of
Morganfield
703 Culver Court
Morganfield, KY 42437-1663
270-389-3066

Morgantown
Housing Authority of
Morgantown
300 Kent Manor Drive
Morgantown, KY 42261-
8815
270-526-3873

Mount Sterling
Housing Authority of
Mount Sterling
335 Barnard Avenue
Mount Sterling, KY 40353-
1565
859-498-5592

Mount Vernon
Housing Authority of
Mount Vernon
50 Lovell Lane
Mount Vernon, KY 40456-
2987
606-256-4185

Murray
Housing Authority of
Murray
716 Nash Drive
Murray, KY 42071-3053
270-753-5000

Newport
Housing Authority of
Newport
301 W Southgate Street
Newport, KY 41071-1066
859-581-2533

Nicholasville
Housing Authority of
Nicholasville

601 Broadway Street
Nicholasville, KY 40356-
1417
859-885-4324

Olive Hill
Housing Authority of Olive
Hill
501 Tygart Street
Olive Hill, KY 41164-7034
606-286-4721

Owensboro
Housing Authority of
Owensboro
2161 E 19th Street
Owensboro, KY 42303-1270
270-683-5365

Owenton
Housing Authority of
Owenton
100 Gaines Village Drive
Owenton, KY 40359-1241
502-484-2939

Owingsville
Housing Authority of
Owingsville
180 Kendall Springs Avenue
Owingsville, KY 40360-2209
606-674-2704

Paducah
Housing Authority of
Paducah
2330 Ohio Street
Paducah, KY 42003-3306
270-443-3634

Paintsville
Housing Authority of
Paintsville
700 6th Street
Paintsville, KY 41240-1334
606-789-1782

Paris
Housing Authority of Paris
2 Horton Drive
Paris, KY 40361-1316
859-987-2575

Pikeville
Housing Authority Pikeville
748 Hambley Boulevard
Pikeville, KY 41501-1155
606-432-8124

Pineville
Housing Authority of
Pineville
911 Alabama Avenue
Pineville, KY 40977-1550
606-337-2900

Prestonsburg
Housing Authority Floyd
County
36 Blaine Hall Drive
Apartment 37
Prestonsburg, KY 41653-
1851
606-285-3833 ext. 11

Prestonsburg
Housing Authority
Prestonsburg
12 Blaine Hall Drive
Prestonsburg, KY 41653-
1851
606-886-2717

Princeton
Housing Authority of
Princeton
100 Hillview Court
Princeton, KY 42445-1300
270-365-5769

Providence
Housing Authority of
Providence
101 Center Ridge Drive
Providence, KY 42450-1169
270-667-5786

Radcliff
Housing Authority of
Radcliff
480 Robbie Valentine Drive
Radcliff, KY 40160-2053
270-351-6772

Richmond
Housing Authority of
Richmond
PO Box 786
Richmond, KY 40476-0786
859-623-5968

Russellville
Housing Authority of
Russellville
940 Hicks Street
Russellville, KY 42276-2178
270-726-7579

Salyersville
Housing Authority of
Salyersville / Magoffin CO.
540 Allen Drive
Salyersville, KY 41465-9191
606-349-6554

Scottsville
Housing Authority of
Scottsville
301 Massey Street

Scottsville, KY 42164-1452
270-237-4062

Shelbyville
Housing Authority of
Shelbyville
41 Cardinal Drive
Shelbyville, KY 40065-1877
502-633-4531

Somerset
Housing Authority of
Somerset
608 Mckinley Street
Somerset, KY 42501-1226
606-679-1332 ext. 104

Springfield
Housing Authority
Springfield
1057 Melavin Circle
Springfield, KY 40069-1100
859-336-7645

Stanford
Housing Authority of
Stanford
100 Lacy Street
Stanford, KY 40484-1401
606-365-7874

Sturgis
Housing Authority of
Sturgis
116 E Old Providence Road
Sturgis, KY 42459-1726
270-333-4231

Tompkinsville
Housing Authority of
Tompkinsville
1023 Green Hills
Tompkinsville, KY 42167-
1664
270-487-6050

Vanceburg
Housing Authority
Vanceburg
802 Fairlane Drive
Vanceburg, KY 41179-1179
606-796-2241

Versailles
Housing Authority of
Versailles
519 Poplar Street
Versailles, KY 40383-1196
859-873-5351

Warfield
Housing Authority of
Martin County
Warfield, KY 41267-9801
606-395-5575

Whitesburg
Housing Authority of
Whitesburg
4 Banks Street 101
Whitesburg, KY 41858-7526
606-633-7144

Williamsburg
Housing Authority of
Williamsburg
600 Brush Arbor
Apartments
Williamsburg, KY 40769-
1711
606-549-0282

Williamstown
Housing Authority of
Williamstown
514 Helton Heights
Williamstown, KY 41097-
9438
859-823-1511

Winchester
Housing Authority of
Winchester
PO Box 56
Winchester, KY 40392-0056
859-744-2960

Wurtland
Elliott County Housing
Authority
C/O Appalachian Foothills
Housing Agency
1214 Riverside Blvd.
Wurtland, KY 41144
606-836-0911

Louisiana

Abbeville
Housing Authority of The
City of Abbeville
1101 E Oak Street
Abbeville, LA 70510-3853
337-893-4643

Alexandria
Housing Authority of The
City of Alexandria
2558 Loblolly Lane
Alexandria, LA 71303-4343
318-442-8843

Basile
Housing Authority of The
Town of Basile
2307 2nd Street
Basile, LA 70515-5546
318-432-5423

Baton Rouge
Housing Authority of East
Baton Rouge
4731 North Blvd.
Baton Rouge, LA 70806
504-923-8100

Berwick
Housing Authority of The
Town of Berwick
2751 5th Street
Berwick, LA 70342-2809
985-385-1546

Bogalusa
Bogalusa Housing
Authority
1015 Union Avenue
Bogalusa, LA 70427-2360
504-735-6533

Bossier City
Bossier Parish Section 8
3022 Old Minden Road
Suite 206
Bossier City, LA 71112
318-747-7823 ext. 22

Housing Authority of The
City of Bossier City
805 E 1st Street
Bossier City, LA 71111-4321
318-549-1556

Boyce
Housing Authority of
Rapides Parish
119 Boyce Garden Drive
Boyce, LA 71409-9649
318-793-4752

Breaux Bridge
Housing Authority of The
City of Breaux Bridge
720 Genny Drive
Breaux Bridge, LA 70517-
6004
337-332-2808

Bunkie
Housing Authority of The
Town of Bunkie
712 Keller Street
Bunkie, LA 71322-2324
318-346-6838

Church Point
Housing Authority of The
Town of Church Point
700 S Wimberly Street
Church Point, LA 70525-
3721
337-684-2195

Colfax
Colfax Housing Authority
300 Park Lane
Colfax, LA 71417-1137
318-627-5945

Columbia
Housing Authority of The
Parish of Caldwell
103 N Alvin Street
Columbia, LA 71418-3373
318-649-5022

Cottonport
Housing Authority of The
Town of Cottonport
650 Jacobs Street
Cottonport, LA 71327-3732
318-876-3457

Covington
Housing Authority of City
of Covington
303 W 33rd Avenue
Covington, LA 70433-1637
504-898-0345

Crowley
Housing Authority of
Crowley
200 Westwood Drive
Crowley, LA 70526-3239
337-783-8521

DelCambre
Housing Authority of The
Town of DelCambre
218 S Pelloat Street
Delcambre, LA 70528-4022
337-685-4455

Denham Springs
Housing Authority of The
City of Denham Springs
600 Eugene Street
Denham Springs, LA 70726-
3933
504-664-3301

Dequincy
Housing Authority of The
City of Dequincy
500 S Grand Avenue
Dequincy, LA 70633-4122
318-786-2381

Deridder
Housing Authority of The
City of Deridder
600 Warren Street
Deridder, LA 70634-3547
318-463-7288

Donaldsonville
Housing Authority of The
City of Donaldsonville
1501 Saint Patrick Street
Donaldsonville, LA 70346-
4138
504-473-9486

Elton
Housing Authority of The
Town of Elton
415 Lafleur Street
Elton, LA 70532-3229
318-584-2224

Erath
Housing Authority of The
Town of Erath
608 N Lahasky Street
Erath, LA 70533-3010
337-937-5128

Eunice
Housing Authority of The
City of Eunice
331 Mill Street
Eunice, LA 70535-6129
337-457-7716

Farmerville
Housing Authority of
Farmerville
810 Doyle Street
Farmerville, LA 71241-2057
318-368-9677

Ferriday
Housing Authority of
Ferriday
27393 Highway 15
Ferriday, LA 71334-3347
318-757-6531

Grambling
Housing Authority of The
Town of Grambling
300 B T Woodard Circle
Grambling, LA 71245-9210
318-247-6035

Gueydan
Housing Authority of The
Town of Gueydan
707 Wilkinson Street
Gueydan, LA 70542-3309
337-536-6949

Haynesville
Housing Authority of The
Town of Haynesville
1953 Mill Street
Haynesville, LA 71038-5610
318-624-1272

Homer
Housing Authority of
Homer
329 S 4th Street
Homer, LA 71040-4507
318-927-3579

Houma
Housing Authority of The
City of Houma
7491 Park Avenue
Houma, LA 70364-3601
504-876-4755

Independence
Town of Independence
Housing Authority
222 Pine Street
Independence, LA 70443-
2350
504-878-9091

Iowa
Housing Authority of The
Town of Iowa
603 N Park Drive
Iowa, LA 70647-3938
318-582-3564

Jena
Housing Authority of Jena
100 Tarver Avenue
Jena, LA 71342-9786
318-992-6413

Jennings
Housing Authority of The
City of Jennings
300 Bangle Drive
Jennings, LA 70546-7530
318-824-5642

Jonesboro
Housing Authority of The
Town of Jonesboro
839 Harvey Place
Jonesboro, LA 71251-2907
318-259-3125

Kenner
Housing Authority of The
City of Kenner
1013 31st Street
Kenner, LA 70065-4366
504-467-9166

LA Place
Housing Authority of St.
John The Baptist Parish
152 Joe Parquet Circle
LA Place, LA 70068-4212
504-652-9036

Lake Arthur
Housing Authority of The
Town of Lake Arthur
118a Mcclure Avenue
Lake Arthur, LA 70549-4420
337-774-3143

Lake Charles
Housing Authority of Lake
Charles
800 Bilbo Street
Lake Charles, LA 70601-
4250
318-439-4189

Lake Providence
East Carroll Parish Housing
Authority
1415 Mike Avenue
Lake Providence, LA 71254-
3653
318-559-3134

Housing Authority of The
Town of Lake Providence
210 Foster Street
Lake Providence, LA 71254-
2153
318-559-2047

Leesville
Housing Authority of The
City of Leesville
213 Blackburn Street
Leesville, LA 71446-3108
318-238-1912

Housing Authority of
Vernon Parish
117 Savannah Circle
Leesville, LA 71446-8407
318-537-0339

Logansport
Housing Authority of The
Town of Logansport
PO Box 470
Logansport, LA 71049-0470
318-697-4380

Lutcher
Housing Authority of St.
James Parish
2627 N King Avenue
Lutcher, LA 70071-5351
504-869-3278

Mamou
Housing Authority of The
Town of Mamou
1016 Maple Street
Mamou, LA 70554-3916
318-468-3539

Mansfield
Housing Authority of The
Town of Mansfield
600 Kennedy Street
Mansfield, LA 71052-3328
318-872-1383

Many
Housing Authority of
Sabine Parish
210 N Highland Drive
Many, LA 71449-3751
318-256-3359

Marksville
Housing Authority of The
Town of Marksville
100 N Hillside Drive
Marksville, LA 71351-2758
318-253-9256

Marrero
Housing Authority of
Jefferson Parish
1718 Betty Street
Marrero, LA 70072-3318
504-347-4381

Merryville
Housing Authority of The
Town of Merryville
100 Hard Times Road
Merryville, LA 70653-3843
318-825-8770

Minden
Housing Authority of The
City of Minden
1209 East Street
Minden, LA 71055-5027
318-377-1077

Monroe
Housing Authority of
Monroe
300 Harrison Street
Monroe, LA 71201-7441
318-388-1500 ext. 310

Morgan City
Housing Authority of The
City of Morgan City
336 Wren Street
Morgan City, LA 70380-
7214
504-384-5118

Natchitoches
Housing Authority of
Natchitoches Parish
529 4th Street
Natchitoches, LA 71457-
4450
318-357-0553

Natchitoches City Housing
Authority
416 Shady Lane
Natchitoches, LA 71457-
6029
318-352-9788

New Iberia
Housing Authority of New
Iberia
325 North Street
New Iberia, LA 70560-3565
318-364-5515

New Orleans
Housing Authority of New
Orleans
4100 Touro Street
New Orleans, LA 70122-
3162
504-670-3300

New Roads
Housing Authority of The
Town of New Roads
151 Cherry Street
New Roads, LA 70760-2411
504-638-8940

Oakdale
Housing Authority of
Oakdale
201 E Lake Street
Oakdale, LA 71463-2738
318-335-2417

Olla
Housing Authority of The
Town of Olla
108 Washington Street
Olla, LA 71465-9723
318-495-5996

Opelousas
Housing Authority of
Opelousas
906 E Laurent Street
Opelousas, LA 70570-7241
337-942-5693

Patterson
Housing Authority of The
Town of Patterson
409 Grout Street
Patterson, LA 70392-4517
504-395-3736

Pineville
Pineville Housing
Authority
2731 Highway 28 E
Pineville, LA 71360-5770
318-473-9729

Ponchatoula
Housing Authority of The
Town of Pontchatoula
1005 Pelican Drive
Ponchatoula, LA 70454-9007
504-386-3257

Rayne
Housing Authority of
Rayne
1011 The Boulevard
Rayne, LA 70578-6132
337-334-3084

Rayville
Housing Authority of The
Town of Rayville
202 Waldorf Street
Rayville, LA 71269-2032
318-728-5217

Ruston
Housing Authority of
Ruston
615 N Farmerville Street
Ruston, LA 71270-3916
318-255-3644

Saint Martinville
Housing Authority of The
City of St. Martinville
13 Bulliard Drive
Saint Martinville, LA 70582-
3403
337-394-6288

Housing Authority of The
Village of Parks
1003 Charles Street
Saint Martinville, LA 70582-
6231
337-845-4003

Shreveport
Housing Authority of
Shreveport
623 Jordan Street
Shreveport, LA 71101-4748
318-227-8174

Sulphur
Housing Authority of The
City of Sulphur
312 Brook Street
Sulphur, LA 70663-2804
318-527-5248

Thibodaux
Housing Authority of The
City of Thibodaux
1425 Eagle Drive
Thibodaux, LA 70301-4204
504-447-2904

Ville Platte
Housing Authority of Ville
Platte
724 N Thompson Street
Ville Platte, LA 70586-3064
318-363-2535

Vinton
Housing Authority of The
Town of Vinton
810 Center Street
Vinton, LA 70668-4104
318-589-5331

Vivian
Housing Authority of
Vivian
609 Redbud Court
Vivian, LA 71082-3344
318-375-2381

Westwego
Housing Authority of
Westwego
PO Box 248
Westwego, LA 70096-0248
504-341-5255

White Castle
Housing Authority of The
Town of White Castle
55050 Veterans Street
White Castle, LA 70788-
2337
504-545-3967

Winnfield
Housing Authority of
Winnfield
901 Neil Wagoner Road
Winnfield, LA 71483-8804
318-628-4960

Winnsboro
Housing Authority of The
Town of Winnsboro
1702 Hatfield Street
Winnsboro, LA 71295-3628
318-435-5426

Youngsville
Housing Authority of The
Town of Youngsville
125 Romero Street
Youngsville, LA 70592-5511
337-856-4534

MAiNE

Auburn
Auburn Housing Authority
PO Box 3037

Auburn, ME 04212-3037
207-784-7351

Bangor
Housing Authority City of
Bangor
161 Davis Road
Bangor, ME 04401-2310
207-942-6365

Bar Harbor
Bar Harbor Housing
Authority
80 Mount Desert Street
Bar Harbor, ME 04609-1335
207-288-4770

Bath
Bath Housing Authority
80 Congress Avenue
Bath, ME 04530-1542
207-443-3116

Brewer
Brewer Housing Authority
1 Colonial Circle
Brewer, ME 04412-1475
207-989-7890

Brunswick
Brunswick Housing
Authority
12 Stone Street
Brunswick, ME 04011-1516
207-725-8711

Ellsworth
Ellsworth Housing
Authority
430 Water Street
Ellsworth, ME 04605-2111
207-288-4770

Fort Fairfield
Fort Fairfield Housing
Authority
18 Fields Lane
Fort Fairfield, ME 04742
207-476-5771

Lewiston
Lewiston Housing
Authority
1 College Street
Lewiston, ME 04240-7175
207-783-1423

Old Town
Old Town Housing
Authority
165 S Main Street
Old Town, ME 04468 -1563
207-827-6151

Portland
Portland Housing Authority
14 Baxter Boulevard
Portland, ME 04101-1802
207-773-4753

Presque Isle
Presque Isle Housing
Authority
58 Birch Street
Presque Isle, ME 04769-2204
207-768-8231

Sanford
Sanford Housing Authority
29 Yale Street
Sanford, ME 04073 -2734
207-324-6747

Van Buren
Van Buren Housing
Authority
16 Champlain Street
Van Buren, ME 04785-1339
207-868-5441

Waterville
Waterville Housing
Authority
60 Elm Street
Waterville, ME 04901-6046
207-873-2155

Westbrook
Westbrook Housing
Authority
30 Liza Harmon Drive
Westbrook, ME 04092-4766
207-854-9779

MARylANd

Annapolis
Annapolis Housing
Authority
1217 Madison Street
Annapolis, MD 21403-2203
410-267-8000

Baltimore
Housing Authority of
Baltimore City
417 E Fayette Street
Baltimore, MD 21202-3431
410-396-3232

Cambridge
Housing Authority of
Cambridge
700 Weaver Avenue
Cambridge, MD 21613-2105
410-228-6856

Centreville
Queen Anne's City Housing
Authority
P.O. Box 327
Centreville, MD 21617
410-758-3977

College Park
College Park Housing
Authority
9014 Rhode Island Avenue
College Park, MD 20740-
1963
301-345-3600

Columbia
Howard Co. Housing
Authority Comm.
Development
6751 Columbia Gateway
Drive
Columbia, MD 21046-2164
410-313-6320

Crisfield
Housing Authority of
Crisfield
115 S 7th Street
Crisfield, MD 21817-1035
410-968-0289

Cumberland
Housing Authority of
Allegany County
701 Furnace Street
Suite 1
Cumberland, MD 21502-
1569
301-759-2880

Easton
Housing Authority of The
Town of Easton
900 Doverbrook Street
Easton, MD 21601-4904
410-822-5358

Elkton
Elkton Housing Authority
150 E Main Street
Elkton, MD 21921-5936
410-398-5018

Frederick
Frederick Housing
Authority
209 Madison Street
Frederick, MD 21701-6536
301-662-8173

Frostburg
Housing Authority of
Frostburg

Meshach Frost Village
Frostburg, MD 21532
301-689-9700

Glen Burnie
Housing Commission of
Anne Arundel County
7885 Gordon Court
Glen Burnie, MD 21060-
7931
410-222-6200

Glenarden
Glenarden Housing
Authority
8639 Glenarden Parkway
Glenarden, MD 20706-1521
301-772-0880

Hagerstown
Hagerstown Housing
Authority
35 W Baltimore Street
Hagerstown, MD 21740-
6059
301-733-6911

Housing Authority of
Washington County
44 North Potomac St
Suite 201
Hagerstown, MD 21740-
4885
301-791-3168 ext. 207

Havre De Grace
Havre De Grace Housing
Authority
101 Stansbury Court
Havre De Grace, MD 21078-
2641
410-939-2097

Kensington
Housing Opportunity Com
of Montgomery Co
10400 Detrick Avenue
Kensington, MD 20895-2440
301-929-6700

Largo
Housing Authority of
Prince Georges County
9400 Peppercorn Place
Suite 200
Largo, MD 20774-5359
301-883-5531

Leonardtown
St Mary's County Housing
Authority
PO Box 653
Leonardtown, MD 20650-
0653
301-475-4405

Rockville
Housing Authority of The
City of Rockville
14 Moore Drive
Rockville, MD 20850-1168
301-424-6265

Saint Michaels
St. Michaels Housing
Authority
PO Box 296
Saint Michaels, MD 21663-
0296
410-745-5121

Salisbury
Wicomico County Housing
Authority
911 Booth Street
Salisbury, MD 21801-3046
410-749-1383

MASSACHUSETTS

Amherst
Amherst Housing
Authority
33 Kellogg Avenue
Amherst, MA 01002-2102
413-256-0206

Auburn
Auburn Housing Authority
200 Oxford Street N
Auburn, MA 01501-1505
508-832-3852

Beverly
Beverly Housing Authority
137 Bridge Street R
Beverly, MA 01915-2800
978-922-3100

Boston
Boston Housing Authority
52 Chauncy Street
Boston, MA 02111-2325
617-988-4000

Brockton
Brockton Housing
Authority
45 Goddard Road
Brockton, MA 02301-3864
508-588-6880

Brookline
Brookline Housing
Authority
90 Longwood Avenue
Brookline, MA 02446-6640
617-277-2022

Cambridge
Cambridge Housing
Authority
675 Massachusetts Avenue
Cambridge, MA 02139-3309
617-864-3020

Chelsea
Chelsea Housing Authority
54 Locke Street
Chelsea, MA 02150-2250
617-884-5617

Chicopee
Chicopee Housing
Authority
128 Meetinghouse Road
Chicopee, MA 01013-1830
413-592-6132

Clinton
Clinton Housing Authority
58 Fitch Road
Clinton, MA 01510-1816
978-365-4150

Concord
Concord Housing Authority
115 Stow Street
Concord, MA 01742-2495
978-369-8435

Danvers
Danvers Housing Authority
14 Stone Street
Danvers, MA 01923-1869
978-777-0909

Dedham
Dedham Housing Authority
163 Dedham Boulevard
Dedham, MA 02026-2541
781-326-3543

Dracut
Dracut Housing Authority
971 Mammoth Road
Dracut, MA 01826-3124
978-957-3515

Fall River
Fall River Housing
Authority
PO Box 989
Fall River, MA 02722-0989
508-675-3500

Falmouth
Falmouth Housing
Authority
115 Scranton Avenue
Falmouth, MA 02540-3560
508-548-1977

Fitchburg
Fitchburg Housing
Authority
50 Day Street
Fitchburg, MA 01420-4368
978-342-5222

Framingham
Framingham Housing
Authority
1 John J Brady Drive
Framingham, MA 01702-2307
508-879-7562

Gloucester
Gloucester Housing
Authority
99 Prospect Street
Gloucester, MA 01930-3742
978-281-4770

Groveland
Groveland Housing
Authority
10 River Pines Drive
Groveland, MA 01834-1347
978-374-0370

Holyoke
Holyoke Housing Authority
475 Maple Street
Holyoke, MA 01040-3775
413-534-0261

Hyannis
Barnstable Housing
Authority
500 Old Colony Road
Hyannis, MA 02601-4029
508-771-7222

Lawrence
Lawrence Housing
Authority
353 Elm Street
Lawrence, MA 01841-3649
978-685-3811

Lexington
Lexington Housing
Authority
1 Countryside Village
Lexington, MA 02420-2530
781-861-0900

Lynn
Lynn Housing Authority
10 Church Street
Lynn, MA 01902-4418
781-592-1966

Malden
Malden Housing Authority

630 Salem Street
Malden, MA 02148-4361
781-322-9460

Maynard
Maynard Housing
Authority
15 Powder Mill Circle
Maynard, MA 01754-1334
978-897-8738

Medford
Medford Housing
Authority
121 Riverside Avenue
Medford, MA 02155-4611
781-396-7200

Methuen
Methuen Housing
Authority
25 Jade Street
Methuen, MA 01844-1478
978-682-8607

Milford
Milford Housing Authority
45 Birmingham Court
Milford, MA 01757-1616
508-473-9521

Needham
Needham Housing
Authority
28 Captain Robert Cooke
Drive
Needham, MA 02494-3139
781-444-3011

New Bedford
New Bedford Housing
Authority
134 South Second Street
P.O. Box A-2081
New Bedford, MA 02740-5852
508-997-4806

Newburyport
Newburyport Housing
Authority
25 Temple Street
Newburyport, MA 01950-2713
978-465-7216

Newton Highlands
Newton Housing Authority
82 Lincoln Street
Newton Highlands, MA
02461-1551
617-964-8080

North Adams
North Adams Housing
Authority

150 Ashland Street
North Adams, MA 01247-4594
413-663-5379

North Andover
North Andover Housing
Authority
PO Box 373
North Andover, MA 01845-0373
978-682-3932

Northampton
Northampton Housing
Authority
49 Old South Street
Northampton, MA 01060-3849
413-584-4030

Norwood
Norwood Housing
Authority
40 William Shyne Circle
Norwood, MA 02062-2719
781-762-8115

Pittsfield
Pittsfield Housing
Authority
65 Columbus Avenue
Pittsfield, MA 01201-5064
413-443-5936

Pocasset
Bourne Housing Authority
871 Shore Road
Pocasset, MA 02559-2080
508-563-7485

Quincy
Quincy Housing Authority
80 Clay Street
Quincy, MA 02170-2745
617-847-4350

Revere
Revere Housing Authority
70 Cooledge Street
Revere, MA 02151-2963
617-284-4394

Salem
Salem Housing Authority
27 Charter Street
Salem, MA 01970-3656
978-744-4432

Saugus
Saugus Housing Authority
19 Talbot Street
Saugus, MA 01906-3465
781-233-2116

Scituate
Scituate Housing Authority
791 Country Way
Scituate, MA 02066-1729
781-545-3375

Shrewsbury
Shrewsbury Housing
Authority
36 N Quinsigamond
Avenue
Shrewsbury, MA 01545-2455
508-757-0323

Somerville
Somerville Housing
Authority
30 Memorial Road
Somerville, MA 02145-1704
617-625-1152

Springfield
Springfield Housing
Authority
25 Saab Court
P.O.Box 1609
Springfield, MA 01101-1609
413-785-4500

Taunton
Taunton Housing Authority
30 Olney Street
Suite B
Taunton, MA 02780-4141
508-823-6308

Wakefield
Wakefield Housing
Authority
26 Crescent Street
Wakefield, MA 01880-2430
781-245-7328

Waltham
Waltham Housing
Authority
110 Pond Street
Waltham, MA 02451-4506
781-894-3357

Watertown
Watertown Housing
Authority
100 Warren Street
Watertown, MA 02472-1723
617-923-3950

Wayland
Wayland Housing
Authority
106 Main Street
Wayland, MA 01778-4939
508-655-6310

Webster
Webster Housing Authority
10 Golden Heights
Webster, MA 01570-1651
508-943-1634

Weymouth
Weymouth Housing
Authority
402 Essex Street
Weymouth, MA 02188-4214
781-331-2323

Winchendon
Winchendon Housing
Authority
108 Ipswich Drive
Winchendon, MA 01475-
1217
978-297-2280 ext. 302

Woburn
Woburn Housing Authority
59 Campbell Street
Woburn, MA 01801-3612
781-935-0818

Worcester
Worcester Housing
Authority
40 Belmont Street
Worcester, MA 01605-2655
508-798-4500

Michigan

Albion
Albion Hgs Comm
1300 Cooper Street
Albion, MI 49224-4009
517-629-2511

Algonac
Algonac Housing
Commission
1205 Saint Clair River Drive
Algonac, MI 48001-1471
810-794-9369

Allen Park
Allen Park Housing
Commission
17000 Champaign Road
Allen Park, MI 48101-1778
313-928-5970

Alma
Alma Housing Commission
400 E Warwick Drive
Alma, MI 48801-1081
517-463-4200

Alpena
Alpena Housing
Commission
2340 S 4th Street
Alpena, MI 49707-3027
989-354-4144

Ann Arbor
Ann Arbor Housing
Commission
727 Miller Avenue
Ann Arbor, MI 48103-3367
734-994-2829

Baldwin
Baldwin Housing
Commission
105 Fournier Drive
Baldwin, MI 49304-9401
231-745-7441

Bangor
Bangor Housing
Commission
820 2nd Street
Bangor, MI 49013-1082
616-427-5535

Baraga
Baraga Housing
Commission
416 Michigan Avenue
Baraga, MI 49908-9613
906-353-6432

Bath
Bath Charter Township
Housing Commission
14379 Webster Road
Bath, MI 48808-9724
517-641-6244

Battle Creek
Battle Creek Hsg
Commission
250 Champion Street
Battle Creek, MI 49017-2368
616-965-0591

Bay City
Bay City Housing
Commission
1200 N Madison Avenue
Bay City, MI 48708-5234
989-892-9581

Belding
Belding Housing
Commission
41 Belhaven Street
Belding, MI 48809-1402
616-794-1740

Benton Harbor
Benton Harbor Hsg Comm
721 Nate Wells Drive
Benton Harbor, MI 49022
616-927-3544

Benton Township Housing
Commission
1216 Blossom Lane
Benton Harbor, MI 49022
616-927-3541

Bessemer
Bessemer Housing
Commission
46 N Fairview Street
Bessemer, MI 49911-1377
906-667-0288

Big Rapids
Big Rapids Housing
Commission
9 Parkview Village
Big Rapids, MI 49307-1500
231-796-8689

Boyne City
Boyne City Hsg Cm
829 S Park Street
Boyne City, MI 49712-1588
616-582-6203

Bronson
Bronson Housing
Commission
318 S Ruggles Street
Bronson, MI 49028-1428
517-369-6265

Cadillac
Cadillac Housing
Commission
111 S Simons Street
Cadillac, MI 49601-2184
231-775-9491

Calumet
Calumet Housing
Commission
1 Park Avenue
Calumet, MI 49913-1829
906-337-0005

Caseville
Caseville Housing
Commission
PO Box 1128
Caseville, MI 48725-1128
517-856-3323

Charlevoix
Charlevoix Housing
Commission
210 W Garfield Avenue

Charlevoix, MI 49720-1665
231-547-5451

Cheboygan
Cheboygan Hsg. Comm.
659 Cuyler Street
Cheboygan, MI 49721-2201
231-627-7189

Clinton Township
Clinton Township Housing
Commission
34947 Village Road
Clinton Township, MI
48035-3674
810-791-7000

Coldwater
Coldwater Housing
Commission
60 S Clay Street
Coldwate, MI 49036-1893
517-278-2660

Covert
Covert Public Housing
Commission
PO Box 66
Covert, MI 49043-0066
616-764-8881

Crystal Falls
Iron County Housing
Commission
210 N 3rd Street
Crystal Falls, MI 49920-1201
906-875-6060

Curtis
Mackinac County Housing
Commission
N9174 Kozy Street 50
Curtis, MI 49820-9628
906-586-3414

Dearborn
Dearborn Housing
Commission
13615 Michigan Avenue
Floor 2
Dearborn, MI 48126-3518
313-943-2390

Dearborn Heights
Dearborn Heights Housing
Commission
26155 Richardson
Dearborn Heights, MI 48127
313-277-7844

Detroit
Detroit Housing
Commission
2211 Orleans Street

Detroit, MI 48207-2731
313-877-8639

Dowagiac
Dowagiac Housing
Commission
100 Chestnut Street
Dowagiac, MI 49047-1963
616-782-3786

Dundee
Dundee Housing
Commission
501 Rawson Street
Dundee, MI 48131-1073
734-529-2828

East Jordan
East Jordan Housing
Commission
451 Water Street
East Jordan, MI 49727-9355
616-536-2051

East Tawas
East Tawas Housing
Commission
304 W Bay Street
East Tawas, MI 48730-1159
517-362-4963

Eastpointe
Eastpointe Housing
Commission
15701 E 9 Mile Road
Eastpointe, MI 48021-2275
810-445-5099

Ecorse
Ecorse Housing
Commission
266 Hyacinthe Street
Ecorse, MI 48229-1629
313-381-9393

Elk Rapids
Elk Rapids Housing
Commission
701 Chippewa Street
Elk Rapids, MI 49629-9583
616-264-5831

Escanaba
Escanaba Housing
Commission
110 S 5th Street
Escanaba, MI 49829-3947
906-786-6229

Essexville
Bay County Housing
Commission
798 N Pine Road

Essexville, MI 48732-2138
989-895-8191

Evart
Evart Housing Commission
601 W 1st Street
Evart, MI 49631-9596
616-734-3301

Ferndale
Ferndale Housing
Commission
415 Withington Street
Ferndale, MI 48220-2918
248-547-9500

Royal Oak Township
Housing Commission
8900 Cloverdale
Ferndale, MI 48220-2125
248-398-8101

Flint
Flint Housing Commission
3820 Richfield Road
Flint, MI 48506-2616
810-736-3050

Gladstone
Gladstone Housing
Commission
217 Dakota Avenue
Gladstone, MI 49837-1943
906-428-2215

Gladwin
Gladwin City Housing
Commission
215 S Antler Street
Gladwin, MI 48624-2051
517-426-5721

Grand Rapids
Grand Rapids Housing
Commission
1420 Fuller Avenue Se
Grand Rapids, MI 49507-
2139
616-235-2600

Grayling
Grayling Housing
Commission
308 Lawndale Street
Grayling, MI 49738-1844
517-348-9314

Greenville
Greenville Housing
Commission
308 E Oak Street
Greenville, MI 48838-2396
616-754-7179

Hamtramck
Hamtramck Housing
Commission
2620 Holbrook Street
Hamtramck, MI 48212-3470
313-868-7445

Hancock
Hancock Housing
Authority
1401 Quincy Street
Hancock, MI 49930-1258
906-482-3252

Hermansville
Hermansville Housing
Commission
W5577 129 W. Third
Hermansville, MI 49847-
0129
906-498-2141

Highland Park
Highland Park Housing
Commission
13725 John R Street
Highland Park, MI 48203-
3155
313-868-4500

Hillsdale
Hillsdale Housing
Commission
45 N West Street
Hillsdale, MI 49242-1554
517-439-1210

Houghton
Houghton Housing
Commission
401 E Montezuma Avenue
Houghton, MI 49931-2145
906-482-0334

Howard City
Montcalm County Hsg.
Comm.
120 Mulberry Street
Howard City, MI 49329-
9767
616-937-4241

Inkster
Inkster Housing
Commission
4500 Inkster Road
Inkster, MI 48141-3068
313-561-2355

Ionia
Ionia Housing Commission
667 Union Street
Ionia, MI 48846-1279
616-527-9060

Iron Mountain
Iron Mountain Housing
Commission
401 E D Street
Iron Mountain, MI 49801-
4052
906-774-2685

Iron River
Iron River Housing
Commission
236 N 3rd Avenue
Iron River, MI 49935-1700
906-265-4398

Ironwood
Ironwood Housing
Commission
515 E Vaughn Street
Ironwood, MI 49938-2200
906-932-3341

Ishpeming
Ishpeming Housing
Commission
111 Bluff Street
Ishpeming, MI 49849-2067
906-485-4100

Jackson
Jackson Housing
Commission
301 Steward Avenue
Jackson, MI 49201-2809
517-787-9241

Kingsford
Kingsford Housing
Commission
1025 Woodward Avenue
Kingsford, MI 49802-4424
906-774-2771

Lake Linden
Lake Linden Housing
Commission
210 Calumet Street
Lake Linden, MI 49945-1333
906-296-0713

Lanse
L'anse Housing
Commission
110 6th Street
Lanse, MI 49946-1460
906-524-6311

Lansing
Lansing Housing
Commission
310 Seymour Avenue
Lansing, MI 48933-1136
517-487-6550

Michigan State Housing
Development Authority
735 E. Michigan
Lansing, MI 48912
517-373-9184

Lapeer
Lapeer Housing
Commission
544 N Saginaw Street
Lapeer, MI 48446-4005
810-664-0591

Laurium
Laurium Housing
Commission
125 Lake Linden Avenue
Laurium, MI 49913-2200
906-337-2306

Lincoln Park
Lincoln Park Housing
Commission
1370 Electric Avenue
Lincoln Park, MI 48146-1887
313-388-4660

Livonia
Livonia Housing
Commission
19300 Purlingbrook Street
Livonia, MI 48152-1948
248-477-7086

Luna Pier
Luna Pier Housing
Commission
10885 Ellen Street
Luna Pier, MI 48157-9794
734-848-2355

Madison Heights
Madison Heights Housing
Commission
300 W. Thirteen Mile Road
Madison Heights, MI 48071
248-583-0843

Manistee
Manistee Housing
Commission
237 6th Avenue
Manistee, MI 49660-1375
616-723-6201

Manistique
Manistique Hsg Comm
400 E Lakeshore Drive
Manistique, MI 49854-1448
906-341-5451

Schoolcraft County Hsg.
Comm.
900 Steuben Street

Manistique MI 49854-1600
906-341-5052

Marquette
Marquette Housing
Commission
316 Pine Street
Marquette, MI 49855-4250
906-226-7559

Marysville
Marysville Housing
Commission
1100 New York Avenue
Marysville, MI 48040-2115
810-364-4020

Melvindale
Melvindale Housing
Commission
3501 Oakwood Boulevard
Melvindale, MI 48122-1181
313-429-1095

Menominee
Menominee Housing
Commission
1801 8th Avenue
Menominee, MI 49858-2559
906-863-8717

Middleville
Middleville Housing
Commission
500 Lincoln Street
Middleville, MI 49333-9154
616-795-7715

Monroe
Monroe Housing
Commission
20 N Roessler Street
Monroe, MI 48162-2463
734-242-5880

Mount Clemens
Mount Clemens Housing
Commission
50 Church Street
Mount Clemens, MI 48043-
2253
810-468-1434

Mount Pleasant
Mount Pleasant Housing
Comm
1 W Mosher Street
Mount Pleasant, MI 48858-
2392
517-773-3784

Munising
Munising Hs Cm
200 City Park Drive

Munising, MI 49862-1100
906-387-4084

Muskegon
Muskegon Housing
Commission
1823 Commerce Street
Muskegon, MI 49441-2608
616-722-2647

Muskegon Heights
Muskegon Heights Housing
Commission
615 E Hovey Avenue
Muskegon Heights, MI
49444-1725
616-733-2033

Negaunee
Negaunee Housing
Commission
98 Croix Street
Negaunee, MI 49866-1158
906-475-9107

New Haven
New Haven Housing
Commission
30100 John Rivers Drive
New Haven, MI 48048-1822
810-749-6570

Niles
Niles Housing Commission
251 Cass Street
Niles, MI 49120-2335
616-683-6235

Okemos
Ingham County Housing
Commission
3882 Dobie Road
Okemos, MI 48864-3784
517-349-1643

Ontonagon
Ontonagon Housing
Commission
100 Cane Court
Ontonagon, MI 49953-1106
906-884-2258

Plymouth
Plymouth Housing
Commission
1160 Sheridan Street
Plymouth, MI 48170-1560
734-455-3670

Pontiac
Pontiac Housing
Commission
132 Franklin Boulevard

Pontiac, MI 48341-1778
248-338-4551

Port Huron
Port Huron Housing
Commission
905 7th Street
Port Huron, MI 48060-5326
810-984-3173

Potterville
Potterville Housing
Commission
210 E Main Street
Potterville, MI 48876-9744
517-645-7076

Rapid River
Rapid River Housing
Commission
10570 N Main Street
Rapid River, MI 49878-9799
906-474-9370

Reed City
Reed City Housing
Commission
802 S Mill Street
Reed City, MI 49677-1357
231-832-2762

River Rouge
River Rouge Housing
Commission
180 Visger Road
River Rouge, MI 48218-1159
313-382-1414

Rockford
Rockford Hsg Comm
59 S Main Street
Rockford, MI 49341-1243
616-866-0371

Rockwood
Rockwood Housing
Commission
32409 Fort Street
Rockwood, MI 48173-1111
313-379-9700

Rogers City
Rogers City Housing
Commission
643 W Erie Street
Rogers City, MI 49779-1650
517-734-7303

Romulus
Romulus Housing
Commission
34200 Beverly Road
Romulus, MI 48174-4444
734-729-5389

Roseville
Roseville Housing
Commission
18330 Eastland Street
Roseville, MI 48066-2174
810-778-1360

Saginaw
Saginaw Housing
Commission
1803 Norman Street
P. O. Box 928
Saginaw, MI 48605
517-755-8183 ext. 137

Saint Clair Shores
St. Clair Shores Housing
Commission
1000 Blossom Heath
Boulevard
Saint Clair Shores, MI
48080-2800
810-773-9200

Saint Louis
Saint Louis Ha
308 S Delaware Street
Saint Louis, MI 48880-1318
517-681-5100

Saranac
Saranac Housing
Commission
203 Parsonage Street
Saranac, MI 48881-8510
616-642-9832

Sault Sainte Marie
Sault Ste Marie Housing
Commission
608 Pine Street
Sault Sainte Marie, MI
49783-1836
906-635-5841

South Haven
South Haven Housing
Commission
220 Broadway Street
South Haven, MI 49090-
2511
616-637-5755

South Lyon
South Lyon Housing
Commission
432 Washington Street
South Lyon, MI 48178-1372
800-898-2848

St Clair
St. Clair Housing
Commission
400 S 3rd Street

St Clair, MI 48079-5362
810-329-9141

St Joseph
Saint Joseph Housing
Commission
601 Port Street
St Joseph, MI 49085-1182
616-983-2814

Stambaugh
Stambaugh Housing
Commission
208 Jefferson Avenue
Stambaugh, MI 49964
906-265-5540

Sterling Heights
Sterling Heights Housing
Commission
40555 Utica Road
P. O. Box 8009
Sterling Heights, MI 48311-
8009
810-264-6410

Sturgis
Sturgis Housing
Commission
128 S Nottawa Street
Sturgis, MI 49091-1701
616-651-8772

Taylor
Taylor Housing
Commission
15270 S Plaza Drive
Taylor, MI 48180-6035
734-287-9460

Temperance
Bedford Township Housing
Commission
8745 Lewis Avenue
Temperance, MI 48182-9357
313-847-3950

Traverse City
Traverse City Housing
Commission
10200 E Carter Center
Traverse City, MI 49684-
7814
616-922-4915

Wakefield
Wakefield Housing
Commission
200 E Pierce Street
Wakefield, MI 49968-1356
906-229-5204

Wayne
Wayne Housing
Commission

4001 S Wayne Road
Wayne, MI 48184-2100
734-721-8602

Wyoming
Wyoming Housing
Commission
2450 36th Street SW
Wyoming, MI 49509-3158
616-534-5471

Ypsilanti
Ypsilanti Housing
Commission
601 Armstrong Drive
Ypsilanti, MI 48197-5281
734-482-4300

MINNESOTA

Aitkin
Housing Authority of
Aitkin County, Minnesota
215 3rd Street SE
Aitkin, MN 56431-1753
218-927-2151

Albert Lea
Hra In And For The City of
Albert Lea, Minnesota
800 S 4th Avenue
Albert Lea, MN 56007-1986
507-377-4330

Alexandria
Douglas County Hra
715 Elm Street
Suite 1060
Alexandria, MN 56308-1760
320-762-3849

Hra of Alexandria,
Minnesota
805 Fillmore Street
Alexandria, MN 56308-1462
320-762-1311

Austin
Hra of Austin, Minnesota
308 2nd Avenue NE
Austin, MN 55912-3429
507-433-1866

Mower County Hra
1105 1/2 8th Avenue NE
Austin, MN 55912-3683
507-437-9527

Backus
Cass County Hra
PO Box 33

Backus, MN 56435-0033
218-947-3993

Bagley
Hra of Bagley, Minnesota
516 Main Avenue N
Bagley, MN 56621-8301
218-694-6548

Barnesville
Hra of Barnesville,
Minnesota
PO Box 158
Barnesville, MN 56514-0158
218-354-7700

Bemidji
Hra of Bemidji, Minnesota
619 America Avenue NW
Bemidji, MN 56601-3017
218-444-4522

Benson
Hra of Benson, Minnesota
300 13th Street N
Benson, MN 56215 1257
320-842-8481

Bloomington
Hra In And For The City of
Bloomington
2215 W Old Shakopee Road
Bloomington, MN 55431-
3033
612-948-8937

Blue Earth
Hra of The City of Blue
Earth, Minnesota
220 E 7th Street
Blue Earth, MN 56013-2001
507-526-2981

Braham
Hra of Braham, Minnesota
409 Central Drive W
Braham, MN 55006-3014
320-396-3580

Brainerd
Hra In And For The City of
Brainerd, Minnesota
410 E River Road
Brainerd, MN 56401-3551
218-829-8634 ext. 15

Breckenridge
Breckenridge Hra of
Breckenridge, Minnesota
200 Park Avenue
Breckenridge, MN 56520-
1247
218-643-6147

Browerville
Todd County Hra
300 Linden Avenue S
Browerville, MN 56438-9409
320-732-2801

Cambridge
Hra of Cambridge,
Minnesota
121 Fern Street S
Cambridge, MN 55008-1454
612-689-3883

Carlton
Hra of Carlton, Minnesota
201 Spruce Avenue
Carlton, MN 55718-9231
218-879-3353

Cass Lake
Hra of Cass Lake,
Minnesota
225 1st Street NW
Cass Lake, MN 56633-8301
218-335-2674

Chisholm
Hra of Chisholm, Minnesota
519 6th Street SW
Chisholm, MN 55719-1935
218-254-2656

Clarkfield
Hra of Clarkfield,
Minnesota
1012 12th Avenue
Clarkfield, MN 56223-1017
320-669-4648

Cloquet
Hra of Cloquet, Minnesota
950 14th Street
Cloquet, MN 55720-2563
218-879-3353

Cold Spring
Stearns County Hra
312 1st Street N, Suite 2
Cold Spring, MN 56320-
1612
320-685-7771

Columbia Heights
Hra of Columbia Heights
965 40th Avenue NE
Columbia Heights, MN
55421-3172
612-782-2855

Cook
Hra of Cook, Minnesota
111 5th Street Se
Cook, MN 55723-9743
218-666-2533

Cottonwood
Hra of Cottonwood,
Minnesota
425 Prairie Street W
Cottonwood, MN 56229-
9798
507-423-6495

Crookston
Hra of Crookston,
Minnesota
110 Sargent Street
Crookston, MN 56716-1263
218-281-5334

Crosby
Hra of Crosby, Minnesota
300 3rd Avenue NE
Crosby, MN 56441-1642
218-546-5088

Dassel
Meeker County Hra
840 3rd Street
Dassel, MN 55325-1057
320-275-3542

Delano
Hra of City of Delano,
Minnesota
125 5th Street S
Delano, MN 55328-9105
612-972-2945

Detroit Lakes
Becker County Hra
829 Lake Avenue
Detroit Lakes, MN 56501-
3017
218-846-7316

Hra of Detroit Lakes,
Minnesota
1111 Washington Avenue
Detroit Lakes, MN 56501-
3410
218-847-7859

Dilworth
Clay County Hra
116 Center Avenue E
Dilworth, MN 56529-1419
218-233-8883 ext. 14

Dodge Center
Housing & Redevelopment
Authority of Dodge Center
111 2nd Street SW
Dodge Center, MN 55927-
9238
507-374-2697

Duluth
Hra of Duluth, Minnesota

PO Box 16900
Duluth, MN 55816-0900
218-529-6300

East Grand Forks
Edha of East Grand Forks
610 2nd Avenue NE
East Grand Forks, MN
56721-2504
218-773-8939

Elbow Lake
Grant County Hra
10 2nd Street NE
Elbow Lake, MN 56531-4330
218-685-4494

Ely
Hra of Ely, Minnesota
114 N 8th Avenue E
Apartment 111
Ely, MN 55731-1657
218-365-3900

Eveleth
Hra of Eveleth, Minnesota
902 Clay Court
Eveleth, MN 55734-1412
218-744-1010

Fairmont
Hra of Fairmont, Minnesota
500 Home Street
Fairmont, MN 56031-4200
507-235-9691

Faribault
Housing & Redevelopment
Authority of Faribault
208 1st Avenue NW
Faribault, MN 55021-5105
507-334-2222

Fergus Falls
Hra of Fergus Falls,
Minnesota
225 W Washington Avenue
Fergus Falls, MN 56537-
2535
218-739-3249

Fergus Falls
Otter Tail County Hra
225 W Washington Avenue
Fergus Falls, MN 56537-
2535
218-739-3249

Forest Lake
Hra of Forest Lake,
Minnesota
7 5th Avenue NE
Forest Lake, MN 55025-1235
651-464-4406

Glenwood
Hra of Glenwood,
Minnesota
507 5th Street SE
Glenwood, MN 56334-1648
320-634-3655

Grand Rapids
Hra of Grand Rapids,
Minnesota
411 NW 7th Street
Grand Rapids, MN 55744-
2567
218-326-9515

Itasca County Hra
19 NE 3rd Street
Grand Rapids, MN 55744-
2742
218-326-7978

Greenbush
Hra of Village of
Greenbush, Minnesota
610 Central Avenue W
Greenbush, MN 56726-4436
218-782-2470

Henning
Hra of Henning, Minnesota
500 Holden Avenue
Henning, MN 56551-4022
218-583-2781

Hibbing
The Hra of Hibbing,
Minnesota
3115 7th Avenue E
Hibbing, MN 55746-2625
218-263-3661

Hopkins
Hra of Hopkins, Minnesota
22 5th Avenue S
Hopkins, MN 55343-1639
612-935-8474

Hutchinson
Hra of Hutchinson,
Minnesota
133 3rd Avenue SW
Hutchinson, MN 55350-2400
320-587-2168

International Falls
Hra of International Falls,
Minnesota
1200 Riverside Drive
International Falls, MN
56649-2157
218-283-4114

Jackson
Hra of Jackson, Minnesota

116 State Street
Jackson, MN 56143-1185
507-847-3926

Janesville
Housing & Redevelopment
Authority of Janesville
106 E North Street
Janesville, MN 56048-9702
507-231-5880

Lake Benton
Housing & Redevelopment
Authority of Lincoln Co.
106 Bluff Street W
Apartment 31
Lake Benton, MN 56149-
1203
507-694-1552

Hra of Lake Benton,
Minnesota
106 Bluff Street W
Lake Benton, MN 56149-
1204
507-368-4600

Le Sueur
Hra of Le Sueur, Minnesota
220 Risedorph Street
Apartment A3
Le Sueur, MN 56058-2034
507-665-3932

Lindstrom
Hra of Lindstrom,
Minnesota
12940 N 1st Avenue
Lindstrom, MN 55045-9506
612-257-5372

Litchfield
Hra of Litchfield, Minnesota
122 W 4th Street
Litchfield, MN 55355-2146
320-693-2104

Little Falls
Hra of Little Falls,
Minnesota
901 1st Avenue SW
Little Falls, MN 56345-1464
320-632-3305

Morrison County Hra
302 West Broadway
Little Falls, MN 56345
320-632-0176

Long Prairie
Hra of Long Prairie,
Minnesota
601 Central Avenue

Long Prairie, MN 56347-
1424
320-732-2801

Luverne
Hra of Luverne, Minnesota
216 N Mckenzie Street
Luverne, MN 56156-1668
507-283-4922

Madison
Hra of Madison, Minnesota
310 Park Avenue
Madison, MN 56256-1761
320-598-3374

Mankato
Blue Earth County Hra
10 Civic Center Plaza
Mankato, MN 56001-7794
507-387-8622

Mankato Eda
10 Civic Center Plaza
Mankato, MN 56001-7794
507-387-8600

Marshall
Public Housing
Commission of The City of
Marshall
202 N 1st Street
Marshall, MN 56258-1884
507-537-7083

Melrose
Hra of City of Melrose,
Minnesota
16 E 1st Street S
Melrose, MN 56352-1383
320-256-4600

Minneapolis
Minneapolis Pha In And
For The City of Minneapolis
1001 Washington Avenue N
Minneapolis, MN 55401-
1032
612-342-1290

Montevideo
Hra of Montevideo,
Minnesota
501 N 1st Street
Montevideo, MN 56265-
1426
320-269-6868

Moorhead
Moorhead Public Housing
Agency
800 2nd Avenue N
Moorhead, MN 56560-2857
218-299-5458

Mora
Hra of Mora, Minnesota
420 Bean Avenue
Mora, MN 55051-1430
612-679-4789

Morris
Hra of Morris, Minnesota
100 S Columbia Avenue
Morris, MN 56267-1540
320-589-3142

Mound
Hra of Mound, Minnesota
2020 Commerce Boulevard
Mound, MN 55364-1575
612-472-5078

Mountain Lake
Hra of Mountain Lake,
Minnesota
1225 3rd Avenue
Mountain Lake, MN 56159-
1444
507-427-2425

New Richland
Hra of New Richland,
Minnesota
221 1st Street NE
New Richland, MN 56072-
2002
507-463-8515

New Ulm
New Ulm Eda
100 N Broadway Street
New Ulm, MN 56073-1716
507-359-8233

North Mankato
Hra of North Mankato,
Minnesota
615 Nicollet Avenue
North Mankato, MN 56003-
3866
507-388-3202

Olivia
Renville County Hra
500 E. Depue Avenue
Olivia, MN 56277
320-523-3656

Ortonville
Big Stone County Hra
301 2nd Street NW
Ortonville, MN 56278-1412
612-839-3304

Park Rapids
Hra of Park Rapids,
Minnesota
500 Riverside Avenue

Park Rapids, MN 56470-
1623
218-732-4158

Pequot Lakes
Hra of Pequot Lakes,
Minnesota
31203 N. Oak St.
Pequot Lakes, MN 56472-
0243
218-568-4555

Perham
Hra of Perham, Minnesota
211 2nd Avenue Se
Perham, MN 56573-1785
218-346-4455

Pine City
Hra of Pine City, Minnesota
905 7th Street
Pine City, MN 55063-2092
320-629-6301

Pine River
Hra of Pine River,
Minnesota
312 1st Street S
Pine River, MN 56474-4035
218-587-4929

Pipestone
Hra of Pipestone,
Minnesota
PO Box 365
Pipestone, MN 56164-0365
507-825-2558

Princeton
Hra of Princeton, Minnesota
801 3rd Street N
Princeton, MN 55371-1551
612-389-2442

Red Lake Falls
Hra of Red Lake Falls,
Minnesota
209 International Drive
Red Lake Falls, MN 56750-
4640
218-253-2022

Red Wing
Hra of Red Wing,
Minnesota
428 W 5th Street
Red Wing, MN 55066-2522
651-388-7571

Redwood Falls
Hra of Redwood Falls,
Minnesota
300 S Minnesota Street

Redwood Falls, MN 56283-
1544
507-637-2221

Rochester
Olmsted County Hra
2122 Campus Drive Se
Rochester, MN 55904-4744
507-285-8224

Rosemount
Dakota County Hra
2496 145th Street W
Rosemount, MN 55068-4929
651-423-4800

Saint Cloud
Hra of St. Cloud, Minnesota
1225 W. Saint Germain
Saint Cloud, MN 56301-3609
320-252-0880

Saint Louis Park
Housing Authority of St
Louis Park, Minnesota
5005 Minnetonka Boulevard
Saint Louis Park, MN
55416-2216
612-924-2578

Saint Paul
Public Housing Agency of
The City of Saint Paul
480 Cedar Street
Suite 600
Saint Paul, MN 55101-1830
651-298-5664

Sauk Centre
Hra of Sauk Centre,
Minnesota
407 1st Street N
Sauk Centre, MN 56378-
1152
320-352-2311

Shakopee
Scott County Hra
323 Naumkeag Street S
Shakopee, MN 55379-1652
612-402-9022

Sleepy Eye
Hra of Sleepy Eye,
Minnesota
313 4th Avenue Se
Sleepy Eye, MN 56085-1700
507-794-5101

South St Paul
Hra of The City of South St
Paul, Minnesota
125 3rd Avenue N

South St Paul, MN 55075-
2097
651-451-1838

St Peter
Hra of St. Peter, Minnesota
1010 S 4th Street
St Peter, MN 56082-1463
507-931-2236

Thief River Falls
Hra of Thief River Falls,
Minnesota
415 Arnold Avenue S
Thief River Falls, MN
56701-3507
218-681-5995

Tracy
Hra of Tracy, Minnesota
760 Morgan Street
Tracy, MN 56175-1181
507-629-3160

Two Harbors
Hra of Two Harbors,
Minnesota
505 1st Avenue
Two Harbors, MN 55616-
1553
218-834-2728

Virginia
Hra of Virginia, Minnesota
442 Pine Mill Court
Virginia, MN 55792-3097
218-741-2610

Wabasha
Southeast MN Multi-
County Hra
134 2nd Street E
Wabasha, MN 55981-1440
651-565-2638

Waconia
Hra of Waconia, Minnesota
325 S Spruce Street
Waconia, MN 55387-1845
612-442-2943

Wadena
Hra of Wadena, Minnesota
222 2nd Street SE
Wadena, MN 56482-1508
218-631-7723

Warren
Hra of Warren, Minnesota
411 N 4th Street
Warren, MN 56762-1394
218-745-4858

Waseca
Hra of Waseca, Minnesota
308 2nd Avenue NW
Waseca, MN 56093-2410
507-835-1753

Willmar
Hra In And For The City of
Willmar, Minnesota
333 6th Street SW
Willmar, MN 56201-3222
320-235-8637

Kandiyohi County Hra
409 19th Avenue SW
Willmar, MN 56201
320-235-0850

Mcleod County Hra
409 19th Avenue SW, Po
Box 1359
Willmar, MN 56201
320-235-7703

Windom
Hra of Windom, Minnesota
605 10th Street
Windom, MN 56101-1374
507-831-1016

Winona
Hra of Winona, Minnesota
1756 Kraemer Drive
Suite 100
Winona, MN 55987-2086
507-454-3665

Worthington
Hra of Worthington,
Minnesota
819 10th Street
Worthington, MN 56187-
2758
507-376-3655

Mississippi

Amory
The Housing Authority of
The City of Amory
401 South Main Street
Amory, MS 38821-3424
662-256-3213

Baldwyn
The Housing Authority of
The City of Baldwyn
101 Eastover Circle 501
Baldwyn, MS 38824-2407
662-365-2335

Bay Saint Louis
The Housing Authority of
The City of Bay St. Louis
601 Bienville Drive
Bay Saint Louis, MS 39520-
2610
601-467-4545

Biloxi
The Housing Authority of
The City of Biloxi
330 Benachi Avenue
Biloxi, MS 39530-1950
228-374-2930

Booneville
The Housing Authority of
The City of Booneville
801 N College Street
Booneville, MS 38829-1704
601-728-4032

Brookhaven
The Housing Authority of
The City of Brookhaven
501 Brookman Drive
Brookhaven, MS 39601-2374
601-833-1781

Canton
The Housing Authority of
The City of Canton
496 Dobson Avenue
Canton, MS 39046-3539
601-859-4032

Clarksdale
The Housing Authority of
The City of Clarksdale
2401 6th Street
Building 9
Clarksdale, MS 38614-6730
601-624-8030

Columbus
Mississippi Regional
Housing Authority No. Iv
2845 S Frontage Road
Columbus, MS 39701-9528
662-327-4121 ext. 17

The Housing Authority of
The City of Columbus
1515 4th Street S
Columbus, MS 39701-7431
601-328-4236

Corinth
Tennessee Valley Regional
Housing Authority
1210 Proper Street
Corinth, MS 38834-5015
662-286-8437

The Housing Authority of
The City of Corinth
1101 Cruise Street
Corinth, MS 38834-5002
601-287-1489

Forest
The Housing Authority of
The City of Forest
518 N 4th Avenue
Forest, MS 39074-3627
601-469-1342

Greenville
South Delta Regional
Housing Authority
PO Box 4769
Greenville, MS 38704-4769
662-334-1786

Greenwood
The Housing Authority of
The City of Greenwood
111 E Washington Street
Greenwood, MS 38930-4433
601-453-4822 ext. 11

Gulfport
Mississippi Regional
Housing Authority No. Viii
2909 26th Avenue
Gulfport, MS 39501-5914
228-863-6272

Hattiesburg
The Housing Authority of
The City of Hattiesburg
208 Gordon Street
Hattiesburg, MS 39401-2101
601-583-1881

Hazlehurst
The Housing Authority of
The City of Hazlehurst
150 Roebuck Court
Apartment 36
Hazlehurst, MS 39083-2025
601-894-1566

Holly Springs
The Housing Authority of
The City of Holly Springs
111 N Market Street
Holly Springs, MS 38635-2314
601-252-2971

Itta Bena
The Housing Authority of
The City of Itta Bena
301 Sunflower Road
Apartment 22
Itta Bena, MS 38941-1826
601-254-9656

Jackson
Mississippi Regional
Housing Authority No. Vi
2180 Terry Road
Jackson, MS 39204-5748
601-373-7040

Jackson
The Housing Authority of
The City of Jackson
2747 Livingston Road
Jackson, MS 39213-6928
601-362-0885

Kosciusko
The Housing Authority of
Attala County
311 Gilliland Street
Kosciusko, MS 39090-4045
662-289-5181

Laurel
The Housing Authority of
The City of Laurel
701 Beacon Street
Laurel, MS 39440-4407
601-425-4651

Long Beach
The Housing Authority of
The City of Long Beach
102 N Girard Avenue
Long Beach, MS 39560-4516
228-863-8256

Louisville
The Housing Authority of
The City of Louisville
605a W Main Street
Louisville, MS 39339-2535
601-773-3761

Mccomb
The Housing Authority of
The City of Mccomb
1002 Sedgewick Street
Mccomb, MS 39648-5058
601-684-7291

The Housing Authority of
The Town of Summit
1002 Sedgewick Street
Mccomb, MS 39648-5058
601-684-7291

Meridian
The Housing Authority of
The City of Meridian
PO Box 870
Meridian, MS 39302-0870
601-693-4285

Mound Bayou
The Housing Authority of
The City of Mound Bayou

504 Banks Avenue
Mound Bayou, MS 38762-9777
601-741-2061

Natchez
Natchez Housing Authority
160 Saint Catherine Street
Natchez, MS 39120-3687
601-446-5301

Newton
Mississippi Regional
Housing Authority No. V
110 Broad Street
Newton, MS 39345-2509
601-683-3371 ext. 20

Okolona
The Housing Authority of
The City of Okolona
PO Box 190
Okolona, MS 38860-0190
662-447-5473

Oxford
The Housing Authority of
The City of Oxford
900 Molly Barr Road
Oxford, MS 38655 -2106
662-234-7524

Picayune
The Housing Authority of
The City of Picayune
1511 7th Avenue
Picayune, MS 39466-3719
601-798-3281

Pontotoc
The Housing Authority of
The City of Pontotoc
206 Hud Street
Pontotoc, MS 38863-1306
601-489-1312

Sardis
The Housing Authority of
The Town of Sardis
321 Greenhill Circle
Sardis, MS 38666-2417
662-487-2441

Senatobia
The Housing Authority of
The City of Senatobia
100 Scotsdale Street
Senatobia, MS 38668-2841
662-562-5071

Starkville
The Housing Authority of
The City of Starkville
101 Pecan Acres

Starkville, MS 39759-3227
662-323-5536

Vicksburg
The Housing Authority of
The City of Vicksburg
131 Elizabeth Circle
Vicksburg, MS 39183-2413
601-638-1661

Waveland
The Housing Authority of
The City of Waveland
500 Camille Circle
Waveland, MS 39576-3104
601-467-4247

Waynesboro
The Housing Authority of
The City of Waynesboro
1069 Wayne Street
Waynesboro, MS 39367-8069
601-735-4522

West Point
The Housing Authority of
The City of West Point
805 Ivy Lane
West Point, MS 39773-3732
601-494-3663

Winona
The Housing Authority of
The City of Winona
200 Briscoe Street
Winona, MS 38967-1709
601-283-2575

Yazoo City
The Housing Authority of
The City of Yazoo City
121 Lindsey Lawn Drive
Yazoo City, MS 39194-2912
601-746-2226

Missouri

Aurora
Aurora Housing Authority
111 W Springfield Street
Aurora, MO 65605-1715
417-678-5437

Ava
Housing Authority of The
City of Ava
802 NE 11th Avenue
Ava, MO 65608
417-683-5252

Bethany
Bethany Housing Authority
2602 Crossan Street
Bethany, MO 64424-2162
660-425-3349

Bloomfield
Housing Authority of The
City of Bloomfield
476 Hester Street
Bloomfield, MO 63825-9771
573-568-2193

Boonville
Housing Authority of The
City of Boonville
506 Powell Court
Boonville, MO 65233-1521
660-882-7332

Branson
Branson Housing Authority
320 W Main Street
Branson, MO 65616-2776
417-334-4236

Brookfield
Brookfield Housing
Authority
61 Joyce Place
Brookfield, MO 64628-2466
660-258-3959

Brunswick
Brunswick Housing
Authority
510 N Adams Street
Brunswick, MO 65236-1380
660-548-3896

Cabool
Housing Authority of The
City of Cabool
6b Cedar Bluff Avenue
Cabool, MO 65689
417-926-3142

Campbell
Housing Authority of The
City of Campbell
930 Poplar Street
Campbell, MO 63933-1834
573-246-3103

Cardwell
Housing Authority of The
City of Cardwell
123 Circle Drive
Cardwell, MO 63829
573-654-3557

Carrollton
Carrollton Housing
Authority

107 N Monroe Street
Carrollton, MO 64633-1379
660-542-3787

Caruthersville
Housing Authority of The
City of Caruthersville
1301 Schults Avenue
Caruthersville, MO 63830-
2161
573-333-4461

Chaffee
Housing Authority of The
City of Chaffee
904 S 2nd Street
Chaffee, MO 63740-1209
573-887-3768

Charleston
Housing Authority of The
City of Charleston
700 S Elm Street
Charleston, MO 63834-1800
573-683-2172

Chillicothe
Chillicothe Housing
Authority
320 Park Lane
Chillicothe, MO 64601-1576
660-646-3215

Clinton
Clinton Housing Authority
7 Bradshaw Drive
Clinton, MO 64735-2538
660-885-5852

Columbia
Housing Authority of The
City of Columbia
201 Switzler Street
Columbia, MO 65203
573-443-2556

East Prairie
Housing Authority of The
City of East Prairie
529 N Lincoln Street
East Prairie MO 63845-1115
573-649-3010

Excelsior Springs
Excelsior Springs Housing
Authority
320 W Excelsior Street
Excelsior Springs, MO
64024-2173
816-630-7361

Fayette
Housing Authority of The
City of Fayette

302 Villers Drive
Fayette, MO 65248-1314
660-248-2213

Festus
Housing Authority of The
City of Festus
1504b Robert Thompson
Drive
Festus, MO 63028-2333
636-937-0044

Fulton
Housing Authority of The
City of Fulton
350 Sycamore Street
Fulton, MO 65251-1278
573-642-7611

Gideon
Housing Authority of The
City of Gideon
135 Haven Street
Gideon, MO 63848-9104
573-448-3215

Glasgow
Housing Authority of The
City of Glasgow
112 2nd Street Terrace
Glasgow, MO 65254-1000
660-338-2151

Hannibal
Housing Authority of The
City of Hannibal
306 Munger Lane
Hannibal, MO 6340- 2361
573-221-7575

Hayti
Housing Authority of The
City of Hayti
212 N 4th Street
Hayti, MO 63851-1462
573-359-0698

Hayti Heights
Housing Authority of The
City of Hayti Heights
100 N Martin Luther King
Drive
Hayti Heights, MO 63851-
9664
573-359-2710

Higginsville
Higginsville Housing
Authority
419 Fairground Avenue
Higginsville, MO 64037-
1726
660-584-3911

Holcomb
Housing Authority of The
City of Holcomb
PO Box 278
Holcomb, MO 63852-0278
573-792-3576

Holcomb
Housing Authority of The
City of Holcomb
PO Box 278
Holcomb, MO 63852-0278
573-792-3576

Hornersville
Housing Authority of The
City of Hornersville
201 Jc Edmonston Circle
Hornersville, MO 63855-
9867
573-737-2533

Houston
Housing Authority of The
City of Houston
200 Chestnut Terrace
Houston, MO 65483-1741
417-967-3394

Independence
Independence Housing
Authority
210 S Pleasant Street
Independence, MO 64050-
3662
816-836-9200

Independence
Independence Housing
Authority
210 S Pleasant Street
Independence, MO 64050
3662
816-836-9200

Jefferson City
Housing Authority of The
City of Jefferson
1040 Myrtle Avenue
Jefferson City, MO 65109-
2525
573-635-6163 ext. 216

Joplin
Joplin Housing Authority
1834 W 24th Street
Joplin, MO 64804-1511
417-624-4514

Kansas City
Housing Authority of
Kansas City
712 Broadway Street

Kansas City, MO 64105-
1545
816-842-2440

Kennett
Housing Authority of The
City of Kennett
900 Kennett Street
Kennett, MO 63857-3817
573-888-4612 ext. 203

Kirksville
Housing Authority of The
City of Kirksville
100 Valley Forge Drive
Kirksville, MO 63501-3116
660-665-8539

Kirkwood
Housing Authority of The
City of Kirkwood
385 S Taylor Avenue
Kirkwood, MO 63122-6159
314-966-5610

Lancaster
Housing Authority of The
City of Lancaster
PO Box 157a
Lancaster, MO 63548-9739
660-457-3030

Lawson
Lawson Housing Authority
517 N Doniphan Street
Lawson, MO 64062-9775
816-296-7150

Lebanon
Lebanon Housing Authority
1225 Maple Lane
Lebanon, MO 65536-3593
417-532-4912

Lees Summit
Lee's Summit Housing
Authority
111 Se Grand Avenue
Lees Summit, MO 64063-
2670
816-524-1100

Lexington
Lexington Housing
Authority
2215 Aull Lane
Lexington, MO 64067-1532
660-259-4232

Macon
Housing Authority of The
City of Macon
1404 S Missouri Street
Macon, MO 63552-4427
660-385-5782 ext. 21

Malden
Housing Authority of The
City of Malden
109 Watson Drive
Malden, MO 63863-1005
573-276-3706

Mansfield
Housing Authority of The
City of Mansfield
100 E Maple Street
Mansfield, MO 65704-9112
417-924-8316

Marceline
Marceline Housing
Authority
229 W Hauser Street
Marceline, MO 64658-2102
660-376-3101

Marionville
Marionville Housing
Authority
PO Box 406
Marionville, MO 65705-0406
417-258-7665

Marshall
Marshall Housing
Authority
PO Box 98
Marshall, MO 65340-0098
660-886-9664

Memphis
Housing Authority of The
City of Memphis
31 Cornelius Avenue
Memphis, MO 63555-9237
660-465-7281

Mexico
Housing Authority of The
City of Mexico
828 Garfield Avenue
Mexico, MO 65265-2513
573-581-2294

Moberly
Housing Authority of The
City of Moberly
23 Kehoe Street
Moberly, MO 65270-2712
660-263-3950

Morehouse
Housing Authority of The
City of Morehouse
PO Box 45
Morehouse, MO 63868-0045
573-667-5579

Mountain Grove
Housing Authority of The
City of Mountain Grove
301 W 1st Street
Mountain Grove, MO
65711-1610
417-926-3142

Neosho
Neosho Housing Authority
321 Hamilton Street
Neosho, MO 64850-1864
417-451-5303

Nevada
Nevada Housing Authority
1117 N West Street
Nevada, MO 64772-1359
417-448-2730

New Madrid
Housing Authority of The
City of New Madrid
550 Line Street
New Madrid, MO 63869-
1736
573-748-2417

Noel
Noel Housing Authority
624 Johnson Drive
Noel, MO 64854-9229
417-475-3195

Osceola
Osceola Housing Authority
102 Goodrich Drive
Apartment 11
Osceola, MO 64776-2547
417-646-8019

Plattsburg
Plattsburg Housing
Authority
PO Box 371
Plattsburg, MO 64477-0371
816-539-2755

Poplar Bluff
Housing Authority of The
City of Poplar Bluff
506 Hazel Street
Poplar Bluff, MO 63901-
6006
573-785-8265

Potosi
Housing Authority of The
City of Potosi
103 W Citadel Drive
Potosi, MO 63664-1801
573-438-2362

Princeton
Princeton Housing
Authority
801 E Hickland Street
Princeton, MO 64673-1282
660-748-4300

Republic
Republic Housing
Authority
621 N Boston Lane
Apartment 24
Republic, MO 65738-1178
417-732-7260

Richland
Richland Housing
Authority
215 S Walnut Street
Richland, MO 65556-7800
573-765-3448

Richmond
Richmond Housing
Authority
302 N Camden Avenue
Richmond, MO 64085-1624
816-776-2308

Rolla
Housing Authority of The
City of Rolla
1440 Forum Drive
Rolla, MO 65401-2509
573-364-6460

Saint Charles
Housing Authority of The
City of St. Charles
1041 Olive Street
Saint Charles, MO 63301-
4711
636-946-6577

Saint Louis
Housing Authority of St.
Louis County
8865 Natural Bridge Road
Saint Louis, MO 63121 3933
314-428-3200

Saint Louis
Housing Authority of The
City of Kinloch
8149 Lurch Avenue
Saint Louis, MO 63134-1338
314-522-3313

Housing Authority of The
City of Olivette
8865 Natural Bridge Road
Saint Louis, MO 63121-3933
314-428-3200

Housing Authority of The
City of St. Louis
4100 Lindell Boulevard
Saint Louis, MO 63108-2914
314-286-4357

Housing Authority of The
City of Wellston
1584 Ogden Avenue
Saint Louis, MO 63133-2413
314-385-4089

Sainte Genevieve
Housing Authority of The
City of Sainte Genevieve
35 Robinwood Drive
Sainte Genevieve, MO
63670-1461
573-883-2160

Salem
Housing Authority of The
City of Salem
606 Mcgrath Lane
Salem, MO 65560-1034
573-729-6453

Scott City
Housing Authority of The
City of Illmo
103 W Hickory Drive
Scott City, MO 63780-2437
573-264-2161

Sikeston
Sikeston Housing Authority
400 Allen Boulevard
Sikeston, MO 63801-1976
573-471-3012

Slater
Slater Housing Authority
14 Emmerson Terrace
Slater, MO 65349-1622
660-886-9664

Smithville
Smithville Housing
Authority
161 County Road F
Smithville, MO 64089-9208
816-532-3744

South West City
Southwest City Housing
Authority
702a Crescent Drive
South West City, MO 64863-
9453
417-762-3487

Springfield
Springfield Housing
Authority

421 W Madison Street
Springfield, MO 65806-2938
417-866-4329

St Joseph
St. Joseph Housing
Authority
502 S 10th Street
St Joseph, MO 64501-2726
816-236-8215

Steele
Housing Authority of The
City of Steele
201 S Elm Street
Steele, MO 63877-1705
573-695-3771

Tarkio
Tarkio Housing Authority
218 S Maple Street
Tarkio, MO 64491-1358
660-736-4212

Webb City
Webb City Housing
Authority
415 N Washington Drive
Webb City, MO 64870-1366
417-673-2288

West Plains
Housing Authority of The
City of West Plains
302 Walnut Street
Apartment 1000
West Plains, MO 65775-3561
417-256-5506

MONTANA

Anaconda
Housing Authority of The
City of Anaconda
10 Main Street
Anaconda, MT 59711-2250
406-563-2921

Billings
Billings Housing Authority
2415 1st Avenue N
Billings, MT 59101-2318
406-245-6391

Butte
Housing Authority of Butte
Curtis & Arizona St.
Butte, MT 59701
406-782-6461

Glendive
Dawson County Housing
Authority

200 California Street
Glendive, MT 59330-3705
406-433-1978

Great Falls
Great Falls Housing
Authority
1500 6th Avenue S
Great Falls, MT 59405-2565
406-777-1180

Helena
Helena Housing Authority
812 Abbey Street
Helena, MT 59601-7924
406-442-7970

Missoula
Missoula Housing
Authority
1319 E Broadway Street
Missoula, MT 59802-4933
406-549-4113

Sidney
Richland County Housing
Authority
1032 6th Street SW
Sidney, MT 59270-3749
406-482-1978

Whitefish
Whitefish Housing
Authority
100 Fourth St. E
Whitefish, MT 59937
406-862-4143

NEBRASKA

Ainsworth
Ainsworth Housing
Authority
524 E 4th Street
Ainsworth, NE 69210-1648
402-387-2550

Albion
Albion Housing Authority
827 W Columbia Street
Albion, NE 68620-1575
402-395-2224

Alliance
Alliance Housing Authority
300 S Potash Avenue
Apartment 27
Alliance, NE 69301-4138
308-762-5130

Alma
Alma Housing Authority

1103 4th Street
Alma, NE 68920-2075
308-928-2161

Auburn
Auburn Housing Authority
1017 H Street
Auburn, NE 68305-1640
402-274-4525

Bassett
Bassett Housing Authority
400 Panzer Street
Bassett, NE 68714
402-684-3329

Bayard
Bayard Housing Authority
501 E 6th Street
Bayard, NE 69334-2008
308-586-1512

Beemer
Beemer Housing Authority
400 Blaine Street
Beemer, NE 68716-4217
402-528-3553

Bellevue
Bellevue Housing Authority
8214 Armstrong Circle
Bellevue, NE 68147-1871
402-734-5448

Benkelman
Benkelman Housing
Authority
100 Rainbow Fountain Park
Benkelman, NE 69021-3045
308-423-2125

Blair
Blair Housing Authority
758 S 16th Street
Blair, NE 68008-2220
402-426-4552

Bridgeport
Bridgeport Housing
Authority
310 W 5th Street
Bridgeport, NE 69336-2514
308-262-1690

Broken Bow
Broken Bow Housing
Authority
825 S 9th Avenue
Broken Bow, NE 68822-2400
308-872-2850

Clay Center
Clay Center Housing
Authority

114 E Division Street
Clay Center, NE 68933-1564
402-762-3503

Coleridge
Coleridge Housing
Authority
106 E Douglas Street
Coleridge, NE 68727-2228
402-283-4222

Columbus
Columbus Housing
Authority
2554 40th Avenue
Columbus, NE 68601-8516
402-564-1131

Cozad
Cozad Housing Authority
421 W 9th Street
Cozad, NE 69130-1346
308-784-3661

Creighton
Creighton Housing
Authority
1106 Millard Avenue
Creighton, NE 68729-3910
402-358-5668

Crete
Crete Housing Authority
1600 Grove Avenue
Crete, NE 68333-1763
402-826-2678

Curtis
Curtis Housing Authority
600 West 4th
Curtis, NE 69025
308-367-4168

David City
David City Housing
Authority
1125 N 3rd Street
David City, NE 68632-1203
402-367-3587

Emerson
Emerson Housing
Authority
207 E 5th Street
Emerson, NE 68733-3608
402-695-2557

Fairbury
Fairbury Housing Authority
105 W 5th Street
Fairbury, NE 68352-2247
402-729-3451

Fairmont
Fairmont Housing
Authority
225 E Main Street
Fairmont, NE 68354-9759
402-268-2891

Falls City
Falls City Housing
Authority
800 E 21st Street
Falls City, NE 68355-2349
402-245-4204

Fremont
Fremont Housing Authority
2510 N Clarkson Street
Fremont, NE 68025-2370
402-727-4848

Friend
Friend Housing Authority
1027 2nd Street
Friend, NE 68359-1101
402-947-6371

Genoa
Genoa Housing Authority
301 E Willard Avenue
Genoa, NE 68640-0401
402-993-2493

Gering
Scotts Bluff County
Housing Authority
89a Woodley Park Road
Gering, NE 69341-1638
308-632-0473

Gibbon
Gibbon Housing Authority
413 1st Street
Gibbon, NE 68840-6163
308-468-6200

Gordon
Gordon Housing Authority
109 N Cornell Street
Gordon, NE 69343-1547
308-282-0202

Gothenburg
Gothenburg Housing
Authority
810 20th Street
Gothenburg, NE 69138-1244
308-537-7275

Grand Island
Hall County Housing
Authority
911 Baumann Drive
Grand Island, NE 68803-
4402
308-385-5530

Greeley
Greeley Housing Authority
Kerry Kourt Apartments
Greeley, NE 68842
308-428-4375

Gresham
Gresham Housing
Authority
120 Maud Street
Gresham, NE 68367-3000
402-735-7292

Harvard
Harvard Housing Authority
502 E Walnut Street
Harvard, NE 68944-3002
402-772-4091

Humboldt
Humboldt Housing
Authority
626 Parkview Drive
Humboldt, NE 68376-6022
402-862-3201

Kearney
Kearney Housing Authority
2715 Avenue I
Kearney, NE 68847-3771
308-234-3000

Lexington
Lexington Housing
Authority
609 E 3rd Street
Lexington, NE 68850-2232
308-324-4633

Lincoln
Lincoln Housing Authority
5700 R Street
Lincoln, NE 68505-2332
402-467-2371

Lyons
Lyons Housing Authority
345 N 3rd Street
Lyons, NE 68038-2596
402-687-2633

Mc Cook
Mccook Housing Authority
502 Missouri Avenue Circle
Mc Cook, NE 69001-2932
308-345-3605

Minden
Minden Housing Authority
849 E 2nd Street
Minden, NE 68959-2432
308-832-2811

Nebraska City
Nebraska City Housing
Authority
200 N 3rd Street
Nebraska City, NE 68410-
2553
402-873-5451

Neligh
Neligh Housing Authority
500 P Street
Neligh, NE 68756-1465
402-887-4912

North Platte
North Platte Housing
Authority
900 Autumn Park Drive
North Platte, NE 69101-7639
308-534-4887

Oakland
Oakland Housing Authority
100 N Aurora Avenue
Oakland, NE 68045-1535
402-685-5440

Omaha
Douglas County Housing
Authority
5404 N 107th Plaza
Omaha, NE 68134-1148
402-444-6203 ext. 17

Omaha
Omaha Housing Authority
540 S 27th Street
Omaha, NE 68105-1520
402-444-6900

Ord
Ord Housing Authority
2410 K Street
Ord, NE 68862-1209
308-728-3770

Oshkosh
Oshkosh Housing
Authority
404 W 6th Street
Apartment 21
Oshkosh, NE 69154-5016
308-772-3941

Oxford
Oxford Housing Authority
103 Pleasant Heights
Oxford, NE 68967-9624
308-824-3188

Pawnee City
Pawnee City Housing
Authority
418 11th Street

Pawnee City, NE 68420-
3539
402-852-2133

Plattsmouth
Plattsmouth Housing
Authority
801 Washington Avenue
Plattsmouth, NE 68048-1255
402-296-3380

Ravenna
Ravenna Housing
Authority
1011 Grand Avenue
Ravenna, NE 68869-1015
308-452-4233

Red Cloud
Red Cloud Housing
Authority
59 N Chestnut Street
Red Cloud, NE 68970-2271
402-746-2262

Sargent
Sargent Housing Authority
701 W Anna Street
Sargent, NE 68874-9767
308-527-4204

Schuyler
Schuyler Housing
Authority
712 F Street
Schuyler, NE 68661-2345
402-352-2431

Shelton
Shelton Housing Authority
306 C Street
Shelton, NE 68876-9622
308-647-6673

St Paul
St. Paul Housing Authority
420 Jay Street
St Paul, NE 68873-1750
308-754-5251

Sutherland
Sutherland Housing
Authority
1200 2nd Street
Sutherland, NE 69165-2056
308-386-4864

Syracuse
Syracuse Housing
Authority
990 Walnut Street
Syracuse, NE 68446-9698
402-269-2851

Tekamah
Tekamah Housing
Authority
211 S 9th Street
Tekamah, NE 68061-1482
402-374-1740

Tilden
Tilden Housing Authority
600 1/2 S Antelope Street
Tilden, NE 68781-4710
402-368-7714

Verdigre
Verdigre Housing
Authority
615 S Main Street
Verdigre, NE 68783-5014
402-668-2237

Wayne
Wayne Housing Authority
409 Dearborn Street
Wayne, NE 68787-2242
402-375-2868

Weeping Water
Weeping Water Housing
Authority
309 W River Street
Weeping Water, NE 68463-
4214
402-267-6565

Wilber
Wilber Housing Authority
316 N Shimerda Street
Wilber, NE 68465-3026
402-821-2298

Wisner
Goldenrod Joint Housing
Authority
1119 Avenue E
Wisner, NE 68791
402-529-3513

Wood River
Wood River Housing
Authority
1413 Main Street
Wood River, NE 68883-9158
308-583-2405

Wymore
Wymore Housing Authority
300 N 7th Street
Wymore, NE 68466-1763
402-645-8241

York
York Housing Authority
215 Lincoln Avenue

York, NE 68467-3500
402-362-4481

Nevada

Las Vegas
City of Las Vegas Housing
Authority
420 N 10th Street
Las Vegas, NV 89101-3106
702-922-6800

County of Clark Housing
Authority
5390 E Flamingo Road
Las Vegas, NV 89122-5338
702-451-8041

North Las Vegas
North Las Vegas Housing
Authority
1632 Yale Street
North Las Vegas, NV 89030-
6827
702-649-2451

Reno
City of Reno Housing
Authority
1525 E 9th Street
Reno, NV 89512-3012
775-329-3630

New Hampshire

Bedford
New Hampshire Housing
Finance Agency
32 Constitution Drive
Bedford, NH 03110
603-472-8623

Claremont
Claremont Housing
Authority
243 Broad Street
Claremont, NH 03743-2674
603-542-6411

Concord
Concord Housing Authority
15 Pitman Street
Concord, NH 03301-4349
603-224-4059

Dover
Dover Housing Authority
62 Whittier Street
Dover, NH 03820-2946
603-742-5804

Exeter
Exeter Housing Authority
277 Water Street
Exeter, NH 03833-1719
603-778-8110

Keene
Keene Housing Authority
105 Castle Street
Keene, NH 03431-3307
603-352-6161 ext. 301

Laconia
Laconia Housing &
Redevelopment Authority
25 Union Avenue
Laconia, NH 03246-3558
603-524-2112

Manchester
Manchester Housing
Authority
198 Hanover Street
Manchester NH 03104-6136
603-624-2100

Nashua
Nashua Housing Authority
101 Major Drive
Nashua, NH 03060-4770
603-883-5661

Newmarket
Newmarket Housing
Authority
34 Gordon Avenue
Newmarket, NH 03857-1802
603-659-5444

Portsmouth
Portsmouth Housing
Authority
245 Middle Street
Portsmouth, NH 03801-5128
603-436-4310 ext. 119

Salem
Housing Authority of The
Town of Salem
70 Telfer Circle
Salem, NH 03079-3340
603-893-6417

Somersworth
Somersworth Housing
Authority
9 Bartlett Avenue
Somersworth, NH 03878-
1802
603-692-2864

West Lebanon
Lebanon Housing Authority
31 Romano Circle

West Lebanon, NH 03784-
1687
603-784-5475

NEW JERSEY

Asbury Park
Asbury Park Housing
Authority
1000 1/2 3rd Avenue
Asbury Park, NJ 07712 -
5806
732-774-2660

Atlantic City
Atlantic City Housing
Authority
227 N Vermont Avenue
Atlantic City, NJ 08401-5563
609-344-1107

Bayonne
Bayonne Housing Authority
50 E 21st Street
Bayonne, NJ 07002-3761
201-339-8700

Belmar
Belmar Housing Authority
710 8th Avenue
Belmar, NJ 07719-2753
732-681-3700 ext. 9229

Beverly
Beverly Housing Authority
100 Magnolia Street
Beverly, NJ 08010-1113
609-387-0250

Boonton
Boonton Housing Authority
125 Chestnut Street
Boonton, NJ 07005-3761
973-335-0846 ext. 6

Bridgeton
Bridgeton Housing
Authority
100 Commerce Street
Bridgeton, NJ 08302-2606
856-451-4454

Burlington
Burlington Housing
Authority
800 Walnut Street
Burlington, NJ 08016-2645
609-386-0246

Camden
Camden Housing Authority
1300 Admiral Wilson Blvd.

Camden, NJ 08109-3908
856-968-2700

Cape May
Cape May Housing
Authority
639 Lafayette Street
Cape May, NJ 08204-1518
856-691-4099

Carteret
Carteret Housing Authority
96 Roosevelt Avenue
Carteret, NJ 07008-3450
732-541-6800

Clementon
Clementon Housing
Authority
22 Gibbsboro Road
Clementon, NJ 08021-4034
609-784-1134

Cliffside Park
Cliffside Park Housing
Authority
500 Gorge Road
Cliffside Park, NJ 07010-
2243
201-941-0655

Collingswood
Collingswood Housing
Authority
30 Washington Avenue
Collingswood, NJ 08108-
1545
609-854-1077

Deptford
Gloucester County Housing
Authority
100 Pop Moylan Boulevard
Deptford, NJ 08096-1947
856-845-4959

Dover
Dover Housing Authority
215 E Blackwell Street
Dover, NJ 07801- 4130
973-361-9444

East Orange
East Orange Housing
Authority
160 Halsted Street
East Orange, NJ 07018-2663
973-678-0250

Edgewater
Edgewater Housing
Authority
300 Undercliff Avenue

Edgewater, NJ 07020-1284
201-943-6000

Elizabeth
Elizabeth Housing
Authority
688 Maple Avenue
Elizabeth, NJ 07202-2624
908-965-2400

Englewood
Englewood Housing
Authority
111 West Street
Englewood, NJ 07631-2341
201-871-3451

Fort Lee
Fort Lee Housing Authority
1403 Teresa Drive
Fort Lee, NJ 07024-2102
201-947-7400

Garfield
Garfield Housing Authority
71 Daniel P Conte Court
Garfield, NJ 07026-2404
973-340-4170

Gloucester City
Gloucester City Housing
Authority
101 Market Street
Gloucester City, NJ 08030-
2049
609-456-5772

Hackensack
Bergen County Housing
Authority
21 Main Street
Room 307w
Hackensack, NJ 07601-7021
201-646-2629

Highland Park
Highland Park Housing
Authority
242 S 6th Avenue
Highland Park, NJ 08904-
2842
732-572-4420

Highlands
Highlands Housing
Authority
215 Shore Drive
Highlands, NJ 07732-1572
732-872-2022

Hightstown
Hightstown Housing
Authority
131 Rogers Avenue

Hightstown, NJ 08520-3725
609-448-2268

Hoboken
Hoboken Housing
Authority
400 Harrison Street
Hoboken, NJ 07030-6202
201-798-0370

Irvington
Irvington Housing
Authority
101 Union Avenue
Irvington, NJ 07111-3261
973-375-2121

Keansburg
Keansburg Housing
Authority
1 Church Street
Keansburg, NJ 07734-1456
732-787-6161

Lakewood
Lakewood Housing
Authority
317 Sampson Avenue
Lakewood, NJ 08701-3565
732-364-1300

Linden
Linden Housing Authority
1601 Dill Avenue
Linden, NJ 07036-1779
908-298-3820

Lodi
Lodi Housing Authority
50 Brookside Avenue
Lodi, NJ 07644-3214
973-470-3650

Madison
Madison Housing
Authority
15 Chateau Thierry Avenue
Madison, NJ 07940 -1165
973-377-0258

Middletown
Middletown Housing
Authority
1 Oakdale Drive
Middletown, NJ 07748-2148
732-671-2990

Millville
Millville Housing Authority
PO Box 803
Millville, NJ 08332-0803
856-825-8860

Minotola
Buena Housing Authority
600 Central Avenue
Minotola, NJ 08341-1014
609-697-4852

Morristown
Morris County Housing
Authority
99 Ketch Road
Morristown, NJ 07960-2606
973-540-0389

New Brunswick
New Brunswick Housing
Authority
65 Morris Street
Second Floor
New Brunswick, NJ 08901
732-745-5147

Newark
Newark Housing Authority
57 Sussex Avenue
Newark, NJ 07103-3941
973-430-2430

Newton
Newton Housing Authority
32 Liberty Street
Newton, NJ 07860-1723
973-383-5191

North Bergen
North Bergen Housing
Authority
6121 Grand Avenue
North Bergen, NJ 07047-
3450
201-868-8605

Orange
Orange City Housing
Authority
340 Thomas Boulevard
Orange, NJ 07050-4151
973-675-1250

Passaic
Passaic Housing Authority
333 Passaic Street
Passaic, NJ 07055 -5814
973-365-6330

Paterson
Paterson Housing Authority
60 Van Houten Street
Paterson, NJ 07505-1028
973-345-5080

Phillipsburg
Phillipsburg Housing
Authority

530 Heckman Street
Phillipsburg, NJ 08865-2624
908-859-0122

Plainfield
Plainfield Housing
Authority
510 E Front Street
Plainfield, NJ 07060-1449
908-769-6335

Pleasantville
Pleasantville Housing
Authority
156 N Main Street
Pleasantville, NJ 08232-2569
609-646-3023

Princeton
Princeton Housing
Authority
50 Clay Street
Princeton, NJ 08542-3108
609-924-3448

Rahway
Rahway Housing Authority
165 E Grand Avenue
Rahway, NJ 07065-4552
732-499-0066

Red Bank
Red Bank Housing
Authority
52 Evergreen Terrace
Red Bank, NJ 07701-1312
732-741-1808

Salem
Salem Housing Authority
205 7th Street
Salem, NJ 08079-1040
856-935-5022

Secaucus
Secaucus Housing
Authority
700 County Avenue
Secaucus, NJ 07094-2700
201-867-2957

Somerset
Franklin Housing Authority
1 Parkside Street
Somerset, NJ 08873-3743
732-545-9430

South Amboy
South Amboy Housing
Authority
250 S Broadway
South Amboy, NJ 08879-
1862
732-721-1831

Summit
Summit Housing Authority
512 Springfield Avenue
Summit, NJ 07901-2607
908-273-6413

Trenton
Trenton Housing Authority
875 New Willow Street
Trenton, NJ 08638-4039
609-278-5042

Union City
Union City Housing
Authority
3911 Kennedy Boulevard
Union City, NJ 07087-2654
201-864-1515

Vineland
Vineland Housing
Authority
191 W Chestnut Avenue
Vineland, NJ 08360-5417
856-691-4099

Weehawken
Weehawken Housing
Authority
525 Gregory Avenue
Weehawken, NJ 07087-5701
201-348-4188

West New York
West New York Housing
Authority
6100 Adams Street
West New York, NJ 07093-
1537
201-868-6100

Westmont
Haddon Housing Authority
25 Wynnewood Avenue
Westmont, NJ 08108-2740
609-854-3700

Wildwood
Wildwood Housing
Authority
3700 New Jersey Avenue
Wildwood, NJ 08260-6154
609-729-0220

Woodbridge
Woodbridge Housing
Authority
20 Bunns Lane
Woodbridge, NJ 07095-1765
732-634-2750

NEW MEXICO

Alamogordo
Housing Authority of The
City of Alamogordo
104 Avenida Amigos
Alamogordo, NM 88310-
3326
505-437-5621 ext. 16

Albuquerque
Albuquerque Department
of Family And Community
Services
1840 University Blvd. SE
Albuquerque, NM 87106 -
3919
505-764-3900

Bernalillo County Housing
Department
2204 Centro Familiar
Boulevard SW
Albuquerque, NM 87105-
4576
505-764-6800

Artesia
Housing Authority of The
City of Artesia
617 W Bush Avenue
Artesia, NM 88210-1330
505-764-3529

Bayard
Housing Authority of The
Town of Bayard
100 Runnels Drive
Bayard, NM 88023
505-537-2296

Bernalillo
Town of Bernalillo Dept. of
Housing Services
857 Calle Los Mayores
Bernalillo, NM 87004
505-867-2792

Chama
Housing Authority of The
Village of Chama
PO Box 695
Chama, NM 87520-0695
505-756-2986

Clayton
Housing Authority of The
Town of Clayton
200 Aspen Street
Clayton, NM 88415-2247
505-374-9580

Clovis
Clovis Housing And
Redevelopment Agency,
Inc.
2101 W Grand Avenue
Clovis, NM 88101-7088
505-769-7902 ext. 11

Gallup
Housing Authority of The
City of Gallup
203 Debra Drive
Gallup, NM 87301-5802
505-722-4388

Grants
Housing Authority of The
City of Grants
508 E Santa Fe Avenue
Grants, NM 87020-2440
505-285-6359

Las Cruces
Housing Authority of Dona
Ana County
926 South San Pedro
Las Cruces, NM 88001
505-523-6100

Housing Authority of The
City of Las Cruces
926 S San Pedro Street
Las Cruces, NM 88001-3637
505-528-2019

Las Vegas
Housing Authority of San
Miguel County
County Courthouse 3rd
Floor
500 West National Suite 304
Las Vegas, NM 87701
505-454-1813

Housing Authority of The
City of Las Vegas
2400 Sagebrush Street
Las Vegas NM 87701-4813
505-425-9463

Lordsburg
Housing Authority of The
City of Lordsburg
1001 Avenida Del Sol
Lordsburg, NM 88045-2705
505-542-8111

Lovington
Housing Authority of The
City of Lovington
1605 S 4th Street
Lovington, NM 88260-5439
505-396-5416

Mora
Housing Authority of The
County of Mora
Main Street Hwy 518
Mora, NM 87732-0041
505-387-5211

Raton
Housing Authority of The
City of Raton
309 Parsons Avenue
Raton, NM 87740 3866
505-445-8021 ext. 16

Roswell
Region VI Housing
Authority
226 N Main St., Suite 301
Roswell, NM 88201-4723
505-622-0881 ext. 31

Santa Fe
Housing Authority of The
County of Santa Fe
52 Camino De Jacobo
Santa Fe, NM 87507-3504
505-992-3060

Santa Fe Civic Housing
Authority
664 Alta Vista Street
Santa Fe, NM 87505-4149
505-988-2859

Silver City
Region V Housing
Authority
2545 N Silver Street
Silver City, NM 88061-7100
505-388-1974

Sunland Park
Housing Authority of The
City of Sunland Park
4420 Mcnutt Rd
Sunland Park, NM 88063
505-589-9414

Taos
Housing Authority of The
County of Taos
962 Ranchitos Road
Taos, NM 87571
505-758-2460 ext. 3930

Housing Authority of The
Town of Taos
106 Gusdorf Circle
Taos, NM 87571
505-758-4312

Truth Or Consequences
Housing Authority of The
City of Truth Or
Consequences

108 S Cedar Street
Truth Or Consequences,
NM 87901-2820
505-894-2244 ext. 27

Tucumcari
Housing Authority of The
City of Tucumcari
323 E Center Street
Tucumcari, NM 88401-2265
505-461-4403

Wagon Mound
Housing Authority of The
Village of Wagon Mound
710 Canton Avenue
Wagon Mound, NM 87752
505-666-2268

New York

Albany
Albany Housing Authority
4 Lincoln Square
Albany, NY 12202-1632
518-445-0711

Amsterdam
Amsterdam Housing
Authority
52 Division St.
Amsterdam, NY 12010-4002
518-842-2894

Batavia
Batavia Housing Authority
4 Macarthur Dr.
Batavia, NY 14020-1543
716-344-1888

Beacon
The City of Beacon Housing
Authority
1 Forrestal Heights
Beacon NY 12508-3701
845-831-1289

Binghamton
Binghamton Housing
Authority
45 Exchange St.
P.O. Box 1906
Binghamton, NY 13902-1906
607-723-9491

Canton
Canton Housing Authority
37 Riverside Dr.
Canton, NY 13617-1064
315-386-8381

Carthage
West Carthage Housing
Authority
63 Madison St.
Carthage NY 13619-1163
315-493-3581

Wilna Housing Authority
600 South Washington St.
Carthage, NY 13619-1581
315-493-1480

Catskill
Catskill Housing Authority
25 Bronson St.
Catskill, NY 12414-1809
518-943-2900

Cortland
Cortland Housing
Authority
42 Church St.
Cortland, NY 13045-2748
607-753-1771

Dunkirk
Dunkirk Housing Authority
15 North Main St.
Dunkirk, NY 14048-1743
716-366-8740

Ellenville
Ellenville Housing
Authority
10 Eastwood Avenue
Ellenville, NY 12428-1228
914-647-8686

Elmira
Elmira Housing Authority
346 Woodlawn Ave.
Elmira, NY 14901-1331
607-737-7100

Freeport
Freeport Housing Authority
3 Buffalo Avenue
Freeport, NY 11520-4013
516-623-2508

Geneva
Geneva Housing Authority
30 Elm St.
Geneva, NY 14456-2319
315-789-8010

Glen Cove
Glen Cove Housing
Authority
140 Glen Cove Avenue
Glen Cove, NY 11542-3414
516-671-3161 ext. 10

Gloversville
Gloversville Housing
Authority
181 West St.
Gloversville, NY 12078-1911
518-773-7308

Great Neck
North Hempstead Housing
Authority
Pond Hill Road
Great Neck, NY 11020-1599
516-627-6433

Great Neck
Village of Great Neck
Housing Authority
700 Middle Neck Road
Great Neck, NY 11023-1242
516-482-2727

Hempstead
Village of Hempstead Ha
260 Clinton Street
Hempstead, NY 11550-2629
516-489-8500

Herkimer
Herkimer Housing
Authority
315 North Prospect St.
Herkimer, NY 13350-1952
315-866-2252

Hoosick Falls
Hoosick Housing Authority
1 Hoosick Meadows Way
Hoosick Falls, NY 12090-
3917
518-686-7316

Hornell
Hornell Housing Authority
87 East Washington St.
Hornell, NY 14843-1453
607-324-7912

Hudson
Hudson Housing Authority
41 North Second St.
Hudson, NY 12534-1820
518-828-5415

Huntington Station
Town of Huntington
Housing Authority
1 Lowndes Avenue A
Huntington Station, NY
11746-1261
631-427-6220

Ilion
Ilion Housing Authority
100 West Main St.

Ilion, NY 13357-1740
315-894-2159

Ithaca
Ithaca Housing Authority
798 South Plain St.
Ithaca, NY 14850-5359
607-273-8629

Jamestown
Jamestown Housing
Authority
110 West Third St.
Jamestown, NY 14701-5112
716-664-3345

Kenmore
Kenmore Municipal
Housing Authority
657 Colvin Blvd.
Kenmore, NY 14217-2852
716-874-6000

Kingston
Kingston Cda
420 Broadway
City Hall
Kingston, NY 12401-0150
914-338-8650

Kingston Housing
Authority
132 Rondout Gardens
Kingston, NY 12401-5513
914-331-1955

Lockport
Lockport Housing
Authority
301 Michigan St.
Lockport, NY 14094-1724
716-434-0001

Long Beach
Housing Authority of Long
Beach
500 Centre Street
Long Beach, NY 11561-2015
516-431-2444

Malone
Malone Housing Authority
215 Elm St.
Malone, NY 12953-1527
518-483-3070

Massena
Massena Housing Authority
20 Robinson Rd.
Massena, NY 13662-2411
315-764-1706

Mechanicville
Mechanicville Housing
Authority

1 Harris Ave.
Mechanicville, NY 12118-
2507
518-664-9897

Monroe
Village of Kiryas Joel Ha
51 Forest Road
Suite 360
Monroe, NY 10950-2938
914-782-7790

Monticello
Monticello Housing
Authority
76 Evergreen Drive
Monticello, NY 12701-1630
914-794-6855

Mount Kisco
Mount Kisco Housing
Authority
200 Carpenter Avenue
Mount Kisco, NY 10549-
1602
914-666-7578

New Rochelle
New Rochelle Housing
Authority
50 Sickles Avenue
New Rochelle, NY 10801-
4029
914-235-1717

New York
New York City Housing
Authority
250 Broadway
Room 912
New York, NY 10007-2516
212-306-3440

Newark
Newark Housing Authority
200 Driving Park Circle
Newark, NY 14513-1156
315-331-1574

Newburgh
Housing Authority of
Newburgh
40 Walsh Road
Newburgh, NY 12550-5327
914-561-0840

Niagara Falls
Niagara Falls Housing
Authority
744 10th St.
Niagara Falls, NY 14301-
1804
716-285-6961

Norwich
Norwich Housing
Authority
13 Brown St.
Norwich, NY 13815-1823
607-334-5358

Oakdale
Town of Islip Housing
Authority
963 Montauk Highway
Oakdale, NY 11769 -1433
631-589-7100

Ogdensburg
Ogdensburg Housing
Authority
1101 Jay St.
Ogdensburg, NY 13669-
2828
315-393-3710

Olean
Olean Housing Authority
610 Martha Ave.
Olean, NY 14760- 3970
716-372-8262

Oneida
Oneida Housing Authority
226 Farrier Ave.
Oneida, NY 13421- 1667
315-363-8450

Oneonta
Oneonta Housing Authority
2 Mitchell St.
Oneonta, NY 13820- 2343
607-432-0170

Peekskill
Peekskill Housing
Authority
807 Main Street
Peekskill, NY 10566- 2040
914-739-1700

Plainview
Town of Oyster Bay
Housing Authority
115 Central Park Road
Plainview, NY 11803 -2027
516-349-1000

Plattsburgh
Plattsburgh Housing
Authority
39 Oak St.
Plattsburgh, NY 12901- 2860
518-561-0720

Port Chester
Port Chester Housing
Authority

PO Box 347
Port Chester, NY 10573 -
0347
914-937-5550

Port Jervis
Port Jervis Housing
Authority
39 Pennsylvania Avenue
Port Jervis, NY 12771- 2144
914-856-8621

Poughkeepsie
Poughkeepsie Housing
Authority
21 Charles Street
Building 4
Poughkeepsie, NY 12601-
2234
914-485-8862

Rensselaer
Rensselaer Housing
Authority
85 Aiken Ave.
Rensselaer, NY 12144 -2518
518-436-0230

Rochester
Rochester Housing
Authority
140 West Ave.
Rochester, NY 14611 -2744
716-697-3600

Rockville Centre
Rockville Centre Ha
160 N Centre Avenue
Rockville Centre, NY 11570-
3907
516-536-4343

Rome
Rome Housing Authority
205 St. Peter`S Ave.
Rome, NY 13440 -5959
315-337-1090

Saranac Lake
Harrietstown Housing
Authority
3-5 Riverside Dr.
Saranac Lake, NY 12983-
2210
518-891-3050

Saratoga Springs
Saratoga Springs Housing
Authority
One South Federal St.
Saratoga Springs, NY 12866-
4206
518-584-6600

Schenectady
Schenectady Housing
Authority
375 Broadway
Schenectady, NY 12305-
2519
518-386-7000

Sleepy Hollow
North Tarrytown Housing
Authority
126 Valley Street
Sleepy Hollow, NY 10591-
2847
914-631-4626

Spring Valley
Village of Spring Valley
Housing Authority
76 Gesner Drive
Spring Valley, NY 10977-
3956
914-352-7677

Suffern
Town of Ramapo Housing
Authority
38 Pondview Drive
Suffern, NY 10901-6504
845-357-7171

Syracuse
Syracuse Housing
Authority
516 Burt St.
Syracuse, NY 13202-3915
315-475-6181

Tarrytown
Tarrytown Municipal
Housing Authority
50 White Street
Tarrytown, NY 10591-3621
914-631-1991

Troy
Troy Housing Authority
1 Eddy`S Lane
Troy, NY 12180-1423
518-272-3211

Tuckahoe
Tuckahoe Housing
Authority
4 Union Place
Tuckahoe, NY 10707-4236
914-961-3373

Uniondale
Town of Hempstead
Housing Authority
760 Jerusalem Avenue
Uniondale, NY 11553-2929
516-485-9666

Utica
Utica Housing Authority
509 Second St.
Utica, NY 13501-2450
315-735-5426

North Carolina

Ahoskie
Ahoskie Housing Authority
200 Pierce Avenue
Ahoskie, NC 27910-4178
252-537-0552

Albemarle
City of Albemarle
Department of Public
Housing
300 S Bell Avenue
Albemarle, NC 28001-5210
704-984-9580

Andrews
Andrews Housing
Authority
291 Whitaker Lane
Andrews, NC 28901-8106
704-321-5257

Asheboro
Asheboro Housing
Authority
338 W Wainman Avenue
Asheboro, NC 27203-5664
336-629-4146 ext. 207

Asheville
Housing Authority of The
City of Asheville
165 S French Broad Avenue
Asheville, NC 28801-3900
828-258-1222

Ayden
Ayden Housing Authority
705 Liberty Street
Ayden, NC 28513-2766
252-746-2021

Beaufort
Housing Authority of The
Town of Beaufort
716 Mulberry Street
Beaufort, NC 28516-1922
252-728-3226

Belmont
Belmont Housing Authority
51 Flowers Court
Belmont, NC 28012-3449
704-825-9376

Benson
Benson Housing Authority
413 Williams Drive
Benson, NC 27504
919-894-8216

Brevard
Brevard Housing Authority
69 W Morgan Street
Brevard, NC 28712-3659
828-884-2146

Burlington
Burlington Housing
Authority
133 N Ireland Street
Burlington, NC 27217-2635
336-226-8421

Chapel Hill
Town of Chapel Hill
Department of Housing
317 Caldwell Street Ext.
Chapel Hill, NC 27516
919-968-2850

Charlotte
Housing Authority of The
City of Charlotte
1301 South Boulevard
Charlotte, NC 28203-4209
704-336-5183

Concord
Housing Authority of The
City of Concord
283 Harold Goodman Circle
SW
Concord, NC 28025-5491
704-788-1139

Dunn
Dunn Housing Authority
601 E Canary Street
Dunn, NC 28334-6003
910-892-5076

Durham
Housing Authority of The
City of Durham
330 E Main Street
Durham, NC 27701-3718
919-683-1551

Edenton
The New Edenton Housing
Authority
115 Blades Street
Edenton, NC 27932-1521
252-482-8164

Elizabeth City
Elizabeth City Housing
Authority

442 Hariot Drive
Elizabeth City, NC 27909-4650
252-335-5411

Fairmont
Fairmont Housing
Authority
501 Mcdaniel Street
Fairmont, NC 28340-2027
910-628-7467

Farmville
Farmville Housing
Authority
172 Anderson Avenue
Farmville, NC 27828-2002
252-753-5347

Fayetteville
Fayetteville Metropolitan
Housing Authority
108 Wiley Street
Fayetteville, NC 28301-4660
910-483-3648

Forest City
Forest City Housing
Authority
147 E Spruce Street
Forest City, NC 28043-5503
704-245-1390

Gaston
Roanoke-Chowan Regional
Housing Authority
205 Gaston Drive
Gaston, NC 27832-9650
252-537-1051

Gastonia
Gastonia Housing
Authority
340 E Long Avenue
Gastonia, NC 28054-2525
704-864-6771

Goldsboro
Eastern Carolina Regional
Housing Authority
300 Myers Avenue
Goldsboro, NC 27530-7332
919-735-0435

Housing Authority of The
City of Goldsboro
1729 Edgerton Street
Goldsboro, NC 27530-3166
919-735-5650

Graham
The Graham Housing
Authority
109 E Hill Street

Graham, NC 27253-2307
336-229-7041

Greensboro
Housing Authority of The
City of Greensboro
450 N Church Street
Greensboro, NC 27401-2001
336-275-8501

Greenville
Housing Authority of The
City of Greenville
1103 Broad Street
Greenville, NC 27834-3952
252-329-4000

Hamlet
Hamlet Housing Authority
1104 Fisher Avenue
Hamlet, NC 28345-4316
910-582-3279

Henderson
Vance County Housing
Authority
224 Lincoln Street
Henderson, NC 27536-2501
252-438-6127

Hendersonville
Hendersonville Housing
Authority
203 N Justice Street
Hendersonville, NC 28739-4943
828-692-6175

Hertford
Hertford Housing
Authority
104 White Street
Hertford, NC 27944-1161
252-426-5663

Hickory
City of Hickory Public
Housing Authority
841 S Center Street
Hickory NC 28602-3611
828-328-5373

High Point
Housing Authority of The
City of High Point
500 E Russell Avenue
High Point, NC 27260-6746
336-887-2661

Hot Springs
Hot Springs Housing
Authority
PO Box 296

Hot Springs, NC 28743-0296
828-622-3237

Kings Mountain
Kings Mountain Housing
Authority
201 Mcgill Court
Kings Mountai, NC 28086-3047
704-739-2816

Kinston
Housing Authority of The
City of Kinston
608 N Queen Street
Kinston, NC 28501-4340
252-523-1195

Laurinburg
Housing Authority of The
Town of Laurinburg
1300 Woodlawn Drive
Laurinburg, NC 28352-5028
910-276-2582

Lenoir
Lenoir Housing Authority
431 Vance Street NW
Lenoir, NC 28645-4168
828-758-5536

Lexington
Lexington Housing
Authority
1 Jamaica Drive
Lexington, NC 27292-2571
336-249-8936

Lincolnton
Lincolnton Housing
Authority
806 Mcbee Street
Lincolnton, NC 28092-3512
704-735-2221 ext. 23

Lumberton
Housing Authority of The
City of Lumberton
900 N Chestnut Street
Lumberton, NC 28358-4854
910-671-8200

Robeson County,
Department of Housing
100 Oxendine Circle
Lumberton, NC 28360-9447
910-738-4866

Madison
Madison Housing
Authority
925 Fern Street
Madison, NC 27025-1554
910-548-6619

Mars Hill
Ha Madison County
160 Ivy Ridge Circle
Apartment Dr
Mars Hill, NC 28754-9759
828-689-2721

Mars Hill Housing
Authority
28 N Main Street
Mars Hill, NC 28754-9317
828-689-4531

Marshall
Marshall Housing
Authority
630 N Main Street
Marshal, NC 28753-7829
828-649-2545

Monroe
Monroe Housing Authority
504 Hough Street
Monroe, NC 28112-5776
704-289-2514

Mooresville
Mooresville Housing
Authority
1046 N Main Street
Mooresville, NC 28115-2358
704-664-1659

Morganton
Morganton Housing
Authority
644 1st Street
Morganton, NC 28655-3028
828-437-9101

Mount Airy
Housing Authority of The
Town of Mount Airy
302 Virginia Street
Mount Airy, NC 27030-3546
336-786-8321

Mount Gilead
Mount Gilead Housing
Authority
106 W. Second Avenue
Mount Gilead, NC 27306
336-544-2300

Mount Holly
City of Mount Holly, Dept.
of Housing
635 Noles Drive
Mount Holly, NC 28120-9549
704-827-9025

Mount Olive
Mount Olive Housing
Authority

108 W Main Street
Mount Olive, NC 28365-2009
919-658-6682

Murphy
Housing Programs of The
Town of Murphy
80 Beal Circle
Murphy, NC 28906-3376
828-837-6662

New Bern
Housing Authority of The
City of New Bern
837 S Front Street
New Bern, NC 28562-5650
919-633-0800

North Wilkesboro
North Wilkesboro Dept. of
Housing & Comm. Dev.
101 Hickory Street
North Wilkesboro, NC
28659-3521
336-667-3203

Oxford
Oxford Housing Authority
101 Hillside Drive
Oxford, NC 27565-3769
919-693-6936

Plymouth
Plymouth Housing
Authority
306 W Water Street
Plymouth, NC 27962-1213
252-793-3188

Princeville
Princeville Housing
Authority
51 Pioneer Court
Princeville, NC 27886-5361
252-823-3889

Raleigh
Housing Authority of The
City of Raleigh
PO Box 28007
Raleigh, NC 27611-8007
919-831-6416

Randleman
The New Randleman
Housing Authority
606 S Main Street
Randleman, NC 27317-2020
336-498-7686

Reidsville
The New Reidsville
Housing Authority

924 3rd Avenue
Reidsville, NC 27320-4440
336-349-1080

Roanoke Rapids
Roanoke Rapids Housing
Authority
200 Creekside Court
Roanoke Rapids, NC 27870-3428
252-537-0552

Robersonville
Robersonville Housing
Authority
302 Grimes Street
Robersonville, NC 27871-9415
252-795-3134

Rockingham
Ha Rockingham
809 Armistead Street
Rockingham, NC 28379-3707
919-997-3316

Rocky Mount
Rocky Mount Housing
Authority
1006 Aycock Street
Rocky Mount, NC 27803-2501
252-977-3141

Roxboro
Roxboro Housing Authority
500 Mount Bethel Church
Road
Roxboro, NC 27573-4795
336-599-8616

Salisbury
Housing Authority of The
City of Salisbury
200 S Boundary Street
Salisbury, NC 28144-5104
704-636-1410

Rowan County Housing
Authority
310 Long Meadow Drive
Salisbury, NC 28147 8200
704-633-8380

Sanford
Sanford Housing Authority
504 N 1st Street
Sanford, NC 27330-3604
919-776-7655

Selma
Selma Housing Authority
711 E Lizzie Street

Selma, NC 27576-2318
919-965-3755

Shelby
City of Shelby, Department
of Housing
801 Logan Street
Shelby, NC 28150-3947
704-484-6830

Smithfield
Smithfield Housing
Authority
801 S 5th Street
Smithfield, NC 27577-4337
919-934-9491

Southern Pines
Southern Pines Housing
Authority
801 S Mechanic Street
Southern Pines, NC 28387-5219
910-692-2042

Spruce Pine
Spruce Pine Housing
Authority
405 Walnut Avenue
Spruce Pine, NC 28777-2864
828-765-9182

Statesville
Statesville Housing
Authority
110 W Allison Street
Statesville, NC 28677-6616
704-872-9811

Tarboro
Redevelopment
Commission of The Town of
Tarboro
947 Simmons Street
Tarboro, NC 27886-3716
252-823-6339

Thomasville
Thomasville Housing
Authority
201 James Avenue
Thomasville, NC 27360-2426
336-475-6137

Troy
Troy Housing Authority
201 Stanley Street
Troy, NC 27371-3245
910-576-0611

Valdese
Valdese Housing Authority
1402 Lydia Avenue NW

Valdese, NC 28690-2138
828-874-0098

Wadesboro
Wadesboro Housing
Authority
200 W Short Plaza
Wadesboro, NC 28170-2944
704-694-4852

Washington
Mid-East Regional Housing
Authority
809 Pennsylvania Avenue
Washington, NC 27889-3824
252-946-0061

Washington
Washington Housing
Authority
809 Pennsylvania Avenue
Washington, NC 27889-3824
252-946-0061

Waynesville
Waynesville Housing
Authority
11 Chestnut Park Drive
Waynesville, NC 28786-4179
828-456-6377

Whiteville
Whiteville Housing
Authority
504 W Burkhead Street
Whiteville, NC 28472-3156
910-642-4979

Williamston
Williamston Housing
Authority
504 E Main Street
Williamston, NC 27892-2543
252-792-7571

Wilmington
Housing Authority of The
City of Wilmington
508 S Front Street
Wilmington, NC 28401-5014
910-341-7700

Wilson
Housing Authority of The
City of Wilson
213 Broad Street W
Wilson, NC 27893 -3887
252-291-2245

Winston-Salem
Housing Authority of The
City of Winston-Salem
901 N Cleveland Avenue

Winston-Salem, NC 27101-
3102
336-727-8500

Zebulon
Housing Authority of The
County of Wake
100 Shannon Drive
Zebulon, NC 27597-8967
919-269-6404

North Dakota

Ashley
Mcintosh County Housing
Authority
112 1st Street NE
Ashley, ND 58413-7009
701-288-3645

Bismarck
Burleigh County Housing
Authority
410 S 2nd Street
Bismarck, ND 58504-5534
701-255-2540

Cando
Towner County Housing
Authority
808 6th Street
Cando, ND 58324-6426
701-968-3922

Carrington
Housing Authority of Foster
County
55 Sixteenth Ave. S.
Carrington, ND 58421
701-652-3276

Cavalier
Pembina County Housing
Authority
100 Tornado Drive
Suite2
Cavalier, ND 58220
701-265-8147

Devils Lake
Ramsey County Housing
Authority
605 3rd Street
Devils Lake, ND 58301-3052
701-662-3099

Dickinson
Stark County Housing
Authority
1449 West Villard

Dickinson, ND 58602-0107
701-225-3120

Fargo
Fargo Housing Authority
325 Broadway
Fargo, ND 58102-4714
701-293-6262

Grafton
Walsh County Housing
Authority
600 E. 9th Street
Grafton ND 58237-1659
701-352-3260

Grand Forks
Grand Forks Housing
Authority
1405 First Avenue N.
Grand Forks, ND 58201
701-746-2545

Harvey
Housing Authority of The
County of Wells
509 Emerson Ave.
Harvey, ND 58341-1227
701-324-4587

Hillsboro
Traill County Housing
Authority
16 W Caledonia Avenue
Hillsboro, ND 58045-4205
701-436-5785

Jamestown
Stutsman County Housing
Authority
217 First Ave. N.
Jamestown ND 58401
701-252-1098

La Moure
Housing Authority of The
County of Ransom
107 2nd Avenue Northeast
La Moure, ND 58458
701-288-3645

Lakota
Nelson County Housing
Authority
210 Main Street
Lakota, ND 58344-7102
701-247-2293

Langdon
Cavalier County Housing
Authority
901 3rd Street
Langdon, ND 58249-2457
701-256-3796

Linton
Emmons County Housing
Authority
813 NE 1st Street
Linton, ND 58552-7408
701-258-0018

Minnewaukan
Benson County Housing
Authority
201 Main Street W
Minnewaukan, ND 58351-
5000
701-473-5671

Minot
Minot Housing Authority
310 2nd Street Se
Minot, ND 58701-3941
701-852-0485

New Rockford
Eddy County Housing
Authority
524 Central Avenue
New Rockford, ND 58356
701-947-2008

Rolette
Rolette County Housing
Authority
509 5th Avenue
Rolette, ND 58366
701-246-3421

Valley City
Barnes County Housing
Authority
120 12th Street NW
Valley City, ND 58072-2136
701-845-2600

West Fargo
Housing Authority of Cass
County
230 8th Avenue W
West Fargo, ND 58078-2660
701-282-3443

Richland County Housing
Authority
230 8th Avenue West
West Fargo, ND 58078
701-282-3443

Williston
Housing Authority of The
City of Williston
1801 8th Avenue W
Apartment 50
Williston, ND 58801-3462
701-572-2006

Ohio

Akron
Akron Metropolitan
Housing Authority
100 W Cedar Street
Akron OH 44307-2502
330-762-9631

Ashtabula
Ashtabula Metropolitan
Housing Authority
3526 Lake Avenue
Ashtabula, OH 44004-5765
440-992-3156

Athens
Athens Metropolitan
Housing Authority
10 Hope Drive
Athens, OH 45701-2137
740-592-4481

Batavia
Clermont Metropolitan
Housing Authority
65 S Market Street
Batavia, OH 45103-2943
513-732-6010

Bellefontaine
Logan County Metropolitan
Housing Authority
116 N Everett Street
Bellefontaine, OH 43311-
1132
937-599-1845

Bidwell
Gallia Metropolitan
Housing Authority
381 Buck Ridge Road
Apartment 14
Bidwell, OH 45614-9209
740-446-0251

Cadiz
Harrison Metropolitan
Housing Authority
82450 Cadiz Jewett Road
Cadiz, OH 43907-9427
740-942-8372

Cambridge
Cambridge Metropolitan
Housing Authority
1100 Maple Court
Cambridge, OH 43725-1768
740-439-6651 ext. 108

Canton
Stark Metropolitan Housing
Authority

400 Tuscarawas Street E
Canton, OH 44702-1131
330-454-8051 ext. 303

Chardon
Geauga Metropolitan
Housing Authority
385 Center Street
Chardon, OH 44024-1155
440-286-7413

Chillicothe
Chillicothe Metropolitan
Housing Authority
178 W 4th Street
Chillicothe, OH 45601-3219
740-775-7881

Cincinnati
Cincinnati Metropolitan
Housing Authority
16 W Central Parkway
Cincinnati, OH 45210-1910
513-721-4580

Circleville
Pickaway Metropolitan
Housing Authority
176 Rustic Drive
Circleville, OH 43113-1500
740-477-2514

Cleveland
Cuyahoga Metropolitan
Housing Authority
1441 W 25th Street
Cleveland, OH 44113-3101
216-348-5000

Columbus
Columbus Metropolitan
Housing Authority
880 East 11th Ave
Columbus, OH 43211-2771
614-421-6000

Coshocton
Coshocton Metropolitan
Housing Authority
823 Magnolia Street
Coshocton, OH 43812-2855
740-622-6300

Crooksville
Perry County Metropolitan
Housing Authority
26 Brown Circle Drive
Crooksville, OH 43731-9793
740-982-5991

Dayton
Dayton Metropolitan
Housing Authority

400 Wayne Ave
Dayton, OH 45401-8750
937-222-9907

East Liverpool
Columbiana Metropolitan
Housing Authority
325 Moore Street
East Liverpool, OH 43920-2572
330-386-5970

Fremont
Sandusky Metropolitan
Housing Authority
1358 Mosser Drive
Fremont, OH 43420-3282
419-334-4426

Georgetown
Brown Metropolitan
Housing Authority
200 S Green Street
Georgetown, OH 45121-1241
937-378-6041

Hamilton
Butler Metropolitan
Housing Authority
4110 Hamilton Middletown Road
Hamilton, OH 45011-6218
513-896-4411 ext. 128

Ironton
Ironton Metropolitan
Housing Authority
720 Washington Street
Ironton, OH 45638-1774
740-532-8658

Lancaster
Fairfield Metropolitan
Housing Authority
1506 Amherst Place SW
Lancaster, OH 43130-8634
740-653-6928

Lebanon
Warren Metropolitan
Housing Authority
990 E Ridge Drive
Lebanon, OH 45036-1678
513-695-1226

Lima
Allen Metropolitan Housing
Authority
600 S Main Street
Lima, OH 45804-1242
419-228-6065

Logan
Hocking Metropolitan
Housing Authority
50 S High Street
Logan, OH 43138-1667
740-385-3883

London
London Metropolitan
Housing Authority
179 S Main Street
London, OH 43140-1549
740-852-1888

Lorain
Lorain Metropolitan
Housing Authority
1600 Kansas Avenue
Lorain, OH 44052-3366
440-288-1600

Manchester
Adams Metropolitan
Housing Authority
401 East 7th St
Manchester, OH 45144-1401
937-549-2648

Martins Ferry
Belmont Metropolitan
Housing Authority
100 S 3rd Street
Martins Ferry, OH 43935-1457
614-633-5085

Mc Connelsville
Morgan Metropolitan
Housing Authority
4512 N State Route 376 NW
McConnelsville, OH 43756-9563
740-962-4930

Medina
Medina Metropolitan
Housing Authority
860 Walter Road
Medina, OH 44256-1542
330-273-9072

Napoleon
Henry Metropolitan
Housing Authority
1044 Chelsea Avenue
Napoleon, OH 43545
419-592-5788

Newark
Licking Metropolitan
Housing Authority
85 W Church Street
Newark, OH 43055-5018
740-349-8069

Painesville
Lake Metropolitan Housing
Authority
189 1st Street
Painesville, OH 44077-3111
440-354-3347

Parma
Parma Public Housing
Agency
5617 Chevrolet Boulevard
Parma, OH 44130-1406
440-885-8076

Piketon
Pike Metropolitan Housing
Authority
2626 Shyville Road
Piketon, OH 45661-9746
740-289-4534

Pomeroy
Meigs Metropolitan
Housing Authority
117 E. Memorial Dr., Suite 7
Pomeroy, OH 45769-9615
740-992-2733

Portsmouth
Portsmouth Metropolitan
Housing Authority
410 Court Street
Portsmouth, OH 45662-3949
740-354-4547

Ravenna
Portage Metropolitan
Housing Authority
2832 State Route 59
Ravenna, OH 44266-1650
330-297-1489

Sandusky
Erie Metropolitan Housing
Authority
322 Warren Street
Sandusky, OH 44870-2265
419-625-0262

Springfield
Springfield Metropolitan
Housing Authority
437 E John Street
Springfield, OH 45505-4036
937-325-7331

Steubenville
Jefferson Metropolitan
Housing Authority
815 N 6th Street
Steubenville, OH 43952-1848
740-282-0994

Toledo
Lucas Metropolitan
Housing Authority
435 Nebraska Avenue
Toledo, OH 43602-1539
419-259-9400

Troy
Miami Metropolitan
Housing Authority
1695 Troy Sidney Road
Troy, OH 45373- 9794
937-339-2111

Warren
Trumbull Metropolitan
Housing Authority
1977 Niles Road Se
Warren, OH 44484-5118
330-369-1533

Wellston
Jackson County Housing
Authority
249 W 13th Street
Wellston, OH 45692-2258
740-384-5627

Wilmington
Clinton Metropolitan
Housing Authority
478 Thorne Avenue
Wilmington, OH 45177-1222
937-382-5749

Wooster
Wayne Metropolitan
Housing Authority
200 S Market Street
Wooster OH 44691-4766
330-264-2727

Xenia
Greene Metropolitan
Housing Authority
538 N Detroit Street
Xenia, OH 45385-2236
937-376-2908

Youngstown
Youngstown Metropolitan
Housing Authority
131 W Boardman Street
Youngstown, OH 44503-1337
330-744-2161

Zanesville
Zanesville Metropolitan
Housing Authority
407 Pershing Road
Zanesville, OH 43701-6871
740-454-8566

Oklahoma

Ada
Housing Authority of The
City of Ada
1100 N Stockton Street
Ada, OK 74820-2067
580-436-1613

Anadarko
Housing Authority of The
City of Anadarko
615 E Texas Drive
Anadarko, OK 73005-5200
405-247-3110

Antlers
Housing Authority of The
Town of Antlers
105 NW 3rd Street
Antlers, OK 74523-2260
580-298-5542

Apache
Housing Authority of The
Town of Apache
PO Box 337
Apache, OK 73006-0337
580-588-3664

Atoka
Housing Authority of The
City of Atoka
80 W Cedar Circle
Atoka, OK 74525-3655
580-889-7311

Bristow
Housing Authority of The
City of Bristow
1110 S Chestnut Street
Bristow, OK 74010-3708
918-367-5558

Broken Bow
Housing Authority of The
City of Broken Bow
710 E 3rd Street
Broken Bow, OK 74728-4326
580-584-6939

Cement
Housing Authority of The
Town of Cement
PO Box 479
Cement, OK 73017-0479
405-489-3674

Cheyenne
Housing Authority of The
Town of Cheyenne
123 Vincent Drive
Cheyenne, OK 73628
580-497-3306

Coalgate
Housing Authority of The
City of Coalgate
51 Levy Annex
Coalgate, OK 74538-2830
580-927-2575

Commerce
Housing Authority of The
City of Commerce
610 D Street
Commerce, OK 74339-3110
918-675-4748

Cushing
Housing Authority of The
Town of Cushing
1713 Cherry Lane
Cushing, OK 74023-4904
918-225-7205

Del City
Housing Authority of The
City of Del City
4613 Tinker Diagonal Street
Del City, OK 73115-3977
405-672-1412

Drumright
Housing Authority of The
City of Drumright
1400 Aspen Drive
Drumright, OK 74030-2020
918-352-9539

Elk City
Housing Authority of The
City of Elk City
1510 W 9th Street
Elk City, OK 73644-6107
580-225-0129

Geary
Housing Authority of The
City of Geary
329 Troxel Drive
Geary, OK 73040-1410
405-884-2710

Grandfield
Housing Authority of The
City of Grandfield
130 E 1st Street
Grandfield, OK 73546-9498
580-479-5256

Granite
Housing Authority of The
Town of Granite
318 S Main Street

Granite OK 73547-9305
580-535-2134

Guthrie
Housing Authority of The
City of Guthrie
1524 E Perkins Avenue
Guthrie, OK 73044-5843
405-282-3246

Hartshorne
Housing Authority of The
City of Hartshorne
615 Wichita Avenue
Hartshorne, OK 74547-4832
918-297-3270

Heavener
Housing Authority of The
City of Heavener
201 E Avenue I
Heavener, OK 74937-3225
918-653-2500

Henryetta
Housing Authority of The
City of Henryetta
1708 W Ragan Street
Henryetta, OK 74437-4607
918-652-9651

Hobart
Housing Authority of The
City of Hobart
329 S Lincoln Street
Hobart, OK 73651-4027
405-726-3121

Holdenville
Housing Authority of The
City of Holdenville
301 Crestview Street
Holdenville, OK 74848-2847
405-379-3375

Hugo
Housing Authority of The
City of Hugo
300 13th Place
Hugo, OK 74743-5202
580-326-3348

Hydro
Housing Authority of The
Town of Hydro
501 W 4th Street
Hydro, OK 73048-8758
405-663-2326

Idabel
Housing Authority of The
City of Idabel
901 Lyndon Road
Idabel, OK 74745-7223
580-286-9444

Konawa
Housing Authority of The
City of Konawa
101 S. East Street
Konawa, OK 74849-0186
580-925-3955

Langston
Housing Authority of The
City of Langston
203 S.W. Bond
Langston, OK 73050
405-466-2619

Lawton
Housing Authority of The
City of Lawton
609 SW F Avenue
Lawton, OK 73501-4540
580-353-7392

Lone Wolf
Housing Authority of The
Town of Lone Wolf
901 Walker Circle
Lone Wolf, OK 73655-9725
580-846-5401

Lookeba
Housing Authority of The
Caddo Electric Cooperative
RR 1 Box 3c
Lookeba, OK 73053-9701
405-457-6323

Madill
Housing Authority of The
City of Madill
1036 Ridgeview Drive
Madill, OK 73446-1471
580-795-2790

Mangum
Housing Authority of The
Town of Mangum
525 E Lincoln Street
Mangum, OK 73554-4407
580-782-3560

Maud
Housing Authority of The
City of Maud
320 E Oak Street
Maud, OK 74854-2500
405-374-2800

Mcalester
Housing Authority of The
City of Mcalester
620 W Kiowa Avenue
Mcalester, OK 74501-5702
918-423-3345

Miami
Housing Authority of The
City of Miami
205 B Street NE
Miami, OK 74354-5903
918-542-3616

Muskogee
Housing Authority of The
City of Muskogee
220 N 40th Street
Muskogee, OK 74401 -2129
918-687-6301

Newkirk
Housing Authority of The
City of Newkirk
311 N Main Street
Newkirk, OK 74647-2200
580-362-3167

Norman
Housing Authority of The
City of Norman
700 N Berry Road
Norman, OK 73069-7562
405-329-0933

Oklahoma City
Housing Authority of The
City of Oklahoma City
1700 NE 4th Street
Oklahoma City, OK 73117-3803
405-239-7551

Pauls Valley
Housing Authority of The
City of Pauls Valley
300 Melville Drive
Pauls Valley, OK 73075-6633
405-238-7507

Pawhuska
Housing Authority of
Osage County
PO Box 818
Pawhuska, OK 74056-0818
918-287-2270

Pawnee
Housing Authority of The
City of Pawnee
406 4th Street
Pawnee, OK 74058-2017
918-762-3316

Picher
Housing Authority of The
City of Picher
116 Devilliers Circle
Picher, OK 74360-1511
918-673-2126

Ponca City
Housing Authority of The
City of Ponca City
201 E Broadway Avenue
Ponca City, OK 74601-4307
580-762-4445

Sayre
Housing Authority of The
City of Sayre
1310 N 2nd Street
Sayre, OK 73662 1831
580-928-3690

Seiling
Housing Authority of The
Town of Seiling
507 N Oak Street
Seiling, OK 73663-9514
580-922-4297

Seminole
Housing Authority of The
City of Seminole
111 Randolph Drive
Seminole, OK 74868-4323
405-382-3081

Shawnee
Housing Authority of The
City of Shawnee
601 W 7th Street
Shawnee, OK 74801-7678
405-275-6330

Snyder
Housing Authority of The
City of Snyder
300 E Street
Snyder, OK 73566-1412
580-569-2827

Stigler
Housing Authority of The
City of Stigler
200 SE B Street
Stigler, OK 74462-2444
918-967-2631

Stillwater
Housing Authority of The
City of Stillwater
807 S Lowry Street
Stillwater, OK 74074-4707
405-372-4906

Stilwell
Housing Authority of The
City of Stilwell
801 N 4th Street
Stilwell, OK 74960-1816
918-696-2494

Tecumseh
Housing Authority of The
City of Tecumseh
601 Leisure Drive
Tecumseh, OK 74873-2432
405-598-3244

Temple
Housing Authority of The
Town of Temple
100 Mcclain Street
Temple, OK 73568-9171
580-342-5013

Tishomingo
Housing Authority of The
Town of Tishomingo
1005 N Byrd Street
Tishomingo, OK 73460-1503
580-371-2543

Tulsa
Housing Authority of The
City of Tulsa
415 E Independence Street
Tulsa, OK 74106-5727
918-582-0021

Tuskahoma
Housing Authority of The
Kiamichi Electric Coop
PO Box 4060
Tuskahoma, OK 74574-9619
918-522-4436

Tuttle
Housing Authority of The
Town of Tuttle
412 E Bond
Tuttle, OK 73089-8844
405-381-2721

Valliant
Housing Authority of The
Town of Valliant
301 E Harris Street
Valliant, OK 74764-9017
580-933-7359

Walters
Housing Authority of The
City of Walters
500 E California Street
Walters, OK 73572-1610
580-875-2310

Watonga
Housing Authority of The
City of Watonga
117 N Spiece Avenue
Watonga, OK 73772-4634
580-623-4623

Waurika
Housing Authority of The
City of Waurika
811 Phillips Avenue
Waurika, OK 73573-3422
580-228-2976

Waynoka
Housing Authority of The
City of Waynoka
PO Box 183
Waynoka, OK 73860-0183
580-824-5331

Wetumka
Housing Authority of The
City of Wetumka
121 N Canadian Street
Wetumka, OK 74883-3001
405-452-3444

Wewoka
Housing Authority of The
City of Wewoka
316 W 4th Street
Wewoka, OK 74884-2527
405-257-5717

Wilburton
Housing Authority of The
City of Wilburton
600 E Ash Avenue
Apartment 19
Wilburton, OK 74578-4436
918-465-2134

Wister
Housing Authority of The
Town of Wister
PO Box 190
Wister, OK 74966-0190
918-655-3323

Wynnewood
Housing Authority of The
City of Wynnewood
806 E Colbert Street
Wynnewood, OK 73098-
3616
405-665-2223

OREGON

Albany
Linn-Benton Housing
Authority
1250 SE Queen Ave.
Albany, OR 97322
541-926-3589

Dallas
Housing and Urban
Renewal Agency of Polk
County

204 SW Walnut Ave.
Dallas, OR 97338
503-623-8387

Eugene
Housing Authority and
Community Services of
Lane County
177 Day Island Rd.
Eugene, OR 97401
541-682-3755

Grants Pass
Josephine Housing
Community Development
Council
1215 SW G St.
Grants Pass, OR 97526
541-479-5529

Hermiston
Housing Authority of the
County of Umatilla
155 SW 10th St.
Hermiston, OR 97838
541-567-3241

Hillsboro
Housing Authority of
Washington County
111 NE Lincoln St.
Hillsboro, OR 97124
503-846-4794

Klamath Falls
Klamath Housing Authority
1445 Avalon St.
Klamath Falls, OR 97603
541-884-0649

La Grande
Northeast Oregon Housing
Authority
2608 May Lane
La Grande, OR 97850
541-963-5360

McMinnville
Housing Authority of
Yamhill County
414 NE Evans St.
McMinnville, OR 97128
503-434-6571

Medford
Housing Authority of
Jackson County
2231 Table Rock Rd.
Medford, OR 97501
541-779-5785

Newport
Housing Authority of
Lincoln County

1039 NW NYE St.
Newport, OR 97365
541-265-5326

North Bend
Coos-Curry Housing
Authority
1700 Monroe St.
North Bend, OR 97459
541-756-4111

Northbend Housing
Authority
1700 Monroe St.
North Bend, OR 97459
541-756-4111

Ontario
Housing Authority of
Malheur County
959 Fortner St.
Ontario, OR 97914
541-889-9661

Oregon City
Housing Authority of the
County of Clackamas
13930 South Gain St.
Oregon City, OR 97045
503-655-8267

Portland
Housing Authority of
Portland
135 SW Ash St.
Portland, OR 97204
503-802-8300

Redmond
Central Oregon Regional
Housing Authority
2445 SW Canal Blvd.
Redmond, OR 97756
541-923-1018

Roseburg
Housing Authority of
Douglas County
902 West Stanton St.
Roseburg, OR 97470
541-673-6548

Salem
Housing Authority of the
City of Salem
360 Church St., SW
Salem, OR 97301
503-588-6368

Marion County Housing
Authority
555 Court St.
Salem, OR 97301
503-373-4448

The Dalles
Mid-Columbis Economic
Development District
506 E. 2nd
The Dalles, OR 97058
541-296-5462

Warrenton
Northwest Oregon Housing
Authority
117 S. Main Ave.
Warrenton, OR 97146
503-861-0119

PENNSYLVANIA

Allentown
Allentown Housing
Authority
1339 W. Allen Street
Allentown, PA 18102-2141
610-439-8678

Altoona
Altoona Housing Authority
2700 Pleasant Valley
Boulevard
Altoona, PA 16602-4460
814-949-2000

Beaver
Beaver County Housing
Authority
300 State Street
Beaver, PA 15009-1735
724-775-1220

Bedford
Bedford County Housing
Authority
201 S Richard Street
Apartment 414
Bedford, PA 15522-1763
814-623-1477

Bellefonte
Centre County Housing
Authority
121 Beaver Farm Lane
Bellefonte, PA 16823-2313
814-355-6830

Bloomsburg
Columbia County Housing
Authority
700 Sawmill Road
Bloomburg, PA 17815-7726
570-784-9373

Blossburg
Bradford County Housing
Authority

4 Riverside Plaza
Bloosburg, PA 16912-1137
570-638-2151

Tioga County Housing
Authority
4 Riverside Plaza
Blossburg, PA 16912-1137
570-638-2151

Boswell
Somerset County Housing
Authority
PO Box 38
Boswell, PA 15531-0038
814-629-5147

Bradford
Bradford City Housing
Authority
2 Bushnell Street
Bradford, PA 16701-1974
814-362-3535

Butler
Butler County Housing
Authority
114 Woody Drive
Butler, PA 16001-5692
724-287-6797

Carbondale
Carbondale Housing
Authority
2 John Street
Carbondale, PA 18407-1832
570-282-0280

Carlisle
Cumberland County
Housing Authority
114 N Hanover Street
Carlisle, PA 17013-2463
717-249-0789

Chambersburg
Franklin County Housing
Authority
436 W. Washington Street
Chambersburg, PA 17201-
2458
717-762-7117

Chester
Chester Housing Authority
1010 Madison Street
Chester, PA 19013-5923
610-876-5561

Clarion
Clarion County Housing
Authority
8 W Main Street

Clarion, PA 16214-1816
814-226-8910 x107

Clearfield
Clearfield County Housing
Authority
222 Leavy Avenue
Clearfield, PA 16830-2241
814-765-2485

Connellsville
Connellsville Housing
Authority
315 N Arch Street
Connellsville, PA 15425-
2600
724-628-4501

Corry
Corry Housing Authority
120 S Center Street
Corry, PA 16407-1923
814-665-5161

Erie County Housing
Authority
120 S Center Street
Corry, PA 16407-1923
814-665-5161

Coudersport
County of Porter Housing
Authority
8 E 7th Street
Coudersport, PA 16915-1711
814-274-7031

Danville
Montour County Housing
Authority
1 Beaver Place
Danville, PA 17821-1002
570-275-3640

Doylestown
Bucks County Housing
Authority
350 S Main Street
Suite 205
Doylestown, PA 18901-4873
215-348-9469

Du Bois
Dubois Housing Authority
21 E Long Avenue
Du Bois, PA 15801-2156
814-371-2290

Dunmore
Lackawanna County
Housing Authority
2019 W Pine Street
Dunmore, PA 18512-2208
570-342-7629

Easton
Easton Housing Authority
157 S 4th Street
Easton, PA 18042-4505
610-258-0806

Emmaus
Lehigh County Housing
Authority
333 Ridge Street
Emmaus, PA 18049-2757
610-965-4514 x204

Erie
Erie City Housing
Authority
606 Holland Street
Erie, PA 16501-1215
814-452-2425

Franklin
Franklin City Housing
Authority
1212 Chestnut Street
Franklin, PA 16323-1462
814-432-3416

Gettysburg
Adams County Housing
Authority
139 Carlisle St.
Gettysburg, PA 17325-1809
717-334-1518

Greensburg
Westmoreland County
Housing Authority
PO Box 223
Greensburg, PA 15601-9308
724-832-7258

Harrisburg
Harrisburg Housing
Authority
351 Chestnut Street
Harrisburg, PA 17101-2751
717-232-6781

Hazelton
Hazelton Housing
Authority
320 W Mine Street
Hazelton, PA 18201-6161
570-455-9503

Hollidaysburg
Blair County Housing
Authority
1407 Blair Street
Hollidaysburg, PA 16648-
2468
814-695-7548

Indiana
Indiana County Housing
Authority
104 Philadelphia Street
Indiana, PA 15701-2132
724-463-4730

Johnsonburg
Elk County Housing
Authority
424 Water Street Extension
Johnsonburg, PA 15845-
1547
814-965-2532

Johnstown
Johnstown Housing
Authority
501 Chestnut Street
Johnstown, PA 15906-2531
814-535-7771

Kingston
Luzerne County Housing
Authority
250 1st Avenue
Kingston, PA 18704-5808
570-287-9661

Kittanning
Armstrong County Housing
Authority
350 S Jefferson Street
Kittanning, PA 16201-2418
724-548-7671

Lancaster
Housing Authority of the
City of Lancaster
325 Church Street
Lancaster, PA 17602-4201
717-397-2835 x3020

Lancaster County Housing
Authority
150 North Queen Street
Lancaster, PA 17603
717-394-0793

Laporte
Sullivan County Housing
Authority
Main and Muncy Sts.
Sullivan County
Courthouse
PO Box 157
Laporte, PA 18626
570-946-7677

Lebanon
Lebanon County Housing
Authority
303 Chestnut Street

Lebanon, PA 17042-6190
717-274-1401

Lehighton
Carbon County Housing
Authority
215 S 3rd Street
Lehighton, PA 18235-2109
610-377-9375

Lewisburg
Housing Authority of
Union County
1610 Industrial Blvd.
Suite 400
Lewisburg, PA 17837-1292
570-522-1300

Lewistown
Housing Authority of
Mifflin County
141 S Pine Road
Lewistown, PA 17044-1894
717-248-2624

Lock Haven
Housing Authority of
Clinton County
369 Linden Circle
Lock Haven , PA 17745-3211
570-748-2954

McKeesport
McKeesport Housing
Authority
301 5th Avenue, Floor 2
McKeesport , PA 15132-2627
412-673-6942 x101

Meadville
Meadville Housing
Authority
1120 Market Street
Meadville, PA 16335-4356
814-336-3177

Mount Union
Huntingdon County
Housing Authority
100 Federal Drive
Mount Union , PA 17066-
1630
814-542-2531

Nazareth
Northampton County
Housing Authority
15 Wood Street
Nazareth, PA 18064-1933
610-759-8488

New Castle
Housing Authority County
of Lawrence

PO Box 988
New Castle, PA 16103-0988
724-656-5100

Norristown
Montgomery County
Housing Authority
1875 New Hope Street
Norristown, PA 19401-3146
215-275-5720

Oil City
Oil City Housing Authority
110 Moran Street
Oil City, PA 16301-3041
814-676-5764

Venango County Housing
Authority
19 Rockwood Avenue
Oil City, PA 16301-1295
814-677-5926

Philadelphia
Philadelphia Housing
Authority
12 S 23rd Street
Philadelphia PA 19103-3014
215-684-4174

Pittsburgh
Allegheny County Housing
Authority
341 4th Avenue
Pittsburgh, PA 15222-2111
412-355-8940

Housing Authority City of
Pittsburgh
200 Ross Street
Pittsburgh, PA 15219-2010
412-456-5000

Pittston
Housing Authority of the
City of Pittston
500 Kennedy Boulevard
Pittston, PA 18640-1720
570-655-3707

Pottsville
Pottsville Housing
Authority
410 Laurel Boulevard
Pottsville, PA 17901-2401
570-628-2702

Punxsutawney
Jefferson County Housing
Authority
201 N Jefferson Street
Punxsutawney, PA 15767-
2057
814-938-7140

Reading
Berks County Housing
Authority
1803 Butler Lane
Reading, PA 19606-1100
610-370-0822

Reading Housing Authority
400 Hancock Boulevard
Reading, PA 19611-1802
610-775-4813

Schuylkill Haven
Schuylkill County Housing
Authority
245 Parkway
Schuylkill Haven, PA
17972-1907
570-385-3400

Scranton
Scranton Housing
Authority
400 Adams Avenue
Scranton, PA 18510-2002
570-348-4401

Shamokin
Shamokin Housing
Authority
1 E Independence Street
Shamokin, PA 17872-6803
570-644-0431

Sharon
Mercer County Housing
Authority
80 Jefferson Avenue
Sharon, PA 16146-3352
724-342-4000

Smethport
Mckean County Housing
Authority
410 E Water Street
Smethport, PA 16749-1419
814-887-5563

Steelton
Dauphin County Housing
Authority
501 Mohn Street
Steelton, PA 17113-2021
717-939-9301

Stroudsburg
Monroe County Housing
Authority
1055 W Main Street
Stroudsburg, PA 18360-1419
717-421-7770

Sunbury
Sunbury Housing Authority

705 Market Street
Sunbury, PA 17801-2368
570-286-8563

Susquehanna
Susquehanna County
Housing Authority
950 Prospect Street
Susquehanna, PA 18847-
1348
570-278-3011

Titusville
Titusville Housing
Authority
217 E Central Avenue
Titusville, PA 16354-1874
814-827-3732

Uniontown
Fayette County Housing
Authority
624 Pittsburgh Road
Uniontown, PA 15401-2214
724-434-2100

Warren
Warren County Housing
Authority
108 Oak Street
Warren, PA 16365-2875
814-723-2312

Washington
Washington County
Housing Authority
100 S Franklin Street
Washington, PA 15301-6943
724-228-6060

Waymart
Wayne County Housing
Authority
130 Carbondale Road
Waymart, PA 18472
570-488-6069

Waynesburg
Greene County Housing
Authority
170 E Greene Street
Waynesburg, PA 15370-
1834
724-627-6523

West Chester
Housing Authority of The
Co of Chester
30 W Barnard Street
West Chester, PA 19382-
3293
610-436-9200

Wilkes Barre
Wilkes Barre Housing
Authority

50 Lincoln Plaza
Wilkes Barre, PA 18702-5132
570-825-6657

Williamsport
Lycoming County Housing Authority
1941 Lincoln Drive
Williamsport, PA 17701-2824
570-323-3755

Williamsport Housing Authority
505 Center Street
Williamsport, PA 17701-4973
570-326-0521

Woodlyn
Delaware County Housing Authority
1855 Constitution Avenue
Woodlyn, PA 19094-1428
610-876-2521

York
York City Housing Authority
31 S Broad Street
York, PA 17403-5648
717-845-2601 ext. 127

Puerto Rico

Hato Rey
Puerto Rico Public Housing Administration
606 Ave Barbosa
Floor 8
Hato Rey, PR 00917-4314
787-753-4409

Rhode Island

Central Falls
Central Falls Housing Authority
30 Washington Street
Central Falls, RI 02863-2842
401-727-9090

Coventry
Coventry Housing Authority
14 Manchester Circle
Coventry, RI 02816-8827
401-828-4367

Cranston
Cranston Housing Authority
50 Birch Street
Cranston, RI 02920-7565
401-944-7210

Cumberland
Cumberland Housing Authority
573 Mendon Road
Suite 3
Cumberland, RI 02864-6221
401-334-2678

East Greenwich
East Greenwich Housing Authority
146 1st Avenue
East Greenwich, RI 02818-3661
401-885-2610

East Providence
East Providence Housing Authority
99 Goldsmith Avenue
East Providence, RI 02914-2240
401-434-7645

Jamestown
Jamestown Housing Authority
45 Pemberton Avenue
Jamestown, RI 02835-1451
401-423-1561

Johnston
Johnston Housing Authority
8 Forand Circle
Johnston, RI 02919-3514
401-231-2007

Lincoln
Lincoln Housing Authority
10 Franklin Street
Lincoln, RI 02865 2049
401-724-8910

Narragansett
Narragansett Housing Authority
25 5th Avenue
Narragansett, RI 02882-3612
401-789-9489

Newport
Newport Housing Authority
1 York Street
Newport, RI 02840-1141
401-847-0185

North Providence
North Providence Housing Authority
945 Charles Street
North Providence, RI 02904-5647
401-728-0930

Pawtucket
Pawtucket Housing Authority
214 Roosevelt Avenue
Pawtucket, RI 02860-2153
401-725-9113

Peace Dale
South Kingstown Housing Authority
364 Curtis Corner Road
Peace Dale, RI 02879-2136
401-783-0126

Portsmouth
Portsmouth Housing Authority
2368 E Main Road
Portsmouth, RI 02871-4039
401-683-3173

Providence
Providence Housing Authority
100 Broad Street
Providence, RI 02903-4154
401-751-6400

Smithfield
Smithfield Housing Authority
7 Church Street
Smithfield, RI 02828-1744
401-949-0270

Tiverton
Tiverton Housing Authority
99 Hancock Street
Tiverton, RI 02878-2360
401-624-4748

Warren
Warren Housing Authority
20 Libby Lane
Warren, RI 02885-2008
401-245-7019

Warwick
Warwick Housing Authority
25 Easton Avenue
Warwick, RI 02888-4156
401-463-7206

West Warwick
West Warwick Housing Authority

62 Roberts Street
West Warwick, RI 02893-5080
401-822-9430

Westerly
Westerly Housing Authority
9 Dixon Street
Westerly, RI 02891-1861
401-596-4918

Woonsocket
Woonsocket Housing Authority
679 Social Street
Woonsocket, RI 02895-2026
401-767-8000

South Carolina

Abbeville
Housing Authority of Abbeville
508 Haigler Street
Abbeville, SC 29620-2064
864-459-4549

Aiken
Housing Authority of Aiken
100 Rogers Terrace
Aiken, SC 29801-3435
803-649-6673

Anderson
Housing Authority of Anderson
1335 E River Street
Anderson, SC 29624-2908
864-260-5132

Barnwell
SC Regional Housing Authority No 3
10938 Ellenton Street
Barnwell, SC 29812-7304
803-259-3588

Beaufort
Housing Authority of Beaufort
1009 Prince Street
Beaufort, SC 29902-5038
843-525-7059

Bennettsville
Housing Authority of Bennettsville
253 Fletcher Street
Bennettsville, SC 29512-3777
843-479-3857

Charleston
Charleston Co Hsg & Redev Auth
PO Box 6188
Charleston, SC 29405-0188
843-722-1942

Housing Authority of Charleston
550 Meeting Street
Charleston, SC 29403-5068
843-720-3970

Cheraw
Housing Authority of Cheraw
1345 Dizzy Gillespie Drive
Cheraw, SC 29520-3527
843-669-4163

Chester
Housing Authority of Chester
2678 Dawson Drive
Building 100
Chester, SC 29706-5121
803-581-6981 ext. 10

Clio
Marlboro Co Hsg & Redev Authority
100 Woods Avenue
Clio, SC 29525-4252
843-669-4163

Columbia
Housing Authority of Columbia
1917 Harden Street
Columbia, SC 29204-1015
803-254-3886

Conway
Housing Authority of Conway
2303 Leonard Avenue
Conway, SC 29527-4515
843-248-7327

Darlington
Housing Authority of Darlington
324 Bacote Street
Darlington, SC 29532-5606
843-393-0437

Easley
Housing Authority of Easley
101 Wallace Drive
Easley, SC 29640-3335
864-855-0629

Florence
Housing Authority of Florence

400 E Pine Street
Florence, SC 29506-3146
843-669-4163

Fort Mill
Housing Authority of Fort Mill
105 Bozeman Drive
Fort Mil, SC 29715-2500
803-547-6787

Gaffney
Housing Authority of Gaffney
125 Beltline Road
Gaffney, SC 29341-1461
864-489-3193

Georgetown
Housing Authority of Georgetown
1 Lincoln Street
Georgetown, SC 29440-2671
843-546-9621

Greenville
Housing Authority of Greenville
PO Box 10047
Greenville SC 29603-0047
864-467-4273

Greer
Housing Authority of Greer
103 School Street
Greer, SC 29651-3437
864-877-5471

Hartsville
Housing Authority of Hartsville
1301 S 5th Street
Hartsville SC 29550-5764
843-332-1583

Kingstree
Housing Authority of Kingstree
1022 Frierson Homes
Kingstree, SC 29556-3034
843-354-7516

Lake City
Housing Authority of Lake City
398 N Matthews Road
Lake City, SC 29560-2026
843-394-3541

Lancaster
Housing Authority of Lancaster
3502 Caroline Court
Lancaster, SC 29720-5226
803-285-7214

Laurens
Housing Authority of Laurens
218 Spring Street
Laurens, SC 29360-1813
864-984-0578

SC Regional Housing Authority No 1
404 Church Street
Laurens SC 29360-2326
864-984-0578

Marion
Housing Authority of Marion
826 Walnut Street
Marion, SC 29571-2714
843-423-5242

Mc Coll
Housing Authority of Mccoll
204 Gilchrist Avenue
Apartment 35
Mc Coll, SC 29570-2221
843-669-4163

Mullins
Housing Authority of Mullins
244 Blanton Court
Mullins, SC 29574-2104
843-464-9822

Myrtle Beach
Housing Authority of Myrtle Beach
605 10th Avenue N
Myrtle Beach, SC 29577-3568
843-918-1525

Newberry
Housing Authority of Newberry
3589 Grant Avenue
Newberry, SC 29108-1423
803-276-1049

North Charleston
Housing Authority of N Charleston
3817 Goodman Boulevard
North Charleston, SC 29405-6305
843-747-1793

North Myrtle Beach
Housing Authority of Atlantic Beach
1020 30th Avenue S

North Myrtle Beach, SC 29582-4549
843-272-4189

Rock Hill
Housing Authority of Rock Hill
467 S Wilson Street
Rock Hill, SC 29730-4444
803-324-6359

Spartanburg
Housing Authority of Spartanburg
325 S Church Street
Spartanburg, SC 29306-5231
864-598-6000

Sumter
Housing Authority of Sumter
15 Caldwell Street
Sumter, SC 29150-5234
803-775-9613

Union
Housing Authority of Union
201 Porter Street
Union, SC 29379-2854
864-427-9679

Woodruff
Housing Authority of Woodruff
110 Miller Drive
Woodruff, SC 29388-2137
864-476-7043

York
Housing Authority of York
PO Box 687
York, SC 29745-0687
803-684-7359

South Dakota

Aberdeen
Aberdeen Housing & Redevelopment Commission
2222 3rd Avenue Se
Aberdeen, SD 57401-5136
605-225-9095

Canton
Canton Housing & Redevelopment Commission
903 W 5th Street
Canton, SD 57013-1562
605-764-5722

Hot Springs
Hot Springs Housing And
Redevelopment
Commission
201 S River Street
Hot Springs, SD 57747-2328
605-745-4067

Howard
Howard Housing And
Redevelopment
Commission
117 N Arthur Street
Howard, SD 57349-9037
605-772-5782

Kennebec
Kennebec Housing &
Redevelopment
Commission
PO Box 93
Kennebec, SD 57544-0093
605-869-2338

Lemmon
Lemmon Housing &
Redevelopment
Commission
206 6th Street E
Lemmon, SD 57638-1931
605-374-5963

Lennox
City of Lennox Housing
And Redevelopment
Commission
217 S Pine Street
Lennox, SD 57039-2100
605-647-2140

Madison
Madison Housing And
Redevelopment
Commission
111 S Washington Avenue
Madison, SD 57042-2948
605-256-2112

Miller
Miller Housing &
Redevelopment
Commission
105 N Broadway Avenue
Miller, SD 57362-1349
605-853-2869

Mitchell
City of Mitchell Housing
And Redevelopment
Commission
200 E 15th Avenue
Mitchell, SD 57301-1183
605-996-6811

Parker
Parker Housing &
Redevelopment
Commission
PO Box 27
Parker, SD 57053-0027
605-297-4918

Pierre
Pierre Housing &
Redevelopment
Commission
301 W Pleasant Drive
Pierre, SD 57501-2451
605-773-7425

Rapid City
Pennington County
Housing And
Redevelopment
Commission
1805 W Fulton Street
Rapid City SD 57702-4333
605-394-5350

Sioux Falls
Sioux Falls Housing And
Redevelopment
Commission
804 S Minnesota Avenue
Sioux Falls, SD 57104-4829
605-332-0704

Sisseton
Sisseton Housing &
Redevelopment
Commission
123 Chestnut Street E
Sisseton, SD 57262-1474
605-698-3463

Sturgis
Meade County Housing
And Redevelopment
Commission
1220 Cedar Street
Sturgis, SD 57785-1805
605-347-3384

Volga
Volga Housing And
Redevelopment
Commission
601 Samara Avenue
Volga, SD 57071-9160
605-627-5249

Watertown
Watertown Housing And
Redevelopment
Commission
24 W Kemp
Watertown, SD 57201-3538
605-886-2867 ext. 2

Webster
Webster Housing And
Redevelopment
Commission
1101 E 7th Street
Webster, SD 57274-1648
605-345-3181

Wessington Springs
Wessington Springs
Housing And
Redevelopment
Commission
519 College Avenue N
Wessington Springs, SD
57382-2054
605-539-1560

Tennessee

Athens
Athens Housing Authority
199 Clark Street
Athens, TN 37303-3141
423-745-0341

Bolivar
Bolivar Housing Authority
621 Hatchie Haven
Bolivar, TN 38008-1533
901-658-3419

Bristol
Bristol Tennessee Housing
& Redevelopment
Authority
100 Ash Street
Bristol, TN 37620-3676
423-274-8150

Brownsville
Brownsville Housing
Authority
205 Summer Oaks Cove
Brownsville, TN 38012-1580
901-772-0274

Carthage
South Carthage Housing
Authority
109 Hazel Drive
Carthage, TN 37030-1928
615-735-1940

Clarksville
Clarksville Housing
Authority
721 Richardson Street
Clarksville, TN 37040-3827
931-647-2303

Cleveland
Cleveland Housing
Authority
450 Walker Street NE
Cleveland, TN 37311-5364
423-479-9659

Clinton
Clinton Housing Authority
825 Mcadoo Street
Clinton, TN 37716-3107
865-457-9692

Columbia
Columbia Housing
Authority
201 Dyer Street
Columbia, TN 38401-4553
931-388-5203

Cookeville
Cookeville Housing
Authority
837 S Willow Avenue
Cookeville, TN 38501-4190
931-526-9793

Covington
Covington Housing
Authority
1701 Shoaf Street
Covington, TN 38019-3342
901-476-6135

Crossville
Crossville Housing
Authority
67 Irwin Avenue
Crossville, TN 38555-4746
931-484-2990

Dayton
Dayton Housing Authority
270 Railroad Street
Dayton, TN 37321-1690
423-775-1871

Dickson
Dickson Housing Authority
333 Martin Luther King Jr
Boulevard
Dickson, TN 37055-2515
615-446-9371

Dyersburg
Dyersburg Housing
Authority
541 Hike Avenue
Dyersburg, TN 38024-3712
731-285-6771

Elizabethton
Elizabethton Housing and
Development Agency

910 Pine Ridge Circle
Elizabethton, TN 37643-4364
423-543-3571

Erwin
Erwin Housing Authority
750 Carolina Avenue
Building 100
Erwin, TN 37650-1094
423-743-5231

Etowah
Etowah Housing Authority
400 Sunset Drive
Etowah, TN 37331-1761
423-263-2674

Fayetteville
The Fayetteville Housing
Authority
402 Calhoun Avenue
Fayetteville, TN 37334-3310
931-433-1587

Franklin
Franklin Housing Authority
100 Spring Street
Franklin, TN 37064-3311
615-794-1247

Gallatin
Gallatin Housing Authority
401 N Boyers Avenue
Gallatin, TN 37066-2389
615-452-1661

Gallaway
Gallaway Housing
Authority
200 Jackson Street
Gallaway, TN 38036
901-867-8101

Greeneville
Greeneville Housing
Authority
100 Cox Circle
Greeneville TN 37743-6976
423-638-3111

Harriman
Harriman Housing
Authority
924 Sewanee Street
Harriman, TN 37748-2824
865-882-9636

Hartsville
Hartsville Housing
Authority
212 Rogers Street
Hartsville, TN 37074-1011
615-374-3959

Hohenwald
Hohenwald Housing
Authority
323 Mill Avenue
Hohenwald, TN 38462-1515
931-796-3642

Humboldt
Humboldt Housing
Authority
3532 Seymour Loop
Humboldt, TN 38343-1584
901-784-9772

Huntingdon
Huntingdon Housing
Authority
433 Hillcourt Circle
Huntingdon, TN 38344-4207
901-986-4442

Jackson
Jackson Housing Authority
125 Preston Street
Jackson, TN 38301-4888
901-422-1671

Jefferson City
Jefferson City Housing
Authority
942 E Ellis Street
Jefferson City, TN 37760-2600
865-475-2064

Jellico
Jellico Housing Authority
189 S Main Street
Jellico, TN 37762-2154
423-784-8809

Johnson City
Johnson City Housing
Authority
901 Pardee Street
Johnson City, TN 37601-4939
423-232-4784

Kingsport
Kingsport Housing And
Redevelopment Authority
906 E Sevier Avenue
Kingsport, TN 37660-5233
423-245-2541

Knoxville
Knox County Housing
Authority
6333 Pleasant Ridge Road
Knoxville, TN 37921-1102
865-637-7942

Knoxville's Community
Devel Corp

901 N Broadway Street
Knoxville, TN 37917-6663
865-594-8800

La Follette
Lafollette Housing
Authority
801 S 4th Street
La Follette, TN 37766-4309
423-562-2261

Lafayette
Lafayette Housing
Authority
613 Dycus Circle
Lafayette, TN 37083-1224
615-666-2140

Lawrenceburg
Lawrenceburg Housing
Authority
1020 Smith Avenue
Lawrenceburg, TN 38464-2549
931-762-7532

Lebanon
Lebanon Housing Authority
49 Lake Drive
Lebanon, TN 37087-7588
615-444-1872

Lenoir City
Lenoir City Housing
Authority
101 Oakwood Drive
Lenoir City, TN 37771-1527
865-986-8707

Lewisburg
Lewisburg Housing
Authority
744 Bark Street
Lewisburg, TN 37091-2674
615-359-4517

Lexington
Lexington Housing
Authority
100 Willow Courts
Lexington, TN 38351-1420
901-968-7506

Livingston
Livingston Housing
Authority
620 E 7th Street
Livingston, TN 38570-1204
931-823-6423

Loudon
Loudon Housing Authority
124 Pathkiller Trail
Loudon, TN 37774-1237
865-458-2061

Manchester
Manchester Housing
Authority
710 Butler Circle
Manchester, TN 37355-1801
931-728-2596

Martin
Martin Housing Authority
100 E Heights Drive
Martin, TN 38237-1541
901-587-3186

Mc Kenzie
Mckenzie Housing
Authority
22 Mcdonald Avenue W
Mc Kenzie, TN 38201-2329
901-352-5335

Mc Minnville
Mcminnville Housing
Authority
301 Hardaway Street
Mc Minnville, TN 37110-3155
931-473-3286

Memphis
Memphis Housing
Authority
700 Adams Avenue
Memphis, TN 38105-5002
901-544-1101

Shelby County Housing
Authority
715 Rouge Bluff Road
Memphis, TN 38127-2614
901-353-0590

Milan
Milan Housing Authority
1000 Northside Terrace
Milan, TN 38358-1616
901-686-8571

Millington
Millington Housing
Authority
PO Box 55
Millington, TN 38083-0055
901-872-3677

Monteagle
Grundy Housing Authority
100 Raulston Avenue
Monteagle, TN 37356-9572
931-924-2496

Morristown
Morristown Housing
Authority
600 Sulphur Springs Road

Morristown, TN 37813-5568
423-586-5115

Mount Pleasant
Mt. Pleasant Housing
Authority
138 Thomas Circle
Mount Pleasant, TN 38474-
1055
931-379-5811

Murfreesboro
Murfreesboro Housing
Authority
318 E Lokey Avenue
Murfreesboro, TN 37130-
2588
615-893-9414

Nashville
Metropolitan Development
& Housing Agency
701 S 6th Street
Nashville, TN 37206-3809
615-252-8400

Newbern
Newbern Housing
Authority
709 Maple Street
Newbern, TN 38059-1157
901-627-2142

Newport
Newport Housing
Authority
375 Alex Street
Newport, TN 37821-2810
423-623-1575

Oliver Springs
Oliver Springs Housing
Authority
113 Wagner Court
Oliver Springs, TN 37840-
1714
865-435-1711

Paris
Paris Housing Authority
917 Minor Street
Paris TN 38242-4663
731-642-4451

Parsons
Parsons-Decatur Ville
Housing Authority
155 Miller Street
Parsons, TN 38363-2329
901-847-2638

Pulaski
Pulaski Housing Authority
2006 Garden Meadows Dr.

Pulaski, TN 38478-4645
931-363-6525

Rockwood
Rockwood Housing
Authority
320 W Carpenter Street
Rockwood TN 37854-3333
865-354-9841 ext. 5

Rogersville
Rogersville Housing
Authority
902 Locust Street
Rogersville, TN 37857-2416
423-272-8540

Savannah
Savannah Housing
Authority
515 Jefferson Street
Savannah, TN 38372-3663
901-925-2020

Sevierville
Sevierville Housing
Authority
500 Leo Sharp Road
Sevierville, TN 37862-4934
865-453-8500

Shelbyville
Shelbyville Housing
Authority
316 Templeton Street
Shelbyville, TN 37160-3295
931-684-1341

Smithville
Smithville Housing
Authority
415 Jackson Street
Smithville, TN 37166-1514
615-597-4140

South Pittsburg
South Pittsburg Housing
Authority
214 Elm Avenue
South Pittsburg, TN 37380-
1312
423-837-6600

Sparta
Sparta Housing Authority
PO Box 419
Sparta, TN 38583-0419
615-836-3357

Springfield
Springfield Housing
Authority
808 Rose Hill Circle
Springfield, TN 37172-2934
615-384-4591

Tullahoma
Tullahoma Housing
Authority
2401 Cedar Lane Village
Drive
Tullahoma, TN 37388-4745
931-455-9319

Union City
Union City Housing
Authority
1409 E Main Street
Union City, TN 38261-2707
901-885-1971

Waverly
Waverly Housing Authority
35 W Brookside Drive
Waverly, TN 37185-1131
931-296-2256

Winchester
Franklin County
Consolidated Housing
Authority
136 Ross Lane
Winchester TN 37398-2601
931-967-0344 ext. 10

Woodbury
Woodbury Housing
Authority
401 Mcferrin Street
Woodbury, TN 37190-1668
615-563-5276

TEXAS

Abilene
Housing Authority of
Abilene
555 Walnut Street
Abilene, TX 79601-5254
915-676-6385

Alamo
Alamo Housing Authority
309 N. 9th St.
Alamo, TX 78516-0445
956-787-2352

Alba
Housing Authority of Alba
102 Lake Fork Highway
Alba, TX 75410-2562
903-765-2541

Alice
Alice Housing Authority
125 Olmito
Alice, TX 78333
361-664-3453

Alpine
Housing Authority of
Alpine
1024 N 5th Street
Alpine, TX 79830-3013
915-837-2648

Andrews
Housing Authority of
Andrews
215 Nw 1st Street
Suite 7
Andrews, TX 79714-6300
915-524-1436

Anson
Housing Authority of
Anson
1302 Avenue J
Anson, TX 79501-4428
915-823-2831

Aransas Pass
Aransas Pass Housing
Authority
254 N 13th Street
Aransas Pass, TX 78336-
4540
512-758-3032

Asherton
Asherton Housing
Authority
Corner of Cleveland And
12th St.
Asherton, TX 78827
830-468-3679

Aspermont
Housing Authority of
Aspermont
PO Box 545
Aspermont, TX 79502-0545
940-989-2721

Atlanta
Housing Authority of
Atlanta
106 S Howe Street
Atlanta, TX 75551-3804
903-796-5065

Austin
Austin Housing Authority
1640b E 2nd Street
Austin, TX 78702-4412
512-477-4488

Travis County Housing
Authority
2200 E. Mlk Blvd
Austin, TX 78702
512-480-8245

Avery
Housing Authority of
Avery
540 S Austin Street
Avery, TX 75554-9780
903-684-3207

Baird
Housing Authority of Baird
401 Chestnut Street
Baird, TX 79504-5317
915-854-1660

Ballinger
Housing Authority of
Ballinger
1401 N 13th Street
Ballinger, TX 76821-2165
915-365-2629

Balmorhea
Housing Authority of
Balmorhea
313 5th Street
Balmorhea, TX 79718
915-375-2459

Bangs
Housing Authority of Bangs
406 E Spencer Street
Bangs, TX 76823-3111
915-752-6522

Bastrop
Bastrop Housing Authority
502 Farm Street
Bastrop, TX 78602-3209
512-321-3398

Bay City
Housing Authority of The
City of Bay City
3012 Sycamore Avenue
Bay City, TX 77414-6859
979-245-2652

Baytown
Housing Authority of The
City of Baytown
805 W Nazro Street
Baytown, TX 77520-7953
281-427-6686

Beaumont
Housing Authority of
Beaumont
4925 Concord Road
Beaumont, TX 77708-5501
409-899-5055

Beckville
Housing Authority of
Beckville
419 Monroe Street

Beckville, TX 75631-1701
903-678-3630

Beeville
Beeville Housing Authority
1101 E Kennedy Street
Beeville, TX 78102-4247
361-358-5865

Bellville
Housing Authority of The
City of Bellville
300 S Thomas Street
Bellville, TX 77418-2142
409-865-3722

Belton
Central Texas Council of
Governments
302 E. Central Avenue
Belton, TX 76513
254-939-5724

Housing Authority of
Belton
715 Saunders Street
Belton, TX 76513-3784
254-939-5321

Big Sandy
Housing Authority of Big
Sandy
401 E Beck Street
Big Sandy, TX 75755-2137
903-636-4914

Blooming Grove
Housing Authority of
Blooming Grove
100 2nd Street
Blooming Grove, TX 76626-
9780
903-695-2834

Blossom
Housing Authority of
Blossom
630 W Division Street
Blossom, TX 75416-2736
903-982-6414

Boerne
Boerne Housing Authority
201 E San Antonio, #230
Boerne, TX 78006
830-249-9343 ext. 351

Bogata
Housing Authority of
Bogotá
PO Box 10
Bogata, TX 75417 0010
903-632-5574

Bonham
Housing Authority of Bells
810 W 16th Street
Bonham, TX 75418-2818
903-583-3336

Housing Authority of
Honey Grove
810 W 16th Street
Bonham, TX 75418-2818
903-583-3336

Housing Authority of Howe
810 W 16th Street
Bonham, TX 75418-2818
903-583-3336

Housing Authority of
Whitewright
810 W 16th Street
Bonham, TX 75418-2818
903-583-3336

Borger
Housing Authority of
Borger
903 Parkway Street
Borger, TX 79007-4343
806-274-2612

Brackettville
Brackettville Housing
Authority
205 S. Sweeney
Brackettville, TX 78832
830-563-2513

Brady
Housing Authority of Brady
405 E Main Street
Brady, TX 76825-4609
915-597-2951

Breckenridge
Housing Authority of
Breckenridge
911 N Payne Street
Breckenridge, TX 76424-
2115
254-559-5996

Bremond
Housing Authority of The
City of Bremond
600 S Main Street
Bremond, TX 76629-9305
254-746-7260

Brenham
Housing Authority of The
City of Brenham
1901 Northview Circle
Drive

Brenham, TX 77833-2138
979-836-9221

Bridgeport
Housing Authority of
Bridgeport
1508 Cobb Street
Bridgeport, TX 76426-3852
940-683-2710

Brownsville
Brownsville Housing
Authority
2606 Boca Chica Boulevard
Brownsville TX 78521-2312
956-541-8315

Brownsville
Cameron County Housing
Authority
65 Castellano Circle
Brownsville, TX 78526-2823
956-541-4983

Brownwood
Housing Authority of
Brownwood
1500 Terrace Drive
Brownwood, TX 76801-2055
915-646-0790

Bryan
Housing Authority of The
City of Bryan
1306 Beck Street
Bryan, TX 77803-3701
979-822-2013

Burkburnett
Housing Authority of
Burkburnett
217 Byerly Street
Burkburnett, TX 76354-2128
940-569-3211

Burnet
Burnet Housing Authority
Hwy 281 S
Burnet, TX 78611
512-756-4745

Cameron
Housing Authority of
Cameron
704 W 6th Street
Cameron, TX 76520-2436
254-697-6523

Canyon
Housing Authority of
Canyon
2617 8th Avenue
Canyon, TX 79015-4715
806-655-0673

Carrizo Springs
Carrizo Springs Housing
Authority
207 N 4th Street
Carrizo Springs, TX 78834-
3241
830-876-5211

Celeste
Housing Authority of
Celeste
103 N 6th Street
Celeste, TX 75423-9796
903-568-4296

Center
Housing Authority of
Center
1600 Sweetgum Trail
Center, TX 75935-9369
936-598-2332

Childress
Housing Authority of
Childress
407 Avenue B Nw
Childress, TX 79201-4404
940-937-3501

Cisco
Housing Authority of Cisco
714 E 10th Street
Cisco, TX 76437-3507
254-442-2662

Clarksville
Housing Authority of
Clarksville
700 S Delaware Street
Clarksville, TX 75426-3817
903-427-3671

Cleveland
Housing Authority of
Cleveland
801 S Franklin Avenue
Cleveland, TX 77327-5307
281-593-1159

Clifton
Housing Authority of
Clifton
608 N Avenue I
Clifton, TX 76634-1506
254-675-8294

Coleman
Housing Authority of
Coleman
605 W 2nd Street
Coleman, TX 76834-4834
915-625-5018

Colorado City
Housing Authority of
Colorado City
439 Oak Street
Colorado City, TX 79512-
6215
915-728-3150

Comanche
Housing Authority of
Comanche
404 E Cedar Avenue
Comanche, TX 76442-1765
915-356-3181

Commerce
Housing Authority of
Commerce
500 Tarter Estate
Commerce, TX 75428-3200
903-886-2946

Como
Housing Authority of Como
101 Home Street
Como, TX 75431-9709
903-488-3090

Copperas Cove
Housing Authority of
Copperas Cove
701 Casa Circle
Copperas Cove, TX 76522-
3973
254-547-9591

Corpus Christi
Corpus Christi Housing
Authority
3701 Ayers Street
Corpus Christi, TX 78415-
4615
361-884-3801

Corrigan
Housing Authority of
Corrigan
600 S Home Street
Corrigan, TX 75939-2656
409-398-5351

Corsicana
Housing Authority of
Corsicana
1360 N 13th Street
Corsicana, TX 75110-3054
903-872-5643

Cotulla
Cotulla Housing Authority
101 S Kerr
Cotulla, TX 78014-3034
830-879-2935

Crockett
Housing Authority of
Crockett
225 S 3rd Street
Crockett, TX 75835-2038
409-544-2057

Crosbyton
Housing Authority of
Crosbyton
111 W Birch Street
Crosbyton, TX 79322-2513
806-675-2842

Cross Plains
Housing Authority of Cross
Plains
119 W 9th Street
Cross Plains, TX 76443-2586
254-725-6116

Crystal City
Crystal City Housing
Authority
1600 N 7th Avenue
Crystal City, TX 78839-1740
830-374-3433

Cuero
Cuero Housing Authority
203 W Church Street
Cuero, TX 77954-3705
361-275-6127

Dallas
Housing Authority of
Dallas
3939 N Hampton Road
Dallas, TX 75212-1630
214-951-8300

Housing Authority of The
City of Buffalo
304 Centre Street
Dallas, TX 75208-6504
903-322-3654

Dawson
Housing Authority of
Dawson
210 Circle Drive
Dawson, TX 76639-9665
254-578-1406

Dayton
Housing Authority of The
City of Dayton
2502 N Winfree Street
Dayton, TX 77535-1567
409-258-5372

De Kalb
Housing Authority of De
Kalb

400 NW North Street
De Kalb, TX 75559-1356
903-667-2818

De Leon
Housing Authority of
Deleon
200 E Navarro Street
De Leon, TX 76444-1166
254-893-2535

Decatur
Housing Authority of
Decatur
500 N Cowan Street
Decatur, TX 76234-1242
940-627-3810

Del Rio
Del Rio Housing Authority
207 Bedell Ave.
Del Rio, TX 78841-4080
830-774-6506

Denison
Housing Authority of
Denison
330 N 8th Avenue
Denison, TX 75021-2769
903-465-2650

Detroit
Housing Authority of
Detroit
165 W. Deport Street
Detroit, TX 75436 -0139
903-674-2185

Devine
Devine Housing Authority
210 S Upson Drive
Devine, TX 7801- 3222
830-665-2831

Diboll
Housing Authority of
Diboll
702 S 1st Street
Diboll, TX 75941-2311
409-829-5440

Dilley
Dilley Housing Authority
400 Ann St
Dilley, TX 78017
830-965-1321

Donna
Donna Housing Authority
705 Silver Avenue
Donna, TX 78537-3152
956-464-4473

Dublin
Housing Authority of
Dublin
201 E May Street
Dublin, TX 76446-2751
254-445-2165

Housing Authority of
Dublin
201 E May Street
Dublin, TX 76446-2751
254-445-2165

Eagle Pass
Eagle Pass Housing
Authority
2095 Main St.
Eagle Pass, TX 78853
830-773-3325

Edcouch
Edcouch Housing Authority
209 Pacific Avenue
Edcouch, TX 78538
956-262-2471

Eden
Housing Authority of Eden
PO Box 991
Eden, TX 76837- 0991
915-869-6491

Edgewood
Housing Authority of
Edgewood
108 Cedar Street
Edgewood, TX 75117-2340
903-896-4655

Edinburg
Edinburg Housing
Authority
201 N 13th Avenue
Edinburg, TX 78539-3500
956-383-3839

Edna
Edna Housing Authority
603 N Kleas Street
Edna, TX 77957-2814
361-782-3842

El Campo
Housing Authority of the
City of El Campo
1303 Delta Street
El Campo, TX 77437-5805
409-543-6991

El Paso
Housing Authority of
Anthony
1007 Francine Street

El Paso, TX 79907-2205
915-886-4650

Housing Authority of El
Paso
5300 E Paisano Drive
El Paso, TX 79905-2931
915-849-3742

Electra
Electra Housing Authority
600 N Moore Street 45
Electra, TX 76360-2259
940-495-3476

Elgin
Elgin Housing Authority
515 Mcdade Road 100
Elgin, TX 78621-3001
512-281-2772

Elsa
Elsa Housing Authority
309 W. 3rd St
Elsa, TX 78543-0098
956-262-1231

Ennis
Housing Authority of Ennis
200 Arnold Street
Ennis, TX 75119-7802
972-878-7451

Fabens
El Paso County Housing
Authority
PO Box 279
Fabens, TX 79838-0279
915-764-3559

Falfurrias
Falfurrias Housing
Authority
924 S Gardner Street
Falfurrias, TX 78355-4826
361-325-5631

Falls City
Falls City Housing
Authority
110 E Meyer
Falls City, TX 78941
830-254-3432

Ferris
Housing Authority of Ferris
401 W 1st Street
Ferris, TX 75125-1502
972-544-2430

Flatonia
Flatonia Housing Authority
701 Mulberry Street

Flatonia, TX 78941-2531
361-865-2534

Floresville
Floresville Housing
Authority
1401 Standish Street
Floresville, TX 78114-1845
830-393-6560

Floydada
Housing Authority of
Floydada
210 E California Street
Floydada, TX 79235-2849
806-983-5165

Fort Worth
Housing Authority of Fort
Worth
1201 E 13th Street
Fort Worth, TX 76102-5764
817-336-2419

Frisco
Housing Authority of Frisco
6891 Main Street
Frisco, TX 75034-3300
972-377-3031

Fruitvale
Housing Authority of
Fruitvale
450 Creagle Circle
Fruitvale, TX 75127-9683
903-896-4381

Galveston
Housing Authority of The
City of Galveston
4700 Broadway Street
Galveston, TX 77551-4241
409-765-1900

Gatesville
Housing Authority of
Gatesville
PO Box 52
Gatesville, TX 76528-0052
254-865-2970

Georgetown
Georgetown Housing
Authority
1702 Hart Street
Georgetown, TX 78626-7820
512-863-5565

Gilmer
Housing Authority of
Gilmer
104 Circle Drive
Gilmer, TX 75644-2007
903-843-3141

Gladewater
Housing Authority of The
City of Gladewater,
604 S Tyler Street
Gladewater, TX 75647-2614
903-845-2493

Goliad
Goliad Housing Authority
360 N Fort Street
Goliad, TX 77963-4029
361-645-2774

Gonzales
Gonzales Housing
Authority
410 Village Dr
Gonzales, TX 78629-0043
830-672-3419

Granbury
Housing Authority of
Granbury
503 N Crockett Street
Granbury, TX 76048-2134
817-573-1107

Grand Saline
Housing Authority of
Grand Saline
304 S Houston Street
Grand Saline, TX 75140-
2214
903-962-4031

Grandview
Housing Authority of
Grandview
303 N 3rd Street
Grandview, TX 76050-1910
817-866-3373

Granger
Granger Housing Authority
North Highway 95
Granger, TX 76530
512-859-2797

Grapevine
Housing Authority of
Grapevine
131 Starr Place
Grapevine, TX 76051-5246
817-488-8132

Gregory
Gregory Housing Authority
103 Granjano Bldg #103
Gregory, TX 78359
512-643-5014

Groesbeck
Housing Authority of
Groesbeck

407 N Leon Street
Groesbeck, TX 76642-1245
254-729-3204

Hallettsville
Hallettsville Housing
Authority
103 Village Drive
Hallettsville, TX 77964
512-798-5845

Haltom City
Housing Authority of
Haltom City
2800 Moneda Avenue
Haltom City, TX 76117-4220
817-834-0691

Hamilton
Housing Authority of
Hamilton
920 S Dempster Street
Hamilton, TX 76531-2815
254-386-5281

Hamlin
Housing Authority of
Hamlin
200 Se Avenue A
Hamlin, TX 79520-4900
915-576-3964

Harlingen
Harlingen Housing
Authority
202 S 1st Street
Harlingen, TX 78550-9154
956-423-2521

Haskell
Housing Authority of
Haskell
702 S Avenue H
Haskell, TX 79521-7134
940-864-3685

Hearne
Housing Authority of The
City of Hearne
809 W Davis Street
Hearne, TX 77859-2851
979-279-3221

Hebbronville
Jim Hogg County Housing
Authority
508 N. Dagmor
Hebbronville, TX 78361
361-527-4353

Henderson
Housing Authority of
Henderson
817 W Main Street

Henderson, TX 75652-3001
903-657-3444

Henrietta
Housing Authority of
Henrietta
1 Parkview Avenue
Henrietta, TX 76365-3029
940-538-4252

Hico
Housing Authority of Hico
PO Box 249
Hico, TX 76457-0249
254-796-4006

Hidalgo
Hidalgo Housing Authority
704 E Tejano Dr
Hidalgo, TX 78557
956-843-8561

Houston
Harris County Housing
And Community Dev.
Agency
8410 Lantern Point Dr.
Houston, TX 77054
713-747-0353

Houston
Housing Authority of The
City of Houston
2640 Fountain View Drive
Houston, TX 77057-7630
713-260-0505

Hubbard
Housing Authority of
Hubbard
640 NE 7th Street
Hubbard, TX 76648-2213
254-576-2978

Hughes Springs
Housing Authority of
Hughes Springs
1314 E 1st
Hughes Springs, TX 75656-
3651
903-639-2251

Ingleside
Ingleside Housing
Authority
2322 First St
Ingleside, TX 78362
361-776-7812

Jasper
Housing Authority of Jasper
200 Myrtis Street
Jasper, TX 75951-4300
409-384-4430

Jefferson
Housing Authority of
Jefferson
505 W Broadway Street
Jefferson, TX 75657-1629
903-665-2671

Johnson City
Johnson City Housing
Authority
304 S Avenue F
Johnson City, TX 78636-4282
830-868-7322

Junction
Housing Authority of
Junction
815 Elm Street
Junction, TX 76849-5344
915-446-3486

Karnes City
Karnes City Housing
Authority
506 N Market Street
Karnes City, TX 78118-2555
830-780-2396

Kemp
Housing Authority of Kemp
400 Dallas Plaza Street
Kemp, TX 75143-8900
903-498-8211

Kenedy
Kenedy Housing Authority
116 Stewart Avenue
Kenedy, TX 78119- 2114
830-583-2321

Kerens
Housing Authority of
Kerens
100 Mcclung Drive
Kerens, TX 75144-3220
903-396-2964

Killeen
Housing Authority of
Killeen
731 Wolf Street
Killeen, TX 76541-7700
254-634-5243

Kingsville
Kingsville Housing
Authority
1000 W Corral Avenue
Kingsville, TX 78363-3035
361-592-6783

Kirbyville
Housing Authority of
Kirbyville

310 W Levert Street
Kirbyville, TX 75956-2026
409-423-4751

Knox City
Housing Authority of Knox
City
201 SW 4th Street
Knox City, TX 79529-2307
940-658-3612

Kyle
Kyle Housing Authority
417 W 2nd Street
Kyle, TX 78640-5602
512-268-7801

La Grange
La Grange Housing
Authority
250 Northwest Circle
La Grange, TX 78945-1227
409-968-3147

Laredo
Housing Authority of The
City of Laredo
2000 San Francisco Avenue
Laredo, TX 78040-4153
956-722-4521

Levelland
Housing Authority of
Levelland
1837 Avenue I
Levelland, TX 79336-6226
806-894-9075

Livingston
Housing Authority of
Livingston
1102 N Pine Avenue
Livingston, TX 77351-2355
409-327-5100

Llano
Llano Housing Authority
1110 Berry Street
Llano, TX 78643-2341
915-247-4931

Lockhart
Lockhart Housing
Authority
809 Redwood Street
Lockhart, TX 78644-1940
512-398-2715

Loraine
Housing Authority of
Loraine
304 W Colorado Avenue
Loraine, TX 79532-2212
915-737-2675

Los Fresnos
Los Fresnos Housing
Authority
801 S Mesquite Street
Los Fresnos, TX 78566-3751
956-233-5012

Lott
Housing Authority of Lott
PO Box 336
Lott, TX 76656-0336
254-584-2841

Lubbock
Housing Authority of
Lubbock
1708 Avenue G
Lubbock, TX 79401-5127
806-762-1191

Luling
Luling Housing Authority
800 E Milam Street
Luling, TX 78648-3135
830-875-5221

Mabank
Housing Authority of
Mabank
200 E Jack Street
Mabank, TX 75147-8500
903-887-4220

Madisonville
Housing Authority of The
City of Madisonville
601 S Madison Street
Madisonville, TX 77864-
1955
936-348-6346

Malakoff
Housing Authority of
Malakoff
200 Terry Plaza
Malakoff, TX 75148-9692
903-489-1517

Marble Falls
Marble Falls Housing
Authority
1110 Broadway Street
Marble Falls, TX 78654-5504
830-693-4521

Marlin
Housing Authority of
Marlin
101 Burnett Street
Marlin, TX 76661-2742
254-803-0072

Marshall
Housing Authority of
Marshall

1401 Poplar Street
Marshall, TX 75670-2115
903-938-0717

Mart
Housing Authority of Mart
201 N Main Street
Mart, TX 76664-1129
254-876-3011

Mathis
Mathis Housing Authority
300 W Fulton Street
Mathis, TX 78368-2275
361-547-3315

Mc Gregor
Housing Authority of
Mcgregor
301 N Johnson Drive
Mc Gregor, TX 76657-1178
254-840-2276

Mc Kinney
Housing Authority of
Mckinney
1200 N Tennessee Street
Mc Kinney, TX 75069-2161
972-542-5641

Mcallen
Mcallen Housing Authority
2301 Jasmine Avenue
Mcallen, TX 78501-7484
956-686-3951

Memphis
Housing Authority of
Memphis
216 S 5th Street
Memphis, TX 79245-3414
806-259-2941

Mercedes
Mercedes Housing
Authority
1025 Anaquitas Street
Mercedes, TX 78570-2242
956-565-3139

Meridian
Housing Authority of
Meridian
205 North First Street
Meridian, TX 76665
254-435-2601

Merkel
Housing Authority of
Merkel
731 N 1st Street
Merkel, TX 79536-4241
915-928-4891

Mexia
Mexia Housing Authority
701 N Sherman Street
Mexia, TX 76667-2347
254-562-6321

Midland
Housing Authority of
Midland
700 W Scharbauer Drive
Midland, TX 79705-8901
915-682-0011

Mineola
Housing Authority of The
City of Mineola
784 Goodson Circle
Mineola, TX 75773-2254
903-569-3519

Mineral Wells
Housing Authority of
Mineral Wells
200 NE 27th Street
Mineral Wells, TX 76067-
2344
940-325-1781

Mission
Mission Housing Authority
906 E 8th Street
Mission, TX 78572-5805
956-585-9747

Monahans
Housing Authority of The
City of Monahans
209 S Dwight Avenue
Monahans, TX 79756-4311
915-943-5962

Moody
Housing Authority of
Moody
1310 Ave E
Moody, TX 76557-3505
254-853-2577

Mount Pleasant
Housing Authority of
Mount Pleasant
601 Stark Street
Mount Pleasant, TX 75455-
4938
903-572-2829

Mount Vernon
Housing Authority of
Mount Vernon
944 Kaufman Street S
Mount Vernon, TX 75457-
3700
903-537-4452

Munday
Housing Authority of
Munday
131 W Cisco Street
Munday, TX 76371-2137
940-422-4941

Nacogdoches
Housing Authority of The
City of Nacogdoches
715 Summit Street
Nacogdoches, TX 75961-
4782
936-569-1151

Navasota
Housing Authority of City
of Navasota
1200 Church Street
Navasota, TX 77868-4350
936-825-7024

New Boston
Housing Authority of New
Boston
303 Rice Street
New Boston, TX 75570-2932
903-628-2951

New Braunfels
New Braunfels Housing
Authority
300 Laurel Lane
P.O. Box 310906
New Braunfels, TX 78130-
6170
830-625-6909

Nixon
Nixon Housing Authority
506 E 4th Street
Nixon, TX 78140-2775
830-582-1433

Nocona
Housing Authority of
Nocona
400 Hobson Street
Nocona, TX 76255-3219
940-825-6515

Odessa
Housing Authority of
Odessa
124 E 2nd Street
Odessa, TX 79761-5405
915-333-1088

Oglesby
Housing Authority of
Oglesby
118 College Avenue
Oglesby, TX 76561-2006
254-456-2590

Olney
Housing Authority of Olney
302 W Main Street
Olney, TX 76374-1851
940-564-5639

Omaha
Housing Authority of
Omaha
PO Box 667
Omaha, TX 75571-0667
903-884-2300

Orange
Housing Authority of
Orange
516 Burton Avenue
Orange, TX 77630-3934
409-883-5882

Overton
Housing Authority of
Overton
220 W Ward Street
Overton, TX 75684-1004
903-834-6213

Paducah
Housing Authority of
Paducah
PO Box 698
Paducah, TX 79248-0698
806-492-3788

Palacios
Housing Authority of The
City of Palacios
45 Seashell Boulevard
Palacios, TX 77465-2600
361-972-3721

Paris
Housing Authority of Paris
PO Box 688
Paris, TX 75461-0688
903-784-6651

Pearsall
Pearsall Housing Authority
501 W Medina Street
Pearsall, TX 78061-2315
830-334-9416

Pecos
Housing Authority of Pecos
600 Meadowbrook Street
Pecos, TX 79772-7534
915-447-2807

Pharr
Pharr Housing Authority
211 W Audry Street
Pharr, TX 78577-3047
956-787-1822

Pittsburg
Housing Authority of
Pittsburg
400 Broach Street
Pittsburg, TX 75686-1075
903-856-3760

Pleasanton
Pleasanton Housing
Authority
402 W Adams Street
Pleasanton, TX 78064-3479
830-569-5558

Point
Housing Authority of Point
212 Avenue A
Point, TX 75472-5636
903-598-2531

Port Arthur
Housing Authority of Port
Arthur
920 Dequeen Boulevard
Port Arthur, TX 77640-5603
409-982-6442

Port Lavaca
Port Lavaca Housing
Authority
627 W George Street
Apartment 174
Port Lavaca, TX 77979-2856
361-552-8831

Post
Housing Authority of Post
709 Caprock Drive
Post, TX 79356-2129
806-495-2233

Poteet
Poteet Housing Authority
120 Avenue E.
Poteet, TX 78065
830-742-3589

Princeton
Housing Authority of
Princeton
702 N 4th Street
Princeton, TX 75407-9537
972-734-3300

Ralls
Housing Authority of Ralls
PO Box 904
Ralls, TX 79357-0904
806-253-2645

Ranger
Housing Authority of
Ranger
526 N Austin Street

Ranger, TX 76470-1343
254-647-3344

Rio Grande City
Starr County Housing
Authority
1601 W Circle Drive
Rio Grande City, TX 78582-
3900
956-487-3216

Rising Star
Housing Authority of
Rising Star
PO Box 29a15
Rising Star, TX 76471-9792
254-643-3812

Robert Lee
Housing Authority of
Robert Lee
PO Box 564
Robert Lee, TX 76945-0564
915-453-2912

Robstown
Robstown Housing
Authority
625 W Avenue F
Robstown, TX 78380-2540
361-387-4525

Rockdale
Housing Authority of
Rockdale
100 Cordova Drive
Rockdale, TX 76567-9307
512-446-4180

Rockwall
Housing Authority of
Rockwall
100 Lake Meadows Drive
Rockwall, TX 75087-3697
972-771-0211

Rogers
Housing Authority of
Rogers
201 Post Oak Street
Rogers, TX 76569-9792
254-939-5321

Roma
Roma Housing Authority
301 N Canales Circle
Roma, TX 78584-8056
956-849-1159

Rosenberg
Housing Authority of The
City of Rosenberg
927 Second Street

Rosenberg, TX 77471
281-342-1456

Rotan
Housing Authority of Rotan
202 W Mcarthur Street
Rotan, TX 79546-3620
915-735-3613

Round Rock
Round Rock Housing
Authority
1505 Lance Lane
Round Rock, TX 78664-4545
512-255-9159

Royse City
Housing Authority of Royse
City
305 N Houston Street
Royse City, TX 75189-3719
972-635-2933

San Angelo
Housing Authority of San
Angelo
115 W 1st Street
San Angelo, TX 76903-5770
915-481-2500

San Antonio
Alamo Area Council of
Government
8700 Tesoro, Suite 700
San Antonio, TX 78217
210-362-5200

San Antonio
Bexar County Housing
Authority
301 S Frio Street
Suite 410
San Antonio, TX 78207-4421
210-225-0071

San Antonio
San Antonio Housing
Authority
818 S Flores Street
San Antonio, TX 78204-1430
210-220-3210

San Augustine
Housing Authority of San
Augustine
700 S Broadway Street
San Augustine, TX 75972-
2400
409-275-5254

San Benito
San Benito Housing
Authority
1400 N Reagan Street

San Benito, TX 78586-5602
956-399-7501

San Diego
Duval County Housing
Authority
Farm Rd 1329
San Diego, TX 78384
361-279-2005

San Marcos
San Marcos Housing
Authority
1201 Thorpe Lane
San Marcos, TX 78666-6508
512-353-5058

San Saba
Housing Authority of San
Saba
1601 W Dry Street
San Saba, TX 76877-4015
915-372-5236

Santa Anna
Housing Authority of Santa
Anna
702 Wallis Avenue
Santa Anna, TX 76878-2032
915-348-3811

Schertz
Schertz Housing Authority
204 Schertz Parkway
Schertz, TX 78154-2165
210-658-1001

Schulenburg
Schulenburg Housing
Authority
702 Baumgarten Street
Schulenburg, TX 78956-2006
979-743-3776

Seguin
Seguin Housing Authority
516 Jefferson Avenue
Seguin, TX 78155-6317
830-379-7091

Seymour
Housing Authority of
Seymour
205 E Idaho Street
Seymour, TX 76380-1765
940-889-3637

Sherman
Grayson County Housing
Authority
223 North Sunset
Sherman, TX 75092
903-892-8717

Sherman
Housing Authority of
Sherman
2001 N Hoard Avenue
Sherman, TX 75090-2311
903-893-3139

Sinton
Sinton Housing Authority
900 Harvill Road
Sinton, TX 78387
361-364-1901

Slaton
Housing Authority of
Slaton
420 E Powers Street
Slaton, TX 79364-5548
806-828-3395

Smiley
Smiley Housing Authority
PO Box 10
Smiley, TX 78159-0010
830-587-6311

Smithville
Smithville Housing
Authority
100 Ken Blaschke Drive
Smithville, TX 78957-2812
512-360-3286

Spearman
Housing Authority of
Spearman
30 SW Court Street
Spearman TX 79081-2649
806-659-2524

Stamford
Housing Authority of
Stamford
110 N Anson Street
Stamford, TX 79553-4202
915-773-3761

Stanton
Housing Authority of
Stanton
PO Box 1529
Stanton, TX 79782-1529
915-756-2812

Stockdale
Housing Authority of The
City of Stockdale
701 W Main Street
Stockdale, TX 78160-6098
830-996-3741

Sweetwater
Housing Authority of
Sweetwater

1217 Coral Drive
Sweetwater, TX 79556-6037
915-235-1764

Taft
Taft Housing Authority
223 Avenue CA
Taft, TX 78390-2623
361-528-3000

Tatum
Housing Authority of
Tatum
200 Forest Acres Circle
Tatum, TX 75691-9720
903-947-6464

Taylor
Taylor Housing Authority
311C East 7th Street
Taylor, TX 76574-3221
512-352-3231

Teague
Housing Authority of
Teague
205 S 5th Avenue
Teague, TX 75860-1801
254-739-2011

Temple
Housing Authority of
Temple
700 W Calhoun Avenue
Temple, TX 76501-4218
254-773-2009

Texarkana
Housing Authority of
Texarkana
1611 N Robison Road
Texarkana, TX 75501-4113
903-838-8548

Texas City
Housing Authority of the
City of Texas City
817 2nd Avenue N
Texas City, TX 77590-7541
409-945-4011

Thorndale
Housing Authority of
Thorndale
306 E Umlang Street
Thorndale, TX 76577-9543
512-898-2777

Throckmorton
Housing Authority of
Throckmorton
PO Box 457
Throckmorton, TX 76483-
0457
940-849-6921

Tioga
Housing Authority of Tioga
208 Ray Roberts Parkway
Tioga, TX 76271-0187
940-437-2563

Trenton
Housing Authority of
Trenton
401 Ballentine Street
Trenton, TX 75490-2304
903-583-3336

Trinidad
Housing Authority of
Trinidad
144 Park Street
Trinidad, TX 75163-6033
903-778-2584

Tulia
Housing Authority of Tulia
301 S Armstrong Avenue
Tulia, TX 79088-2717
806-995-4282

Uvalde
Uvalde Housing Authority
1700 Garner Field Road
Uvalde, TX 78801-6279
830-278-7161

Van
Housing Authority of Van
205 Bluebird Court
Van, TX 75790-3916
903-963-7001

Van Horn
Housing Authority of Van
Horn
PO Box 1119
Van Horn, TX 79855-1119
915-283-2582

Vernon
Housing Authority of
Vernon
1111 Ross Street
Vernon, TX 76384-4143
940-552-5744

Victoria
Victoria Housing Authority
4001 Halsey Street
Victoria, TX 77901-3030
361-575-3682

Vidor
Housing Authority of
Orange County
205 Vidor Drive
Vidor, TX 77662-5635
409-769-8739

Waco
Housing Authority of The
City of Waco
1001 Washington Avenue
Waco, TX 76703
254-752-0324

Waelder
Waelder Housing Authority
PO Box 38
Waelder, TX 78959-0038
361-665-7371

Wake Village
Housing Authority of
Bowie County
1002 Macarthur Avenue
Wake Village, TX 75501-
6170
903-832-8514

Waxahachie
Housing Authority of
Waxahachie
208 Patrick Street
Waxahachie, TX 75165-2953
972-937-5730

Wellington
Housing Authority of
Wellington
1305 Haskell Street
Wellington, TX 79095-3533
806-447-2772

Weslaco
Hidalgo County Housing
Authority
1800 N Texas Boulevard
Weslaco, TX 78596-4000
956-969-5865

Weslaco
Weslaco Housing Authority
303 W 6th Street
Weslaco, TX 78596-6000
956-969-1538

Whitesboro
Housing Authority of
Whitesboro
301 Beauty Lane
Whitesboro, TX 76273-1405
903-564-3700

Whitney
Housing Authority of
Whitney
115 W Polk Avenue
Whitney, TX 76692-2650
254-694-7583

Wichita Falls
Housing Authority of
Wichita Falls

501 Webster Street
Wichita Falls, TX 76306-
2954
940-723-8389

Wichita Falls
Wichita Falls Housing
Assistance Program
1300 Seventh Street
Wichita Falls, TX 76301
940-761-7454

Wills Point
Housing Authority of Wills
Point
914 N 3rd Street
Wills Point, TX 75169-1610
903-873-2152

Wink
Housing Authority of Wink
PO Box 607
Wink, TX 79789-0607
915-527-3008

Winnsboro
Housing Authority of
Winnsboro
612 Autumn Drive
Winnsboro, TX 75494-3410
903-342-6977

Winters
Housing Authority of
Winters
300 N Grant Street
Winters, TX 79567-4717
915-754-4232

Wolfe City
Housing Authority of Wolfe
City
PO Box 73
Wolfe City, TX 75496-9715
903-496-7027

Woodville
Housing Authority of The
City of Woodville
1114 Albert Drive
Woodville, TX 75979-5542
409-283-3628 ext. 11

Yoakum
Yoakum Housing Authority
712 Forrest Street
Yoakum, TX 77995-3007
361-741-5241

Yorktown
Yorktown Housing
Authority
406 N Eckhardt Street

Yorktown, TX 78164-3509
361-564-3132

Utah

Cedar City
Cedar City Housing
Authority
364 S. 100 E
Cedar City, UT 84720
435-586-8462

Farmington
Davis County Housing
Authority
352 S 200 W, Suite 1
Farmington, UT 84025-2423
801-451-2587

Ogden
Housing Authority of The
City of Ogden
2661 Washington
Boulevard, Suite 102
Ogden, UT 84401-3606
801-627-5851

Price
Housing Authority of
Carbon County
251 S 1600 E
Apartment 2647
Price, UT 84501-3776
435-637-5170

Provo
Housing Authority of the
City of Provo
650 W 100 N
Provo, UT 84601-2632
801-852-7080

Utah County Housing
Authority
240 E Center Street
Provo, UT 84606-3107
801-373-8333

Salt Lake City
Housing Authority of Salt
Lake City
1776 S West Temple
Salt Lake City, UT 84115-
1816
801-487-2161 ext. 1202

Housing Authority of The
County of Salt Lake
3595 S Main Street
Salt Lake City, UT 84115-
4434
801-284-4400

West Valley City Housing
Authority
3600 Constitution
Boulevard
Salt Lake City, UT 84119-
3720
801-963-3329

St George
St. George Housing
Authority
975 N 1725 W
Apartment 101
St George, UT 84770-4963
435-628-3648

Tooele
Tooele County Housing
Authority
118 E Vine Street
Tooele, UT 84074 -2152
435-882-7875

Vermont

Barre
Barre Housing Authority
4 Humbert Street
Barre, VT 05641-4529
802-476-3185

Bennington
Bennington Housing
Authority
10 Willow Road
Bennington, VT 05201-1730
802-442-8000

Brattleboro
Brattleboro Housing
Authority
224 Melrose Street
Brattleboro, VT 05301-6527
802-254-6071

Burlington
Burlington Housing
Authority
230 Saint Paul Street
Burlington, VT 05401-4661
802-864-0538

Montpelier
Montpelier Housing
Authority
155 Main Street
Montpelier, VT 05602-2923
802-229-9232

Rutland
Rutland Housing Authority
5 Tremont Street

Rutland, VT 05701-3533
802-775-2926

Springfield
Springfield Housing
Authority
80 Main Street
Springfield, VT 05156-2907
802-885-4905

Winooski
Winooski Housing
Authority
83 Barlow Street
Winooski, VT 05404-2020
802-655-2360

Virginia

Abingdon
Abingdon Redevelopment
Hsg. Auth.
300 Green Spring Road
Abingdon VA 24210-3236
540-628-5661

People Inc. of Southwest
Virginia
1173 West Main Street
Abingdon, VA 24210
276-623-9000 ext. 290

Accomac
Accomack-Northampton
Regional Housing Auth
23372 Front St
Accomac, VA 23301-0387
757-787-2800

Alexandria
Alexandria Redevelopment
& H/A
600 N Fairfax Street
Alexandria, VA 22314-2008
703-549-7115

Bristol
Bristol Redevelopment
Housing Auth.
809 Edmond Street
Bristol, VA 24201-4385
540-642-2001

Charlottesville
Charlottesville
Redevelopment & H/A
PO Box 1405
Charlottesville, VA 22902-
1405
804-970-3253

County of Albemarle/
Office of Housing
Mr. Ron White
Chief of Housing
Charlottesville, VA 22902-
4596
804-296-5839 ext. 3357

Piedmont Housing Alliance
515 Park Street
Charlottesville, VA 22902
434-817-2436

Chesapeake
Chesapeake Redevelopment
& H/A
1468 S Military Highway
Chesapeake, VA 23320-2604
757-523-0401

Coeburn
Wise County
Redevelopment & H/A
107 Litchfield Street Nw
Coeburn, VA 24230-3822
540-395-6104

Danville
Danville Redevelopment
And H/A
651 Cardinal Place
Danville, VA 24541-4411
804-793-1222

Duffield
Scott County
Redevelopment & H/A
100 Anderson Street
Duffield, VA 24244-9776
540-431-2022

Fairfax
Fairfax Co Red And
Housing Authority
3700 Pender Dr., Suite 300
Fairfax, VA 22030-6039
703-246-5100

Franklin
Franklin Redevelopment &
H/A
601 Campbell Avenue
Franklin, VA 23851-1807
757-562-0384

Hampton
Hampton Redevelopment &
Hsg Auth
22 Lincoln Street
Hampton, VA 23669-3522
757-727-6337

Harrisonburg
Harrisonburg
Redevelopment & H/A
286 Kelly Street
Harrisonburg, VA 22802-
4721
540-434-7386

Hopewell
Hopewell Redevelopment
& H/A
350 E Poythress Street
Hopewell, VA 23860-7812
804-458-5160

Lynchburg
Lynchburg Redevelopment
& H/A
1101 Court Street
Lynchburg, VA 24504-4503
804-845-9011

Marion
Marion Redevelopment &
Housing Authority
237 Miller Avenue
Marion, VA 24354-2922
540-783-3381

Newport News
Newport News
Redevelopment & H/A
227 27th Street
Newport News, VA 23607
3901
804-247-9701

Norfolk
Norfolk Redevelopment &
H/A
201 Granby Street
Norfolk, VA 23510-1820
804-623-1111

Norton
Norton Redevelopment &
H/A
200 6th Street Nw
Norton, VA 24273-1954
540-679-0020

Petersburg
Petersburg Redevelopment
& H/A
PO Box 311
Petersburg, VA 23804-0311
804-733-2200

Portsmouth
Portsmouth Redevelopment
& H/A
339 High Street
Portsmouth, VA 23704-3724
757-399-5261

Richmond
Richmond Redevelopment
& H/A
901 Chamberlayne Parkway
Richmond, VA 23220-2309
804-780-4200

Roanoke
Roanoke Redevelopment &
H/A
2624 Salem Turnpike Nw
Roanoke, VA 24017-5334
540-983-9281

Staunton
Staunton Redevelopment &
Housing Authority
900 Elizabeth Miller
Gardens
Staunton, VA 24401-3897
540-886-3413

Suffolk
Suffolk Redevelopment &
H/A
530 E Pinner Street
Suffolk, VA 23434-3023
757-539-2100

Waynesboro
Waynesboro
Redevelopment & H/A
1700 New Hope Road
Waynesboro, VA 22980-
2515
540-946-9230

Williamsburg
Williamsburg Redev. &
Housing Authority
412 N Boundary Street
Williamsburg, VA 23185-
3650
757-220-3477

Wytheville
Wytheville Redev. &
Housing Authority
170 Hedgefield Lane
Wytheville, VA 24382-4022
540-228-6515

Virgin Islands

St Thomas
Virgin Islands Housing
Authority
PO Box 7668
St Thomas, VI 00801-0668
340-775-2741

St. Thomas
Virgin Islands Housing
Authority

P. O. Box 7668
St. Thomas, VI 00801-7668
340-775-2741

Washington

Aberdeen
Housing Authority of Grays Harbor
602 E 1st Street
Aberdeen, WA 98520-3405
360-532-0570

Anacortes
Housing Authority City of Anacortes
719 Q Avenue
Anacortes, WA 98221-4128
360-293-7831

Bellingham
Housing Authority of Whatcom Co.
208 Unity Street, Lower Level
Bellingham, WA 98225-4420
360-676-6887

Bellingham
Housing Authority City of Bellingham
208 Unity Street
Bellingham, WA 98225-4420
360-676-6887

Bremerton
Housing Authority City of Bremerton
110 Russell Road
Bremerton, WA 98312-3478
360-479-3694

Clarkston
Housing Authority of Asotin County
1212 Fair Street
Clarkston, WA 99403-2229
509-758-5751

Coupeville
Housing Authority of Island County
7 Nw 6th Street
Coupeville, WA 98239-3400
360-678-4181

Ellensburg
Housing Authority County of Kittitas
107 W 11th Avenue
Ellensburg, WA 98926-2568
509-962-9006

Everett
Housing Authority City of Everett
3107 Colby Avenue
Everett, WA 98201-4024
425-303-1102

Housing Authority of Snohomish County
12625 4th Avenue W
Suite 200
Everett, WA 98204-6427
425-290-8499

Kalama
Housing Authority City of Kalama
226 Cloverdale Road
Kalama, WA 98625-9740
360-673-3444

Kelso
Housing Authority City of Kelso
1415 S 10th Avenue
Kelso, WA 98626-2729
360-423-3490

Kennewick
Housing Authority City of Kennewick
1915 W 4th Place
Kennewick, WA 99336-5130
509-586-8576

Moses Lake
Housing Authority of Grant County
1139 Larson Boulevard
Moses Lake WA 98837-3308
509-762-5541

Mount Vernon
Housing Authority of Skagit County
2021 E College Way Suite 101
Mount Vernon, WA 98273
360-428-1959

Othello
Housing Authority City of Othello
335 N 3rd Avenue
Othello, WA 99344-1012
509-488-3527

Pasco
Housing Authority City of Pasco
820 N 1st Avenue
Pasco, WA 99301-5362
509-547-3581

Port Angeles
Housing Authority County of Clallam
2603 S Francis Street
Port Angeles, WA 98362-6710
360-452-7631

Renton
Housing Authority City of Renton
970 Harrington Avenue NE
Renton, WA 98056-3088
425-226-1850

Seattle
Housing Authority of King County
600 Andover Park West
Seattle, WA 98188
206-574-1100

Seattle Housing Authority
120 6th Avenue N
Seattle, WA 98109-5002
206-615-3300

Sedro Woolley
Housing Authority City of Sedro Woolley
830 Township
Sedro Woolley, WA 98284
206-244-7750

Silverdale
Kitsap City Consolidated Housing Authority
9307 Bayshore Drive Nw
Silverdale, WA 98383-9113
360-692-5596

Spokane
Housing Authority City of Spokane
55 W Mission Avenue 104
Spokane, WA 99201-2319
509-328-2953

Sunnyside
Housing Authority City of Sunnyside
204 S 13th Street
Sunnyside, WA 98944-1524
509-837-5454

Tacoma
Housing Authority City of Tacoma
902 S L Street
Tacoma, WA 98405-4037
253-207-4400

Housing Authority of Pierce County

603 Polk Street S
Tacoma, WA 98444-5649
253-620-5400

Vancouver
Housing Authority of the City of Vancouver
2500 Main Street
Vancouver, WA 98660-2697
360-694-2501

Walla Walla
Housing Authority City of Walla Walla
501 Cayuse Street
Walla Walla, WA 99362-0702
509-527-4542

Wenatchee
Housing Authority of Chelan County and The City of Wenatchee
1555 S Methow St
Wenatchee, WA 98801
509-663-7421

Yakima
Housing Authority City of Yakima
810 N 6th Street
Yakima, WA 98901-1932
509-453-3106

West Virginia

Beckley
Housing Authority of Raleigh County
282 George Street
Beckley, WV 25801-2641
304-255-5164

Beckley
Housing Authority of The City of Beckley
100 Beckwoods Drive
Beckley, WV 25801-3152
304-256-1772

Benwood
Housing Authority of The City of Benwood
2200 Marshall Street S
Benwood, WV 26031 1323
304-233-0830

Bluefield
Housing Authority of The City of Bluefield
1600 Hill Avenue

Bluefield, WV 24701-2175
304-325-9653

Buckhannon
Housing Authority of The
City of Buckhannon
23 1/2 Hinkle Drive
Buckhannon, WV 26201-2417
304-472-1305

Charleston
Charleston Housing
911 Michael Avenue
Charleston, WV 25312-2024
304-348-6451

Kanawha County Housing
And Redevelopment
Authority
231 Hale Street
Charleston, WV 25301-2207
304-344-5141

Clarksburg
Housing Authority of
Harrison County
301 W Main Street
Clarksburg, WV 26301-2909
304-624-8680

Housing Authority of The
City of Clarksburg
433 Baltimore Avenue
Clarksburg, WV 26301-2550
304-623-3323

Danville
Housing Authority of
Boone County
Black Diamond Arbors
Danville, WV 25053-9626
304-369-3442

Dunbar
Housing Authority of The
City of Dunbar
900 Dutch Hollow Road
Dunbar, WV 25064-1105
304-768-8006

Elkins
Housing Authority of
Randolph County
1404 N Randolph Avenue
Elkins, WV 26241-9667
304-636-6495

Housing Authority of The
City of Elkins
Stoddard Ave.
Gateway Apartments office
Elkins, WV 26241
304-636-6793

Fairmont
Housing Authority of The
City of Fairmont
517 Fairmont Avenue
Fairmont, WV 26554-5101
304-363-0860

Grafton
Housing Authority of The
City of Grafton
131 E Main Street
Grafton, WV 26354-1365
304-265-1183

Huntington
Housing Authority of The
City of Huntington
30 Northcott Court
Huntington, WV 25701-3742
304-526-4400

Keyser
Housing Authority of The
City of Keyser
440 Virginia Street
Keyser, WV 26726-2536
304-788-2225

Martinsburg
Housing Authority of The
City of Martinsburg
703 S Porter Avenue
Martinsburg, WV 25401-1827
304-263-8891

Moundsville
Housing Authority of The
City of Moundsville
501 10th Street
Moundsville, WV 26041-2234
304-845-3141

Mount Hope
Housing Authority of The
City of Mount Hope
9b Midtown Terrace
Mount Hope, WV 25880-1446
304-877-6541

Parkersburg
Housing Authority of The
City of Parkersburg
1901 Cameron Avenue
Parkersburg, WV 26101-9316
304-428-6753

Piedmont
Housing Authority of The
City of Piedmont
51 Jones Street

Piedmont, WV 26750-1041
304-355-2929

Point Pleasant
Housing Authority of The
City of Pt. Pleasant
PO Box 517
Point Pleasant, WV 25550-0517
304-675-4414

Ripley
Housing Authority of The
County of Jackson
Tanglewood Villa
Whispering Way
Ripley, WV 25271-1357
304-372-2343

Romney
Housing Authority of The
City of Romney
100 Valley View Drive
Romney, WV 26757-1019
304-822-5296

Saint Albans
Housing Authority of The
City of St. Albans
650 6th Street
Saint Albans, WV 25177-2971
304-727-5441

South Charleston
Housing Authority of The
City of South Charleston
520 Goshorn Street
South Charleston, WV 25309-1424
304-768-9315

Spencer
Housing Authority of The
City of Spencer
601 Market Street
Spencer, WV 25276-1828
304-927-4181

Weirton
Housing Authority of The
City of Weirton
525 Cove Road
Weirton, WV 26062-4840
304-797-8530

Weston
Housing Authority of The
City of Weston
124 E 1st Street
Weston, WV 26452-1974
304-269-6159

Wheeling
Housing Authority of The
City of Wheeling
11 Community Street
Wheeling, WV 26003-5201
304-242-4447

Williamson
Housing Authority of
Mingo County
75 E 2nd Avenue
Room 334
Williamson, WV 25661-3532
304-235-0388

Housing Authority of The
City of Williamson
16 W 4th Avenue
Williamson, WV 25661-3545
304-235-3270

Wisconsin

Abbotsford
Abbotsford Housing
Authority
310 E Pine Street
Abbotsford, WI 54405-9749
715-223-4631

Albany
Albany Housing Authority
101 W Main Street
Albany, WI 53502-9702
608-862-3424

Algoma
Algoma Housing Authority
145 Grand View Court
Algoma, WI 54201-1158
920-487-5905

Altoona
Altoona Housing Authority
2404 Spooner Avenue
Altoona, WI 54720-1362
715-834-1842

Amery
Amery Housing Authority
300 Harriman Avenue, North
Amery, WI 54001
715-268-2500

Antigo
Antigo Housing Authority
535 3rd Avenue
Antigo, WI 54409-2262
715-623-5768

Appleton
Appleton Housing
Authority
525 N Oneida Street
Appleton, WI 54911-4749
920-739-6811

Ashland
Ashland Housing Authority
319 Chapple Avenue
Ashland, WI 54806-1455
715-682-7066

Baraboo
Baraboo Community
Development Authority
227 First Avenue
Baraboo, WI 53913-1796
608-356-4822

Sauk County Housing
Authority
1211 Eighth Street
Baraboo, WI 53913-2372
608-356-3986

Barron
Barron County Housing
Authority
611 Woodland Avenue
Barron, WI 54812
715-537-5989

Housing Authority of The
City of Barron
123 East Franklin Avenue
Barron, WI 54812
715-537-5533

Beloit
Beloit Community
Development Authority
220 Portland Avenue
Beloit, WI 53511-5277
608-364-8750

Boscobel
Boscobel Housing
Authority
213 Wisconsin Avenue
Boscobel, WI 53805
608-375-4228

Brillion
Brillion Housing Authority
214 S Parkway Drive
Brillion, WI 54110-1100
920-756-3041

Bruce
Bruce Housing Authority
503 South Coleman Street
Bruce, WI 54819-9449
715-868-4731

Chetek
Chetek Housing Authority
801 W Stout Street
Chetek, WI 54728-6331
715-924-3300

Chilton
Chilton Housing Authority
312 Bonk Street
Chilton, WI 53014-1100
920-849-7042

Clintonville
Clintonville Housing
Authority
25 N 12th Street
Clintonville, WI 54929-1478
715-823-3541

Cumberland
Cumberland Housing
Authority
1295 6th Avenue
Cumberland, WI 54829-9131
715-822-2005

Darlington
Lafayette County Housing
Authority
626 Main Street
Room 105
Darlington, WI 53530-1397
608-776-4880

De Forest
Deforest Housing Authority
509 N Main Street
De Forest WI 53532-1160
608-846-4082

De Pere
Depere Housing Authority
850 Morning Glory Lane
De Pere, WI 54115-1300
920-336-0755

Eau Claire
Eau Claire County Housing
Authority
Room 1590
721 Oxford Avenue
Eau Claire, WI 54703-5481
715-839-6240

Eau Claire Housing
Authority
203 S Farwell Street
Eau Claire, WI 54701-3718
715-839-4943

Edgerton
City of Edgerton Housing
Authority
800 Elm Drive

Edgerton, WI 53534-1242
608-884-8454

Fond Du Lac
Fond Du Lac County
Housing Authority
15 North Marr Street
Fond Du Lac, WI 54935-3463
920-929-3107

Frederic
Frederic Housing Authority
104 3rd Avenue S
Frederic, WI 54837-8901
715-327-8490

Grantsburg
Grantsburg Housing
Authority
213 W Burnett Avenue
Grantsburg, WI 54840-7809
715-463-2475

Green Bay
Brown County Housing
Authority
Room 608
100 North Jefferson Street
Green Bay, WI 54301
920-448-3400

Green Bay Housing
Authority
100 N Jefferson Street
Room 608
Green Bay, WI 54301-5006
920-448-3400

Greenwood
Greenwood Housing
Authority
312 N Reese Avenue
Greenwood, WI 54437-9481
715-267-6308

Hayward
Sawyer County Housing
Authority
15918 West 5th Street
Hayward, WI 54843
715-634-4280

Hudson
Hudson Housing Authority
1015 2nd Street
Hudson, WI 54016-1265
715-386-5301

Hurley
Hurley Housing Authority
410 3rd Avenue S
Hurley, WI 54534-1544
715-561-4344

Jefferson
Jefferson Housing
Authority
431 N Elizabeth Avenue
Jefferson, WI 53549-2208
920-674-5294

Kaukauna
Kaukauna Housing
Authority
125 W 10th Street
Kaukauna, WI 54130-2751
920-766-4772

La Crosse
La Crosse Housing
Authority
1307 Badger Street
La Crosse, WI 54601-3636
608-782-2264

Lacrosse County Housing
Authority
615 Plainview Road
La Crosse, WI 54603-1176
608-781-5365

Ladysmith
Ladysmith Housing
Authority
705 E 4th Street S
Ladysmith, WI 54848-2225
715-532-7076

Lake Mills
Lake Mills Housing
Authority
228 Water Street
Lake Mills, WI 53551-1653
920-648-5064

Luck
Luck Housing Authority
416 S 1st Street
Luck, WI 54853-8003
715-472-2032

Madison
Madison Community
Development Authority
215 Martin Luther King Jr.
Blvd.
Madison, WI 53701-1785
608-266-4675

Wisconsin Housing &
Economic Development
Authority
201 West Washington
Avenue, #700
Madison, WI 53703
608-266-7884

Manitowoc
Manitowoc Housing
Authority
1433 N 6th Street
Manitowoc, WI 54220-2066
920-684-5865

Marinette
Marinette Housing
Authority
1520 Ludington Street
Marinette, WI 54143-1329
715-735-6912

Marshfield
Marshfield Community
Development Authority
601 S Cedar Avenue
Marshfield, WI 54449-4267
715-387-0528

Mauston
Mauston Housing
Authority
208 W Monroe Street
Mauston, WI 53948-1134
608-847-4379

Medford
Taylor County Housing
Authority
Courthouse
224 South 2nd Street
Medford, WI 54451
715-748-1456

Mellen
Ashland County Housing
Authority
124 East Bennett Street
Mellen, WI 54546-0349
715-274-8311

Menomonie
Dunn County Housing
Authority
430 Crescent Street
Menomonie, WI 54751
715-235-4511

Menomonie Housing
Authority
1202 10th Street
Menomonie, WI 54751-0296
715-235-0656

Merrill
Merrill Housing Authority
215 Grand Avenue
Merrill, WI 54452-2260
715-536-7386

Milwaukee
Housing Authority of The
City of Milwaukee

809 North Broadway
Milwaukee, WI 53202
414-286-5678

Milwaukee Co Housing
And Community
Development Division
City Campus,
Floor 1, Rm. 102
2711 West Wells Street
Milwaukee, WI 53208
414-278-4894

Mondovi
Mondovi Housing
Authority
600 Buffalo Street
Mondovi, WI 54755-1358
715-926-4943

Monona
Dane County Housing
Authority
2001 W Broadway
Suite 1
Monona, WI 53713-3707
608-224-3636

Middleton Housing
Authority
2001 West Broadway
Suite 1
Monona, WI 53713
608-224-3636

Monroe
Monroe Housing Authority
800 13th Avenue
Monroe, WI 53566-1461
608-325-2949

New London
New London Housing
Authority
505 Division Street
New London WI 54961-1480
920-982-8509

New Richmond
New Richmond Housing
Authority
370 Odanah Avenue
New Richmond, WI 54017-
1445
715-246-2130

Oconto
Oconto County Housing
Authority
1201 Main Street
Oconto, WI 54153
920-834-4621

Oconto Housing Authority
407 Arbutus Avenue
Oconto, WI 54153-1600
920-834-3003

Osceola
Osceola Housing Authority
602 3rd Avenue
Osceola, WI 54020-8057
715-294-3629

Oshkosh
Oshkosh Housing
Authority
600 Merritt Avenue
Oshkosh, WI 54902-0397
920-424-1450

Winnebago County
Housing Authority
600 Merritt Avenue
Oshkosh, WI 54901-5178
920-424-1450

Park Falls
Park Falls Housing
Authority
1175 3rd Avenue S
Park Falls, WI 54552-1850
715-762-2133

Peshtigo
Peshtigo Housing Authority
181 Chicago Court
Peshtigo, WI 54157-1200
715-582-9212

Plymouth
Plymouth Housing
Authority
1214 Reed Street
Plymouth, WI 53073-2509
920-893-5133

Prairie Du Chien
Prairie Du Chien Housing
Authority
695 E Blackhawk Avenue
Prairie Du Chien, WI 53821-
1675
608-326-8323

Pulaski
Pulaski Housing Authority
430 S Saint Augustine Street
Pulaski, WI 54162-8956
920-822-3887

Racine
Racine County Housing
Authority
837 S Main Street
Racine, WI 53403-1522
262-636-3405

Rhinelander
Rhinelander Housing
Authority
411 W Phillip Street
Rhinelander, WI 54501-3066
715-365-7979

Rice Lake
Rice Lake Housing
Authority
132 W Marshall Street
Rice Lake, WI 54868-1675
715-234-3721

Richland Center
Richland Center Housing
Authority
701 W Seminary Street
Richland Center, WI 53581-
2169
608-647-4877

Sauk City
Sauk City Housing
Authority
200 Webster Avenue
Sauk City, WI 53583-1145
608-643-6772

Shawano
Shawano County Housing
Authority
1488 East Green Bay Street
Shawano, WI 54166-0028
715-526-6960

Shawano Housing
Authority
951 E Elizabeth Street
Shawano, WI 54166-3100
715-524-2132

Sheboygan
Sheboygan Housing
Authority
PO Box 1052
Sheboygan WI 53082-1052
920-459-3466

Shell Lake
Shell Lake Housing
Authority
201 2nd Avenue
Shell Lake, WI 5487- 9796
715-468-2730

Slinger
Slinger Housing Authority
205 Slinger Road
Slinger, WI 53086-9406
262-644-8255

South Milwaukee
South Milwaukee Housing
Authority
2906 6th Avenue

South Milwaukee, WI
53172-3316
414-762-4114

Sparta
Monroe County Housing
Authority
1108 W. Wisconsin St., #103
Sparta, WI 54656
608-269-5017

Sparta Housing Authority
307 N Court Street
Sparta, WI 54656-1710
608-269-2188

Spooner
Spooner Housing Authority
713 N Summit Street
Spooner, WI 54801-1343
715-635-2808

Stanley
Stanley Housing Authority
124 W 4th Avenue
Stanley, WI 54768-1064
715-644-5755

Stevens Point
Portage County Housing
Authority
1100 Centerpoint Drive
Suite 201-B
Stevens Point, WI 54481
715-346-1392

Stevens Point Housing
Authority
1300 Briggs Street
Stevens Point, WI 54481-
2839
715-341-3444

Superior
Housing Authority of The
City of Superior
1219 North 8th Street
Superior, WI 54880-6605
715-394-6601

Thorp
Thorp Housing Authority
113 E Lawrence Street
Thorp, WI 54771-9200
715-669-5599

Tomah
Tomah Housing Authority
720 Williams Street
Tomah, WI 54660-1459
608-374-7455

Tomahawk
Lincoln County Housing
Authority
PO Box 213
Tomahawk, WI 54487-0213
715-453-4233

Viroqua
Viroqua Housing Authority
200 Bigley Plaza
Viroqua, WI 54665-1569
608-637-2626

Washburn
Washburn Housing
Authority
420 E 3rd Street
Washburn, WI 54891-9560
715-373-2653

Watertown
Watertown Housing
Authority
201 N Water Street
Watertown, WI 53094-7683
920-261-7795

Waukesha
New Berlin Housing
Authority
120 Corrina Boulevard
Waukesha, WI 53186
262-542-2262

Waukesha
Waukesha County Housing
Authority
120 Corrina Boulevard
Waukesha, WI 53186
262-542-2262

Wausau
Wausau Community
Development Authority
550 E Thomas Street
Wausau, WI 54403-6423
715-845-4144

Wausaukee
Wausaukee Housing
Authority

926 Main Street
Wausaukee, WI 54177-9753
715-856-5231

Webster
Burnett County Housing
Authority
7350 Main Street E
Webster, WI 54893-8331
715-866-8231

West Bend
West Bend Housing
Authority
475 Meadowbrook Drive
West Bend, WI 53090-2470
262-338-0771

Westby
Westby Housing Authority
503 S Main Street
Westby, WI 54667-1331
608-634-4810

Whitehall
Trempealeau County
Housing Authority
PO Box 295
Whitehall, WI 54773-0295
715-538-2274

Wisconsin Rapids
Wisconsin Rapids Housing
Authority
2521 10th Street S
Wisconsin Rapids, WI
54494-6392
715-423-7288

Woodville
Woodville Housing
Authority
240 S Church Street
Woodville, WI 54028-9788
715-698-2487

Wyoming

Buffalo
Housing Authority of The
City of Buffalo

351 S Cedar Street
Buffalo, WY 82834-2337
307-637-8218

Casper
Housing Authority of The
City of Casper
800 Werner Court
Suite 230
Casper, WY 82601-1361
307-266-1388

Wyoming Community
Development Authority
155 N Beech Street
Casper WY 82601-1907
307-265-0603

Cheyenne
Housing Authority of The
City of Cheyenne
3304 Sheridan Street
Cheyenne, WY 82009-5366
307-634-7947

Douglas
Housing Authority of The
Town of Douglas
120 S 5th Street
Douglas, WY 82633-2454
307-358-2440

Evanston
Evanston Housing
Authority
155 Apache Drive, Suite A
Evanston, WY 82930-4544
307-789-2381

Lusk
Lusk Housing Authority
PO Box 117
Lusk, WY 82225-0117
307-334-3224

Rock Springs
Rock Springs Housing
Authority
233 C Street
Rock Springs, WY 82901-
6220
307-352-1471

A Foreclosed Home May Be The Home Of Your Dreams

Want to buy a home, but worried you may be priced out of the market? There are many alternatives from which to choose. Several government agencies have properties to sell. In fact, many sell both single-family homes and multifamily properties. When someone with a mortgage can't meet the payments, the lender forecloses on the home. The agency then quickly sells the property as a foreclosure. Check them out — one might be just what you're looking for!

Purchasing a foreclosure is very similar to purchasing any other type of real estate in many respects. They are usually sold "as is"; therefore an inspection should be made before finalizing the deal. But the one big advantage is that it costs the agency money to own a foreclosed home, so many are willing to offer buyers a good deal in order to get the property off of their books. Often you can get financing through government agencies. And keep in mind that on most HUD sales, the buyer can request HUD to pay all or a portion of the financing and closing costs. You may need to contact a professional real estate agent to place a bid for foreclosed properties.

You can find foreclosed properties listed in a variety of places:

☞ Check your local newspaper, Sheriffs office, or local and city property office for foreclosures in your area.

☞ The Housing and Urban Development Agency (HUD) is another good place to look. You can find them online at {http://www.hud.gov/offices/hsg/sfh/reo/homes.cfm} or at U.S. Department of Housing and Urban Development
451 7th Street SW
Washington, DC 20410
202-708-1112

Once you start looking, you won't believe how many foreclosed homes are waiting for you to call them home!!

You Can Even Buy A House On eBay!

eBay has foreclosed properties from government agencies for auction. The properties are from the inventories of HUD, VA, and major lenders. Check for properties online at {http://www.ebayrealestate.net/foreclosures.html}. You can search available properties by state, city, county or zip code.

You can also receive a list of eBay Real Estate's Properties by Email. This service emails you updates of foreclosed properties when they become available in cities that you select. You must be a registered agent to bid on ebay or have an agent bid for you. The web site can put you in contact with one of over 80,000 registered Agents who are helping buyers every day to purchase homes through eBay Real Estate, at great prices!

Freddie Mac Wants To Sell You A Foreclosed House!

Freddie Mac's mission is to improve the quality of life to all Americans by making the American dream of decent, accessible housing a reality. To do this, Freddie Mac purchases mortgages from banks, and this gives the banks more money to lend to future home buyers. HomeSteps Asset Services is the Freddie Mac unit that markets foreclosed homes, and supports its mission in three major areas:

★ HomeSteps promotes home ownership
★ HomeSteps strengthens communities
★ HomeSteps helps Freddie Mac lower mortgage costs

At any time, HomeSteps has thousands of homes available for sale in neighborhoods across the United States. These include single-family homes, condominiums, town homes and more. You can search for your next home by browsing their database of homes for sale. You can search by features such as city, state, number of bedrooms, etc. {http://www.homesteps.com/}. HomeSteps maintains a professional Call Center at 800-972-7555. You can call them to ask any of your questions. They have information that includes:

★ Tips on how to buy a HomeSteps home
★ News about our latest community development projects
★ Information on upcoming auctions

★ Copies of brochures that explain their programs
★ Information on HomeSteps Special Financing
★ Locations of their Design Centers and Home Buying Centers

Or you may contact HomeSteps by mail:

HomeSteps
Attn: Customer Service
5000 Plano Parkway
Carrollton, TX 75010
800-972-7555

Fannie Mae Can Help You Buy Your Dream Home

Like Freddie Mac, Fannie Mae purchases mortgages from lenders for the secondary market. When they foreclose on a home, they offer it for sale through {www.Homepath.com}. It is full of information to help you find the right home for you. They have homes for sale that you can search by price range and the city, state, and zip code where you would like a property. You can also search for a specific property type, such as single-family, condominium, co-op, or others by selecting the "Property Type" option.

You can sort your results by price, type of property, or zip code by selecting the "Sorted By" option. The site contains information on mortgages, the home buying process, tips on working with your real estate agent as well as Fannie Mae approved lenders.

Fannie Mae properties are sold through real estate agents and are all listed in the local Multiple Listing System (MLS) accessible by any real estate professional. Contact your real estate agent, or the one listed, for more information about a specific property. You may also contact them:

Fannie Mae
3900 Wisconsin Ave., NW
Washington, DC 20016
800-7FANNIE

Bid On A House From The IRS!

The Internal Revenue Service does something else besides collecting taxes, as they have homes available for sale. The properties have been seized or acquired for nonpayment of internal revenue taxes and are sold at auction to the public. You must check the web site for upcoming auctions {http://www.treas.gov/auctions/irs/real1.html}. The web site will provide you with a picture of the property, address, minimum bid and other details. When you've found the perfect home, contact the office listed for more information on how to bid.

U.S Customs Seized Property For Sale!

The U.S. Customs Service sells property that it seizes. You can view the houses to be auctioned on line at {http://www.treas.gov/auctions/customs/realprop.html}. The U.S. Customs Service Support also offers a subscription program for those people interested in receiving sales flyers on real property sales. The subscription is free if you subscribe for email notification. Auctions are open to the public and you do not need a real estate broker to bid

> EG&G Technical Services
> Attention: RP CUS NET
> 7845 Ashton Avenue
> Manassas, VA 20109-2883
> 703-361-3131, ext. 279
> {http://www.treas.gov/auctions/customs/realprop.html}

Get A Great Deal From The Bank

The Federal Deposit Insurance Corporation (FDIC) insures your deposits up to $100,000 in many banks. When someone's home is foreclosed by the FDIC, they offer it for sale. The FDIC sells a wide variety of real estate, including properties in the affordable housing program. A list of properties available for sale is updated weekly. Each property will have a contact name and phone number. The contact name will either be an individual from an FDIC office or an individual associated with the sales initiative (e.g. Auction Company, Real Estate Broker).

Federal Deposit Insurance Corporation
Field Operations Branch
1910 Pacific Avenue
Dallas, TX 75201
888-206-4662
{http://www.fdic.gov/buying/owned/index.html}

This web site can generate a list of properties by type, state, or market price.
{http://www2.fdic.gov/drrore/}

Looking for a bargain? The properties advertised here are sold "as-is, where-is" and with all faults. They may be just what you seek.
{http://www.fdic.gov/buying/owned/bargain/index.html}

Get Your House From The Marshals

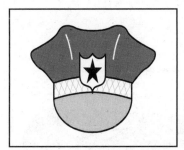

The U.S. Marshals Service (USMS) offers property for sale to the public, which has been forfeited under laws enforced or administered by the United States Department of Justice, its investigative agencies (Drug Enforcement Administration, Federal Bureau of Investigation, and Immigration and Naturalization Service), and certain other federal law enforcement agencies. The property offered for sale consists of residential and commercial real estate and business establishments.

The U.S. Marshals Service maintains neither a list of forfeited property for sale nor a mailing list to notify prospective buyers of upcoming sales.

Contract service providers and federal agencies have been authorized to sell forfeited property for the USMS on a recurring basis. The Contract Service Provider list provides information on company/agency names, locations, and telephone numbers. You must contact the companies/agencies listed for information on property that is currently available for sale, and for sales locations, dates, and other pertinent information. Forfeited real property is also normally listed for sale by authorized brokers in local multiple listing services.

This Contract Service Provider List can be obtained by:

1.   **U.S. Mail**
      Send your name, address and a check or money order for $.50 to: Consumer Information Center (CIC), Dept. 321G, Pueblo, CO. 81009.

2. **Telephone**
   Call 1-888-878-3256 and request Item 321G.
3. **Fax-on-Demand**
   Call 202-307-9777.
4. **World Wide Web**
   CIC website — http://www.pueblo.gsa.gov/.
   Marshals Service website — http://www.usdoj.gov/marshals/.

One online provider for real estate is Bid4Assests. You can check out any properties being auctioned.

Bid4Assets, Inc.
1010 Wayne Avenue, Suite 505
Silver Spring, MD 20910
Toll Free: 877-427-7387
Local: 301-650-9193
Fax: 301-650-9194
http://www.bid4assets.com/

Even You Can Buy a HUD Home!!

HUD sells properties at reduced prices that you might want to buy! When someone with a HUD insured mortgage can't meet the payments, the lender forecloses on the home; HUD pays the lender what is owed; and HUD takes ownership of the home. HUD then sells it at market value as quickly as possible.

To buy a HUD home, start by finding a participating real estate agent. Your real estate agent must submit your bid for you, and homes are usually sold "as is." HUD will not make repairs on the home before selling. Normally, HUD homes are sold in an "Offer Period." At the end of the Offer Period, all offers are opened and, basically, the highest reasonable bid is accepted. For more information contact:

U.S. Department of Housing and Urban Development
451 7th Street S.W.,
Washington, DC 20410
202-708-1112
TTY: 202-708-1455
http://www.hud.gov/offices/hsg/sfh/reo/homes.cfm

State Contacts

Alabama
CitiWest / Best Assets
3420 Norman Berry Dr, Suite 600
Atlanta, GA 30354
404-768-1400
Fax: 404-768-4010
http://bally.towerauction.net/i6
/al/index.html

Alaska
Michaelson, Connor & Boul, Inc.
5312 Bolsa Avenue, Suite 200
Huntington Beach, CA 92649
714-230-3600
Fax: 714-230-3699
http://bally.towerauction.net/a
c/index.html

Arizona
First Preston
1520 Nutmeg Place, Suite 112
Costa Mesa, CA 92626
714-241-1096
Fax: 714-241-1051
http://www.hud.org/fp3/az/

Arkansas
First Preston
1888 Sherman Street, Suite 375
Denver, CO 80203
303-830-0777
Fax: 303-830-1003
http://www.hud.org/fp1/ar/

California (Northern)
Golden Feather Realty Services
1600 Sacramento Inn Way
Suite 220
Sacramento, CA 95815
916-922-2262
Fax: 922-922-8009
http://www.hud.org/g2/nca/

California (Southern)
Golden Feather Realty Services
2500 Michelson Blvd. Suite 100
Irvine, CA 92612
949-477-6300
Fax: 949-477-2225
http://www.hud.org/g1/sca/

Colorado
First Preston
12240 Inwood Road, Suite 400

Dallas, TX 75244
972-788-0026
Fax: 972-392-0635
http://www.hud.org/fp2/co/

Connecticut
Citi West
330 Main Street
Hartford, CT 06106
860-244-2783
Fax: 860-244-2798
http://bally.towerauction.net/n
e/ct/index.html

Delaware
First Preston
475 Sentry Parkway, Suite 5000
Blue Bell, PA 19422
484-530-0700
Fax: 484-530-0794
http://www.hud.org/fp5/de/

District of Columbia
http://www.hud.org/fp5/dc/

Florida
Southeast Alliance
3280 Pointe Parkway, Suite 1000
Norcross, GA 30092
678-832-1000
Fax: 678-832-1015
http://www.hud.org/fp4/fl/

Georgia
CitiWest/BestAssets
3420 Norman Berry Dr, Suite 600
Atlanta, GA 30354
404-768-1400
Fax: 404-768-4010
http://bally.towerauction.net/i6
/ga/index.html

Hawaii
PEMCO, LTD.
1632 S. King Street, Suite 100
Honolulu, HI 96826
808-949-0414
Fax: 808-955-0414
http://www.hudpemco.com/

Idaho
Golden Feather Realty Services
1600 Sacramento Inn Way
Suite 220

Sacramento, CA 95815
916-922-2262
Fax: 922-922-8009
http://bally.towerauction.net/i7
/id/index.html

Illinois
Golden Feather Realty Services
2500 Michelson, Suite 100
Irvine, CA 92612
949-477-6300
Fax: 949-477-2225
http://bally.towerauction.net/i4
/il/index.html

Indiana
Golden Feather Realty Services
2500 Michelson, Suite 100
Irvine, CA 92612
949-477-6300
Fax: 949-477-2225
http://bally.towerauction.net/i4
/in/index.html

Iowa
First Preston
1888 Sherman Street, Suite 375
Denver, CO 80203
303-830-0777
Fax: 303-830-1003
http://www.hud.org/fp2/ia/

Kansas
First Preston
1888 Sherman Street, Suite 375
Denver, CO 80203
303-830-0777
Fax: 303-830-1003
http://www.hud.org/fp1/ks/

Kentucky
Golden Feather Realty Services
2500 Michelson, Suite 100
Irvine, CA 92612
949-477-6300
Fax: 949-477-2225
http://bally.towerauction.net/i4
/ky/index.html

Louisiana
First Preston
1888 Sherman Street, Suite 375
Denver, CO 80203
303-830-0777

Fax: 303-830-1003
http://www.hud.org/fp1/la/

Maine
CitiWest
330 Main Street
Hartford, CT 06106
860-244-2783
Fax: 860-244-2798
http://bally.towerauction.net/n
e/me/index.html

Maryland
Michaelson, Connor & Boul, Inc.
10400 Shaker Dr., Unit F
Columbia, MD 21046
410-772-5800
Fax: 410-772-2299
http://bally.towerauction.net/i3/

Massachusetts
CitiWest
330 Main Street
Hartford, CT 06106
860-244-2783
Fax: 860-244-2798
http://bally.towerauction.net/n
e/ma/index.html

Michigan
Michaelson, Connor & Boul, Inc.
1844 Thunderbird St.
Troy, MI 48084
248-273-0042
Fax: 248-273-0042
http://bally.towerauction.net/i1/

Minnesota
First Preston
1888 Sherman Street, Suite 375
Denver, CO 80203
303-830-0777
Fax: 303-830-1003
http://www.hud.org/fp2/mn/

Mississippi
CitiWest/BestAssets
3420 Norman Berry Drive
Suite 600
Atlanta, GA 30354
404-768-1400
Fax: 404-768-4010
http://bally.towerauction.net/i6
/ms/index.html

Missouri
First Preston
1888 Sherman Street, Suite 375
Denver, CO 80203
303-830-0777
Fax: 303-830-1003
http://www.hud.org/fp1/mo/

Montana
First Preston
1888 Sherman Street, Suite 375
Denver, CO 80203
303-830-0777
Fax: 303-830-1003
http://www.hud.org/fp2/mt/

Nebraska
First Preston
1888 Sherman Street, Suite 375
Denver, CO 80203
303-830-0777
Fax: 303-830-1003
http://www.hud.org/fp2/ne/

Nevada (Northern)
Golden Feather Realty Services
1600 Sacramento Inn Way
Suite 220
Sacramento, CA 95815
916-922-2262
Fax: 916-922-8009
http://www.hud.org/g2/nca/

Nevada (Central/Southern)
First Preston
1520 Nutmeg Place, Suite 112
Costa Mesa, CA 92626
714-241-1096
Fax: 714-241-1051
http://www.hud.org/fp3/nv/

New Hampshire
CitiWest
330 Main Street
Hartford, CT 06106
860-244-2783
Fax: 860-244-2798
http://bally.towerauction.net/n
e/nh/index.html

New Jersey
First Preston
475 Sentry Parkway, Suite 5000
Blue Bell, PA 19422

484-530-0700
Fax: 484-530-0794
http://www.hud.org/fp5/nj/

New Mexico
First Preston
12240 Inwood Road, Suite 400
Dallas, TX 75244
972-788-0026
Fax: 972-392-0635
http://www.hud.org/fp2/nm/

New York
First Preston
475 Sentry Parkway, Suite 5000
Blue Bell, Pennsylvania 19422
484-530-0700
Fax: 484-530-0794
http://www.hud.org/fp5/ny/

North Carolina
Michaelson, Connor & Boul, Inc.
5736 North Tryon St., Suite 104
Charlotte, NC 28213
704-599-1512
Fax: 704-599-1812
http://bally.towerauction.net/i5/

North Dakota
First Preston
1888 Sherman Street, Suite 375
Denver, CO 80203
303-830-0777
Fax: 303-830-1003
http://www.hud.org/fp2/nd/

Ohio
Michaelson, Connor & Boul, Inc.
26250 Euclid Ave., Suite 513
Euclid, OH 44132
216-289-1575
http://bally.towerauction.net/i1
/index.html

Oklahoma
First Preston
1888 Sherman Street, Suite 375
Denver, CO 80203
303-830-0777
Fax: 303-830-1003
http://www.hud.org/fp1/ok/

Oregon
Golden Feather Realty Services
1600 Sacramento Inn Way

Suite 220
Sacramento, CA 95815
916-922-2262
Fax: 916-922-8009
http://bally.towerauction.net/i7
/or/index.html

Pennsylvania

Golden Feather Realty Services
1600 Sacramento Inn Way
Suite 220
Sacramento, CA 95815
916-922-2262
Fax: 916-922-8009
http://paris.towerauction.net/g
2/pa/

Puerto Rico/US Virgin Islands

Southeast Alliance
3280 Pointe Parkway, Suite 1000
Norcross, GA 30092
678-832-1000
Fax: 678-832-1015
http://www.hud.org/fp4/pr/

Rhode Island

CitiWest
330 Main Street
Hartford, CT 06106
860-244-2783
Fax: 860-244-2798
http://bally.towerauction.net/n
e/ri/index.html

South Carolina

Michaelson, Connor & Boul, Inc.
5001 Sunset Blvd., Suite B
Lexington, SC 29072
803-996-2944
Fax: 803-996-2944
http://bally.towerauction.net/i5/

South Dakota

First Preston
12240 Inwood Road, Suite 400
Dallas, TX 75244
972-788-0026
Fax: 972-392-0635
http://www.hud.org/fp2/sd/

Tennessee

Golden Feather Realty Services
2500 Michelson, Suite 100
Irvine, CA 92612
949-477-6300
Fax: 949-477-2225
http://bally.towerauction.net/i4
/tn/index.html

Texas

First Preston
12240 Inwood Road, Suite 400
Dallas, TX 75244
972-788-0026
Fax: 972-392-0635
http://www.hud.org/fp2/tx/

Utah

First Preston
12240 Inwood Road, Suite 400
Dallas, TX 75244
972-788-0026
Fax: 972-392-0635
http://www.hud.org/fp2/ut/

Vermont

CitiWest
330 Main Street
Hartford, CT 06106
860-244-2783
Fax: 860-244-2798
http://bally.towerauction.net/n
e/vt/index.html

Virginia

First Preston
1888 Sherman Street, Suite 375
Denver, CO 80203
303-830-0777
Fax: 303-830-1003
http://www.hud.org/fp5/va/

Washington

Golden Feather Realty Services
1600 Sacramento Inn Way
Suite 220
Sacramento, CA 95815
916-922-2262
Fax: 916-922-8009
http://bally.towerauction.net/i7
/wa/index.html

West Virginia

Michaelson, Connor & Boul, Inc.
26250 Euclid Ave., Suite 513
Euclid, OH 44132
216-289-1575
http://bally.towerauction.net/i1
/index.html

Wisconsin

First Preston
1888 Sherman Street, Suite 375
Denver, CO 80203
303-830-0777
Fax: 303-830-1003
http://www.hud.org/fp2/wi/

Wyoming

First Preston
12240 Inwood Road, Suite 400
Dallas, TX 75244
972-788-0026
Fax: 972-392-0635
http://www.hud.org/fp2/wy/

The VA Has Properties for Sale!!

The U.S. Department of Veterans Affairs (VA) acquires properties that are available for sale to the public through the services of private sector real estate brokers, and are sold to homebuyers and investors who can be veterans or non-veterans. The VA sells mostly single-family properties that they receive as the result of foreclosures on VA guaranteed loans through the facilities of 46 regional offices. Property listings for most offices are available on the Internet or by direct mail. Regional offices whose Internet sites are not fully functional issue sales listings in local newspapers.

U.S. Department of Veterans Affairs
810 Vermont Ave. NW
Washington, DC 20420
800-827-1000
http://www.homeloans.va.gov/homes.htm

VA Regional Offices

Alabama
VA Regional Office
345 Perry Hill Rd.
Montgomery, AL 36109
334-213-3424
www.vamontgomery.com

Alaska
VA Regional Office
2925 Debarr Road
Anchorage, AK 99508
907-257-4736
www.vaalaska.com

Arizona
VA Regional Office
3225 North Central Ave.
Phoenix, AZ 85012
602-530-3574
www.vahomes.org/pn/

Arkansas
VA Regional Office
P O Box 1280, Fort Roots
N Little Rock, AR 72115
800-207-6722
www.vahomes.org/lr/

California (Southern, except San Diego area)
VA Regional Office
11200 Wilshire Blvd
Los Angeles, CA 90024
800-479-5658
www.vahomes.org/la/

California (Northern and Northern Nevada)
VA Regional Office
1301 Clay St, 1300 North
Oakland, CA 94612-5209
510-637-6066
www.vba.va.gov/ro/oakland/index.html

California (San Diego Area)
VA Regional Office
8810 Rio San Diego Drive
San Diego, CA 92108
www.vasandiego.com

Colorado
VA Regional Loan Center
155 Van Gordon St.
Lakewood, CO 80228
888-523-4286
www.vba.va.gov/ro/denver/index.htm

Connecticut
VA Regional Office
275 Chestnut St
Manchester, NH 03101
800-827-6311
http://www.vba.va.gov/ro/manchester/lgymain/loans.html

Delaware
VARO & Insurance Center
5000 Wissahickon Av
Philadelphia, PA 19101
215-842-2000
http://www.vba.va.gov/ro/philly/index.htm

District of Columbia, Northern VA, & Mont. & PG Counties in MD
VA Regional Office
1120 Vermont Ave. NW
Washington, D.C. 20421
202-269-2076
www.vahomeswash.com

Florida
VA Regional Office
P O Box 1437
St. Petersburg, FL 33731
727-319-7500
www.vaflorida.com

Georgia
Department of Veterans Affairs
Regional Loan Center
1700 Clairmont Rd.
PO Box 100023
Decatur, GA 30031-7023
888-768-2132 x3067
www.vba.va.gov/ro/atlanta/rlc
/index.htm

Hawaii
VA Med & RO Center
459 Patterson Road
Honolulu, HI 96819-1522
808-433-0483

Idaho
VA Regional Office
805 West Franklin St.
Boise, ID 83702-5560
800-827-1000
www.vba-boi-lgy.com

Illinois
VA Regional Office
P O Box 8136
Chicago, IL 60680
312-353-2382
www.vahomes.org/ch/

Indiana
VA Regional Office
575 Pennsylvania St
Indianapolis, IN 46204-1541
http://www.vba.va.gov/ro/cen
tral/indy/index.htm

Iowa
VA Regional Office
210 Walnut St
Des Moines, IA 50309
800-827-1000
www.vba.va.gov/ro/desmoines
/index.html

Kansas
VA Med & RO Center
P.O. Box 20077
Wichita, KS 67208-1077

888-878-6881 Ext. 6731
www.vahomes.org/ks

Kentucky
VA Regional Office
545 S 3rd St
Louisville, KY 40202
502-582-5866
www.vba.va.gov/ro/central/lo
uvl/LOAN/Cover.htm

Louisiana
VA Regional Office
701 Loyola Ave.
New Orleans, LA 70113
504-589-3726
http://mirage.towerauction.net
/no/

Maine
VA Regional Office
275 Chestnut St
Manchester, NH 03101
800-827-6311
http://www.vba.va.gov/ro/ma
nchester/lgymain/loans.html

Maryland (except PG and
Mont. Counties)
VA Regional Office
31 Hopkins Plaza
Baltimore, MD 21201
410-962-7874
www.vahomes.org/bt/

Massachusetts
VA Regional Office
275 Chestnut St
Manchester, NH 03101
800-827-6311
http://www.vba.va.gov/ro/ma
nchester/lgymain/loans.html

Michigan
VA Regional Office
477 Michigan Av
Detroit, MI 48226
313-226-4227
www.vba.va.gov/ro/central/de
tr/default.htm

Minnesota
VARO & Insurance Center
Fort Snelling
St. Paul, MN 55111

800-827-0633
www.vba.va.gov/ro/central/st
pau/pages/prpmanag.html

Mississippi
VA Regional Office
1600 E. Woodrow Wilson Ave.
Jackson, MS 39216
601-364-7113
www.vba.va.gov/ro/south/jack
s/LGYListings/LGY.htm

Missouri
VA Regional Office
400 S. 18th St
St. Louis, MO 63103-2271
888-379-9308
www.vahomes.org/sl/

Montana
VA Regional Loan Center
155 Van Gordon St.
Lakewood, CO 80228
800-827-1000
http://www.vba.va.gov/ro/de
nver/index.htm

Nebraska
VA Regional Office
5631 S 48th St
Lincoln, NE 68516
402-421-7480
402-420-4068

Nevada (Northern)
VA Regional Office
1301 Clay St, 1300 North
Oakland, CA 94612-5209
510-637-6066
http://www.vba.va.gov/ro/oak
land/index.html

Nevada (Southern)
VA Regional Office
3225 North Central Ave.
Phoenix, AZ 85012
888-869-0194
http://www.vahomes.org/pn/

New England
VA Regional Office
275 Chestnut St
Manchester, NH 03101
800-827-6311
www.vba.va.gov/ro/mancheste
r/lgymain/loans.html

New Hampshire

VA Regional Office
275 Chestnut St
Manchester, NH 03101
800-827-6311
www.vba.va.gov/ro/mancheste
r/lgymain/loans.html

New Jersey

VA Regional Office
20 Washington Place
Newark, NJ 07102
973-297-4808
www.vba.va.gov/ro/east/newr
k/lgy/index.htm

New Mexico

VA Regional Office
P.O. Box 0968
Albuquerque, NM 87102
800-827-1000
www.vanewmexico.org

New York (Western)

VA Regional Office
111 W Huron St
Buffalo, NY 14202
716-551-5295

New York (Eastern)

VA Regional Office
245 West Houston St
New York, NY 10014
212-807-7229
www.vba.va.gov/ro/east/ny/L
GYHome.htm

North Carolina

VA Regional Office
251 North Main St
Winston Salem, NC 27155
800-827-1000
www.vba.va.gov/ro/winstonsal
em/index.htm

North Dakota

VARO & Insurance Center
Fort Snelling
St. Paul, MN 55111
800-827-0633
http://www.vba.va.gov/ro/cen
tral/stpau/pages/prpmanag.ht
ml

Oklahoma

VA Regional Office
125 Main St
Muskogee, OK 74401
918-687-2364
http://www.gibill.va.gov/musk
ogee/lg.htm

Ohio

VA Regional Office
1240 East 9th St
Cleveland, OH 44199
800-827-1000
www.vba.va.gov/ro/central/cle
ve/index1.htm

Oregon

VA Regional Office
1220 SW Third Av
Portland, OR 97204
503-326-2457
www.pmlgyport.com

Pennsylvania (Western)

VA Regional Office
1000 Liberty Av
Pittsburgh, PA 15222
800-827-1000
www.vba.va.gov/ro/east/pitts/
loan/default.htm

Pennsylvania (Eastern)

VARO & Insurance Center
5000 Wissahickon Av
Philadelphia, PA 19101
215-842-2000
www.vba.va.gov/philly.htm

Puerto Rico

VA Regional Office
GPO Box 4867
San Juan, PR 00936
787-766-5177

Rhode Island

VA Regional Office
275 Chestnut St
Manchester, NH 03101
800-827-6311
http://www.vba.va.gov/ro/ma
nchester/lgymain/loans.html

South Carolina

VA Regional Office
1801 Assembly St
Columbia, SC 29201
803-255-4136
www.vba.va.gov/ro/columbia/
lgy/index.htm

South Dakota

VARO & Insurance Center
Fort Snelling
St. Paul, MN 55111
800-827-0633
http://www.vba.va.gov/ro/cen
tral/stpau/pages/prpmanag.ht
ml

Tennessee

VA Regional Office
110 9th Av S
Nashville, TN 37203
888-768-2132
www.vahomes.org/tn/

Texas

VA Regional Office
6900 Alemda Road
Houston, TX 77030
713-383-3100
888-232-2571
https://www.vahouston.com/d
efault1.htm

Utah

VA Regional Office
P O Box 11500
Salt Lake City, UT 84147
801-524-4515
www.vbaslc.com

Vermont

VA Regional Office
275 Chestnut St
Manchester, NH 03101
800-827-6311
http://www.vba.va.gov/ro/ma
nchester/lgymain/loans.html

Virginia

(except northern VA)
VA Regional Office
210 Franklin Rd, SW

Roanoke, VA 24011
540-857-2735
www.vba-roanoke.com/rlc

Washington
VA Regional Office
915 Second Ave.
Seattle, WA 98174
800-827-1000
www.seattleva.com

West Virginia
VA Regional Office
210 Franklin Rd, SW
Roanoke, VA 24011
800-827-1000
http://www.vba-
roanoke.com/rlc/

Wisconsin
VA Regional Office

5000 National Avenue
Milwaukee, WI 53295
414-382-5060

Wyoming
VA Regional Loan Center
155 Van Gordon St.
Lakewood, CO 80228
800-827-1000
http://www.vba.va.gov/ro/de
nver/index.htm

Need A Home Near A Military Installation??

The US Army Corps of Engineers provides Homeowners Assistance Program, (HAP) to help eligible federal personnel, who were stationed at or near an installation scheduled for closure or realignment and who, through no fault of their own, are unable to sell their homes. The U.S. Army Corps of Engineers acquires single-family homes and other properties, with up to two living units.

The properties are then offered for sale to the public. Local real estate agents may show the properties to prospective buyers and submit offers on behalf of the buyer. In addition, local real estate agents will have information such as location of schools, churches, public transportation, and shopping centers. Anyone can offer to buy these properties regardless of race, color, religion, sex, or national origin.

You can check the web site for a listing of properties or call the US Army Corps of Engineers for your state; {http://www.sas.usace.army.mil/hapinv/haphomes.htm}.

State Contacts

Alabama
U.S. Army Engineer District,
Savannah
Homeowners Assistance
Program Branch
P.O. Box 889
Savannah, GA 31402-0889
800-861-8144
http://www.sas.usace.army.mil
/hapinv/hapinfo.htm

Alaska
U.S. Army Engineer District,
Sacramento
1325 J Street

Sacramento, CA 95814-2922
916-557-6850
800-811-5532
http://www.spk.usace.army.mil
/cespk-re/hap/hapmain.html

Arizona
U.S. Army Engineer District,
Sacramento
1325 J Street
Sacramento, CA 95814-2922
916-557-6850
800-811-5532
http://www.spk.usace.army.mil
/cespk-re/hap/hapmain.html

Arkansas
U.S. Army Engineer District,
Fort Worth
P.O. Box 17300
Ft. Worth, TX 76102-0300
817-978-4047
888-231-7751
http://www.swf.usace.army.mil
/hap/text/hapmain.htm

California
U.S. Army Engineer District,
Sacramento
1325 J Street
Sacramento, CA 95814-2922

916-557-6850
800-811-5532
http://www.spk.usace.army.mil
/cespk-re/hap/hapmain.html

Colorado

U.S. Army Engineer District,
Fort Worth
P.O. Box 17300
Ft. Worth, TX 76102-0300
817-978-4047
888-231-7751
http://www.swf.usace.army.mil
/hap/text/hapmain.htm

Connecticut

U.S. Army Engineer District,
Savannah
Homeowners Assistance
Program Branch
P.O. Box 889
Savannah, GA 31402-0889
800-861-8144
http://www.sas.usace.army.mil
/hapinv/hapinfo.htm

Delaware

U.S. Army Engineer District,
Savannah
Homeowners Assistance
Program Branch
P.O. Box 889
Savannah, GA 31402-0889
800-861-8144
http://www.sas.usace.army.mil
/hapinv/hapinfo.htm

District of Columbia

U.S. Army Engineer District,
Savannah
Homeowners Assistance
Program Branch
P.O. Box 889
Savannah, GA 31402-0889
800-861-8144
http://www.sas.usace.army.mil
/hapinv/hapinfo.htm

Florida

U.S. Army Engineer District,
Savannah
Homeowners Assistance
Program Branch
P.O. Box 889
Savannah, GA 31402-0889

800-861-8144
http://www.sas.usace.army.mil
/hapinv/hapinfo.htm

Georgia

U.S. Army Engineer District,
Savannah
Homeowners Assistance
Program Branch
P.O. Box 889
Savannah, GA 31402-0889
800-861-8144
http://www.sas.usace.army.mil
/hapinv/hapinfo.htm

Hawaii

U.S. Army Engineer District,
Sacramento
1325 J Street
Sacramento, CA 95814-2922
916-557-6850
800-811-5532
http://www.spk.usace.army.mil
/cespk-re/hap/hapmain.html

Idaho

U.S. Army Engineer District,
Sacramento
1325 J Street
Sacramento, CA 95814-2922
916-557-6850
800-811-5532
http://www.spk.usace.army.mil
/cespk-re/hap/hapmain.html

Illinois

U.S. Army Engineer District,
Savannah
Homeowners Assistance
Program Branch
P.O. Box 889
Savannah, GA 31402-0889
800-861-8144
http://www.sas.usace.army.mil
/hapinv/hapinfo.htm

Indiana

U.S. Army Engineer District,
Savannah
Homeowners Assistance
Program Branch
P.O. Box 889
Savannah, GA 31402-0889
800-861-8144
http://www.sas.usace.army.mil
/hapinv/hapinfo.htm

Iowa

U.S. Army Engineer District,
Fort Worth
P.O. Box 17300
Ft. Worth, TX 76102-0300
817-978-4047
888-231-7751
http://www.swf.usace.army.mil
/hap/text/hapmain.htm

Kansas

U.S. Army Engineer District,
Fort Worth
P.O. Box 17300
Ft. Worth, TX 76102-0300
817-978-4047
888-231-7751
http://www.swf.usace.army.mil
/hap/text/hapmain.htm

Kentucky

U.S. Army Engineer District,
Savannah
Homeowners Assistance
Program Branch
P.O. Box 889
Savannah, GA 31402-0889
800-861-8144
http://www.sas.usace.army.mil
/hapinv/hapinfo.htm

Louisiana

U.S. Army Engineer District,
Fort Worth
P.O. Box 17300
Ft. Worth, TX 76102-0300
817-978-4047
888-231-7751
http://www.swf.usace.army.mil
/hap/text/hapmain.htm

Maine

U.S. Army Engineer District,
Savannah
Homeowners Assistance
Program Branch
P.O. Box 889
Savannah, GA 31402-0889
800-861-8144
http://www.sas.usace.army.mil
/hapinv/hapinfo.htm

Maryland

U.S. Army Engineer District,
Savannah

Homeowners Assistance
Program Branch
P.O. Box 889
Savannah, GA 31402-0889
800-861-8144
http://www.sas.usace.army.mil
/hapinv/hapinfo.htm

Massachusetts

U.S. Army Engineer District,
Savannah
Homeowners Assistance
Program Branch
P.O. Box 889
Savannah, GA 31402-0889
800-861-8144
http://www.sas.usace.army.mil
/hapinv/hapinfo.htm

Michigan

U.S. Army Engineer District,
Fort Worth
P.O. Box 17300
Ft. Worth, TX 76102-0300
817-978-4047
888-231-7751
http://www.swf.usace.army.mil
/hap/text/hapmain.htm

Minnesota

U.S. Army Engineer District,
Fort Worth
P.O. Box 17300
Ft. Worth, TX 76102-0300
817-978-4047
888-231-7751
http://www.swf.usace.army.mil
/hap/text/hapmain.htm

Mississippi

U.S. Army Engineer District,
Savannah
Homeowners Assistance
Program Branch
P.O. Box 889
Savannah, GA 31402-0889
800-861-8144
http://www.sas.usace.army.mil
/hapinv/hapinfo.htm

Missouri

U.S. Army Engineer District,
Fort Worth
P.O. Box 17300
Ft. Worth, TX 76102-0300

817-978-4047
888-231-7751
http://www.swf.usace.army.mil
/hap/text/hapmain.htm

Montana

U.S. Army Engineer District,
Savannah
Homeowners Assistance
Program Branch
P.O. Box 889
Savannah, GA 31402-0889
800-861-8144
http://www.sas.usace.army.mil
/hapinv/hapinfo.htm

Nebraska

U.S. Army Engineer District,
Fort Worth
P.O. Box 17300
Ft. Worth, TX 76102-0300
817-978-4047
888-231-7751
http://www.swf.usace.army.mil
/hap/text/hapmain.htm

Nevada

U.S. Army Engineer District,
Sacramento
1325 J Street
Sacramento, CA 95814-2922
916-557-6850
800-811-5532
http://www.spk.usace.army.mil
/cespk-re/hap/hapmain.html

New Hampshire

U.S. Army Engineer District,
Savannah
Homeowners Assistance
Program Branch
P.O. Box 889
Savannah, GA 31402-0889
800-861-8144
http://www.sas.usace.army.mil
/hapinv/hapinfo.htm

New Jersey

U.S. Army Engineer District,
Savannah
Homeowners Assistance
Program Branch
P.O. Box 889
Savannah, GA 31402-0889
800-861-8144

http://www.sas.usace.army.mil
/hapinv/hapinfo.htm

New Mexico

U.S. Army Engineer District,
Fort Worth
P.O. Box 17300
Ft. Worth, TX 76102-0300
817-978-4047
888-231-7751
http://www.swf.usace.army.mil
/hap/text/hapmain.htm

New York

U.S. Army Engineer District,
Savannah
Homeowners Assistance
Program Branch
P.O. Box 889
Savannah, GA 31402-0889
800-861-8144
http://www.sas.usace.army.mil
/hapinv/hapinfo.htm

North Carolina

U.S. Army Engineer District,
Savannah
Homeowners Assistance
Program Branch
P.O. Box 889
Savannah, GA 31402-0889
800-861-8144
http://www.sas.usace.army.mil
/hapinv/hapinfo.htm

North Dakota

U.S. Army Engineer District,
Fort Worth
P.O. Box 17300
Ft. Worth, TX 76102-0300
817-978-4047
888-231-7751
http://www.swf.usace.army.mil
/hap/text/hapmain.htm

Ohio

U.S. Army Engineer District,
Savannah
Homeowners Assistance
Program Branch
P.O. Box 889
Savannah, GA 31402-0889
800-861-8144
http://www.sas.usace.army.mil
/hapinv/hapinfo.htm

Oklahoma

U.S. Army Engineer District,
Fort Worth
P.O. Box 17300
Ft. Worth, TX 76102-0300
817-978-4047
888-231-7751
http://www.swf.usace.army.mil
/hap/text/hapmain.htm

Oregon

U.S. Army Engineer District,
Sacramento
1325 J Street
Sacramento, CA 95814-2922
916-557-6850
800-811-5532
http://www.spk.usace.army.mil
/cespk-re/hap/hapmain.html

Pennsylvania

U.S. Army Engineer District,
Savannah
Homeowners Assistance
Program Branch
P.O. Box 889
Savannah, GA 31402-0889
800-861-8144
http://www.sas.usace.army.mil
/hapinv/hapinfo.htm

Rhode Island

U.S. Army Engineer District,
Savannah
Homeowners Assistance
Program Branch
P.O. Box 889
Savannah, GA 31402-0889
800-861-8144
http://www.sas.usace.army.mil
/hapinv/hapinfo.htm

South Carolina

U.S. Army Engineer District,
Savannah
Homeowners Assistance
Program Branch
P.O. Box 889
Savannah, GA 31402-0889
800-861-8144
http://www.sas.usace.army.mil
/hapinv/hapinfo.htm

South Dakota

U.S. Army Engineer District,
Fort Worth
P.O. Box 17300
Ft. Worth, TX 76102-0300
817-978-4047
888-231-7751
http://www.swf.usace.army.mil
/hap/text/hapmain.htm

Tennessee

U.S. Army Engineer District,
Savannah
Homeowners Assistance
Program Branch
P.O. Box 889
Savannah, GA 31402-0889
800-861-8144
http://www.sas.usace.army.mil
/hapinv/hapinfo.htm

Texas

U.S. Army Engineer District,
Fort Worth
P.O. Box 17300
Ft. Worth, TX 76102-0300
817-978-4047
888-231-7751
http://www.swf.usace.army.mil
/hap/text/hapmain.htm

Utah

U.S. Army Engineer District,
Sacramento
1325 J Street
Sacramento, CA 95814-2922
916-557-6850
800-811-5532
http://www.spk.usace.army.mil
/cespk-re/hap/hapmain.html

Vermont

U.S. Army Engineer District,
Savannah
Homeowners Assistance
Program Branch
P.O. Box 889
Savannah, GA 31402-0889
800-861-8144
http://www.sas.usace.army.mil
/hapinv/hapinfo.htm

Virginia

U.S. Army Engineer District,
Savannah
Homeowners Assistance
Program Branch
P.O. Box 889
Savannah, GA 31402-0889
800-861-8144
http://www.sas.usace.army.mil
/hapinv/hapinfo.htm

Washington

U.S. Army Engineer District,
Sacramento
1325 J Street
Sacramento, CA 95814-2922
916-557-6850
800-811-5532
http://www.spk.usace.army.mil
/cespk-re/hap/hapmain.html

West Virginia

U.S. Army Engineer District,
Savannah
Homeowners Assistance
Program Branch
P.O. Box 889
Savannah, GA 31402-0889
800-861-8144
http://www.sas.usace.army.mil
/hapinv/hapinfo.htm

Wisconsin

U.S. Army Engineer District,
Fort Worth
P.O. Box 17300
Ft. Worth, TX 76102-0300
817-978-4047
888-231-7751
http://www.swf.usace.army.mil
/hap/text/hapmain.htm

Wyoming

U.S. Army Engineer District,
Fort Worth
P.O. Box 17300
Ft. Worth, TX 76102-0300
817-978-4047
888-231-7751
http://www.swf.usace.army.mil
/hap/text/hapmain.htm

Buy From The Government's Supplier

The General Services Administration (GSA) provides workspace, furniture, equipment, supplies and more to Federal agencies. The GSA also operates the Property Disposal Division, which manages the use and disposal of surplus real property government-wide. Surplus properties are made available for various public purposes, including negotiated sale to state and local governments and eligible nonprofit institutions, or are sold competitively to the general public.

The very best place to find the General Services current properties for sale is online at http://propertydisposal.gsa.gov/Property/. The public sales are also advertised in local and national newspapers, in trade publications, on radio, and in a bimonthly leaflet. The Sales List is available in print for free from all of our offices or you may request a copy by writing to Properties, Consumer Information Center, Pueblo, CO 81002.

General Services Administration
Central Office
1800 F Street, NW
Washington, DC 20405
202-501-0084
Fax: 202-208-1714
http://propertydisposal.gsa.gov/Property/PropForSale/SchProperty/search.asp

State Contacts

Alabama
General Services Administration
Region 4
401 West Peachtree St, Suite 2528
Atlanta, GA 30308
404-331-5133
Fax: 404-331-2727

Alaska
General Services Administration
Region 10
400 15th Street, Room 1161
Auburn, WA 98001
253-931-7547
Fax: 253-931-7554

Arizona
General Services Administration
Region 9
450 Golden Gate Avenue, 9PR
San Francisco, CA 94102
888-GSA-LAND
Fax: 415-522-3213

Arkansas
General Services Administration
Region 7
819 Taylor Street, Room 11A09
Ft. Worth, TX 76102
817-978-2331
Fax: 817-978-2063

California
General Services Administration
Region 9
450 Golden Gate Avenue, 9PR
San Francisco, CA 94102
888-GSA-LAND
Fax: 415-522-3213

Colorado
General Services Administration
Region 7
819 Taylor Street, Room 11A09
Ft. Worth, TX 76102
817-978-2331
Fax: 817-978-2063

Connecticut
General Services Administration
Region 1
10 Causeway Street, Room 925
Boston, MA 02222
617-565-5700
Fax: 617-565-5720

Delaware
General Services Administration
Region 4
401 West Peachtree Street
Suite 2528
Atlanta, GA 30308
404-331-5133
Fax: 404-331-2727

District of Columbia
General Services Administration
Region 4
401 West Peachtree Street
Suite 2528
Atlanta, GA 30308
404-331-5133
Fax: 404-331-2727

Florida
General Services Administration
Region 4
401 West Peachtree Street
Suite 2528
Atlanta, GA 30308
404-331-5133
Fax: 404-331-2727

Georgia
General Services Administration
Region 4
401 West Peachtree Street
Suite 2528
Atlanta, GA 30308
404-331-5133
Fax: 404-331-2727

Hawaii
General Services Administration
Region 9
450 Golden Gate Avenue, 9PR
San Francisco, CA 94102
888-GSA-LAND
Fax: 415-522-3213

Idaho
General Services Administration
Region 10
400 15th Street, Room 1161

Auburn, WA 98001
253-931-7547
Fax: 253-931-7554

Illinois
General Services Administration
Region 5
230 South Dearborn Street
Room 3774
Chicago, IL 60604
312-353-6045
Fax: 312-353-0901

Indiana
General Services Administration
Region 5
230 South Dearborn Street
Room 3774
Chicago, IL 60604
312-353-6045
Fax: 312-353-0901

Iowa
General Services Administration
Region 7
819 Taylor Street, Room 11A09
Ft. Worth, TX 76102
817-978-2331
Fax: 817-978-2063

Kansas
General Services Administration
Region 7
819 Taylor Street, Room 11A09
Ft. Worth, TX 76102
817-978-2331
Fax: 817-978-2063

Kentucky
General Services Administration
Region 4
401 West Peachtree Street
Suite 2528
Atlanta, GA 30308
404-331-5133
Fax: 404-331-2727

Louisiana
General Services Administration
Region 7
819 Taylor Street
Room 11A09
Ft. Worth, TX 76102
817-978-2331
Fax: 817-978-2063

Maine
General Services Administration
Region 1
10 Causeway Street, Room 925
Boston, MA 02222
617-565-5700
Fax: 617-565-5720

Maryland
General Services Administration
Region 4
401 West Peachtree Street
Suite 2528
Atlanta, GA 30308
404-331-5133
Fax: 404-331-2727

Massachusetts
General Services Administration
Region 1
10 Causeway Street, Room 925
Boston, MA 02222
617-565-5700
Fax: 617-565-5720

Michigan
General Services Administration
Region 5
230 South Dearborn Street
Room 3774
Chicago, IL 60604
312-353-6045
Fax: 312-353-0901

Minnesota
General Services Administration
Region 5
230 South Dearborn Street
Room 3774
Chicago, IL 60604
312-353-6045
Fax: 312-353-0901

Mississippi
General Services Administration
Region 4
401 West Peachtree Street
Suite 2528
Atlanta, GA 30308
404-331-5133
Fax: 404-331-2727

Missouri
General Services Administration
Region 7

819 Taylor Street, Room 11A09
Ft. Worth, TX 76102
817-978-2331
Fax: 817-978-2063

Montana
General Services Administration
Region 7
819 Taylor Street, Room 11A09
Ft. Worth, TX 76102
817-978-2331
Fax: 817-978-2063

Nebraska
General Services Administration
Region 7
819 Taylor Street, Room 11A09
Ft. Worth, TX 76102
817-978-2331
Fax: 817-978-2063

Nevada
General Services Administration
Region 9
450 Golden Gate Avenue, 9PR
San Francisco, CA 94102
888-GSA-LAND
Fax: 415-522-3213

New Hampshire
General Services Administration
Region 1
10 Causeway Street, Room 925
Boston, MA 02222
617-565-5700
Fax: 617-565-5720

New Jersey
General Services Administration
Region 1
10 Causeway Street, Room 925
Boston, MA 02222
617-565-5700
Fax: 617-565-5720

New Mexico
General Services Administration
Region 7
819 Taylor Street, Room 11A09
Ft. Worth, TX 76102
817-978-2331
Fax: 817-978-2063

New York
General Services Administration

Region 1
10 Causeway Street, Room 925
Boston, MA 02222
617-565-5700
Fax: 617-565-5720

North Carolina
General Services Administration
Region 4
401 West Peachtree Street
Suite 2528
Atlanta, GA 30308
404-331-5133
Fax: 404-331-2727

North Dakota
General Services Administration
Region 7
819 Taylor Street, Room 11A09
Ft. Worth, TX 76102
817-978-2331
Fax: 817-978-2063

Ohio
General Services Administration
Region 5
230 South Dearborn Street
Room 3774
Chicago, IL 60604
312-353-6045
Fax: 312-353-0901

Oklahoma
General Services Administration
Region 7
819 Taylor Street
Room 11A09
Ft. Worth, TX 76102
817-978-2331
Fax: 817-978-2063

Oregon
General Services Administration
Region 10
400 15th Street, Room 1161
Auburn, WA 98001
253-931-7547
Fax: 253-931-7554

Pennsylvania
General Services Administration
Region 4
401 West Peachtree Street
Suite 2528

Atlanta, GA 30308
404-331-5133
Fax: 404-331-2727

Puerto Rico/Virgin Islands
General Services Administration
Region 1
10 Causeway Street, Room 925
Boston, MA 02222
617-565-5700
Fax: 617-565-5720

Rhode Island
General Services Administration
Region 1
10 Causeway Street, Room 925
Boston, MA 02222
617-565-5700
Fax: 617-565-5720

South Carolina
General Services Administration
Region 4
401 West Peachtree St, Suite 2528
Atlanta, GA 30308
404-331-5133
Fax: 404-331-2727

South Dakota
General Services Administration
Region 7
819 Taylor Street, Room 11A09
Ft. Worth, TX 76102
817-978-2331
Fax: 817-978-2063

Tennessee
General Services Administration
Region 4
401 West Peachtree St, Suite 2528
Atlanta, GA 30308
404-331-5133
Fax: 404-331-2727

Texas
General Services Administration
Region 7
819 Taylor Street, Room 11A09
Ft. Worth, TX 76102
817-978-2331
Fax: 817-978-2063

Utah
General Services Administration
Region 7
819 Taylor Street, Room 11A09
Ft. Worth, TX 76102
817-978-2331
Fax: 817-978-2063

Vermont
General Services Administration
Region 1
10 Causeway Street, Room 925
Boston, MA 02222
617-565-5700
Fax: 617-565-5720

Virginia
General Services Administration
Region 4

401 West Peachtree Street
Suite 2528
Atlanta, GA 30308
404-331-5133
Fax: 404-331-2727

Washington
General Services Administration
Region 10
400 15th Street, Room 1161
Auburn, WA 98001
253-931-7547
Fax: 253-931-7554

West Virginia
General Services Administration
Region 4
401 West Peachtree Street
Suite 2528
Atlanta, GA 30308

404-331-5133
Fax: 404-331-2727

Wisconsin
General Services Administration
Region 5
230 South Dearborn Street
Room 3774
Chicago, IL 60604
312-353-6045
Fax: 312-353-0901

Wyoming
General Services Administration
Region 7
819 Taylor Street, Room 11A09
Ft. Worth, TX 76102
817-978-2331
Fax: 817-978-2063

They Are Not Just For Businesses

The Small Business Administration (SBA) is known for their business programs, but they do acquire homes and businesses when someone defaults on a loan. Property acquired by the U.S. Small Business Administration while administering its loan programs is available for purchase by the public. The property ranges from real estate: commercial property, single family homes, vacant land, farms, and personal property: machinery, equipment, furniture, fixtures and inventory. The property list refers to an associated SBA Office and contact person.

For more information, call the listed contact person. If the contact person is not available, we suggest that you call or visit the nearest SBA office.

SBA Headquarters
409 Third St., SW
Washington, DC 20416
800-U-ASK-SBA
http://app1.sba.gov/pfsales/dsp_search.html

SBA District Offices

Alabama
Alabama District Office
801 Tom Martin Drive
Suite 201
Birmingham, AL 35211
205-290-7101
Fax: 205-290-7404
http://www.sba.gov/al/

Alaska
Alaska District Office
510 L Street, Suite 310
Anchorage, AK 99501
907-271-4022
Fax 907-271-4545
Tool-free outside Anchorage
800-755-7034
http://www.sba.gov/ak/

Arizona
Arizona District Office
2828 N. Central Ave, Suite 800
Phoenix, AZ 85004-1093
602-745-7200
Fax: 602-745-7210
http://www.sba.gov/az/

Arkansas
Arkansas District Office
2120 Riverfront Drive, Suite 100
Little Rock, AR 72202-1794
501-324-5871
Fax: 501-324-5199
http://www.sba.gov/ar/

California
California District Office- Fresno
2719 N. Air Fresno Dr, Suite 200
Fresno, CA 93727
800-359-1833
559-487-5791
Fax: 559-487-5636
http://www.sba.gov/ca/fresno/
The Fresno District Office serves
the counties of Alpine,
Fresno, Inyo, Kern, Kings,
Madera, Mariposa, Merced,
Mono, Monterey, San Benito,
San Luis Obispo,
Stanislaus, Tulare and
Tuolumne.

California District Office- Los
Angeles
330 North Brand, Suite 1200
Glendale, California 91203
818-552-3210
http://www.sba.gov/ca/la/
The Los Angeles District Office
serves the counties of Los
Angeles, Santa Barbara, and
Ventura.

California District Office-
Sacramento
650 Capital Mall, Suite 7-500
Sacramento, CA 95814
916-930-3700
Fax: 916-930-3737
http://www.sba.gov/ca/sacr/
The Sacramento District Office
serves the counties of Amador,
Butte, Calaveras, Colusa, El
Dorado, Glenn, Lassen, Modoc,
Nevada, Placer, Plumas,
Sacramento, San Joaquin, Shasta,
Sierra, Siskiyou, Sutter, Tehama,
Trinity, Yolo, and Yuba.

California District Office- San
Diego
550 West "C" Street - Suite 550
San Diego, CA 92101-3500
619-557-7250
Fax: 619-557-5894
http://www.sba.gov/ca/sandie
go/
The San Diego District Office
serves the counties of Imperial
and San Diego.

California District Office- San
Francisco
455 Market Street, 6th Floor
San Francisco, CA 94105-2420
415-744-6820
http://www.sba.gov/ca/sf/

Santa Ana, CA District Office
200 W. Santa Ana Blvd.
Santa Ana, CA 92701
714-550-7420
Fax 714-550-0191
http://www.sba.gov/ca/santa/

The Santa Ana District Office
serves the counties of Orange,
Riverside, and San Bernardino.

Colorado
Colorado District Office
721 19th Street, Suite 426
Denver, CO 80202-2517
Phone: 303-844-2607
Fax: 303-844-6468
http://www.sba.gov/co/

Connecticut
Connecticut District Office
330 Main Street, 2nd Floor
Hartford, CT 06106-1800
860-240-4700
Fax: 860-240-4659
http://www.sba.gov/ct/

District of Columbia
District of Columbia District
Office
1110 Vermont Avenue, NW.
9th Floor
Washington, D.C. 20005
202-606-4000
http://www.sba.gov/dc/

Delaware
Delaware District Office
824 N. Market St.
Wilmington, DE 19801-3011
302-573-6294
Fax: 302-573-6060
http://www.sba.gov/de/

Florida
Florida District Office North
7825 Baymeadows Way
Suite 100B
Jacksonville, FL 32256-7504
904-443-1900
http://www.sba.gov/fl/north/

Florida District Office South
100 S. Biscayne Blvd – 7th Floor
Miami, FL 33131
305-536-5521
Fax: 305-536-5058
http://www.sba.gov/fl/south/

Georgia

Georgia District Office
233 Peachtree St. NE, Suite 1900
Atlanta, GA 30303
404-331-0100
http://www.sba.gov/ga/

Guam

Guam District Office
400 Route 8, Suite 302
First Hawaiian Bank Building
Mongmong, GU 96927
671-472-7419
Fax: 671-472-7365
http://www.sba.gov/gu/

Hawaii

Hawaii District Office
300 Ala Moana Blvd
Room 2-235
Box 50207
Honolulu, HI 96850
808-541-2990
Fax: 808-541-2976
http://www.sba.gov/hi/

Idaho

Idaho District Office
Alaska Center Building
1020 Main Street, Suite 290
Boise, ID 83702-5745
208-334-1696 ext. 234
Fax: 208-334-9353
http://www.sba.gov/id/

Illinois

Illinois District Office
500 W. Madison St, Suite 1250
Chicago, IL 60661-2511
312-353-4528
Fax: 312-886-5688
http://www.sba.gov/il/

Indiana

Indiana District Office
429 North Pennsylvania Street
Suite 100
Indianapolis, IN 46204-1873
317-226-7272
Fax: 317-226-7264
http://www.sba.gov/in/

Iowa

Iowa District Office- Cedar
Rapids

215 4th Ave SE, Suite 200
Cedar Rapids IA 52401-1806
319-362-6405
http://www.sba.gov/ia/cedar/

Iowa District Office- Des Moines
210 Walnut St, Room 749
Des Moines IA 50309-2186
515-284-4422
http://www.sba.gov/ia/desmo/

Kansas

Kansas District Office
271 West Third Street North
Suite 2500
Wichita, KS 67202-1212
316-269-6616
Fax: 316-269-6499
http://www.sba.gov/ks/

Kentucky

Kentucky District Office
600 Dr. MLK Jr. PL
Louisville, KY 40202
502-582-5761
http://www.sba.gov/ky/

Louisiana

Louisiana District Office
365 Canal St., Suite 2820
New Orleans, LA 70130
504-589-6685
http://www.sba.gov/la/

Maine

Maine District Office
40 Western Avenue
Augusta, ME 04330
207-622-8274
Fax: 207-622-8277
http://www.sba.gov/me/

Maryland

Maryland District Office
City Crescent Building, 6th Floor
10 South Howard Street
Baltimore, MD 21201
410-962-4392
Fax: 410-962-1805
http://www.sba.gov/md/

Massachusetts

Massachusetts District Office
10 Causeway Street, Room-265
Boston, MA 02222-1093

617-565-5590
Fax: 617-565-5598
http://www.sba.gov/ma/

Michigan

Michigan District Office
Patrick V. McNamara Building
477 Michigan Avenue, Suite 515
Detroit, MI 48226
313-226-6075
Fax: 313-226-4769
http://www.sba.gov/mi/

Minnesota

Minnesota District Office
100 North Sixth Street, Suite 210-
C Butler Square
Minneapolis, MN 55403
612-370-2324
Fax: 612-370-2303
http://www.sba.gov/mn/

Mississippi

Mississippi District Office
AmSouth Bank Plaza
210 E. Capitol Street, Suite 900
Jackson, MS 39201
601-965-4378
Fax: 601-965-5629
http://www.sba.gov/ms/

Missouri

Kansas District Office
323 West 8th Street, Suite 501
Kansas City, MO 64105
816-374-6708
Fax: 816-374-6759
http://www.sba.gov/mo/kansas/

Missouri District Office
200 North Broadway, Suite 1500
St. Louis, MO 63102
314-539-6600
Fax: 314-539-3785
http://www.sba.gov/mo/stlouis/

Montana

Montana District Office
Federal Building
10 West 15th Street, Suite 1100
Helena, MT 59626
406-441-1081
http://www.sba.gov/mt/

Nebraska

Nebraska District Office
11145 Mill Valley Rd
Omaha, NE 68154
402-221-4691
Fax: 402-221-3680
http://www.sba.gov/ne/

Nevada

Nevada District Office
300 Las Vegas Boulevard South
Suite 1100
Las Vegas, NV 89101
702-388-6611
Fax: 702-388-6469
http://www.sba.gov/nv/

New Hampshire

New Hampshire District Office
143 N. Main St
Concord, NH 03301
603-225-1400
Fax: 603-225-1409
http://www.sba.gov/nh/

New Jersey

New Jersey District Office
Two Gateway Center, 15th Floor
Newark, NJ 07102
973-645-2434
http://www.sba.gov/nj/

New Mexico

New Mexico District Office
625 Silver SW Suite 320
Albuquerque, NM 87102
505-346-7909
Fax: 505-346-6711
http://www.sba.gov/nm/

New York

New York District Office-Buffalo
111 West Huron St, Suite 1311
Buffalo, NY 14202
716-551-4301
Fax: 716-551-4418
http://www.sba.gov/ny/buffalo/

New York District Office-New
York
26 Federal Plaza, Suite 3100
New York, NY 10278
212-264-4354
Fax: 212-264-4963
http://www.sba.gov/ny/ny/

The San Diego District Office
serves the counties of Bronx,
Dutchess, Kings, Manhattan,
Nassau, Orange, Putnam,
Queens, Richmond, Rockland,
Suffolk, Sullivan, Ulster and
Westchester.

North Carolina

North Carolina District Office
6302 Fairview Road, Suite 300
Charlotte, NC 28210-2227
704-344-6563
Fax: 704-344-6769
http://www.sba.gov/nc/

North Dakota

North Dakota District Office
657 Second Avenue North
Room 219
Fargo, ND 58108
701-239-5131
Fax: 701-239-5645
http://www.sba.gov/nd/

Ohio

Ohio District Office-Cleveland
1111 Superior Avenue, Suite 630
Cleveland, OH 44114-2507
216-522-4180
Fax: 216-522-2038
http://www.sba.gov/oh/clevel
and/

Ohio District Office-Columbus
2 Nationwide Plaza, Suite 1400
Columbus, OH 43215-2542
614-469-6860
Fax: 614-469-2391
http://www.sba.gov/oh/colum
bus/

Oklahoma

Oklahoma District Office
210 Park Avenue, Suite 1300
Oklahoma City, OK 73102
405-231-5521
Fax: 405-231-4876
http://www.sba.gov/ok/

Oregon

Oregon District Office
1515 SW 5th Avenue, Suite 1050
Portland, OR 97201-5494
503-326-2682

Fax: 503-326-2808
http://www.sba.gov/or/

Pennsylvania

Pennsylvania District Office-
Philadelphia
Robert N.C. Nix Federal
Building
900 Market Street, 5th Floor
Philadelphia, PA 19107
215-580-2SBA
Fax: 215-580-2762
http://www.sba.gov/pa/phil/

Pennsylvania District Office-
Pittsburgh
Federal Building - Room 1128
1000 Liberty Avenue
Pittsburgh, PA 15222
412-395-6560
Fax: 412-395-6562
http://www.sba.gov/pa/pitt/

Puerto Rico

Puerto Rico District Office
252 Ponce De Leon Ave.
Citibank Tower, Suite 201
Hato Rey, PR 00918
787-766-5572
800-669-8049
Fax: 787-766-5309
http://www.sba.gov/pr/

Rhode Island

Rhode Island District Office
380 Westminster Street
Providence, RI 02903
401-528-4561
Fax: 401-528-4539
http://www.sba.gov/ri/

South Carolina

South Carolina District Office
1835 Assembly Street, Room 358
Columbia, SC 29201
803-765-5377
Fax: 803-765-5962
http://www.sba.gov/sc/

South Dakota

South Dakota District Office
110 S. Phillips Avenue, Suite 200
Sioux Falls SD 57104-6727
605-330-4231
http://www.sba.gov/sd/

TENNESSEE

Tennessee District Office
50 Vantage Way, Suite 201
Nashville, TN 37228
615-736-5881
Fax: 615-736-7232
http://www.sba.gov/tn/

TEXAS

Texas District Office-
Dallas/Fort Worth
4300 Amon Carter Blvd.
Suite 114
Fort Worth, TX 75155
817-684-5500
Fax: 817-684-5516
http://www.sba.gov/tx/dallas/
The Dallas/Fort Worth District
Office serves the counties of
Anderson, Archer, Baylor, Bell,
Bosque, Bowie, Brown, Callahan,
Camp, Cass, Cherokee, Clay,
Coleman, Collin, Comanche,
Cooke, Coryell, Dallas, Delta,
Eastland, Ellis, Erath, Falls,
Fannin, Franklin, Freestone,
Grayson, Gregg, Hamilton,
Harrison, Henderson, Hill,
Hood, Hipkins, Hunt, Jack,
Johnson, Kaufman, Lamar,
Limestone, Marion, McLennan,
Mills, Montague, Morris,
Nacogdoches, Navarro, Palo
Pinto, Panola, Parker, Rains, Red
River, Rockwall, Rusk,
Schackelford, Sabine, San
Augustine, Shelby, Smith,
Somervell, Stephens, Tarrant,
Throckmorton, Titus, Upshur,
Van Zandt, Wichita, Wilbarger,
Wise, Wood, and Young.

Texas District Office-El Paso
10737 Gateway West
El Paso, TX 79935
915-633-7001
Fax: 915-633-7005
http://www.sba.gov/tx/elpaso/
The El Paso District Office serves
the counties of Brewster,
Culberson, Hudspeth, El Paso,
Jeff Davis, Loving, Pecos,
Presidio, Reeves, Terrell and
Ward.

Texas District Office-Harlingen
222 East Van Buren St, Suite 500
Harlingen, TX 78550
956-427-8533
Fax: 956-427-8537
http://www.sba.gov/tx/harlin
gen/
The Harlingen District Office
serves the counties of The Lower
Rio Grande Valley serves;
Cameron, Hidalgo, Jim Hogg,
Kenedy, Starr, Willacy, and
Zapata counties in southern
Texas.

Texas District Office-Houston
8701 S. Gessner Drive, Suite 1200
Houston, TX 77074
713-773-6500
Fax: 713-773.6550
http://www.sba.gov/tx/hous/
The Houston District Office
serves the counties of Angelina,
Austin, Brazos, Burleson,
Chambers, Colorado, Fort Bend,
Galveston, Grimes, Hardin,
Harris, Houston, Jasper,
Jefferson, Leon, Liberty,
Madison, Matagorda, Milam,
Montgomery, Newton, Orange,
Polk, Robertson, San Jacinto,
Trinity, Tyler, Waller, Walker,
Washington, Wharton

Texas District Office-Lubbock
1205 Texas Avenue, Room 408
Lubbock, TX 79401-2693
806-472-7462
Fax: 800-676-1005
http://www.sba.gov/tx/lubbock/
The Lubbock District Office
serves the counties of Andrews,
Armstrong, Bailey, Borden,
Briscoe, Carson, Castro,
Childress, Cochran, Coke,
Collinsworth, Cottle, Crane,
Crosby, Dallum, Dawson, Deaf
Smith, Dickens, Donley, Ector,
Fisher, Floyd, Foard, Gaines,
Garza, Glasscock, Gray, Hale,
Hall, Hansford, Hardman,
Hartley, Haskell. Hutchinson,
Jones, Kent, King, Knox, Lamb,
Lipscomb, Lubbock, Lynn,
Martin, Midland, Mitchell,
Moore, Motley, Nolan, Ochil

Tree, Oldham, Parmer, Potter,
Randall, Reagan, Roberts,
Runnels, Scurry, Sherman,
Sterling, Stonewall, Swisher,
Taylor, Terry, Upton, Ward,
Wheeler, Winkler, and Yoakum.

Texas District Office-San
Antonio
727 E. Durango, Room A-527
San Antonio, TX 78206.
210-472-5900.
http://www.sba.gov/tx/sanant
onio/
The San Antonio District Office
serves the counties of Atascosa
Bandera Bastrop Bee Bexar
Blanco Burnet Caldwell Calhoun
Concho Comal Crockett DeWitt
Dimmit, Edwards, Fayette, Frio,
Gillespie, Goliad, Gonzales,
Guadalupe, Hays, Irion, Jackson,
Karnes, Kendall, Kimble,
Kinney, Kerr, La Salle,
Lampasas, Lavaca, Lee, Live
Oak, Llano, Mason, Maverick,
McCulloch, McMullen, Medina,
Menard, Real, San Saba,
Schleicher, Sutton, Tom Green,
Travis, Uvalde, Val Verde,
Victoria, Webb, Williamson,
Wilson, Zavala.

UTAH

Utah District Office
125 South State St, Room 2231
Salt Lake City, UT 84138
801-524-3209
Fax: 801-524-4160 or 4410
http://www.sba.gov/ut/

VERMONT

Vermont District Office
87 State Street, Room 205
Montpelier, VT 05602
802-828-4422
http://www.sba.gov/vt/

VIRGINIA

Virginia District Office
400 North 8th Street, Suite 1150
Richmond, VA 23240
Phone: 804-771-2400
http://www.sba.gov/va/

Washington
Washington District Office-
Seattle
1200 Sixth Avenue, Suite 1700
Seattle, WA 98101-1128
206-553-7310
http://www.sba.gov/wa/seattle/

Washington District Office-
Spokane
801 W. Riverside Ave, Suite 200
Spokane, WA 99201
509-353-2800
http://www.sba.gov/wa/spoka
ne/

Wisconsin
Wisconsin District Office-
Madison
740 Regent Street, Suite 100
Madison, WI 53715
608-441-5263
Fax: 608-441-5541
http://www.sba.gov/wi/

Wisconsin District Office-
Spokane
310 West Wisconsin Ave
Suite 400

Milwaukee, WI 53203
414-297-3941
Fax: 414-297-1377
http://www.sba.gov/wi/

Wyoming
Wyoming District Office
100 East B Street
Rm 4001, Box 2839
Casper, WY 82602
307-261-6500
Fax: 307-261-6535
http://www.sba.gov/wy/

Buy a Home from the U.S. Department of Agriculture

The U. S. Department of Agriculture Rural
Development Office has single-family foreclosed
housing available for sale to the public. These
houses are available in any state and many
counties within the state. Check the current lists
of homes available by going to the web site and
clicking on the state you are interested in finding
a home. {http://www.resales.usda.gov/}.

The site will give you information on the location
of the property and other property details
sometimes even including a picture. Your state
office can refer you to your area and local offices
that may have other information on foreclosed properties near you. See Page 111 for a
complete listing of local rural housing offices.

National Office
Rural Housing Service National Office
U.S. Department of Agriculture
Room 5037, South Building
14th Street and Independence Ave, SW
Washington, D.C. 20250
202-720-4323
www.rurdev.usda.gov/rhs/

*National Centralized Servicing
Center*
1520 Market Street
St. Louis, MO 63103
800-414-1226

State Contacts

Alabama
State Office
Alabama USDA Rural
Development Office
Suite 601, Sterling Centre
4121 Carmichael Road
Montgomery, AL 36106-3683
334-279-3400
Fax: 334-279-3403
TDD/TTY: 334-279-3495
http://www.rurdev.usda.gov/a
l/index.html

Alaska
Rural Development State Office
800 West Evergreen, Suite 201
Palmer, AK 99645
907-761-7705
Fax: 907-761-7783
http://www.rurdev.usda.gov/a
k/index.html

America Samoa, Hawaii and Western Pacific
(See Hawaii)
American Samoa Local Office
USDA Rural Development
Pago Plaza, Suite 203
P. O. Box 2447
Pago Pago, AS 96799-2447
011-684-633-1131
Fax: 011-684-633-4329

Arizona
USDA Rural Development
Rural Housing Program State
Office
3003 N. Central Ave, Suite 900
Phoenix, AZ 85012 -2906
602-280-8755
Fax: 602-280-8879
http://www.rurdev.usda.gov/a
z/index.html

Arkansas
USDA Service Center State
Office
700 West Capitol, Room 3416
Little Rock, AR 72201-3225
501-301-3200
Fax: 501-301-3278
http://www.rurdev.usda.gov/a
r/index.html

California
USDA Rural Development State
Office
430 G Street, #4169
Davis, CA 95616-4169
530-792-5800 ext. 1
Fax: 530-792-5838
http://www.rurdev.usda.gov/c
a/index.html

Colorado
Rural Development State Office
Lakewood State Office
655 Parfet Street, Room E-100
Lakewood, CO 80215
720-544-2903
800-659-3656
TTY 720-544-2976
http://www.rurdev.usda.gov/c
o/index.html

Connecticut (Southern New England)
Rural Development State Office
451 West Street, Suite 2
Amherst MA 01002-2999
413-253-4300
Fax: 413-253-4347
http://www.rurdev.usda.gov/
ma/index.html

Delaware
Delaware USDA Rural
Development
4607 South DuPont Highway
Post Office Box 400
Camden, DE 19934
302-697-4300
Fax: 302-697-4390
http://www.rurdev.usda.gov/d
e/index.html

Florida/Virgin Islands
USDA Rural Development State
Office
4440 NW 25th Place
Gainesville, FL 32606
352-338-3402
Fax: 352-338-3405
http://www.rurdev.usda.gov/fl
/index.html

Georgia
USDA Rural Development State
Office
Stephens Federal Building
335 East Hancock Avenue
Athens, GA 30601-2768
706-546-2162
Fax: 706-546-2152
http://www.rurdev.usda.gov/g
a/index.html

Hawaii, American Samoa, Western Pacific
Rural Development Area Office
Room 311, Federal Building
154 Waianuenue Avenue
Hilo, HI 96720
808-933-8380
Fax: 808-933-8327
http://www.rurdev.usda.gov/h
i/index.html

Idaho
Idaho State Office
USDA Rural Development
9173 West Barnes, Suite A 1
Boise, ID 83709
208-378-5600
Fax: 208-378-5643
http://www.rurdev.usda.gov/i
d/index.html

Illinois
USDA Rural Development State
Office
2118 West Park Court, Suite A
Champaign, IL 61821
217-403-6202
Fax 217-403-6243
http://www.rurdev.usda.gov/il
/index.html

Indiana
State Office
Indiana USDA Rural
Development
5975 Lakeside Boulevard
Indianapolis, IN 46278
317-290-3100 (extension 400)
Fax: 317-290-3095
http://www.rurdev.usda.gov/i
n/index.html

Iowa
Iowa USDA Rural Development
State Office
210 Walnut Street, Room 873
Des Moines, IA 50309-2196

515-284-4663
Fax: 515-284-4821
http://www.rurdev.usda.gov/i
a/index.html

Kansas
USDA - Rural Development
State Office
1303 First American Place
Suite 100
Topeka, KS 66604
785-271-2700
Fax: 785-271-2708
http://www.rurdev.usda.gov/k
s/index.html

Kentucky
USDA Rural Development State
Office
771 Corporate Drive, Suite 200
Lexington, KY 40503
859-224-7300
Fax: 859-224-7425
http://www.rurdev.usda.gov/k
y/index.html

Louisiana
USDA, Rural Development
LA State Office
3727 Government Street
Alexandria, LA 71302
318-473-7921
Fax: 318-473-7963
http://www.rurdev.usda.gov/l
a/index.html

Maine
State Office
USDA Rural Development
967 Illinois Avenue
P.O. Box 405
Bangor, ME 04402-0405
207-990-9100
Fax: 207-990-9165
http://www.rurdev.usda.gov/
me/index.html

Maryland
MD USDA Rural Development
4607 South DuPont Highway
Post Office Box 400
Camden, DE 19934
302-697-4300
Fax: 302-697-4390
http://www.rurdev.usda.gov/
md/index.html

Massachusetts (Southern
New England)
Rural Development State Office
451 West Street, Suite 2
Amherst MA 01002-2999
413-253-4300
Fax: 413-253-4347
http://www.rurdev.usda.gov/
ma/index.html

Michigan
East Lansing, State Office
3001 Coolidge Road, Suite 200
East Lansing, MI 48823
517-324-5210
Fax: 517-324-5225
http://www.rurdev.usda.gov/
mi/index.html

Minnesota
Rural Development State Office
410 Farm Credit Service Building
375 Jackson Street
St. Paul, MN 55101-1853
651-602-7800
Fax: 651-602-7824
http://www.rurdev.usda.gov/
mn/index.html

Mississippi
USDA Rural Development State
Office
100 West Capitol St., Suite 831
Federal Building
Jackson, MS 39269
601-965-4318
Fax: 601-965-5384
http://www.rurdev.usda.gov/
ms/index.html

Missouri
USDA Rural Development State
Office
601 Business Loop 70 West
Parkade Center, Suite 235
Columbia, MO 65203
573-876-0976
Fax: 573-876-0977
http://www.rurdev.usda.gov/
mo/index.html

Montana
USDA Rural Development State
Office
P.O. Box 850

Bozeman, MT 59771
406-585-2580
Fax: 406-585-2565
http://www.rurdev.usda.gov/
mt/index.html

Nebraska
USDA Rural Development State
Office
Federal Building Room 152
100 Centennial Mall North
Lincoln, NE 68508.
402-437-5551
Fax: 402-437-5408
http://www.rurdev.usda.gov/n
e/index.html

Nevada
USDA Rural Development State
Office
1390 S. Curry Street
Carson City, NV 89703
775-887-1222
Fax: 775-885-0841
http://www.rurdev.usda.gov/n
v/index.html

New Hampshire
USDA Rural Development State
Office
Suite 218, Box 317
10 Ferry Street
Concord, NH 03301-5004
603-223-6035
Fax: 603-223-6061
http://www.rurdev.usda.gov/n
h/index.html

New Jersey
Rural Development State Office
5th Floor North, Suite 500
8000 Midlantic Drive
Mt. Laurel, NJ 08054
856-787-7700
Fax: 856-787-7783
http://www.rurdev.usda.gov/n
j/index.html

New Mexico
USDA Rural Housing State
Office
6200 Jefferson NE, Room 255
Albuquerque, NM 87109
505-761-4944
Fax: 505-761-4976

http://www.rurdev.usda.gov/nm/index.html

New York
Syracuse State Office
441 S Salina St
Syracuse, NY 13202-2405
315-477-6518
Fax: 315-477-6550
http://www.rurdev.usda.gov/ny/index.html

North Carolina
USDA Rural Development State Office
4405 Bland Road
Raleigh, NC 27609
919-873-2000
Fax: 919-873-2075
http://www.rurdev.usda.gov/nc/index.html

North Dakota
USDA Rural Development State Office
Federal Building, Room 208
220 East Rosser Ave.
P.O. Box 1737
Bismarck, ND 58502
701-530-2037
Fax: 701-530-2108
http://www.rurdev.usda.gov/nd/index.html

Ohio
USDA Rural Development
Federal Building, Room 507
200 North High Street
Columbus, OH 43215
614-255-2500
http://www.rurdev.usda.gov/oh/index.html

Oklahoma
USDA Rural Development State Office
100 USDA, Suite 108
Stillwater, OK 74074
405-742-1000
Fax: 405-742-1005
http://www.rurdev.usda.gov/ok/index.html

Oregon
USDA Rural Development State Office
101 SW Main, Suite 1410
Portland, OR 97204-3222
503-414-3300
Fax: 503-414-3392
http://www.rurdev.usda.gov/or/index.html

Pennsylvania
USDA Rural Development State Office
Suite 330, One Credit Union Pl.
Harrisburg, PA 17110-2996
717-237-2186
Fax: 717-237-2193
http://www.rurdev.usda.gov/pa/index.html

Puerto Rico
USDA Rural Development State Office
IBM Building
654 Munoz Rivera Ave, Suite 601
San Juan, PR 00918
787-766-5095
Fax: 787-766-5844
http://www.rurdev.usda.gov/pr/index.html

Rhode Island
Southern New England
Rural Development State Office
451 West Street, Suite 2
Amherst MA 01002-2999
413-253-4300
Fax: 413-253-4347
http://www.rurdev.usda.gov/ma/index.html

South Carolina
USDA Rural Development State Office
Strom Thurmond Federal Bldg.
1835 Assembly St, Room 1007
Columbia, SC, 29201
803-765-5163
Fax: 803-765-5633
http://www.rurdev.usda.gov/sc/index.html

South Dakota
USDA Rural Development State Office
200 4th Street SW
Federal Building, Room 210
Huron, SD 57350
605-352-1100
Fax: 605-352-1146
http://www.rurdev.usda.gov/sd/index.html

Tennessee
USDA Rural Development State Office
3322 West End Ave, Suite 300
Nashville, TN 37203
615-783-1300
Toll Free: 800-342-3149
Fax: 615-783-1301
http://www.rurdev.usda.gov/tn/index.html

Texas
Texas USDA Rural Development State Office
101 South Main Street, Suite 102
Temple, TX 76501
254-742-9700
Fax: 254-742-9709
http://www.rurdev.usda.gov/tx/index.html

Utah
USDA Rural Development State Office
Wallace F. Bennett Federal Bldg.
Room 4311, 125 South State St
P.O. Box 11350
Salt Lake City, UT 84147-0350
801-524-4321
Fax: 801-524-4406
http://www.rurdev.usda.gov/ut/index.html

Vermont
Montpelier Office Staff
3rd Floor, City Center
89 Main Street
Montpelier, VT 05602
802-828-6010
Fax: 802-828-6076
http://www.rurdev.usda.gov/vt/index.html

Virginia
USDA Rural Development State Office
Culpeper Building, Suite 238
1606 Santa Rosa Road
Richmond, VA 23229
804-287-1552

Fax: 804-287-1718
http://www.rurdev.usda.gov/va/index.html

Washington
USDA Rural Development State Office
1835 Black Lake Boulevard SW, Suite B
Olympia, WA 98501-5715
360-704-7740
Fax: 360-704-7742
http://www.rurdev.usda.gov/wa/index.html

West Virginia
USDA Rural Development State Office
75 High Street, Room 320
Federal Building
Morgantown, WV 26505
304-284-4860
Fax: 304-284-4893
http://www.rurdev.usda.gov/wv/index.html

Wisconsin
USDA Rural Development State Office

4949 Kirschling Ct.
Stevens Point, WI 54481
715-345-7671
http://www.rurdev.usda.gov/wi/index.html

Wyoming
USDA Rural Development State Office
100 E. B Street, Room 1005
Casper, WY 82601
307-261-6300
Fax: 307-261-6327
http://www.rurdev.usda.gov/wy/index.html

Free Grants, Low Interest Loans, and Tax Credits to Renovate Historic Homes and Buildings

Renovating an old house can be very time consuming and expensive. If only there were a way to get someone else to pay for all that time consuming work...well, there is, if you know where to look. About 20 states offer some kind of grant or loan program for individual homeowners who are renovating historic homes. Here are a few examples:

- ◆ Iowa offers matching grants for renovation projects
- ◆ Kansas offers up to $75,000 in matching grants for renovation
- ◆ South Carolina offers up to $25,000 in matching grants
- ◆ Maryland offers low interest loans for historic renovation
- ◆ Tennessee offers 50/50 matching grants for renovation

To qualify for these grant and loan programs, you first need to have your house qualify for the National Register of Historic Places. This isn't as difficult as it might seem. Your house doesn't have to have national significance, such as at one time being George Washington's weekend retreat. It can have local historic or architectural significance to qualify for the National Register. It could be an early example of 18th century Greek Revival style—or have been owned at one time by a locally significant family. You'd be surprised how many older houses have some sort of local significance, and that might be just enough to qualify for these programs. Contact your State Office of Historic Preservation listed below for more information about how to get your property qualified for historic status.

Federal Tax Credits

If you happen to live in one of the 30 states that don't offer renovation grants to individual homeowners, you still may be able to qualify for some types of financial benefits. Under the Federal Tax Credit Program, individuals who have rehabilitated an income producing building used for commercial or industrial purposes can receive a 20% tax credit on expenses incurred during that renovation. To be eligible for funding, buildings must be listed on the National Register of Historic Places or be eligible for membership into that organization.

What this means is that if you renovate your house and use part of it to run your own business, like a gift shop, you may be able to receive a federal tax deduction of 20% of the renovation costs. If you spent $50,000 on renovations, that comes out to a $10,000 tax deduction on next year's taxes. Not bad. Not only would you get the benefit of writing off 20% of your renovation expenses, but you'll also be able to write off part of your mortgage as a business expense.

Nonprofits Get The Breaks

Starting up a nonprofit, or looking to relocate an existing one? Think of moving into an historic building in need of renovation. Most states offer nonprofits matching grant money and low interest loans to buy and renovate historic buildings. Yes, that's right — some states actually offer nonprofits money to buy historic buildings.

Check In Often

The availability of money for historic renovation changes from year to year, depending on the state in which you live. Just because your state isn't awarding grants or loans this year, they may change within the next year or two, so continue to check the resources. Don't forget that some states, like South Dakota and Iowa, allow renovating homeowners of historic places up to 8 years of not having to pay property taxes—in the long run that could be even better for you than getting grant money.

State Contacts

Alabama
Alta Cassady
State Historic Preservation Officer
Alabama Historical Commission
468 South Perry
Montgomery, AL 36104
334-242-3184
Fax: 334-240-3477
www.preserveala.org
Email: acassady@mail.preserveala.org
There are no state grant funds available to individual homeowners. However, owners of commercial property listed in the National Register of Historic Places are eligible for a 50% reduction in property taxes. Nonprofits, local government, and universities are eligible to apply for the Alabama Cultural Resources Preservation Trust Fund, a 50/50 matching grant program. Eligible funding categories include survey and registration, education and public awareness, planning for historic rehabilitation, and planning archaeological project and eligible projects are those that encourage good community

preservation. The agency also administers the Federal Rehabilitation Tax Credit Program. Individuals who have rehabilitated an income producing building used for commercial or industrial purposes can receive a 20% tax credit on eligible expenses incurred during renovation. To be eligible for funding, buildings must be listed on the National Register of Historic Places or be eligible for membership.

Alaska
Judith Bittner
State Historic Preservation Officer
Alaska Department of Natural Resources
Office of History and Archeology
550 West 7th Avenue, Suite 1310
Anchorage, AK 99501-3565
907-269-8721
Fax: 907-269-8908
www.dnr.state.ak.us/parks/oha_web
Email: oha@alaska.net
There are no funding programs available to individual property owners. Communities can

become eligible for matching grant funds for historic preservation activities through Alaska's Historic Preservation Program. In order to qualify, the community must first become a Certified Local Government. As such, they can share in the 10% of federal funds that are passed on to the State Historic Preservation Office. The Federal Tax Rehabilitation Tax Credit is also available, it offers a 20% tax credit on money spent on an eligible rehabilitation of an income producing building that will be used for commercial or industrial purposes. Buildings must be listed on the National Register of Historic Places or be eligible for membership to qualify.

Arizona

Joe Roth
State Historic Preservation Officer
Arizona State Parks
1300 West Washington
Phoenix, AZ 85007
602-542-4009
Fax: 602-542-4180
www.pr.state.az.us
Email: jroth@pr.state.az.us

Although $1.7 million is available in historical renovation grants, funds are not directly awarded to individual property owners. Homeowners must have the support of a sponsoring agency to apply for funding. This may include a certified local government, nonprofit organization, Indian tribe, or a national register listed district or educational institution. Matching funds of 40% are usually required. The office also administers the Federal Investment Tax Credit Program. Through this program, individuals receive a 20% tax credit on expenses they incurred while rehabilitating an income producing building that will be used for commercial or industrial purposes. There is also a State property tax reduction program for non-income producing properties and a State property tax incentive program for commercial or industrial properties. Buildings must be listed on the National Register of Historic Places or be eligible for membership to qualify.

Arkansas

Cathie Matthews
State Historic Preservation Officer
Suite 1500 Tower Buildings
323 Center Street
Little Rock, AR 72201
501-324-9880
Fax: 501-324-9184
www.arkansaspreservation.org
Email: info@arkansaspreservation.org

Owners of historic homes can apply for a 50/50 matching grant from the Historic Preservation

Restoration Program. The property must be listed on the Arkansas Register of Historic Places and if the grant will make it eligible for the National Register of Historic Places, the owner must follow through with the listing. The Federal Rehabilitation Tax Credit Program offers a 20% tax credit to individuals who have spent money rehabilitating an income producing building to be used for commercial, industrial, or residential rental purposes. Federal tax deductions can be gained through the donation of a conservation easement of a historic structure. Buildings must be listed on the National Register of Historic Places to qualify for either of these benefits. The Arkansas city governments that participate in the Certified Local Government (CLG) program are eligible for federal pass-through grants. These funds can be used for local historic preservation projects which include the rehabilitation of local historic structures. Individuals that are currently renovating or considering a renovation can receive technical assistance. The agency will provide on-site visits, consultations, and explanations. While cemeteries are not generally included in the National Register of Historic Places, they can be eligible under some circumstances. The Cemetery Preservation Program will consider assistance to those cemeteries where there are a significant amount of older markers and where the graves contain people of historic importance, or if there is a distinctive design feature.

California

Dr. Knox Mellon
Acting State Historic Preservation Officer
Office of Historic Preservation
Department of Parks and Recreation
P.O. Box 942896
Sacramento, CA 94296-0001
916-653-6624
Fax: 916-653-9824
http://ohp.parks.ca.gov
Email: calshpo@ohp.parks.ca.gov

There are occasionally state grants available to nonprofit organizations, local governments, and educational organizations. Various cities in California are Certified Local Governments. As such, they are eligible for 10% of the federal funds given to this agency. That money is used for historic preservation activities in each of their communities. The Mills Act provides property tax relief for owners of historic buildings. If the owner pledges to rehabilitate and maintain the historical and architectural character of their building, for a 10-year period they may receive a property tax savings of around 50%. This is not a state program, it is adopted by city and county governments. Another program the agency administers is the Federal Historic Preservation Tax

Incentive program. Individuals who have rehabilitated an income producing building used for commercial or industrial purposes can receive a 20% tax credit on expenses incurred during renovation. To be eligible for funding, buildings must be listed on the National Register of Historic Places or be eligible for membership.

Colorado

Georgianna Contiguglia
State Historic Preservation Officer
Colorado Historical Society
1300 Broadway
Denver, CO 80203
303-866-3395
Fax: 303-866-2711
www.coloradohistory-oahp.org
The State Historical Fund awards grants to public and nonprofit entities. Individuals can obtain funding if they find a public or nonprofit organization to apply for and administer funds on their behalf. Eligible categories include acquisition and development, education, and survey and planning projects. Funding is divided into four types: 1) General Grant: Competitive grants from $10,000 or less to multi-year grants; 2) Preservation Initiative Grants: No dollar amount specified; 3) Historic Structure Assessment Grants: Non-competitive grants of $10,000 or less whose purpose is to prepare a historic building for assessment; 4) Emergency Grants: Non-competitive grants that generally do not exceed $10,000 for historic properties in danger of being destroyed or seriously damaged. The agency also administers the Colorado Historic Preservation Income Tax Credit. Approved preservation/ rehabilitation projects that cost more than $5,000 and are completed within a 24 month period can receive a 20% credit on state income taxes. Properties must be over 50 years old and listed on the State Register of Historic Places or be landmarked by a Certified Local Government. Another tax savings can be attained through the donation of a preservation easement to this agency. The property must be listed on the National or State Registers of Historic Places to be eligible. There is also the Federal Rehabilitation Tax Credit Program. This is a 20% tax credit on the expenses incurred during the renovation of an income producing building that is used for commercial or industrial purposes. The building must be listed on the National Register of Historic Places or be eligible for a membership.

Connecticut

John W. Shannahan
State Historic Preservation Officer
Connecticut Historical Commission
59 South Prospect Street

Hartford, CT 06106
860-566-3005
Fax: 860-566-5078
www.chc.state.ct.us
Email: cthist@neca.com
There are no state grants or loans for homeowner's renovation projects at this time. There is a state tax incentive program, but it is only available to corporations that purchase homes in certain census tracts. There is however, the Federal Rehabilitation Tax Credit Program. This is a 20% tax credit on the expenses incurred during the renovation of an income producing building that is used for commercial or industrial purposes. The building must be listed on the National Register of Historic Places or be eligible for a membership. Another program available is the federally funded program called the Certified Local Government Program. The CLG's receive 10% of the funds passed on to the Historical Commission to be used for local restoration projects.

Delaware

Daniel R. Griffith
State Historic Preservation Officer
Division of Historical and Cultural Affairs
Hall of Records
P.O. Box 1401
406 Otis Drive
Dover, DE 19901
302-739-5313
Fax: 302-739-6711
www.state.de.us/shpo/index.htm
Email: dgriffith@state.de.us
There are no funding programs available to individuals. The office does administer the Federal Rehabilitation Tax Credit Program. Through this program individuals receive a 20% tax credit on expenses they incurred while rehabilitating a commercial or industrial building. Buildings must be listed on the National Register of Historic Places or be eligible for membership to qualify. The Certified Local Government Program is a federally funded program. The CLG's receive 10% of the funds passed on to the Department of Consumer and Regulatory Affairs to be used for local restoration projects.

District of Columbia

David Maloney, Deputy SHPO
Historic Preservation Division
801 N. Capitol St., NE, 3rd Floor
Washington, DC 20002
202-442-8818
Fax: 202-535-2497
www.planning.dc.gov/main.shtm
At this time there are no funds available from the District of Columbia for individuals to complete

restoration projects. However, the agency does administer the Federal Rehabilitation Tax Credit Program. Individuals who have rehabilitated an income producing building used for commercial or industrial purposes can receive a 20% tax credit on expenses incurred during renovation. To be eligible for funding, buildings must be listed on the National Register of Historic Places or be eligible for membership. A federally funded program is the Certified Local Government Program. The CLG's receive 10% of the funds passed on to the Department of Consumer and Regulatory Affairs to be used for local restoration projects.

Florida

Dr. Janet Snyder Matthews
State Historic Preservation Officer
Division of Historical Resources
Department of State
R.A. Gary Building, Room 305
500 S. Bronaugh Street
Tallahassee, FL 32399-0250
850-245-6300
Fax: 850-488-3353
http://dhr.dos.state.fl.us/
State agencies, units of local government, and nonprofit organizations are eligible to submit applications and compete for funding. Funding categories include acquisition and development, survey and planning and community education. In general, grants will provide 50/50 matching assistance. The agency also administers the Federal Rehabilitation Tax Credit Program. Individuals who have rehabilitated an income producing building used for commercial or industrial purposes can receive a 20% tax credit on expenses incurred during renovation. To be eligible for funding, buildings must be listed on the National Register of Historic Places or be eligible for membership. Another federal program is the Certified Local Government Program. With this, the CLG's receive 10% of the funds passed on to the Division of Historical Resources to be used for local restoration projects.

Georgia

Ray Luce
State Historic Preservation Officer
156 Trinity Avenue, SW, Suite 101
Atlanta, GA 30303-3600
404-656-2840
Fax: 404-651-8739
www.dnr.state.ga.us/dnr/histpres
There are no state grant programs available to home owners. However, this office does administer two federal and one state tax incentive programs. The Federal Rehabilitation Tax Credit Program allows for a 20% tax credit on expenses incurred while rehabilitating an income producing building used for commercial or industrial purposes. The Historic Preservation State Tax Incentive Program offers an 8 year freeze on property tax assessments when a substantial rehabilitation has been done on an individual or business property. There is also a Charitable Contribution Deduction that gives a one time tax deduction to the owner of a historic property that donates a conservation easement. For all of these programs the building must be listed in the National Register of Historic Places or be eligible for membership, and have approval for the project to qualify. There are also cities that are Certified Local Governments in Georgia. Those cities are eligible for a portion of the federal funding to be used for their communities' historic preservation projects and technical assistance.

Hawaii

Don Hibbard
Department of Land and Natural Resources
State Historic Preservation Division
Kakuhihewa Building
601 Kamokila Boulevard, Suite 555
P.O. Box 621
Honolulu, HI 96809
808-692-8015
Fax: 808-692-8020
www.hawaii.gov/dlnr/hpgreeting.htm
Email: dlnr@exec.state.hi.us
A state grant program provides funding, if funds are available, to local and county governments, nonprofit organizations and responsible corporations and individuals. These are 50/50 matching grants, although there are rarely funds for historic property renovation. The agency also administers the Federal Rehabilitation Tax Credit Program Individuals who have rehabilitated an income producing building used for commercial or industrial purposes can receive a 20% tax credit on expenses incurred during renovation. To be eligible for funding, building must be listed on the National Register of Historic Places or be eligible for membership. There is also a property tax exemption available to individuals who won homes listed on the Historic Register. Local county tax offices can provide information and materials. A local government that is deemed a Certified Local Government becomes eligible for federal funding to fund historic renovation projects and technical assistance.

Idaho

Steve Guerber
State Historic Preservation Officer
Idaho State Historical Society

1109 Main Street, Suite 250
Boise, ID 83702-5640
208-334-2682/3847
Fax: 208-334-2774
www.idahohistory.net
There are no funding programs available to
individuals in Idaho. However, this office does
administer the Federal Tax Credit Program. Through
this program individuals receive a 20% tax credit on
expenses they incurred while rehabilitating a building
used for commercial or industrial purposes. Buildings
must be listed on the National Register of Historic
Places or be eligible for membership to qualify. They
also have the Certified Local Government Program in
which CLG's receive 10% of the federal funds passed
on to the Historical Society in the form of matching
grants. The funds are used for local preservation
projects in the CLG's community.

Illinois

William Wheeler, SHPO
State Historic Preservation Agency
1 Old State Capitol Plaza
Springfield, IL 62701-1512
217-785-4512
TDD: 217-524-7128
Fax: 217-524-7525
www.state.il.us/HPA
Email: historicpreservation@yahoo.com
Homeowners must have a sponsoring agency to
apply for state grant funding. Sponsoring agencies
include nonprofit organizations or Certified Local
Governments. The agency administers the Federal
Tax Credit Program. Individuals who have
rehabilitated a building used for commercial or
industrial purposes can receive a 20% tax credit on
approved expenses that were incurred. Another tax
incentive program for owner-occupied residences is
the State Property Tax Assessment Freeze. When at
least 25% of the fair market value of the property is
spent on a rehabilitation project, the owner can
receive a freeze of the assessed valuation of the
property at the pre-rehabilitation level for 8 years.
After that time, the assessed value will increase in
quarter increments for 4 years. Buildings must be
listed on the National Register of Historic Places or be
eligible for membership to qualify. They also have the
Certified Local Government program. With this, a
CLG will receive 10% of the federal funds given to the
Historic Preservation Agency to be used for historic
preservation of their community.

Indiana

Larry D. Macklin, Director, DNR
Division of Historic Preservation & Archaeology
402 Washington Street, Room W274

Indiana Government Center South
Indianapolis, IN 46204
317-232-1646
Fax: 317-232-0693
www.in.gov/dnr/historic
Email: dhpa@dnr.state.in.us
Grants are available to public agencies, nonprofit
organizations with a ceiling up to $30,000. These are
50/50 matching grants. The agency also administers
the Federal Rehabilitation Tax Credit Program.
Individuals who have rehabilitated an income
producing building used for commercial or industrial
purposes can receive a 20% tax credit on approved
expenses incurred during renovation. To be eligible
for funding, the building must be listed on the
National Register of Historic Places or be eligible for
membership. With the Certified Local Government
Program, local communities that have preservation
zoning ordinances receive 10% of the federal funds
passed on to the Historic Preservation Office. With
these matching grants, the CLG's fund local
preservation activities in their community.

Iowa

Anita Walker
State Historic Preservation Officer
State Historical Society of Iowa
Capitol Complex
600 E. Locust Street
Des Moines, IA 50319
515-281-5111
Fax: 515-242-6498
www.iowahistory.org/preservation/
Email: anita.walker@dca.state.ia.us
The Historic Resource Development Program offers
matching grants for work on historic properties,
museums and their collections, and documentary
collections. The program is open to individuals,
nonprofit organizations, Certified Local
Governments, businesses, state agencies, school
districts and Native American tribes. There is another
matching grant available to nonprofits, government
bodies and Indian Tribes. For both the buildings must
be listed on the National Register of Historic Places or
be reviewed by the State Preservation Office to
determine eligibility. Local government agencies that
become Certified Local Governments receive federal
matching grants to fund local preservation planning
activities in their communities. This agency also offers
a state tax incentive for substantial rehabilitation. This
is a combination of a 4-year exemption from any
increase of property valuation because of the project
and 4 years of decreasing exemptions. Buildings must
be evaluated as eligible for membership on the
National Register of Historic Places. There is a Federal
Rehabilitation Tax Credit Program for rehabilitated

income producing buildings used for industrial or commercial purposes. They will receive a 20% tax credit for approved renovations to the buildings. The property must be listed on the National Register of Historic Places or be eligible for membership to participate in the program.

KANSAS

Mary R. Allman
State Historic Preservation Officer
Kansas State Historical Society
6425 SW Sixth Avenue
Topeka, KS 66615-1099
785-272-8681
TTY: 785-272-8683
Fax: 785-272-8682
www.kshs.org/resource/histpres.htm
Email: rpowers@kshs.org
Nonprofit organizations, city or county governments, or individuals may apply for the Heritage Trust Fund Program, an annual grant with a funding ceiling of $75,000. This is a matching grant with 80% provided in grant money and a 20% cash match required on the part of the recipient. The deadline for applications is in February. Eligible properties must be listed on national or state registers of historic places. The agency also administers the Federal Rehabilitation Tax Credit Program. Individuals who have rehabilitated an income producing building used for commercial or industrial purposes can receive a 20% tax credit on approved expenses incurred during renovation. To be eligible for funding, the building must be listed on the National Register of Historic Places or be eligible for membership. With the Certified Local Government Program, local communities that have preservation zoning ordinances receive 10% of the federal funds passed on to the Historic Preservation Office. With these matching grants, the CLG's fund local preservation activities in their community.

KENTUCKY

David Morgan, Director, SHPO
Kentucky Heritage Council
300 Washington Street
Frankfort, KY 40601
502-564-7005
Fax: 502-564-5820
www.state.ky.us/agencies/khc/khchome.htm
Email: dmorgan@mail.state.ky.us
The State Restoration Grant Program that is available to all owners of historic properties, including individuals. However, nonprofit organizations and government agencies that restore structures for public use generally take precedence. It is a 50/50 matching grant. They have an African American Heritage Grant

Program that has funding for projects relating to African American sites. The grants are sometimes used for building restoration, otherwise, it is for research and exhibits. The agency also administers the Federal Tax Credit Program from which individuals may benefit. Individuals who have rehabilitated an income producing building used for commercial or industrial purposes can receive a 20% tax credit on approved expenses incurred during renovation. To be eligible for the credit, buildings must be listed on the National Register of Historic Places or be eligible for membership. With the Certified Local Government Program, local communities that have preservation zoning ordinances receive 10% of the federal funds passed on to the Historic Preservation Office. With these matching grants, the CLG's fund local preservation activities in their community.

LOUISIANA

Laurel Wyckoff
State Historic Preservation Officer
Department of Culture, Recreation & Tourism
Division of Historic Preservation
P.O. Box 44247
Baton Rouge, LA 70804-4247
225-342-8200
Fax: 225-342-8173
www.crt.state.la.us/crt/ocd/hp/ocdhp.htm
At present, state funding is not available to individual property owners. They may however, apply to a Certified Local Government for renovation funding. The CLG's receive a portion of the federal funds given to the Division of Historic Preservation to be used for renovation programs in their communities. These are generally matching grants. The agency does administer the Federal Preservation Tax Credit Program. Individuals who have rehabilitated an income producing building used for commercial or industrial purposes can receive a 20% tax credit on approved expenses incurred during renovation. They also have the Restoration Tax Abatement Program available for business and owner occupied properties that are going to improve, renovate, or create an addition on their buildings. The program creates a freeze on the assessed value and property taxes at the re-improvement level for 5 years. That can be renewed for an additional 5 years in many parishes. This state program can be used in addition to the Federal Tax Credit Program. To be eligible for funding, the building must be listed on the National Register of Historic Places or be eligible for membership.

MAINE

Earle G. Shettleworth, Jr.
State Historic Preservation Officer

Maine Historic Preservation Commission
55 Capitol Street
State House Station 65
Augusta, ME 04333-0065
207-287-2132
Fax: 207-287-2335
www.state.me.us/mhpc
Email: earle.shettleworth@state.me.us
At present, federal and state funding is not available to individual property owners, nonprofit organizations or local county governments. The agency does administer the Federal Historic Preservation Tax Credit Program. Individuals who have rehabilitated an income producing building used for commercial or industrial purposes can receive a 20% tax credit on approved expenses incurred during renovation. To be eligible for funding, the building must be a certified historic structure. With the Certified Local Government Program, local communities that have preservation zoning ordinances receive 10% of the federal funds passed on to the Historic Preservation Office. With these matching grants, the CLG's fund local preservation activities in their community.

Maryland
Rodney Little
State Historic Preservation Officer
Maryland Historical Trust
100 Community Place, 3rd Floor
Crownsville, MD 21032-2023
410-514-7600
Fax: 410-514-7678
www.marylandhistoricaltrust.net
Email: mdshpo@ari.net
There is a loan and a grant program available to individuals for projects to acquire, rehabilitate or restore eligible properties. The Historic Preservation Grant Fund has awards of $40,000 per year, per project. In order to participate in this program, the owner must give a perpetual historic preservation easement to the Trust before receiving any funds. The Historic Preservation Loan Fund is a low interest loan. They are available on a first come, first serve basis. A perpetual historic preservation easement must be conveyed for this program also. The agency also administers the Federal Rehabilitation Tax Credit Program. Individuals who have rehabilitated an income producing building used for commercial or industrial purposes can receive a 20% tax credit on approved expenses incurred during renovation. To be eligible for funding, the building must be listed on the National Register of Historic Places or be eligible for membership. The state tax incentive program is the Heritage Preservation Tax Credit Program. The owner of a certified heritage structure can receive a

tax credit equal to 25% of the qualified capital costs of the rehabilitation project. It also includes a mortgage credit certificate option. With this, a property owner can choose to transfer the credit to his/her mortgage lender for a reduction in the principal amount or interest rate of the loan. There is also a Certified Local Government Program where those local governments receive a portion of the federal funds given to the Historical Division for historic preservation programs.

Massachusetts
Cara Metz
State Historic Preservation Officer
Massachusetts Historical Commission
220 Morrissey Boulevard
Boston, MA 02125-3314
617-727-8470
TDD: 800-392-6090
Fax: 617-727-5128
www.state.ma.us/sec/mhc
Email: cara.metz@sec.state.ma.us
At present, state grants are not available to individual property owners. The Massachusetts Preservation Projects Fund will provide approximately $9 million in matching grants over the next 3 years available to municipalities and nonprofits. Money will be used to support the preservation and maintenance of properties and sites listed in the State Register of Historic Places. Eligible categories will include pre-development, development and acquisition projects. Request for pre-development costs range from $5,000 to $30,000; requests for development or acquisition projects can range from $7,500 to $100,000. Local governments that become Certified Local Governments will receive 10 % of the federal funds given to the Historical Commission for renovation projects in their communities. Individual property owners may benefit from the Federal Rehabilitation Tax Credit Program. Individuals who have rehabilitated an income producing building used for commercial or industrial purposes can receive a 20% tax credit on approved expenses incurred during renovation. To be eligible for funding, the building must be listed on the National Register of Historic Places or be eligible for membership.

Michigan
Brian Conway
State Historic Preservation Office
Michigan Historical Center
Box 30740
Department of History, Arts and Libraries
702 W. Kalamazoo St.
Lansing, MI 48909
517-373-1630

Fax: 517-373-1630
www.sos.state.mi.us/history/preserve/preserve.html
Email: preservation@sos.state.mi.us
State grants are not available to individual property owners. The agency does, however, administer the Federal Rehabilitation Tax Credit Program. Individuals who have rehabilitated an income producing building used for commercial or industrial purposes can receive a 20% tax credit on expenses incurred during renovation. There is also the Michigan Historic Preservation Tax Incentive. This is an income tax credit of up to 25% for owners of an historic home that are going to start a rehabilitation project. To be eligible for funding, buildings must be listed on the National Register of Historic Places or be eligible for membership. There is a federal funding program for Certified Local Governments. They receive 10% of the State Historical Center's federal appropriation in the form of matching grants. These funds are used for local preservation projects in the CLG's community.

Minnesota

Nina Archabal
State Historic Preservation Officer
Minnesota Historical Society
345 West Kellogg Boulevard
St. Paul, MN 55102-1906
651-296-6126
Fax: 651-296-1004
www.mnhs.org
There is no state funding program available to individual property owners. The agency does, however, offer technical advice concerning restoration projects. They do administer a Federal Rehabilitation Tax Credit Program to individuals that have rehabilitated an income producing building. The credit is for 20% of eligible expenses incurred during renovation and the building must be used for commercial or industrial purposes. In order to be eligible, the building must be listed on the National Register of Historic Places, or be eligible for membership. They also have the Certified Local Government Program. With this program, cities, townships, and counties with qualified local historic preservation ordinances receive federally funded matching grants to be used for local preservation projects.

Mississippi

Elbert Hilliard
State Historic Preservation Officer
Mississippi Department of Archives and History
618 East Pearl Street
Jackson, MS 39201
Mailing Address:

P.O. Box 571
Jackson, MS 39205-0571
601-359-6940
Fax: 601-359-6975
www.mdah.state.ms.us/hpres/hprestxt.html
Email: msshpo@mdah.state.ms.us
They do have a pending program called the Mississippi Landmark Program. If a property is designated as a Landmark it can be eligible for funding, however, it is not clear if individual property owners will be able to benefit from the grants. They do have the Certified Local Government Program. With this program, cities, townships, and counties with qualified local historic preservation ordinances receive federally funded matching grants to be used for local preservation projects. They also administer a Federal Rehabilitation Tax Credit Program to individuals that have rehabilitated an income producing building. The credit is for 20% of eligible expenses incurred during renovation and the building must be used for commercial or industrial purposes. In order to be eligible, the building must be listed on the National Register of Historic Places, or be eligible for membership.

Missouri

Stephen Mahfood
State Historic Preservation Officer
State Department of Natural Resources
Division of State Parks
205 Jefferson
P.O. Box 176
Jefferson City, MO 65102
573-751-4422
Fax: 573-751-7627
www.dnr.state.mo.us/shpo/homepage.htm
The Historic Preservation Fund Grant is a federal 60/40 matching grant that is open to individuals, state agencies, municipal governments, incorporated organizations, nonprofits and educational institutions. The eligible activities for funding are survey, National Register, predevelopment, development and planning. These activities must be directly related to the protection of historical or architectural resources, among other things. The recipient of the grant must fund the entire project and then receive a reimbursement up to the total amount of the grant. The agency also administers the Federal Tax Credit Program. It offers a 20% tax credit on money spent on approved rehabilitation of an income producing building that will be used for commercial or industrial purposes. There is a state investment tax credit for 25% of qualified rehabilitation efforts. Homeowners as well as developers of income producing buildings can qualify for this credit and it can be used in combination with the federal credit for

owners of eligible buildings. The Certified Local Government is a federal program administered through local communities. The CLG's receive 10% of the federal funds passed on to the Historical Division to be used for local renovation projects.

Montana

Mark Baumler, Program Manager
State Historic Preservation Office
1410 8th Avenue
P.O. Box 201202
Helena, MT 59620-1202
406-444-7717
Fax: 406-444-6575
www.his.state.mt.us/
Email: mbaumler@state.mt.us
There is not any funding available for individual homeowners. The Certified Local Government Program is a federal program administered through local communities. The CLG's receive 10% of the federal funds passed on to the Historical Division to be used for local renovation projects. The agency also administers the Federal Tax Credit Program. It offers a 20% tax credit on money spent on approved rehabilitation of an income producing building that will be used for commercial or industrial purposes. There is a state investment tax credit for 25% of qualified rehabilitation efforts. Homeowners as well as developers of income producing buildings can qualify for this credit and it can be used in combination with the federal credit for owners of eligible buildings.

Nebraska

Lawrence Sommer
State Historic Preservation Officer
Nebraska State Historical Society
P.O. Box 82554
1500 R Street
Lincoln, NE 68501
402-471-4745
Fax: 402-471-3316
www.nebraskahistory.org
Email: hpnshs@nebraskahistory.org/histpres.index.htm
There are no state grant programs that provide funds for historic preservation to homeowners. Individual property owners may apply for the Federal Tax Credit Program if they have rehabilitated an income producing property used for commercial or industrial purposes. They would receive a 20% tax credit on expenses they incurred during the project. To be eligible, the building must be either listed on the National Register of Historic Places, or be eligible for membership. With the Certified Local Government Program, local communities that have preservation zoning ordinances receive 10% of the federal funds

passed on to the Historic Preservation Office. With these matching grants, the CLG's fund local preservation activities in their community.

Nevada

Ronald James
State Historic Preservation Officer
Historic Preservation Office
100 N. Stewart Street
Carson City, NV 89710-4285
775-684-3448
Fax: 775-684-3442
http://dmla.clan.lib.nv.us/docs/shpo
Presently, there are no state grant programs for individuals. They do have a program to rehabilitate buildings that are used for cultural purposes. However, they do have the Certified Local Government Program. With this program, cities, townships, and counties with qualified local historic preservation ordinances receive federally funded matching grants to be used for local preservation projects. Individuals may be able to become sponsored through the CLG Program for their restoration project. Individual property owners may also apply for the Federal Rehabilitation Tax Credit Program. Rehabilitation of an income producing building that is used for commercial or industrial purposes can receive a 20% tax credit on expenses incurred during renovation. To be eligible for funding, buildings must be listed on the National Register of Historic Places or be eligible for membership.

New Hampshire

James McConaha
State Historic Preservation Officer
State Historic Preservation Office
Division of Historical Resources and
State Historic Preservation Office
19 Pillsbury Street
P.O. Box 2043
Concord, NH 03301-2043
603-271-3483/3558
TDD: 800-735-2964
Fax: 603-271-3433
http://webster.state.nh.us/nhdhr
Email: preservation@mndhr.state.nh.us
Presently, there are no state grants available for individuals or nonprofit organizations. However, they do have the Certified Local Government Program. With this program, cities, townships, and counties with qualified local historic preservation ordinances receive federally funded matching grants to be used for local preservation projects. There is also the Federal Rehabilitation Tax Credit Program that may benefit individual property owners. They can

receive a 20% tax credit on eligible expenses incurred during a renovation of an income producing building used for commercial or industrial purposes. To qualify, the building must be listed on the National Register of Historic Places or be eligible for membership.

New Jersey

Robert C. Shinn
State Historic Preservation Officer
New Jersey Historic Trust
P.O. Box 404
Trenton, NJ 08625-0404
609-292-2023
Fax: 609-984-0578
www.state.nj.us/dep/hpo
The state has both grant and loan programs for nonprofits, government agencies, and educational institutions, however, none for individual homeowners. There are two programs that individuals can use as tax benefits. With the New Jersey Legacies Program, the charitable donation of a historic property allows for reduced estate tax as well as other tax benefits. The Preservation Easement Program gives legal protection to a historic property by the donation of an easement. It also has property and federal tax benefits. The property must be listed on the National Register of Historic Places. There is also the Federal Rehabilitation Tax Credit Program that may benefit individual property owners. They can receive a 20% tax credit on eligible expenses incurred during a renovation of an income producing building used for commercial or industrial purposes. To qualify, the building must be listed on the National Register of Historic Places or be eligible for membership. With the Certified Local Government Program, local communities that have preservation zoning ordinances receive 10% of the federal funds passed on to the Historic Preservation Office. With these matching grants, the CLG's fund local preservation activities in their community.

New Mexico

Elmo Baca
State Historic Preservation Officer
Historic Preservation Division
Office of Cultural Affairs
Room 320, LaVilla Rivera
228 East Palace Avenue
Santa Fe, NM 87501
505-827-6320
Fax: 505-827-6338
www.museums.state.nm.us/hpd
While there are no state grants currently available, funds from the federal Historic Preservation Fund are being administered by this division through

categorical projects. There are ten small grants of up to $2,000 for the promotion of preservation activities available to individuals, local governments, historic and archaeological and preservation groups. The New Mexico Historic Preservation Loan Fund offers rehabilitation incentives to owners of registered cultural properties. This revolving loan fund combines monies of the state and participating local lenders. To obtain funding, projects must be on the State and/or National Register of Historic Places and reviewed for compliance with the Secretary of the Interior's Standards for Rehabilitation and with the Historic Preservation Division Staff. Borrowers are subject to the lending criteria applied by the participating bank. The maximum principal for a loan is $200,000 with a low interest rate and a term of 5 years. Individual property owners can also apply for the Federal Tax Credit Program. Through this program building owners receive a 20% tax credit on allowed expenses they incurred while rehabilitating a building used for commercial or industrial purposes. Buildings must be listed on the National Register of Historic Places or be eligible for membership to qualify. There is a state tax credit program that is available to homeowners and business owners for expenses incurred during a restoration/rehabilitation project. Those projects that have been approved by the Cultural Properties Review Committee are eligible for a 50% credit for expenditures up to a maximum credit of $25,000. Certified Local Governments get a portion of the federal funding received by the Historic Preservation Division in the form of matching grants. The grants fund local preservation activities in the CLG's community.

New York

Ruth Pierpont
Deputy State Historic Preservation Officer
Field Services Bureau
New York State Parks, Recreation and Historic Preservation
New York State Parks
Albany, NY 12238
Physical Address:
    20th Floor, Agency Building #1
    Empire State Plaza
    Albany, NY 12238
518-474-0456
TTY: 518-486-1899
Email: ruth.pierpont@oprhp.state.ny.us
http://nyparks.state.ny.us/
There are no state funds available to individual property owners. Funding to nonprofit organizations and local municipal governments made available by the Environmental Protection Act of 1993 and provides up to 50% matching grants for acquisition

and restoration. Also, the Historic Barn Tax Credit has established a state income tax credit which provides a reduction in state income tax to barn owners based on the rehabilitation of the barn. This office administers the Federal Rehabilitation Tax Credit Program. Through this program individuals receive a 20% tax credit on allowable expenses they incurred while rehabilitating a building used for commercial or industrial purposes. Buildings must be listed on the National Register of Historic Places or be eligible for membership to qualify. New York also has two tax abatement programs that allow local municipalities to establish property tax abatement programs for locally designated landmarks. These will allow for the increase in assessed value of a rehabilitated historic building or barn to be phased-in over time. With the Certified Local Government Program, local communities that have preservation zoning ordinances receive 10% of the federal funds passed on to the Historic Preservation Office. With these matching grants, the CLG's fund local preservation activities in their community.

North Carolina

David Brook
Deputy State Historic Preservation Officer
State Historic Preservation Office
Department of Culture Resources
Division of Archives and History
4617 Mail Service Center
Raleigh, NC 27699-4617
919-733-4763
Fax: 919-733-8653
www.hpo.dcr.state.nc.us
Email: dbrook@ncsl.dcr.state.nc.us
North Carolina has no state funding program for individual property owners. The Division of Archives and History provides grants to nonprofit organizations and local county governments for historical preservation activities. Individual property owners can, however, benefit from the Federal Tax Credit Program. Through this program individuals receive a 20% tax credit on expenses they incurred while rehabilitating a building used for commercial or industrial purposes. Buildings must be listed on the National Register of Historic Places or be eligible for membership to qualify. Private residences that are going to take on a substantial rehabilitation of their historic home may take advantage of a 30% state tax credit. The project must be certified and the home must be listed on that National Register or be located within a National Register district. The Certified Local Government Program funds local community preservation activities in communities that have preservation zoning ordinances.

North Dakota

Merlan Paaverud, Jr.
State Historic Preservation Officer
State Historical Society of North Dakota
Archeology & Historic Preservation Division
Heritage Center
612 East Boulevard
Bismarck, ND 58505-0830
701-328-2666
Fax: 701-328-3710
www.state.nd.us/hist
Email: mpaaverud@state.nd.us
The Restoration Grant Program is available to individuals, but it is offered sporadically. The matching grant comes from federal sources and can be used for approved rehabilitation projects of homes listed on the National Register of Historic Places. The agency also administers the Federal Preservation Tax Credit Program. Individuals who have rehabilitated an income producing building used for commercial or industrial purposes can receive a 20% tax credit on eligible expenses incurred during renovation. To be eligible, the building must be either listed on the National Register of Historic Places, or be eligible for membership. With the Certified Local Government Program, local communities that have preservation zoning ordinances receive 10% of the federal funds passed on to the Historic Preservation Office. With these matching grants, the CLG's fund local preservation activities in their community.

Ohio

Amos J. Loveday
State Historic Preservation Officer
Ohio Historical Society
Historic Preservation Office
567 East Hudson Street
Columbus, OH 43211-1030
614-298-2000
Fax: 614-298-2037
www.ohiohistory.org/resource/histpres
Email: ajloveday@aol.com
There is no state funding available to individual property owners. However, they do have the Certified Local Government Program. With this program, cities, townships, and counties with qualified local historic preservation ordinances receive federally funded matching grants to be used for local preservation projects. Individual property owners may benefit from the Federal Tax Credit Program. Individuals who have rehabilitated an income producing building used for commercial or industrial purposes can receive a 20% tax credit on expenses incurred during renovation. To be eligible for funding, buildings must either be listed on the National Register of Historic Places or be eligible for

membership. Federal Rehabilitation Tax Credit Program.

Oklahoma

Bob Blackburn
State Historic Preservation Officer
State Historic Preservation Office
2704 Villa Prom
Shepherd Mall
Oklahoma City, OK 73107
405-521-6249
Fax: 405-947-2918
www.ok-history.mus.ok.us
There is no state or federal funding available to individual property owners at the present time. The agency does, however, administer the Federal Tax Credit Program. Individuals who have rehabilitated an income producing building used for commercial or industrial purposes can receive a 20% tax credit on eligible expenses incurred during renovation. They also have a state tax credit that can be used on top of the federal credit for historic hotels and historic economic development areas. To be eligible for funding for both credits, the buildings must be listed on the National Register of Historic Places, or be eligible for membership. They have another federal program called the Certified Local Government Program. With this program, cities, townships, and counties with qualified local historic preservation ordinances receive federally funded matching grants to be used for local preservation projects.

Oregon

Michael Carrier
State Historic Preservation Officer
State Parks and Recreation Department
State Historic Preservation Office
1115 Commercial St., NE, Suite 2
Salem, OR 97301-1012
503-378-6305
Fax: 503-378-8936
www.prd.state.or.us/about_shpo.html
Email: shpo.info@state.or.us
They offer competitive grants programs for assistance to National Register properties when they have funding available. Currently, there is no funding but they hope to have it available next year. However, they do have the Certified Local Government Program. With this program, cities, townships, and counties with qualified local historic preservation ordinances receive federally funded matching grants to be used for local preservation projects. Individual property owners may also benefit from the Special Assessment for Historic Properties Program which provides a fifteen year tax abatement on increases in land and improvement. Properties must be listed on

the National Register of Historic Places and be approved by a State Historic Preservation committee. This office also administers the Federal Rehabilitation Tax Credit Program. Income producing buildings that are used for commercial or industrial purposes can receive a 20% tax credit for eligible expenses incurred during a renovation. To be eligible, the building must be listed on the National Register of Historic Places, or be eligible for membership.

Pennsylvania

Brent Glass
State Historic Preservation Officer
Bureau for Historic Preservation
400 North Street
Harrisburg, PA 17108-0093
717-783-8946
Fax: 717-772-0920
www.phmc.state.pa.us
There are no state funds available to residential homeowners at the present time. Nonprofit organizations and public agencies may apply for the Keystone Historic Preservation Grant to renovate/restore historic properties that are open to the public. This is a 50/50 matching grant program. The agency also administers the Federal Tax Credit Program. There is also the Certified Local Government Program. With this program, cities, townships, and counties with qualified local historic preservation ordinances receive federally funded matching grants to be used for local preservation projects. Individuals who have rehabilitated an income producing building used for commercial or industrial purposes can receive a 20% tax credit on approved expenses incurred during renovation. To be eligible for funding, buildings must be listed on the National Register of Historic Places or be eligible for its membership.

Rhode Island

Frederick C. Williamson
State Historic Preservation Officer
Historical Preservation Commission
Old State House
150 Benefit Street
Providence, RI 02903
401-222-2678
Fax: 401-222-2968
www.rihphc.state.ri.us
While there are no state grant programs, they do have a low interest loan program that individual homeowners can apply to for restoration projects. The Historical Preservation Loan Fund has an interest rate of 2% less than prime. The maximum loan is for $200,000 with a term of 5 years. The agency also administers the Federal Rehabilitation Tax Credit

Program. Individuals who have rehabilitated an income producing building used for commercial or industrial purposes can receive a 20% tax credit on expenses incurred during renovation. To be eligible for funding, buildings must be listed on the National Register of Historic Places or be eligible for membership. The state's Historic Preservation Residential Tax Credit Program provides a 10% income tax credit for eligible rehabilitation and maintenance costs for homeowners. With the Certified Local Government Program, local communities that have preservation zoning ordinances receive 10% of the federal funds passed on to the Historic Preservation Office. With these matching grants, the CLG's fund local preservation activities in their community.

South Carolina

Roger E. Stroup
State Historic Preservation Officer
Historic Preservation Office
8301 Parklane Rd.
Columbia, SC 29223-4905
803-896-6100
Fax: 803-896-6168
www.state.sc.us/scdah
This office administers both federal and state grant programs to support preservation efforts of individuals, organizations, institutions and local governments. Owners of South Carolina properties that are listed in the National Register of Historic Places or determined eligible for membership may apply for State Development Grants and Federal Survey & Planning Grants. Funds from State Development grants assist preservation work on historic structures. Awards generally range from $5,000 to $20,000. The Federal Survey & Planning Grant assists historic preservation projects in a variety of categories. The work must be done by professionals and must comply with the agencies' guidelines and standards. Both of these are reimbursable 50/50 matching grants. They do also have the Certified Local Government Program. With this program, cities, townships, and counties with qualified local historic preservation ordinances receive federally funded matching grants to be used for local preservation projects. There are two tax incentive programs available. The Special Property Tax Assessments for Rehabilitated Historic Buildings encourages the revitalization of neighborhoods and downtown commercial districts. Municipal and county governments can freeze tax assessments when a property owner finishes a substantial rehabilitation of a historic building and low and moderate income rental properties. The freeze is in effect for up to 2 years if the rehabilitation is completed within those

years. For the following 8 years, it will be taxed at the greater of 40% of the post-rehabilitation assessment, or 100% of the pre-rehabilitation assessment.

South Dakota

Jay D. Vogt
State Historic Preservation Officer
State Historical Society Historic Preservation Center
900 Governor's Drive
Pierre, SD 57501-2217
605-773-3458
Fax: 605-773-6041
www.state.sd.us/state/executive/deca/cultural/histpres.htm
Email: jay.vogt@state.sd.us
There are no state grants available to individual property owners at the present time. However, individuals, public agencies and nonprofits are eligible to apply for the Deadwood Fund which makes loans and grants available to purchase, restore, or develop historic property for residential, commercial, or public purposes. The agency also administers the Federal Rehabilitation Tax Credit Program. Individuals who have rehabilitated an income producing building used for commercial or industrial purposes can receive a 20% tax credit on expenses incurred during renovation. There is an additional 10% credit for the renovation of buildings that were constructed before 1936. To be eligible for funding, buildings must be listed on the National Register of Historic Places or be eligible for membership. The South Dakota Legislature has also approved an eight year moratorium on property tax assessment for improvements on historical buildings. Buildings must be on the National Register of Historic Places to qualify. There is also the Certified Local Government Program. With this program, cities, townships, and counties with qualified local historic preservation ordinances receive federally funded matching grants to be used for local preservation projects.

Tennessee

Herbert L. Harper
Deputy State Historic Preservation Officer
Tennessee Historical Commission
Clover Bottom Mansion
2941 Lebanon Road
Nashville, TN 37243-0422
615-532-1550
Fax: 615-532-1549
www.state.tn.us/environment/hist/index.html
The Federal Preservation Grant is open to individuals, local governmental bodies, private organizations or educational institutions. While historic survey projects will be emphasized, funding is also available

for other projects that are needed to undertake a restoration. The agency also administers the Federal Renovation Tax Credit Program. Individuals who have rehabilitated an income producing building used for commercial or industrial purposes can receive a 20% tax credit on expenses incurred during renovation. To be eligible for funding, buildings must be listed on the National Register of Historic Places or be eligible for its membership. There is also the Certified Local Government Program. With this program, cities, townships, and counties with qualified local historic preservation ordinances receive federally funded matching grants to be used for local preservation projects.

Texas

Lawrence Oaks
State Historic Preservation Officer
Texas Historical Commission
P.O. Box 12276
Austin, TX 78711-2276
512-463-6100
Fax: 512-463-8222
www.thc.state.tx.us
Email: l.oakes@thc.state.tx.us
The Texas Preservation Trust Fund Grant Program provides funding to public or private entities in the form of two for one matching grants. Although individuals may apply, the large majority of grants are awarded to nonprofit organizations and municipal governments. There is also the Certified Local Government Program. With this program, cities, townships, and counties with qualified local historic preservation ordinances receive federally funded matching grants to be used for local preservation projects. This agency administers the Federal Renovation Tax Credit Program. Individuals who have rehabilitated an income producing building used for commercial or industrial purposes can receive a 20% tax credit on expenses incurred during renovation. To be eligible for funding, buildings must be listed on the National Register of Historic Places or be eligible for its membership.

Utah

Max Evans
State Historic Preservation Officer
Utah State Historical Society
Office of Preservation
300 South Rio Grande
Salt Lake City, UT 84101-1143
801-533-3500
TDD: 801-533-3502
Fax: 801-533-3503
http://history.utah.org
Email: ushs@history.state.ut.us

At present, there are no state or federal funds directly available to individual property owners. However, individuals may be able to apply for funding through Utah's Certified Local Government Program. Homeowners qualify if they have support of a sponsoring agency. Matching funds are usually required. The agency also administers the State and Federal Tax Credit Programs. Through these programs individuals can receive a 20% tax credit on expenses they incurred while rehabilitating a building that will be used for residences (state tax credit only), commercial or industrial purposes. Buildings must be either listed on the National Register of Historic Places, or be eligible for membership to qualify.

Vermont

Emily Wadhams
State Historic Preservation Officer
Vermont Division for Historic Preservation
National Life Building, Drawer 20
Montpelier, VT 05620-0501
802-828-3211
www.historicvermont.org
Vermont has no state funding for privately owned properties other than a state grant program that provides funding for the renovation of old barns. There is a 50/50 matching grant program available to nonprofit organizations and municipalities. The agency also administers the Federal Tax Credit Program. Individuals who have rehabilitated an income producing building used for commercial or industrial purposes can receive a 20% tax credit on expenses incurred during renovation. To be eligible for funding, buildings must be listed on the National Register of Historic Places or be eligible for its membership. There is also the Certified Local Government Program. With this program, cities, townships, and counties with qualified local historic preservation ordinances receive federally funded matching grants to be used for local preservation projects.

Virginia

Kathleen Kilpatrick
State Historic Preservation Officer
Department of Historic Resources
Commonwealth of Virginia
2801 Kensington Avenue
Richmond, VA 23221
804-367-2323
Fax: 804-367-2391
www.dhr.state.va.us
Email: kkilpatrick@dhr.state.va.us
The state grant program is available for local governments, nonprofit historical associations, and museum organizations. However, individuals with

state tax liability may benefit from the State Rehabilitation Tax Credit Program which provides a 25% credit for eligible rehabilitation expenses. The agency also administers the Federal Tax Credit Program. Individuals who have rehabilitated an income producing building used for commercial or industrial purposes can receive a 20% tax credit on expenses incurred during renovation. To be eligible for funding, buildings must be listed on the National Register of Historic Places or be eligible for its membership. There is also the Certified Local Government Program. With this program, cities, townships, and counties with qualified local historic preservation ordinances receive federally funded matching grants to be used for local preservation projects.

Washington

Allyson Brooks
State Historic Preservation Officer
Office of Archeology and Historic Preservation
1063 S. Capitol Way, Suite 106
P.O. Box 48343
Olympia, WA 98504-8343
360-586-3065
Fax: 360-586-3067
www.ocd.wa.gov/info/lgd/oahp
At present, state grant funding is not available to individual property owners, nonprofit organizations or local county governments, although, there is the Certified Local Government Program. With this program, cities, townships, and counties with qualified local historic preservation ordinances receive federally funded matching grants to be used for local preservation projects. This agency administers the Federal Rehabilitation Tax Credit Program. Individuals who have rehabilitated an income producing building used for commercial or industrial purposes can receive a 20% tax credit on expenses incurred during renovation. To be eligible for funding, buildings must be either listed on the National Register of Historic Places, or be eligible for membership.

West Virginia

Susan Pierce
Deputy State Historic Preservation Officer
West Virginia Division of Culture and History
1900 Kanawha Boulevard, East
Charleston, WV 25305-0300
304-558-0220
TDD: 304-558-3562
Fax: 304-558-2779
www.wvculture.org/shpo/index.html
State Development Grants are available to individuals who wish to renovate an historic home. Grants range

from $1,000 to $20,000 depending upon the scope of the project. There is also the Certified Local Government Program. With this program, cities, townships, and counties with qualified local historic preservation ordinances receive federally funded matching grants to be used for local preservation projects. The Federal Rehabilitation Tax Credit Program is administered by this agency. Individuals who have rehabilitated an income producing building used for commercial or industrial purposes can receive a 20% tax credit on expenses incurred during renovation. In addition, there is a state tax credit program for both residential and commercial property owners that undergo a rehabilitation project. To be eligible for funding, buildings must be either listed on the National Register of Historic Places, or be eligible for membership.

Wisconsin

George Vogt
State Historic Preservation Officer
Historic Preservation Division
State Historical Society
816 State St.
Madison, WI 53706-1842
608-264-6500
Fax: 608-264-6504
www.shsw.wisc.edu/about/index.html
There are no state or federal grants available to individual homeowners. Individuals can, however, apply for tax assistance under the Federal Tax Credit Program. Individuals who have rehabilitated an income producing building used for commercial or industrial purposes can receive a 20% tax credit on expenses incurred during renovation. To be eligible for funding, buildings must be either listed on the National Register of Historic Places, or be eligible for membership. There is also the Certified Local Government Program. With this program, cities, townships, and counties with qualified local historic preservation ordinances receive federally funded matching grants to be used for local preservation projects.

Wyoming

Richard Currit
State Historic Preservation Officer
2301 Central Avenue, 3rd Floor
Cheyenne, WY 82002
307-777-7013
Fax: 307-777-3543
http://wyoshpo.state.wy.us
There are currently no state or federal grant programs available to individuals. Individuals can, however, apply for tax assistance under the Federal Tax Credit Program. Those who have rehabilitated an income

producing building used for commercial or industrial purposes can receive a 20% tax credit on expenses incurred during renovation. To be eligible for funding, buildings must be either listed on the National Register of Historic Places, or be eligible for membership. There is also the Certified Local Government Program. With this program, cities, townships, and counties with qualified local historic preservation ordinances receive federally funded matching grants to be used for local preservation projects.

Want To Buy A House or Can't Afford What You Have?

Trouble in the house? HUD may be able to help. Layoffs and threatened unemployment causes many homeowners to worry about making their mortgage payments. HUD provides a list of HUD-approved housing counseling agencies! HUD funds housing counseling agencies throughout the country that can give you advice on buying a home, renting, defaults, foreclosures, credit issues, reverse mortgages and working with lenders. Just contact the agency nearest to you or call 1-888-466-3487. Homeowners with problems that could result in default of their mortgage or foreclosure on their property need to contact a HUD-approved housing counseling agency immediately.

The Housing Counseling Clearinghouse (HCC) operates a toll-free, 24-hour a day automated voice response system that provides homeowners and homebuyers referrals to local housing counseling agencies toll-free at 1-800-569-4287.

> The Housing Counseling Clearinghouse
> P.O. Box 10423
> McLean, VA 22102
> www.hud.gov
> 888-466-3487 (toll-free)
> TDD: 703-734-1444
> Fax: 703-734-7929

For those homeowners with FHA mortgages, another resource also exists. The goal of HUD's National Servicing Center is to help FHA homeowners by working with lenders to find creative solutions to avoid foreclosure.

> Department of Housing and Urban Development
> National Servicing Center
> 500 W. Main Street, Suite 400
> Oklahoma City, OK 73102
> 888-297-8685 (toll-free)

HUD Approved Housing Counseling Agencies

(Agencies with a ** have not been individually HUD approved, but are affiliates of one of the HUD funded National Intermediaries.)

Alabama

COMMUNITY SERVICES OF CALHOUN COUNTIES
1702 Noble Street, Suite 112
Anniston, AL 36202
256-231-1798
Fax: 256-241-2965
Email: eftcsccc@aol.com
Type of Counseling:
Default/Foreclosure Counseling,
Prepurchase Counseling, Rental
Counseling, HECM Counseling

CONSUMER CREDIT COUNSELING SERVICE OF WEST FLORIDA/POARCH CREEK INDIAN RESERVATION
5811 Jack Springs Road
Atmore, AL 36502
334-368-9136
Fax: 850-432-5078
Type of Counseling:
Prepurchase Counseling, Rental
Counseling, Default/Foreclosure
Counseling, HECM Counseling

ALABAMA COUNCIL ON HUMAN RELATIONS, INCORPORATED
319 W Glenn Ave
Auburn, AL 368310409
334-821-8336
Fax: 334-826-6397
Type of Counseling:
HECM Counseling,
Default/Foreclosure Counseling,
Rental Counseling, Prepurchase
Counseling

AUBURN HOUSING AUTHORITY
931 Booker St
Auburn, AL 36832-2902
334-821-2262
Fax: 334-821-2264
Type of Counseling:
HECM Counseling,
Default/Foreclosure Counseling,
Rental Counseling, Prepurchase
Counseling

JEFFERSON COUNTY COMMITTEE FOR ECONOMIC OPPORTUNITY
300 Eighth Avenue, West
Birmingham, AL 352043039
205-327-7500
Fax: 205-326-4179
Type of Counseling:
Prepurchase Counseling,
Default/Foreclosure Counseling,
HECM Counseling, Rental
Counseling

BIRMINGHAM URBAN LEAGUE, INCORPORATED
1229 3rd Avenue North
Birmingham, AL 35202-1269
205-326-0162
Fax: 205-521-6951
Email: burbanleag@aol.com
Type of Counseling:
HECM Counseling,
Default/Foreclosure Counseling,
Rental Counseling, Prepurchase
Counseling

JEFFERSON COUNTY HOUSING AUTHORITY
3700 Industrial Parkway
Birmingham, AL 35217
205-849-0123
Fax: 205-849-0137
Type of Counseling:
HECM Counseling,
Default/Foreclosure Counseling,
Rental Counseling, Prepurchase
Counseling

****BIRMINGHAM NEIGHBORHOOD HOUSING SERVICES**
1200 Tuscaloosa Ave SW
Birmingham, AL 35203-
205-328-4292
Fax: 205-328-1057
Type of Counseling:
Prepurchase Counseling, HECM
Counseling
Affiliate of: NEIGHBORHOOD
REINVESTMENT
CORPORATION

****CONSUMER CREDIT COUNSELING SERVICES, DIVISION OF UNITED FAMILY SERVICES**
2000 First Avenue North, Suite
600
Birmingham, AL 35203-4117
205-251-1572
Fax: 205-251-1574
Type of Counseling:
Prepurchase Counseling,
Default/Foreclosure Counseling,
HECM Counseling, Rental
Counseling
Affiliate of: NATIONAL
FOUNDATION FOR
CONSUMER CREDIT,
INCORPORATED

****LEGAL SERVICES OF METRO BIRMINGHAM, INCORPORATED**
1820 McFarland
Birmingham, AL 35202
205-328-3540
Fax: 205-328-3548
Email: kenc@lsmbi.com
Type of Counseling:
Prepurchase Counseling,
Default/Foreclosure Counseling,
Rental Counseling, HECM
Counseling
Affiliate of: WEST TENNESSEE
LEGAL SERVICES,
INCORPORATED

HOUSING AUTHORITY OF BIRMINGHAM DISTRICT
1826 3rd Ave S
Birmingham, AL 35233-1905
205-521-0686
Fax: 205-521-7789
Type of Counseling:
Default/Foreclosure Counseling,
Rental Counseling, Prepurchase
Counseling

COMMUNITY ACTION AND
COMMUNITY DEVELOPMENT
AGENCY OF NORTH
ALABAMA, INCORPORATED
207 Commerce Circle SW
Decatur, AL 35601
256-355-7843
Fax: 256-355-7953
Email: mail@cacdana.org
Type of Counseling:
HECM Counseling,
Default/Foreclosure Counseling,
Rental Counseling, Prepurchase
Counseling

**LEGAL SERVICES OF
NORTH CENTRAL ALABAMA,
INCORPORATED
17 Vine Street NW
Decatur, AL 35602-
256-350-3551
Fax: 256-350-6722
Type of Counseling:
Prepurchase Counseling,
Default/Foreclosure Counseling,
Rental Counseling, HECM
Counseling
Affiliate of: WEST TENNESSEE
LEGAL SERVICES,
INCORPORATED

**LEGAL SERVICES
CORPORATION OF
ALABAMA, INCORPORATED
119 South Foster Street Suite 101
Dothan, AL 36301-
334-793-2882
Toll-Free:
TTY/TDD:
Fax: 334-793-7932
Type of Counseling:
Prepurchase Counseling,
Default/Foreclosure Counseling,
Rental Counseling, HECM
Counseling
Affiliate of: WEST TENNESSEE
LEGAL SERVICES,
INCORPORATED

HUMAN RESOURCE
DEVELOPMENT
CORPORATION
100 George Wallace Dr
Enterprise, AL 36331
334-678-0084
Fax: 334-393-0048

Type of Counseling:
HECM Counseling,
Default/Foreclosure Counseling,
Rental Counseling, Prepurchase
Counseling

COMMUNITY ACTION
AGENCY OF NORTHWEST
ALABAMA, INCORPORATED
745 Thompson St
Florence, AL 35630
256-766-4330
Fax: 256-766-4367
Type of Counseling:
HECM Counseling,
Default/Foreclosure Counseling,
Rental Counseling, Prepurchase
Counseling

**LEGAL SERVICES
CORPORATION OF
ALABAMA, INCORPORATED
412 S. Court Street
Florence, AL 35631-
256-767-2020
Fax: 256-767-2212
Type of Counseling:
Prepurchase Counseling,
Default/Foreclosure Counseling,
Rental Counseling, HECM
Counseling
Affiliate of: WEST TENNESSEE
LEGAL SERVICES,
INCORPORATED

**LEGAL SERVICES
CORPORATION OF
ALABAMA, INCORPORATED
802 Chestnut Street
Gadsden, AL 35901-
256-543-2435
Fax: 256-543-2438
Type of Counseling:
Prepurchase Counseling,
Default/Foreclosure Counseling,
Rental Counseling, HECM
Counseling
Affiliate of: WEST TENNESSEE
LEGAL SERVICES,
INCORPORATED

WIL-LOW NONPROFIT
HOUSING CORPORATION,
INCORPORATED
200 A Commerce Street
Hayneville, AL 36040

334-548-2191
Fax: 334-548-2576
Email: willowa@htcnet.net
Type of Counseling:
Default/Foreclosure Counseling,
Rental Counseling

COMMUNITY ACTION
AGENCY - HUNTSVILLE,
MADISON, LIMESTONE
3516 Stringfield Rd NW
Huntsville, AL 35810-1758
256-851-9800
Fax: 256-851-9803
Type of Counseling:
HECM Counseling,
Default/Foreclosure Counseling,
Rental Counseling, Prepurchase
Counseling

**LEGAL SERVICES OF
NORTH CENTRAL ALABAMA,
INCORPORATED
2000-C Vemon Drive
Huntsville, AL 35804
256-536-9645
Fax: 256-536-1544
Email: tkeith00@lsnca.org
Type of Counseling:
Prepurchase Counseling,
Default/Foreclosure Counseling,
Rental Counseling, HECM
Counseling
Affiliate of: WEST TENNESSEE
LEGAL SERVICES,
INCORPORATED

CONSUMER CREDIT
COUNSELING SERVICE OF
JACKSON
P.O. Box 1432
Jackson, AL 36545
251-246-9898
Toll-Free: 888-880-1413
Fax: 251-246-9898
Email: dunaway@mobilecan.org
Type of Counseling:
Prepurchase Counseling,
Default/Foreclosure Counseling,
HECM Counseling, Rental
Counseling
Affiliate of: NATIONAL
FOUNDATION FOR
CONSUMER CREDIT,
INCORPORATED

MOBILE HOUSING BOARD
HOUSING COUNSELING
SERVICES
151 S Clairborne St
Mobile, AL 36633-1345
334-434-2202
Fax: 334-434-2220
Type of Counseling:
HECM Counseling,
Default/Foreclosure Counseling,
Rental Counseling, Prepurchase
Counseling

CONSUMER CREDIT
COUNSELING SERVICE OF
MONTROSE
P.O. Box 91068
Mobile, AL 36609-
251-990-8499
Fax: 251-666-6854
Type of Counseling:
Prepurchase Counseling,
Default/Foreclosure Counseling,
HECM Counseling

CONSUMER CREDIT
COUNSELING SERVICE OF
MOBILE
705 Oak Circle Drive East
Mobile, AL 36609
251-602-0011
Toll-Free: 888-880-1416
Fax: 251-666-6850
Email: dunaway@mobilecan.org
Type of Counseling:
Prepurchase Counseling,
Default/Foreclosure Counseling,
HECM Counseling
Affiliate of: NATIONAL
FOUNDATION FOR
CONSUMER CREDIT,
INCORPORATED

**LEGAL SERVICES
CORPORATION OF
ALABAMA, INCORPORATED
103 Dauphin Street, Suite 601
Mobile, AL 36602-
334-433-1032
Fax: 334-433-2488
Type of Counseling:
Prepurchase Counseling,
Default/Foreclosure Counseling,
Rental Counseling, HECM
Counseling

Affiliate of: WEST TENNESSEE
LEGAL SERVICES,
INCORPORATED

CONSUMER CREDIT
COUNSELING SERVICE OF
WEST FLORIDA
4365 Midwest Drive Suite 5
Mobile, AL 36609-
251-460-4600
Toll-Free: 800-343-3317
Fax: 251-460-9090
Type of Counseling:
Prepurchase Counseling, Rental
Counseling, Default/Foreclosure
Counseling, HECM Counseling

CONSUMER CREDIT
COUNSELING SERVICE OF
ALABAMA, INCORPORATED
777 S Lawrence St Ste 101
Montgomery, AL 36104-5075
334-265-8545
Toll-Free: 800-662-6119
Fax: 334-265-5926
Website: www.budgethelp.com
Type of Counseling:
HECM Counseling,
Default/Foreclosure Counseling,
Rental Counseling, Prepurchase
Counseling
Affiliate of: NATIONAL
FOUNDATION FOR
CONSUMER CREDIT,
INCORPORATED

HOUSING AUTHORITY OF
THE CITY OF MONTGOMERY
1020 Bell St
Montgomery, AL 36104-3006
334-206-7200
Fax: 334-206-7222
Type of Counseling:
Default/Foreclosure Counseling,
Rental Counseling, Prepurchase
Counseling

**LEGAL SERVICES
CORPORATION OF
ALABAMA
207 Montgomery St., 500 Bell
Bldg.
Montgomery, AL 36104
334-264-1471
Fax: 334-264-1474

Email:
mwaters@compumise.com
Type of Counseling:
Prepurchase Counseling,
Default/Foreclosure Counseling,
Rental Counseling, HECM
Counseling
Affiliate of: WEST TENNESSEE
LEGAL SERVICES,
INCORPORATED

**LEGAL SERVICES
CORPORATION OF
ALABAMA, INCORPORATED
207 Montgomery Street, Suite
500
Montgomery, AL 36104-
334-264-1471
Fax: 334-264-1474
Type of Counseling:
Prepurchase Counseling,
Default/Foreclosure Counseling,
Rental Counseling, HECM
Counseling
Affiliate of: WEST TENNESSEE
LEGAL SERVICES,
INCORPORATED

CONSUMER CREDIT
COUNSELING SERVICE OF
MONTROSE
22787 U. S. Highway 98,
Building B-2
Montrose, AL 36559-
251-990-8499
Toll-Free: 888-880-1412
Fax: 251-990-8406
Email: dunaway@mobilecan.org
Type of Counseling:
Rental Counseling, Prepurchase
Counseling, Default/Foreclosure
Counseling, HECM Counseling
Affiliate of: NATIONAL
FOUNDATION FOR
CONSUMER CREDIT,
INCORPORATED

DALLAS-SELMA
COMMUNITY ACTION AND
COMMUNITY DEVELOPMENT
713 Jeff Davis Ave
Selma, AL 367020988
334-875-2450
Fax: 334-872-3590
Type of Counseling:

HECM Counseling,
Default/Foreclosure Counseling,
Rental Counseling, Prepurchase
Counseling

**LEGAL SERVICES
CORPORATION OF
ALABAMA, INCORPORATED
1114 Church Street
Selma, AL 36702-
334-875-3770
Fax: 334-875-3773
Type of Counseling:
Prepurchase Counseling,
Default/Foreclosure Counseling,
Rental Counseling, HECM
Counseling
Affiliate of: WEST TENNESSEE
LEGAL SERVICES,
INCORPORATED

ORGANIZED COMMUNITY
ACTION PROGRAM
507 North Three Notch Street
Troy, AL 36081-0908
334-566-1712
Fax: 334-566-7417
Type of Counseling:
HECM Counseling,
Default/Foreclosure Counseling,
Rental Counseling, Prepurchase
Counseling

CITY OF TUSCALOOSA
COMMUNITY PLANNING
AND DEVELOPMENT
DEPARTMENT
1802 41st Avenue/Westgate
office
Tuscaloosa, AL 35401
205-349-0175
Fax: 205-349-0397
Type of Counseling:
HECM Counseling,
Default/Foreclosure Counseling,
Rental Counseling, Prepurchase
Counseling

COMMUNITY SERVICE
PROGRAMS OF WEST
ALABAMA, INCORPORATED
601 17th St
Tuscaloosa, AL 35401-4807
205-752-5429
Fax: 205-758-7229
Type of Counseling:

Default/Foreclosure Counseling,
Rental Counseling, Prepurchase
Counseling, HECM Counseling

**LEGAL SERVICES
CORPORATION OF
ALABAMA, INCORPORATED
131 McFarland Blvd E.
Tuscaloosa, AL 35402-
205-758-7503
Fax: 205-758-6041
Type of Counseling:
Prepurchase Counseling,
Default/Foreclosure Counseling,
Rental Counseling, HECM
Counseling
Affiliate of: WEST TENNESSEE
LEGAL SERVICES,
INCORPORATED

Alaska

CONSUMER CREDIT
COUNSELING SERVICE
(CCCS) OF ALASKA
208 E 4th Ave
Anchorage, AK 99501-2508
907-279-6501
Toll-Free: 800-478-6501
Fax: 907-276-6083
Email: jjones@cccsofak.com
Type of Counseling:
Default/Foreclosure Counseling,
Rental Counseling, Prepurchase
Counseling, HECM Counseling

**ANCHORAGE
NEIGHBORHOOD HOUSING
SERVICES, INCORPORATED
480 West Tudor Road
Anchorage, AK 99503-
907-677-8490
Fax: 907-677-8450
Email: cparker@alaska.net
Type of Counseling:
Default/Foreclosure Counseling,
Rental Counseling, Prepurchase
Counseling
Affiliate of: NEIGHBORHOOD
REINVESTMENT
CORPORATION

**FAIRBANKS
NEIGHBORHOOD HOUSING
SERVICES, INCORPORATED
1616 South Cushman St Ste 201

Fairbanks, AK 99707
907-451-7230
Fax: 907-451-7236
Email: fnhs@ptialaska.net
Type of Counseling:
Prepurchase Counseling
Affiliate of: NEIGHBORHOOD
REINVESTMENT
CORPORATION

Arizona

SOUTHEASTERN ARIZONA
GOVERNMENTS
ORGANIZATION
118 Arizona St
Bisbee, AZ 85603-1800
520-432-5301
Fax: 520-432-5858
Type of Counseling:
HECM Counseling,
Default/Foreclosure Counseling,
Rental Counseling, Prepurchase
Counseling

COMMUNITY SERVICES OF
ARIZONA
670 N Arizona Ave Ste 23
Chandler, AZ 85225
480-899-8717
Toll-Free: 800-471-8247
Fax: 480-786-4173
Type of Counseling:
Prepurchase Counseling, HECM
Counseling
Affiliate of: THE HOUSING
PARTNERSHIP NETWORK

**HOUSING FOR MESA,
INCORPORATED
251 W. Main Street
Mesa, AZ 85211-4457
480-649-1335
Fax: 480-649-1020
Email: hfm@uswest.net
Type of Counseling:
Prepurchase Counseling
Affiliate of: NATIONAL
COUNCIL OF LA RAZA

CHICANOS POR LA
LACAUSA, INC
1242 E Washington St Ste 103
Phoenix, AZ 85034-1149
602-253-0838
Fax: 602-253-4203

Type of Counseling:
Default/Foreclosure Counseling,
Prepurchase Counseling
Affiliate of: NATIONAL
COUNCIL OF LA RAZA

CITY OF PHOENIX
NEIGHBORHOOD
IMPROVEMENT AND
HOUSING SERVICES
200 W Washington St 4th Fl
Phoenix, AZ 85003-1611
602-534-4446
Fax: 602-534-1555
Type of Counseling:
Rental Counseling

**NEIGHBORHOOD HOUSING
SERVICES OF PHOENIX,
INCORPORATED
320 E McDowell Rd Ste 120
Phoenix, AZ 85004-4514
602-258-1659
Fax: 602-258-1666
Email: ritac@dancris.com
Affiliate of: NEIGHBORHOOD
REINVESTMENT
CORPORATION

ADMINISTRATION OF
RESOURCES AND CHOICES
1366 East Thomas Road, Suite
108
Phoenix, AZ 85014-
602-241-6169
Toll-Free: 888-264-2258
TTY/TDD: 602-241-6110
Fax: 602-230-9132
Email: kwhitearc@earthlink.net
Type of Counseling:
Prepurchase Counseling,
Default/Foreclosure Counseling,
HECM Counseling

**ACORN HOUSING
CORPORATION
1018 W Roosevelt St
Phoenix, AZ 85007-2107
602-253-7501
Fax: 602-258-7143
Type of Counseling:
HECM Counseling,
Default/Foreclosure Counseling,
Rental Counseling, Prepurchase
Counseling

Affiliate of: ACORN HOUSING
CORPORATION

LABOR'S COMMUNITY
SERVICE AGENCY
5818 N 7th St Ste 100
Phoenix, AZ 85014-5810
602-263-5741
Fax: 602-263-0815
Type of Counseling:
Default/Foreclosure Counseling

**ARIZONA FEDERATION OF
HOUSING COUNSELING
2502 N. 22nd Avenue
Phoenix, AZ 85009-1926
602-257-1715
Fax: 602-254-6080
Type of Counseling:
Default/Foreclosure Counseling,
Rental Counseling, Prepurchase
Counseling
Affiliate of: HOUSING
OPPORTUNITIES,
INCORPORATED

COMMUNITY HOUSING
RESOURCES OF ARIZONA
500 E Thomas Rd Ste 300
Phoenix, AZ 85012-3207
602-631-9780
Fax: 602-631-9757
Email: chr1@aol.com
Type of Counseling:
Default/Foreclosure Counseling,
Prepurchase Counseling
Affiliate of: NATIONAL
COUNCIL OF LA RAZA

**HOUSING AMERICA
CORPORATION
130 North State Avenue
Somerton, AZ 85350
520-627-4221
Fax: 520-627-4213
Email: nogalesm@juno.com
Type of Counseling:
Prepurchase Counseling
Affiliate of: NATIONAL
COUNCIL OF LA RAZA

ADMINISTRATION OF
RESOURCES AND CHOICES
P.O. Box 86802
Tucson, AZ 85754-
520-327-8250

TTY/TDD: 520-623-9577
Fax: 520-327-2665
Email: kwhitearc@earthlink.net
Type of Counseling:
Prepurchase Counseling,
Default/Foreclosure Counseling,
HECM Counseling

FAMILY HOUSING
RESOURCES
3777 E. Broadway, Ste. 100
Tucson, AZ 85716
520-318-0993
Toll-Free: 800-622-7462
Fax: 520-323-3788
Email: cpoor@quest.net
Type of Counseling:
Prepurchase Counseling

**CHICANOS POR LA CAUSA-
TUCSON
200 N. Stone
Tucson, AZ 85701
520-882-0018
Fax: 520-884-9007
Email: edcplc@azstarnet.com
Type of Counseling:
Prepurchase Counseling,
Default/Foreclosure Counseling,
Rental Counseling
Affiliate of: NATIONAL
COUNCIL OF LA RAZA

**TUCSON URBAN LEAGUE
INCORPORATED
2305 South Park Avenue
Tucson, AZ 85713-
520-620-1988
Fax: 520-620-1987
Email:
bcrobinsonbc@netscape.net
Type of Counseling:
Prepurchase Counseling,
Default/Foreclosure Counseling,
HECM Counseling, Rental
Counseling
Affiliate of: NATIONAL
URBAN LEAGUE

Arkansas

CONSUMER DEBT
COUNSELING
555 St. Louis Street
Batesville, AR 72501
870-793-7807

Toll-Free: 877-786-3328
Fax: 314-647-1359
Type of Counseling:
Default/Foreclosure Counseling

CONSUMER DEBT
COUNSELING
422 W. Main Street
Blytheville, AR 72315
870-763-2227
Toll-Free: 877-786-3328
Fax: 314-647-1359
Type of Counseling:
Default/Foreclosure Counseling

FAMILY SERVICE
AGENCY/CONSUMER
CREDIT COUNSELING
SERVICE
740 S. Salem Road Suite 104
Conway, AR 72032
501-450-9399
Fax: 501-450-3036
Email: wcohns@fsainc
Website:
www.HELPINGFAMILIES.ORG
Type of Counseling:
Prepurchase Counseling, Rental
Counseling, Default/Foreclosure
Counseling, HECM Counseling

ARKANSAS RIVER VALLEY
AREA COUNCIL,
INCORPORATED
613 North 5th Street
Dardanells, AR 72834-0808
501-229-4861
Fax: 501-229-4863
Type of Counseling: HECM
Counseling, Default/Foreclosure
Counseling, Rental Counseling,
Prepurchase Counseling

FAMILY SERVICE AGENCY
CONSUMER CREDIT
COUNSELING SERVICE
1301-B So. Waldron Road
Fort Smith, AR 72903-
501-450-9399
Fax: 501-450-3036
Email: wcohns@fsainc.org
Type of Counseling:
Prepurchase Counseling,
Default/Foreclosure Counseling,
HECM Counseling, Rental
Counseling

CRAWFORD-SEBASTIAN
COMMUNITY DEVELOPMENT
COUNCIL, INCORPORATED
4831 Armour St.
Fort Smith, AR 72914
501-785-2303
Fax: 501-785-2341
Type of Counseling:
HECM Counseling,
Default/Foreclosure Counseling,
Rental Counseling, Prepurchase
Counseling

EAST ARKANSAS LEGAL
SERVICES
402 Franklin St
Helena, AR 72342-3206
870-338-9834
Fax: 870-338-9837
Type of Counseling:
HECM Counseling,
Default/Foreclosure Counseling,
Prepurchase Counseling

FAMILY SERVICE AGENCY
CONSUMER CREDIT
COUNSELING SERVICE
1401 Malvern Avenue, Suite 100
Hot Springs, AR 71913-
501-321-1238
Fax: 501-624-5636
Email: wcohns@fsainc.org
Type of Counseling:
Prepurchase Counseling,
Default/Foreclosure Counseling,
HECM Counseling, Rental
Counseling

CONSUMER DEBT
COUNSELING
2218 East Race Street
Jonesboro, AR 724017217
870-932-8277
Toll-Free: 877-786-3328
Fax: 314-647-1359
Type of Counseling:
Default/Foreclosure Counseling

CROWLEY'S RIDGE
DEVELOPMENT COUNCIL,
INCORPORATED
249 S Main St
Jonesboro, AR 72403-1497
870-935-8610
Fax: 870-935-0291
Type of Counseling:

HECM Counseling,
Default/Foreclosure Counseling,
Rental Counseling, Prepurchase
Counseling

FAMILY SERVICE AGENCY
CONSUMER CREDIT
COUNSELING SERVICE
4504 Burrow Dr
Little Rock, AR 72231-6615
501-753-0202
Fax: 501-812-4309
Email: wcohns@fsainc.org
Type of Counseling:
HECM Counseling,
Default/Foreclosure Counseling,
Prepurchase Counseling, Rental
Counseling

FAMILY SERVICE
AGENCY/CONSUMER
CREDIT COUNSELING
SERVICE
300 S. Rodney Parham, Suite 6
Little Rock, AR 72205
501-219-2208
Fax: 501-219-2214
Email:
LRACCCS@HELPINGFAMILIE
S.ORG
Website: www.HELPING
FAMILIES.ORG
Type of Counseling:
Prepurchase Counseling,
Default/Foreclosure Counseling,
HECM Counseling, Rental
Counseling

IN AFFORDABLE HOUSING,
INCORPORATED
1200 John Barrow Rd # 109
Little Rock, AR 72205-6523
501-221-2203
Fax: 501-221-2279
Type of Counseling:
Default/Foreclosure Counseling,
Prepurchase Counseling

**ARGENTA COMMUNITY
DEVELOPMENT
CORPORATION
401 Main Street, Suite 200
North Little Rock, AR 72114
501-372-6936
Fax: 501-374-0496
Type of Counseling:

Prepurchase Counseling,
Default/Foreclosure Counseling,
Rental Counseling
Affiliate of: NEIGHBORHOOD
REINVESTMENT
CORPORATION

FAMILY SERVICE
AGENCY/CONSUMER
CREDIT COUNSELING
SERVICE
121 West 6th Ave. Suite 7C
Pine Bluff, AR 71601
870-536-6003
Fax: 870-535-4741
Email: wcohns@fsainc.org
Type of Counseling:
Prepurchase Counseling, Rental
Counseling, Default/Foreclosure
Counseling, HECM Counseling

UNIVERSAL HOUSING
DEVELOPMENT
301 E 3rd St
Russellville, AR 72811-5109
501-968-5001
Fax: 501-968-5002
Type of Counseling:
Default/Foreclosure Counseling,
Rental Counseling, Prepurchase
Counseling

FAMILY SERVICE AGENCY
CONSUMER CREDIT
COUNSELING SERVICE
5204 S Thompson Ste C
Springdale, AR 72764
501-751-4575
Fax: 501-751-7114
Email: wcohns@fsainc.org
Type of Counseling:
Default/Foreclosure Counseling,
Rental Counseling, Prepurchase
Counseling, HECM Counseling

LEGAL AID OF ARKANSAS
2126 E. Broadway
West Memphis, AR 723033201
870-732-6370
Fax: 870-732-6373
Type of Counseling:
Default/Foreclosure Counseling,
Rental Counseling, Prepurchase
Counseling

CONSUMER DEBT
COUNSELING
310 Mid-Continent Plaza, Suite
320
West Memphis, AR 723011748
870-735-2022
Toll-Free: 877-786-3328
Fax: 314-647-1359
Type of Counseling:
Default/Foreclosure Counseling

California

ANAHEIM HOUSING
AUTHORITY
201 S. Anaheim Blvd. 2nd Floor
Anaheim, CA 92085-
714-765-4340
Fax: 714-765-4654
Type of Counseling:
Prepurchase Counseling,
Default/Foreclosure Counseling,
Rental Counseling

**NEIGHBORHOOD HOUSING
SERVICES OF ORANGE
COUNTY
198 West Lincoln Ave., 2nd floor
Anaheim, CA 92805
714-490-1250
Fax: 714-490-1263
Type of Counseling:
Prepurchase Counseling
Affiliate of: NEIGHBORHOOD
REINVESTMENT
CORPORATION

CONSUMER CREDIT
COUNSELING SERVICE OF
ORANGE COUNTY
2450 E. Lincoln
Anaheim, CA 92809-4272
714-547-2227
Fax: 714-245-1690
Email: gbengoch@cccsoc.org
Website: www.cccsoc.org/
Type of Counseling:
Default/Foreclosure Counseling,
Rental Counseling, Prepurchase
Counseling

CONSUMER CREDIT
COUNSELING SERVICES OF
EAST BAY
3700 Delta Fair Boulevard #202
Antioch, CA 94509-

510-729-6966
Toll-Free: 888-788-8528
Fax: 510-729-6961
Website: www.cccsebay.org
Type of Counseling:
Prepurchase Counseling,
Default/Foreclosure Counseling,
Rental Counseling

CONSUMER CREDIT
COUNSELING SERVICE OF
KERN AND TULARE
COUNTIES
5300 Lennox Ave Ste 200
Bakersfield, CA 93309-1662
661-324-9628
Toll-Free: 800-272-2482
Fax: 661-324-0750
Email:
nancyjohnsoncccsbakersfield@at
t.net
Type of Counseling:
HECM Counseling,
Default/Foreclosure Counseling,
Prepurchase Counseling

SPRINGBOARD-BARSTOW
170 North Yucca (SBCCCU)
Barstow, CA 92311
800 -947-3752
Fax: 909-781-8027
Type of Counseling:
Default/Foreclosure Counseling,
Prepurchase Counseling

SPRINGBOARD-BEAUMONT
499 E 6th St
Beaumont, CA 92223-2215
800-947-3752-
Fax: 909-781-8027
Type of Counseling: HECM
Counseling, Default/Foreclosure
Counseling, Rental Counseling,
Prepurchase Counseling

CONSUMER CREDIT
COUNSELING SERVICES OF
LOS ANGELES
6510 Atlantic Ave.
Bell, CA 90201-
800-750-2227
Toll-Free: 800-750-2227
Fax: 213-890-9589
Type of Counseling:
Prepurchase Counseling,
Default/Foreclosure Counseling,

HECM Counseling, Rental
Counseling

**CONSUMER CREDIT
COUNSELING SERVICES OF
EAST BAY**
2326 Fourth Street #2
Berkeley, CA 94710-
510-729-6966
Toll-Free: 888-788-8528
Fax: 510-729-6961
Website: www.cccsebay.org
Type of Counseling:
Prepurchase Counseling,
Default/Foreclosure Counseling,
Rental Counseling

SPRINGBOARD-BISHOP
362 North Main St, 2nd Floor
Bishop, CA 93514
800-947-3752
Fax: 909-781-1003
Email: www.credit.org
Type of Counseling:
Prepurchase Counseling, Rental
Counseling, Default/Foreclosure
Counseling, HECM Counseling

**CONSUMER CREDIT
COUNSELING SERVICE OF
ORANGE COUNTY**
695 Madison Way
Brea, CA 92821-5732
714-547-2227
Fax: 714-245-1690
Email: gbengoch@cccsoc.org
Website: www.cccsoc.org
Type of Counseling:
Prepurchase Counseling,
Default/Foreclosure Counseling,
HECM Counseling, Rental
Counseling

**CONSUMER CREDIT
COUNSELING SERVICE OF
VENTURA COUNTY
INCORPORATED**
80 N Wood Rd Ste 312
Camarillo, CA 93010
800-540-2227
Toll-Free: 800-540-2227
Fax: 805-383-7721
Type of Counseling:
HECM Counseling,
Default/Foreclosure Counseling,

Rental Counseling, Prepurchase
Counseling
Affiliate of: NATIONAL
FOUNDATION FOR
CONSUMER CREDIT,
INCORPORATED

**SPRINGBOARD-CANOGA
PARK**
22048 Sherman Way, Suite 212
Canoga Park, CA 91303-
800-947-3752
Type of Counseling:
Prepurchase Counseling,
Default/Foreclosure Counseling

**HOUSING AUTHORITY OF
THE COUNTY OF SANTA
CRUZ**
2160 41st Ave
Capitola, CA 95010-2060
831-464-0170
Fax: 831-475-3861
Type of Counseling:
Default/Foreclosure Counseling,
HECM Counseling

**CONSUMER CREDIT
COUNSELING SERVICE OF
VENTURA COUNTY,
INCORPORATED**
4140 Jade Street
Capitola, CA 95010-
831-476-7733
Fax: 831-462-6606
Type of Counseling:
Default/Foreclosure Counseling,
Prepurchase Counseling, Rental
Counseling
Affiliate of: NATIONAL
FOUNDATION FOR
CONSUMER CREDIT,
INCORPORATED

**CONSUMER CREDIT
COUNSELING SERVICE OF
LOS ANGELES**
11829 South St Ste 101
Cerritos, CA 90703-6825
323-890-9500
Toll-Free: 800-750-2227
Fax: 323-890-9590
Type of Counseling: HECM
Counseling, Default/Foreclosure
Counseling, Rental Counseling,
Prepurchase Counseling

**COMMUNITY HOUSING AND
CREDIT COUNSELING
CENTER**
1001 Willow Street
Chico, CA 95928
530-891-4124
Toll-Free: 888-423-6333
Fax: 530-891-8547
Email:
srodriguez@chiphousing.org
Type of Counseling:
Prepurchase Counseling, Rental
Counseling, Default/Foreclosure
Counseling

**CONSUMER CREDIT
COUNSELING SERVICE OF
KERN AND TULARE
COUNTIES**
610 Blandy-NAWS Family
Service Center
China Lake, CA 93555
661-324-9628
Toll-Free: 800-272-2482
Fax: 661-324-0750
Email:
nancyjohnsoncccsbakersfield@at
t.net
Type of Counseling:
HECM Counseling,
Default/Foreclosure Counseling,
Prepurchase Counseling

SPRINGBOARD-CHINO
12150 Ramona Ave. Suite 12B
Chino, CA 91710
800-947-3752
Fax: 909-781-8027
Type of Counseling:
HECM Counseling, Prepurchase
Counseling, Default/Foreclosure
Counseling

**CONSUMER CREDIT
COUNSELORS OF SAN DIEGO
AND IMPERIAL COUNTY**
660 Bay Blvd Ste 114
Chula Vista, CA 91910-5200
619-498-0600
Fax: 619-498-0642
Type of Counseling: HECM
Counseling, Default/Foreclosure
Counseling, Rental Counseling,
Prepurchase Counseling

SPRINGBOARD-CHULA VISTA
229 "F" Street, Suite F
Chula Vista, CA 91910-
800-947-3752
Type of Counseling:
Prepurchase Counseling,
Default/Foreclosure Counseling,
HECM Counseling

SPRINGBOARD-CITY OF
COMMERCE
8900 Southeastern Avenue
City of Commerce, CA 90040-
800-947-3752
Type of Counseling:
Prepurchase Counseling,
Default/Foreclosure Counseling

CONSUMER CREDIT
COUNSELING SERVICE OF
LOS ANGELES
500 Citadel Dr Ste 300
Commerce, CA 90040
213-890-9511
Toll-Free: 800-750-2227
Fax: 323-869-5196
Email: cccsla.org.com
Type of Counseling: HECM
Counseling, Default/Foreclosure
Counseling, Rental Counseling,
Prepurchase Counseling

CONSUMER CREDIT
COUNSELING SERVICE OF
LOS ANGELES
600 Citadel Dr Ste 400
Commerce, CA 90040
323-890-9500
Toll-Free: 800-750-2227
Fax: 323-890-9590
Type of Counseling: HECM
Counseling, Default/Foreclosure
Counseling, Rental Counseling,
Prepurchase Counseling

CONSUMER CREDIT
COUNSELING SERVICES OF
EAST BAY
1070 Concord Avenue #170
Concord, CA 94510-
510-729-6966
Toll-Free: 888-788-8528
Fax: 510-729-6961
Website: www.cccsebay.org
Type of Counseling:
Prepurchase Counseling,

Default/Foreclosure Counseling,
Rental Counseling

SPRINGBOARD-CORONA
370 W Grand Blvd Ste 104
Corona, CA 91720-2174
800-947-3752
Fax: 909-781-8027
Type of Counseling:
Default/Foreclosure Counseling,
Prepurchase Counseling

CONSUMER CREDIT
COUNSELING SERVICE OF
ORANGE COUNTY
2701 S. Harbor Boulevard, E-6
Costa Mesa, CA 92626-
714-547-2227
Fax: 714-245-1680
Email: gbengoch@cccsoc.org
Type of Counseling:
Prepurchase Counseling,
Default/Foreclosure Counseling,
HECM Counseling, Rental
Counseling

CONSUMER CREDIT
COUNSELING SERVICE OF
LOS ANGELES
6167 Bristol Pkwy Ste 340
Culver City, CA 90230
323-890-9500
Toll-Free: 800-750-2227
Fax: 323-890-9590
Type of Counseling:
HECM Counseling,
Default/Foreclosure Counseling,
Prepurchase Counseling

CONSUMER CREDIT
COUNSELING SERVICE OF
SAN FRANCISCO, DALY CITY
2171 Junipero Serra Blvd.
Suite 300
Daly City, CA 94015
800-777-7526
Toll-Free: 800-777-7526
Fax: 415-788-7817
Type of Counseling:
Prepurchase Counseling,
Default/Foreclosure Counseling,
Rental Counseling, HECM
Counseling

SPRINGBOARD-DOWNEY
8444 Florence Ave

Downey, CA 90241-
800-947-3752
Type of Counseling:
Prepurchase Counseling,
Default/Foreclosure Counseling

CONSUMER CREDIT
COUNSELING SERVICES OF
EAST BAY
6500 Dublin Court #213
Dublin, CA 94568
510-729-6966
Toll-Free: 888-788-8528
Fax: 510-729-6961
Website: www.cccsebay.org
Type of Counseling:
Default/Foreclosure Counseling,
Prepurchase Counseling, Rental
Counseling

SPRINGBOARD-EL CAJON
1150 Broadway, Suite 230
El Cajon, CA 92021-
800-947-3752
Type of Counseling:
Prepurchase Counseling,
Default/Foreclosure Counseling

CONSUMER CREDIT
COUNSELORS OF SAN DIEGO
AND IMPERIAL COUNTY
700 North Johnson Ave Ste G
El Cajon, CA 92020
619-447-5700
Fax: 619-447-0519
Type of Counseling: HECM
Counseling, Default/Foreclosure
Counseling, Rental Counseling,
Prepurchase Counseling

CONSUMER CREDIT
COUNSELORS OF SAN DIEGO
AND IMPERIAL COUNTY
370 Aurora St Ste A & B
El Centro, CA 92243
760-337-2300
Fax: 760-233-8196
Type of Counseling: HECM
Counseling, Default/Foreclosure
Counseling, Rental Counseling,
Prepurchase Counseling

SPRINGBOARD- ESCONDIDO
139 East Third Ave. Suite 108
Escondido, CA 92025-
800-947-3752

Type of Counseling:
Prepurchase Counseling,
Default/Foreclosure Counseling

PACIFIC COMMUNITY
SERVICES FAIRFIELD
934 Missouri St., Ste. D
Fairfield, CA 94533
925-439-1056
Toll-Free: 800-914-6874
Type of Counseling:
Prepurchase Counseling,
Default/Foreclosure Counseling,
Rental Counseling

CONSUMER CREDIT
COUNSELING SERVICES OF
EAST BAY
609 Jefferson Street, G2
Fairfield, CA 94533-
510-729-6966
Toll-Free: 888-788-8528
Fax: 510-729-6961
Website: www.cccsebay.org
Type of Counseling:
Prepurchase Counseling,
Default/Foreclosure Counseling,
Rental Counseling

SPRINGBOARD- FOUNTANA
8275 Sierra Ave,Suite 106
Fountana, CA 92335
800-947-3752
Fax: 909-781-8027
Type of Counseling:
Prepurchase Counseling,
Default/Foreclosure Counseling

CONSUMER CREDIT
COUNSELING SERVICES OF
EAST BAY
3100 Mowry Avenue #403A
Fremont, CA 94538-
510-729-6966
Toll-Free: 888-788-8528
Fax: 510-729-6961
Website: www.cccsebay.org
Type of Counseling:
Prepurchase Counseling,
Default/Foreclosure Counseling,
Rental Counseling

CONSUMER CREDIT
COUNSELING SERVICE OF
CENTRAL VALLEY
4969 E McKinley Ave Ste 107

Fresno, CA 93727-1968
559-454-1700
Toll-Free: 800-773-9009
Fax: 559-454-1405
Type of Counseling: HECM
Counseling, Default/Foreclosure
Counseling, Rental Counseling,
Prepurchase Counseling

CONSUMER CREDIT
COUNSELING SERVICE OF
MID COUNTIES FRESNO
4270 N. Blackstone, Ste. 312
Fresno, CA 93726
559-650-7658
Fax: 559-650-7657
Type of Counseling:
Prepurchase Counseling,
Default/Foreclosure Counseling,
Rental Counseling, HECM
Counseling

CONSUMER CREDIT
COUNSELING SERVICES OF
CENTRAL VALLEY
3170 N. Chestnut Avenue, Suite
101
Fresno, CA 93703-
559-454-5090
Fax: 559-454-0672
Type of Counseling:
Prepurchase Counseling,
Default/Foreclosure Counseling,
HECM Counseling, Rental
Counseling

SPRINGBOARD- FORT IRWIN
Fort Irwin Military Base
Ft. Irwin, CA 92310
800-947-3752
Fax: 909-781-9896
Type of Counseling:
Default/Foreclosure Counseling,
Prepurchase Counseling

SPRINGBOARD- FULLERTON
801 E. Chapman Ave., Suite 213
Fullerton, CA 92831-
800-947-3752
Type of Counseling:
Prepurchase Counseling,
Default/Foreclosure Counseling

CONSUMER CREDIT
COUNSELING SERVICE OF
ORANGE COUNTY

2501 E Chapman Ave Ste 100
Fullerton, CA 92631
714-547-2227
Fax: 714-245-1680
Email: gbengoch@cccsoc.org
Website: www.cccsoc.org
Type of Counseling:
Default/Foreclosure Counseling,
Prepurchase Counseling, HECM
Counseling

CONSUMER CREDIT
COUNSELING SERVICE OF
VENTURA COUNTY,
INCORPORATED
8339 Church Street, Suite 106
Gilroy, CA 95020-
408-842-1927
Fax: 408-842-0035
Type of Counseling:
Default/Foreclosure Counseling,
Prepurchase Counseling, Rental
Counseling
Affiliate of: NATIONAL
FOUNDATION FOR
CONSUMER CREDIT,
INCORPORATED

PROJECT SENTINEL
7365 Monterey Rd., Ste. D1
Gilroy, CA 95020
408-842-7740
Toll-Free: 800-468-7464
Fax: 408-842-8054
Type of Counseling: Rental
Counseling, Prepurchase
Counseling

CONSUMER CREDIT
COUNSELING SERVICE OF
LOS ANGELES
112 West Broadway, Suite 212
Glendale, CA 91204
323-890-9500
Toll-Free: 800-750-2227
Fax: 323-890-9590
Type of Counseling: HECM
Counseling, Default/Foreclosure
Counseling, Rental Counseling,
Prepurchase Counseling

CONSUMER CREDIT
COUNSELING SERVICE OF
LOS ANGELES
16800 Devonshire Ste 301
Granada Hills, CA 91344

323-890-9500
Toll-Free: 800-750-2227
Fax: 323-890-9590
Type of Counseling:
HECM Counseling,
Default/Foreclosure Counseling,
Rental Counseling, Prepurchase
Counseling

CATHOLIC CHARITIES
221 Turner Street
Guasti, CA 91743
909-390-2424
Fax: 909-390-2433
Type of Counseling: Rental
Counseling

CONSUMER CREDIT
COUNSELING SERVICES OF
CENTRAL VALLEY
598 W. Grangeville Blvd.
Suite 102
Hanford, CA 93230
559-454-1700
Fax: 559-454-1405
Type of Counseling:
Prepurchase Counseling,
Default/Foreclosure Counseling,
HECM Counseling, Rental
Counseling

EDEN COUNCIL FOR HOPE
AND OPPORTUNITY/ECHO
HOUSING
770 A St
Hayward, CA 94541-3956
510-581-9380
Fax: 510-537-4793
Type of Counseling:
Prepurchase Counseling,
Default/Foreclosure Counseling,
HECM Counseling, Rental
Counseling

SPRINGBOARD- HEMET
1700 E Florida Ave
Hemet, CA 92544-4679
800-947-3752
Fax: 909-781-8027
Type of Counseling: HECM
Counseling, Default/Foreclosure
Counseling, Prepurchase
Counseling

CONSUMER CREDIT
COUNSELING SERVICE OF
ORANGE COUNTY
8907 Warner Avenue Ste 215

Huntington Beach, CA 92647
714-547-2227
Fax: 714-245-1690
Type of Counseling: HECM
Counseling, Default/Foreclosure
Counseling, Rental Counseling,
Prepurchase Counseling

SPRINGBOARD- INDIO
81730 Highway 111, Unit #3
Indio, CA 92201-3937
800-947-3752
Fax: 909-781-8027
Type of Counseling: HECM
Counseling, Default/Foreclosure
Counseling, Rental Counseling,
Prepurchase Counseling

CATHOLIC CHARITIES
45149 Smurr St
Indio, CA 92201
760-347-1188
Fax: 760-347-8388
Type of Counseling: Rental
Counseling

**INGLEWOOD
NEIGHBORHOOD HOUSING
SERVICES, INCORPORATED
335 E Manchester Blvd
Inglewood, CA 90301
310-674-3756
Fax: 310-674-6915
Email:
Nwinglewood@earthlink.net
Type of Counseling:
Prepurchase Counseling,
Default/Foreclosure Counseling
Affiliate of: NEIGHBORHOOD
REINVESTMENT
CORPORATION

CONSUMER CREDIT
COUNSELING SERVICES OF
CENTRAL VALLEY
Null
Kingsburg, CA 93631
559-454-1700
Fax: 559-454-1405
Type of Counseling:
Prepurchase Counseling,
Default/Foreclosure Counseling,
HECM Counseling, Rental
Counseling

EDEN COUNCIL FOR HOPE
AND OPPORTUNITY/ECHO
HOUSING
3311 Pacific Ave
Livermore, CA 94705
925-449-7340
Fax: 925-449-0704
Type of Counseling:
Default/Foreclosure Counseling,
Rental Counseling, Prepurchase
Counseling, HECM Counseling

CONSUMER CREDIT
COUNSELING SERVICES OF
VENTURA COUNTY,
INCORPORATED LOMPOC
1320 N. H St.
Lompoc, CA 93436
800-540-2227
Toll-Free: 800-540-2227
Fax: 805-383-7722
Type of Counseling:
Prepurchase Counseling,
Default/Foreclosure Counseling,
Rental Counseling, HECM
Counseling

HOUSING AUTHORITY OF
THE COUNTY OF SANTA
BARBARA
815 W Ocean Ave
Lompoc, CA 93436-6526
805-736-3423
Fax: 805-735-7672
Type of Counseling: HECM
Counseling, Default/Foreclosure
Counseling, Rental Counseling,
Prepurchase Counseling

CONSUMER CREDIT
COUNSELING SERVICE OF
LOS ANGELES
2501 Cherry Ave Ste 260
Long Beach, CA 90806-2034
323-890-9500
Toll-Free: 800-750-2227
Fax: 323-890-9590
Type of Counseling: HECM
Counseling, Default/Foreclosure
Counseling, Rental Counseling,
Prepurchase Counseling

CONSUMER CREDIT
COUNSELING SERVICE OF
LOS ANGELES
500 Citadel Drive Suite 300

Los Angeles, CA 90040-
323-890-9500
Toll-Free: 800-750-2227
Fax: 323-890-9590
Type of Counseling: HECM
Counseling, Default/Foreclosure
Counseling, Prepurchase
Counseling, Rental Counseling

CONSUMER CREDIT
COUNSELING SERVICES OF
LOS ANGELES
4929 Wilshire Blvd. #400
Los Angeles, CA 90010-
800-750-2227
Toll-Free: 800-750-2227
Fax: 213-890-9589
Type of Counseling:
Prepurchase Counseling,
Default/Foreclosure Counseling,
HECM Counseling, Rental
Counseling

**ACORN HOUSING
CORPORATION
3655 South Grand Street Suite
250
Los Angeles, CA 90007-
213-748-1345
Fax: 213-747-4221
Type of Counseling:
Default/Foreclosure Counseling,
Prepurchase Counseling
Affiliate of: ACORN HOUSING
CORPORATION

SPRINGBOARD- LOS
ANGELES
1605 W. Olympic Blvd. Ste. 9023
Los Angeles, CA 90015-
800-947-3752
Type of Counseling:
Prepurchase Counseling,
Default/Foreclosure Counseling

CONSUMER CREDIT
COUNSELING SERVICE OF
LOS ANGELES
4060 S Figueroa St
Los Angeles, CA 90037-2042
323-890-9500
Toll-Free: 800-750-2227
Fax: 323-890-9590
Type of Counseling: HECM
Counseling, Default/Foreclosure

Counseling, Rental Counseling,
Prepurchase Counseling

**LOS ANGELES
NEIGHBORHOOD HOUSING
SERVICES, INCORPORATED
3111 S Flower St
Los Angeles, CA 90007-3727
213-749-7797
Fax: 213-749-3325
Email: lorig@lanhs.corpusa.com
Type of Counseling:
Default/Foreclosure Counseling,
Prepurchase Counseling
Affiliate of: NEIGHBORHOOD
REINVESTMENT
CORPORATION

CONSUMER CREDIT
COUNSELING SERVICES OF
CENTRAL VALLEY
800 E. Yosemite
Madera, CA 93638
559-454-1700
Fax: 559-454-1405
Type of Counseling:
Prepurchase Counseling,
Default/Foreclosure Counseling,
HECM Counseling, Rental
Counseling

CONSUMER CREDIT
COUNSELING SERVICE OF
MID COUNTIES MERCED
885 W. 18th St.
Merced, CA 95340
209-723-9982
Fax: 209-723-4315
Type of Counseling:
Prepurchase Counseling,
Default/Foreclosure Counseling,
Rental Counseling, HECM
Counseling

PROJECT SENTINEL
79 S. Main Street
Milpitas, CA 95035-
408-946-6582
Fax: 650-321-4173
Type of Counseling:
Prepurchase Counseling,
Default/Foreclosure Counseling,
HECM Counseling, Rental
Counseling

CONSUMER CREDIT
COUNSELING SERVICE OF
ORANGE COUNTY
28570 Marguerite Pkwy, Ste 213
Mission Viejo, CA 92692
714-547-2227
Fax: 714-245-1690
Email: gbengoch@cccsoc.org
Website: www.cccsoc.org
Type of Counseling: HECM
Counseling, Default/Foreclosure
Counseling, Rental Counseling,
Prepurchase Counseling

STANISLAUS COUNTY
AFFORDABLE HOUSING
CORPORATION
201 East Rumble Road, Suite E
Modesto, CA 95350
209-574-1155
Fax: 209-574-0586
Type of Counseling: HECM
Counseling, Default/Foreclosure
Counseling, Rental Counseling,
Prepurchase Counseling

CONSUMER CREDIT
COUNSELING SERVICE OF
MID COUNTIES MODESTO
1800 Tully Rd., Ste. A-1
Modesto, CA 95350
209-522-1261
Fax: 209-522-5845
Type of Counseling:
Prepurchase Counseling,
Default/Foreclosure Counseling,
Rental Counseling, HECM
Counseling

COMMUNITY HOUSING AND
SHELTER SERVICES
936 McHenry Avenue Room 230
Modesto, CA 95354
209-574-1149
Fax: 209-575-9818
Type of Counseling:
Default/Foreclosure Counseling,
Rental Counseling, Prepurchase
Counseling

**NEIGHBORHOOD
PARTNERSHIP OF
MONTCLAIR
9916 Central Ave
Montclair, CA 91763
909-624-9110

Fax: 909-624-9263
Email: margaret@npnhs.com
Type of Counseling:
Default/Foreclosure Counseling,
Prepurchase Counseling
Affiliate of: NEIGHBORHOOD
REINVESTMENT
CORPORATION

SPRINGBOARD- MONTCLAIR
4959 Palo Verde St Ste 100C
Montclair, CA 91763-2330
909-781-0114
Toll-Free: 800-947-3752
Fax: 909-781-8027
Type of Counseling:
HECM Counseling,
Default/Foreclosure Counseling,
Prepurchase Counseling

CONSUMER CREDIT
COUNSELING SERVICE OF
VENTURA COUNTY,
INCORPORATED
801 Lighthouse Ave., Suite 106
Monterey, CA 93940-
831-643-0531
Fax: 831-643-0532
Type of Counseling:
Default/Foreclosure Counseling,
Rental Counseling, Prepurchase
Counseling, HECM Counseling
Affiliate of: NATIONAL
FOUNDATION FOR
CONSUMER CREDIT,
INCORPORATED

CATHOLIC CHARITIES
23-700 Sunnymead Blvd
Moreno Valley, CA 92556
909-485-2125
Fax: 909-485-2188
Type of Counseling: Rental
Counseling

SPRINGBOARD- MORENO
VALLEY
23800 Sunnymead Blvd Suite F
Moreno Valley, CA 92553
800-947-3752
Fax: 909-781-8027
Type of Counseling:
HECM Counseling,
Default/Foreclosure Counseling,
Prepurchase Counseling

CONSUMER CREDIT
COUNSELING SERVICE OF
SACRAMENTO VALLEY -
NORTH HIGHLANDS
4636 Watt Ave.
North Highlands, CA 95660
916-379-3600
Toll-Free: 800-736-2227
Fax: 916-379-0636
Type of Counseling:
Prepurchase Counseling,
Default/Foreclosure Counseling,
HECM Counseling

**ACORN HOUSING
CORPORATION
3205 Farnam Ave
Oakland, CA 94601
510-436-6532
Fax: 510-436-6395
Type of Counseling:
Default/Foreclosure Counseling,
Prepurchase Counseling
Affiliate of: ACORN HOUSING
CORPORATION

CONSUMER CREDIT
COUNSELING SERVICES OF
EAST BAY
587 15th Street
Oakland, CA 94612
510-729-6966
Toll-Free: 888-788-8528
Fax: 510-729-6961
Website: www.cccsebay.org
Type of Counseling:
Prepurchase Counseling,
Default/Foreclosure Counseling,
Rental Counseling

**SPANISH SPEAKING UNITY
COUNCIL
1900 Fruitvale Avenue, Suite 2-A
Oakland, CA 94601
510-535-6941
Fax: 510-534-7771
Email: wleone@unitycouncil.org
Type of Counseling:
Prepurchase Counseling
Affiliate of: NATIONAL
COUNCIL OF LA RAZA

**HOME BUYER ASSISTANCE
CENTER
1611 Telegraph Ave. #620
Oakland, CA 94612

510-832-6925
Fax: 510-832-1335
Website: www.hbac.org
Type of Counseling:
Prepurchase Counseling
Affiliate of: THE HOUSING
PARTNERSHIP NETWORK

CONSUMER CREDIT
COUNSELING SERVICES OF
EAST BAY
333 Hegenberger Rd Ste 710
Oakland, CA 94621-1462
510-729-6969
Toll-Free: 888-788-8528
Fax: 510-729-6961
Email: ljd8421@aol.com
Website: www.cccsebay.org
Type of Counseling:
Default/Foreclosure Counseling,
Prepurchase Counseling, Rental
Counseling

EDEN COUNCIL FOR HOPE
AND OPPORTUNITY/ECHO
HOUSING
1305 Franklin St Ste 305
Oakland, CA 94612-3213
510-271-7931
Fax: 510-763-3736
Type of Counseling:
Prepurchase Counseling,
Default/Foreclosure Counseling,
HECM Counseling, Rental
Counseling

**CATHOLIC CHARITIES OF
THE EAST BAY
433 Jefferson Street
Oakland, CA 94607
510-768-3100
Type of Counseling:
Prepurchase Counseling,
Default/Foreclosure Counseling,
HECM Counseling, Rental
Counseling
Affiliate of: CATHOLIC
CHARITIES USA

EDEN COUNCIL FOR HOPE
AND OPPORTUNITY/ECHO
HOUSING
4768 Lucchesi Court
Oakley, CA 94561
925-679-8023
Fax: 925-625-4189

Type of Counseling: HECM
Counseling

CONSUMER CREDIT
COUNSELORS OF SAN DIEGO
AND IMPERIAL COUNTY
2741 Vista Way Ste 205
Oceanside, CA 92054-6372
760-757-2227
Fax: 760-757-9600
Type of Counseling:
HECM Counseling,
Default/Foreclosure Counseling,
Rental Counseling, Prepurchase
Counseling

INLAND FAIR HOUSING
MEDIATION BOARD
1005 N Begonia Ave
Ontario, CA 91762
909-984-2254
Toll-Free: 800-321-0911
Fax: 909-460-0274
Type of Counseling: HECM
Counseling, Default/Foreclosure
Counseling, Rental Counseling,
Prepurchase Counseling

CONSUMER CREDIT
COUNSELING SERVICE OF
SACRAMENTO VALLEY -
ORANGEVALE
6000 Main Ave.
Orangevale, CA 95662
916-379-3600
Toll-Free: 800-736-2227
Fax: 916-379-0636
Type of Counseling:
Prepurchase Counseling,
Default/Foreclosure Counseling,
HECM Counseling

CONSUMER CREDIT
COUNSELING SERVICE OF
VENTURA COUNTY,
INCORPORATED OXNARD
750 W. Gonzales Rd., Ste.
Oxnard, CA
800-540-2227
Toll-Free: 800-540-2227
Fax: 805-383-7722
Type of Counseling:
Prepurchase Counseling,
Default/Foreclosure Counseling,
Rental Counseling, HECM
Counseling

SPRINGBOARD- PALM
SPRINGS
1001 South Palm Canyon Ste 103
Palm Springs, CA 92262
800-947-3752
Fax: 909-781-8027
Type of Counseling: HECM
Counseling, Default/Foreclosure
Counseling, Rental Counseling,
Prepurchase Counseling

CONSUMER CREDIT
COUNSELING SERVICE OF
LOS ANGELES
1605 E Palmdale Blvd Ste E
Palmdale, CA 93550
661-265-8142
Toll-Free: 800-750-2227
Fax: 661-265-8508
Type of Counseling: HECM
Counseling, Default/Foreclosure
Counseling, Rental Counseling,
Prepurchase Counseling

PROJECT SENTINEL
430 Sherman Avenue Suite 308
Palo Alto, CA 94306
650-321-6291
Fax: 650-321-4173
Type of Counseling:
Default/Foreclosure Counseling,
Prepurchase Counseling, Rental
Counseling, HECM Counseling

CONSUMER CREDIT
COUNSELING SERVICE OF
VENTURA COUNTY,
INCORPORATED
480 Lytton Ave.
Palo Alto, CA 74301
650-329-9674
Fax: 650-322-2302
Type of Counseling:
Default/Foreclosure Counseling,
Prepurchase Counseling, Rental
Counseling
Affiliate of: NATIONAL
FOUNDATION FOR
CONSUMER CREDIT,
INCORPORATED

CONSUMER CREDIT
COUNSELING SERVICE OF
LOS ANGELES
505 E. Colorado Blvd
Pasadena, CA 91101

323-890-9500
Toll-Free: 800-750-2227
Fax: 323-890-9590
Type of Counseling: HECM
Counseling, Default/Foreclosure
Counseling, Rental Counseling,
Prepurchase Counseling

CONSUMER CREDIT
COUNSELING SERVICE OF
VENTURA COUNTY,
INCORPORATED PASO
ROBLES
Null
Paso Robles, CA 93446
800-540-2227
Toll-Free: 800-540-2227
Fax: 805-383-7722
Type of Counseling:
Prepurchase Counseling,
Default/Foreclosure Counseling,
Rental Counseling, HECM
Counseling

PACIFIC COMMUNITY
SERVICES
329 Railroad Ave
Pittsburg, CA 94565-2245
925-439-1056
Fax: 925-439-0831
Type of Counseling: Rental
Counseling, Default/Foreclosure
Counseling, Prepurchase
Counseling

CONSUMER CREDIT
COUNSELING SERVICE OF
LOS ANGELES
281 S.Thomas Street Suite 505
Pomona, CA 91766
909-622-7203
Toll-Free: 800-750-2227
Fax: 909-622-5625
Email: fharris@cccsla.org
Type of Counseling: HECM
Counseling, Default/Foreclosure
Counseling, Rental Counseling,
Prepurchase Counseling

SPRINGBOARD- RANCHO
CUCAMONGA
9267 Haven Avenue, Suite 101
Rancho Cucamonga, CA 91730-
800-947-3752
Fax: 909-328-7742
Type of Counseling:

Default/Foreclosure Counseling, Prepurchase Counseling

CONSUMER CREDIT
COUNSELING SERVICE OF
SACRAMENTO VALLEY -
REDDING
3609 Bechelli Lane, Ste. I
Redding, CA 96002
916-379-3600
Toll-Free: 8007362227
Fax: 9163790636
Type of Counseling:
Prepurchase Counseling,
Default/Foreclosure Counseling,
HECM Counseling

**RICHMOND
NEIGHBORHOOD HOUSING
SERVICES, INCORPORATED
500 S 15th St
Richmond, CA 94804-3709
510-237-6459
Fax: 510-237-3317
Email: rnhs-ca@ix.netcom.com
Type of Counseling:
Prepurchase Counseling,
Default/Foreclosure Counseling
Affiliate of: NEIGHBORHOOD
REINVESTMENT
CORPORATION

CONSUMER CREDIT
COUNSELING SERVICES OF
EAST BAY
700 Barrett Avenue
Richmond, CA 94801-
510-729-6966
Toll-Free: 888-788-8528
Fax: 510-729-6961
Website: www.cccsebay.org
Type of Counseling:
Prepurchase Counseling,
Default/Foreclosure Counseling,
Rental Counseling

**VOLUNTEER CENTER OF
RIVERSIDE COUNTY
2060 University Avenue
Riverside, CA 92517
909-686-4402
Fax: 909-686-7417
Type of Counseling: Rental
Counseling
Affiliate of: HOUSING
OPPORTUNITIES,
INCORPORATED

SPRINGBOARD NON PROFIT
CONSUMER CREDIT
MANAGEMENT
6370 Magnolia Ave Ste 200
Riverside, CA 92517-2149
909-781-0114
Toll-Free: 800-947-3752
Fax: 909-781-9896
Email: springboard@credit.org
Website: www.credit.org
Type of Counseling:
Default/Foreclosure Counseling,
Rental Counseling, Prepurchase
Counseling

CONSUMER CREDIT
COUNSELING SERVICE OF
SACRAMENTO VALLEY
8795 Folsom Blvd., Suite 250
Sacramento, CA 95826
916-379-3600
Toll-Free: 800-736-2227
Fax: 916-379-0626
Website: www.cccssacto.org
Type of Counseling:
HECM Counseling,
Default/Foreclosure Counseling,
Prepurchase Counseling

**ACORN HOUSING
CORPORATION
4921 San Francisco Blvd.
Sacramento, CA 95820
916-451-9659
Fax: 916-455-1797
Type of Counseling:
Prepurchase Counseling,
Default/Foreclosure Counseling
Affiliate of: ACORN HOUSING
CORPORATION

CONSUMER CREDIT
COUNSELING SERVICE OF
SACRAMENTO VALLEY -
DOWNTOWN
800 H St.
Sacramento, CA 95814
916-379-3600
Toll-Free: 800-736-2227
Fax: 916-379-0636
Type of Counseling:
Prepurchase Counseling,
Default/Foreclosure Counseling,
HECM Counseling

SACRAMENTO
NEIGHBORHOOD HOUSING
SERVICES HOMEOWNERSHIP
CENTER
3447 5th Avenue
Sacramento, CA 95817-
916-452-5361
Fax: 916-431-3209
Type of Counseling:
Prepurchase Counseling,
Default/Foreclosure Counseling,
Rental Counseling

CONSUMER CREDIT
COUNSELING SERVICE OF
VENTURA COUNTY,
INCORPORATED
601 E Romie Ln Ste 9
Salinas, CA 93901-4229
831-751-9517
Fax: 831-751-9521
Type of Counseling:
Default/Foreclosure Counseling,
Rental Counseling, Prepurchase
Counseling, HECM Counseling

**NEIGHBORHOOD HOUSING
SERVICES OF THE INLAND
EMPIRE, INCORPORATED
1390 North D ST
San Bernardino, CA 92405
909-884-6891
Fax: 909-884-6893
Email: dawkins@nhsie.org
Type of Counseling:
HECM Counseling,
Default/Foreclosure Counseling,
Rental Counseling, Prepurchase
Counseling
Affiliate of: NEIGHBORHOOD
REINVESTMENT
CORPORATION

SPRINGBOARD- SAN
BERNARDINO
1814 Commerce Center West,
Suite B
San Bernardino, CA 92408
800 947-3752
Fax: 909-781-8027
Type of Counseling:
Prepurchase Counseling, Rental
Counseling, Default/Foreclosure
Counseling, HECM Counseling

SPRINGBOARD- SAN
BERNARDINO
1814 Commerce Center West
Suite B
San Bernardino, CA 92408-
800-947-3752
Toll-Free: 800-947-3752
Fax: 909-890-4071
Type of Counseling:
Default/Foreclosure Counseling,
Rental Counseling, Prepurchase
Counseling

SPRINGBOARD- SAN
BERNARDINO
7285 Boulder Ave.
San Bernardino, CA 92402
800 947 3752
Fax: 909-781-8027
Type of Counseling: HECM
Counseling, Prepurchase
Counseling, Default/Foreclosure
Counseling, Rental Counseling

**SAN DIEGO URBAN
LEAGUE
720 Gateway Center Drive
San Diego, CA 92102-
619-263-3115
Fax: 619-263-3660
Email: michelle@sdul.org
Type of Counseling:
Prepurchase Counseling,
Default/Foreclosure Counseling,
HECM Counseling, Rental
Counseling
Affiliate of: NATIONAL
URBAN LEAGUE

**SAN DIEGO
NEIGHBORHOOD HOUSING
SERVICES, INCORPORATED
4336 54th St., Ste B
San Diego, CA 92115
619-229-2370
Fax: 619-229-2375
Type of Counseling:
Prepurchase Counseling
Affiliate of: NEIGHBORHOOD
REINVESTMENT
CORPORATION

CONSUMER CREDIT
COUNSELORS OF SAN DIEGO
AND IMPERIAL COUNTY
1550 Hotel Cir N Ste 110

San Diego, CA 92108-2901
888-298-2227
Fax: 619-542-1328
Type of Counseling: HECM
Counseling, Default/Foreclosure
Counseling, Rental Counseling,
Prepurchase Counseling

SAN DIEGO HOME LOAN
COUNSELING AND
EDUCATION CENTER
3180 University Avenue Suite
430
San Diego, CA 92104
619-624-2330
Fax: 619-624-0314
Type of Counseling:
Default/Foreclosure Counseling,
Prepurchase Counseling

UNION OF PAN ASIAN
COMMUNITIES
3288 El Cahon Boulevard, #3
San Diego, CA 92104
619-280-5197
Fax: 619-235-9002
Type of Counseling:
Default/Foreclosure Counseling,
Prepurchase Counseling

SPRINGBOARD- SAN DIEGO
8998 El Cajon Boulevard
San Diego, CA 92115
800-947-3752
Type of Counseling:
Prepurchase Counseling,
Default/Foreclosure Counseling

SPRINGBOARD- SAN DIEGO
7710 Balboa Avenue, Suite 218-F
San Diego, CA 92111
800-947-3752
Type of Counseling:
Prepurchase Counseling,
Default/Foreclosure Counseling

CONSUMER CREDIT
COUNSELORS OF SAN DIEGO
AND IMPERIAL COUNTY
15373 Innovation Dr Ste 115
San Diego, CA 92128-3413
888-298-2227
Fax: 858-276-0296
Type of Counseling: HECM
Counseling, Default/Foreclosure

Counseling, Rental Counseling,
Prepurchase Counseling

SPRINGBOARD- SAN DIEGO
2550 Fifth Ave, Suite 169
San Diego, CA 92103
800-947-3752
Type of Counseling:
Prepurchase Counseling,
Default/Foreclosure Counseling

UNION OF PAN ASIAN
COMMUNITIES
1031 25th Street
San Diego, CA 92102
619-232-6454
Fax: 619-235-9002
Type of Counseling:
Default/Foreclosure Counseling,
Prepurchase Counseling

NEIGHBORHOOD HOUSE
ASSOCIATION
841 S 41st St
San Diego, CA 92113-1801
619-263-7761
Fax: 619-263-6398
Email:
ebrown@neighborhoodhouse.or
g
Type of Counseling: HECM
Counseling, Default/Foreclosure
Counseling, Rental Counseling,
Prepurchase Counseling

CONSUMER CREDIT
COUNSELING SERVICES
1406 A Valencia St
San Francisco, CA 94110
800-777-7526
Toll-Free: 800-777-7526
Fax: 415-788-7817
Type of Counseling:
Default/Foreclosure Counseling,
Rental Counseling, Prepurchase
Counseling, HECM Counseling

CONSUMER CREDIT
COUNSELING SERVICES OF
SAN FRANCISCO
150 Post Street, 5th floor
San Francisco, CA 94108-
800-777-7526
Toll-Free: 800-777-7526
Fax: 415-788-7817
Type of Counseling:

HECM Counseling,
Default/Foreclosure Counseling,
Rental Counseling, Prepurchase
Counseling
Affiliate of: NATIONAL
FOUNDATION FOR
CONSUMER CREDIT,
INCORPORATED

PROJECT SENTINEL
25 Van Ness Avenue #800
San Francisco, CA
415-468-7464
Fax: 650-321-4173
Type of Counseling:
Prepurchase Counseling,
Default/Foreclosure Counseling,
HECM Counseling, Rental
Counseling

SAN FRANCISCO HOUSING
DEVELOPMENT
CORPORATION
5266 Third St.
San Francisco, CA 94124
415-822-1022
Fax: 415-822-1077
Type of Counseling:
Default/Foreclosure Counseling,
Prepurchase Counseling, Rental
Counseling

CONSUMER CREDIT
COUNSELING SERVICE OF
VENTURA COUNTY,
INCORPORATED
2150 Alum Rock
San Jose, CA 95116-
408-923-3914
Fax: 408-251-0218
Type of Counseling:
Default/Foreclosure Counseling,
Prepurchase Counseling, Rental
Counseling
Affiliate of: NATIONAL
FOUNDATION FOR
CONSUMER CREDIT,
INCORPORATED

PROJECT SENTINEL
111W. St. John Street Suite 302
San Jose, CA
408-287-2943
Fax: 650-321-4173
Type of Counseling:Prepurchase
Counseling, Default/Foreclosure

Counseling, HECM Counseling,
Rental Counseling

CONSUMER CREDIT
COUNSELING SERVICE OF
VENTURA COUNTY,
INCORPORATED SAN LUIS
OBISPO
3220 S. Higuera, Ste. 232
San Luis Obispo, CA 93401
800-540-2227
Toll-Free: 800-540-2227
Fax: 805-383-7722
Type of Counseling:
Prepurchase Counseling,
Default/Foreclosure Counseling,
Rental Counseling, HECM
Counseling

CONSUMER CREDIT
COUNSELING SERVICE OF
SAN FRANCISCO, SAN
MATEO
520 El Camino Real
Suite 310
San Mateo, CA 94402
800-777-7526
Toll-Free: 800-777-7526
Fax: 415-788-7817
Type of Counseling:
Prepurchase Counseling,
Default/Foreclosure Counseling,
Rental Counseling, HECM
Counseling

HUMAN INVESTMENT
PROJECT, INCORPORATED
364 S Railroad Ave
San Mateo, CA 94401-4024
650-341-5679
Fax: 650-348-0284
Type of Counseling: HECM
Counseling

CONSUMER CREDIT
COUNSELING SERVICE OF
EAST BAY, INCORPORATED
13925 San Pablo Ave
Suite 110
San Pablo, CA 94806-3675
510-729-6966
Fax: 510-729-6961
Type of Counseling: HECM
Counseling, Default/Foreclosure
Counseling, Rental Counseling,
Prepurchase Counseling

CONSUMER CREDIT
COUNSELING SERVICES OF
SAN FRANCISCO, SAN
RAFAEL
950 Northgate Ave., Ste. 204
San Rafael, CA 94903
800-777-7526
Toll-Free: 800-777-7526
Fax: 415-788-7817
Type of Counseling:
Prepurchase Counseling,
Default/Foreclosure Counseling,
Rental Counseling, HECM
Counseling

CONSUMER CREDIT
COUNSELING SERVICE OF
ORANGE COUNTY
2115 N Broadway
Santa Ana, CA 92706-2613
714-547-2227
Fax: 714-245-1690
Type of Counseling:
HECM Counseling,
Default/Foreclosure Counseling,
Rental Counseling, Prepurchase
Counseling

CONSUMER CREDIT
COUNSELING SERVICE OF
ORANGE COUNTY
1920 Old Tustin Ave
Santa Ana, CA 92705
714-247-2227
Fax: 714-245-1680
Email: gbengoch@cccsoc.org
Type of Counseling: HECM
Counseling, Default/Foreclosure
Counseling, Rental Counseling,
Prepurchase Counseling

FAIR HOUSING COUNCIL OF
ORANGE COUNTY
201 S. Broadway
Santa Ana, CA 92701-5633
714-569-0825
Toll-Free: 800-698-3247
Fax: 714-835-0281
Type of Counseling: HECM
Counseling, Default/Foreclosure
Counseling, Rental Counseling,
Prepurchase Counseling

CATHOLIC CHARITIES OF
ORANGE COUNTY
1506 Brookhollow Dr Ste 112

Santa Ana, CA 92705-5405
714-957-4671
Fax: 714-957-4612
Type of Counseling:
Default/Foreclosure Counseling,
Rental Counseling, Prepurchase
Counseling

CATHOLIC CHARITIES OF
ORANGE COUNTY,
INCORPORATED
3631 W Warner Ave
Santa Ana, CA 92704-5216
714-668-1130
Fax: 714-957-2523
Type of Counseling: Rental
Counseling

CONSUMER CREDIT
COUNSELING SERVICES OF
VENTURA COUNTY,
INCORPORATED SANTA
BARBARA
5276 Hollister Ave., Ste. 405
Santa Barbara, CA 93105
800-540-2227
Toll-Free: 800-540-2227
Fax: 805-383-7722
Type of Counseling:
Prepurchase Counseling,
Default/Foreclosure Counseling,
Rental Counseling, HECM
Counseling

CONSUMER CREDIT
COUNSELING SERVICE OF
VENTURA COUNTY,
INCORPORATED
1825 de La Cruz Blvd Ste 204
Santa Clara, CA 95050-3012
408-988-7881
Toll-Free: 800-969-7526
Fax: 408-988-0911
Website: www.cccssc.org
Type of Counseling:
Rental Counseling, Prepurchase
Counseling, HECM Counseling,
Default/Foreclosure Counseling
Affiliate of: NATIONAL
FOUNDATION FOR
CONSUMER CREDIT,
INCORPORATED

CONSUMER CREDIT
COUNSELING SERVICES OF
VENTURA COUNTY,

INCORPORATED SANTA
MARIA
1203 S. Broadway St.
Santa Maria, CA 93454
800-540-2227
Toll-Free: 800-540-2227
Fax: 805-383-7722
Type of Counseling:
Prepurchase Counseling,
Default/Foreclosure Counseling,
Rental Counseling, HECM
Counseling

CONSUMER CREDIT
COUNSELING SERVICE OF
LOS ANGELES
2444 Wilshire Blvd
Suite 501
Santa Monica, CA 90403-5808
323-890-9500
Toll-Free: 800-750-2227
Fax: 323-890-9590
Type of Counseling: HECM
Counseling, Default/Foreclosure
Counseling, Rental Counseling,
Prepurchase Counseling

**CATHOLIC CHARITIES,
DIOCESE OF SANTA ROSA
PO Box 4900
Santa Rosa, CA 95402-4900
707-528-8712
Fax: 707-575-4910
Type of Counseling:
Prepurchase Counseling,
Default/Foreclosure Counseling,
Rental Counseling, HECM
Counseling
Affiliate of: CATHOLIC
CHARITIES USA

CONSUMER CREDIT
COUNSELING SERVICE OF
SAN FRANCISCO, SANTA
ROSA
85 Brookwood Ave., Ste. 14
Santa Rosa, CA 95404
800-777-7526
Toll-Free: 800-777-7526
Fax: 415-788-7817
Type of Counseling:
Prepurchase Counseling,
Default/Foreclosure Counseling,
Rental Counseling, HECM
Counseling

**CABRILLO ECONOMIC
DEVELOPMENT
CORPORATION
11011 Azahar Street
Saticoy, CA 93004
805-659-3791
Fax: 805-659-3195
Email: cdc@rain.org
Type of Counseling:
Prepurchase Counseling
Affiliate of: NATIONAL
COUNCIL OF LA RAZA

CONSUMER CREDIT
COUNSELING SERVICE OF
LOS ANGELES
25129 The Old Road Ste 200
Stevenson Ranch, CA 91381
323-890-9500
Toll-Free: 800-750-2227
Fax: 323-890-9590
Type of Counseling: HECM
Counseling, Default/Foreclosure
Counseling, Rental Counseling,
Prepurchase Counseling
CONSUMER CREDIT
COUNSELING SERVICE OF
MID-COUNTY
2575 Grand Canal Blvd., Ste 100
Stockton, CA 95207
209-956-1170
Fax: 209-956-1178
Type of Counseling: HECM
Counseling, Default/Foreclosure
Counseling, Prepurchase
Counseling, Rental Counseling

PROJECT SENTINEL
1055 Sunnyvale Saratoga Rd
Suite 3
Sunnyvale, CA 94087-2539
888-331-3332
Toll-Free: 888-321-3332
Fax: 408-720-0810
Type of Counseling:
Default/Foreclosure Counseling,
Rental Counseling

CONSUMER CREDIT
COUNSELING SERVICE OF
LOS ANGELES
18401 Burbank Blvd Ste 127
Tarzana, CA 91356-2803
323-890-9500
Toll-Free: 800-750-2227
Fax: 323-890-9590

Type of Counseling: HECM Counseling, Default/Foreclosure Counseling, Rental Counseling, Prepurchase Counseling

SPRINGBOARD- TEMECULA
27715 Jefferson Ave Ste 113 E
Temecula, CA 92590-2660
800-947 3752
Fax: 909-781-8027
Type of Counseling: Default/Foreclosure Counseling, Rental Counseling

CONSUMER CREDIT COUNSELING SERVICE OF VENTURA COUNTY, INCORPORATED THOUSAND OAKS
80 E. Hillcrest Dr., Ste. 102
Thousand Oaks, CA 91360
800-540-2227
Toll-Free: 800-540-2227
Fax: 805-383-7722
Type of Counseling: Prepurchase Counseling, Default/Foreclosure Counseling, Rental Counseling, HECM Counseling

CONSUMER CREDIT COUNSELING SERVICE OF LOS ANGELES
3848 Carson St
Suite E103
Torrance, CA 90503-6701
323-890-9500
Toll-Free: 800-750-2227
Fax: 323-890-9500
Type of Counseling: HECM Counseling, Default/Foreclosure Counseling, Rental Counseling, Prepurchase Counseling

SPRINGBOARD- TWENTY-NINE PALMS
29 Palms Military Base
Twenty-Nine Palms, CA 92278
909-781-0114
Fax: 909-781-9896
Type of Counseling: Default/Foreclosure Counseling, Rental Counseling, Prepurchase Counseling

CONSUMER CREDIT COUNSELING SERVICE OF SACRAMENTO VALLEY - VACAVILLE
11 Cemon St.
Vacaville, CA 95688
916-379-3600
Toll-Free: 8007362227
Fax: 9163790636
Type of Counseling: Prepurchase Counseling, Default/Foreclosure Counseling, HECM Counseling

CITY OF VACAVILLE OFFICE OF HOUSING AND REDEVELOPMENT
40 Eldridge Ave #1-5
Vacaville, CA 95688-6800
707-449-5675
Fax: 707-449-6242
Email: jdias@ci.vacaville.ca.us
Type of Counseling: HECM Counseling, Default/Foreclosure Counseling, Rental Counseling, Prepurchase Counseling

**VALLEJO NEIGHBORHOOD HOUSING SERVICES, INCORPORATED
610 Lemon St
Vallejo, CA 94590-7276
707-552-4663
Fax: 707-643-2143
Email: reneew@fmcompserve.com
Type of Counseling: HECM Counseling, Default/Foreclosure Counseling, Prepurchase Counseling, Rental Counseling
Affiliate of: NEIGHBORHOOD REINVESTMENT CORPORATION

CONSUMER CREDIT COUNSELING SERVICES OF EAST BAY
515 Broadway Street, D3
Vallejo, CA 94590-
510-729-6966
Toll-Free: 888-788-8528
Fax: 510-729-6961
Website: www.cccsebay.org
Type of Counseling: Prepurchase Counseling,

Default/Foreclosure Counseling, Rental Counseling

CONSUMER CREDIT COUNSELING SERVICE OF VENTURA COUNTY, INCORPORATED VENTURA
1915 E. Main St.
Ventura, CA 93001
800-540-2227
Toll-Free: 800-540-2227
Fax: 805-383-7722
Type of Counseling: Prepurchase Counseling, Default/Foreclosure Counseling, Rental Counseling, HECM Counseling

SPRINGBOARD- VICTORVILLE
14298 Saint Andrews Dr Ste 1
Victorville, CA 92392-4367
909-781-0114
Toll-Free: 800-947-3752
Fax: 909-781-9896
Type of Counseling: Default/Foreclosure Counseling

CONSUMER CREDIT COUNSELING SERVICE OF KERN AND TULARE COUNTIES
718 W Center Ave Ste C
Visalia, CA 93291-6016
559-732-2227
Toll-Free: 800-272-2482
Fax: 661-324-0750
Email: nancyjohnsoncccsbakersfield@att.net
Type of Counseling: HECM Counseling, Default/Foreclosure Counseling, Prepurchase Counseling

**SELF HELP ENTERPRISES
8445 W. Elowin Court
Visalia, CA 93279-
559-651-1000
Fax: 559-651-3634
Email: tomc@selfhelpenterprises.org
Type of Counseling: Prepurchase Counseling
Affiliate of: NATIONAL COUNCIL OF LA RAZA

CONSUMER CREDIT
COUNSELING SERVICE OF
VENTURA COUNTY,
INCORPORATED
406 Main Street, Room 319
Watsonville, CA 95077-
831-728-5160
Fax: 831-728-5195
Type of Counseling:
Default/Foreclosure Counseling,
Prepurchase Counseling, Rental
Counseling
Affiliate of: NATIONAL
FOUNDATION FOR
CONSUMER CREDIT,
INCORPORATED

CONSUMER CREDIT
COUNSELING SERVICE OF
LOS ANGELES
1700 West Cameron
Suite 108
West Covina, CA 91790-2707
323-890-9500
Toll-Free: 800-750-2227
Fax: 323-890-9500
Type of Counseling:
HECM Counseling,
Default/Foreclosure Counseling,
Rental Counseling, Prepurchase
Counseling

SPRINGBOARD- WEST
COVINA
100 N. Barranca Ave.
7th Floor, Suite 17
West Covina, CA 91791-1600
800-947-3752
Type of Counseling:
Prepurchase Counseling,
Default/Foreclosure Counseling

CONSUMER CREDIT
COUNSELING SERVICE OF
SACRAMENTO VALLEY -
WOODLAND
266 W. Main St.
Woodland, CA 95695
916-379-3600
Toll-Free: 800-736-2227
Fax: 916-379-0636
Type of Counseling:
Prepurchase Counseling,
Default/Foreclosure Counseling,
HECM Counseling

CONSUMER CREDIT
COUNSELING SERVICES OF
SOUTHERN OREGON
999 Main St., #D
Yreka, CA 96097
530-841-1516
Fax: 530-841-1516
Type of Counseling:
Prepurchase Counseling, Rental
Counseling

Colorado

CITY OF AURORA
COMMUNITY DEVELOPMENT
DIVISION
9801 E. Colfax Ave.
Aurora, CO 80010
303-739-7900
Fax: 303-361-2989
Type of Counseling:
Prepurchase Counseling, Rental
Counseling, Default/Foreclosure
Counseling, HECM Counseling

BOULDER COUNTY HOUSING
AUTHORITY
3482 North Broadway
Boulder, CO 80306-0471
303-441-3929
Fax: 303-441-1537
Email: njcho@co.boulder.co.us
Type of Counseling: HECM
Counseling, Default/Foreclosure
Counseling, Rental Counseling,
Prepurchase Counseling

**CONSUMER CREDIT
COUNSELING SERVICE OF
GREATER DENVER,
INCORPORATED
5350 Manhattan Circle, #231
Boulder, CO 80303
303-632-2100
Toll-Free: 800-224-9885
Fax: 303-543-9814
Type of Counseling:
Default/Foreclosure Counseling,
Prepurchase Counseling, Rental
Counseling

SUMMIT HOUSING
AUTHORITY
106 North Ridge
Breckenridge, CO 80424
970-453-3555

Fax: 970-453-3554
Website:
www.co.summit.co.us/housing/
Type of Counseling:
Prepurchase Counseling

CONSUMER CREDIT
COUNSELING SERVICE OF
SOUTHERN COLORADO
1233 Lake Plaza Dr Ste A
Colorado Springs, CO 80906-
3555
719-576-0909
Toll-Free: 888-258-0685
Fax: 719-576-3756
Email: cccs@codenet.net
Type of Counseling:
HECM Counseling,
Default/Foreclosure Counseling,
Rental Counseling, Prepurchase
Counseling
Affiliate of: NATIONAL
FOUNDATION FOR
CONSUMER CREDIT,
INCORPORATED

ADAMS COUNTY HOUSING
AUTHORITY
7190 Colorado Blvd 6th Fl
Commerce City, CO 80022-1812
303-227-2075
Fax: 303-227-2098
Type of Counseling: HECM
Counseling, Default/Foreclosure
Counseling, Rental Counseling,
Prepurchase Counseling

**CONSUMER CREDIT
COUNSELING SERVICE OF
GREATER DENVER,
INCOPRORATED
928 E. Main
Cortez, CO 81321
303-632-2100
Toll-Free: 800-224-9885
Fax: 218-726-1251
Type of Counseling:
Default/Foreclosure Counseling,
Prepurchase Counseling, Rental
Counseling

**CONSUMER CREDIT
COUNSELING SERVICE OF
GREATER DENVER,
INCORPORATED
1740 Broadway

Denver, CO 80202
303-632-2100
Toll-Free: 800-224-9885
Fax: 303-863-5865
Type of Counseling:
Default/Foreclosure Counseling,
Prepurchase Counseling, Rental
Counseling

**NEWSED COMMUNITY
DEVELOPMENT
CORPORATION
1029 Santa Fe Drive
Denver, CO 80204
303-534-8342
Fax: 303-534-7418
Email: laura@newsed.org
Type of Counseling:
Prepurchase Counseling
Affiliate of: NATIONAL
COUNCIL OF LA RAZA

**ACORN HOUSING
CORPORATION
1760 High St
Denver, CO 80205
303-388-1989
Fax: 303-393-1451
Type of Counseling:
Prepurchase Counseling,
Default/Foreclosure Counseling
Affiliate of: ACORN HOUSING
CORPORATION

**DEL NORTE
NEIGHBORHOOD
DEVELOPMENT
CORPORATION
2926 Zuni Street, #202
Denver, CO 80211
303-477-4774
Fax: 303-433-0924
Email: delnortndc@aol.com
Type of Counseling:
Prepurchase Counseling
Affiliate of: NATIONAL
COUNCIL OF LA RAZA

**CONSUMER CREDIT
COUNSELING SERVICE OF
GREATER DENVER,
INCORPORATED
10375 East Harvard Ave #300
Denver, CO 80231
303-632-2100
Toll-Free: 800-224-9885

Fax: 303-632-2013
Type of Counseling:
Default/Foreclosure Counseling,
Rental Counseling, Prepurchase
Counseling
Affiliate of: NATIONAL
FOUNDATION FOR
CONSUMER CREDIT,
INCORPORATED

**CONSUMER CREDIT
COUNSELING SERVICE OF
GREATER DENVER,
INCORPORATED
5353 W. Dartmouth, Suite 305
Denver, CO 80227
303-632-2100
Toll-Free: 800-224-9885
Fax: 303-969-9137
Type of Counseling:
Default/Foreclosure Counseling,
Rental Counseling, Prepurchase
Counseling

BROTHERS
REDEVELOPMENT,
INCORPORATED
2250 Eaton St
Denver, CO 80214-1210
303-202-6340
Fax: 303-274-1314
Email: meganb@briathome.org
Website: www.briathome.org
Type of Counseling:
HECM Counseling,
Default/Foreclosure Counseling,
Rental Counseling, Prepurchase
Counseling

**ROCKY MOUNTAIN
MUTUAL HOUSING
ASSOCIATION,
INCORPORATED
1550 Park Avenue
Denver, CO 80218-
303-863-8651
Fax: 303-866-0850
Type of Counseling:
Prepurchase Counseling
Affiliate of: THE HOUSING
PARTNERSHIP NETWORK

**SOUTHWEST
IMPROVEMENT COUNCIL
1000 South Lowell Blvd.
Denver, CO 80219

303-934-8057
Fax: 303-934-0035
Email: lizswic@hotmail.com
Type of Counseling:
Prepurchase Counseling
Affiliate of: NATIONAL
COUNCIL OF LA RAZA

NORTHEAST DENVER
HOUSING CENTER
1735 Gaylord St
Denver, CO 80206-1208
303-377-3334
Fax: 303-377-3327
Type of Counseling:
HECM Counseling,
Default/Foreclosure Counseling,
Rental Counseling, Prepurchase
Counseling

SOUTHWEST COMMUNITY
RESOURCES
295 Girard St
Durango, CO 81303
970-259-1086
Fax: 970-259-2037
Type of Counseling:
HECM Counseling,
Default/Foreclosure Counseling,
Rental Counseling, Prepurchase
Counseling

CONSUMER CREDIT
COUNSELING SERVICE OF
NORTHERN COLORADO AND
SOUTHEAST WYOMING
1247 Riverside Avenue
Fort Collins, CO 80524-3258
970-229-0695
Toll-Free: 800-424-2227
Fax: 970-229-0721
Website: www.cccsnc.org
Type of Counseling:
HECM Counseling,
Default/Foreclosure Counseling,
Rental Counseling, Prepurchase
Counseling
Affiliate of: NATIONAL
FOUNDATION FOR
CONSUMER CREDIT,
INCORPORATED

NEIGHBOR TO NEIGHBOR
424 Pine St Ste 203
Fort Collins, CO 80524
970-484-7498

Fax: 970-407-7045
Type of Counseling:
HECM Counseling,
Default/Foreclosure Counseling,
Rental Counseling, Prepurchase
Counseling

TRI-COUNTY HOUSING,
INCORPORATED
34385 Highway 167
Fowler, CO 81039-5460
719-263-5460
Fax: 719-261-5168
Type of Counseling:
Prepurchase Counseling

**CONSUMER CREDIT
COUNSELING SERVICE OF
GREATER DENVER,
INCORPORATED
901 Grand Avenue
Glenwood Springs, CO 81602
303-632-2100
Toll-Free: 800-224-9885
Fax: 218-726-1251
Type of Counseling:
Default/Foreclosure Counseling,
Prepurchase Counseling, Rental
Counseling

GRAND JUNCTION HOUSING
AUTHORITY
1011 North 10th Street
Grand Junction, CO 81501
970-245-0388
Fax: 970-254-8347
Type of Counseling:
Default/Foreclosure Counseling,
Prepurchase Counseling

**CONSUMER CREDIT
COUNSELING OF GREATER
DENVER, INCORPORATED
2764 Compassor, Suite 217-5
Grand Junction, CO 81506
303-632-2100
Toll-Free: 800-224-9885
Fax: 303-243-6005
Type of Counseling:
Default/Foreclosure Counseling,
Prepurchase Counseling, Rental
Counseling

CONSUMER CREDIT
COUNSELING SERVICE
NORTHERN COLORADO AND
SOUTHEAST WYOMING

1228 8th St Ste 101
Greeley, CO 80631
970-229-0695
Fax: 970-229-0721
Website: www.cccsnc.org
Type of Counseling:
HECM Counseling,
Default/Foreclosure Counseling,
Rental Counseling, Prepurchase
Counseling
Affiliate of: NATIONAL
FOUNDATION FOR
CONSUMER CREDIT,
INCORPORATED

CONSUMER CREDIT
COUNSELING SERVICE
NORTHERN COLORADO AND
SOUTHEAST WYOMING
2919 W. 17th Avenue
Longmont, CO 80503-
800-424-2227
Toll-Free: 800-424-2227
Fax: 970-229-0721
Website: www.cccsnc.org
Type of Counseling:
HECM Counseling,
Default/Foreclosure Counseling,
Rental Counseling, Prepurchase
Counseling

NEIGHBOR TO NEIGHBOR
565 North Cleveland Avenue
Loveland, CO 80537-4801
970-663-4163
Fax: 970-663-2860
Type of Counseling:
HECM Counseling,
Default/Foreclosure Counseling,
Rental Counseling, Prepurchase
Counseling

CONSUMER CREDIT
COUNSELING SERVICE N
COLORADO AND
SOUTHEAST WYOMING
315 E 7th St
Loveland, CO 80537-4801
970-229-0695
Fax: 970-229-0721
Website: www.cccsnc.org
Type of Counseling:
HECM Counseling,
Default/Foreclosure Counseling,
Rental Counseling, Prepurchase
Counseling

**NEIGHBORHOOD HOUSING
SERVICES OF PUEBLO,
INCORPORATED
825 N Greenwood Ave
Pueblo, CO 81003-2925
719-544-8078
Fax: 719-544-0271
Email: nhs5@ix.netcom.com
Type of Counseling:
Prepurchase Counseling,
Default/Foreclosure Counseling
Affiliate of: NEIGHBORHOOD
REINVESTMENT
CORPORATION

CONSUMER CREDIT
COUNSELING SERVICE OF
SOUTHERN COLORADO
200 West 1st Street, Suite 302
Pueblo, CO 81003
719-542-6620
Fax: 719-542-7057
Type of Counseling:
HECM Counseling,
Default/Foreclosure Counseling,
Rental Counseling, Prepurchase
Counseling

CATHOLIC CHARITIES OF
THE DIOCESE OF PUEBLO,
INCORPORATED
429 W. 10th Street, Suite 101
Pueblo, CO 81003
800-303-4690
Toll-Free: 800-303-4690
Fax: 719-544-4215
Type of Counseling:
HECM Counseling,
Default/Foreclosure Counseling,
Rental Counseling, Prepurchase
Counseling
Affiliate of: CATHOLIC
CHARITIES USA

CONSUMER CREDIT
COUNSELING SERVICE
NORTHERN COLORADO AND
SOUTHEAST WYOMING
508 S. 10th Avenue
Sterling, CO 80751
800-424-2227
Toll-Free: 800-424-2227
Fax: 970-229-0721
Website: www.cccsnc.org
Type of Counseling:

HECM Counseling,
Default/Foreclosure Counseling,
Rental Counseling, Prepurchase
Counseling

**CONSUMER CREDIT
COUNSELING SERVICE OF
GREATER DENVER,
INCORPORATED
9101 Harlan
Westminister, CO 80030
303-632-2100
Toll-Free: 800-224-9885
Fax: 303-426-9029
Type of Counseling:
Default/Foreclosure Counseling,
Prepurchase Counseling, Rental
Counseling

COLORADO RURAL
HOUSING DEVELOPMENT
CORPORATION
3621 West 73rd Avenue, Suite C
Westminster, CO 80030
303-428-1448
Fax: 303-428-1989
Type of Counseling:
Prepurchase Counseling

CONNECTICUT

BRIDGEPORT
NEIGHBORHOOD TRUST
177 State St, 5th Floor
Bridgeport, CT 06604-4806
203-332-7977
Fax: 203-579-2338
Type of Counseling:
Rental Counseling, Prepurchase
Counseling, Default/Foreclosure
Counseling

**ACORN HOUSING
CORPORATION
2310 Main St. 3rd Fl.
Bridgeport, CT 06606
203-366-4180
Fax: 203-366-0020
Type of Counseling:
Prepurchase Counseling,
Default/Foreclosure Counseling
Affiliate of: ACORN HOUSING
CORPORATION

CONSUMER CREDIT
COUNSELING SERVICE OF
CONNECTICUT
40 Old Ridgebury Rd Ste. 105
Danbury, CT 06810
800-450-2808
Toll-Free: 800-450-2808
Fax: 203-798-2725
Type of Counseling:
HECM Counseling,
Default/Foreclosure Counseling,
Prepurchase Counseling

CONSUMER CREDIT
COUNSELING SERVICE OF
CONNECTICUT,
INCORPORATED
111 Founders Plz Ste 1400
East Hartford, CT 06108-3212
800-450-2808
Fax: 860-282-2001
Type of Counseling:
Prepurchase Counseling, Rental
Counseling, Default/Foreclosure
Counseling, HECM Counseling

URBAN LEAGUE OF GREATER
HARTFORD
1229 Albany Ave, 3rd floor
Hartford, CT 06112-2156
860-527-0147 x1421
Fax: 860-520-1159
Type of Counseling:
Prepurchase Counseling,
Default/Foreclosure Counseling,
Rental Counseling, HECM
Counseling
Affiliate of: NATIONAL
URBAN LEAGUE

**CO-OPPORTUNITY
117 Murphy Rd
Hartford, CT 06114
860-236-3617
Fax: 860-808-1757
Email: jerryd@co-
opportunity.org
Type of Counseling:
Prepurchase Counseling,
Default/Foreclosure Counseling
Affiliate of: CITIZENS'
HOUSING AND PLANNING
ASSOCIATION,
INCORPORATED

**HOUSING EDUCATION
RESOURCE CENTER
901 Wethersfield Ave.
Hartford, CT 06114
860-296-4242
Fax: 860-296-1317
Email: herc@hartnet.org
Type of Counseling:
Prepurchase Counseling, Rental
Counseling
Affiliate of: CITIZENS'
HOUSING AND PLANNING
ASSOCIATION,
INCORPORATED

HARTFORD AREAS RALLY
TOGETHER
227 Lawrence Street
Hartford, CT 06106
860-525-3449
Fax: 860-525-7759
Type of Counseling:
Prepurchase Counseling
Affiliate of: CITIZENS'
HOUSING AND PLANNING
ASSOCIATION,
INCORPORATED

**CO-OP INITIATIVES
999 Asylum Ave. Suite 506
Hartford, CT 06105
860-724-4940
Fax: 860-724-7102
Email:
TNADEAU@COOPINIT.ORG
Type of Counseling:
Prepurchase Counseling
Affiliate of: CITIZENS'
HOUSING AND PLANNING
ASSOCIATION,
INCORPORATED

CONSUMER CREDIT
COUNSELING SERVICE OF
CONNECTICUT
185 Plains Rd Ste W201
Milford, CT 06460-2474
800-450-2808
Fax: 203-882-3429
Type of Counseling:
HECM Counseling,
Default/Foreclosure Counseling,
Rental Counseling, Prepurchase
Counseling

NEIGHBORHOOD HOUSING
SERVICES OF NEW BRITAIN,
INCORPORATED
223 Broad St
New Britain, CT 06053-4107
860-224-2433
Fax: 860-225-6131
Type of Counseling:
Default/Foreclosure Counseling,
Rental Counseling, Prepurchase
Counseling

**NEIGHBORHOOD HOUSING
SERVICES OF NEW HAVEN,
INCORPORATED
333 Sherman Ave
New Haven, CT 06511-3107
203-562-0598
Fax: 203-772-2876
Email: paley2@ix.netcom.com
Type of Counseling:
Prepurchase Counseling,
Default/Foreclosure Counseling
Affiliate of: NEIGHBORHOOD
REINVESTMENT
CORPORATION

**ACORN HOUSING
CORPORATION
215 Grand Avenue
New Haven, CT 06513
203-789-8671
Type of Counseling:
Prepurchase Counseling,
Default/Foreclosure Counseling
Affiliate of: ACORN HOUSING
CORPORATION

HILL DEVELOPMENT
CORPORATION OF NEW
HAVEN
649 Howard Avenue
New Haven, CT 06519-1506
203-776-3759
Fax: 203-785-1321
Type of Counseling:
Prepurchase Counseling,
Default/Foreclosure Counseling,
Rental Counseling

**SHILOH DEVELOPMENT
CORP.
3 Garvin Street
New London, CT 06320
860-443-9647
Fax: 860-447-8812

Type of Counseling:
Prepurchase Counseling
Affiliate of: CONGRESS OF
NATIONAL BLACK
CHURCHES, INCORPORATED

**NEIGHBORHOOD HOUSING
SERVICES OF NORWALK,
INCORPORATED
23 Leonard St
Norwalk, CT 068502074
203-852-1717
Fax: 203-852-0879
Email: nhsnwlk@ix.netcom.com
Type of Counseling:
Default/Foreclosure Counseling,
Rental Counseling, Prepurchase
Counseling
Affiliate of: NEIGHBORHOOD
REINVESTMENT
CORPORATION

**CATHOLIC CHARITIES
1020 Market Street
Norwich, CT 06360-
860-889-8346
Type of Counseling:
Prepurchase Counseling, Rental
Counseling, Default/Foreclosure
Counseling
Affiliate of: CATHOLIC
CHARITIES USA

CONNECTICUT HOUSING
FINANCE AGENCY
999 West Street
Rocky Hill, CT 06067
860-721-9501
Fax: 860-571-4367
Type of Counseling:
Prepurchase Counseling,
Default/Foreclosure Counseling,
HECM Counseling

**NEIGHBORHOOD HOUSING
SERVICE OF WATERBURY,
INCORPORATED
139 Prospect St
Waterbury, CT 06710-2318
203-753-1896
Fax: 203-757-6496
Email: wbynhs@ix.netcom.com
Prepurchase Counseling,
Default/Foreclosure Counseling
Affiliate of: NEIGHBORHOOD
REINVESTMENT
CORPORATION

Delaware

NATIONAL COUNCIL ON
AGRICULTURAL LIFE AND
LABOR RESEARCH,
INCORPORATED
20 E Division St
Dover, DE 199031092
302-678-9400
Fax: 302-678-9058
Type of Counseling:
Prepurchase Counseling

FIRST STATE COMMUNITY
ACTION AGENCY,
INCORPORATED
308 N Railroad Ave
Georgetown, DE 19947-1252
302-856-7761
Toll-Free: 800-372-2240
Fax: 302-856-2599
Type of Counseling:
HECM Counseling,
Default/Foreclosure Counseling,
Rental Counseling, Prepurchase
Counseling

DELAWARE STATE HOUSING
AUTHORITY
Carvel StateOffice Building
Wilmington, DE 19801
302-577-5001
Fax: 302-577-5021
Type of Counseling:
Prepurchase Counseling

YOUNG WOMEN'S
CHRISTIAN ASSOCIATION,
CENTERS FOR
HOMEOWNERSHIP
233 King St
Wilmington, DE 19801-2521
302-888-7790
Fax: 302-658-7547
Type of Counseling:
Prepurchase Counseling,
Default/Foreclosure Counseling

NEIGHBORHOOD HOUSE,
INCORPORATED
1218 B St
Wilmington, DE 19801-5844
302-652-3928
Fax: 302-652-3983
Email: karenqbrady@msn.com
Type of Counseling:

HECM Counseling,
Default/Foreclosure Counseling,
Rental Counseling, Prepurchase
Counseling

COMMUNITY HOUSING,
INCORPORATED
613 N Washington St
Wilmington, DE 19801-2135
302-652-3991
Fax: 302-652-3945
Type of Counseling:
HECM Counseling,
Default/Foreclosure Counseling,
Rental Counseling, Prepurchase
Counseling

INTERFAITH HOUSING
DELAWARE, INCORPORATED
2 S. Augustine Street Ste B
Wilmington, DE 19804
302-995-7428
Fax: 302-225-4770
Email: ckarnai@ihd.sbs.dca.net
Type of Counseling:
Rental Counseling, Prepurchase
Counseling, HECM Counseling
Affiliate of: HOUSING
OPPORTUNITIES,
INCORPORATED

HOUSING OPPORTUNITIES
OF NORTHERN DELAWARE
100 W. 10th Street, Ste 1004
Wilmington, DE 19501
302-429-0974
Fax: 302-429-0795
Type of Counseling:
Prepurchase Counseling,
Default/Foreclosure Counseling,
HECM Counseling, Rental
Counseling

District Of Columbia

NEIGHBORHOOD
REINVESTMENT
CORPORATION
1325 G St NW
Washington, DC 20005-3104
202-220-2300
Fax: 202-376-2600

NEAR NORTHEAST
COMMUNITY IMPROVEMENT
CORPORATION

1326 Florida Ave NE
Washington, DC 20002-7108
202-399-6900
Fax: 202-399-6942
Email: WyHodgesl@aol.com
Type of Counseling:
HECM Counseling,
Default/Foreclosure Counseling,
Rental Counseling, Prepurchase
Counseling

PEOPLES INVOLVEMENT
CORPORATION
2146 Georgia Ave NW
Washington, DC 20001-3029
202-797-3900
Fax: 202-332-7891

UNIVERSITY LEGAL
SERVICES
300 I St NE Ste 202
Washington, DC 20002-4389
202-547-4747
Fax: 202-547-2083
Type of Counseling:
HECM Counseling,
Default/Foreclosure Counseling,
Rental Counseling, Prepurchase
Counseling

DISTRICT OF COLUMBIA
HOUSING FINANCE AGENCY
815 Florida Ave.Suite 209,NW
Washington, DC 20001
202-777-1600
Fax: 202-986-6705
Type of Counseling:
Prepurchase Counseling

MARSHALL HEIGHTS
COMMUNITY DEVELOPMENT
ORGANIZATION,
INCORPORATED
3939 Benning Road, NE
Washington, DC 20019-2662
202-396-1200
Fax: 202-396-4106
Type of Counseling:
HECM Counseling,
Default/Foreclosure Counseling,
Rental Counseling, Prepurchase
Counseling

GREATER WASHINGTON
URBAN LEAGUE
3501 14th St NW

Washington, DC 20010
202-265-8200
Fax: 202-328-3064
Email: jex6@aol.com
Type of Counseling:
Default/Foreclosure Counseling,
Prepurchase Counseling, Rental
Counseling, HECM Counseling
Affiliate of: NATIONAL
URBAN LEAGUE

HOUSING COUNSELING
SERVICES, INCORPORATED
2430 Ontario Rd NW
Washington, DC 20009-2705
202-667-7006
Fax: 202-462-5305
Type of Counseling:
HECM Counseling,
Default/Foreclosure Counseling,
Rental Counseling, Prepurchase
Counseling

CONSUMER CREDIT
COUNSELING SERVICE OF
GREATER WASHINGTON
1275 K St NW
Washington, DC 20005-4006
202-682-1500
Fax: 202-682-1505
Type of Counseling:
HECM Counseling,
Default/Foreclosure Counseling,
Rental Counseling, Prepurchase
Counseling

UNIVERSITY LEGAL
SERVICES
3220 Pennsylvania Avenue SE,
Suite 4
Washington, DC 20020
202-645-7175
Fax: 202-654-7178
Type of Counseling:
HECM Counseling,
Default/Foreclosure Counseling,
Rental Counseling, Prepurchase
Counseling

NATIONAL COUNCIL OF LA
RAZA
1111 19th Street NW
Suite 1000
Washington, DC 20036
202-785-1670
Fax: 202-776-1792

HOMEFREE - U S A
318 Riggs Rd NE
Washington, DC 20011-2534
202-526-2000
Fax: 202-526-4072
Type of Counseling:
HECM Counseling,
Default/Foreclosure Counseling,
Prepurchase Counseling

**ACORN HOUSING
CORPORATION
739 8th St SE
Washington, DC 20003-2802
202-547-9295
Fax: 202-546-2483
Type of Counseling:
Prepurchase Counseling,
Default/Foreclosure Counseling
Affiliate of: ACORN HOUSING
CORPORATION

**CATHOLIC CHARITIES OF
THE ARCHDIOCESE OF
WASHINGTON, D C
1438 Rhode Island Ave NE
Washington, DC 20018-3709
202-526-4100 ext.206
Fax: 202-526-1829
Type of Counseling:
Prepurchase Counseling,
Default/Foreclosure Counseling,
Rental Counseling, HECM
Counseling
Affiliate of: CATHOLIC
CHARITIES USA

CONGRESS OF NATIONAL
BLACK CHURCHES,
INCORPORATED
2000 L Street NW
Suite 225
Washington, DC 20036-4962
202-296-5637
Fax: 202-296-4939
Type of Counseling:
Prepurchase Counseling

**LYDIA'S HOUSE
4101 Martin Luther King Jr.
Avenue SW
Washington, DC 20032
202-563-7629
Fax: 202-563-7621
Type of Counseling:

Prepurchase Counseling,
Default/Foreclosure Counseling,
Rental Counseling
Affiliate of: CONGRESS OF
NATIONAL BLACK
CHURCHES, INCORPORATED

LATINO ECONOMIC
DEVELOPMENT
CORPORATION
2316 18th Street NW
Washington, DC 20009
202-588-5102
Fax: 202-588-5204
Type of Counseling:
Prepurchase Counseling, Rental
Counseling

Florida

HOMES IN PARTNERSHIP,
INCORPORATED
235 E 5th St
Apopka, FL 32703-5315
407-886-2451
Fax: 407-886-5304
Type of Counseling:
Prepurchase Counseling

CONSUMER CREDIT
COUNSELING SERVICE OF
WEST FLORIDA/ COUNTY
COURTHOUSE
425 E. Central Ave. Rm 321
Blountstown, FL 32424
850-674-2678
Fax: 850-432-5078
Type of Counseling:
Prepurchase Counseling, Rental
Counseling, Default/Foreclosure
Counseling, HECM Counseling

CONSUMER CREDIT
COUNSELING SERVICES
9045 La Fontana Blvd STE C6-B
Boca Raton, FL 33434-5633
800-330-2227
Fax: 561-470-1390
Email: derrick@cccsinc.com
Website: www.cccsinc.com
Type of Counseling:
HECM Counseling,
Default/Foreclosure Counseling,
Rental Counseling, Prepurchase
Counseling

CONSUMER CREDIT
COUNSELING SERVICE OF
THE FLORIDA GULF
4910 14th St W Ste 104
Bradenton, FL 34207-2482
941-746-4476
Toll-Free: 800-741-7040
Fax: 813-755-6944
Email: LPICHCCCS@aol.com
Website: www.cccsfl.org
Type of Counseling:
HECM Counseling,
Default/Foreclosure Counseling,
Rental Counseling, Prepurchase
Counseling

MANATEE OPPORTUNITY
COUNCIL, INCORPORATED
236 9th Ave W
Bradenton, FL 34205-8833
941-708-8440
Fax: 941-708-8445
Email: mocsandy@aol.com
Type of Counseling:
HECM Counseling,
Default/Foreclosure Counseling,
Rental Counseling, Prepurchase
Counseling

CONSUMER CREDIT
COUNSELING SERVICE OF
THE FLORIDA GULF
407 N. Parsons, Suite 104A
Brandon, FL 33510-
813-289-8923
Fax: 813-289-6452
Email: LPICHCCCS@aol.com
Website: www.cccsfl.org
Type of Counseling:
HECM Counseling,
Default/Foreclosure Counseling,
Rental Counseling, Prepurchase
Counseling

CONSUMER CREDIT
COUNSELING SERVICE OF
THE FLORIDA GULF
1 East Jefferson Street
Brooksville, FL 34605-3460
352-754-9675
Fax: 352-754-5545
Email: LPICHCCCS@aol.com
Website: www.cccsfl.org
Type of Counseling:
HECM Counseling,
Default/Foreclosure Counseling,

Rental Counseling, Prepurchase
Counseling

CONSUMER CREDIT
COUNSELING SERVICE OF
THE FLORIDA GULF
2503 Del Prado Blvd.
Cape Coral, FL 33990
914-278-3121
Fax: 941-772-7112
Email: LPICHCCCS@aol.com
Website: www.cccsfl.org
Type of Counseling:
HECM Counseling,
Default/Foreclosure Counseling,
Rental Counseling, Prepurchase
Counseling

**UNIVERSAL TRUTH
COMMUNITY DEVELOPMENT
CORPORATION
21310 NW 37th Ave.
Carol City, FL 33056
305-624-4991
Fax: 305-628-2008
Type of Counseling:
Prepurchase Counseling,
Default/Foreclosure Counseling
Affiliate of: CONGRESS OF
NATIONAL BLACK
CHURCHES, INCORPORATED

**CLEARWATER
NEIGHBORHOOD HOUSING
SERVICES, INCORPORATED
608 N Garden Ave
Clearwater, FL 33755
727-442-4155
Fax: 727-446-4911
Email: clwnhs@ix.netcom.com
Type of Counseling:
Prepurchase Counseling,
Default/Foreclosure Counseling
Affiliate of: NEIGHBORHOOD
REINVESTMENT
CORPORATION

THE HOMEBUYER'S CLUB
2139 NE Coachman Road
Clearwater, FL 33765
727-446-6222
Fax: 727-446-8727
Website: www.tampabaycdc.org
Type of Counseling:
Prepurchase Counseling,
Default/Foreclosure Counseling

CONSUMER CREDIT
COUNSELING SERVICE OF
WEST FLORIDA
648-B North Wilson
Crestview, FL 32536
850-689-0177
Fax: 850-432-5078
Type of Counseling:
Prepurchase Counseling, Rental
Counseling, Default/Foreclosure
Counseling, HECM Counseling

CENTRAL FLORIDA
COMMUNITY DEVELOPMENT
CORPORATION
847 Orange Avenue
Daytona Beach, FL 32114
386-258-7520
Fax: 386-238-3428
Type of Counseling:
Prepurchase Counseling, Rental
Counseling

MID-FLORIDA HOUSING
COUNSELING PARTNERSHIP,
INCORPORATED
330 North Street
Daytona Beach, FL 32114
386-252-7200
Toll-Free: 800-644-6125
Fax: 386-239-7119
Email: MFHP330@aol.com
Type of Counseling:
Default/Foreclosure Counseling,
Prepurchase Counseling, Rental
Counseling

CONSUMER CREDIT
COUNSELING SERVICE OF
CENTRAL FLORIDA
1176 Pelican Bay Drive
Daytona Beach, FL 32119
386-761-5361
Toll-Free: 800-388-2227
Fax: 386-756-6705
Email: counselor@cccscfl.com
Type of Counseling:
Prepurchase Counseling, HECM
Counseling, Default/Foreclosure
Counseling, Rental Counseling

CONSUMER CREDIT
COUNSELING SERVICE OF
WEST FLORIDA
11-B East Nelson
DeFuniak Springs, FL 32433

850-892-5234
Fax: 850-432-5078
Type of Counseling:
Prepurchase Counseling, Rental
Counseling, Default/Foreclosure
Counseling, HECM Counseling

URBAN LEAGUE SOUTH
COUNTY OFFICE
301 SW 14th Ave
Delray Beach, FL 33444-1455
561-265-3318
Fax: 561-265-3318
Type of Counseling:
HECM Counseling,
Default/Foreclosure Counseling,
Rental Counseling, Prepurchase
Counseling

CONSUMER CREDIT
COUNSELING SERVICE OF
WEST FLORIDA/EGLIN AIR
FORCE BASE
502 W. Van Matre Ave. Suite 1
Eglin Air Force Base, FL 32542
850-678-7726
Fax: 850-432-5078
Type of Counseling:
Prepurchase Counseling, Rental
Counseling, Default/Foreclosure
Counseling, HECM Counseling

CREDIT COUNSELORS OF
NORTH AMERICA
3317 NW 10 Terrace #408
Fort Lauderdale, FL 33309
800-330-1616
Toll-Free: 800-330-1616
Fax: 954-563-3052
Type of Counseling:
Default/Foreclosure Counseling,
Prepurchase Counseling, Rental
Counseling

**NEW VISIONS COMMUNITY
DEVELOPMENT
CORPORATION
1214 NE Fourth Avenue
Fort Lauderdale, FL 33304
954-768-0920
Fax: 954-768-0964
Type of Counseling:
Prepurchase Counseling,
Default/Foreclosure Counseling
Affiliate of: CONGRESS OF
NATIONAL BLACK
CHURCHES, INCORPORATED

CONSUMER CREDIT
COUNSELING SERVICE OF
THE FLORIDA GULF
12811 Kenwood Lane
Suite 111
Fort Myers, FL 33907
941-278-3121
Fax: 941-278-9097
Email: LPICHCCCS@aol.com
Website: www.cccsfl.org
Type of Counseling:
HECM Counseling,
Default/Foreclosure Counseling,
Rental Counseling, Prepurchase
Counseling

CONSUMER CREDIT
COUNSELING SERVICES OF
WEST FLORIDA
244 Racetrack Rd NE
Fort Walton Beach, FL 32547-
1866
850-314-9888
Fax: 850-314-9891
Type of Counseling:
HECM Counseling,
Default/Foreclosure Counseling,
Prepurchase Counseling

CONSUMER CREDIT
COUNSELING SERVICE OF
MID-FLORIDA,
INCORPORATED
1227 NW 16th Ave
Gainesville, FL 32601-4023
352-867-1865
Fax: 352-867-8490
Type of Counseling:
HECM Counseling,
Default/Foreclosure Counseling,
Rental Counseling, Prepurchase
Counseling

CITY OF GAINESVILLE
HOUSING AND ECON0MIC
DEVELOPMENT
200 E University Ave Rm. 341
Gainesville, FL 32602-0490
352-334-5026
Fax: 352-334-2272
Type of Counseling:
HECM Counseling,
Default/Foreclosure Counseling,
Rental Counseling, Prepurchase
Counseling

**NEIGHBORHOOD HOUSING
AND DEVELOPMENT
CORPORATION OF GREATER
GAINESVILLE
633 NW 8th Ave
Gainesville, FL 32601
352-380-9119
Fax: 352-380-9170
Email: dlherk@aol.com
Type of Counseling:
Prepurchase Counseling,
Default/Foreclosure Counseling
Affiliate of: NEIGHBORHOOD
REINVESTMENT
CORPORATION

GOULDS COMMUNITY
DEVELOPMENT
CORPORATION
11293 S. W. 216th St.
Goulds, FL 33170
305-278-6950
Fax: 305-278-1519
Type of Counseling:
Prepurchase Counseling, Rental
Counseling

CONSUMER CREDIT
COUNSELING SERVICES
1800 W 49th St Ste 303
Hialeah, FL 33012-2900
954-828-0585
Toll-Free: 800-928-2227
Fax: 305-828-1030
Type of Counseling:
HECM Counseling,
Default/Foreclosure Counseling,
Rental Counseling, Prepurchase
Counseling

BROWARD COUNTY
HOUSING AUTHORITY
7481 NW 33rd St
Hollywood, FL 33024-2376
954-432-6506
Fax: 954-484-5650
Type of Counseling:
HECM Counseling,
Default/Foreclosure Counseling,
Rental Counseling, Prepurchase
Counseling

BROWARD COUNTY
HOUSING AUTHORITY
3100 N 24th Ave #8
Hollywood, FL 33020-1401

954-921-2702
Fax: 954-920-6573
Type of Counseling:
HECM Counseling,
Default/Foreclosure Counseling,
Rental Counseling, Prepurchase
Counseling

CONSUMER CREDIT
COUNSELING SERVICE OF
JACKSONVILLE
1639 Atlantic Blvd
Jacksonville, FL 32207-3346
904-396-4846
Fax: 904-398-6649
Type of Counseling:
HECM Counseling,
Default/Foreclosure Counseling,
Rental Counseling, Prepurchase
Counseling
Affiliate of: NATIONAL
FOUNDATION FOR
CONSUMER CREDIT,
INCORPORATED

**OAKLAND TRACE
COMMUNITY DEVELOPMENT
CORPORATION
1025 Jessie Street
Jacksonville, FL 32206
904-354-0776
Toll-Free:
TTY/TDD:
Fax: 904-354-0630
Type of Counseling:
Prepurchase Counseling
Affiliate of: CONGRESS OF
NATIONAL BLACK
CHURCHES, INCORPORATED

CONSUMER CREDIT
COUNSELING SERVICE OF
FAMILY COUNSELING
C Avenue Naval Air Station
Jacksonville, FL 32207
904-396-4846
Fax: 904-398-6649
Type of Counseling:
HECM Counseling,
Default/Foreclosure Counseling,
Rental Counseling, Prepurchase
Counseling

JACKSONVILLE URBAN
LEAGUE
903 W. Union St

Jacksonville, FL 32204-1161
904-356-8336
Fax: 904-356-8369
Type of Counseling:
HECM Counseling,
Default/Foreclosure Counseling,
Rental Counseling, Prepurchase
Counseling

**JACKSONVILLE HOUSING
PARTNERSHIP
4401 Emerson St. Suite 1
Jacksonville, FL 322074954
904-398-4424
Fax: 904-398-0828
Type of Counseling:
Default/Foreclosure Counseling,
Prepurchase Counseling
Affiliate of: THE HOUSING
PARTNERSHIP NETWORK

CATHOLIC CHARITIES
BUREAU, INCORPORATED
134 E Church St Ste 2
Jacksonville, FL 32202-3130
904-354-4846
Fax: 904-354-4718
Type of Counseling:
Prepurchase Counseling, HECM
Counseling, Default/Foreclosure
Counseling, Rental Counseling
Affiliate of: CATHOLIC
CHARITIES USA

CONSUMER CREDIT
COUNSELING SERVICE OF
FAMILY COUNSELING
1316 3rd St N
Jacksonville Beach, FL 32250-
7348
904-246-6539
Fax: 904-398-6649
Type of Counseling:
HECM Counseling,
Default/Foreclosure Counseling,
Rental Counseling, Prepurchase
Counseling

CONSUMER CREDIT
COUNSELING SERVICE OF
SOUTH FLORIDA,
INCORPORATED
1010 Kennedy Dr
Key West, FL 33040-4019
800-928-2227
Fax: 305-892-1667

Type of Counseling:
HECM Counseling,
Default/Foreclosure Counseling,
Prepurchase Counseling

CONSUMER CREDIT
COUNSELING SERVICE OF
CENTRAL FLORIDA
1935 E Edgewood Dr
Lakeland, FL 33803-3473
941-687-2515
Fax: 941-683-9793
Type of Counseling:
HECM Counseling,
Default/Foreclosure Counseling,
Rental Counseling, Prepurchase
Counseling

BROWARD COUNTY
HOUSING AUTHORITY
1773 North State Road 7
Lauderhill, FL 33313
954-739-1114
Fax: 954-484-5650
Email: bchabm@mail.state.fl.us
Website: www.bchafl.org
Type of Counseling:
HECM Counseling,
Default/Foreclosure Counseling,
Rental Counseling, Prepurchase
Counseling

CONSUMER CREDIT
COUNSELING SERVICE OF
CENTRAL FLORIDA
1211 North Boulevard West
Leesburg, FL 34748-3959
352-326-9004
Fax: 352-326-1916
Type of Counseling:
HECM Counseling,
Default/Foreclosure Counseling,
Rental Counseling, Prepurchase
Counseling

CONSUMER CREDIT
COUNSELING SERVICE OF
WEST FLORIDA
2878 Green St. Suite 209
Marianna, FL 32446
850-526-1221
Fax: 850-432-5078
Type of Counseling:
Prepurchase Counseling, Rental
Counseling, Default/Foreclosure
Counseling, HECM Counseling

COMMUNITY HOUSING
INITIATIVE
3033 College Wood Drive
Melbourne, FL 32934
321-253-0053
Fax: 321-253-1575
Type of Counseling:
Default/Foreclosure Counseling,
Prepurchase Counseling

CONSUMER CREDIT
COUNSELING SERVICE OF
BREVARD
507 N Harbor City Blvd
Melbourne, FL 32935-6837
321-259-1070
Fax: 321-259-5202
Email: cccsjulie@aol.com
Type of Counseling:
HECM Counseling,
Default/Foreclosure Counseling,
Rental Counseling, Prepurchase
Counseling

ACORN HOUSING
CORPORATION HOUSING
COUNSELING OFFICES -
MIAMI
6025 NW 6 Court
Miami, FL
305-756-7166
Fax: 305-756-7765
Type of Counseling:
Prepurchase Counseling, Rental
Counseling, Default/Foreclosure
Counseling

CONSUMER CREDIT
COUNSELING SERVICES
16201 SW 95th Ave Ste 210
Miami, FL 33157-3459
305-233-2480
Fax: 305-893-4466
Type of Counseling:
HECM Counseling,
Default/Foreclosure Counseling,
Rental Counseling, Prepurchase
Counseling

**MIAMI-DADE
NEIGHBORHOOD HOUSING
SERVICES, INCORPORATED
7100 Biscayne Blvd, 2nd Floor
Miami, FL 33137
305-751-5511
Fax: 305-751-2228

Type of Counseling:
Default/Foreclosure Counseling,
Prepurchase Counseling
Affiliate of: NEIGHBORHOOD
REINVESTMENT
CORPORATION

WEST PERRINE COMMUNITY
DEVELOPMENT
CORPORATION,
INCORPORATED
17747 Homestead Ave
Miami, FL 33157-5341
305-252-0129
Fax: 305-235-5809
Type of Counseling:
Default/Foreclosure Counseling,
Rental Counseling, Prepurchase
Counseling

WEST PERRINE HOUSING
OPPORTUNITY CENTER
17623 Homestead Ave
Miami, FL 33157-5340
305-233-2997
Fax: 305-233-4165
Type of Counseling:
Default/Foreclosure Counseling,
Prepurchase Counseling

**ACORN HOUSING
CORPORATION
3510 Biscayne Blvd, Suite 201
Miami, FL 33137-4143
305-438-9061
Fax: 305-438-9064
Type of Counseling:
Prepurchase Counseling
Affiliate of: ACORN HOUSING
CORPORATION

**GREATER MIAMI
NEIGHBORHOODS
300 NW 12th Ave
Miami, FL 33128
305-324-5505
Fax: 305-324-5506
Type of Counseling:
Prepurchase Counseling, Rental
Counseling, Default/Foreclosure
Counseling, HECM Counseling
Affiliate of: THE HOUSING
PARTNERSHIP NETWORK

MIAMI BEACH COMMUNITY
DEVELOPMENT CORP

945 Pennsylvania Ave. 2nd Floor
Miami Beach, FL 33139
305-538-0090
Fax: 305-538-2863
Type of Counseling:
Default/Foreclosure Counseling,
Prepurchase Counseling, HECM
Counseling, Rental Counseling

HOMES IN PARTNERSHIP,
INCORPORATED
75 Lucerne Drive
Mount Dora, FL 32757-
352-383-7300
Fax: 407-886-5304
Type of Counseling:
Prepurchase Counseling

CONSUMER CREDIT
COUNSELING SERVICE OF
CENTRAL FLORIDA
2400 Tamiami Trail, North Suite
402
Naples, FL 34112-4883
941-775-6688
Fax: 941-430-1153
Type of Counseling:
HECM Counseling,
Default/Foreclosure Counseling,
Rental Counseling, Prepurchase
Counseling
Affiliate of: NATIONAL
FOUNDATION FOR
CONSUMER CREDIT,
INCORPORATED

CONSUMER CREDIT
COUNSELING SERVICE OF
SOUTH FLORIDA,
INCORPORATED
11645 Biscayne Blvd Ste 205
North Miami, FL 33181-3155
305-893-5225
Toll-Free: 800-928-2227
Fax: 305-892-1667
Email: MARCIA@cccs-sfl.com
Type of Counseling:
HECM Counseling,
Default/Foreclosure Counseling,
Prepurchase Counseling

CONSUMER CREDIT
COUNSELING SERVICE OF
MID-FLORIDA,
INCORPORATED
1539 NE 22nd Ave

Ocala, FL 34478
352-867-1865
Fax: 352-867-8490
Type of Counseling:
HECM Counseling,
Default/Foreclosure Counseling,
Rental Counseling, Prepurchase
Counseling

OCALA HOUSING
AUTHORITY
233 SW 3rd Street
Ocala, FL 344782468
352-369-2636
Fax: 352-369-2642
Type of Counseling:
Prepurchase Counseling, Rental
Counseling, Default/Foreclosure
Counseling

CONSUMER CREDIT
COUNSELING SERVICES
205 N Parrot Ave Barnett Bank
Okeechobee, FL 34972
800-330-2227
Fax: 561-434-2540
Type of Counseling:
HECM Counseling,
Default/Foreclosure Counseling,
Rental Counseling, Prepurchase
Counseling

CONSUMER CREDIT
COUNSELING SERVICE OF
CENTRAL FLORIDA
815 S Volusia Ave Ste1
Orange City, FL 32763-6568
407-895-8886
Fax: 407-895-3807
Type of Counseling:
HECM Counseling,
Default/Foreclosure Counseling,
Rental Counseling, Prepurchase
Counseling

CONSUMER CREDIT
COUNSELING SERVICE OF
FAMILY COUNSELING
1409 Kingsley Ave Bld 4 Ste B
Orange Park, FL 32073-4537
904-269-6679
Fax: 904-269-4111
Type of Counseling:
HECM Counseling,
Default/Foreclosure Counseling,

Rental Counseling, Prepurchase
Counseling

METROPOLITAN ORLANDO
URBAN LEAGUE,
INCORPORATED
2512 W Colonial Dr
Orlando, FL 32804-8009
407-841-7654
Fax: 407-841-9114
Type of Counseling:
HECM Counseling,
Default/Foreclosure Counseling,
Rental Counseling, Prepurchase
Counseling
Affiliate of: NATIONAL
URBAN LEAGUE

CONSUMER CREDIT
COUNSELING SERVICE OF
CENTRAL FLORIDA
6220 S Orange Blossom Trl Ste
145
Orlando, FL 32809-4630
407-895-8886
Fax: 407-895-3807
Type of Counseling:
HECM Counseling,
Default/Foreclosure Counseling,
Rental Counseling, Prepurchase
Counseling

-PALMETTO CATHOLIC
CHARITIES HOUSING
COUNSELING
506 26th St W
Palmetto, FL 34221
941-721-0924
Fax: 941-722-1063
Type of Counseling:
Rental Counseling, Prepurchase
Counseling
Affiliate of: CATHOLIC
CHARITIES USA

CONSUMER CREDIT
COUNSELING SERVICE OF
WEST FLORIDA/TYNDALL
AIR FORCE BASE
721 Suwannee Rd.
Panama City, FL 32403
850-283-4205
Fax: 850-432-5078
Type of Counseling:
Prepurchase Counseling, Rental
Counseling, Default/Foreclosure
Counseling, HECM Counseling

CONSUMER CREDIT
COUNSELING SERVICES OF
WEST
FLORIDA/Bonifay/Chipley
121 W 23rd St
Panama City, FL 32405-4504
850-784-6301
Fax: 850-784-2980
Type of Counseling:
HECM Counseling,
Default/Foreclosure Counseling,
Prepurchase Counseling

**SOUTH MISSISSIPPI LEGAL
SERVICES CORPORATION
P.O. Box 1654
Pascagoula, FL 39568-1654
228-769-7817
Fax: 228-769-7477
Type of Counseling:
Prepurchase Counseling,
Default/Foreclosure Counseling,
Rental Counseling, HECM
Counseling
Affiliate of: WEST TENNESSEE
LEGAL SERVICES,
INCORPORATED

CONSUMER CREDIT
COUNSELING SERVICE OF
WEST FLORIDA/Whiting Field
Naval Air Station
14 S Palafox Pl
Pensacola, FL 32501
850-434-0268
Toll-Free: 800-343-3317
Fax: 850-432-5078
Website: www.cccs-wfla.com
Type of Counseling:
HECM Counseling,
Default/Foreclosure Counseling,
Prepurchase Counseling, Rental
Counseling

COMMUNITY EQUITY
INVESTMENTS,
INCORPORATED
302 North Barcelona St
Pensacola, FL 32501
850-595-6234
Fax: 850-595-6264
Type of Counseling:
Prepurchase Counseling

CONSUMER CREDIT
COUNSELING SERVICE OF
WEST FLORIDA

Pensacola Naval Air Station FSC
Bldg. 625
Pensacola, FL 32508
850-452-5101
Fax: 850-432-5078
Type of Counseling:
Prepurchase Counseling, Rental
Counseling, Default/Foreclosure
Counseling, HECM Counseling

BROWARD COUNTY
HOUSING AUTHORITY
3801 NE 8th Ave
Pompano Beach, FL 33064-4364
954-941-0664
Fax: 954-484-5650
Type of Counseling:
HECM Counseling,
Default/Foreclosure Counseling,
Rental Counseling, Prepurchase
Counseling

CONSUMER CREDIT
COUNSELING SERVICES
9466 S US Highway 1
Port Saint Lucie, FL 34952-5001
800-330-2227
Fax: 561-398-3479
Email: derric@cccsinc.com
Website: www.cccsinc.com
Type of Counseling:
HECM Counseling,
Default/Foreclosure Counseling,
Rental Counseling, Prepurchase
Counseling

CONSUMER CREDIT
COUNSELING SERVICE OF
WEST FLORIDA
305 Fifth Street
Port St. Joe, FL 32456
850-784-6301
Fax: 850-432-5078
Type of Counseling:
Prepurchase Counseling, Rental
Counseling, Default/Foreclosure
Counseling, HECM Counseling

CONSUMER CREDIT
COUNSELING SERVICE OF
BREVARD
220 Coral Sands Dr
Rockledge, FL 32955-2702
321-259-1070
Fax: 321-259-5202
Type of Counseling:

HECM Counseling,
Default/Foreclosure Counseling,
Rental Counseling, Prepurchase
Counseling

THE CENTER FOR
AFFORDABLE HOUSING
INCORPORATED
203 E. 3rd Street, Suite 201
Sanford, FL 32771-
407-323-3268
Fax: 407-323-3800
Type of Counseling:
Prepurchase Counseling,
Default/Foreclosure Counseling

CONSUMER CREDIT
COUNSELING SERVICE OF
THE FLORIDA GULF
1750 17th Street, Unot D
Sarasota, FL 34234-
941-316-9600
Fax: 941-951-7788
Email: LPICHCCCS@aol.com
Website: www.cccsfl.org
Type of Counseling:
HECM Counseling,
Default/Foreclosure Counseling,
Rental Counseling, Prepurchase
Counseling

CONSUMER CREDIT
COUNSELING SERVICE
SARASOTA-EAST
5899 Whitfield Ave NW Suite
100 Mail Code 0327
Sarasota, FL 34243
941-316-9600
Toll-Free: 800-741-7040
Fax: 813-289-6452
Type of Counseling:
Prepurchase Counseling, Rental
Counseling, Default/Foreclosure
Counseling, HECM Counseling

CONSUMER CREDIT
COUNSELING SERVICE OF
CENTRAL FLORIDA
228 N Ridgewood Dr 2nd Fl
Sebring, FL 33870
941-385-3485
Fax: 941-382-5425
Type of Counseling:
HECM Counseling,
Default/Foreclosure Counseling,

Rental Counseling, Prepurchase
Counseling

CONSUMER CREDIT
COUNSELING SERVICE OF
FAMILY COUNSELING
SERVICES
2535 US 1 South
St. Augustine, FL 32086
904-396-4846
Fax: 904-398-6649
Type of Counseling:
HECM Counseling,
Default/Foreclosure Counseling,
Rental Counseling, Prepurchase
Counseling

**CATHOLIC CHARITIES OF
SAINT PETERSBURG
6533 9th Avenue, North Suite 1E
St. Petersburg, FL 33710
727-893-1313
Fax: 727-893-1307
Email: scanlancch@aol.com
Type of Counseling:
Default/Foreclosure Counseling,
Prepurchase Counseling, Rental
Counseling, HECM Counseling
Affiliate of: CATHOLIC
CHARITIES USA

**SAINT PETERSBURG
NEIGHBORHOOD HOUSING
SERVICES, INCORPORATED
1640 Martin Luther King St S
St. Petersburg, FL 33701
727-821-6897
Fax: 727-821-7457
Type of Counseling:
Prepurchase Counseling,
Default/Foreclosure Counseling
Affiliate of: NEIGHBORHOOD
REINVESTMENT
CORPORATION

**MOUNT ZION HUMAN
SERVICES COMMUNITY
DEVELOPMENT
CORPORATION
945-20th Street South
St. Petersburg, FL 33712
727-894-4311
Fax: 727-823-8002
Type of Counseling:
Prepurchase Counseling,
Default/Foreclosure Counseling

Affiliate of: CONGRESS OF
NATIONAL BLACK
CHURCHES, INCORPORATED

CONSUMER CREDIT
COUNSELING SERVICE OF
WEST FLORIDA
1311 Executive Center Dr. Suite
222
Tallahassee, FL 32301
850-402-0378
Fax: 850-432-5078
Type of Counseling:
Prepurchase Counseling, Rental
Counseling, Default/Foreclosure
Counseling, HECM Counseling

TALLAHASSEE URBAN
LEAGUE
923 Old Bainbridge Road
Tallahassee, FL 323036042
850-222-6111
Fax: 850-561-8390
Type of Counseling:
Prepurchase Counseling

FLORIDA HOUSING FINANCE
CORPORTATION
227 N. Bronough Street Suite
5000
Tallahassee, FL 32301
850-488-4197
Fax: 850-488-9809
Type of Counseling:
Prepurchase Counseling

TALLAHASSEE LENDERS
CONSORTIUM
1114 East Tennessee St
Tallahassee, FL 32308
850-222-6609
Fax: 850-222-6687
Email: tucc22095@aol.com
Type of Counseling:
HECM Counseling,
Default/Foreclosure Counseling,
Prepurchase Counseling, Rental
Counseling

CONSUMER CREDIT
COUNSELING SERVICE OF
CENTRAL FLORIDA
1648 Metropolitan Cir Ste 2
Tallahassee, FL 32308-3740
850-878-0975
Fax: 850-878-2716

Type of Counseling:
HECM Counseling,
Default/Foreclosure Counseling,
Rental Counseling, Prepurchase
Counseling

CONSUMER CREDIT
COUNSELING SERVICE OF
THE FLORIDA GULF
5201 W Kennedy Blvd Ste 110
Tampa, FL 33609-1845
813-289-8923
Fax: 813-289-6452
Email: LPICHCCCS@aol.com
Website: www.cccsfl.org
Type of Counseling:
HECM Counseling,
Default/Foreclosure Counseling,
Rental Counseling, Prepurchase
Counseling

CITY OF TAMPA
COMMUNITY
REDEVELOPMENT AGENCY
2105 N Nebraska Ave
Tampa, FL 33602-2529
813-274-7954
Fax: 813-274-7927
Type of Counseling:
Prepurchase Counseling

CONSUMER CREDIT
COUNSELING SERVICE OF
BREVARD
725 S Deleon Ave
Titusville, FL 32780-4115
321-636-9210
Fax: 321-259-5202
Type of Counseling:
HECM Counseling,
Default/Foreclosure Counseling,
Rental Counseling, Prepurchase
Counseling

CONSUMER CREDIT
COUNSELING SERVICE OF
THE FLORIDA GULF
3700 South Tamiami Trail
Venice, FL 34285
941-493-3180
Toll-Free: 800-741-7040
Fax: 941-488-9483
Email: LPICHCCCS@aol.com
Website: www.cccsfl.org
Type of Counseling:

Prepurchase Counseling, Rental
Counseling, Default/Foreclosure
Counseling, HECM Counseling

CONSUMER CREDIT
COUNSELING SERVICE OF
BREVARD
2046 14th Ave
Vero Beach, FL 32960-3430
561-562-6512
Fax: 407-259-5202
Email: cccsjulie@aol.com
Type of Counseling:
HECM Counseling,
Default/Foreclosure Counseling,
Rental Counseling, Prepurchase
Counseling

URBAN LEAGUE OF PALM
BEACH COUNTY,
INCORPORATED
1700 N Austrian Ave
West Palm Beach, FL 33407
561-833-1461
Fax: 561-833-6050
Email: ulwest@aol.com
Type of Counseling:
HECM Counseling,
Default/Foreclosure Counseling,
Rental Counseling, Prepurchase
Counseling
Affiliate of: NATIONAL
URBAN LEAGUE

CONSUMER CREDIT
COUNSELING SERVICE OF
GREATER ATLANTA, INC
2330 S Congress Ave Ste 1A
West Palm Beach, FL 33406-7666
561-434-2544
Toll-Free: 800-330-2227
Fax: 561-434-2540
Email: derrick@cccsinc.com
Website: www.cccsinc.com
Type of Counseling:
HECM Counseling,
Default/Foreclosure Counseling,
Rental Counseling, Prepurchase
Counseling

**WEST PALM BEACH
HOUSING PARTNERSHIP
4016 Broadway Ave.
West Palm Beach, FL 33407
561-841-3500
Fax: 561-841-3555

Type of Counseling:
HECM Counseling,
Default/Foreclosure Counseling,
Rental Counseling, Prepurchase
Counseling
Affiliate of: NEIGHBORHOOD
REINVESTMENT
CORPORATION

CONSUMER CREDIT
COUNSELING SERVICES OF
SOUTH FLORIDA
2101 N Andrews Ave Ste 405
Wilton Manors, FL 33311-3940
800-928-2227
Fax: 954-561-4084
Type of Counseling:
HECM Counseling,
Default/Foreclosure Counseling,
Prepurchase Counseling

THE AGRICULTURE AND
LABOR PROGRAM,
INCORPORATED
7301 Lynchburg Rd
Winter Haven, FL 33885
863-956-3491
Toll-Free: 800-330-3491
Fax: 863-956-5560
Type of Counseling:
Default/Foreclosure Counseling,
Rental Counseling, Prepurchase
Counseling

HANDS HOUSING AND
NEIGHBORHOOD
DEVELOPMENT SERVICES OF
CENTRAL FLORIDA
INCORPORATED
990 N Bennett Ave., Ste 200
Winter Park, FL 32789
407-740-0805
Fax: 407-740-8576
Type of Counseling:
Default/Foreclosure Counseling,
Rental Counseling, Prepurchase
Counseling

Georgia

CITY OF ALBANY
COMMUNITY AND
ECONOMIC DEVELOPMENT
230 South Jackson St Ste 315
Albany, GA 31701
229-430-5283

Toll-Free: 800-251-2910
Fax: 229-430-2737
Type of Counseling:
Default/Foreclosure Counseling,
Rental Counseling, Prepurchase
Counseling

**GEORGIA LEGAL SERVICES
PROGRAM
111 West Oglethorpe Boulevard
Albany, GA 31701-
912-430-4261
Fax: 912-430-4344
Type of Counseling:
Prepurchase Counseling,
Default/Foreclosure Counseling,
Rental Counseling, HECM
Counseling
Affiliate of: WEST TENNESSEE
LEGAL SERVICES,
INCORPORATED

ATHENS-CLARKE COUNTY
UNIFIED GOVERNMENT
HUMAN AND ECONOMIC
DEVELOPMENT
375 Satula Ave.
Athens, GA 30601-2746
706-613-3155
Fax: 706-613-3158
Type of Counseling:
HECM Counseling,
Default/Foreclosure Counseling,
Rental Counseling, Prepurchase
Counseling

EAST ATHENS
DEVELOPMENT
CORPORATION,
INCORPORATED
410 McKinley drive, Suite 101
Athens, GA 30601-
706-208-0048
Fax: 706-208-0015
Type of Counseling:
Prepurchase Counseling,
Default/Foreclosure Counseling,
Rental Counseling

HOUSING AND ECONOMIC
LEADERSHIP PARTNERS,
INCORPORATED
485 Huntington Road, Suite 200
Athens, GA 30606
706-549-5200
Fax: 706-549-5004

Type of Counseling:
HECM Counseling, Prepurchase
Counseling, Rental Counseling,
Default/Foreclosure Counseling

ATLANTA URBAN LEAGUE,
INCORPORATED
100 Edgewood Ave NE Ste 600
Atlanta, GA 30303-3066
404-659-1150
Fax: 404-230-9950
Email: au1198@bellsouth.net
Type of Counseling:
Default/Foreclosure Counseling,
Rental Counseling, Prepurchase
Counseling
Affiliate of: NATIONAL
URBAN LEAGUE

CONSUMER CREDIT
COUNSELING OF GREATER
ATLANTA, INCORPORATED
100 Edgewood Ave NE Ste 1500
Atlanta, GA 30303-3026
866-255-2227
Toll-Free: 866-255-2227
Fax: 404-653-8883
Email: jjordan@cccsatl.org
Type of Counseling:
Default/Foreclosure Counseling,
Rental Counseling, Prepurchase
Counseling, HECM Counseling

**ACORN HOUSING
CORPORATION HOUSING
COUNSELING OFFICES -
ATLANTA
250 Auburn Ave. Ste 304
Atlanta, GA 30303
404-525-0033
Fax: 404-525-2655
Type of Counseling:
Prepurchase Counseling, Rental
Counseling, Default/Foreclosure
Counseling
Affiliate of: ACORN HOUSING
CORPORATION

LATIN AMERICAN
ASSOCIATION
2750 Buford Highway
Atlanta, GA 30324
404-638-1800
Fax: 404-638-1806
Email: rconcepcion@
latinamericanassoc.org

Type of Counseling:
Prepurchase Counseling,
Default/Foreclosure Counseling

ATLANTA CENTER FOR
HOME OWNERSHIP
228 Auburn Avenue
Atlanta, GA 30315
404-588-3700
Fax: 404-588-3733
Type of Counseling:
Prepurchase Counseling
Affiliate of: HOUSING
OPPORTUNITIES,
INCORPORATED

FULTON ATLANTA
COMMUNITY ACTION
AUTHORITY
1690 Chantilly Drive, N.E.
Atlanta, GA 30324-
404-320-0166
Fax: 404-810-0098
Type of Counseling:
Default/Foreclosure Counseling,
Rental Counseling, Prepurchase
Counseling

GEORGIA HOUSING AND
FINANCE AUTHORITY
60 Exec Park South, NE
Atlanta, GA 30340
404-679-0670
Fax: 404-679-4844
Email: tchilds@dca.state.ga.us
Type of Counseling:
Rental Counseling, Prepurchase
Counseling

**CHRISTIAN FAMILY
WORSHIP CENTER
1401 Hosea L. Williams Dr., SE
Atlanta, GA 30317-1703
404-584-7429
Fax: 404-222-9444
Type of Counseling:
Prepurchase Counseling, Rental
Counseling
Affiliate of: CONGRESS OF
NATIONAL BLACK
CHURCHES, INCORPORATED

ATLANTA CENTER FOR
HOMEOWNERSHIP
818 Pollard Boulevard
Atlanta, GA 30315

404-588-3700
Fax: 404-588-3733
Type of Counseling:
Prepurchase Counseling

**GEORGIA LEGAL SERVICES
PROGRAM
1100 Spring St. NW, Ste. 200-A
Atlanta, GA 303092848
404-206-5378
Fax: 404-206-5346
Email: sreif@glsp.org
Type of Counseling:
Prepurchase Counseling,
Default/Foreclosure Counseling,
Rental Counseling, HECM
Counseling
Affiliate of: WEST TENNESSEE
LEGAL SERVICES,
INCORPORATED

DEKALB/FULTON HOUSING
COUNSELING CENTER
233 Mitchell St SW Ste 100
Atlanta, GA 30303-3300
404-659-6744
Fax: 404-659-6739
Type of Counseling:
HECM Counseling,
Default/Foreclosure Counseling,
Rental Counseling, Prepurchase
Counseling

CONSUMER CREDIT
COUNSELING SERVICE OF
THE CENTRAL SAVANNAH
RIVER AREA
1341 Druid Park Ave.
Augusta, GA 30904
706-736-2090
Fax: 706-736-0637
Type of Counseling:
Prepurchase Counseling,
Default/Foreclosure Counseling,
Rental Counseling

**GEORGIA LEGAL SERVICES
PROGRAM
811 Telfair Street Suite 202
Augusta, GA 30901-
706-721-2327
Fax: 706-721-4897
Type of Counseling:
Prepurchase Counseling,
Default/Foreclosure Counseling,

Rental Counseling, HECM
Counseling
Affiliate of: WEST TENNESSEE
LEGAL SERVICES,
INCORPORATED

**GEORGIA LEGAL SERVICES
PROGRAM
1311 Union Street
Brunswick, GA 31520-7226
912-264-7301
Fax: 912-262-2312
Type of Counseling:
Prepurchase Counseling,
Default/Foreclosure Counseling,
Rental Counseling, HECM
Counseling
Affiliate of: WEST TENNESSEE
LEGAL SERVICES,
INCORPORATED

**GEORGIA LEGAL SERVICES
PROGRAM
1214 First Avenue
Columbus, GA 31902-
706-649-7493
Fax: 706-649-7519
Type of Counseling:
Prepurchase Counseling,
Default/Foreclosure Counseling,
Rental Counseling, HECM
Counseling
Affiliate of: WEST TENNESSEE
LEGAL SERVICES,
INCORPORATED

METRO COLUMBUS URBAN
LEAGUE, INCORPORATED
802 1st Ave
Columbus, GA 31901-2702
706-323-3687
Fax: 706-596-2144
Type of Counseling:
Default/Foreclosure Counseling,
Prepurchase Counseling

**GEORGIA LEGAL SERVICES
PROGRAM
107 King Street
Dalton, GA 30722-2204
706-272-2359
Fax: 706-272-2259
Type of Counseling:
Prepurchase Counseling,
Default/Foreclosure Counseling,

Rental Counseling, HECM
Counseling
Affiliate of: WEST TENNESSEE
LEGAL SERVICES,
INCORPORATED

**GREEN FOREST
COMMUNITY DEVELOPMENT
CORPORATION
3299 Rainbow Drive
Decatur, GA 30034
404-284-7799
Fax: 404-284-8727
Type of Counseling:
Prepurchase Counseling,
Default/Foreclosure Counseling
Affiliate of: HOUSING
OPPORTUNITIES,
INCORPORATED

CONSUMER CREDIT
COUNSELING SERVICE OF
GREATER ATLANTA
5304 Panola Industrial Blvd.
Suite N
Decatur, GA 30035-
866-255-2227
Toll-Free: 866-255-2227
Fax: 404-653-8883
Email: jjordan@cccsatl.org
Type of Counseling:
Prepurchase Counseling,
Default/Foreclosure Counseling,
HECM Counseling, Rental
Counseling

THE HOUSING AUTHORITY
OF THE CITY OF DECATUR,
GEORGIA
325 Swanton Way
Decatur, GA
404-377-0425
Fax: 404-378-7249
Type of Counseling:
Rental Counseling, Prepurchase
Counseling, Default/Foreclosure
Counseling

DEKALB/FULTON HOUSING
COUNSELING CENTER
4151 Memorial Dr Suite 107E
Decatur, GA 30032-1504
404-508-0922
Fax: 404-508-0967
Type of Counseling:

HECM Counseling,
Default/Foreclosure Counseling,
Rental Counseling, Prepurchase
Counseling

HEART OF GEORGIA
COMMUNITY ACTION
COUNCIL
213 Pine Street
Eastman, GA 31203
478-374-4301
Fax: 478-374-7648
Type of Counseling:
Default/Foreclosure Counseling

CONSUMER CREDIT
COUNSELING SERVICE OF
GREATER ATLANTA
140 Carnegie Place Suite 106
Fayetteville, GA 30214-
866-255-2227
Toll-Free: 866-255-2227
Fax: 404-653-8883
Email: jjordan@cccsatl.org
Prepurchase Counseling,
Default/Foreclosure Counseling,
HECM Counseling, Rental
Counseling

**GEORGIA LEGAL SERVICES
PROGRAM
1276 Jesse Jewel Parkway
Gainesville, GA 30503-
404-535-5717
Fax: 404-531-6011
Type of Counseling:
Prepurchase Counseling,
Default/Foreclosure Counseling,
Rental Counseling, HECM
Counseling
Affiliate of: WEST TENNESSEE
LEGAL SERVICES,
INCORPORATED

GAINESVILLE-HALL COUNTY
NEIGHBORHOOD
REVITALIZATION
924 Athens Street
Gainesville, GA 30503
770-297-1800
Fax: 770-297-1097
Type of Counseling:
Prepurchase Counseling,
Default/Foreclosure Counseling

CONSUMER CREDIT
COUNSELING SERVICE OF
FAMILY COUNSELING
1063 Tennessee Ave
Bldg. 1051
Kings Bay, GA 31547
912-673-4512
Fax: 912-673-2031
Email:
qlharvem@subasekb.navy.mil
Type of Counseling:
HECM Counseling,
Default/Foreclosure Counseling,
Rental Counseling, Prepurchase
Counseling

LATIN AMERICAN
ASSOCIATION
134 S. Clayton Street, Suite 32
Lawrenceville, GA 30045
770-339-4335
Fax: 770-339-9154
Type of Counseling:
Default/Foreclosure Counseling,
Prepurchase Counseling

CONSUMER CREDIT
COUNSELING SERVICE OF
MIDDLE GEORGIA,
INCORPORATED
277 M.L.K. Jr. W
Suite 202
Macon, GA 31201
478-745-6197
Fax: 478-745-6270
Email: counselor@cccsmacon.org
Type of Counseling:
Default/Foreclosure Counseling,
Rental Counseling, Prepurchase
Counseling

**GEORGIA LEGAL SERVICES
PROGRAM
111 Third Street, Suite 230
Macon, GA 31202-1507
912-751-6261
Fax: 912-751-6581
Type of Counseling:
Prepurchase Counseling,
Default/Foreclosure Counseling,
Rental Counseling, HECM
Counseling
Affiliate of: WEST TENNESSEE
LEGAL SERVICES,
INCORPORATED

CONSUMER CREDIT
COUNSELING SERVICE OF
GREATER ATLANTA
1341 Canton Road Suite F
Marietta, GA 30066-
866-255-2227
Toll-Free: 866-255-2227
Fax: 404-653-8883
Email: jjordan@cccsatl.org
Type of Counseling:
Prepurchase Counseling,
Default/Foreclosure Counseling,
HECM Counseling, Rental
Counseling

LATIN AMERICAN
ASSOCIATION
48 Henderson Street
Marietta, GA 30064
770-420-6556
Fax: 678-354-0500
Type of Counseling:
Default/Foreclosure Counseling,
Prepurchase Counseling

COBB HOUSING,
INCORPORATED
700 Sandy Plains Rd Ste B8
Marietta, GA 30062-6370
770-429-4400
Fax: 770-429-4405
Type of Counseling:
Default/Foreclosure Counseling,
Rental Counseling, Prepurchase
Counseling

CONSUMER CREDIT
COUNSELING SERVICE OF
GREATER ATLANTA
6000 Live Oak Pkwy Suite 113
Norcross, GA 30093-
866-255-2227
Toll-Free: 866-255-2227
Fax: 404-653-8883
Email: jjordan@cccsatl.org
Type of Counseling:
Prepurchase Counseling,
Default/Foreclosure Counseling,
HECM Counseling, Rental
Counseling

GWINNETT HOUSING
RESOURCE PARTNERSHIP,
INCORPORATED
3453 Holcomb Bridge Rd Ste 140
Norcross, GA 30092

770-448-0702
Fax: 770-448-6958
Type of Counseling:
HECM Counseling,
Default/Foreclosure Counseling,
Rental Counseling, Prepurchase
Counseling

APPALACHIAN HOUSING
COUNSELING AGENCY
800 Avenue B
Rome, GA 30162-
706-378-9917
Fax: 706-290-0042
Type of Counseling:
Prepurchase Counseling, Rental
Counseling, Default/Foreclosure
Counseling, HECM Counseling

NATIONAL ASSOCIATION OF
HOUSING COUNSELORS AND
AGENCIES
PO Box 5607
Savannah, GA 31414-5607
912-236-9670
Fax: 912-238-2977
Type of Counseling:
HECM Counseling,
Default/Foreclosure Counseling,
Rental Counseling, Prepurchase
Counseling

ECONOMIC OPPORTUNITY
AUTHORITY FOR
SAVANNAH-CHATHAM
COUNTY AREA,
INCORPORATED
618 W Anderson St
Savannah, GA 31404
912-238-2960
Fax: 912-238-2977
Type of Counseling:
Default/Foreclosure Counseling,
Rental Counseling, Prepurchase
Counseling

**GEORGIA LEGAL SERVICES
PROGRAM
10 Whittaker Street 2nd floor
Savannah, GA 31401-
912-651-2180
Fax: 912-651-3300
Type of Counseling:
Prepurchase Counseling,
Default/Foreclosure Counseling,

Rental Counseling, HECM
Counseling
Affiliate of: WEST TENNESSEE
LEGAL SERVICES,
INCORPORATED

CONSUMER CREDIT
COUNSELING SERVICE OF
WEST FLORIDA
Chamber of Commerce Building
St. Mary's, GA 31558
912-673-1526
Fax: 850-432-5078
Type of Counseling:Prepurchase
Counseling, Rental Counseling,
Default/Foreclosure Counseling,
HECM Counseling

**GEORGIA LEGAL SERVICES
PROGRAM
150 South Ridge Avenue
Tifton, GA 31794-
912-386-3566
Fax: 912-386-3880
Type of Counseling:
Prepurchase Counseling,
Default/Foreclosure Counseling,
Rental Counseling, HECM
Counseling
Affiliate of: WEST TENNESSEE
LEGAL SERVICES,
INCORPORATED

**GEORGIA LEGAL SERVICES
PROGRAM
114 N. Toombs Street
Valdosta, GA 31601-
912-333-5252
Fax: 912-333-5236
Type of Counseling:
Prepurchase Counseling,
Default/Foreclosure Counseling,
Rental Counseling, HECM
Counseling
Affiliate of: WEST TENNESSEE
LEGAL SERVICES,
INCORPORATED

CONSUMER CREDIT
COUNSELING SERVICE OF
MIDDLE GEORGIA,
INCORPORATED
511 N. Houston Road Suite C-1
Warner Robins, GA 31093-
912-745-6197
Fax: 912-745-6270

Email: counselor@cccsmacon.org
Type of Counseling:
Prepurchase Counseling

MIDDLE GEORGIA
COMMUNITY ACTION
AGENCY, INCORPORATED
708 Elberta Rd
Warner Robins, GA 31093-1734
478-922-4464
Toll-Free: 800-422-9053
Fax: 478-329-0959
Type of Counseling:
Prepurchase Counseling

GEORGIA LEGAL SERVICES
PROGRAM
1057 Grove Avenue
Waycross, GA 31501-
912-285-6181
Fax: 912-285-6187
Type of Counseling:
Prepurchase Counseling,
Default/Foreclosure Counseling,
Rental Counseling, HECM
Counseling
Affiliate of: WEST TENNESSEE
LEGAL SERVICES,
INCORPORATED

CONSUMER CREDIT
COUNSELING SERVICE OF
FAMILY COUNSELING
505 Haines Ave
Waycross, GA 31501-2266
912-284-2261
Fax: 912-284-2284
Type of Counseling:
HECM Counseling,
Default/Foreclosure Counseling,
Rental Counseling, Prepurchase
Counseling

Hawaii

LEGAL AID SOCIETY OF
HAWAII
305 Wailuku Dr
Hilo, HI 96720-2448
808-536-4302
Fax: 808-527-8088
Type of Counseling:
Default/Foreclosure Counseling,
Rental Counseling, Prepurchase
Counseling

LEGAL AID SOCIETY OF
HAWAII
924 Bethel Street
Honolulu, HI 96813
808-536-4302
Fax: 808-527-8088
Type of Counseling:
HECM Counseling,
Default/Foreclosure Counseling,
Rental Counseling, Prepurchase
Counseling

CATHOLIC CHARITIES
COMMUNITY AND
IMMIGRANT SERVICES
712 North School Street
Honolulu, HI 96817
808-528-5233
Fax: 808-531-1970
Email: dmilazzolevy@
catholiccharitieshawaii.org
Type of Counseling:
Rental Counseling, Prepurchase
Counseling, Default/Foreclosure
Counseling, HECM Counseling
Affiliate of: CATHOLIC
CHARITIES USA

HALE MAHAOLU
HOMEOWNERSHIP/HOUSIN
G COUNSELING
200 Hina Ave
Kahului, HI 96732-1821
808-872-4114
Fax: 808-872-4120
Email: hmahaolu@maui.net
Type of Counseling:
HECM Counseling,
Default/Foreclosure Counseling,
Rental Counseling, Prepurchase
Counseling

LEGAL AID SOCIETY OF
HAWAII
47-200 Waihee Rd Ste 104
Kaneohe, HI 96744-4947
808-536-4302
Fax: 808-527-8088
Type of Counseling:
Rental Counseling, HECM
Counseling, Prepurchase
Counseling

LEGAL AID SOCIETY OF
HAWAII
19-23 Ala Malama St
Kaunakakai, HI 96748
808-536-4302

Toll-Free: 800-499-4302
Fax: 808-527-8088
Type of Counseling:
Default/Foreclosure Counseling,
Rental Counseling

LEGAL AID SOCIETY OF
HAWAII
3-3359 Kuhio Hwy
Lihue, HI 96766
808-536-4302
Fax: 808-499-4302
Type of Counseling:
Default/Foreclosure Counseling,
Rental Counseling

LEGAL AID SOCIETY OF
HAWAII
85-555 Farrington Hwy Ste A
Waianae, HI 96792-2354
808-536-4302
Fax: 808-527-8088
Type of Counseling:
Default/Foreclosure Counseling,
Rental Counseling

LEGAL AID SOCIETY OF
HAWAII
2287 Main St
Wailuku, HI 96793-1655
808-436-4302
Fax: 808-527-8088
Type of Counseling:
Default/Foreclosure Counseling,
Rental Counseling

IdAho

IDAHO HOUSING AND
FINANCE ASSOCIATION
565 West Myrtle
Boise, ID 83702
208-331-4847
Fax: 208-331-4801
Type of Counseling:
Prepurchase Counseling

CALDWELL BOARD OF
REALTORS
PO Box 1516
Caldwell, ID 836051516
208-463-2727
Fax: 208-453-8875
Type of Counseling:
Prepurchase Counseling

ST VINCENT DE PAUL
108 East Walnut
Coeur d' Alene, ID 83814
208-664-3095
Fax: 208-664-3095
Type of Counseling:
Prepurchase Counseling

**IDAHO FALLS
ASSOCIATION OF REALTORS
1388 Cambridge
Idaho Falls, ID 83401
208-523-1477
Fax: 208-522-7867
Type of Counseling:
Prepurchase Counseling

COMMUNITY ACTION
AGENCY
124 New Sixth Street
Lewiston, ID 83501
208-746-3351
Fax: 208-746-5456
Email: s.smith@caanid.org
Type of Counseling:
HECM Counseling,
Default/Foreclosure Counseling,
Rental Counseling, Prepurchase
Counseling

NAMPA NEIGHBORHOOD
HOUSING SERVICES
704 11th Avenue North
Nampa, ID 83687
208-467-7336
Fax: 208-463-9136
Type of Counseling:
Prepurchase Counseling

**COLLEGE OF SOUTHERN
IDAHO COMMUNITY
EDUCATION CENTER
315 Falls Ave
Twin Falls, ID 83301
208-733-9554
Fax: 208-736-3014
Type of Counseling:
Prepurchase Counseling

Illinois

MADISON COUNTY URBAN
LEAGUE
210 William St
Alton, IL 62002-6146
618-463-1906

Fax: 618-463-9021
Email: sjh95@aol.com
Type of Counseling:
HECM Counseling,
Default/Foreclosure Counseling,
Rental Counseling, Prepurchase
Counseling
Affiliate of: NATIONAL
URBAN LEAGUE

CONSUMER CREDIT
COUNSELING SERVICE-
SAINT LOUIS
1623 Washington Ave., Suite 200
Alton, IL 620023933
618-463-1660
Toll-Free: 800-966-3328
Fax: 314-647-1359
Email: sueash@dellepro.com
Type of Counseling:
Default/Foreclosure Counseling

**JOSEPH CORPORATION
32 South Broadway Avenue
Aurora, IL 60507
630-906-9400
Fax: 630-906-9406
Type of Counseling:
Prepurchase Counseling,
Default/Foreclosure Counseling
Affiliate of: HOUSING
OPPORTUNITIES,
INCORPORATED

NEIGHBORS UNITED FOR
PROGRESS
19 Public Square
Suite 300
Belleville, IL 62220
618-234-9165
Fax: 618-234-9217
Type of Counseling:
Prepurchase Counseling,
Default/Foreclosure Counseling

MID CENTRAL COMMUNITY
ACTION
923 E Grove St
Bloomington, IL 61701-4201
309-829-0691
Fax: 309-828-8811
Type of Counseling:
Default/Foreclosure Counseling,
Rental Counseling, Prepurchase
Counseling

NEIGHBORS UNITED FOR
PROGRESS
5701 Bond Avenue
Centreville, IL 62207
618-274-4206
Fax: 618-234-9217
Type of Counseling:
Prepurchase Counseling

CONSUMER CREDIT
COUNSELING
201 W. Springfield Avenue, Suite
702
Champaign, IL 61820-
217-425-0654
Toll-Free: 800-959-2227
Fax: 217-425-4793
Email: cris@cccsillinois.org
Type of Counseling:
HECM Counseling, Prepurchase
Counseling, Default/Foreclosure
Counseling, Rental Counseling

URBAN LEAGUE OF
CHAMPAIGN COUNTY
17 Taylor Street
Champaign, IL 61820
217-356-6018
Fax: 217-356-1310
Email: tparson@prarienet.org
Type of Counseling:
Prepurchase Counseling,
Default/Foreclosure Counseling
Affiliate of: NATIONAL
URBAN LEAGUE

**ACORN HOUSING
CORPORATION
650 S. Clark Street #301
Chicago, IL 60605
312-939-1611
Fax: 312-939-4239
Type of Counseling:
Default/Foreclosure Counseling,
Prepurchase Counseling
Affiliate of: ACORN HOUSING
CORPORATION

CONSUMER CREDIT
COUNSELING SERVICE OF
GREATER CHICAGO
150 N Wacker Dr Ste 1400
Chicago, IL 606061607
312-849-2227
Toll-Free: 888-527-3328
Fax: 312-849-2135

Website: www.cccsgrchicago.org
Type of Counseling:
Rental Counseling, Prepurchase
Counseling, HECM Counseling
Affiliate of: NATIONAL
FOUNDATION FOR
CONSUMER CREDIT,
INCORPORATED

**RESURRECTION PROJECT
1818 S. Paulina
Chicago, IL 60608
312-666-1323
Toll-Free:
TTY/TDD:
Fax: 312-942-1123
Email:
maricruz_poncedeleon@yahoo.c
om
Website:
Type of Counseling:
Prepurchase Counseling,
Default/Foreclosure Counseling,
Rental Counseling, HECM
Counseling
Affiliate of: NATIONAL
COUNCIL OF LA RAZA

LATIN UNITED COMMUNTIY
HOUSING ASSOCIATION
3541 West North Avenue
Chicago, IL 60647
773-276-5338
Toll-Free: 800-217-6970
Fax: 773-276-5358
Email: jmartens@lucha.org
Type of Counseling:
Prepurchase Counseling, Rental
Counseling, Default/Foreclosure
Counseling

SPANISH COALITION FOR
HOUSING
4035 W North Ave
Chicago, IL 60639
773-342-7575
Fax: 773-342-8528
Type of Counseling:
HECM Counseling,
Default/Foreclosure Counseling,
Rental Counseling, Prepurchase
Counseling

CHICAGO ROSELAND
COALITION FOR
COMMUNITY CONTROL

11015 S Michigan Ave
Chicago, IL 60628-4308
773-264-3500
Fax: 773-264-9634
Email: crcc@cnt.org
Type of Counseling:
HECM Counseling,
Default/Foreclosure Counseling,
Prepurchase Counseling

COMMUNITY AND
ECONOMIC DEVELOPMENT
ASSOCIATION - CEDA
208 S La Salle St Ste 1900
Chicago, IL 60604-1104
312-795-8961
Fax: 312-795-1034
Type of Counseling:
HECM Counseling,
Default/Foreclosure Counseling,
Rental Counseling, Prepurchase
Counseling

CHICAGO URBAN LEAGUE
DEVELOPMENT
CORPORATION
4510 S Michigan Ave
Chicago, IL 60653-3898
773-451-3606
Fax: 773-285-0879
Email: Sstanley@cul-chicago.org
Type of Counseling:
HECM Counseling,
Default/Foreclosure Counseling,
Rental Counseling, Prepurchase
Counseling
Affiliate of: NATIONAL
URBAN LEAGUE

CHICAGO COMMONS
HOUSING RESOURCE
CENTER
6247c South Halsted Street
Chicago, IL 60621
773-783-2472
Fax: 773-783-0667
Email: CommonsHRC@aol.com
Type of Counseling:
Prepurchase Counseling,
Default/Foreclosure Counseling,
Rental Counseling

ILLINOIS HOUSING
DEVELOPMENT AUTHORITY
401 North Michigan Ave. Suite
900

Chicago, IL 60611
312-836-5200
Fax: 312-832-2170

LEADERSHIP COUNCIL FOR
METROPOLITAN OPEN
COMMUNITIES
111 Wesr Jackson Blvd
12th Floor
Chicago, IL 60604-
312-341-5678
Fax: 312-341-1958
Type of Counseling:
Prepurchase Counseling, Rental
Counseling

ROGERS PARK COMMUNITY
COUNCIL
1530 West Morse Avenue
Chicago, IL 60626
773-338-7722
Fax: 773-338-7774
Type of Counseling:
HECM Counseling,
Default/Foreclosure Counseling,
Prepurchase Counseling

AGENCY METROPOLITAN
PROGRAM SERVICES
3210 West Arthington Street
Chicago, IL 60624
773-533-0242
Fax: 773-533-0243
Type of Counseling:
Prepurchase Counseling, Rental
Counseling

LOGAN SQUARE
NEIGHBORHOOD
ASSOCIATION
3321 Wrightwood Avenue
Chicago, IL 60647
773-384-4370
Fax: 773-384-0624
Type of Counseling:
HECM Counseling,
Default/Foreclosure Counseling,
Rental Counseling, Prepurchase
Counseling

LEGAL ASSISTANCE
FOUNDATION OF
METROPOLITAN CHICAGO
111 West Jackson Ste 300
Chicago, IL 60604
312-341-1070

Fax: 312-341-1041
Type of Counseling:
HECM Counseling, Prepurchase
Counseling, Default/Foreclosure
Counseling, Rental Counseling

CITY OF CHICAGO
DEPARTMENT OF HOUSING
318 S Michigan Ave
Chicago, IL 60604-4208
312-747-2858
Fax: 312-747-1670
Type of Counseling:
HECM Counseling,
Default/Foreclosure Counseling,
Rental Counseling, Prepurchase
Counseling

CHICAGO HEIGHTS
COMMUNITY SERVICE
CENTER - CEDA
1203 W End Ave
Chicago Heights, IL 60411-2746
708-754-4575
Fax: 708-754-4595
Type of Counseling:
HECM Counseling,
Default/Foreclosure Counseling,
Rental Counseling, Prepurchase
Counseling

CEDA NEAR WEST
5142 West 25th Street
Cicero, IL 60804-
708-222-3824
Fax: 708-222-0026
Type of Counseling:
HECM Counseling,
Default/Foreclosure Counseling,
Rental Counseling, Prepurchase
Counseling

CONSUMER CREDIT
COUNSELING
220 N Vermilion St
Danville, IL 61832-
217-425-0654
Toll-Free: 800-959-2227
Fax: 217-425-4793
Email: cris@cccsillinois.org
Type of Counseling:
HECM Counseling,
Default/Foreclosure Counseling,
Rental Counseling, Prepurchase
Counseling

Affiliate of: NATIONAL
FOUNDATION FOR
CONSUMER CREDIT,
INCORPORATED

CONSUMER CREDIT
COUNSELING SERVICE OF
EAST CENTRAL ILLINOIS
222 E. North Street
Decatur, IL 62523
217-425-0654
Toll-Free: 800-959-2227
Fax: 217-425-4793
Email: cris@cccsillinois.org
Type of Counseling:
HECM Counseling,
Default/Foreclosure Counseling,
Rental Counseling, Prepurchase
Counseling
Affiliate of: NATIONAL
FOUNDATION FOR
CONSUMER CREDIT,
INCORPORATED

COMMUNITY DEVELOPMENT
BLOCK GRANT OPERATIONS
CORPORATION
301 River Park Dr. 3rd Floor
East St Louis, IL 62201-3022
618-482-6635
Fax: 618-271-8194
Type of Counseling:
Rental Counseling,
Default/Foreclosure Counseling

CEFS EFFINGHAM
OUTREACH OFFICE
202 N Banker Street
Effiingham, IL 62401-
217-347-7514
Fax: 217-347-5331
Email: outreach@effengham.net
Type of Counseling:
HECM Counseling,
Default/Foreclosure Counseling,
Rental Counseling, Prepurchase
Counseling

CONSUMER CREDIT
COUNSELING SERVICE-
SAINT LOUIS
1901 South 4th Street, Suite 201,
Lincoln Land Building
Effingham, IL 62401
217-342-6761
Toll-Free: 800-966-3328

Fax: 314-647-1359
Type of Counseling:
Default/Foreclosure Counseling

EFFINGHAM ECONOMIC
OPPORTUNITY
CORPORATION
204 W Washington Ave
Effingham, IL 62401-2357
217-347-7514
Fax: 217-347-5331
Type of Counseling:
HECM Counseling,
Default/Foreclosure Counseling,
Rental Counseling, Prepurchase
Counseling

CEFS ECONOMIC
OPPORTUNITY
CORPORATION
1805 S Banker St
Effingham, IL 62401-3482
217-342-2193
Fax: 217-342-4701
Type of Counseling:
HECM Counseling,
Default/Foreclosure Counseling,
Rental Counseling, Prepurchase
Counseling

LEADERSHIP COUNCIL FOR
METROPOLITAN OPEN
COMMUNITIES NORTHWEST
SUBURBAN HOUSING
CENTER
25 Turner Avenue Suite 204
Elk Grove Village, IL 60007-
847-290-0148
Fax: 847-290-0451
Type of Counseling:
Prepurchase Counseling, Rental
Counseling

COMMUNITY AND
ECONOMIC DEVELOPMENT
ASSOCIATION NEIGHBORS
AT WORK
1229 Emerson St
Evanston, IL 60201-3524
847-328-5166
Fax: 847-328-9262
Type of Counseling:
HECM Counseling,
Default/Foreclosure Counseling,
Rental Counseling, Prepurchase
Counseling

LEADERSHIP COUNCIL FOR
METROPOLITAN OPEN
COMMUNITIES
9730 S. Western Avenue, Suite
828
Evergreen Park, IL 60305
708-636-2811
Fax: 708-636-9360
Type of Counseling:
Prepurchase Counseling, Rental
Counseling

CONSUMER CREDIT
COUNSELING SERVICE OF
GREATER CHICAGO-
EVERGREEN PARK
3317 W. 95th Street, Ste 3
Evergreen Park, IL 60805-
888-527-3328
Fax: 312-849-2135
Email: jgarcia@cccsgrchicago.org
Type of Counseling:
Prepurchase Counseling, HECM
Counseling, Rental Counseling

CONSUMER CREDIT
COUNSELING SERVICE -
SAINT LOUIS
10314 Lincoln Trail, Suite 100
Fairview Heights, IL 622081801
618-394-1137
Toll-Free: 800-966-3328
Fax: 314-647-1359
Type of Counseling:
Default/Foreclosure Counseling

CLAY ECONOMIC
OPPORTUNITY
CORPORATION
832 W North Ave
Flora, IL 62839-1219
618-662-4024
Fax: 618-662-2721
Type of Counseling:
HECM Counseling,
Default/Foreclosure Counseling,
Rental Counseling, Prepurchase
Counseling

CEFS CLAY COUNTY
OUTREACH OFFICE
832B West North
Flora, IL 62839-
618-662-4024
Fax: 618-662-2721
Email: ccefs@wabash.net

Type of Counseling:
HECM Counseling,
Default/Foreclosure Counseling,
Rental Counseling, Prepurchase
Counseling

FORD HEIGHTS COMMUNITY
SERVICE CENTER - CEDA
1647 Cottage Grove Ave
Ford Heights, IL 60411-3899
708-758-2510
Fax: 708-758-0825
Type of Counseling:
HECM Counseling,
Default/Foreclosure Counseling,
Rental Counseling, Prepurchase
Counseling

CONSUMER CREDIT
COUNSELING SERVICES OF
CENTRAL ILLINOIS,
INCORPORATED
180 s. Soangetaha Road, Knox
Agricultural Center Building
Galesburg, IL 61401-
309-676-2941
Toll-Free: 888-671-2227
Fax: 309-676-6143
Email: cris@cccsillinois.org
Type of Counseling:
Rental Counseling, Prepurchase
Counseling, Default/Foreclosure
Counseling, HECM Counseling

HOUSING AUTHORITY OF
THE COUNTY LAKE ILLINOIS
33928 North Route 45
Grayslake, IL 60030
847-223-1170
TTY/TDD: 847-223-1270
Fax: 847-223-1174
Type of Counseling:
HECM Counseling,
Default/Foreclosure Counseling,
Rental Counseling, Prepurchase
Counseling

AFFORDABLE HOUSING
CORPORATION OF LAKE
COUNTY
3701 W. Grand Avenue, Suite H
Gurnee, IL 60031
847-263-7478
Fax: 847-263-9381
Type of Counseling:

Prepurchase Counseling,
Default/Foreclosure Counseling
Affiliate of: HOUSING
OPPORTUNITIES,
INCORPORATED

COMMUNITY AND
ECONOMIC SEVELOPMENT
ASSOCIATION CENTER OF
COMMUNITY ACTION
53 E 154th St
Harvey, IL 60426-3645
708-339-3610
Fax: 708-331-4539
Type of Counseling:
HECM Counseling,
Default/Foreclosure Counseling,
Rental Counseling, Prepurchase
Counseling

SOUTH SUBURBAN HOUSING
CENTER
18220 Harwood Avenue, Suite 1
Homewood, IL 60430
708-957-4874
Fax: 708-957-4761
Type of Counseling:
Prepurchase Counseling, Rental
Counseling

WILL COUNTY CENTER FOR
COMMUNITY CONCERNS
309 N. Scott Street
Joliet, IL 60432-
815-722-0722
Fax: 815-722-6344
Type of Counseling:
HECM Counseling,
Default/Foreclosure Counseling,
Rental Counseling, Prepurchase
Counseling

**KANKAKEE
NEIGHBORHOOD HOUSING
SERVICES, INCORPORATED
512 S Chicago Ave
Kankakee, IL 60901-0831
815-939-9700
Fax: 815-939-3730
Email: knhs@colint.com
Type of Counseling:
HECM Counseling,
Default/Foreclosure Counseling,
Prepurchase Counseling
Affiliate of: NEIGHBORHOOD
REINVESTMENT
CORPORATION

CEFS MONTGOMERY
CORPORATION OUTREACH
OFFICE
311 S. State
Litchfield, IL 62056-
217-324-2367
Fax: 217-324-2241
Email: montcefs@mcleodusa.net
Type of Counseling:
HECM Counseling,
Default/Foreclosure Counseling,
Rental Counseling, Prepurchase
Counseling

CONSUMER CREDIT
COUNSELING SERVICE-
SAINT LOUIS
1616 West Main Street, Suite 200
Marion, IL 62959-1144
618-997-1880
Toll-Free: 800-966-3328
Fax: 314-647-1359
Type of Counseling:
Default/Foreclosure Counseling

CONSUMER CREDIT
COUNSELING SERVICE-
SAINT LOUIS
613 Lake Land Blvd.
Mattoon, IL 61938
217-235-3570
Toll-Free: 800-966-3328
Fax: 314-647-1359
Type of Counseling:
Default/Foreclosure Counseling

PROVISO-LEYDEN COUNCIL
FOR COMMUNITY ACTION -
CEDA
411 Madison St
Maywood, IL 60153-1939
708-450-3500
Fax: 708-449-2699
Type of Counseling:
HECM Counseling,
Default/Foreclosure Counseling,
Rental Counseling, Prepurchase
Counseling

CEDA NORTHWEST SELF-
HELP CENTER,
INCORPORATED
1300 W Northwest Hwy
Mount Prospect, IL 60056-2217
847-392-2332
Fax: 847-392-2427

Type of Counseling:
HECM Counseling,
Default/Foreclosure Counseling,
Rental Counseling, Prepurchase
Counseling

CONSUMER CREDIT
COUNSELING SERVICE-
SAINT LOUIS
123 S. 10TH Street, Suite 205
Mt. Vernon, IL 62864
618-241-9102
Toll-Free: 800-966-3328
Fax: 314-647-1359
Type of Counseling:
Default/Foreclosure Counseling

CONSUMER CREDIT
COUNSELING SERVICE OF
GREATER CHICAGO-OAK
PARK
1515 N Harlem Ave Ste 205
Oak Park, IL 60302-1205
888-527-3328
Fax: 312-849-2135
Type of Counseling:
HECM Counseling, Rental
Counseling, Prepurchase
Counseling

PANA ECONOMIC
OPPORTUNITY
CORPORATION
Raymond and Route 16
Pana, IL 62557
217-562-2311
Fax: 217-342-4701
Type of Counseling:
HECM Counseling,
Default/Foreclosure Counseling,
Rental Counseling, Prepurchase
Counseling

CEFS CHRISTIAN COUNTY
OUTREACH OFFICE
2295 Illinois Street, Route 16
Pana, IL 62557
217-562-2311
Fax: 217-824-5018
Email: chcefs@mcleodusa.net
Type of Counseling:
HECM Counseling,
Default/Foreclosure Counseling,
Rental Counseling, Prepurchase
Counseling

CONSUMER CREDIT
COUNSELING SERVICES OF
CENTRAL ILLINOIS,
INCORPORATED
110 N. 5th Street, Suite 210
Pekin, IL 61554
309-676-2941
Toll-Free: 888-671-2227
Fax: 309-676-6143
Email: cris@cccsillinois.org
Type of Counseling:
Rental Counseling, Prepurchase
Counseling, Default/Foreclosure
Counseling, HECM Counseling

CONSUMER CREDIT
COUNSELING SERVICES OF
CENTRAL ILLINOIS,
INCORPORATED
719 Main Street
Peoria, IL 61602
309-676-2941
Toll-Free: 888-671-2227
Fax: 309-676-6143
Email: cris@cccsillinois.org
Type of Counseling:
Prepurchase Counseling,
Default/Foreclosure Counseling,
HECM Counseling, Rental
Counseling
Affiliate of: NATIONAL
FOUNDATION FOR
CONSUMER CREDIT,
INCORPORATED

CONSUMER CREDIT
COUNSELING SERVICES OF
CENTRAL ILLINOIS,
INCORPORATED
Backbone Road East, Options
EAP
Princeton, IL 61356-
309-676-2941
Toll-Free: 888-671-2227
Fax: 309-676-6143
Email: cris@cccsillinois.org
Type of Counseling:
Rental Counseling, Prepurchase
Counseling, Default/Foreclosure
Counseling, HECM Counseling

CONSUMER CREDIT
COUNSELING SERVICE -
SAINT LOUIS
1890 Maine Street
Quincy, IL 623014231

217-222-0621
Toll-Free: 800-966-3328
Fax: 314-647-1359
Type of Counseling:
Default/Foreclosure Counseling

SOUTHEAST CEDA
3518 W 139th St
Robbins, IL 60472-2002
708-371-1522
Fax: 708-371-1247
Type of Counseling:
HECM Counseling,
Default/Foreclosure Counseling,
Rental Counseling, Prepurchase
Counseling

**ROCK ISLAND ECONOMIC
GROWTH CORPORATION
120 16 1/2 Street
Rock Island, IL 61201
309-788-6311
Fax: 309-788-6323
Type of Counseling:
Prepurchase Counseling
Affiliate of: HOUSING
OPPORTUNITIES,
INCORPORATED

CONSUMER CREDIT
COUNSELING SERVICE OF
GREATER CHICAGO-
ROCKFORD
810 E State St Ste 306
Rockford, IL 61104-1001
888-527-3328
Fax: 312-849-2135
Email: jgarcia@cccsgrchicago.org
Type of Counseling:
HECM Counseling, Rental
Counseling, Prepurchase
Counseling

ROCKFORD AREA
AFFORDABLE HOUSING
COALITION
205 N. Church St.
Rockford, IL 611051354
815-962-2011
Fax: 815-964-0144
Type of Counseling:
Prepurchase Counseling,
Default/Foreclosure Counseling,
Rental Counseling

Affiliate of: HOUSING
OPPORTUNITIES,
INCORPORATED

COMMUNITY SERVICE
COUNCIL OF NORTHERN
WILL COUNTY
719 Parkwood Ave
Romeoville, IL 60446-1134
815-886-5000
Fax: 815-886-6700
Type of Counseling:
HECM Counseling,
Default/Foreclosure Counseling,
Prepurchase Counseling

CONSUMER CREDIT
COUNSELING SERVICE OF
GREATER CHICAGO-
SCHAUMBURG
1320 Tower Rd Suite 150
Schaumburg, IL 60173
888-527-3328
Fax: 847-519-7095
Email: jgarcia@cccsgrchicago.org
Type of Counseling:
HECM Counseling, Rental
Counseling, Prepurchase
Counseling

CEFS SHELBY COUNTY
OUTREACH OFFICE
Route 16 Main Street
Shelbyville, IL 62565
217-774-4541
Fax: 217-774-3532
Email: shelbycocefs@
mcleodusa.net
Type of Counseling:
HECM Counseling,
Default/Foreclosure Counseling,
Rental Counseling, Prepurchase
Counseling

SHELBY ECONOMIC
OPPORTUNITY
CORPORATION
County Courthouse
Shelbyville, IL 62565
217-774-4541
Fax: 217-774-3532
Type of Counseling:
HECM Counseling,
Default/Foreclosure Counseling,
Rental Counseling, Prepurchase
Counseling

CEFS MOULTRIE COUNTY
OUTREACH OFFICE
114 E Harrison Street
Sillivan, IL 61951-
217-728-7721
Fax: 217-728-2923
Email: cefsoutreach@one-
eleven.net
Type of Counseling:
HECM Counseling,
Default/Foreclosure Counseling,
Rental Counseling, Prepurchase
Counseling

**SPRINGFIELD URBAN
LEAGUE
100 North 11th Street
Springfield, IL 62798-
217-789-0830
Fax: 217-789-9838
Email: kadavis59@hotmail.com
Type of Counseling:
Prepurchase Counseling,
Default/Foreclosure Counseling,
HECM Counseling, Rental
Counseling
Affiliate of: NATIONAL
URBAN LEAGUE

CONSUMER CREDIT
COUNSELING SERVICE-
SAINT LOUIS
3111 Normandy Road
Springfield, IL 62703
217-585-2227
Toll-Free: 800-966-3328
Fax: 314-647-1359
Type of Counseling:
Default/Foreclosure Counseling

THE SPRINGFIELD PROJECT
HOPE, INCORPORATED
1507 East Cook Street
Springfield, IL 62708
217-206-7690
Fax: 217-522-6442
Type of Counseling:
Prepurchase Counseling,
Default/Foreclosure Counseling,
Rental Counseling

SPRINGFIELD DEPARTMENT
OF COMMUNITY RELATIONS
800 E Monroe St Ste 108
Springfield, IL 62701-1900
217-789-2271

Fax: 217-789-2268
Type of Counseling:
Default/Foreclosure Counseling,
Rental Counseling, Prepurchase
Counseling

MOULTRIE ECONOMIC
OPPORTUNITY
CORPORATION
County Courthouse
Sullivan, IL 61951
217-728-7721
Fax: 217-728-4743
Type of Counseling:
HECM Counseling,
Default/Foreclosure Counseling,
Rental Counseling, Prepurchase
Counseling

SOUTHWEST DEVELOPMENT
ASSOCIATION - CEDA
5818 S Archer Rd
Summit Argo, IL 60501-1410
708-458-2736
Fax: 708-458-5242
Type of Counseling:
HECM Counseling,
Default/Foreclosure Counseling,
Rental Counseling, Prepurchase
Counseling

MONTGOMERY ECONOMIC
OPPORTUNITY
CORPORATION
South Rt. 127
Taylor Springs, IL 62089
217-532-5971
Fax: 217-532-3551
Type of Counseling:
HECM Counseling,
Default/Foreclosure Counseling,
Rental Counseling, Prepurchase
Counseling

CEFS MONTGOMERY
CORPORATION OUTREACH
OFFICE
S. Route 127, Box 128
Taylor Springs, IL 62089-
217-532-5971
Fax: 217-532-2367
Email: montcefs@mcleodusa.net
Type of Counseling:
HECM Counseling,
Default/Foreclosure Counseling,

Rental Counseling, Prepurchase
Counseling

CEFS CHRISTIAN COUNTY
OUTREACH OFFICE
311 S. Main Street
Taylorville, IL 62568-
217-824-4712
Fax: 217-824-5018
Email: chcefs@mcleodusa.net
Type of Counseling:
HECM Counseling,
Default/Foreclosure Counseling,
Rental Counseling, Prepurchase
Counseling

CHRISTIAN ECONOMIC
OPPORTUNITY
CORPORATION
124 S Main
Taylorville, IL 62568
217-824-4712
Fax: 217-824-5018
Type of Counseling:
HECM Counseling,
Default/Foreclosure Counseling,
Rental Counseling, Prepurchase
Counseling

CONSUMER CREDIT
COUNSELING SERVICE OF
GREATER CHICAGO-TINLEY
PARK
16860 Oak Park Ave Ste 102
Tinley Park, IL 60477-2761
888-527-3328
Fax: 312-849-2135
Email: jgarcia@cccsgrchicago.org
Type of Counseling:
HECM Counseling, Rental
Counseling, Prepurchase
Counseling

CEFS FAYETTE COUNTY
OUTREACH OFFICE
517 W. Gattatin Street
Vandalia, IL 62471-
618-283-2631
Fax: 618-283-2715
Email: cefs@swetland.net
Type of Counseling:
HECM Counseling,
Default/Foreclosure Counseling,
Rental Counseling, Prepurchase
Counseling

FAYETTE ECONOMIC
OPPORTUNITY
CORPORATION
517 West Gallatin St
Vandalia, IL 62471-0044
618-283-2631
Fax: 618-283-2715
Type of Counseling:
HECM Counseling,
Default/Foreclosure Counseling,
Rental Counseling, Prepurchase
Counseling

LAKE COUNTY COMMUNITY
ACTION PROJECT
102-6 S Sheridan Rd
Waukegan, IL 60085-5610
847-249-4330
Fax: 847-249-4393
Type of Counseling:
HECM Counseling,
Default/Foreclosure Counseling,
Rental Counseling, Prepurchase
Counseling

POSITIVE SYSTEMATIC
TRANSFORMATIONS,
INCORPORATED
1528 Washington St
Waukegan, IL 60085-5347
847-625-8629
Fax: 847-625-8631
Type of Counseling:
Rental Counseling, Prepurchase
Counseling

CATHOLIC CHARITIES OF
THE ARCHDIOCESE OF
CHICAGO
671 S Lewis Ave
Waukegan, IL 60085
847-782-4160
Fax: 847-249-0116
Type of Counseling:
HECM Counseling,
Default/Foreclosure Counseling,
Rental Counseling, Prepurchase
Counseling
Affiliate of: CATHOLIC
CHARITIES USA

LEADERSHIP COUNCIL FOR
METROPOLITAN OPEN
COMMUNITIES NEARWEST
SUBURBAN HOUSING
CENTER

9999 W. Roosevelt Road, Suite
203
Westchester, IL 60154-
708-450-0070
Fax: 708-450-0082
Type of Counseling:
Rental Counseling, Prepurchase
Counseling

DU PAGE HOMEOWNERSHIP
CENTER
1333 N Main St
Wheaton, IL 60187-3579
630-260-2500
Fax: 630-260-2505
Type of Counseling:
Default/Foreclosure Counseling,
Prepurchase Counseling

CONSUMER CREDIT
COUNSELING SERVICE OF
GREATER CHICAGO-
WHEELING
212 S Milwaukee Ave Ste D
Wheeling, IL 60090-5080
888-527-3328
Fax: 312-849-2135
Type of Counseling:
HECM Counseling,
Default/Foreclosure Counseling,
Rental Counseling, Prepurchase
Counseling

INTERFAITH HOUSING
DEVELOPMENT
CORPORATION
620 Lincoln Avenue
Winnetka, IL 600935722
847-501-3278
Fax: 847-501-5722
Type of Counseling:
Prepurchase Counseling, Rental
Counseling

**CONSUMER CREDIT
COUNSELING SERVICE OF
MCHENRY COUNTY,
INCORPORATED
400 Russel Ct Ste A
Woodstock, IL 60098-2640
815-338-5757
Fax: 815-338-9646
Type of Counseling:
HECM Counseling,
Default/Foreclosure Counseling,

Rental Counseling, Prepurchase
Counseling
Affiliate of: NATIONAL
FOUNDATION FOR
CONSUMER CREDIT,
INCORPORATED

Indiana

ANDERSON HOUSING
AUTHORITY
528 West 11th St
Anderson, IN 46016-1228
765-641-2620
Fax: 765-641-2629
Type of Counseling:
HECM Counseling,
Default/Foreclosure Counseling,
Rental Counseling, Prepurchase
Counseling

**CONSUMER CREDIT
COUNSELING SERVICE OF
CENTRAL INDIANA
931 Meridian Plaza, Ste 704
Anderson, IN 46016
317-266-1300
Toll-Free: 888-711-7227
TTY/TDD: 317-266-1324
Fax: 317-266-1315
Email:
mwright@cccsmidwest.org
Website: www.cccsmidwest.org
Type of Counseling:
Prepurchase Counseling,
Default/Foreclosure Counseling,
HECM Counseling, Rental
Counseling
Affiliate of: NATIONAL
FOUNDATION FOR
CONSUMER CREDIT,
INCORPORATED

KNOX COUNTY HOUSING
AUTHORITY
Tilly Estates Office
Bicknell, IN 47512
812-882-0220
Fax: 812-735-2004
Type of Counseling:
Rental Counseling

CITY OF BLOOMINGTON
HOUSING AND
NEIGHBORHOOD
DEVLOPMENT

401 N Morton St
Bloomington, IN 47404-3729
812-349-3576
Fax: 812-349-3582
Email:
hand@city.bloomington.in.us
Type of Counseling:
HECM Counseling,
Default/Foreclosure Counseling,
Rental Counseling, Prepurchase
Counseling

**CONSUMER CREDIT
COUNSELING SERVICE OF
CENTRAL INDIANA
205 N. College, Suite 014
Bloomington, IN 47404
812-333-6083
Toll-Free: 888-711-7227
TTY/TDD: 317-266-1324
Fax: 317-266-1315
Email:
mwright@cccsmidwest.org
Website: www.cccsmidwest.org
Type of Counseling:
Default/Foreclosure Counseling,
Rental Counseling, Prepurchase
Counseling, HECM Counseling
Affiliate of: NATIONAL
FOUNDATION FOR
CONSUMER CREDIT,
INCORPORATED

**CONSUMER CREDIT
COUNSELING SERVICE OF
CENTRAL INDIANA
551 First Street
Columbus, IN 47201
812-372-1015
Toll-Free: 888-711-7227
TTY/TDD: 317-266-1324
Fax: 317-266-1315
Email:
mwright@cccsmidwest.org
Website: www.cccsmidwest.org
Type of Counseling:
Default/Foreclosure Counseling,
Rental Counseling, Prepurchase
Counseling, HECM Counseling
Affiliate of: NATIONAL
FOUNDATION FOR
CONSUMER CREDIT,
INCORPORATED

**CONSUMER CREDIT
COUNSELING SERVICE OF
CENTRAL INDIANA
Fayette Senior Center

477 Grand Avenue
Connersville, IN 47331
888-711-7227
Toll-Free: 888-711-7227
TTY/TDD: 317-266-1324
Fax: 317-266-1315
Email:
mwright@cccsmidwest.org
Website: www.cccsmidwest.org
Type of Counseling:
Default/Foreclosure Counseling,
Rental Counseling, Prepurchase
Counseling, HECM Counseling
Affiliate of: NATIONAL
FOUNDATION FOR
CONSUMER CREDIT,
INCORPORATED

LAKE COUNTY COMMUNITY
ECONOMIC DEPARTMENT
2293 N Main St
Crown Point, IN 46307-1885
219-755-3232
Fax: 219-736-5925
Type of Counseling:
HECM Counseling,
Default/Foreclosure Counseling,
Rental Counseling, Prepurchase
Counseling

**CONSUMER CREDIT
COUNSELING SERVICE OF
CENTRAL INDIANA
1500 E. Main Street
Danville, IN 46112
888-711-7227
Toll-Free: 888-711-7227
TTY/TDD: 317-266-1324
Fax: 317-266-1315
Email:
mwright@cccsmidwest.org
Website: www.cccsmidwest.org
Type of Counseling:
Default/Foreclosure Counseling,
Rental Counseling, Prepurchase
Counseling, HECM Counseling
Affiliate of: NATIONAL
FOUNDATION FOR
CONSUMER CREDIT,
INCORPORATED

ELKHART HOUSING
AUTHORITY
1396 Benham Ave
Elkhart, IN 46516-3341
219-295-0065

Fax: 219-293-6878
Type of Counseling:
HECM Counseling,
Default/Foreclosure Counseling,
Rental Counseling, Prepurchase
Counseling

**CONSUMER CREDIT
COUNSELING SERVICE OF
NORTHERN INDIANA
3422 S Main St
Elkhart, IN 46517-3124
574-293-0075
Toll-Free: 800-794-6559
Fax: 574-293-0365
Type of Counseling:
Default/Foreclosure Counseling,
Rental Counseling, Prepurchase
Counseling, HECM Counseling
Affiliate of: NATIONAL
FOUNDATION FOR
CONSUMER CREDIT,
INCORPORATED

CONSUMER CREDIT
COUNSELING OF THE TRI-
STATE. INCORPORATED
715 First Ave, 3rd Floor
Evansville, IN 47710
812-422-1108
Toll-Free: 800-451-6293
Fax: 812-424-9050
Type of Counseling:
HECM Counseling,
Default/Foreclosure Counseling,
Rental Counseling, Prepurchase
Counseling
Affiliate of: NATIONAL
FOUNDATION FOR
CONSUMER CREDIT,
INCORPORATED

HOPE OF EVANSVILLE,
INCORPORATED
608 Cherry St
Evansville, IN 47713
812-423-3169
Fax: 812-424-2848
Email: hope@sigecom.net
Type of Counseling:
HECM Counseling,
Default/Foreclosure Counseling,
Rental Counseling, Prepurchase
Counseling

FORT WAYNE URBAN
LEAGUE, INCORPORATED
227eAST Washington Blvd.
Fort Wayne, IN 46802-
260-424-6326
Fax: 260-422-1626
Type of Counseling:
Prepurchase Counseling,
Default/Foreclosure Counseling,
Rental Counseling

**CONSUMER CREDIT
COUNSELING SERVICE OF
NORTHEASTERN INDIANA
4105 W Jefferson Blvd
Fort Wayne, IN 46858
219-432-8200
Toll-Free: 800-432-0420
Fax: 219-432-7415
Type of Counseling:
Prepurchase Counseling,
Default/Foreclosure Counseling,
HECM Counseling, Rental
Counseling
Affiliate of: NATIONAL
FOUNDATION FOR
CONSUMER CREDIT,
INCORPORATED

FORT WAYNE HOUSING
AUTHORITY
2013 S Anthony Blvd
Ft. Wayne, IN 46869-3489
219-449-7800
Fax: 219-449-7133
Email: mmorris@fwha.org
Type of Counseling:
HECM Counseling,
Default/Foreclosure Counseling,
Prepurchase Counseling

**CATHOLIC CHARITIES
GARY, INDIANA
520 El Camino Real, Suite 204
Gary, IN 46402-
650-696-1255
Type of Counseling:
Prepurchase Counseling,
Default/Foreclosure Counseling,
Rental Counseling
Affiliate of: CATHOLIC
CHARITIES USA

URBAN LEAGUE OF
NORTHWEST INDIANA,
INCORPORATED

3101 Broadway
Gary, IN 46409-1006
219-887-9621
Fax: 219-887-0020
Type of Counseling:
HECM Counseling,
Default/Foreclosure Counseling,
Rental Counseling, Prepurchase
Counseling

CONSUMER CREDIT
COUNSELING SERVICE
3637 Grant St
Gary, IN 46408-1423
219-980-4800
Fax: 219-980-5012
Email: CCCSofNWIN@aol.com
Type of Counseling:
HECM Counseling,
Default/Foreclosure Counseling,
Rental Counseling, Prepurchase
Counseling

**CONSUMER CREDIT
COUNSELING SERVICE OF
CENTRAL INDIANA
98 E. North St.
Greenfield, IN 46140
888-711-7227
Toll-Free: 888-711-7227
TTY/TDD: 317-266-1324
Fax: 317-266-1315
Email:
mwright@cccsmidwest.org
Website: www.cccsmidwest.org
Type of Counseling:
Default/Foreclosure Counseling,
Rental Counseling, Prepurchase
Counseling, HECM Counseling
Affiliate of: NATIONAL
FOUNDATION FOR
CONSUMER CREDIT,
INCORPORATED

**CONSUMER CREDIT
COUNSELING SERVICE OF
CENTRAL INDIANA
1025 Freeland Rd.
Greensburg, IN 47240
812-662-6458
Toll-Free: 888-711-7227
TTY/TDD: 317-266-1324
Fax: 317-266-1315
Email:
mwright@cccsmidwest.org
Website: www.cccsmidwest.org

Type of Counseling:
Default/Foreclosure Counseling,
Rental Counseling, Prepurchase
Counseling, HECM Counseling
Affiliate of: NATIONAL
FOUNDATION FOR
CONSUMER CREDIT,
INCORPORATED

**CONSUMER CREDIT
COUNSELING SERVICE OF
CENTRAL INDIANA
500 S. Polk, Suite 18
Greenwood, IN 46142
317-865-4979
Toll-Free: 888-711-7227
TTY/TDD: 317-266-1324
Fax: 317-266-1315
Email:
mwright@cccsmidwest.org
Website: www.cccsmidwest.org
Type of Counseling:
Default/Foreclosure Counseling,
Rental Counseling, Prepurchase
Counseling, HECM Counseling
Affiliate of: NATIONAL
FOUNDATION FOR
CONSUMER CREDIT,
INCORPORATED

HAMMOND HOUSING
AUTHORITY
4923 Hohman Avenue
Hammond, IN 46320
219-937-8660
Fax: 219-937-8670
Type of Counseling:
HECM Counseling,
Default/Foreclosure Counseling,
Rental Counseling, Prepurchase
Counseling

HAMMOND HOUSING
AUTHORITY
7329 Columbia Circle West
Hammond, IN 46324-2831
219-989-3265
Fax: 219-989-3275
Type of Counseling:
Default/Foreclosure Counseling,
Rental Counseling, Prepurchase
Counseling

**INDIANAPOLIS
NEIGHBORHOOD HOUSING

PARTNERSHIP,
INCORPORATED
3550 N Washington Blvd
Indianapolis, IN 46205-3719
317-925-1400
Fax: 317-610-4678
Type of Counseling:
Default/Foreclosure Counseling,
Prepurchase Counseling
Affiliate of: THE HOUSING
PARTNERSHIP NETWORK

COMMUNITY ACTION OF
GREATER INDIANAPOLIS,
INCORPORATED
2445 N Meridian St
Indianapolis, IN 46208-5731
317-924-4397
Fax: 317-396-1528
Type of Counseling:
Default/Foreclosure Counseling,
Prepurchase Counseling

INDIANAPOLIS URBAN
LEAGUE
777 Indiana Ave.
Indianapolis, IN 46202
317-693-7603
Fax: 317-693-7611
Type of Counseling:
Prepurchase Counseling, Rental
Counseling

**CONSUMER CREDIT
COUNSELING SERVICE OF
CENTRAL INDIANA
615 N Alabama St Ste 134
Indianapolis, IN 46204-1431
317-266-1300
Toll-Free: 888-711-7227
TTY/TDD: 317-266-1324
Fax: 317-266-1315
Email:
mwright@cccsmidwest.org
Website: www.cccsmidwest.org
Type of Counseling:
Default/Foreclosure Counseling,
Rental Counseling, Prepurchase
Counseling, HECM Counseling
Affiliate of: NATIONAL
FOUNDATION FOR
CONSUMER CREDIT,
INCORPORATED

**FAMILY SERVICE
ASSOCIATION OF CENTRAL
INDIANA INCORPORATED

615 North Alabama Suite 220
Indianapolis, IN 46204-
317-634-6341
Fax: 317-464-9575
Type of Counseling:
Default/Foreclosure Counseling,
Rental Counseling, Prepurchase
Counseling
Affiliate of: HOUSING
OPPORTUNITIES,
INCORPORATED

MARTIN LUTHER KING
CENTER
40 West 40th Street
Indianapolis, IN 46208
317-923-4581
Fax: 317-923-4583
Type of Counseling:
Prepurchase Counseling, Rental
Counseling, Default/Foreclosure
Counseling, HECM Counseling

**LAFAYETTE
NEIGHBORHOOD HOUSING
SERVICES, INCORPORATED
1119 Ferry St
Lafayette, IN 47902-0252
765-423-1284
Fax: 765-742-2874
Type of Counseling:
Default/Foreclosure Counseling,
Prepurchase Counseling
Affiliate of: NEIGHBORHOOD
REINVESTMENT
CORPORATION

**CONSUMER CREDIT
COUNSELING SERVICE OF
CENTRAL INDIANA
327 N. Lebanon St. Suite 103
Lebanon, IN 46052
765-482-6396
Toll-Free: 888-711-7227
TTY/TDD: 317-266-1324
Fax: 317-266-1315
Email:
mwright@cccsmidwest.org
Website: www.cccsmidwest.org
Type of Counseling:
Default/Foreclosure Counseling,
Rental Counseling, Prepurchase
Counseling, HECM Counseling
Affiliate of: NATIONAL
FOUNDATION FOR

CONSUMER CREDIT,
INCORPORATED

AFFORDABLE HOUSING
CORPORATION OF MARION
INDIANA, INCORPORATED
601 S. Adams Street
Marion, IN
765-664-5194
Fax: 765-668-3045
Type of Counseling:
Prepurchase Counseling, Rental
Counseling

THE GREATER MICHIGAN
CITY COMMUNITY
DEVELOPMENT CORP
1709 East Michigan Blvd
Michigan City, IN 46360
219-873-1207
Fax: 219-873-1208
Type of Counseling:
Prepurchase Counseling, Rental
Counseling

HOOSIER UPLANDS
ECONOMIC DEVELOPMENT
CORPORATION
521 W Main St
Mitchell, IN 47446-1410
812-849-4447
Toll-Free: 800-827-2219
Fax: 812-849-0627
Type of Counseling:
Rental Counseling

MUNCIE HOMEOWNERSHIP
AND DEVELOPMENT
CENTER/URBAN ENTERPRISE
ASSOCIATION,
INCORPORATED
407 S Walnut St
Muncie, IN 47308
765-282-6656
Fax: 765-282-8391
Type of Counseling:
HECM Counseling,
Default/Foreclosure Counseling,
Rental Counseling, Prepurchase
Counseling

**CONSUMER CREDIT
COUNSELING SERVICE OF
CENTRAL INDIANA
2803 N. Oakwood
Muncie, IN 47304

765-284-7154
Toll-Free: 888-711-7227
TTY/TDD: 317-266-1324
Fax: 317-266-1315
Email:
mwright@cccsmidwest.org
Website: www.cccsmidwest.org
Type of Counseling:
Default/Foreclosure Counseling,
Rental Counseling, Prepurchase
Counseling, HECM Counseling
Affiliate of: NATIONAL
FOUNDATION FOR
CONSUMER CREDIT,
INCORPORATED

CRAIG STANLEY AGENCY
133 Edgemont Drive
New Albany, IN 47150
812-949-9997
Fax: 812-948-4603
Type of Counseling:
HECM Counseling,
Default/Foreclosure Counseling,
Rental Counseling, Prepurchase
Counseling

**CONSUMER CREDIT
COUNSELING SERVICE OF
CENTRAL INDIANA
100 S. Main Street
New Castle, IN 47388-
765-533-6390
Toll-Free: 888-711-7227
TTY/TDD: 317-266-1324
Fax: 317-266-1315
Email:
mwright@cccsmidwest.org
Website: www.cccsmidwest.org
Type of Counseling:
Default/Foreclosure Counseling,
Rental Counseling, Prepurchase
Counseling, HECM Counseling
Affiliate of: NATIONAL
FOUNDATION FOR
CONSUMER CREDIT,
INCORPORATED

**CONSUMER CREDIT
COUNSELING SERVICE OF
CENTRAL INDIANA
942 N. 10th Street
Noblesville, IN 46060
317-776-3480
Toll-Free: 888-711-7227
TTY/TDD: 317-266-1324

Fax: 317-266-1315
Email:
mwright@cccsmidwest.org
Website: www.cccsmidwest.org
Type of Counseling:
Default/Foreclosure Counseling,
Rental Counseling, Prepurchase
Counseling, HECM Counseling
Affiliate of: NATIONAL
FOUNDATION FOR
CONSUMER CREDIT,
INCORPORATED

**CONSUMER CREDIT
COUNSELING SERVICE OF
CENTRAL INDIANA
50 Hancock Street, Suite 5
Seymour, IN 47274
812-523-3760
Toll-Free: 888-711-7227
TTY/TDD: 317-266-1324
Fax: 317-266-1315
Email:
mwright@cccsmidwest.org
Website: www.cccsmidwest.org
Type of Counseling:
Default/Foreclosure Counseling,
Rental Counseling, Prepurchase
Counseling, HECM Counseling
Affiliate of: NATIONAL
FOUNDATION FOR
CONSUMER CREDIT,
INCORPORATED

**CONSUMER CREDIT
COUNSELING SERVICE OF
NORTHERN INDIANA
1635 N. Ironwood Drive
South Bend, IN 46553
574-273-2121
Toll-Free: 800-794-6559
Fax: 574-273-9478
Type of Counseling:
Default/Foreclosure Counseling,
Rental Counseling, Prepurchase
Counseling, HECM Counseling
Affiliate of: NATIONAL
FOUNDATION FOR
CONSUMER CREDIT,
INCORPORATED

HOUSING ASSISTANCE
OFFICE, INCORPORATED
1138 Lincoln Way E
South Bend, IN 46601-3728
219-233-9305

Fax: 219-282-3429
Type of Counseling:
HECM Counseling, Rental
Counseling, Prepurchase
Counseling

REAL SERVICES OF SAINT
JOSEPH COUNTY,
INCORPORATED AREA 2
AGENCY ON AGING
1151 S Michigan St
South Bend, IN 46634
219-284-2644
Toll-Free: 800-552-7928
Fax: 219-284-2691
Type of Counseling: HECM
Counseling

HOUSING AUTHORITY OF
THE CITY OF SOUTH BEND
501 S Scott St
South Bend, IN 46601-2766
219-235-9346
Fax: 219-235-9440
Type of Counseling:
HECM Counseling,
Default/Foreclosure Counseling,
Rental Counseling, Prepurchase
Counseling

HOUSING DEVELOPMENT
CORPORATION OF SAINT
JOSEPH COUNTY
1200 County-City Building
South Bend, IN 46601
219-235-9475
Fax: 219-235-9697
Type of Counseling:
Default/Foreclosure Counseling,
Prepurchase Counseling, Rental
Counseling, HECM Counseling

LINCOLN HILLS
DEVELOPMENT
CORPORATION
302 Main St
Tell City, IN 47586-0336
812-547-3435
Fax: 812-547-3466
Email:
sharon@LHDC.Dubois.net
Type of Counseling:
Prepurchase Counseling

**CONSUMER CREDIT
COUNSELING SERVICE OF
CENTRAL INDIANA
2901 Ohio Boulevard, Suite 139

Terre Haute, IN 47803
812-232-1803
Toll-Free: 888-711-7227
TTY/TDD: 317-266-1324
Fax: 317-266-1315
Email:
mwright@cccsmidwest.org
Website: www.cccsmidwest.org
Type of Counseling:
Default/Foreclosure Counseling,
Rental Counseling, Prepurchase
Counseling, HECM Counseling
Affiliate of: NATIONAL
FOUNDATION FOR
CONSUMER CREDIT,
INCORPORATED

HOUSING OPPORTUNITES,
INCORPORATED
2801 Evans Avenue
Valparaiso, IN 46383-
219-464-9621
Fax: 219-464-9635
Type of Counseling:
Rental Counseling, Prepurchase
Counseling, Default/Foreclosure
Counseling

SWITZERLAND COUNTY
COMMUNITY HOUSING
DEVELOPMENT
ORGANIZATION
317 Ferry Street
Vevay, IN 47043
812-427-2533
Fax: 812-427-9173
Type of Counseling:
Prepurchase Counseling, Rental
Counseling

Iowa

IOWA STATE UNIVERSITY-
FINANCIAL COUNSELING
CLINIC
Palmer HDFS Building #1331
Ames, IA 50011-4380
515-294-8644
Fax: 515-294-5464
Type of Counseling:
Default/Foreclosure Counseling,
Prepurchase Counseling, Rental
Counseling, HECM Counseling

CONSUMER CREDIT
COUNSELING SERVICES OF
AMES
2546 Lincolnway, Suite 110
Ames, IA 50010
515-296-1968
Toll-Free: 866-723-7468
Fax: 515-296-1968
Type of Counseling:
Prepurchase Counseling,
Default/Foreclosure Counseling,
Rental Counseling, HECM
Counseling

FAMILY HOUSING ADVISORY
SERVICES, INCORPORATED
500 West Broadway, Suite 403
Council Bluffs, IA 51503
712-322-4436
Fax: 402-934-7928
Type of Counseling:
Default/Foreclosure Counseling,
Prepurchase Counseling, Rental
Counseling, HECM Counseling

**MISSISSIPPI VALLEY
NEIGHBORHOOD HOUSING
SERVICES
131 W. 3rd Street
Davenport, IA 528072114
563-324-1556
Fax: 563-324-3540
Type of Counseling:
Prepurchase Counseling,
Default/Foreclosure Counseling
Affiliate of: NEIGHBORHOOD
REINVESTMENT
CORPORATION

UNITED NEIGHBORS
INCORPORATED
808 Harrison St.
Davenport, IA 52803
319-322-7363
Type of Counseling:
Prepurchase Counseling,
Default/Foreclosure Counseling

CITIZENS FOR COMMUNITY
IMPROVEMENT
2005 Forest Avenue
Des Moines, IA 50311
515-255-0800
Fax: 515-255-1314
Type of Counseling:

Default/Foreclosure Counseling,
Prepurchase Counseling

SERVICES FOR
HOMEOWNERS PROGRAM
602 E 1st St
Des Moines, IA 503091812
515-283-4787
Fax: 515-237-1687
Type of Counseling:
HECM Counseling,
Default/Foreclosure Counseling,
Rental Counseling, Prepurchase
Counseling

NEIGHBORHOOD HOUSING
SERVICES OF DES MOINES
1153 24th Street
Des Moines, IA 50311
515-277-6647
Fax: 515-277-6681
Email: nhsdm@aol.com
Type of Counseling:
Default/Foreclosure Counseling,
Prepurchase Counseling
Affiliate of: NEIGHBORHOOD
REINVESTMENT
CORPORATION

CONSUMER CREDIT
COUNSELING SERVICES OF
DUBUQUE
2255 JF Kennedy Rd.
Dubuque, IA 52001
563-582-2885
Toll-Free: 866-720-9049
Fax: 563-582-4504
Type of Counseling:
Prepurchase Counseling,
Default/Foreclosure Counseling,
Rental Counseling, HECM
Counseling

HAWKEYE AREA
COMMUNITY ACTION
PROGRAM, INCORPORATED
1515 Hawkeye Dr.
Hiawatha, IA 52233
319-393-7811
Fax: 319-739-1533
Email: jwhite@hacap.org
Type of Counseling:
HECM Counseling,
Default/Foreclosure Counseling,
Rental Counseling, Prepurchase
Counseling

CONSUMER CREDIT
COUNSELING SERVICES OF
MARSHALLTOWN
24 East Main St.
Marshalltown, IA 50158
641-752-6161
Toll-Free: 866-720-9048
Fax: 641-754-6970
Type of Counseling:
Prepurchase Counseling,
Default/Foreclosure Counseling,
Rental Counseling, HECM
Counseling

CONSUMER CREDIT
COUNSELING SERVICES OF
MASON CITY
520 S. Pierce Suite 202
Mason City, IA 50401
641-421-7619
Toll-Free: 866-720-9050
Fax: 515-421-7738
Type of Counseling:
HECM Counseling,
Default/Foreclosure Counseling,
Rental Counseling, Prepurchase
Counseling

THE CENTER FOR
ASSISTANCE, INFORMATION
AND DIRECTION
715 Douglas St
Sioux City, IA 51101-1208
877-580-5526
Toll-Free: 877-580-5526
Fax: 712-255-1352
Type of Counseling:
HECM Counseling,
Default/Foreclosure Counseling,
Rental Counseling, Prepurchase
Counseling

LA CASA LATINA
206 6th Street
Sioux City, IA 51101-1208
712-252-4259
Fax: 712-252-5655
Email: cccs@willinet.net
Website:
www.cccsofsiouxland.com
Type of Counseling:
Prepurchase Counseling,
Default/Foreclosure Counseling,
Rental Counseling, HECM
Counseling

CONSUMER CREDIT
COUNSELING SERVICE OF
GREATER SIOUXLAND
705 Douglas Street, Suite 350
Sioux City, IA 51101-1018
712-252-5666
Toll-Free: 800-509-5601
Fax: 712-252-1621
Email: cccs@willienet.net
Website:
www.cccsofsiouxland.com
Type of Counseling:
HECM Counseling,
Default/Foreclosure Counseling,
Rental Counseling, Prepurchase
Counseling

CONSUMER CREDIT
COUNSELING SERVICE OF
GREATER SIOUXLAND
515 Grand
Spencer, IA 51301-3913
800-509-5601
Toll-Free: 800-509-5601
Fax: 712-252-1621
Email: cccs@willienet.net
Website:
www.cccsofsiouxland.com
Type of Counseling:
Prepurchase Counseling,
Default/Foreclosure Counseling,
Rental Counseling, HECM
Counseling

CONSUMER CREDIT
COUNSELING SERVICE OF
NORTHEASTERN IOWA,
INCORPORATED
1003 W 4th St
Waterloo, IA 50702-2803
319-234-0661
Toll-Free: 800-714-4388
Fax: 319-234-7533
Type of Counseling:
HECM Counseling,
Default/Foreclosure Counseling,
Rental Counseling, Prepurchase
Counseling
Affiliate of: NATIONAL
FOUNDATION FOR
CONSUMER CREDIT,
INCORPORATED

FAMILY MANAGEMENT
CREDIT COUNSELORS,
INCORPORATED

1409 W 4th St
Waterloo, IA 50702-2907
319-234-6695
Fax: 319-236-6626
Type of Counseling:
Default/Foreclosure Counseling,
Rental Counseling, Prepurchase
Counseling, HECM Counseling

KANSAS

21ST CENTURY HOMESTEAD,
INCORPORATED
600 S. Houston Street
Altamont, KS 67330
620-784-2177
Fax: 620-784-2665
Type of Counseling:
HECM Counseling,
Default/Foreclosure Counseling,
Rental Counseling, Prepurchase
Counseling

HOUSING AND CREDIT
COUNSELING
INCORPORATED
417 Commercial, Ste. 7
Emporia, KS 66801
620-342-7766
Toll-Free: 800-383-0217
TTY/TDD:
Fax: 785-234-0237
Type of Counseling:
Prepurchase Counseling,
Default/Foreclosure Counseling,
Rental Counseling

CONSUMER CREDIT
COUNSELING SERVICE,
INCORPORATED
1608 Belmont Place
Garden City, KS 67846-
800-279-2227
Toll-Free: 800-279-2227
Fax: 785-827-8280
Email: cccs@salhelp.org
Website: www.salhelp.org/cccs
Type of Counseling:
Prepurchase Counseling,
Default/Foreclosure Counseling,
HECM Counseling, Rental
Counseling

CONSUMER CREDIT
COUNSELING SERVICE,
INCORPORATED

1200 N. Main, Room 414
Hays, KS 67601
785-827-6731
Toll-Free: 800-279-2227
Fax: 785-827-8280
Email: cccs@salhelp.org
Website: www.salhelp.org/cccs
Type of Counseling:
HECM Counseling,
Default/Foreclosure Counseling,
Rental Counseling, Prepurchase
Counseling

NORTHEAST KANSAS
COMMUNITY ACTION
PROGRAM, INCORPORATED
1260 220th Rd
Hiawatha, KS 66434-0380
785-742-2222
Fax: 785-742-2164
Type of Counseling:
HECM Counseling,
Default/Foreclosure Counseling,
Rental Counseling, Prepurchase
Counseling

CONSUMER CREDIT
COUNSELING SERVICE,
INCORPORATED
Quest Building, 1 E 9th Suite 201
Hutchinson, KS 67501-
800-279-2227
Toll-Free: 800-279-2227
Fax: 785-827-8280
Email: cccs@salhelp.org
Website: www.salhelp.org/cccs
Type of Counseling:
Prepurchase Counseling,
Default/Foreclosure Counseling,
HECM Counseling, Rental
Counseling

ECONOMIC OPPORTUNITY
FOUNDATION
1542 Minnesota Ave
Kansas City, KS 66102-4312
913-371-7800
Fax: 913-371-0457
Type of Counseling:
Default/Foreclosure Counseling,
Rental Counseling

CONSUMER CREDIT
COUNSELING SERVICE OF
GREATER KANSAS CITY
1314 N 38th St

Kansas City, KS 66102-2231
816-753-0535
Fax: 816-753-3374
Type of Counseling:
Default/Foreclosure Counseling,
Prepurchase Counseling

**EL CENTRO,
INCORPORATED
1333 South 27th Street
Kansas City, KS 66106
913-677-0100
Fax: 913-362-8250
Email: mimio8@aol.com
Type of Counseling:
Prepurchase Counseling,
Default/Foreclosure Counseling
Affiliate of: NATIONAL
COUNCIL OF LA RAZA

CITY VISION MINISTRIES,
INCORPORATED
1321 North 7th Street
Kansas City, KS 66101
913-371-5200
Fax: 913-371-2555
Type of Counseling:
Prepurchase Counseling

HOUSING AND CREDIT
COUNSELING
INCORPORATED
2518 Ridge Court, Ste. 207
Lawrence, KS 66046
785-749-4224
Toll-Free: 800-383-0217
Fax: 785-234-0237
Type of Counseling:
Prepurchase Counseling,
Default/Foreclosure Counseling,
Rental Counseling, HECM
Counseling

CONSUMER CREDIT
COUNSELING SERVICE OF
GREATER KANSAS CITY
2830 S 4th St
Leavenworth, KS 66048-4519
816-753-0535
Fax: 816-753-3374
Type of Counseling:
Default/Foreclosure Counseling,
Prepurchase Counseling

HOUSING AND CREDIT
COUNSELING
INCORPORATED
513 Leavenworth, Ste. C
Manhattan, KS 66502
785-539-6666
Toll-Free: 800-383-0217
Fax: 785-234-0237
Type of Counseling:
Prepurchase Counseling,
Default/Foreclosure Counseling,
Rental Counseling, HECM
Counseling

HOUSING INFORMATION
CENTER
333 East Poplar, Suite D
Olathe, KS 66061-
913-829-4584
Fax: 816-931-0722
Type of Counseling:
Prepurchase Counseling, Rental
Counseling

CONSUMER CREDIT
COUNSELING SERVICE OF
GREATER KANSAS CITY
11111 West 9th Street Suite 1200
Overland Park, KS 66214
816-753-0535
Fax: 816-753-3374
Type of Counseling:
Default/Foreclosure Counseling,
Prepurchase Counseling

CONSUMER CREDIT
COUNSELING SERVICE,
INCORPORATED
1201 W Walnut St
Salina, KS 67402-0843
785-827-6731
Toll-Free: 800-279-2227
Fax: 785-827-8280
Email: cccs@salhelp.org
Website: www.salhelp.org/cccs
Type of Counseling:
HECM Counseling,
Default/Foreclosure Counseling,
Rental Counseling, Prepurchase
Counseling

HOUSING AND CREDIT
COUNSELING,
INCORPORATED
1195 SW Buchanan St, Ste 101
Topeka, KS 66604-1183

800-383-0217
Toll-Free: 800-383-0217
Fax: 785-234-0237
Type of Counseling:
HECM Counseling,
Default/Foreclosure Counseling,
Rental Counseling, Prepurchase
Counseling

KANSAS DEPARTMENT OF
COMMERCE AND HOUSING
700 SW Harrison, Suite 1300
Topeka, KS 66603-3712
785-296-5865
Fax: 785-296-8985
Type of Counseling:
Prepurchase Counseling, Rental
Counseling, Default/Foreclosure
Counseling

CONSUMER CREDIT
COUNSELING SERVICE,
INCORPORATED
1515 E Lewis St
Wichita, KS 67211-1836
316-265-2000
Fax: 316-265-8507
Website: www.salhelp.org/cccs
Type of Counseling:
HECM Counseling,
Default/Foreclosure Counseling,
Rental Counseling, Prepurchase
Counseling

URBAN LEAGUE OF
WICHITA, INCORPORATED
1802 E 13th St N
Wichita, KS 67214-1704
316-262-2463
Fax: 316-262-8841
Type of Counseling:
HECM Counseling,
Default/Foreclosure Counseling,
Prepurchase Counseling

MENNONITE HOUSING
REHABILITATION SERVICES,
INCORPORATED
2145 North Topeka
Wichita, KS 67214-1140
316-942-4848
Fax: 316-942-0190
Type of Counseling:
Default/Foreclosure Counseling,
Rental Counseling, Prepurchase
Counseling

Kentucky

**NORTHERN KENTUCKY
LEGAL AID SOCIETY,
INCORPORATED
1312 Highway Drive
Ashland, KY 41105-
606-329-1321
Fax: 606-325-0615
Type of Counseling:
Prepurchase Counseling,
Default/Foreclosure Counseling,
Rental Counseling, HECM
Counseling
Affiliate of: WEST TENNESSEE
LEGAL SERVICES,
INCORPORATED

KENTUCKY LEGAL AID
520 E. Main Street
Bowling Green, KY 42102-1776
270-782-1924
Toll-Free: 800-782-1924
Fax: 270-782-1993
Email:
ctls@ctls.bowlinggreen.net
Website:
www.ctls.bowlinggreen.net
Type of Counseling:
Rental Counseling,
Default/Foreclosure Counseling,
Prepurchase Counseling, HECM
Counseling
Affiliate of: WEST TENNESSEE
LEGAL SERVICES,
INCORPORATED

HOUSING AND COMMUNITY
DEVELOPMENT
DEPARTMENT CITY OF
BOWLING GREEN
1017 College Street
Bowling Green, KY 42102-0430
270-393-3630
Fax: 270-393-3168
Type of Counseling:
Prepurchase Counseling

CAMPBELLSVILLE HOUSING
AND REDEVELOPMENT
AUTHORITY
400 Ingram Ave
Campbellsville, KY 42718-1627
270-465-3576
Fax: 270-465-2444
Type of Counseling:

Default/Foreclosure Counseling,
Rental Counseling, Prepurchase
Counseling, HECM Counseling

KENTUCKY LEGAL AID
120 E 1st St
Campbellsville, KY 42719-0059
270-789-2366
Fax: 270-465-2368
Type of Counseling:
Rental Counseling,
Default/Foreclosure Counseling,
Prepurchase Counseling, HECM
Counseling

**APPALACHIAN RESEARCH
AND DEFENSE FUND OF
KENTUCKY, INCORPORATED
p. o. Box 460
Columbia, KY 42728-0460
502-384-5907
Fax: 502-384-4707
Type of Counseling:
Default/Foreclosure Counseling,
Prepurchase Counseling, HECM
Counseling, Rental Counseling
Affiliate of: WEST TENNESSEE
LEGAL SERVICES,
INCORPORATED

**NORTHERN KENTUCKY
LEGAL AID SOCIETY,
INCORPORATED
302 Greenup Street
Covington, KY 41011
859-431-8200
Fax: 859-431-3009
Email: blcnklas@hotmail.com
Type of Counseling:
Prepurchase Counseling,
Default/Foreclosure Counseling,
Rental Counseling, HECM
Counseling
Affiliate of: WEST TENNESSEE
LEGAL SERVICES,
INCORPORATED

NORTHERN KENTUCKY
COMMUNITY CENTER
824 Greenup St
Covington, KY 41011-3210
859-431-5700
Fax: 859-392-2672
Type of Counseling:
HECM Counseling,
Default/Foreclosure Counseling,

Rental Counseling, Prepurchase
Counseling

**CATHOLIC SOCIAL
SERVICES OF NORTHERN
KENTUCKY
3629 Church Street
Covington, KY 41015
859-581-8974
Fax: 859-581-9595
Type of Counseling:
Prepurchase Counseling, HECM
Counseling, Rental Counseling
Affiliate of: CATHOLIC
CHARITIES USA

KENTUCKY HOUSING
CORPORATION
1231 Louisville Road
Frankfort, KY 40601
502-564-7630
Fax: 502-564-7664
Email:
mcrawfor@mail.kentuckyhousin
g .org
Type of Counseling:
Default/Foreclosure Counseling,
Prepurchase Counseling

**APPALACHIAN RESEARCH
AND DEFENSE FUND OF
KENTUCKY, INCORPORATED
108 S. Main Street suite 202
Harlan, KY 40831-2100
606-573-6301
Fax: 606-573-6301
Type of Counseling:
Default/Foreclosure Counseling,
Prepurchase Counseling, HECM
Counseling, Rental Counseling
Affiliate of: WEST TENNESSEE
LEGAL SERVICES,
INCORPORATED

**APPALACHIAN RESEARCH
AND DEFENSE FUND OF
KENTUCKY, INCORPORATED
P.O. Box 7220
Hazard, KY 41702-7220
606-439-2315
Fax: 606-439-4364
Type of Counseling:
Default/Foreclosure Counseling,
Prepurchase Counseling, HECM
Counseling, Rental Counseling

Affiliate of: WEST TENNESSEE
LEGAL SERVICES,
INCORPORATED

CONSUMER CREDIT
COUNSELING SERVICE OF
THE TRI-STATE,
INCORPORATED
435 First Street
Henderson, KY 42420
812-422-1108
Toll-Free: 800-451-6293
Fax: 812-424-9050
Type of Counseling:
HECM Counseling, Prepurchase
Counseling, Default/Foreclosure
Counseling, Rental Counseling

PENNYRILE ALLIED
COMMUNITY SERVICES,
INCORPORATED
1100 S Liberty St
Hopkinsville, KY 42241-0582
270-885-4959
Fax: 270-885-6078
Type of Counseling:
Default/Foreclosure Counseling,
Rental Counseling, Prepurchase
Counseling

**APPALACHIAN RESEARCH
AND DEFENSE FUND OF
KENTUCKY, INCORPORATED
P.O. Box 725
Jackson, KY 41339-0725
606-666-4941
Fax: 606-666-9815
Type of Counseling:
Default/Foreclosure Counseling,
Prepurchase Counseling, HECM
Counseling, Rental Counseling
Affiliate of: WEST TENNESSEE
LEGAL SERVICES,
INCORPORATED

TENANT SERVICES AND
HOUSING COUNSELING,
INCORPORATED
136 N Martin Luther King Blvd
Lexington, KY 40507-1526
859-258-3960
Fax: 859-258-3968
Type of Counseling:
HECM Counseling,
Default/Foreclosure Counseling,

Rental Counseling, Prepurchase
Counseling

**REALTOR-COMMUNITY
HOUSING FOUNDATION**
2250 Regency Rd
Lexington, KY 40503-2302
859-276-2693
Fax: 859-277-0286
Type of Counseling:
Default/Foreclosure Counseling,
Prepurchase Counseling

LOUISVILLE URBAN LEAGUE
1535 W Broadway
Louisville, KY 40203-3515
502-585-4622
Fax: 502-568-4663
Email: KDUNLAP@lul.org
Type of Counseling:
HECM Counseling,
Default/Foreclosure Counseling,
Rental Counseling, Prepurchase
Counseling

**HOME OWNERSHIP
PARTNERS**
NIA Center- 2900 West
Broadway, Suite 310
Louisville, KY 40202
502-585-5451
Fax: 502-585-5568
Type of Counseling:
HECM Counseling,
Default/Foreclosure Counseling,
Prepurchase Counseling, Rental
Counseling

**THE HOUSING
PARTNERSHIP/ HOME
OWNERSHIP PARTNERS**
333 Guthrie Green, Suite 404
Louisville, KY 40202
502-585-5451
Fax: 502-585-5568
Type of Counseling:
HECM Counseling,
Default/Foreclosure Counseling,
Prepurchase Counseling, Rental
Counseling
Affiliate of: THE HOUSING
PARTNERSHIP NETWORK

**CONSUMER CREDIT
COUNSELING**
510 East Chestnut Street

Louisville, KY 40201
502-458-8840
Toll-Free: 800-278-9219
Fax: 502-458-9361
Email: cccservices.com
Type of Counseling:
HECM Counseling,
Default/Foreclosure Counseling,
Rental Counseling, Prepurchase
Counseling

**CONSUMER CREDIT
COUNSELING SERVICE OF
THE TRI STATE**
1002 1/2 Main St
Madisonville, KY 42431
800-451-6293
Fax: 812-424-9050
Type of Counseling:
HECM Counseling,
Default/Foreclosure Counseling,
Rental Counseling, Prepurchase
Counseling

****APPALACHIAN RESEARCH
AND DEFENSE FUND OF
KENTUCKY, INCORPORATED**
P.O. Box 613
Manchester, KY 40962-0613
606-598-6188
Fax: 606-886-3704
Type of Counseling:
Default/Foreclosure Counseling,
Prepurchase Counseling, HECM
Counseling, Rental Counseling
Affiliate of: WEST TENNESSEE
LEGAL SERVICES,
INCORPORATED

**PURCHASE AREA HOUSING
CORPORATION**
1002 Medical Dr
Mayfield, KY 42066-0588
270-247-7171
Fax: 270-251-6110
Type of Counseling:
Default/Foreclosure Counseling,
Rental Counseling, Prepurchase
Counseling

****NORTHERN KENTUCKY
LEGAL AID**
320 E. Main Street
Morehead, KY 403511040
606-784-8921
Toll-Free: 800-274-5863

Fax: 606-783-1342
Email: blcnklas@hotmail.com
Type of Counseling:
Prepurchase Counseling,
Default/Foreclosure Counseling,
Rental Counseling, HECM
Counseling
Affiliate of: WEST TENNESSEE
LEGAL SERVICES,
INCORPORATED

**CONSUMER CREDIT
COUNSELING SERVICE-
SAINT LOUIS**
The Village 1406 North 12th
Street. Suite D
Murray, KY 42071-
270-753-4200
Toll-Free: 800-966-3328
Fax: 314-647-1359
Type of Counseling:
Default/Foreclosure Counseling

**BRIGHTON CENTER,
INCORPORATED**
741 Central Ave
Newport, KY 410721222
859-431-5649
Fax: 859-491-8702
Type of Counseling:
HECM Counseling,
Default/Foreclosure Counseling,
Rental Counseling, Prepurchase
Counseling

**CONSUMER CREDIT
COUNSELING SERVICE OF
THE TRI STATE**
920 Frederica St Ste 213
Owensboro, KY 42301-3050
800-451-6293
Fax: 812-424-9050
Type of Counseling:
HECM Counseling,
Default/Foreclosure Counseling,
Rental Counseling, Prepurchase
Counseling

**CONSUMER CREDIT
COUNSELING SERVICE-
SAINT LOUIS**
546 Lone Oak Rd, Suite 1
Paducah, KY 42003-4538
270-443-7917
Toll-Free: 800-966-3328
Fax: 314-647-1359

Type of Counseling:
Default/Foreclosure Counseling

**APPALACHIAN RESEARCH AND DEFENSE FUND OF KENTUCKY, INCORPORATED
410 Third Street
Pikeville, KY 41501-1249
606-432-2181
Fax: 606-432-2183
Type of Counseling:
Default/Foreclosure Counseling,
Prepurchase Counseling, HECM
Counseling, Rental Counseling
Affiliate of: WEST TENNESSEE
LEGAL SERVICES,
INCORPORATED

**APPALACHIAN RESEARCH AND DEFENSE FUND OF KENTUCKY, INCORPORATED
28 North Front Street
Prestonsburg, KY 416531221
606-886-3876
Fax: 606-886-3704
Email: ardfpres@se-tel.com
Type of Counseling:
Default/Foreclosure Counseling,
Prepurchase Counseling, HECM
Counseling, Rental Counseling
Affiliate of: WEST TENNESSEE
LEGAL SERVICES,
INCORPORATED

Louisiana

CENLA COMMUNITY ACTION COMMITTEE, INCORPORATED
230 Bolton Ave
Alexandria, LA 71301-7126
318-487-5878
Fax: 318-487-5858
Type of Counseling:
HECM Counseling,
Default/Foreclosure Counseling,
Rental Counseling, Prepurchase
Counseling

CONSUMER CREDIT COUNSELING
3915 Independence Blvd
Alexandria, LA 71303-3551
225-923-2227
Toll-Free: 800-364-5595
Fax: 225-926-7912

Type of Counseling:
HECM Counseling,
Default/Foreclosure Counseling,
Rental Counseling, Prepurchase
Counseling

JEFFERSON COMMUNITY ACTION PROGRAM
4008 U.S. Highway 90
Avondale, LA 70092
504-349-5414
Fax: 504-349-5417
Type of Counseling:
Prepurchase Counseling,
Default/Foreclosure Counseling,
HECM Counseling, Rental
Counseling

CONSUMER CREDIT COUNSELING SERVICES - BATON ROUGE
615 Chevelle Ct.
Baton Rouge, LA 70896-6478
225-923-2227
Toll-Free: 800-364-5595
Fax: 225-926-7912
Email: info@cccs-la.com
Website: www.cccs-la.com
Type of Counseling:
HECM Counseling,
Default/Foreclosure Counseling,
Rental Counseling, Prepurchase
Counseling
Affiliate of: NATIONAL
FOUNDATION FOR
CONSUMER CREDIT,
INCORPORATED

SAINT JAMES PARISH DEPARTMENT OF HUMAN RESOURCES
5153 Canatelle Street
Convent, LA 70723-0087
225-562-2300
Fax: 225-562-2425
Type of Counseling:
Prepurchase Counseling,
Default/Foreclosure Counseling,
Rental Counseling

CONSUMER CREDIT COUNSELING OF GREATER NEW ORLEANS, INCORPORATED
1 Courtano Dr.
Covington, LA 70433

504-893-0650
Fax: 504-641-4159
Type of Counseling:
HECM Counseling,
Default/Foreclosure Counseling,
Rental Counseling, Prepurchase
Counseling

**SEVENTH DISTRICT PAVILLION
225 North Avenue C
Crowley, LA 70527
318-788-3103
Fax: 318-783-0278
Type of Counseling:
Prepurchase Counseling, Rental
Counseling, Default/Foreclosure
Counseling
Affiliate of: CONGRESS OF
NATIONAL BLACK
CHURCHES, INCORPORATED

ASSIST AGENCY
125 West 3rd Street
Crowley, LA 705271404
337-783-7490
Fax: 337-783-9353
Type of Counseling:
Default/Foreclosure Counseling,
Prepurchase Counseling

SAINT MARY COMMUNITY ACTION AGENCY, INCORPORATED
1407 Barrow St
Franklin, LA 70538-3514
337-828-5703
Fax: 337-828-5754
Type of Counseling:
HECM Counseling,
Default/Foreclosure Counseling,
Rental Counseling, Prepurchase
Counseling

CONSUMER CREDIT COUNSELING
401 Whitney Ave Ste 301
Gretna, LA 70056-2558
504-366-8952
Fax: 504-367-5360
Type of Counseling:
HECM Counseling,
Default/Foreclosure Counseling,
Rental Counseling, Prepurchase
Counseling

JEFFERSON COMMUNITY
ACTION PROGRAM
1501 Estalote Street
Harvey, LA
504-227-1221
Fax: 504-227-1229
Type of Counseling:
Prepurchase Counseling,
Default/Foreclosure Counseling,
HECM Counseling, Rental
Counseling

JEFFERSON HOUSING
FOUNDATION
2418 Westbank Expressway
Harvey, LA 70058
504-368-5809
Fax: 504-368-5816
Type of Counseling:
Default/Foreclosure Counseling,
Rental Counseling, Prepurchase
Counseling

**CATHOLIC SOCIAL SERVICE
1220 Aycock Street
Houma, LA 70361
985-876-0490
Fax: 985-876-7751
Type of Counseling:
Default/Foreclosure Counseling,
Prepurchase Counseling, Rental
Counseling, HECM Counseling
Affiliate of: CATHOLIC
CHARITIES USA

CONSUMER CREDIT
COUNSELING
1340 W Tunnel Blvd Ste 500
Houma, LA 70360-2801
504-876-2225
Fax: 504-876-2182
Type of Counseling:
HECM Counseling,
Default/Foreclosure Counseling,
Rental Counseling, Prepurchase
Counseling

JEFFERSON COMMUNITY
ACTION PROGRAM
1221 Elmwood Park Blvd Ste 402
Jefferson, LA 70123
504-736-6158
Fax: 504-736-7093
Type of Counseling:
HECM Counseling,
Default/Foreclosure Counseling,

Rental Counseling, Prepurchase
Counseling

JEFFERSON COMMUNITY
ACTION PROGRAM
1121 Causeway Blvd
Jefferson, LA 70121-1925
504-838-4277
Fax: 504-838-1179
Type of Counseling:
HECM Counseling,
Default/Foreclosure Counseling,
Rental Counseling, Prepurchase
Counseling

CONSUMER CREDIT
COUNSELING
3701 Williams Blvd Ste 310
Kenner, LA 70065-3070
504-443-1015
Fax: 504-443-1527
Type of Counseling:
HECM Counseling,
Default/Foreclosure Counseling,
Rental Counseling, Prepurchase
Counseling

PEOPLE'S ORGANIZATION
FOR SOCIAL EQUALITY,
INCORPORATED
625 Veterans Boulevard
Kenner, LA 70062
504-468-2063
Fax: 504-468-3469
Type of Counseling:
Default/Foreclosure Counseling,
Prepurchase Counseling, Rental
Counseling

CONSUMER CREDIT
COUNSELING SERVICES
117 Liberty Ave.
Lafayette, LA 70508-6821
225-923-2227
Toll-Free: 800-364-5595
Fax: 225-926-7912
Type of Counseling:
HECM Counseling,
Default/Foreclosure Counseling,
Rental Counseling, Prepurchase
Counseling

SAINT MARTIN, IBERIA,
LAFAYETTE COMMUNITY
ACTION AGENCY,
INCORPORATED

501 Saint John St
Lafayette, LA 70501-5709
337-234-3272
Fax: 337-234-3274
Email: smilecaa@netconnect.net
Type of Counseling:
HECM Counseling,
Default/Foreclosure Counseling,
Rental Counseling, Prepurchase
Counseling

LAFAYETTE CONSOLIDATED
GOVERNMENT
1017 Mudd Avenue
Lafayette, LA 70501
337-291-8447
Fax: 337-291-5459
Type of Counseling:
Prepurchase Counseling, Rental
Counseling, Default/Foreclosure
Counseling, HECM Counseling

NEIGHBORHOOD
COUNSELING SERVICES
Jessie L. Taylor Center 1017
Mudd Ave.
Lafayette, LA 70501
337-291-8447
Fax: 337-291-5459
Type of Counseling:
HECM Counseling,
Default/Foreclosure Counseling,
Rental Counseling, Prepurchase
Counseling

CONSUMER CREDIT
COUNSELING SERVICES
2021 Oak Park Blvd
Lake Charles, LA 70601-7827
225-923-2227
Toll-Free: 800-364-5595
Fax: 225-926-7912
Type of Counseling:
HECM Counseling,
Default/Foreclosure Counseling,
Rental Counseling, Prepurchase
Counseling

MARRERO-MULTI SERVICE
CENTER
2001 Lincolnshire Dr
Marrero, LA 70072-4617
504-349-5458
Fax: 504-349-5495
Type of Counseling:

HECM Counseling,
Default/Foreclosure Counseling,
Rental Counseling, Prepurchase
Counseling

DOROTHY B. WATSON
MEMORIAL CENTER
1300 S Myrtle St
Metairie, LA 70003-5928
504-736-6480
Fax: 504-731-4480
Type of Counseling:
Prepurchase Counseling,
Default/Foreclosure Counseling,
Rental Counseling, HECM
Counseling

OUACHITA MULTI-PURPOSE
COMMUNITY ACTION
AGENCY
315 Plum St
Monroe, LA 71210-3086
318-322-7151
Fax: 318-387-0449
Type of Counseling:
HECM Counseling,
Default/Foreclosure Counseling,
Rental Counseling, Prepurchase
Counseling

CONSUMER CREDIT
COUNSELING AGENCY
2912 Evangeline Street
Monroe, LA 71201
225-923-2227
Toll-Free: 800-364-5595
Fax: 225-926-7912
Type of Counseling:
HECM Counseling,
Default/Foreclosure Counseling,
Rental Counseling, Prepurchase
Counseling

NORTH LOUISIANA LEGAL
ASSISTANCE CORPORATION
200 Washington Street
Monroe, LA 71201
318-323-8851
Toll-Free: 800-256-1262
Fax: 318-323-8856
Email: nnls@nnls.org
Type of Counseling:
Prepurchase Counseling,
Default/Foreclosure Counseling,
Rental Counseling

CONSUMER CREDIT
COUNSELING SERVICES
Offshore Oil Cntr Ste 108 6502
Highway 90 E
Morgan City, LA 70380
504-385-2055
Fax: 504-876-2182
Type of Counseling:
HECM Counseling,
Default/Foreclosure Counseling,
Rental Counseling, Prepurchase
Counseling

FAMILY RESOURCES OF NEW
ORLEANS
1418 N. Claiborne Ave., Suite 1
New Orleans, LA 70116
504-947-1555
Fax: 504-947-1575
Type of Counseling:
Default/Foreclosure Counseling,
Rental Counseling, Prepurchase
Counseling

DESIRE COMMUNITY
HOUSING CORPORATION
2709 Piety Street
New Orleans, LA 70126
504-944-6425
Fax: 504-949-8646
Type of Counseling:
HECM Counseling,
Default/Foreclosure Counseling,
Rental Counseling, Prepurchase
Counseling

CONSUMER CREDIT
COUNSELING SERVICES OF
NEW ORLEANS EAST
6800 Plaza Dr Ste 150
New Orleans, LA 70127
504-241-9760
Fax: 504-241-4245
Type of Counseling:
HECM Counseling,
Default/Foreclosure Counseling,
Rental Counseling, Prepurchase
Counseling

**LIVING WATER BAPTIST
CHURCH
2114 Elysian Fields Ave.
New Orleans, LA 70117
504-944-1795
Fax: 504-944-1212

Type of Counseling:
Prepurchase Counseling,
Default/Foreclosure Counseling
Affiliate of: CONGRESS OF
NATIONAL BLACK
CHURCHES, INCORPORATED

CONSUMER CREDIT
COUNSELING SERVICE OF
GREATER NEW ORLEANS,
INCORPORATED
1539 Jackson Ave Ste 501
New Orleans, LA 70130-5858
504-529-2396
Toll-Free: 888-818-2275
Fax: 504-598-6366
Website: www.cccsno.org
Type of Counseling:
HECM Counseling,
Default/Foreclosure Counseling,
Rental Counseling, Prepurchase
Counseling
Affiliate of: NATIONAL
FOUNDATION FOR
CONSUMER CREDIT,
INCORPORATED

**NEIGHBORHOOD HOUSING
SERVICE OF NEW ORLEANS,
INCORPORATED
4700 Freret St
New Orleans, LA 70115
504-899-5900
Fax: 504-899-6190
Email: nhsno@worldnet.att.net
Type of Counseling:
Prepurchase Counseling, Rental
Counseling, HECM Counseling,
Default/Foreclosure Counseling
Affiliate of: NEIGHBORHOOD
REINVESTMENT
CORPORATION

**ACORN HOUSING
CORPORATION
1024 Elysian Fields Ave
New Orleans, LA 70117-8402
504-943-7513
Fax: 504-943-3842
Type of Counseling:
Rental Counseling, Prepurchase
Counseling, Default/Foreclosure
Counseling
Affiliate of: ACORN HOUSING
CORPORATION

**NEW ORLEANS
NEIGHBORHOOD
DEVELOPMENT
FOUNDATION**
3801 Canal Street Suite 329
New Orleans, LA 70119
504-488-0155
Fax: 504-488-2275
Type of Counseling:
HECM Counseling,
Default/Foreclosure Counseling,
Rental Counseling, Prepurchase
Counseling
Affiliate of: THE HOUSING
PARTNERSHIP NETWORK

**CENTRAL CITY HOUSING
DEVELOPMENT**
2020 Jackson Ave
New Orleans, LA 70113-1475
504-522-4273
Fax: 504-522-7948
Type of Counseling:
HECM Counseling,
Default/Foreclosure Counseling,
Rental Counseling, Prepurchase
Counseling

**SAINT LANDRY COMMUNITY
ACTION AGENCY**
1065 Hwy. 749, suite E
Opelousas, LA 70589
337-948-3651
Fax: 337-948-4153
Type of Counseling:
HECM Counseling,
Default/Foreclosure Counseling,
Rental Counseling, Prepurchase
Counseling

**CONSUMER CREDIT
COUNSELING AGENCY**
8575 Business Park Dr.
Shreveport, LA 71105-5655
225-923-2227
Toll-Free: 800-364-5595
Fax: 225-726-7912
Type of Counseling:
HECM Counseling,
Default/Foreclosure Counseling,
Rental Counseling, Prepurchase
Counseling

**QUEENSBOROUGH
NEIGHBORHOOD
ASSOCIATION**

2805 Missouri Avenue
Shreveport, LA 71109-
318-631-6573
Fax: 318-635-8100
Type of Counseling:
Prepurchase Counseling

**CADDO COMMUNITY
ACTION AGENCY**
4055 Saint Vincent Ave
Shreveport, LA 71108-2542
318-861-4808
Fax: 318-861-4958
Type of Counseling:
HECM Counseling,
Default/Foreclosure Counseling,
Rental Counseling, Prepurchase
Counseling

**NEW SHREVEPORT
COMMUNITY HOUSING
DEVELOPMENT
ORGANIZATION,
INCORPORATED**
2210 Line Avenue, Suite 201
Shreveport, LA 71104
318-425-5540
Fax: 318-425-5549
Type of Counseling:
Prepurchase Counseling, Rental
Counseling

**CONSUMER CREDIT
COUNSELING**
1338 Gause Blvd Ste 202
Slidell, LA 70458-3040
504-641-4158
Fax: 504-641-4159
Type of Counseling:
HECM Counseling,
Default/Foreclosure Counseling,
Rental Counseling, Prepurchase
Counseling

Maine

**MAINE STATE HOUSING
AUTHORITY**
353 Water Street
Augusta, ME 04330
207-626-4600
Toll-Free: 800-452-4668
TTY/TDD: 800-452-4603
Fax: 207-626-4678
Type of Counseling:

Prepurchase Counseling,
Default/Foreclosure Counseling

**PINE TREE LEGAL SERVICES,
INCORPORATED**
39 Green St
Augusta, ME 04330-7436
207-622-4731
TTY/TDD: 207-623-7770
Fax: 207-623-7774
Website: www.ptla.org
Type of Counseling:
HECM Counseling, Rental
Counseling, Prepurchase
Counseling

SENIOR SPECTRUM
One Weston Court.
Augusta, ME 04338-2589
800-639-1553
Fax: 207-622-7857
Email:
dashby@seniorspectrum.com
Type of Counseling:
HECM Counseling

**PENQUIS COMMUNITY
ACTION PROGRAM**
262 Harlow St.
Bangor, ME 04401-
207-973-3500
Fax: 207-973-3699
Email: laverill@penquiscap.org
Website: www.penquiscap.org
Type of Counseling:
Prepurchase Counseling,
Default/Foreclosure Counseling

**PENQUIS COMMUNITY
ACTION PROGRAM**
PO BOX 1162
Bangor, ME 04402
207-973-3500
Fax: 207-973-3699
Email: laverhill@penquiscap.org
Type of Counseling:
Prepurchase Counseling,
Default/Foreclosure Counseling
Affiliate of: CITIZENS'
HOUSING AND PLANNING
ASSOCIATION,
INCORPORATED

**PINE TREE LEGAL SERVICES,
INCORPORATED**
61 Main St Rm. 41

Bangor, ME 04401
207-942-8241
TTY/TDD: 207-942-1060
Fax: 207-942-8323
Website: www.ptla.org
Type of Counseling:
HECM Counseling, Rental
Counseling, Prepurchase
Counseling

COASTAL ECONOMIC
DEVELOPMENT
CORPORATION
39 Andrews Rd
Bath, ME 04530-2105
207-442-7963
Fax: 207-443-7447
Type of Counseling: Rental
Counseling

PINE TREE LEGAL SERVICES,
INCORPORATED
145 Lisbon Street
Lewiston, ME 04042
207-784-1558
TTY/TDD: 207-828-2308
Fax: 207-828-2300
Website: www.ptla.org
Type of Counseling:
HECM Counseling, Rental
Counseling, Prepurchase
Counseling

PINE TREE LEGAL SERVICES,
INCORPORATED
1 School Street
Machias, ME
207-255-8656
TTY/TDD: 207-255-6179
Fax: 207-255-8657
Website: www.ptla.org
Type of Counseling:
Prepurchase Counseling, Rental
Counseling, HECM Counseling

SOUTHERN MAINE AREA
AGENCY ON AGING
307 Cumberland Ave
Portland, ME 04104
207-775-6503
Toll-Free: 800-427-7411
TTY/TDD: 207-775-6503
Fax: 207-775-7319
Email: sdavis@smaaa.org
Type of Counseling: HECM
Counseling

**PEOPLES REGIONAL
OPPORTUNITY PROGRAM
510 Cumberland Avenue
Portland, ME 04101
207-874-1140
Fax: 207-874-1155
Type of Counseling:
Prepurchase Counseling
Affiliate of: CITIZENS'
HOUSING AND PLANNING
ASSOCIATION,
INCORPORATED

PINE TREE LEGAL SERVICES,
INCORPORATED
88 Federal St
Portland, ME 04112
207-774-8211
TTY/TDD: 207-828-2308
Fax: 207-828-2300
Website: www.ptla.org
Type of Counseling:
HECM Counseling, Rental
Counseling, Prepurchase
Counseling

PINE TREE LEGAL SERVICES,
INCORPORATED
373 Main St
Presque Isle, ME 04769-2811
207-764-4349
TTY/TDD: 207-764-2453
Fax: 207-764-2455
Website: www.ptla.org
Type of Counseling:
HECM Counseling, Rental
Counseling, Prepurchase
Counseling

SOUTHERN MAINE AREA
AGENCY ON AGING
Kimball Center
Saco, ME 04072
207-775-6503
Fax: 207-775-7319
Type of Counseling:
HECM Counseling

YORK COUNTY COMMUNITY
ACTION AGENCY
11 Cottage St
Sanford, ME 04073
207-324-5762
Fax: 207-490-5025
Type of Counseling:

Prepurchase Counseling,
Default/Foreclosure Counseling,
Rental Counseling, HECM
Counseling
Affiliate of: CITIZENS'
HOUSING AND PLANNING
ASSOCIATION,
INCORPORATED

**KENNEBEC VALLEY
COMMUNITY ACTION
PROGRAM
Mary Street; RR1 Box 4747
Skowhegan, ME 04976
207-873-2122
Fax: 207-474-6614
Type of Counseling:
Prepurchase Counseling
Affiliate of: NEIGHBORHOOD
REINVESTMENT
CORPORATION

**COMMUNITY CONCEPTS,
INC.
PO Box 278
South Paris, ME 04281
207-743-7716
Fax: 207-743-6513
Type of Counseling:
Prepurchase Counseling
Affiliate of: CITIZENS'
HOUSING AND PLANNING
ASSOCIATION,
INCORPORATED

CONSUMER CREDIT
COUNSELING SERVICE OF
MAINE, INCORPORATED
111 Westcott Rd
South Portland, ME 04106
207-773-1411
Toll-Free: 800-539-2227
Fax: 207-773-1824
Email: cccs@ccsme.org
Website: www.cccsme.org
Type of Counseling:
HECM Counseling,
Default/Foreclosure Counseling,
Rental Counseling, Prepurchase
Counseling

COASTAL ENTERPRISES,
INCORPORATED
36 Water Street
Wiscasset, ME 04578-0268
207-882-7552

Fax: 207-882-4457
Email: els@ceimaine.org
Type of Counseling:
HECM Counseling,
Default/Foreclosure Counseling,
Rental Counseling, Prepurchase
Counseling

Maryland

ANNE ARUNDEL COUNTY
ECONOMIC OPPORTUNITY
COMMITTEE,
INCORPORATED
251 West St
Annapolis, MD 21401-3427
410-626-1941
Fax: 410-626-1920
Email: incoi@aol.com
Type of Counseling:
HECM Counseling,
Default/Foreclosure Counseling,
Rental Counseling, Prepurchase
Counseling

ANNE ARUNDEL
DEPARTMENT OF AGING
2666 Riva Rd Ste 400
Annapolis, MD 21401-0675
410-222-4464
Toll-Free: 800-492-2499
Fax: 410-222-4346
Type of Counseling:
HECM Counseling

ARUNDEL COMMUNITY
DEVELOPMENT SERVICE INC
2660 Riva Road Suite 210
Annapolis, MD 21401-
410-222-7600
Fax: 410-222-7619
Type of Counseling:
Prepurchase Counseling,
Default/Foreclosure Counseling

COMMUNITY ORGANIZED
TO IMPROVE LIFE
9-11 S Carrollton Ave
Baltimore, MD 21223-2626
410-752-8500
Fax: 410-332-1804
Type of Counseling:
HECM Counseling,
Default/Foreclosure Counseling,
Rental Counseling, Prepurchase
Counseling

ASSOCIATED CATHOLIC
CHARITIES, INCORPORATED
4367 Hollins Ferry Rd suite 3-D
Baltimore, MD 21227
410-354-6811
Fax: 410-659-0750
Type of Counseling:
Rental Counseling, Prepurchase
Counseling

**NEIGHBORHOOD HOUSING
SERVICES OF BALTIMORE,
INCORPORATED
244 North Patterson Park Ave
Baltimore, MD 21231
410-327-1200
Fax: 410-675-1855
Email: nhsbalto@ix.netcom.com
Type of Counseling:
Default/Foreclosure Counseling,
Prepurchase Counseling
Affiliate of: NEIGHBORHOOD
REINVESTMENT
CORPORATION

**ACORN HOUSING
CORPORATION
825 Park Ave.
Baltimore, MD 21218
410-752-4213
Fax: 410-685-3521
Type of Counseling:
Prepurchase Counseling,
Default/Foreclosure Counseling
Affiliate of: ACORN HOUSING
CORPORATION

HARBEL HOUSING
PARTERSHIP
5807 Harford Rd.
Baltimore, MD 21214
410-444-9152
Fax: 410-444-9181
Type of Counseling:
Prepurchase Counseling

DRUID HEIGHTS
COMMUNITY DEVELOPMENT
CORPORATION
1821 McCullough Street
Baltimore, MD 21217
410-523-1350
Fax: 410-523-1374
Email: dheights@smart.net
Type of Counseling:
HECM Counseling,
Default/Foreclosure Counseling,

Rental Counseling, Prepurchase
Counseling

MIDDLE EAST COMMUNITY
DEVELOPMENT
730 N Collington Ave
Baltimore, MD 21205-2311
410-675-0900
Fax: 410-327-8204
Type of Counseling:
HECM Counseling,
Default/Foreclosure Counseling,
Rental Counseling, Prepurchase
Counseling

THE DEVELOPMENT
CORPORATION OF
NORTHWEST BALTIMORE
3521 W. Belvedere Avenue
Baltimore, MD 21215-
410-578-7190
Fax: 410-578-7193
Type of Counseling:
Prepurchase Counseling,
Default/Foreclosure Counseling,
HECM Counseling

BEA GADDY FAMILY
CENTERS, INC.
140 N Collington Ave
Baltimore, MD 21231-1635
410-563-2749
Fax: 410-675-5830
Type of Counseling:
HECM Counseling, Rental
Counseling, Prepurchase
Counseling

BALTIMORE URBAN LEAGUE
512 Orchard St
Baltimore, MD 21201-1947
410-523-8150
Fax: 410-523-4022
Email: twjordan@hotmail.com
Type of Counseling:
HECM Counseling,
Default/Foreclosure Counseling,
Rental Counseling, Prepurchase
Counseling
Affiliate of: NATIONAL
URBAN LEAGUE

HOMEOWNERSHIP AND
REHABILITATION SERVICES
DIVISION
417 E Fayette St Rm 1125

Baltimore, MD 21202-3431
410-396-3124
Fax: 410-545-6912
Type of Counseling:
HECM Counseling,
Default/Foreclosure Counseling,
Rental Counseling, Prepurchase
Counseling

SAINT AMBROSE HOUSING
AID CENTER
321 E 25th St
Baltimore, MD 21218-5303
410-235-5770
Fax: 410-366-8795
Type of Counseling:
HECM Counseling,
Default/Foreclosure Counseling,
Rental Counseling, Prepurchase
Counseling

HARLEM PARK
REVITALIZATION
CORPORATION
1017 Edmondson Ave
Baltimore, MD 21223-1325
410-728-5086
Fax: 410-728-4186
Email:
HPRCORP@WORLDNET.ATT.
NET
Type of Counseling:
HECM Counseling,
Default/Foreclosure Counseling,
Rental Counseling, Prepurchase
Counseling

TRI-CHURCHES HOUSING,
INCORPORATED
815 Scott St
Baltimore, MD 21230-2509
410-385-1463
Fax: 410-752-4643
Type of Counseling:
Prepurchase Counseling

SOUTHEAST DEVELOPMENT,
INCORPORATED
10 S Wolfe St
Baltimore, MD 21231-1912
410-327-1626
Fax: 410-276-5807
Type of Counseling:
HECM Counseling,
Default/Foreclosure Counseling,

Rental Counseling, Prepurchase
Counseling

**PAYNE MEMORIAL
OUTREACH CENTER
1505 Eutaw Place
Baltimore, MD 21217
410-462-3800
Fax: 410-462-3810
Type of Counseling:
Prepurchase Counseling
Affiliate of: CONGRESS OF
NATIONAL BLACK
CHURCHES, INCORPORATED

COMMUNITY ASSISTANCE
NETWORK
7701 Dunmanway
Baltimore, MD 21222-5437
410-285-4674
Fax: 410-285-6707
Type of Counseling:
HECM Counseling,
Default/Foreclosure Counseling,
Rental Counseling, Prepurchase
Counseling

GOVANS ECONOMIC
MANAGEMENT SENATE,
INCORPORATED
4324 York Road, Ste 203
Baltimore, MD 21212
410-433-3400
Fax: 410-433-7140
Email:
GEMS4234@YAHOO.COM
Type of Counseling:
HECM Counseling,
Default/Foreclosure Counseling,
Rental Counseling, Prepurchase
Counseling

EASTERN BALTIMORE AREA
CHAMBER OF COMMERCE
7835 Eastern Ave Ste 302
Baltimore, MD 21224
410-282-9100
Fax: 410-284-9864
Email: rruddle@ebacc.org
Type of Counseling:
HECM Counseling,
Default/Foreclosure Counseling,
Rental Counseling, Prepurchase
Counseling

HARFORD COUNTY
HOUSING AGENCY
15 S Main Street Ste 106
Bel Air, MD 21014
410-638-3045
Fax: 410-893-9816
Type of Counseling:
HECM Counseling,
Default/Foreclosure Counseling,
Prepurchase Counseling, Rental
Counseling

HOME PARTNERSHIP,
INCORPORATED
1221 B Brass Mill Road
Belcamp, MD 21017
410-297-6700
Fax: 410-297-6613
Type of Counseling:
HECM Counseling,
Default/Foreclosure Counseling,
Rental Counseling, Prepurchase
Counseling

DORCHESTER COMMUNITY
DEVELOPMENT
CORPORATION
435 High St
Cambridge, MD 21613-0549
410-228-3600
Fax: 410-228-4531
Type of Counseling:
HECM Counseling,
Default/Foreclosure Counseling,
Rental Counseling, Prepurchase
Counseling

MARYLAND DEPARTMENT
OF HOUSING AND
COMMUNITY DEVELOPMENT
100 Community Place
Crownsville, MD 21032
410-514-7530
Fax: 410-987-4136

**CUMBERLAND
NEIGHBORHOOD HOUSING
SERVICES, INCORPORATED
400 N Mechanic St
Cumberland, MD 21502
301-722-6958
Fax: 301-722-6966
Type of Counseling:
Prepurchase Counseling

Affiliate of: NEIGHBORHOOD
REINVESTMENT
CORPORATION

AFFORDABLE HOUSING
ALLIANCE
4785 Dorsey Hall Drive
Ellicott, MD 21042
410-995-5815
Fax: 301-596-5817
Email: wrossr106@aol.com
Type of Counseling:
HECM Counseling,
Default/Foreclosure Counseling,
Rental Counseling, Prepurchase
Counseling

HOUSING AUTHORITY -CITY
OF FREDERICK
209 Madison Street
Frederick, MD 21701
301-662-8173
Fax: 301-663-1464
Type of Counseling:
Default/Foreclosure Counseling,
Rental Counseling, Prepurchase
Counseling

FREDERICK COMMUNITY
ACTION AGENCY
100 S Market St
Frederick, MD 21701-5527
301-694-1506
Fax: 301-662-9079
Type of Counseling:
HECM Counseling,
Default/Foreclosure Counseling,
Rental Counseling, Prepurchase
Counseling

CONSUMER CREDIT
COUNSELING SERVICE OF
GREATER WASHINGTON
10 N. Jefferson St Suite 403
Frederick, MD 21701-4802
301-695-0369
Fax: 301-695-4878
Type of Counseling:
HECM Counseling,
Default/Foreclosure Counseling,
Rental Counseling, Prepurchase
Counseling

MARYLAND RURAL
DEVELOPMENT
CORPORATION

101 Cedar Ave
Greensboro, MD 21639-0739
410-479-3566
Fax: 410-479-3710
Email: dothouse@dmv.com
Type of Counseling:
Rental Counseling, Prepurchase
Counseling, Default/Foreclosure
Counseling

WASHINGTON COUNTY CAP
101 Summit Ave.
Hagerstown, MD 21740-
301-797-4161
Fax: 301-791-9062
Type of Counseling:
Prepurchase Counseling,
Default/Foreclosure Counseling,
Rental Counseling

CONSUMER CREDIT
COUNSELING SERVICE OF
GREATER WASHINGTON
44 N Potomac St Ste 101
Hagerstown, MD 21740-4855
301-416-8284
Fax: 301-791-1641
Type of Counseling:
HECM Counseling,
Default/Foreclosure Counseling,
Rental Counseling, Prepurchase
Counseling

SOUTHERN MARYLAND TRI-
COUNTY COMMUNITY
ACTION COMMITTEE,
INCORPORATED
8383 Leonardtown Rd.
Hughesville, MD 20637
301-274-4474
Fax: 301-274-0637
Type of Counseling:
HECM Counseling, Prepurchase
Counseling, Default/Foreclosure
Counseling, Rental Counseling

HOUSING INITIATIVES
PARTNERSHIP,
INCORPORATED
4310 Gallatin Street
Hyattsville, MD 20781-
301-699-3835
Fax: 301-699-8184
Type of Counseling:

Prepurchase Counseling,
Default/Foreclosure Counseling,
Rental Counseling

GREATER WASHINGTON
URBAN LEAGUE
5012 Rhode Island Ave
Hyattsville, MD 20781
301-985-3519
Fax: 301-985-3523
Type of Counseling:
Default/Foreclosure Counseling,
Prepurchase Counseling

HOUSING OPPORTUNITIES
COMMISSION OF
MONTGOMERY COUNTY
10400 Detrick Ave
Kensington, MD 20895-2440
301-933-9750
Fax: 301-929-4336
Type of Counseling:
Prepurchase Counseling, Rental
Counseling

GARRETT COUNTY
COMMUNITY ACTION
COMMITTEE,
INCORPORATED
104E E Center St
Oakland, MD 21550-1328
301-334-9431
Fax: 301-334-8555
Type of Counseling:
Default/Foreclosure Counseling,
Rental Counseling, Prepurchase
Counseling

COMMUNITY ASSISTANCE
NETWORK
8737-B Liberty Rd
Randallstown, MD 21133-4708
410-887-0600
Fax: 410-887-0713
Type of Counseling:
Default/Foreclosure Counseling,
Rental Counseling, Prepurchase
Counseling

CONSUMER CREDIT
COUNSELING SERVICE OF
GREATER WASHINGTON
5515 Security Ln Ste 525
Rockville, MD 20852
301-231-5833
Fax: 301-881-3670

Type of Counseling:
HECM Counseling,
Default/Foreclosure Counseling,
Rental Counseling, Prepurchase
Counseling

CONSUMER CREDIT
COUNSELING SERVICE OF
GREATER WASHINGTON
15848 Crabbs Branch Way
Rockville, MD 20855-2635
301-590-1010
Toll-Free: 800-747-4222
Fax: 301-948-7498
Email: hdrivon@cccswdc.org
Type of Counseling:
HECM Counseling,
Default/Foreclosure Counseling,
Rental Counseling, Prepurchase
Counseling

MAC INCORPORATED - AREA
AGENCY ON AGING
1504 Riverside Dr
Salisbury, MD 21801-6740
410-742-0505
Fax: 410-742-0525
Type of Counseling:
HECM Counseling

**SALISBURY
NEIGHBORHOOD HOUSING
SERVICES, INCORPORATED
513 Camden Ave
Salisbury, MD 21801
410-543-4626
Fax: 410-543-9204
Type of Counseling:
Default/Foreclosure Counseling,
Prepurchase Counseling
Affiliate of: NEIGHBORHOOD
REINVESTMENT
CORPORATION

SHORE UP
520 Snow Hill Rd
Salisbury, MD 218030430
410-749-1142
Fax: 410-742-9191
Email: tchase@shoreup.org
Type of Counseling:
HECM Counseling,
Default/Foreclosure Counseling,
Rental Counseling, Prepurchase
Counseling

NATIONAL FOUNDATION
FOR CONSUMER CREDIT,
INCORPORATED
8611 2nd Ave Ste 100
Silver Spring, MD 20910-3372
301-589-5600
Fax: 301-495-5623

SPANISH SPEAKING
COMMUNITY OF
MARYLAND,
INCORPORATED
8519 Piney Branch Rd
Silver Spring, MD 20901-3919
301-587-7217
Fax: 301-589-1397
Type of Counseling:
Rental Counseling

ROOTS OF MANKIND
CORPORATION
Park Place Professional Center,
5835 Allentown Road
Suitland, MD 20746-
301-899-6800
Toll-Free: 866-490-6800
Fax: 301-899-8444
Website:
www.ROMKIND.ORG/INDEX.
HTM
Type of Counseling:
Prepurchase Counseling, Rental
Counseling, Default/Foreclosure
Counseling

CARROLL COUNTY BUREAU
OF HOUSING AND
COMMUNITY DEVELOPMENT
10 Distillery Drive Ste 101
Westminster, MD 21157
410-386-3600
Toll-Free: 888-302-8978
TTY/TDD: 410-848-9747
Fax: 410-876-5255
Type of Counseling:
Default/Foreclosure Counseling,
Rental Counseling, HECM
Counseling

MassachUsetts

**ALLSTON BRIGHTON
COMMUNITY DEVELOPMENT
CORPORATION
15 North Beacon Street
Allston, MA 02134

617-787-3874
Fax: 617-787-0425
Email:
MHN@ALLSTONBRIGHTONC
DC.ORG
Type of Counseling:
Prepurchase Counseling
Affiliate of: CITIZENS'
HOUSING AND PLANNING
ASSOCIATION,
INCORPORATED

HOMEOWNER OPTIONS FOR
MASSACHUSETTS ELDERS
30 Winter S 7th Floor
Boston, MA 02108-4720
617-451-0680
Fax: 617-451-5838
Type of Counseling:
HECM Counseling,
Default/Foreclosure Counseling,
Prepurchase Counseling
Affiliate of: HOUSING
OPPORTUNITIES,
INCORPORATED

CONSUMER CREDIT
COUNSELING SERVICES OF
MASSACHUSETTS
8 Winter St 10th floor
Boston, MA 02108-4705
617-426-6644
Toll-Free: 800-282-6196
Fax: 617-960-1492
Website: www.cccsma.org
Type of Counseling:
HECM Counseling,
Default/Foreclosure Counseling,
Rental Counseling, Prepurchase
Counseling

CITIZENS' HOUSING AND
PLANNING ASSOCIATION,
INCORPORATED
18 Tremont Street, Suite 401
Boston, MA 02108
617-742-0820
Fax: 617-742-3953
Website: www.chapa.org
Affiliate of: CITIZENS'
HOUSING AND PLANNING
ASSOCIATION,
INCORPORATED

GREATER BOSTON LEGAL
SERVICES

197 Friend St
Boston, MA 02114-1802
617-371-1234
Fax: 617-371-1222
Type of Counseling: Rental
Counseling

THE HOUSING PARTNERSHIP
NETWORK
160 State Street, 5th Fl
Boston, MA 02109
617-720-1999
Fax: 617-720-3939
Email: turner@nahp.net

MASSACHUSETTS HOUSING
FINANCE AGENCY
One Beacon Street
Boston, MA 02108
617-854-1000
Fax: 617-854-1029
Type of Counseling:
Prepurchase Counseling

**METROPOLITAN BOSTON
HOUSING PARTNERSHIP,
INCORPORATED
569 Columbus Ave
Boston, MA 02118-1180
617-425-6767
Fax: 617-437-9311
Type of Counseling:
Rental Counseling, Prepurchase
Counseling, Default/Foreclosure
Counseling
Affiliate of: THE HOUSING
PARTNERSHIP NETWORK

**ACORN HOUSING
CORPORATION
13 1/2 Perkins St.
Brockton, MA 02302
508-580-4111
Fax: 508-580-0278
Type of Counseling:
Prepurchase Counseling,
Default/Foreclosure Counseling
Affiliate of: ACORN HOUSING
CORPORATION

**FAMILY SERVICE OF
NORFOLK COUNTY
18 Norfolk Street
Dedham, MA 02026
781-326-0400
Fax: 781-326-1141

Type of Counseling:
Prepurchase Counseling, Rental
Counseling, Default/Foreclosure
Counseling
Affiliate of: HOUSING
OPPORTUNITIES,
INCORPORATED

**ACORN HOUSING
CORPORATION
1453 Dorchester Ave
Dorchester, MA 02122-1338
617-436-6161
Fax: 617-436-4878
Type of Counseling:
Prepurchase Counseling,
Default/Foreclosure Counseling
Affiliate of: ACORN HOUSING
CORPORATION

**MASSACHUSETTS
AFFORDABLE HOUSING
ALLIANCE
1803 Dorchester Ave.
Dorchester, MA 02124
617-265-8995
Fax: 617-265-7503
Email:
FHAGINS@MAHAHOME.ORG
Type of Counseling:
Prepurchase Counseling
Affiliate of: CITIZENS'
HOUSING AND PLANNING
ASSOCIATION,
INCORPORATED

**NEIGHBORHOOD OF
AFFORDABLE HOUSING
22 Paris St
East Boston, MA 02128
617-567-5882
Fax: 617-567-7563
Email: NOAH22@ix.netcom.com
Type of Counseling:
Default/Foreclosure Counseling,
Rental Counseling, Prepurchase
Counseling
Affiliate of: NEIGHBORHOOD
REINVESTMENT
CORPORATION

**CATHOLIC SOCIAL
SERVICES
783 Slade St
Fall River, MA 02724-2509
508-674-4682

Fax: 508-675-2224
Type of Counseling:
Rental Counseling, Prepurchase
Counseling, Default/Foreclosure
Counseling, HECM Counseling
Affiliate of: CATHOLIC
CHARITIES USA

**TWIN CITIES COMMUNITY
DEVELOPMENT
CORPORATION
195 Kimball Street
Fitchburg, MA 01420
978-342-9561
Fax: 978-345-7905
Email: twincdc@ix.netcom.com
Type of Counseling:
Prepurchase Counseling, Rental
Counseling
Affiliate of: NEIGHBORHOOD
REINVESTMENT
CORPORATION

CATHOLIC CHARITIES
NORTH
11-15 Parker St
Gloucester, MA 01930-3017
978-740-6923
Fax: 978-745-1863
Type of Counseling:
Default/Foreclosure Counseling,
Rental Counseling, Prepurchase
Counseling

**HOUSING ASSISTANCE
CORPORATION
460 West Main Street
Hyannis, MA 02601
508-771-5400
Fax: 508-775-7434
Website:
www.haconcapecod.org
Type of Counseling:
Default/Foreclosure Counseling,
Rental Counseling, Prepurchase
Counseling, HECM Counseling
Affiliate of: THE HOUSING
PARTNERSHIP NETWORK

LEGAL SERVICES OF CAPE
COD AND ISLANDS,
INCORPORATED
460 W Main St
Hyannis, MA 02601-3653
508-428-8161
Toll-Free: 800-742-4107

Fax: 508-790-3955
Type of Counseling:
HECM Counseling,
Default/Foreclosure Counseling,
Rental Counseling, Prepurchase
Counseling

**ECUMENICAL SOCIAL
ACTION COMMITTEE,
INCORPORATED
3134 Washington St
Jamaica Plain, MA 02130
617-524-2555
Fax: 617-524-2315
Type of Counseling:
Default/Foreclosure Counseling
Affiliate of: HOUSING
OPPORTUNITIES,
INCORPORATED

**CITY LIFE/ VIDA URBANA
3353 Washington Street
Jamaica Plain, MA 02130
617-524-3541
Fax: 617-524-3555
Type of Counseling:
Prepurchase Counseling, Rental
Counseling
Affiliate of: HOUSING
OPPORTUNITIES,
INCORPORATED

MERRIMACK VALLEY
HOUSING PARTNERSHIP
10 Kirk Street
Lowell, MA 01852
978-459-8490
Fax: 978-459-0194
Email: MVHP1@aol.com
Type of Counseling:
Rental Counseling, Prepurchase
Counseling
Affiliate of: CITIZENS'
HOUSING AND PLANNING
ASSOCIATION,
INCORPORATED

**COMMUNITY TEAMWORK,
INC.
167 Dutton Street
Lowell, MA 01852
978-459-0551
Fax: 978-453-9128
Email:
CBCAUREGARD@COMTEAM.
ORG

Type of Counseling:
Prepurchase Counseling,
Default/Foreclosure Counseling
Affiliate of: CITIZENS'
HOUSING AND PLANNING
ASSOCIATION,
INCORPORATED

**COALITION FOR A BETTER
ACRE
450 Merrimack Street
Lowell, MA 01854
508-452-7523
Fax: 508-452-4923
Type of Counseling:
Prepurchase Counseling
Affiliate of: NEIGHBORHOOD
REINVESTMENT
CORPORATION

HOUSING ALLOWANCE
PROJECT, INCORPORATED
20 Hampton Ave Suite 185
Northampton, MA 01060
413-584-8495
Toll-Free: 800-851-8495
Fax: 413-586-3571
Type of Counseling:
HECM Counseling,
Default/Foreclosure Counseling,
Rental Counseling, Prepurchase
Counseling

BERKSHIRE HOUSING
DEVELOPMENT
CORPORATION
74 North St
Pittsfield, MA 01201-5116
413-499-1630
Fax: 413-445-7633
Email:
dblacklo@bershirehousing.com
Type of Counseling:
Prepurchase Counseling

PLYMOUTH
REDEVELOPMENT
AUTHORITY
11 Lincoln Street
Plymouth, MA 02360
508-830-4115
Fax: 508-830-4116
Type of Counseling:
Prepurchase Counseling,
Default/Foreclosure Counseling,

HECM Counseling, Rental
Counseling

QUINCY COMMUNITY
ACTION PROGRAMS,
INCORPORATED
1509 Hancock St
Quincy, MA 02169-5200
617-479-8181
Fax: 617-479-7228
Email: Agardner@QCAP.org
Type of Counseling:
HECM Counseling,
Default/Foreclosure Counseling,
Rental Counseling, Prepurchase
Counseling

**URBAN EDGE HOUSING
CORPORATION
2010 Columbus Ave
Roxbury, MA 02119
617-522-5515
Fax: 617-522-5584
Type of Counseling:
Prepurchase Counseling,
Default/Foreclosure Counseling
Affiliate of: NEIGHBORHOOD
REINVESTMENT
CORPORATION

**ACORN HOUSING
CORPORATION
1655 Main Street #204
Springfield, MA 01103
413-736-7713
Fax: 413-736-7715
Type of Counseling:
Default/Foreclosure Counseling,
Prepurchase Counseling, Rental
Counseling
Affiliate of: ACORN HOUSING
CORPORATION

HAMPDEN HAMPSHIRE
HOUSING PARTNERSHIP
322 Main St
Springfield, MA 01105
800-332-9667
Toll-Free: 800-332-9667
Fax: 413-731-8723
Type of Counseling:
HECM Counseling,
Default/Foreclosure Counseling,
Rental Counseling, Prepurchase
Counseling

Affiliate of: THE HOUSING
PARTNERSHIP NETWORK

COMMUNITY SERVICE
NETWORK, INCORPORATED
52 Broadway
Stoneham, MA 02180-1003
781-438-1977
Fax: 781-438-6037
Type of Counseling:
Prepurchase Counseling,
Default/Foreclosure Counseling,
HECM Counseling, Rental
Counseling

PRO-HOME INCORPORATED
PO Box 2793
Taunton, MA 02780
508-821-1092
Fax: 508-821-1091
Type of Counseling:
Prepurchase Counseling,
Default/Foreclosure Counseling,
Rental Counseling, HECM
Counseling

**RURAL DEVELOPMENT
INCORPORATED
42 Canal Road
Turners Falls, MA 01376-
413-863-9781
Fax: 413-863-8160
Affiliate of: HOUSING
OPPORTUNITIES,
INCORPORATED

HOUSING ALLOWANCE
PROJECT, INCORPORATED
79 Broad St
Westfield, MA 01085-2925
413-568-7200
Fax: 413-785-1251
Type of Counseling:
HECM Counseling,
Default/Foreclosure Counseling,
Rental Counseling, Prepurchase
Counseling

RURAL HOUSING
IMPROVEMENT,
INCORPORATED
218 Central St
Winchendon, MA 01475-1633
978-297-5300
Fax: 978-297-2606

Type of Counseling:
Rental Counseling

Michigan

GREENPATH DEBT
SOLUTIONS
7445 Allen Rd Rm. 260
Allen Park, MI 48101-1963
800-547-5005
Toll-Free: 800-547-5005
Fax: 313-381-3158
Type of Counseling:
HECM Counseling,
Default/Foreclosure Counseling,
Rental Counseling, Prepurchase
Counseling
Affiliate of: NATIONAL
FOUNDATION FOR
CONSUMER CREDIT,
INCORPORATED

WASHTENAW HOMEBUYERS
PROGRAM
2301 Platt Road
Ann Arbor, MI 48104
734-975-0559
Fax: 734-975-1665
Type of Counseling:
Prepurchase Counseling,
Default/Foreclosure Counseling

GREENPATH DEBT
SOLUTIONS
3840 Packard Rd Ste. 270
Ann Arbor, MI 48108
734-477-0700
Fax: 734-477-0706
Type of Counseling:
HECM Counseling,
Default/Foreclosure Counseling,
Rental Counseling, Prepurchase
Counseling
Affiliate of: NATIONAL
FOUNDATION FOR
CONSUMER CREDIT,
INCORPORATED

GREENPATH DEBT
SOLUTIONS
131 Columbia Ave E Ste 204
Battle Creek, MI 49015-3761
616-963-4575
Fax: 616-963-6123
Type of Counseling:

HECM Counseling,
Default/Foreclosure Counseling,
Rental Counseling, Prepurchase
Counseling

**NEIGHBORHOODS
INCORPORATED OF BATTLE
CREEK
47 N Washington Avenue
Battle Creek, MI 49017
616-968-1113
Fax: 616-963-7022
Type of Counseling:
Default/Foreclosure Counseling,
Prepurchase Counseling, Rental
Counseling
Affiliate of: NEIGHBORHOOD
REINVESTMENT
CORPORATION

SOUTHWEST CMMUNITY
ACTION AGENCY
185 E. Main, 2nd. Floor
Benton Harbor, MI 49022-
616-925-9077
Fax: 616-925-9271
Type of Counseling:
Prepurchase Counseling

GREENPATH DEBT
SOLUTIONS
2525 Telegraph Road, Suite 306
Bloomfield Hills, MI 48302-0289
248-332-5273
Fax: 248-332-5537
Type of Counseling:
Prepurchase Counseling,
Default/Foreclosure Counseling,
HECM Counseling, Rental
Counseling
Affiliate of: NATIONAL
FOUNDATION FOR
CONSUMER CREDIT,
INCORPORATED

GREENPATH DEBT
SOLUTIONS
211 North First Street, Suite 300
Brighton, MI 48116-1297
810-227-0200
Fax: 810-227-0474
Type of Counseling:
Prepurchase Counseling,
Default/Foreclosure Counseling,
HECM Counseling, Rental
Counseling

Affiliate of: NATIONAL
FOUNDATION FOR
CONSUMER CREDIT,
INCORPORATED

NORTHWEST MICHIGAN
HUMAN SERVICES AGENCY,
INCORPORATED
1640 Marty Paul St
Cadillac, MI 49601-9608
616-775-9781
Fax: 616-775-1448
Type of Counseling:
HECM Counseling,
Default/Foreclosure Counseling,
Rental Counseling, Prepurchase
Counseling

HUMAN DEVELOPMENT
COMMISSION
429 Montague Ave
Caro, MI 48723-1921
989-673-4121
Fax: 989-673-2031
Type of Counseling:
HECM Counseling,
Default/Foreclosure Counseling,
Rental Counseling, Prepurchase
Counseling

DETROIT NONPROFIT
HOUSING CORPORATION
2990 West Grand Blvd., Suite 200
Detroit, MI
313-972-1111
Fax: 313-972-1125
Email: detroitnon@aol.com
Type of Counseling:
Default/Foreclosure Counseling,
Rental Counseling, Prepurchase
Counseling, HECM Counseling

PEOPLE UNITED AS ONE
660 Martin Luther King Blvd.
Detroit, MI 48201-
313-993-9077
Fax: 313-993-6502
Type of Counseling:
Prepurchase Counseling, Rental
Counseling, HECM Counseling,
Default/Foreclosure Counseling

**ACORN HOUSING
CORPORATION
1249 Washington Blvd Ste 1301
Detroit, MI 48226-1822

313-963-1841
Fax: 313-963-6905
Type of Counseling:
Prepurchase Counseling,
Default/Foreclosure Counseling
Affiliate of: ACORN HOUSING
CORPORATION

PHOENIX NONPROFIT,
INCORPORATED
1640 Porter St
Detroit, MI 48216-1936
313-964-4207
Fax: 313-964-3861
Email: FatMarv@AOL.COM
Type of Counseling:
Default/Foreclosure Counseling,
Prepurchase Counseling

U SNAP BAC
11101 Morang Dr
Detroit, MI 48224-1702
313-640-1100
Fax: 313-640-1112
Type of Counseling:
Default/Foreclosure Counseling,
Rental Counseling, Prepurchase
Counseling

GREENPATH DEBT
SOLUTIONS
3011 W Grand Blvd Ste 561
Fisher Bldg
Detroit, MI 48202
313-872-2401
Fax: 313-872-3041
Type of Counseling:
HECM Counseling,
Default/Foreclosure Counseling,
Rental Counseling, Prepurchase
Counseling

NEIGHBORHOOD SERVICE
ORGANIZATION
18829 McNichols
Detroit, MI 48221-
313-537-5268
Fax: 313-537-5358
Type of Counseling:
Prepurchase Counseling,
Default/Foreclosure Counseling

DETROIT NEIGHBORHOOD
HOUSING SERVICES
3839 Woodward Avenue
Detroit, MI 482012009

313-833-1943
Type of Counseling:
HECM Counseling,
Default/Foreclosure Counseling,
Rental Counseling, Prepurchase
Counseling

MICHIGAN STATE
UNIVERSITY EXTENSION
SERVICES
108 Agricultural Hall
East Lansing, MI 48224-
517-432-7686
Fax: 517-353-4846
Website:
www.msue.msu.edu/home/
Type of Counseling:
Prepurchase Counseling,
Default/Foreclosure Counseling,
HECM Counseling, Rental
Counseling

GREENPATH DEBT
SOLUTIONS
38505 Country Club Dr Ste 210
Farmington Hills, MI 483313429
248-553-5400
Toll-Free: 800-547-5005
Fax: 248-553-2224
Type of Counseling:
HECM Counseling,
Default/Foreclosure Counseling,
Prepurchase Counseling
Affiliate of: NATIONAL
FOUNDATION FOR
CONSUMER CREDIT,
INCORPORATED

URBAN LEAGUE OF FLINT
5005 Cloverlawn Dr
Flint, MI 48504-2067
810-789-7611
Fax: 810-787-4518
Email: ulflint@aol.com
Type of Counseling:
Default/Foreclosure Counseling,
Prepurchase Counseling, HECM
Counseling, Rental Counseling
Affiliate of: NATIONAL
URBAN LEAGUE

**METRO HOUSING
PARTNERSHIP,
INCORPORATED
503 S Saginaw St, Suite 519
Flint, MI 48502

810-767-4622
Fax: 810-767-4664
Type of
Counseling:Default/Foreclosure
Counseling, Prepurchase
Counseling, HECM Counseling
Affiliate of: THE HOUSING
PARTNERSHIP NETWORK

GREENPATH DEBT
SOLUTIONS
2222 South Linden Rd Ste I
Flint, MI 48532
810-230-1077
Fax: 810-230-7508
Type of Counseling:
HECM Counseling,
Default/Foreclosure Counseling,
Rental Counseling, Prepurchase
Counseling
Affiliate of: NATIONAL
FOUNDATION FOR
CONSUMER CREDIT,
INCORPORATED

MICHIGAN HOUSING
COUNSELORS
G1173 N Ballenger Hwy Ste 100
Flint, MI 48504-4462
810-235-4649
Fax: 810-235-4649
Type of Counseling:
HECM Counseling,
Default/Foreclosure Counseling,
Rental Counseling, Prepurchase
Counseling

MISSION OF PEACE
Windmill Place, 877 East Fifth
Ave.
Flint, MI 48503
810-232-0104
Toll-Free: 877-334-0104
Fax: 810-235-6878
Type of Counseling:
Prepurchase Counseling, Rental
Counseling, Default/Foreclosure
Counseling, HECM Counseling
Affiliate of: CONGRESS OF
NATIONAL BLACK
CHURCHES, INCORPORATED

GREENPATH DEBT
SOLUTIONS
3051 Commerce Dr Ste 3
Fort Gratiot, MI 48059-3820

810-385-8562
Fax: 810-385-8569
Type of Counseling:
HECM Counseling,
Default/Foreclosure Counseling,
Rental Counseling, Prepurchase
Counseling
Affiliate of: NATIONAL
FOUNDATION FOR
CONSUMER CREDIT,
INCORPORATED

GREENPATH DEBT
SOLUTIONS
810 South Otsego Avenue, Suite
105
Gaylord, MI 49735-1780
989-732-2260
Fax: 989-732-1054
Type of Counseling:
Prepurchase Counseling,
Default/Foreclosure Counseling,
HECM Counseling, Rental
Counseling
Affiliate of: NATIONAL
FOUNDATION FOR
CONSUMER CREDIT,
INCORPORATED

GARFIELD DEVELOPMENT
CORPORATION
1725 S Division Ave
Grand Rapids, MI 49507-1603
616-248-3235
Fax: 616-248-3445
Email: gdc@iserv.net
Type of Counseling:
Prepurchase Counseling

GREENPATH DEBT
SOLUTIONS
2922 Fuller Ave NE
Suite B203
Grand Rapids, MI 49505-3459
616-281-0013
Fax: 616-361-5573
Type of Counseling:
HECM Counseling,
Default/Foreclosure Counseling,
Rental Counseling, Prepurchase
Counseling
Affiliate of: NATIONAL
FOUNDATION FOR
CONSUMER CREDIT,
INCORPORATED

GRAND RAPIDS URBAN
LEAGUE
745 Eastern Ave SE
Grand Rapids, MI 49503-5544
616-245-2207
Fax: 616-245-6510
Type of Counseling:
HECM Counseling,
Default/Foreclosure Counseling,
Rental Counseling, Prepurchase
Counseling

EIGHTCAP, INCORPORATED
904 Oak Dr-Turk Lake
Greenville, MI 48838
989-772-0110
Fax: 989-775-3907
Type of Counseling:
Default/Foreclosure Counseling,
Rental Counseling, Prepurchase
Counseling

GREENPATH DEBT
SOLUTIONS
675 E 16th St Ste 220
Holland, MI 49423-3752
616-394-9003
Fax: 616-394-4308
Type of Counseling:
HECM Counseling,
Default/Foreclosure Counseling,
Rental Counseling, Prepurchase
Counseling
Affiliate of: NATIONAL
FOUNDATION FOR
CONSUMER CREDIT,
INCORPORATED

GREENPATH DEBT
SOLUTIONS
Plaza Central 415 Stephenson
Ave
Iron Mountain, MI 49801
906-774-7565
Fax: 906-774-0461
Type of Counseling:
HECM Counseling,
Default/Foreclosure Counseling,
Rental Counseling, Prepurchase
Counseling

GREENPATH DEBT
SOLUTIONS
127 East Ayer Street, East Side
Ironwood, MI 49938-2037
906-932-4169

Fax: 906-932-2635
Type of Counseling:
Prepurchase Counseling,
Default/Foreclosure Counseling,
HECM Counseling, Rental
Counseling
Affiliate of: NATIONAL
FOUNDATION FOR
CONSUMER CREDIT,
INCORPORATED

GREENPATH DEBT
SOLUTIONS
211 W Ganson St
Jackson, MI 49201-1241
517-788-9866
Fax: 517-788-9248
Type of Counseling:
HECM Counseling,
Default/Foreclosure Counseling,
Rental Counseling, Prepurchase
Counseling
Affiliate of: NATIONAL
FOUNDATION FOR
CONSUMER CREDIT,
INCORPORATED

**KALAMAZOO
NEIGHBORHOOD HOUSING
SERVICES, INCORPORATED
814 S Westnedge Ave
Kalamazoo, MI 49008
616-385-2916
Fax: 616-385-9912
Type of Counseling:
Prepurchase Counseling,
Default/Foreclosure Counseling
Affiliate of: NEIGHBORHOOD
REINVESTMENT
CORPORATION

GREENPATH DEBT
SOLUTIONS
2450 44th St SE Ste 204
Kentwood, MI 49512-9081
616-281-0013
Fax: 616-281-0293
Type of Counseling:
HECM Counseling,
Default/Foreclosure Counseling,
Prepurchase Counseling
Affiliate of: NATIONAL
FOUNDATION FOR
CONSUMER CREDIT,
INCORPORATED

GREENPATH DEBT
SOLUTIONS
612 S Creyts Rd Ste C
Lansing, MI 48917-9201
517-321-5836
Fax: 517-321-5863
Type of Counseling:
HECM Counseling,
Default/Foreclosure Counseling,
Rental Counseling, Prepurchase
Counseling

MICHIGAN STATE HOUSING
DEVELOPMENT AUTHORITY
735 E. Michigan Avenue
Lansing, MI 48909
517-373-6208
Fax: 517-241-4756
Type of Counseling:
Prepurchase Counseling,
Default/Foreclosure Counseling

FERRIS DEVELOPMENT
820 N. Capitol Avenue
Lansing, MI 48906-
517-485-9100
Fax: 517-485-0179
Email: tmunson@ferris.org
Type of Counseling:
Prepurchase Counseling,
Default/Foreclosure Counseling

GREENPATH DEBT
SOLUTIONS
712 Chippewa Sq. Ste 103
Marquette, MI 49855-4827
906-228-5505
Fax: 906-228-5856
Type of Counseling:
HECM Counseling,
Default/Foreclosure Counseling,
Rental Counseling, Prepurchase
Counseling

GREENPATH DEBT
SOLUTIONS
25 S Monroe St Rm 307
Monroe, MI 48161-2230
734-457-0370
Fax: 734-457-3856
Type of Counseling:
HECM Counseling,
Default/Foreclosure Counseling,
Rental Counseling, Prepurchase
Counseling

Affiliate of: NATIONAL
FOUNDATION FOR
CONSUMER CREDIT,
INCORPORATED

GREENPATH DEBT
SOLUTIONS
37060 Garfield Rd Ste T-4
Mount Clemens, MI 48036
810-263-1160
Fax: 810-263-0715
Type of Counseling:
HECM Counseling,
Default/Foreclosure Counseling,
Rental Counseling, Prepurchase
Counseling
Affiliate of: NATIONAL
FOUNDATION FOR
CONSUMER CREDIT,
INCORPORATED

MICHIGAN HOUSING
COUNSELORS
237 Southbound Gratiot Ave
Mount Clemens, MI 48043-2410
810-468-4594
Fax: 810-468-0119
Type of Counseling:
HECM Counseling,
Default/Foreclosure Counseling,
Rental Counseling, Prepurchase
Counseling

GREENPATH DEBT
SOLUTIONS
950 W Norton Ave Ste 210
Muskegon, MI 49441-4169
616-737-6404
Fax: 616-739-7510
Type of Counseling:
HECM Counseling,
Default/Foreclosure Counseling,
Rental Counseling, Prepurchase
Counseling
Affiliate of: NATIONAL
FOUNDATION FOR
CONSUMER CREDIT,
INCORPORATED

NELSON NEIGHBORHOOD
IMPROVEMENT
ASSOCIATION,
INCORPORATED
1330 5th St
Muskegon, MI 49441-2004
231-722-0529

Fax: 231-722-3201
Type of Counseling:
Default/Foreclosure Counseling,
Rental Counseling, Prepurchase
Counseling

NORTHWEST MICHIGAN
HUMAN SERVICES AGENCY,
INCORPORATED
441 Bay St
Petoskey, MI 49770-2408
616-347-9070
Fax: 616-347-3664
Type of Counseling:
Default/Foreclosure Counseling,
Rental Counseling

OAKLAND COUNTY -
HOUSING COUNSELING
1200 N Telegraph Rd/Bldg. 34,
Rm 112
Pontiac, MI 48341-0435
248-858-5402
Fax: 248-858-5311
Email:
FrederiksenA@CO.Oakland.MI.
US
Type of Counseling:
HECM Counseling,
Default/Foreclosure Counseling,
Rental Counseling, Prepurchase
Counseling

OAKLAND LIVINGSTON
HUMAN SERVICE AGENCY
196 Cesar Chavez Ave.
Pontiac, MI 48343-0598
248-209-2767
Fax: 248-209-2777
Type of Counseling:
Prepurchase Counseling,
Default/Foreclosure Counseling,
HECM Counseling, Rental
Counseling

PONTIAC NEIGHBORHOOD
HOUSING SERVICES
69 S Ardmore
Pontiac, MI 48342
248-335-5840
Fax: 248-335-2014
Type of Counseling:
Default/Foreclosure Counseling,
Rental Counseling, Prepurchase
Counseling

GREENPATH DEBT
SOLUTIONS
576 Romence Rd Ste 220
Portage, MI 49024-3472
616-329-7153
Fax: 616-329-7498
Type of Counseling:
HECM Counseling,
Default/Foreclosure Counseling,
Rental Counseling, Prepurchase
Counseling
Affiliate of: NATIONAL
FOUNDATION FOR
CONSUMER CREDIT,
INCORPORATED

MICHIGAN STATE
UNIVERSITY EXTENSION
SERVICE
MONTMORENEY/PRESQUE
ILSE COUNTY BRANCH
151 E. Huron Avenue
Rogers City, MI 49779-0110
989-785-8013
Fax: 989-785-4183
Type of Counseling:
Prepurchase Counseling,
Default/Foreclosure Counseling,
HECM Counseling, Rental
Counseling

MICHIGAN STATE
UNIVERSITY EXTENSION
SERVICES
One Tuscola Street
Saginaw, MI 48607-
989-758-2500
Fax: 989-758-2509
Type of Counseling:
Prepurchase Counseling,
Default/Foreclosure Counseling,
HECM Counseling, Rental
Counseling

**NEIGHBORHOOD
RENEWAL SERVICES OF
SAGINAW, INCORPORATED
427 Atwater
Saginaw, MI 48605
517-753-4900
Fax: 517-753-8545
Type of Counseling:
Default/Foreclosure Counseling,
Prepurchase Counseling

Affiliate of: NEIGHBORHOOD
REINVESTMENT
CORPORATION

SAGINAW COUNTY
COMMUNITY ACTION
COMMITTEE,
INCORPORATED
2824 Perkins St
Saginaw, MI 48601-1505
989-753-7741
Fax: 989-753-2439
Type of Counseling:
HECM Counseling,
Default/Foreclosure Counseling,
Rental Counseling, Prepurchase
Counseling

GREENPATH DEBT
SOLUTIONS
4600 Fashion Square Blvd Ste
110
Saginaw, MI 48604-2616
517-793-5623
Fax: 517-793-2898
Type of Counseling:
HECM Counseling,
Default/Foreclosure Counseling,
Rental Counseling, Prepurchase
Counseling
Affiliate of: NATIONAL
FOUNDATION FOR
CONSUMER CREDIT,
INCORPORATED

GREENPATH DEBT
SOLUTIONS
24725 W 12 Mile Rd Ste 240
Southfield, MI 48034-1801
248-352-5344
Fax: 248-352-9938
Type of Counseling:
Default/Foreclosure Counseling,
Rental Counseling, Prepurchase
Counseling
Affiliate of: NATIONAL
FOUNDATION FOR
CONSUMER CREDIT,
INCORPORATED

NORTHWEST MICHIGAN
HUMAN SERVICES AGENCY,
INCORPORATED
3963 3 Mile Rd
Traverse City, MI 49686-9164
231-947-3780

Fax: 231-947-4935
Type of Counseling:
HECM Counseling,
Default/Foreclosure Counseling,
Rental Counseling, Prepurchase
Counseling

MICHIGAN STATE
UNIVERSITY EXTENSION
SERVICE BENZIE/GRAND
TRAVERSE/LEEIANAU
COUNTY BRANCH
Grand Traverse County
Extension, Suite A
Traverse City, MI 49684-2208
231-922-4821
Fax: 231-922-4633
Type of Counseling:
Prepurchase Counseling,
Default/Foreclosure Counseling,
HECM Counseling, Rental
Counseling

GREENPATH DEBT
SOLUTIONS
812 South Garfield Avenue,
Suite 7
Traverse City, MI 49686-3456
231-933-4980
Fax: 231-933-0975
Type of Counseling:
Prepurchase Counseling,
Default/Foreclosure Counseling,
HECM Counseling, Rental
Counseling
Affiliate of: NATIONAL
FOUNDATION FOR
CONSUMER CREDIT,
INCORPORATED

GREENPATH DEBT
SOLUTIONS
675 E Big Beaver Rd Rm 101
Troy, MI 48083-1418
248-689-2440
Fax: 248-689-6527
Type of Counseling:
HECM Counseling,
Default/Foreclosure Counseling,
Rental Counseling, Prepurchase
Counseling
Affiliate of: NATIONAL
FOUNDATION FOR
CONSUMER CREDIT,
INCORPORATED

GREENPATH DEBT
SOLUTIONS
38545 Ford Rd Ste 202
Westland, MI 48185-7901
734-326-4466
Fax: 734-326-3060
Type of Counseling:
HECM Counseling,
Default/Foreclosure Counseling,
Rental Counseling, Prepurchase
Counseling
Affiliate of: NATIONAL
FOUNDATION FOR
CONSUMER CREDIT,
INCORPORATED

MINNESOTA

**CONSUMER CREDIT
COUNSELING SERVICE OF
DULUTH
2409 Forthun Roads
Baxter, MN 56425-
218-829-5000
Fax: 218-829-9726
Type of Counseling:
Default/Foreclosure Counseling,
Prepurchase Counseling, Rental
Counseling

LEGAL AID SERVICE OF
NORTHEASTERN
MINNESOTA BRAINERD
LAKES OFFICE
1342 Highway 210 West
Baxter, MN 56425
218-829-1701
Fax: 218-829-4792
Type of Counseling:
Default/Foreclosure Counseling,
Rental Counseling

**CONSUMER CREDIT
COUNSELING OF DULUTH
403 4TH Street NW #120
Bemidji, MN 56601
218-751-1305
Fax: 218-751-0703
Type of Counseling:
Default/Foreclosure Counseling,
Rental Counseling

ANOKA COUNTY
COMMUNITY ACTION
PROGRAM, INCORPORATED
1201 89th Ave NE Ste 345
Blaine, MN 55434-3373

763-783-4705
Fax: 763-783-4700
Type of Counseling:
Default/Foreclosure Counseling,
Prepurchase Counseling, Rental
Counseling, HECM Counseling

CARVER COUNTY HOUSING
AND REDEVELOPMENT
AUTHORITY
500 N Pine St Ste 300
Chaska, MN 55318-1953
952-448-7715
Fax: 952-448-6506
Type of Counseling:
Default/Foreclosure Counseling,
Rental Counseling, Prepurchase
Counseling

CONSUMER CREDIT
COUNSELING SERVICE OF
MINNESOTA
277 Coon Rapids Blvd NW Ste
410 Rm. 16
Coon Rapids, MN 55433-5843
612-874-8164
Fax: 612-874-8465
Type of Counseling:
Default/Foreclosure Counseling,
Rental Counseling, Prepurchase
Counseling

**NEIGHBORHOOD HOUSING
SERVICES OF DULUTH,
INCORPORATED
2910 West 3rd Street
Duluth, MN 55806-
218-628-1057
Fax: 218-628-1060
Type of Counseling:
Default/Foreclosure Counseling,
Prepurchase Counseling
Affiliate of: NEIGHBORHOOD
REINVESTMENT
CORPORATION

LAW OFFICES OF LEGAL AID
SERVICE OF NORTHEASTERN
MINNESOTA
302 Ordean Building, 424 West
Superior St.
Duluth, MN 55802
218-726-4800
Fax: 218-726-4804
Type of Counseling:
Default/Foreclosure Counseling,
Rental Counseling

**CONSUMER CREDIT COUNSELING SERVICE OF DULUTH/LUTHERAN SOCIAL SERVICES
424 West Superior Street
Duluth, MN 558020306
218-726-4767
Fax: 218-726-1251
Email: cedland@lss-dul.usa.com
Type of Counseling:
Prepurchase Counseling,
Default/Foreclosure Counseling
Affiliate of: NATIONAL FOUNDATION FOR CONSUMER CREDIT, INCORPORATED

LEGAL AID SERVICE OF NORTHEASTERN MINNESOTA ITASCA OFFICE
204 1st Ave. Northwest, Suite 7
Grand Rapids, MN 55744
218-326-6695
Fax: 218-326-2298
Type of Counseling:
Rental Counseling,
Default/Foreclosure Counseling

**CONSUMER CREDIT COUNSELING SERVICE OF DULUTH
501 Pokegama Avenue South
Grand Rapids, MN 55744
218-326-1269
Fax: 218-326-1147
Type of Counseling:
Default/Foreclosure Counseling,
Prepurchase Counseling, Rental
Counseling

**CONSUMER CREDIT COUNSELING OF DULUTH
301 e. Howard Street #106
Hibbing, MN 55746
218-262-3372
Fax: 213-362-7701
Type of Counseling:
Default/Foreclosure Counseling,
Prepurchase Counseling, Rental
Counseling

COMMUNITY ACTION FOR SUBURBAN HENNEPIN, INCORPORATED
33 10th Ave South, Ste 150
Hopkins, MN 55343-1303

952-933-9639
Fax: 952-933-8016
Email: mtimm@Cashenn.org
Type of Counseling:
HECM Counseling,
Default/Foreclosure Counseling,
Prepurchase Counseling

**CONSUMER CREDIT COUNSELING SERVICE OF DULUTH
710 South 2nd Street
Mankato, MN 56001
507-625-8021
Fax: 507-625-8998
Type of Counseling:
Default/Foreclosure Counseling,
Prepurchase Counseling, Rental
Counseling

SENIOR HOUSING, INCORPORATED
2021 E Hennepin Ave Ste 372
Minneapolis, MN 55413-
612-617-1925
Toll-Free: 888-399-4663
Fax: 612-617-1022
Type of Counseling:
HECM Counseling

PILOT CITY REGIONAL CENTER
1315 Penn Ave N
Minneapolis, MN 55411-3047
612-348-4752
Fax: 612-348-4434
Type of Counseling:
Default/Foreclosure Counseling,
Rental Counseling, Prepurchase
Counseling

CONSUMER CREDIT COUNSELING SERVICE OF MINNESOTA
10560 Wayzata Blvd Ste 11
Woodside Complex
Minnetonka, MN 55305-1524
651-874-8164
Fax: 651-439-4894
Type of Counseling:
Default/Foreclosure Counseling,
Rental Counseling, Prepurchase
Counseling

**THE VILLAGE FAMILY CENTER

715 N. 11th Street, Suite 302
Moorhead, MN 56560
218-291-1227
Fax: 218-233-7930
Type of Counseling:
HECM Counseling,
Default/Foreclosure Counseling,
Prepurchase Counseling, Rental
Counseling

**CONSUMER CREDIT COUNSELING SERVICE OF DULUTH
602 East First Street
Park Rapids, MN 56470
218-732-4320
Type of Counseling:
Default/Foreclosure Counseling,
Prepurchase Counseling, Rental
Counseling

LEGAL AID SERVICE OF NORTHEASTERN MINNESOTA PINE CITY OFFICE
235 6th St.
Pine City, MN 55063
320-629-7166
Fax: 320-629-0185
Type of Counseling:
Rental Counseling,
Default/Foreclosure Counseling

CATHOLIC CHARITIES/CARITAS FAMILY SERVICES
305 North 7th Avenue
Saint Cloud, MN 56303-3633
320-650-1660
Fax: 320-650-1672
Email: Bcorson@gw.stcdio.org
Type of Counseling:
HECM Counseling,
Default/Foreclosure Counseling,
Rental Counseling, Prepurchase
Counseling
Affiliate of: CATHOLIC CHARITIES USA

TRI-COUNTY ACTION PROGRAMS, INCORPORATED
700 W Saint Germain St
Saint Cloud, MN 56301-3507
320-251-1612
Toll-Free: 888-765-5597
Fax: 320-251-6469

Email:
caroleen.boeder@tricap.org
Type of Counseling:
Default/Foreclosure Counseling

**SOUTHWEST MINNESOTA
HOUSING PARTNERSHIP
2401 Broadway Ave, Suite 204
Slayton, MN 56172-1142
507-836-8673
Fax: 507-836-8866
Email: swmhp@rconnect.com
Type of Counseling:
Prepurchase Counseling
Affiliate of: THE HOUSING
PARTNERSHIP NETWORK

SOUTHERN MINNESOTA
REGIONAL LEGAL SERVICES,
INCORPORATED
46 E 4th St 300 Minnesota Bldg
St. Paul, MN 55101-1121
651-222-5863
Fax: 651-297-6457
Type of Counseling:
Default/Foreclosure Counseling,
Rental Counseling, Prepurchase
Counseling

SAINT PAUL HOUSING
INFORMATION CENTER
25 4th St W Room 150 CHA
St. Paul, MN 55102-1634
651-266-6000
Fax: 651-298-5054
Type of Counseling:
Default/Foreclosure Counseling,
Rental Counseling, Prepurchase
Counseling

SAINT PAUL URBAN LEAGUE
401 Selby Ave
St. Paul, MN 55102-1724
651-224-5771
Fax: 651-224-8009
Type of Counseling:
Rental Counseling, Prepurchase
Counseling, Default/Foreclosure
Counseling

**ACORN HOUSING
CORPORATION
Security Building 757 Raymond
Avenue
St. Paul, MN 55114
651-203-0008

Fax: 651-642-0060
Type of Counseling:
Prepurchase Counseling, Rental
Counseling, Default/Foreclosure
Counseling
Affiliate of: ACORN HOUSING
CORPORATION

MINNESOTA HOUSING
FINANCE AGENCY
400 Sibley Street, Suite 300
St. Paul, MN 55101
651-296-7608
Fax: 651-296-8139
Type of Counseling:
Prepurchase Counseling, Rental
Counseling, Default/Foreclosure
Counseling

**HOME OWNERSHIP
CENTER
1885 University Ave W Ste 350
St. Paul, MN 55104-3403
651-659-9336
Fax: 651-659-9518
Email: hocenter@qwest.net
Website: www.hocmn.org
Type of Counseling:
Default/Foreclosure Counseling,
Prepurchase Counseling
Affiliate of: THE HOUSING
PARTNERSHIP NETWORK

**COMMUNITY
NEIGHBORHOOD HOUSING
SERVICES, INCORPORATED
35 W. Water St
St. Paul, MN 55107
651-292-8710
Fax: 651-292-0473
Type of Counseling:
Prepurchase Counseling
Affiliate of: NEIGHBORHOOD
REINVESTMENT
CORPORATION

FAMILY SERVICE,
INCORPORATED SAINT PAUL
166 4th St E Ste 200
St. Paul, MN 55101-1464
651-222-0311
Fax: 651-222-8920
Type of Counseling:
Default/Foreclosure Counseling,
Rental Counseling, Prepurchase
Counseling

**DAYTON'S BLUFF
NEIGHBORHOOD HOUSING
SERVICES, INCORPORATED
823 E 7th St
St. Paul, MN 55106
651-774-6995
Fax: 651-774-0445
Type of Counseling:
Prepurchase Counseling
Affiliate of: NEIGHBORHOOD
REINVESTMENT
CORPORATION

LEGAL AID SERVICE OF
NORTHEASTERN
MINNESOTA IRON RANGE
OFFICE
Olcott Plaza
820 N. 9th St., Suite 150
Virginia, MN 55792
218-749-3270
Fax: 218-749-0706
Type of Counseling:
Default/Foreclosure Counseling,
Rental Counseling

**CONSUMER CREDIT
COUNSELING SERVICE OF
DULUTH
333 Litchfield Avenue SW
Wilmar, MN 56201
320-235-7916
Fax: 320-231-1619
Type of Counseling:
Default/Foreclosure Counseling,
Prepurchase Counseling, Rental
Counseling

Mississippi

**SOUTH MISSISSIPPI LEGAL
SERVICES CORPORATION
202 Fountain Square Building
Suite 203
Biloxi, MS 395331386
228-374-4160
Fax: 228-374-6045
Email: smlsc01@aol.com
Type of Counseling:
Prepurchase Counseling,
Default/Foreclosure Counseling,
Rental Counseling, HECM
Counseling
Affiliate of: WEST TENNESSEE
LEGAL SERVICES,
INCORPORATED

NORTH MISSISSIPPI RURAL
LEGAL SERVICES OF
CLARKSDALE
606 DeSoto Avenue
Clarksdale, MS 38614
662-627-4184
Toll-Free: 800-388-3163
Fax: 662-624-4009
Email: watsa@nmrls.com
Website: www.nmrls.com
Type of Counseling:
Prepurchase Counseling, Rental
Counseling, Default/Foreclosure
Counseling
Affiliate of: WEST TENNESSEE
LEGAL SERVICES,
INCORPORATED

**NORTH MISSISSIPPI RURAL
LEGAL SERVICES
606 Desoto Avenue
Clarksdale, MS 38614-
601-627-4184
Fax: 601-624-4009
Type of Counseling:
Prepurchase Counseling,
Default/Foreclosure Counseling,
Rental Counseling, HECM
Counseling
Affiliate of: WEST TENNESSEE
LEGAL SERVICES,
INCORPORATED

**NORTH MISSISSIPPI RURAL
LEGAL SERVICES
301 Washington Street
Greenville, MS 38701-
601-335-8203
Fax: 601-335-7500
Type of Counseling:
Prepurchase Counseling,
Default/Foreclosure Counseling,
Rental Counseling, HECM
Counseling
Affiliate of: WEST TENNESSEE
LEGAL SERVICES,
INCORPORATED

NORTH MISSISSIPPI RURAL
LEGAL SERVICES OF
GREENVILLE
835 Main Street
Greenville, MS 38701
662-335-8203
Toll-Free: 800-545-1909
Fax: 662-335-7500

Email: watsa@nmrls.com
Website: www.nmrls.com
Type of Counseling:
Prepurchase Counseling, Rental
Counseling, Default/Foreclosure
Counseling
Affiliate of: WEST TENNESSEE
LEGAL SERVICES,
INCORPORATED

GULF COAST COMMUNITY
ACTION AGENCY
500 24th St
Gulfport, MS 39507-1711
228-868-4250
Fax: 228-868-4163
Type of Counseling:
HECM Counseling,
Default/Foreclosure Counseling,
Rental Counseling, Prepurchase
Counseling

**SOUTHEAST MISSISSIPPI
LEGAL SERVICES
CORPORATION
111 East Front Street
Hattiesburg, MS 39403-
601-545-2950
Fax: 601-545-2935
Type of Counseling:
Prepurchase Counseling,
Default/Foreclosure Counseling,
Rental Counseling, HECM
Counseling
Affiliate of: WEST TENNESSEE
LEGAL SERVICES,
INCORPORATED

HOUSING EDUCATION AND
ECONOMIC DEVELOPMENT
3405 Medgar Evers Blvd
Jackson, MS 39213-6360
601-981-1960
Fax: 601-981-0258
Type of Counseling:
HECM Counseling,
Default/Foreclosure Counseling,
Rental Counseling, Prepurchase
Counseling

DIVISION OF AGING AND
ADULT SERVICES
750 N State St
Jackson, MS 39202-
601-359-4366
Fax: 601-359-9664

Email: ELAnderson@
MDHS.State.MS.US
Type of Counseling:
Prepurchase Counseling, Rental
Counseling, Default/Foreclosure
Counseling, HECM Counseling

URBAN LEAGUE OF GREATER
JACKSON
2310 Highway 80 W.,
Bldg. 1, Ste.E
Jackson, MS 39204
601-714-4600
Fax: 601-714-4040
Email: jul@netdoor.com
Type of Counseling:
HECM Counseling,
Default/Foreclosure Counseling,
Rental Counseling, Prepurchase
Counseling
Affiliate of: NATIONAL
URBAN LEAGUE

JACKSON METRO HOUSING
PARTNERSHIP,
INCORPORATED
1217 N. West St
Jackson, MS 39202
601-969-1895
Fax: 601-969-5300
Type of Counseling:
Default/Foreclosure Counseling,
Rental Counseling, Prepurchase
Counseling, HECM Counseling
Affiliate of: THE HOUSING
PARTNERSHIP NETWORK

**CENTRAL MISSISSIPPI
LEGAL SERVICES
PO Box 951
Jackson, MS 392050951
601-948-6752
Fax: 601-948-6757
Email: hn6720@handsnet.org
Type of Counseling:
Prepurchase Counseling,
Default/Foreclosure Counseling,
Rental Counseling, HECM
Counseling
Affiliate of: WEST TENNESSEE
LEGAL SERVICES,
INCORPORATED

MISSISSIPPI CHILDREN'S
HOME SOCIETY AND FAMILY
SERVICES ASSOCIATION

1900 North West St.
Jackson, MS 392021034
601-352-7784
Toll-Free: 800-388-6247
Fax: 601-968-0028
Type of Counseling:
Prepurchase Counseling, HECM
Counseling, Default/Foreclosure
Counseling, Rental Counseling

**SOUTHWEST MISSISSIPPI
LEGAL SERVICES
CORPORATION
221 Main Street
McComb, MS 39649
601-684-0578
Fax: 601-684-0575
Type of Counseling:
Prepurchase Counseling,
Default/Foreclosure Counseling,
Rental Counseling, HECM
Counseling
Affiliate of: WEST TENNESSEE
LEGAL SERVICES,
INCORPORATED

**SOUTHEAST MISSISSIPPI
LEGAL SERVICES
2305 5th St., 2nd Fl.
Meridian, MS 39302
601-693-5470
Fax: 601-693-5473
Type of Counseling:
Prepurchase Counseling,
Default/Foreclosure Counseling,
Rental Counseling, HECM
Counseling
Affiliate of: WEST TENNESSEE
LEGAL SERVICES,
INCORPORATED

**SOUTHWEST MISSISSIPPI
LEGAL SERVICES
CORPORATION
261 D'Evereux Drive Unit 20
Natchez, MS 39121-0427
601-446-7590
Fax: 601-446-7592
Type of Counseling:
Prepurchase Counseling,
Default/Foreclosure Counseling,
Rental Counseling, HECM
Counseling
Affiliate of: WEST TENNESSEE
LEGAL SERVICES,
INCORPORATED

NORTH MISSISSIPPI RURAL
LEGAL SERVICES OF OXFORD
P.O. Box 928
Oxford, MS 38655
662-234-2918
Toll-Free: 800-559-5074
Fax: 662-234-2965
Email: watsa@nmrls.com
Website: www.nmrls.com
Type of Counseling:
Prepurchase Counseling, Rental
Counseling, Default/Foreclosure
Counseling
Affiliate of: WEST TENNESSEE
LEGAL SERVICES,
INCORPORATED

NORTH MISSISSIPPI RURAL
LEGAL SERVICES -
ADMINISTRATIVE OFFICE
2134 West Jackson Avenue
Oxford, MS 38655
662-234-8731
Toll-Free: 800-898-8731
Fax: 662-236-3263
Email: watsa@nmrls.com
Website: www.nmrls.com
Type of Counseling:
Prepurchase Counseling,
Default/Foreclosure Counseling,
Rental Counseling
Affiliate of: WEST TENNESSEE
LEGAL SERVICES,
INCORPORATED

**NORTH MISSISSIPPI RURAL
LEGAL SERVICES
658 W. Main Street
Tupelo, MS 38802
601-842-3702
Fax: 601-840-8060
Type of Counseling:
Prepurchase Counseling,
Default/Foreclosure Counseling,
Rental Counseling, HECM
Counseling
Affiliate of: WEST TENNESSEE
LEGAL SERVICES,
INCORPORATED

NORTH MISSISSIPPI RURAL
LEGAL SERVICES OF TUPELO
658 West Main Street
Tupelo, MS 38802
662-842-3702
Toll-Free: 800-898-3702

Fax: 662-840-8060
Email: watsa@nmrls.com
Website: www.nmrls.com
Type of Counseling:
Prepurchase Counseling, Rental
Counseling, Default/Foreclosure
Counseling
Affiliate of: WEST TENNESSEE
LEGAL SERVICES,
INCORPORATED

**CENTRAL MISSISSIPPI
LEGAL SERVICES
CORPORATION
P.O.Box 52
Vicksburg, MS 39181-052
601-636-8322
Fax: 601-636-8405
Type of Counseling:
Prepurchase Counseling,
Default/Foreclosure Counseling,
Rental Counseling, HECM
Counseling
Affiliate of: WEST TENNESSEE
LEGAL SERVICES,
INCORPORATED

SACRED HEART SOUTHERN
MISSIONS HOUSING
CORPORATION
6144 Highway 161 N
Walls, MS 38680-0365
662-781-1516
Fax: 662-781-3534
Type of Counseling:
Default/Foreclosure Counseling,
Rental Counseling, Prepurchase
Counseling, HECM Counseling

**NORTH MISSISSIPPI RURAL
LEGAL SERVICES
221 Commerce Street
West Point, MS 39773
601-494-6122
Fax: 601-898-6122
Type of Counseling:
Prepurchase Counseling,
Default/Foreclosure Counseling,
Rental Counseling, HECM
Counseling
Affiliate of: WEST TENNESSEE
LEGAL SERVICES,
INCORPORATED

NORTH MISSISSIPPI RURAL
LEGAL SERVICES OF WEST
POINT
221 Commerce Street

West Point, MS 39773
662-494-6122
Toll-Free: 800-898-6122
Fax: 662-494-0670
Email: watsa@nmrls.com
Website: www.nmrls.com
Type of Counseling:
Prepurchase Counseling,
Default/Foreclosure Counseling,
Rental Counseling
Affiliate of: WEST TENNESSEE
LEGAL SERVICES,
INCORPORATED

Missouri

WEST CENTRAL MISSOURI
RURAL COMMUNITY
ACTION AGENCY
106 W 4th St
Appleton City, MO 64724
660-476-2184
Fax: 660-476-2259
Email: wchsghc@iland.net
Type of Counseling:
HECM Counseling,
Default/Foreclosure Counseling,
Rental Counseling, Prepurchase
Counseling

CONSUMER CREDIT
COUNSELING SERVICE -
SAINT LOUIS
1699 Jeffco Boulevard
Arnold, MO 630102281
636-282-2227
Toll-Free: 800-966-3328
Fax: 314-647-1359
Type of Counseling:
Default/Foreclosure Counseling

NORTH EAST COMMUNITY
ACTION CORPORATION
16 North Court Street
Bowling Green, MO 633340470
573-324-2231
Fax: 573-324-6335
Type of Counseling:
Default/Foreclosure Counseling,
Prepurchase Counseling, Rental
Counseling

CONSUMER CREDIT
COUNSELING SERVICE-
SAINT LOUIS
1301 N. Kingshighway, Suite A

Cape Girardeau, MO 63701-
573-334-7050
Toll-Free: 800-966-3328
Fax: 314-647-1359
Type of Counseling:
Default/Foreclosure Counseling

EDUCATION, TRAINING,
RESEARCH, AND
DEVELOPMENT, INC.
608 E. Cherry Street, Suite 103
Columbia, MO 65201
573-442-1122
Toll-Free: 877-355-3135
Fax: 573-443-2677
Type of Counseling:
Prepurchase Counseling

CONSUMER CREDIT
COUNSELING OF MID-
MISSOURI, INCORPORATED
1900 N Providence Ste 301
Columbia, MO 65202
573-449-5199
Toll-Free: 8007360535
Fax: 573-875-4953
Type of Counseling:
HECM Counseling,
Default/Foreclosure Counseling,
Rental Counseling, Prepurchase
Counseling

CONSUMER DEBT
COUNSELING
2401 Bernadette Drive, Suite 115
Columbia, MO 65203
573-234-1851
Toll-Free: 877-786-3328
Fax: 314-647-1359
Type of Counseling:
Default/Foreclosure Counseling

CONSUMER CREDIT
COUNSELING SERVICE-
SAINT LOUIS
400 N. Washington, Suite 118
Farmington, MO 63640
573-760-1510
Toll-Free: 800-966-3328
Fax: 314-647-1359
Type of Counseling:
Default/Foreclosure Counseling

CONSUMER CREDIT
COUNSELING SERVICE-
SAINT LOUIS
493 Rue St., Francois, Suite 6

Florissant, MO 63031
314-830-6464
Toll-Free: 800-966-3328
Fax: 314-647-1359
Type of Counseling:
Default/Foreclosure Counseling

CONSUMER CREDIT
COUNSELING SERVICE -
SAINT LOUIS
2801 St. Mary's Avenue (lower
level)
Hannibal, MO 634014443
573-248-0059
Toll-Free: 800-966-3328
Fax: 314-647-1359
Type of Counseling:
Default/Foreclosure Counseling

COMMUNITY SERVICES
LEAGUE
300 W Maple Ave
Independence, MO 64050-2818
816-254-4100
Fax: 816-252-9906
Type of Counseling:
HECM Counseling,
Default/Foreclosure Counseling,
Rental Counseling, Prepurchase
Counseling

CONSUMER DEBT
COUNSELING
1110 Missouri Blvd.
Jefferson City, MO 65109
573-556-5578
Toll-Free: 877-786-3328
Fax: 314-647-1359
Type of Counseling:
Default/Foreclosure Counseling

CONSUMER CREDIT
COUNSELING SERVICE-
SAINT LOUIS
1288 St. Cyr Road
Jennings, MO 63137
314-867-7049
Toll-Free: 800-966-3328
Fax: 314-647-1359
Type of Counseling:
Default/Foreclosure Counseling

CONSUMER CREDIT
COUNSELING SERVICE OF
GREATER KANSAS CITY
211 West Armour Blvd Ste 304

Kansas City, MO 64111
816-753-0535
Fax: 816-753-3374
Type of Counseling:
Default/Foreclosure Counseling,
Prepurchase Counseling

HOUSING INFORMATION
CENTER
3201 Southwest Trafficway
Kansas City, MO 64108-
816-759-4170
Fax: 816-931-0722
Type of Counseling:
Prepurchase Counseling,
Default/Foreclosure Counseling,
Rental Counseling

**ACORN HOUSING
CORPORATION
3931 Main St Fl 2
Kansas City, MO 64111-1916
816-931-3310
Fax: 816-931-5522
Type of Counseling:
Prepurchase Counseling
Affiliate of: ACORN HOUSING
CORPORATION

HOUSING INFORMATION
CENTER
3810 Paseo Blvd
Kansas City, MO 64109-2721
816-931-0443
Fax: 816-931-0722
Type of Counseling:
Default/Foreclosure Counseling,
Rental Counseling, Prepurchase
Counseling

MISSOURI VALLEY HUMAN
RESOURCE COMMUNITY
ACTION AGENCY
PO Box 550
Marshall, MO 65340-0550
660-886-7476
Fax: 660-886-5868
Type of Counseling:
HECM Counseling,
Default/Foreclosure Counseling,
Rental Counseling, Prepurchase
Counseling

CONSUMER CREDIT
COUNSELING SERVICE-
SAINT LOUIS

2300 West Osage, Suite 1
Pacific, MO 63069
636-257-8186
Toll-Free: 800-966-3328
Fax: 314-647-1359
Type of Counseling:
Default/Foreclosure Counseling

CONSUMER CREDIT
COUNSELING SERVICE-
SAINT LOUIS
3069A N. Westwood Blvd.
Poplar Bluff, MO 639012808
573-686-3323
Toll-Free: 800-966-3328
Fax: 314-647-1359
Type of Counseling:
Default/Foreclosure Counseling

**CATHOLIC CHARITIES-
KANSAS CITY/ST. JOSEPH
426 S. Jefferson, Suite 207
Springfield, MO 65806-
417-865-0050
Fax: 417-865-0070
Email: tonya@infac.com
Affiliate of: CATHOLIC
CHARITIES USA

SOUTHWEST MISSOURI
OFFICE ON AGING
1735 S. Fort
Springfield, MO 65807
417-862-0762
Toll-Free: 800-497-0822
Fax: 417-865-2683
Type of Counseling: HECM
Counseling

CONSUMER CREDIT
COUNSELING SERVICE -
SAINT LOUIS
1600 Heritage Landing, Suite 211
St. Charles, MO 633038442
636-441-9107
Toll-Free: 800-966-3328
Fax: 314-647-1359
Type of Counseling:
Default/Foreclosure Counseling

ECONOMIC OPPORTUNITY
CORPORATION OF GREATER
SAINT JOSEPH
817 Monterey
St. Joseph, MO 64503
816-233-8281

Fax: 816-233-8262
Type of Counseling:
Prepurchase Counseling

**ACORN HOUSING
CORPORATION OF SAINT
LOUIS
4304 Manchester Ave
St. Louis, MO 63110-2138
314-531-6204
Fax: 314-531-4942
Type of Counseling:
Prepurchase Counseling,
Default/Foreclosure Counseling
Affiliate of: ACORN HOUSING
CORPORATION

**CATHOLIC COMMISSION
ON HOUSING
4140 Lindell Blvd
St. Louis, MO 63108-2998
314-371-4980
Fax: 314-371-0058
Type of Counseling:
Default/Foreclosure Counseling,
Prepurchase Counseling
Affiliate of: CATHOLIC
CHARITIES USA

**NEIGHBORHOOD HOUSING
SERVICES OF SAINT LOUIS,
INCORPORATED
4156 Manchester St
St. Louis, MO 63110-3847
314-533-0600
Fax: 314-533-0476
Type of Counseling:
Default/Foreclosure Counseling,
Prepurchase Counseling
Affiliate of: NEIGHBORHOOD
REINVESTMENT
CORPORATION

LEGAL SERVICES OF
EASTERN MISSOURI,
INCORPORATED
4232 Forest Park Ave
St. Louis, MO 63108-2811
314-534-4200
Toll-Free: 800-444-0514
Fax: 314-534-1028
Type of Counseling:
Default/Foreclosure Counseling,
Rental Counseling, Prepurchase
Counseling

A J H HOUSING
INCORPORATED
4545 Gravois Ave
St. Louis, MO 63116
314-352-7248
Fax: 314-352-3444
Type of Counseling:
Prepurchase Counseling

URBAN LEAGUE OF
METROPOLITAN SAINT
LOUIS
3701 Grandel Sq
St. Louis, MO 63108-3627
314-615-3600
Fax: 314-615-3611
Type of Counseling:
Default/Foreclosure Counseling,
Rental Counseling, Prepurchase
Counseling

BETTER FAMILY LIFE, INC.
1017 Olive, 6th Floor
St. Louis, MO 63101
314-241-8704
Fax: 314-241-1277
Type of Counseling:
Prepurchase Counseling, Rental
Counseling, Default/Foreclosure
Counseling

JUSTINE PETERSEN HOUSING
AND REINVESTMENT
CORPORATION
5031 Northrup
St. Louis, MO 63110
314-664-5051
Fax: 314-664-5364
Email:
sflanigan@justinepetersen.org
Type of Counseling:
Default/Foreclosure Counseling,
Prepurchase Counseling, Rental
Counseling

ST. LOUIS REINVESTMENT
CORPORATION
55 Plaza Square, Suite 202
St. Louis, MO 63103
314-588-9334
Fax: 314-588-9354
Type of Counseling:
Default/Foreclosure Counseling,
Prepurchase Counseling

CONSUMER CREDIT
COUNSELING SERVICE
1300 Hampton Ave at West Park
St. Louis, MO 63139-8901
314-647-9004
Toll-Free: 800-966-3328
Fax: 314-647-1359
Type of Counseling:
Default/Foreclosure Counseling

HOUSING OPTIONS
PROVIDED FOR THE ELDERLY
4265 Shaw Blvd
St. Louis, MO 63110-3526
314-776-0155
Fax: 314-776-0852
Type of Counseling: HECM
Counseling

URBAN LEAGUE OF
METROPOLITAN SAINT
LOUIS
9860 Jennings Station Road
St. Louis, MO 63136-1413
314-388-9840
Fax: 314-389-9845
Type of Counseling:
Default/Foreclosure Counseling,
Rental Counseling, Prepurchase
Counseling

BETTER FAMILY LIFE, INC.
724 North Union Boulevard,
Suite 301
St. Louis, MO 63108
314-367-3440
Fax: 314-367-1414
Type of Counseling:
Prepurchase Counseling, Rental
Counseling, Default/Foreclosure
Counseling

MONTANA

DISTRICT 7 HUMAN
RESOURCES DEVELOPMENT
COUNCIL
7 N 31 St
Billings, MT 59103
406-247-4736
Toll-Free: 800-433-1411
Fax: 406-248-2943

Type of Counseling:
HECM Counseling,
Default/Foreclosure Counseling,
Rental Counseling, Prepurchase
Counseling

**NEIGHBORHOOD HOUSING
SERVICES OF GREAT FALLS,
INCORPORATED
509 First Avenue, South
Great Falls, MT 59401
406-761-5861
Fax: 406-761-5852
Type of Counseling:
Prepurchase Counseling,
Default/Foreclosure Counseling
Affiliate of: NEIGHBORHOOD
REINVESTMENT
CORPORATION

HELENA HOUSING
AUTHORITY
812 Abbey St
Helena, MT 59601-7924
406-443-8211
Fax: 406-442-0574
Type of Counseling:
HECM Counseling,
Default/Foreclosure Counseling,
Rental Counseling, Prepurchase
Counseling

NORTH WEST MONTANA
HUMAN RESOURCES
214 Main St
Kalispell, MT 59904-1300
406-752-6565
Toll-Free: 800-344-5979
Fax: 406-752-6582
Type of Counseling:
HECM Counseling,
Default/Foreclosure Counseling,
Rental Counseling, Prepurchase
Counseling

WOMEN'S OPPORTUNITY
RESOURCE DEVELOPMENT,
INCORPORATED
127 N Higgins Ave, Room 307
Missoula, MT 59802-4457
406-543-3550
Fax: 406-721-4584
Type of Counseling:
Default/Foreclosure Counseling,
Rental Counseling, Prepurchase
Counseling, HECM Counseling

Nebraska

HIGH PLAINS COMMUNITY DEVELOPMENT CORPORATION
130 E. 2nd Street
Chadron, NE 69337
308-432-4346
Fax: 308-432-4655
Type of Counseling:
Default/Foreclosure Counseling,
Prepurchase Counseling, Rental
Counseling

**CONSUMER CREDIT COUNSELING OF NEBRASKA
2121 North Webb Road, Suite
307
Grand Island, NE 68802
308-381-4551
Fax: 308-381-1434
Type of Counseling:
HECM Counseling,
Default/Foreclosure Counseling,
Prepurchase Counseling, Rental
Counseling

**CONSUMER CREDIT COUNSELING SERVICE OF NEBRASKA
1001 S. 70th Street, Suite 200
Lincoln, NE 68505
402-484-7200
Fax: 402-484-7332
Type of Counseling:
HECM Counseling,
Default/Foreclosure Counseling,
Prepurchase Counseling, Rental
Counseling

**NEIGHBORHOOD HOUSING SERVICES OF LINCOLN, INCORPORATED
2121 N 27th St
Lincoln, NE 68503
402-477-7181
Fax: 402-477-7406
Type of Counseling:
Prepurchase Counseling
Affiliate of: NEIGHBORHOOD
REINVESTMENT
CORPORATION

LINCOLN ACTION PROGRAM, INCORPORATED
210 O Street

Lincoln, NE 68508
402-416-6970
Fax: 402-471-4844
Type of Counseling:
HECM Counseling,
Default/Foreclosure Counseling,
Rental Counseling, Prepurchase
Counseling

**CONSUMER CREDIT COUNSELING SERVICE OF NEBRASKA
125 S. 4th Street, Suite 213
Norfolk, NE 68701
402-371-4656
Fax: 402-371-7462
Type of Counseling:
HECM Counseling,
Default/Foreclosure Counseling,
Prepurchase Counseling, Rental
Counseling

NORTHERN PONCA HOUSING AUTHORITY
1501 Michigan Ave.
Norfolk, NE 68701
402-379-8224
Fax: 402-379-8557
Type of Counseling:
Prepurchase Counseling,
Default/Foreclosure Counseling,
Rental Counseling

**CONSUMER CREDIT COUNSELING SERVICE OF NEBRASKA
509 East Fourth Street, Suite F
North Platte, NE 69103
308-532-9760
Fax: 308-532-9439
Type of Counseling:
HECM Counseling,
Default/Foreclosure Counseling,
Prepurchase Counseling, Rental
Counseling

FAMILY HOUSING ADVISORY SERVICES, INCORPORATED
3605 Q Street
Omaha, NE 68107
402-546-1013
Fax: 402-734-8887
Email: fhc_is@fhasinc.org
Website: www.fhasinc.org
Type of Counseling: Rental
Counseling

**CONSUMER CREDIT COUNSELING SERVICE OF NEBRASKA
10843 Old Mill Rd Ste 401
Omaha, NE 68154
402-333-2227
Fax: 402-333-8443
Type of Counseling:
Default/Foreclosure Counseling,
Rental Counseling, HECM
Counseling, Prepurchase
Counseling
Affiliate of: NATIONAL
FOUNDATION FOR
CONSUMER CREDIT,
INCORPORATED

**MMMBC DEVELOPMENT CORPORATION
3223 North 45th St.
Omaha, NE 681043711
402-457-7811
Fax: 402-457-7814
Type of Counseling:
Prepurchase Counseling
Affiliate of: CONGRESS OF
NATIONAL BLACK
CHURCHES, INCORPORATED

FAMILY HOUSING ADVISORY SERVICES, INCORPORATED
2416 Lake St
Omaha, NE 68111-3831
402-934-7921
Fax: 402-934-7928
Email: fhc_is@fhasinc.org
Website: www.fhasinc.org
Type of Counseling:
HECM Counseling,
Default/Foreclosure Counseling,
Rental Counseling, Prepurchase
Counseling

FAMILY HOUSING ADVISORY SERVICES, INCORPORATED
2505 N. 24th Street, Suite 219
Omaha, NE 68110
402-934-6675
Fax: 402-934-7928
Email: fhc_is@fhasinc.org
Website: www.fhasinc.org
Type of Counseling:
HECM Counseling,
Default/Foreclosure Counseling,
Rental Counseling, Prepurchase
Counseling

Nevada

CITIZENS FOR AFFORDABLE
HOMES, INCORPORATED
308 N Curry St Ste 210
Carson City, NV 89703
775-883-7101
Fax: 775-883-7115
Type of Counseling:
Default/Foreclosure Counseling,
Rental Counseling, Prepurchase
Counseling

CONSUMER CREDIT
COUNSELING SERVICE OF
NORTHERN NEVADA
625 Fairview Ste 123
Carson City, NV 89701
702-887-1442
Fax: 702-887-0407
Type of Counseling:
Default/Foreclosure Counseling,
Rental Counseling, Prepurchase
Counseling

CONSUMER CREDIT
COUNSELING SERVICE OF
NORTHERN NEVADA
368 7th St
Elko, NV 89801
775-753-4966
Fax: 775-753-4050
Type of Counseling:
Default/Foreclosure Counseling,
Rental Counseling, Prepurchase
Counseling

CONSUMER CREDIT
COUNSELING SERVICE OF SO.
NEVADA
2920 N. Green Valley Parkway
Henderson, NV 89014
702-364-0344
Fax: 702-364-0773
Email: cccsnv@aol.com
Website: www.cccsnevada.com
Type of Counseling:
HECM Counseling,
Default/Foreclosure Counseling,
Prepurchase Counseling, Rental
Counseling

CONSUMER CREDIT
COUNSELING OF SO.
NEVADA
Nellis Air Force Base, NV

Las Vegas, NV 89119
702-364-0344
Fax: 702-364-0773
Email: cccsnv@aol.com
Website: www.cccsnevada.org
Type of Counseling:
HECM Counseling,
Default/Foreclosure Counseling,
Prepurchase Counseling, Rental
Counseling

**LIVING WORD AMEZ
5240 Ferrell Mountain Court
Las Vegas, NV 89031
702-631-0098
Fax: 702-631-0098
Type of Counseling:
Prepurchase Counseling
Affiliate of: CONGRESS OF
NATIONAL BLACK
CHURCHES, INCORPORATED

COMMUNITY DEVELOPMENT
PROGRAMS CENTER OF
NEVADA
2009 Alta Drive
Las Vegas, NV 89106
702-873-8882
Fax: 702-873-8942
Email:
dora_d_lagrande@hotmail.com
Type of Counseling:
Prepurchase Counseling

WOMEN'S DEVELOPMENT
CENTER
953 E Sahara Ave Ste 201
Las Vegas, NV 89104-3016
702-796-7770
Fax: 702-796-3007
Type of Counseling:
Rental Counseling, Prepurchase
Counseling

ECONOMIC OPPORTUNITY
BOARD OF CLARK COUNTY
3674 N Rancho Dr Ste 32
Las Vegas, NV 89130
702-647-7816
Fax: 702-647-3125
Type of Counseling:
Default/Foreclosure Counseling,
HECM Counseling

CONSUMER CREDIT
COUNSELING SERVICE OF
SOUTHERN NEVADA
3650 S Decatur Blvd.

Suite 30
Las Vegas, NV 89103-5864
702-364-0344
Fax: 702-364-0773
Email: cccsnv@aol.com
Website: www.cccsnevada.com
Type of Counseling:
HECM Counseling,
Default/Foreclosure Counseling,
Rental Counseling, Prepurchase
Counseling

CONSUMER CREDIT
COUNSELING OF SO.
NEVADA
2290 McDaniel
N. Las Vegas, NV 89030
702-364-0344
Fax: 702-364-0773
Email: cccsnv@aol.com
Website: www.cccsnevada.org
Type of Counseling:
HECM Counseling,
Default/Foreclosure Counseling,
Prepurchase Counseling, Rental
Counseling

CONSUMER CREDIT
COUNSELING OF SOUTH
NEVADA
3100 Mill Street, Ste.111
Reno, NV 89502
775-337-6363
Fax: 775-337-6679
Email: cccsnv@aol.com
Website: www.cccsnevada.org
Type of Counseling:
HECM Counseling,
Default/Foreclosure Counseling,
Prepurchase Counseling, Rental
Counseling

WASHOE LEGAL SERVICES
650 Tahoe St
Reno, NV 89509-1721
775-329-2727
Fax: 775-324-5509
Website:
www.washoelegalservices.org
Type of Counseling:
HECM Counseling,
Default/Foreclosure Counseling,
Rental Counseling, Prepurchase
Counseling

WASHOE COUNTY SENIOR
LAW PROJECT
1155 E Ninth St
Reno, NV 89512
775-328-2592
Fax: 775-328-6193
Type of Counseling:
HECM Counseling,
Default/Foreclosure Counseling,
Rental Counseling

CONSUMER CREDIT
COUNSELING SERVICE OF
NORTHERN NEVADA
575 E Plumb Lane, Suite 101
Reno, NV 89502-3540
775-322-6557
Toll-Free: 888-298-9622
Fax: 775-322-2059
Website: www.vrpr.com/fcs/
Type of Counseling:
Default/Foreclosure Counseling,
Rental Counseling, Prepurchase
Counseling

New Hampshire

TRI-COUNTY CAP
30 Exchange Street
Berlin, NH 03570-
603-536-1911
Toll-Free: 800-552-4617
Fax: 603-536-8222
Type of Counseling:
Prepurchase Counseling,
Default/Foreclosure Counseling,
Rental Counseling

NEW HAMPSHIRE HOUSING
FINANCE AUTHORITY
P. O. Box 5087
Manchester, NH 03108
603-472-8623
Fax: 603-472-2663
Type of Counseling:
Prepurchase Counseling, HECM
Counseling

**MANCHESTER
NEIGHBORHOOD HOUSING
SERVICES, INCORPORATED
969 Elm Street
Manchester, NH 03103
603-626-4663
Fax: 603-623-8011
Email: john@mnhs.net

Type of Counseling:
Prepurchase Counseling,
Default/Foreclosure Counseling
Affiliate of: NEIGHBORHOOD
REINVESTMENT
CORPORATION

THE WAY HOME
214 Spruce Street
Manchester, NH 03103-
603-627-3491
Fax: 603-644-7949
Type of Counseling: Rental
Counseling

NEIGHBORHOOD HOUSING
SERVICES OF GREATER
NASHUA, INCORPORATED
50 Tolles St
Nashua, NH 03060
603-882-2077
Fax: 603-881-9894
Email: fhnhs@ix.netcom.com
Type of Counseling:
Default/Foreclosure Counseling,
Prepurchase Counseling

New Jersey

FAMILY
SERVICE/CONSUMER CREDIT
COUNSELING SERVICE
312 E White Horse Pike
Absecon, NJ 08201
800-473-2227
Toll-Free: 800-473-2227
Fax: 609-748-1498
Website: www.aclink.crg.fsa.htm
Type of Counseling:
HECM Counseling,
Default/Foreclosure Counseling,
Rental Counseling
Affiliate of: NATIONAL
FOUNDATION FOR
CONSUMER CREDIT,
INCORPORATED

CHECK MATE
INCORPORATED
550 Cookman Ave
Asbury Park, NJ 07712-7120
732-774-3100
Fax: 732-774-3220
Email:
KEVIN@BEONLINE.COM
Type of Counseling:

Default/Foreclosure Counseling,
Rental Counseling, Prepurchase
Counseling

NEW JERSEY CITIZEN
ACTION
1 Municipal Plaza
Asbury Park, NJ 07712
800-656-9637
Toll-Free: 800-656-9637
Fax: 732-714-5386
Email:
jennifer@njcitizenaction.org
Website:
www.njcitizenaction.org
Type of Counseling:
HECM Counseling,
Default/Foreclosure Counseling,
Rental Counseling, Prepurchase
Counseling

FAMILY SERVICE
ASSOCIATION/CONSUMER
CREDIT COUNSELING
SERVICES OF SOUTH JERSEY
1 S. New York Avenue
Atlantic City, NJ 08401
609-569-0239
Toll-Free: 800-473-2227
Fax: 609-569-1752
Type of Counseling:
Default/Foreclosure Counseling,
Prepurchase Counseling, Rental
Counseling
Affiliate of: NATIONAL
FOUNDATION FOR
CONSUMER CREDIT,
INCORPORATED

ATLANTIC HUMAN
RESOURCES, INCORPORATED
1 S New York Ave Ste 303
Atlantic City, NJ 08401-8012
609-348-4131
Fax: 609-345-5750
Type of Counseling:
HECM Counseling,
Default/Foreclosure Counseling,
Rental Counseling, Prepurchase
Counseling

BAYONNE ECONOMIC
OPPORTUNITY FOUNDATION
555 Kennedy Blvd
Bayonne, NJ 07002-2627
201-437-7222

Fax: 201-437-2810
Type of Counseling:
Rental Counseling, Prepurchase
Counseling

FAMILY SERVICE
ASSOCIATION/CONSUMER
CREDIT COUNSELING
SERVICES OF SOUTH JERSEY
150 S. WHP, Hudson Savings
Bank
Berlin, NJ
609-569-0239
Toll-Free: 800-473-2227
Fax: 609-569-1752
Type of Counseling:
Default/Foreclosure Counseling,
Prepurchase Counseling, Rental
Counseling
Affiliate of: NATIONAL
FOUNDATION FOR
CONSUMER CREDIT,
INCORPORATED

JERSEY COUNSELING AND
HOUSING DEVELOPMENT,
INCORPORATED
29 S Black Horse Pike
Blackwood, NJ 08012-2952
856-227-3683
Fax: 856-228-0662
Type of Counseling:
HECM Counseling,
Default/Foreclosure Counseling,
Rental Counseling, Prepurchase
Counseling

TRI-COUNTY COMMUNITY
ACTION AGENCY
110 Cohansey St.
Bridgeton, NJ 08302
856-453-0803
Fax: 856-455-7288
Type of Counseling:
HECM Counseling, Prepurchase
Counseling, Default/Foreclosure
Counseling, Rental Counseling

CATHOLIC CHARITIES OF
THE DIOCESE OF METUCHEN
540-550 Route 22 East
Bridgewater, NJ 08807
908-722-1881
Fax: 908-704-0215
Type of Counseling:

Default/Foreclosure Counseling,
Rental Counseling, Prepurchase
Counseling

BURLINGTON COUNTY
COMMUNITY ACTION
PROGRAM
718 Rt. 130 S.
Burlington, NJ 08016
609-386-5800
Fax: 609-386-7380
Type of Counseling:
Prepurchase Counseling,
Default/Foreclosure Counseling,
Rental Counseling

JERSEY COUNSELING AND
HOUSING DEVELOPMENT,
INCORPORATED
1840 S Broadway
Camden, NJ 08104-1334
856-541-1000
Fax: 856-541-8836
Type of Counseling:
HECM Counseling,
Default/Foreclosure Counseling,
Rental Counseling, Prepurchase
Counseling

**NEIGHBORHOOD HOUSING
SERVICES OF CAMDEN,
INCORPORATED
601 Clinton St
Camden, NJ 08103-1415
856-541-0720
Fax: 856-541-8440
Type of Counseling:
Prepurchase Counseling,
Default/Foreclosure Counseling,
HECM Counseling, Rental
Counseling

NEW JERSEY CITIZEN
ACTION
527 Cooper St
Camden, NJ 08102-1210
800-656-9637
Toll-Free: 800-656-9637
Fax: 732-714-5386
Email:
Jennifer@njcitizenaction.org
Website:
www.njcitizenaction.org
Type of Counseling:
HECM Counseling,
Default/Foreclosure Counseling,

Rental Counseling, Prepurchase
Counseling

**CENTER FOR FAMILY
SERVICES
584 Benson Street
Camden, NJ 08103
856-964-9508
Fax: 856-964-0242
Type of Counseling:
Prepurchase Counseling,
Default/Foreclosure Counseling,
Rental Counseling
Affiliate of: HOUSING
OPPORTUNITIES,
INCORPORATED

FAMILY SERVICES
ASSOCIATION/CONSUMER
CREDIT COUNSELING
SERVICE
217 N. Main St., Ste. 201, 2nd
floor
Cape May Court House, NJ
08210-2191
800-473-2227
Toll-Free: 800-473-2227
Fax: 609-569-1752
Type of Counseling:
HECM Counseling,
Default/Foreclosure Counseling,
Rental Counseling, Prepurchase
Counseling
Affiliate of: NATIONAL
FOUNDATION FOR
CONSUMER CREDIT,
INCORPORATED

CONSUMER CREDIT
COUNSELING SERVICE OF
NEW JERSEY
185 Ridgedale Ave.
Cedar Knolls, NJ 07927
973-264-4324
Toll-Free: 888-726-3260
Fax: 973-267-0484
Website: www.cccsnj.com
Type of Counseling:
HECM Counseling,
Default/Foreclosure Counseling,
Prepurchase Counseling

NEW JERSEY CITIZEN ACTON
556 Haddon Ave
Collingswood, NJ 08108-1444
800-656-9637

Toll-Free: 800-656-9637
Fax: 732-714-5386
Email:
Jennifer@njcitizenaction.org
Website:
www.njcitizenaction.org
Type of Counseling:
HECM Counseling,
Default/Foreclosure Counseling,
Rental Counseling, Prepurchase
Counseling

FAMILY SERVICE
ASSOCIATION/CONSUMER
CREDIT COUNSELING
SERVICES OF SOUTH JERSEY
1675 Clemens Bridge Road, First
Union Bank
Deptford, NJ 08096-
609-569-0239
Toll-Free: 800-473-2227
Fax: 609-569-1752
Type of Counseling:
Default/Foreclosure Counseling,
Prepurchase Counseling, Rental
Counseling
Affiliate of: NATIONAL
FOUNDATION FOR
CONSUMER CREDIT,
INCORPORATED

HOUSING PARTNERSHIP FOR
MORRIS COUNTY
2 E. Blackwell St. Ste 29
Dover, NJ 07801
973-659-9222
Fax: 973-659-9220
Type of Counseling:
Prepurchase Counseling, Rental
Counseling

**YES LORD COMMUNITY
DEVELOPMENT
CORPORATION
10 South Oraton Pkwy.
East Orange, NJ 07018
973-399-0416
Fax: 973-399-0416
Type of Counseling:
Prepurchase Counseling, Rental
Counseling, Default/Foreclosure
Counseling
Affiliate of: CONGRESS OF
NATIONAL BLACK
CHURCHES, INCORPORATED

FAMILY SERVICE
ASSOCIATION/CONSUMER
CREDIT COUNSELING
SERVICES OF SOUTH JERSEY
3073 English Creek Avenue Ste 3
Egg Harbor TWP, NJ 08234-
609-569-0239
Toll-Free: 800-473-2227
Fax: 609-569-1752
Type of Counseling:
Default/Foreclosure Counseling,
Prepurchase Counseling, Rental
Counseling
Affiliate of: NATIONAL
FOUNDATION FOR
CONSUMER CREDIT,
INCORPORATED

COMMUNITY ACCESS
UNLIMITED
80 West Grand Avenue
Elizabeth, NJ 07202-
908-354-3040
Fax: 908-354-2665
Type of Counseling:
Prepurchase Counseling, Rental
Counseling, HECM Counseling,
Default/Foreclosure Counseling

URBAN LEAGUE OF UNION
COUNTY
288 N Broad St
Elizabeth, NJ 07208-3789
908-351-7200
Fax: 908-527-9881
Type of Counseling:
HECM Counseling,
Default/Foreclosure Counseling,
Rental Counseling, Prepurchase
Counseling

URBAN LEAGUE FOR
BERGEN COUNTY
106 W Palisade Ave
Englewood, NJ 07631-2619
201-568-4988
Fax: 201-568-3192
Type of Counseling:
HECM Counseling,
Default/Foreclosure Counseling,
Prepurchase Counseling

MONMOUTH COUNTY
DIVISION OF SOCIAL
SERVICES
Kozloski Road

Freehold, NJ 07728
732-845-2071
Fax: 732-577-6605
Type of Counseling:
HECM Counseling,
Default/Foreclosure Counseling,
Rental Counseling, Prepurchase
Counseling

FAIR HOUSING COUNCIL OF
NORTHERN NEW JERSEY
131 Main St, Suite 140
Hackensack, NJ 07601-7140
201-489-3552
Fax: 201-489-8472
Email: fhcnnj@bellatlantic.net
Type of Counseling:
Default/Foreclosure Counseling,
Rental Counseling, Prepurchase
Counseling

COUNTY OF BERGEN,
DEPARTMENT OF HUMAN
SERVICES
21 Main St Rm 109W
Hackensack, NJ 07601-7021
201-336-7575
Fax: 201-336-7450
Type of Counseling:
HECM Counseling

NEW JERSEY CITIZEN
ACTION
400 Main St
Hackensack, NJ 07601-5903
800-656-9637
Toll-Free: 800-656-9637
Fax: 732-714-5386
Email:
jennifer@njcitizenaction.org
Website:
www.njcitizenaction.org
Type of Counseling:
HECM Counseling,
Default/Foreclosure Counseling,
Rental Counseling, Prepurchase
Counseling

CONSUMER CREDIT
COUNSELING SERVICE OF
NEW JERSEY
Airport 17 Office Center 377
Route 17 South Room 108
Hasbrouck Heights, NJ 07604
973-267-4324
Toll-Free: 888-726-3260

Fax: 973-267-0484
Type of Counseling:
HECM Counseling,
Default/Foreclosure Counseling,
Prepurchase Counseling

NEW JERSEY CITIZEN
ACTION
85 Raritan Ave Ste 100
Highland Park, NJ 08904
800-656-9637
Toll-Free: 800-656-9637
Fax: 732-714-5386
Email:
Jennifer@njcitizenaction.org
Website:
www.njcitizenaction.org
Type of Counseling:
HECM Counseling,
Default/Foreclosure Counseling,
Rental Counseling, Prepurchase
Counseling

NEW JERSEY CITIZEN
ACTION
583 Newark Ave. 2nd Floor
Jersey City, NJ 07306-4551
800-656-9637
Toll-Free: 800-656-9637
Fax: 732-714-5386
Email:
Jennifer@njcitizenaction.org
Website:
www.njcitizenaction.org
Type of Counseling:
HECM Counseling,
Default/Foreclosure Counseling,
Rental Counseling, Prepurchase
Counseling

**ACORN HOUSING
CORPORATION
22 Journal Square, 3rd Fl.
Jersey City, NJ 07306-4307
201-222-7741
Fax: 201-222-1199
Type of Counseling:
Default/Foreclosure Counseling,
Rental Counseling, Prepurchase
Counseling
Affiliate of: ACORN HOUSING
CORPORATION

NEW JERSEY CITIZEN
ACTION
213 Broadway

Long Branch, NJ 07740-7005
800-656-9637
Toll-Free: 800-656-9637
Fax: 732-714-5386
Email:
Jennifer@njcitizenaction.org
Website:
www.njcitizenaction.org
Type of Counseling:
HECM Counseling,
Default/Foreclosure Counseling,
Rental Counseling, Prepurchase
Counseling

CONSUMER CREDIT
COUNSELING SERVICE OF
NEW JERSEY
479 Route 17 North-Constantine
Rd. 2nd Floor
Mahwah, NJ 07430
973-267-4324
Toll-Free: 888-726-3260
Fax: 973-267-0484
Type of Counseling:
Default/Foreclosure Counseling,
Prepurchase Counseling, HECM
Counseling

CONSUMER CREDIT AND
BUDGET COUNSELING
299 S. Shore Road, Route 9 South
Marmora, NJ 082230866
888-738-8233
Toll-Free: 888-738-8233
Type of Counseling:
HECM Counseling,
Default/Foreclosure Counseling,
Prepurchase Counseling, Rental
Counseling

AFFORDABLE HOMES OF
MILLVILLE ECUMENICAL
511 Buck Street
Millville, NJ 08332
856-293-0100
Fax: 856-293-0101
Email: ahomeinc@juno.com
Type of Counseling:
Prepurchase Counseling,
Default/Foreclosure Counseling

CONSUMER CREDIT
COUNSELING SERVICE OF
NEW JERSEY
484 Bloomfield Avenue
Montclair, NJ 07042

973-267-4324
Toll-Free: 888-726-3260
Fax: 973-267-0484
Type of Counseling:
Default/Foreclosure Counseling,
HECM Counseling, Prepurchase
Counseling

**FAMILY SERVICE LEAGUE,
INC
204 Claremont Avenue
Montclair, NJ 07042-
973-746-0800
Fax: 973-746-2822
Email:
dfann@familyserviceleague.org
Type of Counseling:
Rental Counseling
Affiliate of: HOUSING
OPPORTUNITIES,
INCORPORATED

MORRIS COUNTY FAIR
HOUSING COUNCIL
65 Spring St.
Morristown, NJ 07963-0773
973-538-2975
Fax: 973-292-9392
Type of Counseling:
HECM Counseling, Rental
Counseling, Prepurchase
Counseling

SENIOR CITIZENS UNITED
COMMUNITY SERVICES
146 Black Horse Pike
Mount Ephraim, NJ 08059-2007
856-456-1121
Fax: 856-456-1076
Type of Counseling:
HECM Counseling

CONSUMER CREDIT
COUNSELING SERVICE OF
NEW JERSEY
374 Livingston Avenue
New Brunswick, NJ 08901
973-267-4324
Toll-Free: 888-726-3260
Fax: 973-267-0484
Type of Counseling:
Default/Foreclosure Counseling,
Prepurchase Counseling, HECM
Counseling

HOUSING COALITION OF
CENTRAL JERSEY
78 New St
New Brunswick, NJ 08901-2502
732-249-9700
Fax: 732-249-4121
Type of Counseling:
HECM Counseling, Rental
Counseling, Prepurchase
Counseling, Default/Foreclosure
Counseling

NEW JERSEY CITIZEN
ACTION
432 Lafayette St
Newark, NJ 07105-2704
800-656-9637
Toll-Free: 800-656-9637
Fax: 732-714-5386
Email:
Jennifer@njcitizenaction.org
Website:
www.njcitizenaction.org
Type of Counseling:
HECM Counseling,
Default/Foreclosure Counseling,
Rental Counseling, Prepurchase
Counseling

URBAN LEAGUE OF ESSEX
COUNTY
508 Central Ave
Newark, NJ 07107
973-624-9535
Fax: 973-624-1103
Type of Counseling:
HECM Counseling, Prepurchase
Counseling

NEW JERSEY CITIZEN
ACTION
346 Mount Prospect Ave
Newark, NJ 07104-2106
800-656-9637
Toll-Free: 800-656-9637
Fax: 732-714-5386
Email:
Jennifer@njcitizenaction.org
Website:
www.njcitizenaction.org
Type of Counseling:
HECM Counseling,
Default/Foreclosure Counseling,
Rental Counseling, Prepurchase
Counseling

**CATHOLIC COMMUNITY
SERVICES- DOMUS
CORPORATION
494 Broad Street, 5th Fl.
Newark, NJ 07102
973-596-5117
Fax: 973-424-9596
Email:
catherinedaly@ccsnewark.org
Type of Counseling:
Default/Foreclosure Counseling,
Prepurchase Counseling, Rental
Counseling, HECM Counseling
Affiliate of: CATHOLIC
CHARITIES USA

ST. JAMES COMMUNITY
DEVELOPMENT
CORPORATION
260 Broadway, Suite 300
Newark, NJ 07104
973-482-5700
Fax: 973-482-0176
Type of Counseling:
Prepurchase Counseling, Rental
Counseling, Default/Foreclosure
Counseling

MIDDLESEX COUNTY
ECONOMIC OPPORTUNITIES
CORPORATION
1215 Livingston Avenue
North Brunswick, NJ 08902
732-846-6600
Fax: 732-846-3728
Type of Counseling:
Prepurchase Counseling,
Default/Foreclosure Counseling,
Rental Counseling, HECM
Counseling

ATLANTIC COUNTY
INTERGENERATIONAL
SERVICES
101 S Shore Rd Shoreview Bldg
Northfield, NJ 08225
609-645-7700
Fax: 609-645-5907
Type of Counseling:
HECM Counseling

NEW JERSEY CITIZEN
ACTION
336 Oakwood Ave
Orange, NJ 07050-3223
800-656-9637

Toll-Free: 800-656-9637
Fax: 732-714-5386
Email:
Jennifer@njcitizenaction.org
Website:
www.njcitizenaction.org
Type of Counseling:
HECM Counseling,
Default/Foreclosure Counseling,
Rental Counseling, Prepurchase
Counseling

**CHILDREN'S AID AND
FAMILY SERVICES, INC
200 Robin Road
Paramus, NJ 07652
201-261-2800
Fax: 201-261-6013
Type of Counseling:
Rental Counseling
Affiliate of: HOUSING
OPPORTUNITIES,
INCORPORATED

NEW JERSEY CITIZEN
ACTION
128 Market St.
Passaic, NJ 07055
800-656-9637
Toll-Free: 800-656-9637
Fax: 732-714-5386
Email:
jennifer@njcitizenaction.org
Website:
www.njcitizenaction.org
Type of Counseling:
HECM Counseling,
Default/Foreclosure Counseling,
Rental Counseling, Prepurchase
Counseling

PATTERSON HOUSING
AUTHORITY
60 Van Houten Street
Paterson, NJ 07505
973-345-5650
Fax: 973-977-9085
Type of Counseling:
Prepurchase Counseling

NEW JERSEY CITIZEN
ACTION
90 Martin St
Paterson, NJ 07501-3622
800-656-9637
Toll-Free: 800-656-9637

Fax: 732-714-5386
Email:
Jennifer@njcitizenaction.org
Website:
www.njcitizenaction.org
Type of Counseling:
HECM Counseling,
Default/Foreclosure Counseling,
Rental Counseling, Prepurchase
Counseling

PATERSON TASK FORCE FOR
COMMUNITY ACTION,
INCORPORATED
155 Ellison St
Paterson, NJ 07505-1304
973-279-2333
Fax: 973-279-2334
Type of Counseling:
HECM Counseling,
Default/Foreclosure Counseling,
Rental Counseling, Prepurchase
Counseling

PATERSON COALITION FOR
HOUSING, INCORPORATED
262 Main St, 5th floor
Paterson, NJ 07505-1704
973-684-5911
Fax: 973-684-7538
Type of Counseling:
Rental Counseling, Prepurchase
Counseling, HECM Counseling,
Default/Foreclosure Counseling

NEW JERSEY CITIZEN
ACTION
280 McClellan St
Perth Amboy, NJ 08861-4320
800-656-9637
Toll-Free: 800-656-9637
Fax: 732-714-5386
Email:
Jennifer@njcitizenaction.org
Website:
www.njcitizenaction.org
Type of Counseling:
HECM Counseling,
Default/Foreclosure Counseling,
Rental Counseling, Prepurchase
Counseling

NORTH WEST NEW JERSEY
COMMUNITY ACTION
PROGRAM
350 Marshall St.

Phillipsburg, NJ 08865
908-454-7000
Toll-Free: 888-454-4778
Fax: 908-454-3768
Type of Counseling:
HECM Counseling

NORTH STELTON ECONOMIC
DEVELOPMENT
CORPORATION
6 Ethel Road
Piscataway, NJ 088550756
732-287-6111
Fax: 732-287-0828
Type of Counseling:
Rental Counseling, Prepurchase
Counseling, Default/Foreclosure
Counseling, HECM Counseling

CITY OF PLAINFIELD
DIVISION OF PLANNING
AND COMMUNITY
DEVELOPMENT
515 Watchung Ave
Plainfield, NJ 07060-1720
908-753-3377
Fax: 908-753-3500
Type of Counseling:
Prepurchase Counseling

NEW JERSEY CITIZEN
ACTION
1613 Beaver Dam Road, Suite 1
Point Pleasant, NJ 08742
800-656-9637
Toll-Free: 800-656-9637
Fax: 732-714-5386
Email:
jennifer@njcitizenaction.org
Website:
www.njcitizenaction.org
Type of Counseling:
HECM Counseling,
Default/Foreclosure Counseling,
Rental Counseling, Prepurchase
Counseling

CONSUMER CREDIT
COUNSELING SERVICE OF
NEW JERSEY
148 Prospect Street
Ridgewood, NJ 07450
973-267-4324
Toll-Free: 888-726-3260
Fax: 973-267-0484
Type of Counseling:

Default/Foreclosure Counseling,
Prepurchase Counseling, HECM
Counseling

CONSUMER CREDIT
COUNSELING SERVICE OF
NEW JERSEY
148 W. Main Street
Somerville, NJ 08876
973-267-4324
Toll-Free: 888-726-3260
Fax: 973-267-0484
Type of Counseling:
Default/Foreclosure Counseling,
Prepurchase Counseling, HECM
Counseling

SOMERSET COUNTY
COALITION ON AFFORDABLE
HOUSING
One W Main St 2nd Fl
Somerville, NJ 08876-2201
908-704-8901
Fax: 908-704-9235
Type of Counseling:
Prepurchase Counseling, HECM
Counseling, Rental Counseling,
Default/Foreclosure Counseling

NEW JERSEY HOUSING
FINANCE AND MORTGAGE
FINANCE AGENCY
63 Clinton Avenue
Trenton, NJ 08650
609-278-7400
Fax: 609-278-1754
Type of Counseling:
Prepurchase Counseling,
Default/Foreclosure Counseling,
Rental Counseling

**NEIGHBORHOOD HOUSING
SERVICES OF TRENTON,
INCORPORATED
1100 West State Street
Trenton, NJ 08618-
609-392-5494
Fax: 609-392-5615
Type of Counseling:
Default/Foreclosure Counseling,
Prepurchase Counseling, HECM
Counseling
Affiliate of: NEIGHBORHOOD
REINVESTMENT
CORPORATION

ISLES, INCORPORATED
10 Wood St
Trenton, NJ 08618-3921
609-393-5656
Fax: 609-393-2124
Type of Counseling:
Prepurchase Counseling

MERCER COUNTY HISPANIC
ASSOCIATION
200 East State Street
Trenton, NJ 08607
609-392-2446
Fax: 609-695-7618
Type of Counseling:
Rental Counseling, Prepurchase
Counseling, HECM Counseling,
Default/Foreclosure Counseling

NEW JERSEY CITIZEN
ACTION
130 Parkway Ave
Trenton, NJ 08618-3010
800-656-9637
Toll-Free: 800-656-9637
Fax: 732-714-5386
Email:
Jennifer@njcitizenaction.org
Website:
www.njcitizenaction.org
Type of Counseling:
HECM Counseling,
Default/Foreclosure Counseling,
Rental Counseling, Prepurchase
Counseling

FAMILY SERVICE
ASSOCIATION/CONSUMER
CREDIT COUNSELING
SERVICES OF SOUTH JERSEY
5581 Route 42, Plaza Office
Center Unit #6
Turnersville, NJ 08012-
609-569-0239
Toll-Free: 800-473-2227
Fax: 609-569-1752
Type of Counseling:
Default/Foreclosure Counseling,
Prepurchase Counseling, Rental
Counseling
Affiliate of: NATIONAL
FOUNDATION FOR
CONSUMER CREDIT,
INCORPORATED

FAMILY SERVICES
ASSOCIATION/CONSUMER
CREDIT COUNSELING
SERVICE
744 E Landis Ave
Vineland, NJ 08360-8017
800-473-2227
Toll-Free: 800-473-2227
Fax: 609-569-1752
Type of Counseling:
HECM Counseling,
Default/Foreclosure Counseling,
Rental Counseling, Prepurchase
Counseling
Affiliate of: NATIONAL
FOUNDATION FOR
CONSUMER CREDIT,
INCORPORATED

GENESIS HOUSING
CORPORATION
217 S Barber Ave
Woodbury, NJ 08096
856-848-8863
Fax: 856-848-1934
Type of Counseling:
Default/Foreclosure Counseling,
Rental Counseling, Prepurchase
Counseling

New Mexico

HOME-NEW MEXICO,
INCORPORATED
2300 Menaul Blvd.
Albuquerque, NM 87107-
505-889-9486
Type of Counseling:
Prepurchase Counseling

NEW MEXICO MORTGAGE
FINANCE AUTHORITY
344 Fourth Street, SW
Albuquerque, NM 87102
505-843-6880
Fax: 505-243-3289
Type of Counseling:
Prepurchase Counseling,
Default/Foreclosure Counseling,
Rental Counseling

**ACORN HOUSING
CORPORATION
1202 Central Avenue N.W.
Albuquerque, NM 87102-3047
505-244-1086

Fax: 505-244-1088
Type of Counseling:
Prepurchase Counseling,
Default/Foreclosure Counseling
Affiliate of: ACORN HOUSING
CORPORATION

LEGAL AID SOCIETY OF
ALBUQUERQUE.
INCORPORATED
121 Tijeras NE, Suite 3100
Albuquerque, NM 87125-5486
505-243-7871
Fax: 505-842-9864
Type of Counseling:
Prepurchase Counseling,
Default/Foreclosure Counseling,
Rental Counseling

**NEIGHBORHOOD HOUSING
SERVICES OF ALBUQUERQUE,
INCORPORATED
1500 Lomas Blvd NW Ste. B
Albuquerque, NM 87194
505-243-5511
Fax: 505-242-2911
Email: albnhs@ix.netcom.com
Type of Counseling:
Default/Foreclosure Counseling,
Prepurchase Counseling
Affiliate of: NEIGHBORHOOD
REINVESTMENT
CORPORATION

CONSUMER CREDIT
COUNSELING SERVICES
SOUTHWEST
2727 San Pedro Dr NE Ste 117
Albuquerque, NM 87110-3364
505-880-1892
Fax: 505-880-1891
Type of Counseling:
HECM Counseling,
Default/Foreclosure Counseling,
Rental Counseling, Prepurchase
Counseling

GREATER ALBUQUERQUE
HOUSING PARTNERSHIP
7717 Zuni SE
Albuquerque, NM 87108
505-262-9697
Fax: 505-244-0137
Type of Counseling:
Prepurchase Counseling

**UNITED SOUTH BROADWAY CORPORATION
2301 Yale Blvd S.E.
Albuquerque, NM 87102
505-764-8867
Fax: 505-764-9121
Type of Counseling:
Prepurchase Counseling,
Default/Foreclosure Counseling
Affiliate of: HOUSING OPPORTUNITIES, INCORPORATED

CONSUMER CREDIT COUNSELING SERVICE OF GREATER DALLAS, CLOVIS NEW MEXICO
1800 Sheffield Ste B
Clovis, NM 88101
800-538-2227
Fax: 505-769-3245
Type of Counseling:
HECM Counseling,
Default/Foreclosure Counseling,
Rental Counseling, Prepurchase Counseling

CONSUMER CREDIT COUNSELING SERVICE OF SOUTHWEST
3001 Northridge Dr Ste A
Farmington, NM 87401-2084
505-325-5431
Fax: 505-325-5191
Type of Counseling:
HECM Counseling,
Default/Foreclosure Counseling,
Rental Counseling, Prepurchase Counseling

CONSUMER CREDIT COUNSELING SERVICE OF GREATER FORT WORTH
726 E Michigan Dr Ste 138
Hobbs, NM 88240-3456
800-867-2227
Fax: 817-332-2247
Type of Counseling:
HECM Counseling,
Default/Foreclosure Counseling,
Rental Counseling, Prepurchase Counseling

CONSUMER CREDIT COUNSELING SERVICES SOUTHWEST

1065 S Main St Ste B12
Las Cruces, NM 88005-2956
505-527-2585
Fax: 505-527-1975
Type of Counseling:
HECM Counseling,
Default/Foreclosure Counseling,
Prepurchase Counseling

CONSUMER CREDIT COUNSELING SERVICES SOUTHWEST
228 S Saint Francis Dr Ste C2
Santa Fe, NM 87501-2453
505-984-8707
Fax: 505-984-8798
Type of Counseling:
HECM Counseling,
Default/Foreclosure Counseling,
Rental Counseling, Prepurchase Counseling

New York

**AFFORDABLE HOUSING PARTNERSHIP
175 Central Ave.
Albany, NY 12205
518-434-1730
Fax: 518-434-1767
Type of Counseling:
Prepurchase Counseling,
Default/Foreclosure Counseling
Affiliate of: THE HOUSING PARTNERSHIP NETWORK

CONSUMER CREDIT COUNSELING SERVICE OF CENTRAL NEW YORK, INCORPORATED
2 Computer Dr W
Albany, NY 12205-1622
518-482-2227
Toll-Free: 800-479-6026
Fax: 518-482-2296
Type of Counseling:
HECM Counseling,
Default/Foreclosure Counseling,
Rental Counseling, Prepurchase Counseling

UNITED TENANTS OF ALBANY, INCORPORATED
33 Clinton Ave
Albany, NY 12207-2221
518-436-8997

Fax: 518-436-0320
Type of Counseling:
HECM Counseling,
Default/Foreclosure Counseling,
Rental Counseling, Prepurchase Counseling

**CATHOLIC CHARITIES OF THE DIOCESE OF ALBANY
40 North Main Avenue
Albany, NY 19903
518-453-6605
Type of Counseling:
Prepurchase Counseling,
Default/Foreclosure Counseling,
HECM Counseling, Rental Counseling
Affiliate of: CATHOLIC CHARITIES USA

CAPITOL HILL IMPROVEMENT CORPORATION
148 Dove St
Albany, NY 12202-1329
518-462-9696
Fax: 518-462-9698
Email: mbesse@iname.com
Type of Counseling:
HECM Counseling,
Default/Foreclosure Counseling,
Prepurchase Counseling

CAYUGA COUNTY HOMESITE DEVELOPMENT CORPORATION
60 Clark St.
Auburn, NY 13021-3343
315-253-8451
Fax: 315-255-6114
Type of Counseling:
HECM Counseling,
Default/Foreclosure Counseling,
Rental Counseling, Prepurchase Counseling

CORNELL COOPERATIVE EXTENSION
50 W High St
Ballston Spa, NY 12020-1979
518-885-8995
Fax: 518-885-9078
Type of Counseling:
HECM Counseling, Prepurchase Counseling

BELLPORT, HAGERMAN,
EAST PATCHOQUE
ALLIANCE
1492 Montaugh Highway
Bellport, NY 11713
631-286-9236
Fax: 631-286-3948
Type of Counseling:
HECM Counseling,
Default/Foreclosure Counseling,
Rental Counseling, Prepurchase
Counseling

TRI-COUNTY HOUSING
COUNCIL
143 Hibbard Road
Big Flats, NY 14814
607-562-2477
Fax: 607-562-3856
Email:
info@tricountyhousing.org
Type of Counseling:
Rental Counseling, Prepurchase
Counseling, Default/Foreclosure
Counseling, HECM Counseling

METRO-INTERFAITH
SERVICES, INCORPORATED
21 New St.
Binghamton, NY 13903
607-723-0723
Fax: 607-722-8912
Email: metrohc@aol.com
Type of Counseling:
HECM Counseling,
Default/Foreclosure Counseling,
Rental Counseling, Prepurchase
Counseling

CONSUMER CREDIT
COUNSELING OF CENTRAL
NEW YORK, INCORPORATED
49 Court St.
Binghamton, NY 13901
607-723-2984
Fax: 607-723-3007
Type of Counseling:
HECM Counseling,
Default/Foreclosure Counseling,
Rental Counseling, Prepurchase
Counseling

LONG ISLAND HOUSING
SERVICES
3900 Veterans Memorial Hwy
Suite 251

Bohemia, NY 11716
631-467-5111
Fax: 631-467-5131
Email:
LongIslandHousingServices@ya
hoo.com
Type of Counseling:
HECM Counseling,
Default/Foreclosure Counseling,
Rental Counseling, Prepurchase
Counseling

SOUTH BRONX ACTION
GROUP, INCORPORATED
384 E 149th St Ste 220
Bronx, NY 10455-3908
718-993-5869
Fax: 718-993-7904
Type of Counseling: Rental
Counseling

2 OR 3 GATHERED
TOGETHER, INCORPORATED
5301 Avenue N
Brooklyn, NY 11234
718-436-1754
Fax: 718-854-3541
Type of Counseling: Rental
Counseling, Prepurchase
Counseling

CYPRESS HILLS LOCAL
DEVELOPMENT
CORPORATION
3214 Fulton St
Brooklyn, NY 11208-1908
718-647-8100
Fax: 718-647-2104
Type of Counseling:
HECM Counseling,
Default/Foreclosure Counseling,
Rental Counseling, Prepurchase
Counseling

CARROLL GARDENS
ASSOCIATION,
INCORPORATED
201 Columbia St
Brooklyn, NY 11231-1402
718-243-9301
Fax: 718-243-9304
Type of Counseling:
Rental Counseling, Prepurchase
Counseling

NEIGHBORS HELPING
NEIGHBORS
443 39th Street, Suite 202
Brooklyn, NY 11232
718-686-7946
Fax: 718-686-7948
Email: info@nhnhome.org
Website: www.nhnhome.org
Type of Counseling:
HECM Counseling,
Default/Foreclosure Counseling,
Rental Counseling, Prepurchase
Counseling

NEIGHBORHOOD HOUSING
SERVICES
1 Hanson Place
Brooklyn, NY 11243-
718-230-7610
Fax: 718-230-0032
Type of Counseling:
HECM Counseling,
Default/Foreclosure Counseling,
Rental Counseling, Prepurchase
Counseling

BROOKLYN NEIGHBORHOOD
IMPROVEMENT
ASSOCIATION
1482 Saint Johns Place Ste 1F
Brooklyn, NY 11213-3929
718-773-4116
Fax: 718-221-1711
Type of Counseling:
HECM Counseling,
Default/Foreclosure Counseling,
Rental Counseling

**ACORN HOUSING
CORPORATION
88 3rd Ave -3rd Floor
Brooklyn, NY 11217
718-246-8080
Fax: 718-246-7939
Type of Counseling:
Prepurchase Counseling,
Default/Foreclosure Counseling
Affiliate of: ACORN HOUSING
CORPORATION

BUFFALO URBAN LEAGUE
13 East Genesee St
Buffalo, NY 14203-1405
716-854-7625
Fax: 716-854-8960
Email: jbaun@buffalourban.org

Type of Counseling:
HECM Counseling,
Default/Foreclosure Counseling,
Rental Counseling, Prepurchase
Counseling
Affiliate of: NATIONAL
URBAN LEAGUE

**FILLMORE-LEROY AREA
RESIDENTS**
307 Leroy Ave
Buffalo, NY 14214-2520
716-838-6740
Fax: 716-838-6919
Type of Counseling:
Prepurchase Counseling, Rental
Counseling
Affiliate of: HOUSING
OPPORTUNITIES,
INCORPORATED

****KENSINGTON-BAILEY
NEIGHBORHOOD HOUSING
SERVICES**
995 Kensington Ave.
Buffalo, NY 14215
716-836-3600
Fax: 716-836-3686
Email: kbnhsivy@yahoo.com
Type of Counseling:
Prepurchase Counseling
Affiliate of: NEIGHBORHOOD
REINVESTMENT
CORPORATION

**BELMONT SHELTER
CORPORATION**
1195 Main Street
Buffalo, NY 14209-
716-884-7791
Fax: 716-884-8026
Email:
mriegel@belmontshelter.org
Type of Counseling:
Prepurchase Counseling, Rental
Counseling, Default/Foreclosure
Counseling, HECM Counseling

****WEST SIDE
NEIGHBORHOOD HOUSING
SERVICES, INCORPORATED**
359 Connecticut St
Buffalo, NY 14213
716-885-2344
Fax: 716-885-2346
Type of Counseling:

Prepurchase Counseling,
Default/Foreclosure Counseling
Affiliate of: NEIGHBORHOOD
REINVESTMENT
CORPORATION

**ORANGE COUNTY RURAL
DEVELOPMENT ADVISORY
CORPORATION**
Route 207 Professional Bldg
Campbell Hall, NY 10916
845-291-7300
Fax: 845-291-7322
Type of Counseling: HECM
Counseling

**BISHOP SHEEN ECUMENICAL
HOUSING FOUNDATION**
2520 Country Rd
Canandaigua, NY 14424
716-461-4263
Fax: 716-461-5177
Email: sheen@netacc.net
Type of Counseling:
HECM Counseling,
Default/Foreclosure Counseling,
Rental Counseling, Prepurchase
Counseling

**STONELEIGH HOUSING,
INCORPORATED**
120 East Center Street
Canastota, NY 13032
315-697-3737
Fax: 315-697-3700
Email: stonelie@twcny.rr.com
Type of Counseling:
HECM Counseling,
Default/Foreclosure Counseling,
Rental Counseling, Prepurchase
Counseling

**ST. LAWRENCE COUNTY
HOUSING COUNCIL**
19 Main Street
Canton, NY 13617
315-386-8576
Fax: 315-386-1564
Type of Counseling:
HECM Counseling,
Default/Foreclosure Counseling,
Prepurchase Counseling, Rental
Counseling

**PUTNAM COUNTY HOUSING
CORPORATION**

11 Seminary Hill Rd
Carmel, NY 10512
845-225-8493
Fax: 845-225-8532
Type of Counseling:
HECM Counseling,
Default/Foreclosure Counseling,
Rental Counseling, Prepurchase
Counseling

**CATSKILL MOUNTAIN
HOUSING DEVELOPMENT
CORPORATION**
448 Main St
Catskill, NY 12414
518-943-6700
Fax: 518-943-0113
Email: cmh@mhonline.net
Type of Counseling:
HECM Counseling,
Default/Foreclosure Counseling,
Rental Counseling, Prepurchase
Counseling

**COMMUNITY DEVELOPMENT
CORPORATION OF LONG
ISLAND**
2100 Middle Country Road
Suite 300
Centereach, NY 11720
631-471-1215
Fax: 631-471-2167
Type of Counseling:
Default/Foreclosure Counseling,
Prepurchase Counseling

**ROCKLAND HOUSING
ACTION COALITION**
747 Chestnut Ridge Road
Suite 300
Chestnut Ridge, NY 10977-6224
845-352-3819
Fax: 845-352-2126
Type of Counseling:
Prepurchase Counseling,
Default/Foreclosure Counseling

**CORTLAND HOUSING
ASSISTANCE COUNCIL,
INCORPORATED**
159 Main St
Cortland, NY 13045
607-753-8271
Fax: 607-756-6267
Type of Counseling:

HECM Counseling,
Default/Foreclosure Counseling,
Rental Counseling, Prepurchase
Counseling

DELAWARE OPPORTUNITIES,
INCORPORATED
47 Main St
Delhi, NY 137531124
607-746-2165
Fax: 607-746-6269
Email: houseoff@catskill.net
Type of Counseling:
Prepurchase Counseling, Rental
Counseling, Default/Foreclosure
Counseling, HECM Counseling

CHAUTAUQUA
OPPORTUNITIES,
INCORPORATED
17 W Courtney St
Dunkirk, NY 14048-2754
716-366-3333
Fax: 716-366-7366
Email: lesliefagan@hotmail.com
Type of Counseling:
HECM Counseling,
Default/Foreclosure Counseling,
Rental Counseling, Prepurchase
Counseling

**VICTORY HOUSING
DEVELOPMENT FUND
1415 Montauk Hwy.
East Patchogue, NY 11772
631-286-5525
Fax: 631-286-0325
Type of Counseling:
Prepurchase Counseling, Rental
Counseling
Affiliate of: HOUSING
OPPORTUNITIES,
INCORPORATED

HOUSING ASSISTANCE
PROGRAM OF ESSEX
COUNTY, INCORPORATED
2 Church St
Elizabethtown, NY 12932
518-873-6888
Fax: 518-873-9102
Type of Counseling:
HECM Counseling,
Default/Foreclosure Counseling,
Rental Counseling, Prepurchase
Counseling

**CATHOLIC CHARITIES
ELMIRA NEW YORK THE
SOUTHERN TIER
25 East Church Street
Elmira, NY 14901
607-734-9784
Type of Counseling:
Prepurchase Counseling,
Default/Foreclosure Counseling,
HECM Counseling, Rental
Counseling
Affiliate of: CATHOLIC
CHARITIES USA

MARGERT COMMUNITY
CORPORATION
1931 Mott Avenue Room 412
Far Rockaway, NY 11691-4103
718-471-3724
Fax: 718-471-5342
Email: stephanielawes@nyct.net
Type of Counseling:
HECM Counseling,
Default/Foreclosure Counseling,
Prepurchase Counseling, Rental
Counseling

ROCKAWAY DEVELOPMENT
AND REVITALIZATION
CORPORATION
1920 Mott Ave Ste 2
Far Rockaway, NY 11691-4102
718-471-6040
Fax: 718-327-4990
Type of Counseling:
HECM Counseling,
Default/Foreclosure Counseling,
Rental Counseling, Prepurchase
Counseling

MARBLE CITY HOUSING
CORPORATION
68 W Main St
Gouverneur, NY 13642-0430
315-287-0143
Fax: 315-287-2492
Type of Counseling:
Default/Foreclosure Counseling,
Rental Counseling, Prepurchase
Counseling

HOUSING HELP,
INCORPORATED
91-101 Broadway, Suite 6
Greenlawn, NY 11740-
631-754-0373

Fax: 631-754-0821
Type of Counseling:
Rental Counseling, Prepurchase
Counseling, Default/Foreclosure
Counseling

NORTH FORK HOUSING
ALLIANCE, INCORPORATED
110 South St
Greenport, NY 11944-1619
631-477-1070
Fax: 631-477-1769
Type of Counseling:
HECM Counseling,
Default/Foreclosure Counseling,
Rental Counseling, Prepurchase
Counseling
Affiliate of: HOUSING
OPPORTUNITIES,
INCORPORATED

**LONG ISLAND HOUSING
PARTNERSHIP,
INCORPORATED
180 Osner Ave, Suite 800
Hauppauge, NY 11788-3709
631-435-4710
Fax: 631-435-4751
Type of Counseling:
Default/Foreclosure Counseling,
Prepurchase Counseling, HECM
Counseling
Affiliate of: THE HOUSING
PARTNERSHIP NETWORK

HOUSING OPPORTUNITIES
FOR GROWTH,
ADVANCEMENT AND
REVITILIZATION,
INCORPORATED
12 Broadway
Haverstraw, NY 10927-1605
845-429-1100
Fax: 845-429-0193
Email: rivers4556@aol.com
Type of Counseling:
HECM Counseling,
Default/Foreclosure Counseling,
Prepurchase Counseling

FAMILY AND CHILDREN'S
ASSOCIATION
336 Fulton Ave
Hempstead, NY 11550
516-485-5600
Fax: 516-538-2548

Type of Counseling:
HECM Counseling,
Default/Foreclosure Counseling,
Rental Counseling, Prepurchase
Counseling

**HOUSING RESOURCES OF
COLUMBIA COUNTY,
INCORPORATED
605 State St
Hudson, NY 12534
518-822-0707
Fax: 518-822-0367
Email:
margaret@housingresources.org
Website:
www.housingresources.org
Type of Counseling:
HECM Counseling,
Default/Foreclosure Counseling,
Rental Counseling, Prepurchase
Counseling
Affiliate of: NEIGHBORHOOD
REINVESTMENT
CORPORATION

TOWN OF HUNTINGTON
HOUSING AUTHORITY
1 Lowndes Ave Ste A
Huntington Station, NY 11746-
1261
516-427-6220
Fax: 516-427-6288
Type of Counseling:
Default/Foreclosure Counseling,
Rental Counseling

HOST PROGRAM OF
TOMPKINS COUNTY OFFICE
FOR THE AGING
320 N Tioga St
Ithaca, NY 14850-4206
607-274-5482
Fax: 607-274-5495
Email:
David_Stoyell@einstein.co.tomp
kins.NY.US
Type of Counseling: HECM
Counseling

**ITHACA NEIGHBORHOOD
HOUSING SERVICES,
INCORPORATED
115 W Clinton St
Ithaca, NY 14850
607-277-4500

Fax: 607-277-4536
Email: pdm@claritycomm
Type of Counseling:
Rental Counseling, Prepurchase
Counseling
Affiliate of: NEIGHBORHOOD
REINVESTMENT
CORPORATION

JAMAICA HOUSING
IMPROVEMENT,
INCORPORATED
161-10 Jamaica Ave Ste 601
Jamaica, NY 11432-6149
718-658-5050
Fax: 718-658-5065
Type of Counseling:
HECM Counseling,
Default/Foreclosure Counseling,
Rental Counseling, Prepurchase
Counseling

COMMISSION ON HUMAN
RIGHTS
89-31 161 St. 2nd Floor #210
Jamaica, NY 11432
718-657-9333
Fax: 718-262-8834
Type of Counseling:
HECM Counseling,
Default/Foreclosure Counseling

CHAUTAUQUA
OPPORTUNITIES,
INCORPORATED
610 W 3rd St
Jamestown, NY 14701-4705
716-661-9430
Fax: 716-661-9436
Type of Counseling:
HECM Counseling,
Default/Foreclosure Counseling,
Rental Counseling, Prepurchase
Counseling

RURAL ULSTER
PRESERVATION COMPANY
289 Fair St
Kingston, NY 12401
845-331-2140
Fax: 845-331-6217
Type of Counseling:
HECM Counseling,
Default/Foreclosure Counseling,
Prepurchase Counseling

COMMUNITY ACTION IN
SELF HELP, INCORPORATED
48 Water St
Lyons, NY 14489-1244
315-946-6992
Fax: 315-946-3314
Type of Counseling:
Rental Counseling, Prepurchase
Counseling

KIRYAS JOEL COMMUNITY
HOUSING DEVELOPMENT
ORGANIZATION,
INCORPORATED
51 Forest Road, Suite 360
Monroe, NY 10950
845-782-7790
Fax: 845-783-7415
Type of Counseling:
Prepurchase Counseling,
Default/Foreclosure Counseling,
HECM Counseling, Rental
Counseling

RURAL SULLIVAN COUNTY
HOUSING OPPORTUNITIES,
INCORPORATED
6 Pelton Street
Monticello, NY 12701-1128
845-794-0348
Fax: 845-794-3042
Type of Counseling:
HECM Counseling,
Default/Foreclosure Counseling,
Rental Counseling, Prepurchase
Counseling

NEW ROCHELLE CAP
95 Lincoln Ave
New Rochelle, NY 10801-3912
914-636-3050
Fax: 914-633-0617
Type of Counseling:
Default/Foreclosure Counseling,
Rental Counseling, Prepurchase
Counseling

OPEN HOUSING CENTER,
INCORPORATED
45 John St. Rm 308
New York, NY 10038
212-231-7080
Fax: 212-231-7087
Type of Counseling:
Prepurchase Counseling

ASIAN AMERICANS FOR
EQUALITY
129 Rivington St
New York, NY 10002-6103
212-477-2265
Fax: 212-477-2429
Type of Counseling:
HECM Counseling,
Default/Foreclosure Counseling,
Rental Counseling, Prepurchase
Counseling

**NEW YORK MORTGAGE
COALITION
305 Seventh Avenue, Suite 2001
New York, NY 10001
646-336-8609
Fax: 212-463-9606
Email:
c.alleyne@worldnet.att.net
Type of Counseling:
Default/Foreclosure Counseling,
Prepurchase Counseling
Affiliate of: THE HOUSING
PARTNERSHIP NETWORK

NATIONAL URBAN LEAGUE
120 Wall Street
New York, NY 10005
212-558-5453
Fax: 212-344-8948

NORTHERN MANHATTAN
IMPROVEMENT
CORPORATION
76 Wadsworth Ave
New York, NY 10033-7000
212-568-9166
Fax: 212-740-9646
Type of Counseling:
Rental Counseling

HARLEM COMMUNITY
DEVELOPMENT
CORPORATION
163 West 125th Street, 17th floor
New York, NY 10027
212-961-4100
Fax: 212-961-4143
Email:
dphillpotts@empire.state.ny.us
Type of Counseling:
Prepurchase Counseling,
Default/Foreclosure Counseling,
HECM Counseling, Rental
Counseling

WEST HARLEM GROUP
ASSISTANCE,
INCORPORATED
1528 Amsterdam Avenue
New York City, NY 10031-
212-862-1399
Fax: 212-862-3281
Type of Counseling:
Prepurchase Counseling,
Default/Foreclosure Counseling,
HECM Counseling, Rental
Counseling

COALITION FOR PEOPLE'S
RIGHTS
13 Paddock Place
Newburgh, NY 12550
914-564-4259
Fax: 914-564-4259
Type of Counseling:
Default/Foreclosure Counseling,
Rental Counseling

CENTER CITY
NEIGHBORHOOD
DEVELOPMENT
CORPORATION
1824 Main St
Niagara Falls, NY 14305-2661
716-282-3738
Fax: 716-282-9607
Email:
mfrancisco@centercitynf.org
Type of Counseling:
Rental Counseling, Prepurchase
Counseling, Default/Foreclosure
Counseling

OPPORTUNITIES FOR
CHENANGO,
INCORPORATED
44 W Main St
Norwich, NY 13815-1613
607-334-7114
Fax: 607-336-6958
Type of Counseling:
HECM Counseling,
Default/Foreclosure Counseling,
Rental Counseling, Prepurchase
Counseling

OSWEGO HOUSING
DEVELOPMENT COUNCIL,
INCORPORATED
2822 St. Rt. 29
Parish, NY 13131

315-625-4520
Fax: 315-625-7347
Type of Counseling:
HECM Counseling,
Default/Foreclosure Counseling,
Rental Counseling, Prepurchase
Counseling

ECONOMIC OPPORTUNITY
COUNCIL OF SUFFOLK INC.
475 E. Main Street, Suite 206
Patchogue, NY 11772
800-300-4362
Toll-Free: 800-300-4362
Fax: 631-289-2178
Type of Counseling:
Prepurchase Counseling, Rental
Counseling, Default/Foreclosure
Counseling, HECM Counseling

SHARP COMMITTEE,
INCORPORATED
98 Main St
Phoenicia, NY 12464
845-688-5777
Fax: 845-688-5007
Type of Counseling:
HECM Counseling,
Default/Foreclosure Counseling,
Rental Counseling, Prepurchase
Counseling

DUTCHESS COUNTY OFFICE
FOR THE AGING
27 High Street
Poughkeepsie, NY 12601
845-486-2555
Fax: 845-486-2571
Email: dc4@mhv.net
Type of Counseling: HECM
Counseling

NEW JERSEY CITIZEN
ACTION
80 Elm St.
Rahway, NY 07065
800-656-9637
Toll-Free: 800-656-9637
Fax: 732-714-5386
Email:
jennifer@njcitizenaction.org
Website:
www.njcitizenaction.org
Type of Counseling:
HECM Counseling,
Default/Foreclosure Counseling,

Rental Counseling, Prepurchase
Counseling

HOUSING COUNCIL IN
MONROE COUNTY,
INCORPORATED
183 Main St E
Suite 1100
Rochester, NY 14604
716-546-3700
Fax: 716-546-2946
Type of Counseling:
HECM Counseling,
Default/Foreclosure Counseling,
Rental Counseling, Prepurchase
Counseling

**RURAL OPPORTUNITIES,
INCORPORATED
400 East Ave
Rochester, NY 14607-1910
716-546-7180
Fax: 716-340-3337
Type of Counseling:
Prepurchase Counseling
Affiliate of: NEIGHBORHOOD
REINVESTMENT
CORPORATION

**NEIGHBORHOOD HOUSING
SERVICES OF ROCHESTER,
INCORPORATED
570 South Ave
Rochester, NY 14620-1345
716-325-4170
Fax: 716-325-2587
Type of Counseling:
Prepurchase Counseling
Affiliate of: NEIGHBORHOOD
REINVESTMENT
CORPORATION

BISHOP SHEEN ECUMENICAL
HOUSING FOUNDATION
935 East Ave
Suite 300
Rochester, NY 14607-2216
716-461-4263
Fax: 716-461-5177
Email: sheen@netacc.net
Type of Counseling:
HECM Counseling,
Default/Foreclosure Counseling,
Rental Counseling, Prepurchase
Counseling

**CATHOLIC CHARITIES OF
THE DIOCESE OF ROCHESTER
NEW YORK
1150 Buffalo Road
Rochester, NY
716-328-3210
Type of Counseling:
Prepurchase Counseling,
Default/Foreclosure Counseling,
HECM Counseling, Rental
Counseling
Affiliate of: CATHOLIC
CHARITIES USA

ROOSEVELT ASSISTANCE
CORPORATION
455D Nassau Road
Roosevelt, NY 11575-
516-223-7077
Fax: 516-223-0863
Type of Counseling:
Prepurchase Counseling,
Default/Foreclosure Counseling,
HECM Counseling

CATTARAUGUS
PRESERVATION
CORPORATION
25 Jefferson St
Salamanca, NY 14779
716-945-1041
Fax: 716-945-1301
Type of Counseling:
Default/Foreclosure Counseling,
Rental Counseling, Prepurchase
Counseling

BETTER NEIGHBORHOODS,
INCORPORATED
986 Albany St
Schenectady, NY 12307
518-372-6469
Fax: 518-372-6460
Type of Counseling:
HECM Counseling,
Default/Foreclosure Counseling,
Rental Counseling, Prepurchase
Counseling

WESTERN CATSKILLS
COMMUNITY
REVITALIZATION COUNCIL,
INCORPORATED
125 Main Street, Box A
Stamford, NY 12167
607-652-2823

Fax: 607-652-2825
Type of Counseling:
Prepurchase Counseling, Rental
Counseling, Default/Foreclosure
Counseling

NORTHFIELD COMMUNITY
LOCAL DEVELOPMENT
CORPORATION
160 Heberton Ave.
Staten Island, NY 10302
718-442-7351
Fax: 718-981-3441
Type of Counseling:
Prepurchase Counseling, Rental
Counseling, Default/Foreclosure
Counseling

CONSUMER CREDIT
COUNSELING SERVICE OF
CENTRAL NEW YORK,
INCORPORATED
500 S Salina St Ste 600
Syracuse, NY 132023394
315-474-6026
Toll-Free: 800-479-6026
Fax: 315-479-8421
Website: www.cccscny.org
Type of Counseling:
HECM Counseling,
Default/Foreclosure Counseling,
Rental Counseling, Prepurchase
Counseling
Affiliate of: NATIONAL
FOUNDATION FOR
CONSUMER CREDIT,
INCORPORATED

NORTHEAST HAWLEY
DEVELOPMENT
ASSOCIATION,
INCORPORATED
101 Gertrude St
Syracuse, NY 13203-2417
315-425-1032
Fax: 315-425-1089
Email: nehda@a-znet.com
Type of Counseling:
Prepurchase Counseling

HOME HEADQUARTERS,
INCORPORATED
124 E Jefferson St
Syracuse, NY 13202
315-474-1939
Fax: 315-474-0637

Email: homehq.org
Type of Counseling:
Prepurchase Counseling,
Default/Foreclosure Counseling
Affiliate of: NEIGHBORHOOD
REINVESTMENT
CORPORATION

URBAN LEAGUE OF
ONONDAGA COUNTY,
INCORPORATED
1211 S. Salina Street
Syracuse, NY 13205-
315-472-6955
Fax: 315-472-6445
Email:
urbanleaguesyr@hotmail.com
Type of Counseling:
HECM Counseling,
Default/Foreclosure Counseling,
Rental Counseling, Prepurchase
Counseling

HOUSING ASSISTANCE
CENTER OF NIAGARA
FRONTIER, INCORPORATED
200 Niagara St
Tonawanda, NY 14150-1003
716-695-1807
Fax: 716-881-2378
Type of Counseling:
HECM Counseling,
Default/Foreclosure Counseling,
Rental Counseling, Prepurchase
Counseling

RENSSELAER COUNTY
HOUSING RESOURCES
415 River St, Third floor
Troy, NY 12180
518-272-8289
Fax: 518-272-1950
Type of Counseling:
HECM Counseling,
Default/Foreclosure Counseling,
Prepurchase Counseling, Rental
Counseling

TROY REHABILITATION AND
IMPROVEMENT PROGRAM,
INCORPORATED
251 River Street
Troy, NY 12180-2834
518-690-0020
Fax: 518-690-0025
Email: tripinc@ix.netcom

Type of Counseling:
HECM Counseling,
Default/Foreclosure Counseling,
Prepurchase Counseling
Affiliate of: NEIGHBORHOOD
REINVESTMENT
CORPORATION

**UTICA NEIGHBORHOOD
HOUSING SERVICES,
NEIGHBORWORKS
HOMEOWNERSHIP CENTER
1611 Genesee St.
Utica, NY 13501
315-724-4197
Toll-Free: 866-724-4197
Fax: 315-724-1415
Email: jforte@unhs.org
Website:
www.thehomeownershipcenter.
org
Type of Counseling:
Default/Foreclosure Counseling,
Prepurchase Counseling, HECM
Counseling
Affiliate of: NEIGHBORHOOD
REINVESTMENT
CORPORATION

CONSUMER CREDIT
COUNSELING SERVICE OF
CENTRAL NEW YORK
289 Genesee St
Utica, NY 13501-3804
315-797-5366
Fax: 315-797-9410
Type of Counseling:
HECM Counseling,
Default/Foreclosure Counseling,
Rental Counseling, Prepurchase
Counseling

ALBANY COUNTY RURAL
HOUSING ALLIANCE,
INCORPORATED
24 Martin Road
Voorheesville, NY 12186
518-765-2425
Fax: 518-765-9014
Email: acrha@gateway.net
Website:
www.timesunion.com/commun
ities/acrha
Type of Counseling:
HECM Counseling,
Default/Foreclosure Counseling,

Rental Counseling, Prepurchase
Counseling

WESTCHESTER RESIDENTIAL
OPPORTUNITIES,
INCORPORATED
470 Mamaroneck Ave,suite 410
White Plains, NY 10605-1830
914-428-4507
Fax: 914-428-9455
Email: toni@wroinc.org
Type of Counseling:
HECM Counseling,
Default/Foreclosure Counseling,
Rental Counseling, Prepurchase
Counseling

WYANDANCH COMMUNITY
DEVELOPMENT
CORPORATION
30 William St VFW Bldg
Wyandanch, NY 11798-3326
631-643-4786
Fax: 631-253-0139
Type of Counseling:
HECM Counseling,
Default/Foreclosure Counseling,
Prepurchase Counseling, Rental
Counseling

North Carolina

CONSUMER CREDIT
COUNSELING CENTERS OF
GREATER GREENSBORO IN
ASHEBORO
135 Sunset Avenue
Asheboro, NC 27204-
336-373-8882
Fax: 336-387-9167
Type of Counseling:
Prepurchase Counseling,
Default/Foreclosure Counseling,
HECM Counseling, Rental
Counseling
Affiliate of: NATIONAL
FOUNDATION FOR
CONSUMER CREDIT,
INCORPORATED

AFFORDABLE HOUSING
COALITION OF ASHEVILLE
AND BUNCOMBE COUNTY
34 Wall Street, Suite 607
Asheville, NC 28801
828-259-9216

Fax: 828-259-9469
Type of Counseling:
Prepurchase Counseling,
Default/Foreclosure Counseling,
Rental Counseling

CONSUMER CREDIT
COUNSELING OF WESTERN
NORTH CAROLINA
50 S French Broad Ave Ste 227
Asheville, NC 288013217
828-255-5166
Toll-Free: 800-737-5485
Fax: 828-255-5129
Website: www.cccsofwnc.org
Type of Counseling:
HECM Counseling,
Default/Foreclosure Counseling,
Rental Counseling, Prepurchase
Counseling

**NEIGHBORHOOD HOUSING
SERVICES OF ASHEVILLE,
NORTH CAROLINA
135 Cherry St
Asheville, NC 28801-2223
828-251-5054
Fax: 828-251-1323
Type of Counseling:
Prepurchase Counseling

NORTHWESTERN REGIONAL
HOUSING AUTHORITY
869 Highway 105 Ext Ste 10
Boone, NC 28607-2510
828-264-6683
Fax: 828-264-0160
Type of Counseling:
Default/Foreclosure Counseling,
Prepurchase Counseling, Rental
Counseling, HECM Counseling

**CONSUMER CREDIT
COUNSELING SERVICE OF
GREATER GREENSBORO IN
BURLINGTON
719 Hermitage Road
Burlington, NC 27215
336-373-8882
Fax: 336-387-9167
Type of Counseling:
HECM Counseling,
Default/Foreclosure Counseling,
Prepurchase Counseling, Rental
Counseling

Affiliate of: NATIONAL
FOUNDATION FOR
CONSUMER CREDIT,
INCORPORATED

NORTHEASTERN
COMMUNITY DEVELOPMENT
CORPORATION,
INCORPORATED
154 Highway 158 East
Camden, NC 27921-0367
252-338-5466
Fax: 252-338-5639
Email: ncdc@net-change.com
Type of Counseling:
Prepurchase Counseling,
Default/Foreclosure Counseling,
Rental Counseling

SANDHILLS COMMUNITY
ACTION PROGRAM,
INCORPORATED
103 Saunders St
Carthage, NC 28327-0937
910-947-5675
Fax: 910-947-5514
Email:
kristanb@portlandhousingcenter
.org
Type of Counseling:
HECM Counseling,
Default/Foreclosure Counseling,
Rental Counseling, Prepurchase
Counseling

EMPOWERMENT
INCORPORATED
109 North Grahm Street Suite
200
Chapel Hill, NC 27516
919-967-8779
Fax: 919-967-0710
Type of Counseling:
Prepurchase Counseling

CONSUMER CREDIT
COUNSELING AND HOUSING
SERVICES/ UNITED FAMILY
SERVICES
200 North Sharon Amity
Charlotte, NC 28211
704-332-4191
Fax: 704-362-3137
Email: agreene@UFSCLT.org

HECM Counseling, Prepurchase
Counseling, Rental Counseling,
Default/Foreclosure Counseling

CHARLOTTE-MECKLENBURG
HOUSING PARTNERSHIP,
INCORPORATED
1201 Greenwood Cliff Ste 300
Charlotte, NC 28204-2822
704-342-0933
TTY/TDD: 704-343-4692
Fax: 704-342-2745
Email: info@cmhp.org
Website: www.cmhp.org
Type of Counseling:
Prepurchase Counseling
Affiliate of: THE HOUSING
PARTNERSHIP NETWORK

URBAN LEAGUE OF
CENTRAL CAROLINAS,
INCORPORATED
740 West 5th Street
Charlotte, NC 28202
704-373-2256
Fax: 704-373-2262
Email: cnuljerri@aol.com
Website:
www.urbanleaguecc.org
Type of Counseling:
Prepurchase Counseling, Rental
Counseling, Default/Foreclosure
Counseling
Affiliate of: NATIONAL
URBAN LEAGUE

CONSUMER CREDIT
COUNSELING SERVICE
212 Le Phillip Ct Ste 106
Concord, NC 28025-2954
704-786-7918
Fax: 704-786-7709
Type of Counseling:
Default/Foreclosure Counseling

DURHAM AFFORDABLE
HOUSING COALITION
331 W Main St Ste 408
Durham, NC 27701-3232
919-683-1185
Fax: 919-688-0082
Type of Counseling:
HECM Counseling,
Default/Foreclosure Counseling,
Prepurchase Counseling, Rental
Counseling

Affiliate of: HOUSING
OPPORTUNITIES,
INCORPORATED

**CONSUMER CREDIT
COUNSELING SERVICE OF
DURHAM
413 East Chapel Hill Street
Durham, NC 27701-3221
919-688-3381
Toll-Free: 888-562-3732
Fax: 919-682-4021
Type of Counseling:
HECM Counseling,
Default/Foreclosure Counseling,
Prepurchase Counseling, Rental
Counseling
Affiliate of: NATIONAL
FOUNDATION FOR
CONSUMER CREDIT,
INCORPORATED

ELIZABETH CITY STATE
UNIVERSITY
1704 Weeksville Rd.
Elizabeth City, NC 27909
252-335-3702
Fax: 252-335-3735
Type of Counseling:
Prepurchase Counseling, Rental
Counseling, Default/Foreclosure
Counseling

RIVER CITY COMMUNITY
DEVELOPMENT
CORPORATION
501 East Main St
Elizabeth City, NC 27909
252-331-2925
Fax: 252-331-1425
Type of Counseling:
Default/Foreclosure Counseling,
Rental Counseling, Prepurchase
Counseling

SANDHILLS COMMUNITY
ACTION PROGRAM,
INCORPORATED
122 Railroad St
Ellerbe, NC 28338-0389
910-652-6167
Fax: 910-947-5514
Type of Counseling:
HECM Counseling,
Default/Foreclosure Counseling,

Rental Counseling, Prepurchase
Counseling

CUMBERLAND COUNTY
COMMUNITY ACTION
PROGRAM, INCORPORATED
PO Box 2009
Fayetteville, NC 28301
910-323-3192
Fax: 910-323-4990
Type of Counseling:
HECM Counseling,
Default/Foreclosure Counseling,
Rental Counseling, Prepurchase
Counseling

CONSUMER CREDIT
COUNSELING SERVICE
130 South Oakland Street
Gastonia, NC 28052
704-862-0702
Toll-Free: 888-213-8853
Fax: 704-862-0239
Type of Counseling:
HECM Counseling,
Default/Foreclosure Counseling,
Rental Counseling, Prepurchase
Counseling
Affiliate of: NATIONAL
FOUNDATION FOR
CONSUMER CREDIT,
INCORPORATED

CONSUMER CREDIT
COUNSELING SERVICE OF
GOLDSBORO
678 North Spence Avenue
Goldsboro, NC 27534
919-751-3868
Fax: 919-751-0382
Type of Counseling:
HECM Counseling,
Default/Foreclosure Counseling,
Rental Counseling, Prepurchase
Counseling

HOMEKEEPING MORTGAGE
DEFAULT COUNSELING,
INCORPORATED
2808 Four Seasons Blvd.
Greensboro, NC 27406
336-299-3827
Fax: 336-299-3827
Type of Counseling:

Prepurchase Counseling,
Default/Foreclosure Counseling,
Rental Counseling

**CONSUMER CREDIT
COUNSELING SERVICE OF
GREATER GREENSBORO
315 E. Washington Street
Greensboro, NC 27401
336-373-8882
Fax: 336-387-9167
Type of Counseling:
Prepurchase Counseling,
Default/Foreclosure Counseling,
HECM Counseling, Rental
Counseling
Affiliate of: NATIONAL
FOUNDATION FOR
CONSUMER CREDIT,
INCORPORATED

ALBEMARLE COMMISSION
512 South Church St
Hertford, NC 27944
252-426-5753
Fax: 252-426-8482
Type of Counseling:
HECM Counseling

WESTERN PIEDMONT
COUNCIL OF GOVERNMENTS
736 4th Street South-West
Hickory, NC 28602
828-322-9191
Fax: 828-322-5991
Type of Counseling:
HECM Counseling

**CONSUMER CREDIT
COUNSELING SERVICE OF
GREATER GREENSBORO IN
HIGH POINT
1401 Long Street
High Point, NC 27262
336-373-8882
Fax: 336-387-9167
Type of Counseling:
Prepurchase Counseling,
Default/Foreclosure Counseling,
Rental Counseling
Affiliate of: NATIONAL
FOUNDATION FOR
CONSUMER CREDIT,
INCORPORATED

HOUSING AUTHORITY OF
THE CITY OF HIGH POINT
500E Russell Avenue
High Point, NC 272611779
336-878-2300
Fax: 336-887-9366
Type of Counseling:
Prepurchase Counseling, Rental
Counseling, Default/Foreclosure
Counseling

DAVIDSON COUNTY
COMMUNITY ACTION
INCORPORATED
701 S Salisbury St
Lexington, NC 27292
336-249-0234
Fax: 336-249-2078
Type of Counseling:
Prepurchase Counseling, Rental
Counseling, Default/Foreclosure
Counseling, HECM Counseling

**FAMILY SERVICE CREDIT
COUNSELORS
235 East CenterStreet
Lexington, NC 27292
336-249-0237
Fax: 336-243-7685
Type of Counseling:
HECM Counseling,
Default/Foreclosure Counseling,
Prepurchase Counseling, Rental
Counseling

COASTAL COMMUNITY
DEVELOPMENT
CORPORATION
1017 A Broad St
New Bern, NC 28563
252-636-0893
Fax: 252-636-1062
Type of Counseling:
HECM Counseling,
Default/Foreclosure Counseling,
Prepurchase Counseling

TWIN RIVERS
OPPORTUNITIES, INC.
318 Craven St.
New Bern, NC 28563
252-637-3599
Fax: 252-637-7101
Type of Counseling:
Prepurchase Counseling, Rental
Counseling

NORTH CAROLINA HOUSING
FINANCE AGENCY
3508 Bush Street
Raleigh, NC 27609-8066
919-877-5700
Fax: 919-877-5701

**DOWNTOWN HOUSING
IMPROVEMENT
CORPORATION
113 S. Wilmington Street
Raleigh, NC 27601
919-832-4345
Fax: 919-832-2206
Website: www.dhic.org
Type of Counseling:
Prepurchase Counseling,
Default/Foreclosure Counseling,
Rental Counseling
Affiliate of: NEIGHBORHOOD
REINVESTMENT
CORPORATION

RESOURCES FOR SENIORS
1110 Navaho Dr. Ste 400
Raleigh, NC 27609-7318
919-872-7933
Fax: 919-872-9574
Type of Counseling: HECM
Counseling

ISOTHERMAL PLANNING
AND DEVELOPMENT
COMMISSION
101 W Court St
Rutherfordton, NC 28139-2804
828-287-2281
Fax: 828-287-2735
Type of Counseling: HECM
Counseling

JOHNSTON-LEE COMMUNITY
ACTION, INCORPORATED
1102 Massey Street
Smithfield, NC 27577-0711
919-934-2145
Fax: 919-934-6231
Email: jlca.usa.net
Type of Counseling:
HECM Counseling,
Default/Foreclosure Counseling,
Rental Counseling, Prepurchase
Counseling

CONSUMER CREDIT
COUNSELING SERVICE OF

THE CAROLINA FOOTHILLS,
INCORPORATED
200 Ohio St
Spindale, NC 28160-0006
828-286-7062
Fax: 828-286-7064
Type of Counseling:
HECM Counseling,
Default/Foreclosure Counseling,
Rental Counseling, Prepurchase
Counseling
Affiliate of: NATIONAL
FOUNDATION FOR
CONSUMER CREDIT,
INCORPORATED

SANDHILLS COMMUNITY
ACTION PROGRAM,
INCORPORATED
217 S Main St Ste B
Troy, NC 27371-3200
910-576-9071
Fax: 910-947-5514
Type of Counseling:
HECM Counseling,
Default/Foreclosure Counseling,
Rental Counseling, Prepurchase
Counseling

SANDHILLS COMMUNITY
ACTION PROGRAM,
INCORPORATED
208 Rutherford Street
Wadesboro, NC 28170-0065
704-694-5161
Fax: 910-947-5514
Type of Counseling:
HECM Counseling,
Default/Foreclosure Counseling,
Rental Counseling, Prepurchase
Counseling

MID-EAST COMMISSION-
AREA AGENCY ON AGING
1385 John Small Avenue
Washington, NC 27889-1787
252-974-1835
Fax: 252-948-1884
Type of Counseling: HECM
Counseling

**CONSUMER CREDIT
COUNSELING SERVICE OF
GREATER GREENSBORO IN
WENTWORTH
525 NC-65

Wentworth, NC 27320
336-373-8882
Fax: 336-387-9167
Type of Counseling:
HECM Counseling,
Default/Foreclosure Counseling,
Prepurchase Counseling, Rental
Counseling
Affiliate of: NATIONAL
FOUNDATION FOR
CONSUMER CREDIT,
INCORPORATED

WILMINGTON HOUSING
FINACE AND
DEVELOPMENT,
INCORPORATED
310 North Fron Street
Wilmington, NC 28401
910-763-7775
Fax: 910-763-7705
Type of Counseling:
Prepurchase Counseling,
Default/Foreclosure Counseling,
Rental Counseling

**SCOTLAND NECK
COMMUNITY OUTREACH
CENTER
135 New Street
Williamston, NC 27892
252-826-0314
Type of Counseling:
Prepurchase Counseling
Affiliate of: CONGRESS OF
NATIONAL BLACK
CHURCHES, INCORPORATED

WILSON COMMUNITY
IMPROVEMENT
ASSOCIATION,
INCORPORATED
504 E Green St
Wilson, NC 27893
252-243-4855
Fax: 252-243-2945
Type of Counseling:
HECM Counseling, Prepurchase
Counseling

CONSUMER CREDIT
COUNSELING SERVICE OF
FORSYTH COUNTY
8064 North Point Boulevard,
Suite 204
Winston Salem, NC 27106

336-896-1191
Fax: 336-896-0481
Type of Counseling:
HECM Counseling,
Default/Foreclosure Counseling,
Rental Counseling, Prepurchase
Counseling

EAST WINSTON COMMUNITY
DEVELOPMENT
CORPORATION,
INCORPORATED
1225 E Fifth St
Winston-Salem, NC 27101
336-723-1783
Fax: 336-761-8014
Type of Counseling:
Prepurchase Counseling,
Default/Foreclosure Counseling,
Rental Counseling, HECM
Counseling

North Dakota

COMMUNITY ACTION
PROGRAM REGION VII,
INCORPORATED
2105 Lee Ave
Bismarck, ND 58504-6798
701-258-2240
Fax: 701-258-2245
Type of Counseling:
HECM Counseling,
Default/Foreclosure Counseling,
Rental Counseling, Prepurchase
Counseling

INDUSTRIAL COMMISSION
OF NORTH DAKOTA
North Dakota Housing Finance
Agency
P.O. Box 1535
Bismarck, ND 58502
701-328-8080
Fax: 701-328-8090
Type of Counseling:
Rental Counseling,
Default/Foreclosure Counseling,
Prepurchase Counseling

COMMUNITY ACTION AND
DEVELOPMENT PROGRAM
202 E Villard St
Dickinson, ND 58601-5247
701-227-0131
Fax: 701-227-4750

Email:
comact1@dickinson.ctctel.com
Type of Counseling:
Prepurchase Counseling, Rental
Counseling, Default/Foreclosure
Counseling, HECM Counseling

VILLAGE FAMILY SERVICE
CENTER (CCCS)
1201 25th Street South
Fargo, ND 58106
701-451-4900
Toll-Free: 800-627-8220
Fax: 701-235-9693
Email:
www.thefamilyvillage.org
Type of Counseling:
Prepurchase Counseling
Affiliate of: NATIONAL
FOUNDATION FOR
CONSUMER CREDIT,
INCORPORATED

SOUTHEASTERN NORTH
DAKOTA COMMUNITY
ACTION AGENCY
3233 S University Dr
Fargo, ND 58104-6221
701-232-2452
Fax: 701-298-3115
Type of Counseling:
HECM Counseling,
Default/Foreclosure Counseling,
Rental Counseling, Prepurchase
Counseling

VILLAGE FAMILY SERVICE
CENTER (CCCS)
Riverview Center, 215 North 3rd
Street #104
Grand Forks, ND 58203
701-746-4584
Fax: 701-746-1239
Email:
bflickinger@thevillagefamily.org
Website:
www.thevillagefamily.org
Type of Counseling:
Prepurchase Counseling

RED RIVER VALLEY
COMMUNITY ACTION
1013 N 5th St
Grand Forks, ND 58203-2442
701-746-5431
Fax: 701-746-0406

Type of Counseling:
HECM Counseling,
Default/Foreclosure Counseling,
Rental Counseling, Prepurchase
Counseling

COMMUNITY ACTION
OPPORTUNITIES,
INCORPORATED
220 8th Ave. SE
Minot, ND 58701
701-839-7221
Toll-Free: 800-726-8645
Fax: 701-839-1747
Email: cao@minot.ndak.net
Type of Counseling:
Default/Foreclosure Counseling,
Rental Counseling, Prepurchase
Counseling

Ohio

FAIR HOUSING CONTACT
SERVICE
333 South Main Street, Suite 300
Akron, OH 44308
330-376-6191
Fax: 330-376-8391
Type of Counseling:
Prepurchase Counseling, Rental
Counseling, HECM Counseling

CATHOLIC CHARITIES OF
ASHTABULA COUNTY
4200 Park Avenue
Ashtabula, OH 44004
440-992-0300
Fax: 440-992-5974
Type of Counseling:
HECM Counseling,
Default/Foreclosure Counseling,
Rental Counseling, Prepurchase
Counseling

CONSUMER CREDIT
COUNSELING OF
NORTHEAST OHIO,
INCORPORATED
4274 Manhattan Ave
Brunswick, OH 44212-3523
216-771-0790
Fax: 216-781-8852
Type of Counseling:
HECM Counseling,
Default/Foreclosure Counseling,
Prepurchase Counseling

CATHOLIC COMMUNITY
SERVICES OF STARK
COUNTY, INCORPORATED
1500 Market Ave. N, Suite 3
Canton, OH 44714
330-454-2220
Fax: 330-454-2255

BETTER HOUSING LEAGUE
OF GREATER CINCINNATI
2400 Reading Rd
Cincinnati, OH 452021429
513-721-6855
Fax: 513-721-8160
Type of Counseling:
HECM Counseling,
Default/Foreclosure Counseling,
Prepurchase Counseling

**HOME OWNERSHIP
CENTER OF GREATER
CINCINNATI,
INCORPORATED
2820 Vernon Place
Cincinnati, OH 45219
513-961-2800
Fax: 513-961-8222
Type of Counseling:
Default/Foreclosure Counseling,
Prepurchase Counseling
Affiliate of: NEIGHBORHOOD
REINVESTMENT
CORPORATION

**NEIGHBORHOOD HOUSING
SERVICES OF CLEVELAND,
INCORPORATED
3210 Euclid Avenue
Cleveland, OH 44115
216-361-0516
Fax: 216-361-1252
Type of Counseling:
Prepurchase Counseling
Affiliate of: NEIGHBORHOOD
REINVESTMENT
CORPORATION

CONSUMER PROTECTION
ASSOCIATION
3030 Euclid Ave Ste 105
Cleveland, OH 44115-2521
216-881-3434
Fax: 216-881-6524
Type of Counseling:
Default/Foreclosure Counseling,

Rental Counseling, Prepurchase
Counseling

CLEVELAND HOUSING
NETWORK, INCORPORATED
2999 Payne Ave Ste 306
Cleveland, OH 44114-4400
216-574-7100
Fax: 216-574-7130
Email: jciammai@chnnet.com
Website: www.chnnet.com
Type of Counseling:
Rental Counseling, Prepurchase
Counseling
Affiliate of: THE HOUSING
PARTNERSHIP NETWORK

CONSUMER CREDIT
COUNSELING OF
NORTHEAST OHIO,
INCORPORATED
1228 Euclid Ave Ste 390
Cleveland, OH 44115-1831
216-781-8624
Fax: 216-781-8852
Type of Counseling:
HECM Counseling,
Default/Foreclosure Counseling,
Prepurchase Counseling
Affiliate of: NATIONAL
FOUNDATION FOR
CONSUMER CREDIT,
INCORPORATED

NEAR WEST SIDE MULTI-
SERVICE CORPORATION
4115 Bridge Ave
Cleveland, OH 44113-3304
216-631-5800
Fax: 216-631-4595
Email:
maydugan@multiverse.com
Type of Counseling:
Prepurchase Counseling

LUTHERAN HOUSING
CORPORATION-WEST SIDE
OFFICE
1967 W 45th St
Cleveland, OH 44102-3449
216-651-0077
Fax: 216-651-0072
Type of Counseling:
HECM Counseling,
Default/Foreclosure Counseling,

Rental Counseling, Prepurchase
Counseling

**LUTHERAN HOUSING
CORPORATION-LARCHMERE
OFFICE**
12114 Larchmere Blvd
Cleveland, OH 44120-1139
216-231-5815
Fax: 216-231-5845
Type of Counseling:
HECM Counseling,
Default/Foreclosure Counseling,
Rental Counseling, Prepurchase
Counseling

**CONSUMER CREDIT
COUNSELING OF
NORTHEAST OHIO,
INCORPORATED**
2490 Lee Blvd Ste 310 Maylee
Bldg.
Cleveland Heights, OH 44118-
1255
216-771-0790
Fax: 216-781-8852
Type of Counseling:
HECM Counseling,
Default/Foreclosure Counseling,
Prepurchase Counseling

****COLUMBUS
NEIGHBORHOOD HOUSING
SERVICES, INCORPORATED**
604 E Rich St 3rd Fl
Columbus, OH 43215-5341
614-224-3603
Fax: 614-224-5946
Email: CNHS@ix.netcom.com
Type of Counseling:
Default/Foreclosure Counseling,
Prepurchase Counseling
Affiliate of: NEIGHBORHOOD
REINVESTMENT
CORPORATION

CONSOC CONSULTANTS
3632 Indianola Avenue, Ste A
Columbus, OH 432143734
614-267-8970
Fax: 614-267-8976
Type of Counseling:
HECM Counseling,
Default/Foreclosure Counseling,
Rental Counseling, Prepurchase
Counseling

**CONSUMER CREDIT
COUNSELING OF COLUMBUS**
697 E Broad St
Columbus, OH 43215-3948
614-464-2227
Fax: 614-464-2124
Type of Counseling:
Prepurchase Counseling,
Default/Foreclosure Counseling,
HECM Counseling

**MID-OHIO REGIONAL
PLANNING COMMISSION**
285 E Main St
Columbus, OH 43215-5272
614-233-4181
Fax: 614-228-1904
Email: morpc.org
Type of Counseling:
HECM Counseling, Rental
Counseling, Prepurchase
Counseling

HOMES ON THE HILL
12 South Terrace Avenue
Columbus, OH 43204
614-275-4663
Fax: 614-275-3060
Type of Counseling:
Default/Foreclosure Counseling,
Rental Counseling, Prepurchase
Counseling

**COLUMBUS HOUSING
PARTNERSHIP**
562 East Main St.
Columbus, OH 43215-5312
614-221-8889
Fax: 614-221-8591
Type of Counseling:
Default/Foreclosure Counseling,
Prepurchase Counseling, HECM
Counseling
Affiliate of: THE HOUSING
PARTNERSHIP NETWORK

FAMILY SOLUTIONS
2100 Front Street - Mall
Cuyahoga, OH 44221
330-928-1159
Fax: 330-928-2191
Type of Counseling:
Default/Foreclosure Counseling,
Rental Counseling, Prepurchase
Counseling

**LUTHERAN SOCIAL
SERVICES**
3131 S Dixie Dr Suite 300
Dayton, OH 45439
937-643-5599
Toll-Free: 800-359-0831
Fax: 937-643-9970
Email: jclifton@lssma.org
Type of Counseling:
Default/Foreclosure Counseling,
Prepurchase Counseling, HECM
Counseling
Affiliate of: NATIONAL
FOUNDATION FOR
CONSUMER CREDIT,
INCORPORATED

**LUTHERAN HOUSING
CORPORATION**
13944 Euclid Ave Ste 208
East Cleveland, OH 44112-3832
216-651-0077
Fax: 216-651-0072
Type of Counseling:
HECM Counseling,
Default/Foreclosure Counseling,
Rental Counseling, Prepurchase
Counseling

****HAMILTON
NEIGHBORHOOD HOUSING
SERVICES, INCORPORATED**
100 S. Martin Luther King, Jr.
Blvd.
Hamilton, OH 45011
513-737-9301
Toll-Free: 800-525-5420
Fax: 513-737-9304
Type of Counseling:
Default/Foreclosure Counseling,
Prepurchase Counseling
Affiliate of: NEIGHBORHOOD
REINVESTMENT
CORPORATION

**CONSUMER CREDIT
COUNSELING OF
NORTHEAST OHIO,
INCORPORATED**
763 Broadway Ste 202
Lorain, OH 44052-1857
216-771-0790
Fax: 216-781-8852
Type of Counseling:

HECM Counseling,
Default/Foreclosure Counseling,
Prepurchase Counseling

MARION-CRAWFORD
COMMUNITY ACTION
COMMISSION
1183 Bellefontaine Ave
Marion, OH 43302-7007
740-383-2154
Fax: 740-387-3407
Type of Counseling:
Default/Foreclosure Counseling,
Rental Counseling, Prepurchase
Counseling

MASSILLON URBAN LEAGUE
325 Third Street, SE
Massillon, OH 44646-
330-833-2804
Fax: 330-833-0126
Type of Counseling:
Default/Foreclosure Counseling,
Rental Counseling

CONSUMER CREDIT
COUNSELING OF
NORTHEAST OHIO,
INCORPORATED
7519 Mentor Avenue Rm. A104
Mentor, OH 44060
216-771-0790
Fax: 216-781-8852
Type of Counseling:
HECM Counseling,
Default/Foreclosure Counseling,
Prepurchase Counseling

CONSUMER CREDIT
COUNSELING OF
NORTHEAST OHIO,
INCORPORATED
5339 Ridge Rd Ste 201
Parma, OH 44129-1467
216-771-0790
Fax: 216-781-8852
Type of Counseling:
HECM Counseling,
Default/Foreclosure Counseling,
Prepurchase Counseling

PORTSMOUTH-INNER CITY
CORPORATION
1206 Waller St
Portsmouth, OH 45662-3524
740-354-6626

Fax: 740-353-2695
Type of Counseling:
HECM Counseling,
Default/Foreclosure Counseling,
Rental Counseling, Prepurchase
Counseling

**PORTAGE AREA
DEVELOPMENT
CORPORATION
218 West Main Street
Ravenna, OH 44266
330-297-6400
Fax: 330-297-5305
Type of Counseling:
Prepurchase Counseling
Affiliate of: NEIGHBORHOOD
REINVESTMENT
CORPORATION

COMMUNITY ACTION
COMMISSION OF BELMONT
COUNTY, INCORPORATED
100 W. Main Street, Suite 209
Saint Clairsville, OH 43950-
740-695-5477
Fax: 740-695-5477
Email: cachousing@aol.com
Type of Counseling:
HECM Counseling, Prepurchase
Counseling, Default/Foreclosure
Counseling

JEFFERSON COUNTY
COMMUNITY ACTION
COUNCIL
114 N. Fourth Street
Steubenville, OH 43952-
740-282-0971
Fax: 740-282-8631
Type of Counseling:
Prepurchase Counseling, HECM
Counseling, Rental Counseling

**NEIGHBORHOOD HOUSING
SERVICES OF TOLEDO,
INCORPORATED
704 Second St
Toledo, OH 43605
419-691-2900
Fax: 419-244-4035
Email: wfarnsel@toledolink.com
Type of Counseling:
Default/Foreclosure Counseling,
Prepurchase Counseling

Affiliate of: NEIGHBORHOOD
REINVESTMENT
CORPORATION

CATHOLIC CHARITIES,
DIOCESE OF TOLEDO,
HOUSING AND
EMPLOYMENT SERVICES
One Stranahan Square, Suite 354
Toledo, OH 436041495
419-244-6711
Fax: 419-242-4220
Type of Counseling:
HECM Counseling,
Default/Foreclosure Counseling,
Rental Counseling, Prepurchase
Counseling
Affiliate of: CATHOLIC
CHARITIES USA

CONSUMER CREDIT
COUNSELING SERVICE-
COMMUNITY SOLUTIONS
ASSOCIATION
320 High Street NE
Warren, OH 44481-1222
330-394-9090
Fax: 330-394-5910
Type of Counseling:
Default/Foreclosure Counseling,
Rental Counseling, Prepurchase
Counseling
Affiliate of: NATIONAL
FOUNDATION FOR
CONSUMER CREDIT,
INCORPORATED

**CATHOLIC COMMUNITY
SERVICES, INCORPORATED
175 Laird Ave NE 3rd Fl
Warren, OH 44482-1740
330-393-5254
Fax: 330-393-4050
Type of Counseling:
Rental Counseling, Prepurchase
Counseling, Default/Foreclosure
Counseling, HECM Counseling
Affiliate of: CATHOLIC
CHARITIES USA

COMMUNITY ACTION
COMMISSION OF FAYETTE
COUNTY
324 E Court St
Washington Court House, OH
43160-1402

740-335-7282
Fax: 740-335-6802
Type of Counseling:
HECM Counseling, Rental
Counseling, Prepurchase
Counseling

JACKSON-VINTON
COMMUNITY ACTION,
INCORPORATED
14333 State Route 327
Wellston, OH 45692-9307
740-384-3722
Fax: 740-384-5815

FAMILY SERVICE AGENCY
CONSUMER CREDIT
COUNSELING
535 Marmion Ave
Youngstown, OH 44502-2323
330-782-9113
Fax: 330-782-1614
Type of Counseling:
HECM Counseling,
Default/Foreclosure Counseling,
Rental Counseling, Prepurchase
Counseling
Affiliate of: NATIONAL
FOUNDATION FOR
CONSUMER CREDIT,
INCORPORATED

**CATHOLIC CHARITIES
HOUSING OPPORTUNITIES
225 Elm St
Youngstown, OH 44503-1005
330-744-8451
Fax: 330-742-6447
Type of Counseling:
Prepurchase Counseling,
Default/Foreclosure Counseling,
Rental Counseling, HECM
Counseling
Affiliate of: CATHOLIC
CHARITIES USA

YOUNGSTOWN AREA URBAN
LEAGUE
1350 5th Ave Ste 300
Youngstown, OH 44504-1728
330-744-4111
Fax: 330-744-1140
Type of Counseling:
HECM Counseling,
Default/Foreclosure Counseling,
Rental Counseling, Prepurchase
Counseling

UNIVERSAL CREDIT
COUNSELING SERVICES,
INCORPORATED
531 Market St
Zanesville, OH 43701-3610
740-450-2227
Toll-Free: 888-900-8227
Fax: 740-454-3933
Type of Counseling:
HECM Counseling,
Default/Foreclosure Counseling,
Rental Counseling, Prepurchase
Counseling

Oklahoma

CONSUMER CREDIT
COUNSELING SERVICE
Irving Center
704 North Oak, Room 7
Ada, OK 74820
800-364-2227
Toll-Free: 800-364-2227
Fax: 405-789-5052
Email: lhoover@cccsok.com
Type of Counseling:
Prepurchase Counseling, Rental
Counseling, Default/Foreclosure
Counseling, HECM Counseling

THE CHICKASAW NATION
601 W. 33rd St.
Ada, OK 74820
580-421-8800
Fax: 580-421-8879
Email:
carolynB@Chickasaw.com
Type of Counseling:
Rental Counseling, Prepurchase
Counseling, Default/Foreclosure
Counseling

CONSUMER CREDIT
COUNSELING SERVICE
Midfirst Bank, 2511 North Main
Altus, OK 73521
800-364-2227
Toll-Free: 800-364-2227
Fax: 405-789-5052
Email: lhoover@cccsok.com
Type of Counseling:
Prepurchase Counseling, Rental
Counseling, Default/Foreclosure
Counseling, HECM Counseling

CONSUMER CREDIT
COUNSELING SERVICE OF
GREATER
DALLAS/ARDMORE OK
333 W. Main, Suite 150
Ardmore, OK 73402
800-944-3826
Toll-Free: 800-944-3826
Fax: 580-224-9196
Type of Counseling:
Prepurchase Counseling, Rental
Counseling, Default/Foreclosure
Counseling, HECM Counseling

CREDIT COUNSELING
CENTERS OF OKLAHOMA,
INCORPORATED
210 S. Keeler
Bartlesville, OK 74006-
918-336-7619
Toll-Free: 800-324-5611
Fax: 918-336-2722
Type of Counseling:
Prepurchase Counseling,
Default/Foreclosure Counseling,
HECM Counseling, Rental
Counseling
Affiliate of: NATIONAL
FOUNDATION FOR
CONSUMER CREDIT,
INCORPORATED

CONSUMER CREDIT
COUNSELING SERVICE
3230 N Rockwell Ave
Bethany, OK 730081789
800-364-2227
Toll-Free: 800-364-2227
Fax: 405-789-5052
Email: lhoover@cccsok.com
Type of Counseling:
HECM Counseling,
Default/Foreclosure Counseling,
Rental Counseling, Prepurchase
Counseling

CREDIT COUNSELING
CENTERS OF OKLAHOMA,
INCORPORATED
828 N. Sycamore Ave.
Broken Arrow, OK 77012
918-259-0164
Toll-Free: 800-324-5611
Fax: 918-258-6237
Type of Counseling:

Prepurchase Counseling,
Default/Foreclosure Counseling,
HECM Counseling, Rental
Counseling
Affiliate of: NATIONAL
FOUNDATION FOR
CONSUMER CREDIT,
INCORPORATED

CONSUMER CREDIT
COUNSELING SERVICE
Canadian Valley Technology
Center, 1401N. Michigan
Chickasha, OK 73018
800-364-2227
Toll-Free: 800-364-2227
Fax: 405-789-5052
Email: lhoover@cccsok.com
Type of Counseling:
Prepurchase Counseling, Rental
Counseling, Default/Foreclosure
Counseling, HECM Counseling

CREDIT COUNSELING
CENTERS OF OKLAHOMA,
INCORPORATED
400 W. Will Rogers Blvd.
Claremore, OK 74017
918-343-3313
Toll-Free: 800-324-5611
Fax: 918-343-2712
Type of Counseling:
Prepurchase Counseling,
Default/Foreclosure Counseling,
HECM Counseling, Rental
Counseling
Affiliate of: NATIONAL
FOUNDATION FOR
CONSUMER CREDIT,
INCORPORATED

CENTRAL OKLAHOMA
COMMUNITY ACTION
ACENCY
122 N. Cleveland
Cushing, OK 74023
918-225-7469
Fax: 405-275-9442
Type of Counseling:
Prepurchase Counseling,
Default/Foreclosure Counseling,
HECM Counseling, Rental
Counseling

CONSUMER CREDIT
COUNSELING SERVICE

Del West Center, 3907 SE 29th St
Del City, OK 73115-2639
800-364-2227
Toll-Free: 800-364-2227
Fax: 405-789-5052
Email: lhoover@cccsok.com
Type of Counseling:
HECM Counseling,
Default/Foreclosure Counseling,
Rental Counseling, Prepurchase
Counseling

CONSUMER CREDIT
COUNSELING SERVICE
Local Oklahoma Bank, 2210
North Hwy 81 Suite A
Duncan, OK 73533
800-364-2227
Toll-Free: 800-364-2227
Fax: 405-789-5052
Email: lhoover@cccsok.com
Type of Counseling:
Prepurchase Counseling, Rental
Counseling, Default/Foreclosure
Counseling, HECM Counseling

CONSUMER CREDIT
COUNSELING SERVICE
Broadway South Building
2 East 11th Street Suite 109
Edmond, OK 73034-3922
800-364-2227
Toll-Free: 800-364-2227
Fax: 405-789-5052
Email: lhoover@cccsok.com
Type of Counseling:
HECM Counseling,
Default/Foreclosure Counseling,
Rental Counseling, Prepurchase
Counseling

COMMUNITY DEVELOPMENT
SUPPORT ASSOCIATION
2615 E Randolph
Enid, OK 73701
580-242-6131
Fax: 580-234-3554
Type of Counseling:
HECM Counseling,
Default/Foreclosure Counseling,
Rental Counseling, Prepurchase
Counseling

CONSUMER CREDIT
COUNSELING SERVICE
317 West Cherokee Ste A

Enid, OK 73701
800-364-2227
Toll-Free: 800-364-2227
Fax: 405-789-5052
Email: lhoover@cccsok.com
Type of Counseling:
HECM Counseling,
Default/Foreclosure Counseling,
Rental Counseling, Prepurchase
Counseling

CONSUMER CREDIT
COUNSELING SERVICE
Army Community Service
Building, 1651 Randolph Road
Ft. Sill, OK 73503
800-364-2227
Toll-Free: 800-364-2227
Fax: 405-789-5052
Email: lhoover@cccsok.com
Type of Counseling:
Prepurchase Counseling, Rental
Counseling, Default/Foreclosure
Counseling, HECM Counseling

CONSUMER CREDIT
COUNSELING SERVICE
First Capital Bank, 110 East
Cleveland
Guthrie, OK 73044
800-364-2227
Toll-Free: 800-364-2227
Fax: 405-789-5052
Email: lhoover@cccsok.com
Type of Counseling:
Prepurchase Counseling, Rental
Counseling, Default/Foreclosure
Counseling, HECM Counseling

CENTRAL OKLAHOMA
COMMUNITY ACTION
ACENCY
109 Oklahoma
Guthrie, OK 73044
405-282-4332
Fax: 405-275-9442
Type of Counseling:
Prepurchase Counseling,
Default/Foreclosure Counseling,
HECM Counseling, Rental
Counseling

CONSUMER CREDIT
COUNSELING SERVICE OF
NORTH CENTRAL TEXAS,
HUGO, OK

502 E. Rosewood
Hugo, OK 74743
580-326-5434
Fax: 972-542-3623
Type of Counseling:
Prepurchase Counseling, Rental
Counseling, Default/Foreclosure
Counseling, HECM Counseling

CONSUMER CREDIT
COUNSELING SERVICES OF
NORTH CENTRAL
TEXAS/HUGO, OK
502 E Rosewood
Hugo, OK 74743
580-326-5434
Fax: 972-542-3623
Type of Counseling:
Prepurchase Counseling, Rental
Counseling, Default/Foreclosure
Counseling, HECM Counseling

**LITTLE DIXIE COMMUNITY
ACTION AGENCY
502 West Duke Street
Hugo, OK 74743
580-326-5434
Fax: 580-326-0556
Type of Counseling:
Prepurchase Counseling,
Default/Foreclosure Counseling,
HECM Counseling
Affiliate of: NEIGHBORHOOD
REINVESTMENT
CORPORATION

CHOCTAW HOUSING
AUTHORITY
1005 S. 5th Street
Hugo, OK 74743
580-326-7521
Fax: 580-326-7641
Type of Counseling:
Rental Counseling,
Default/Foreclosure Counseling

CONSUMER CREDIT
COUNSELING SERVICE
Bank First
501 C Avenue Ste 308 C
Lawton, OK 735014325
800-364-2227
Toll-Free: 800-364-2227
Fax: 405-789-5052
Email: lhoover@cccsok.com
Type of Counseling:

HECM Counseling,
Default/Foreclosure Counseling,
Rental Counseling, Prepurchase
Counseling

HOUSING AUTHORITY OF
THE CITY OF LAWTON
609 SW F Avenue
Lawton, OK 73501
580-353-7392
Fax: 580-353-6111
Type of Counseling:
Prepurchase Counseling, Rental
Counseling, Default/Foreclosure
Counseling, HECM Counseling

CENTRAL OKLAHOMA
COMMUNITY ACTION
ACENCY
131 S. Main
Lexington, OK 73051
405-527-5883
Fax: 405-275-9442
Type of Counseling:
Prepurchase Counseling,
Default/Foreclosure Counseling,
HECM Counseling, Rental
Counseling

CENTRAL OKLAHOMA
COMMUNITY ACTION
ACENCY
410 W. Main Street
Maud, OK 74854
405-374-2222
Fax: 405-275-9442
Type of Counseling:
Prepurchase Counseling,
Default/Foreclosure Counseling,
HECM Counseling, Rental
Counseling

CREDIT COUNSELING
CENTERS OF OKLAHOMA,
INCORPORATED
100 North 5th
McAlester, OK 74501
918-423-2193
Toll-Free: 800-324-5611
Fax: 918-420-5901
Type of Counseling:
Prepurchase Counseling,
Default/Foreclosure Counseling,
HECM Counseling, Rental
Counseling

Affiliate of: NATIONAL
FOUNDATION FOR
CONSUMER CREDIT,
INCORPORATED

CENTRAL OKLAHOMA
COMMUNITY ACTION
ACENCY
2026 N. Broadway
Moore, OK 73160
405-799-5778
Fax: 405-275-9442
Type of Counseling:
Prepurchase Counseling,
Default/Foreclosure Counseling,
HECM Counseling, Rental
Counseling

CREDIT COUNSELING
CENTERS OF OKLAHOMA,
INCORPORATED
917 W. Broadwat
Muskogee, OK 74401
918-683-2778
Toll-Free: 800-324-5611
Fax: 918-683-5571
Type of Counseling:
Prepurchase Counseling,
Default/Foreclosure Counseling,
HECM Counseling, Rental
Counseling
Affiliate of: NATIONAL
FOUNDATION FOR
CONSUMER CREDIT,
INCORPORATED

THE HOUSING AUTHORITY
OF THE CITY OF MUSKOGEE
220 North 40th Street
Muskogee, OK 74401
918-687-6301
Fax: 918-687-3249
Email: blake@mhastaff.org
Website: www.mhastaff.org
Type of Counseling:
Prepurchase Counseling, Rental
Counseling, Default/Foreclosure
Counseling

CONSUMER CREDIT
COUNSELING SERVICE
Midtown Plaza
330 W Gray Ste 410
Norman, OK 73069-7111
800-364-2227
Toll-Free: 800-364-2227

Fax: 405-789-5052
Email: lhoover@cccsok.com
Type of Counseling:
HECM Counseling,
Default/Foreclosure Counseling,
Rental Counseling, Prepurchase
Counseling

HOUSING AUTHORITY OF
THE CITY OF NORMAN
700 N Berry Rd
Norman, OK 73069
405-329-0933
Fax: 405-329-2542
Type of Counseling:
HECM Counseling,
Default/Foreclosure Counseling,
Rental Counseling, Prepurchase
Counseling

CENTRAL OKLAHOMA
COMMUNITY ACTION
ACENCY
1121E. Main
Norman, OK 73071
405-701-2120
Fax: 405-275-9442
Type of Counseling:
Prepurchase Counseling,
Default/Foreclosure Counseling,
HECM Counseling, Rental
Counseling

CONSUMER CREDIT
COUNSELING SERVICE
Western Tower Building, 5350
South Western, Suite 601
Oklahoma City, OK 73139-2740
800-364-2227
Toll-Free: 800-364-2227
Fax: 405-789-5052
Email: lhoover@cccsok.com
Type of Counseling:
HECM Counseling,
Default/Foreclosure Counseling,
Rental Counseling, Prepurchase
Counseling

OKLAHOMA HOUSING
FINANCE AGENCY
1140 Northwest 63rd, Suite 200
Oklahoma City, OK 73126-0720
405-848-1144
Fax: 405-840-1109
Type of Counseling:

Prepurchase Counseling, Rental
Counseling, Default/Foreclosure
Counseling

COMMUNITY ACTION
AGENCY OF OKLAHOMA
CITY AND
OKLAHOMA/CANADIAN
COUNTIES
1900 NW 10th St
Oklahoma City, OK 73106-2428
405-232-0199
Fax: 405-232-9074
Type of Counseling:
HECM Counseling,
Default/Foreclosure Counseling,
Rental Counseling, Prepurchase
Counseling

CONSUMER CREDIT
COUNSELING
CLEARINGHOUSE
420 Southwest 10th
Oklahoma City, OK 73109
800-364-2227
Toll-Free: 800-364-2227
Fax: 405-789-5052
Email: lhoover@cccsok.com
Type of Counseling:
Prepurchase Counseling, Rental
Counseling, Default/Foreclosure
Counseling, HECM Counseling

**NEIGHBORHOOD HOUSING
SERVICES OF OKLAHOMA
CITY, INCORPORATED
1320 Classen Dr. Ste 200
Oklahoma City, OK 73103
405-231-4663
Fax: 405-231-5137
Email: nhsokc@ixnetcom.com
Type of Counseling:
Prepurchase Counseling,
Default/Foreclosure Counseling
Affiliate of: NEIGHBORHOOD
REINVESTMENT
CORPORATION

CONSUMER CREDIT
COUNSELING SERVICE
Urban League Building, 3017
North Martin Luther King Blvd.
Oklahoma City, OK 73111
800-364-2227
Toll-Free: 800-364-2227
Fax: 405-789-5052

Email: lhoover@cccsok.com
Type of Counseling:
Prepurchase Counseling, Rental
Counseling, Default/Foreclosure
Counseling, HECM Counseling

**LATINO COMMUNITY
DEVELOPMENT AGENCY
420 SW 10th
Oklahoma City, OK 73109
405-236-0701
Fax: 405-236-0737
Email:
LCDACHODO@juno.com
Type of Counseling:
Prepurchase Counseling
Affiliate of: NATIONAL
COUNCIL OF LA RAZA

CONSUMER CREDIT
COUNSELING SERVICE
Macarthur Executive Building,
4614 North MacArthur Suite 232
Oklahoma City, OK 73122
800-364-2227
Toll-Free: 800-364-2227
Fax: 405-789-5052
Email: lhoover@cccsok.com
Type of Counseling:
Prepurchase Counseling, Rental
Counseling, Default/Foreclosure
Counseling, HECM Counseling

DEEP FORK COMMUNITY
ACTION FOUNDATION,
INCORPORATED
313 W 8th St
Okmulgee, OK 74447-5006
918-756-2826
Fax: 918-756-6829
Type of Counseling:
Rental Counseling, Prepurchase
Counseling, HECM Counseling

CREDIT COUNSELING
CENTERS OF OKLAHOMA,
INCORPORATED
114 N. Grand, suite 212
Okmulgee, OK 74447
918-756-5170
Toll-Free: 800-324-5611
Fax: 918-756-5170
Type of Counseling:
Prepurchase Counseling,
Default/Foreclosure Counseling,

HECM Counseling, Rental
Counseling
Affiliate of: NATIONAL
FOUNDATION FOR
CONSUMER CREDIT,
INCORPORATED

CREDIT COUNSELING
CENTERS OF OKLAHOMA,
INCORPORATED
207 S. Cedar
Owasso, OK 74055
918-272-3226
Toll-Free: 800-324-5611
Fax: 918-274-0601
Type of Counseling:
Prepurchase Counseling,
Default/Foreclosure Counseling,
HECM Counseling, Rental
Counseling
Affiliate of: NATIONAL
FOUNDATION FOR
CONSUMER CREDIT,
INCORPORATED

CONSUMER CREDIT
COUNSELING SERVICE
Pioneer Technology Center, 2015
North Ash, Room D107
Ponca City, OK 74601
800-364-2227
Toll-Free: 800-364-2227
Fax: 405-789-5052
Email: lhoover@cccsok.com
Type of Counseling:
Prepurchase Counseling, Rental
Counseling, Default/Foreclosure
Counseling, HECM Counseling

CENTRAL OKLAHOMA
COMMUNITY ACTION
ACENCY
807 Jim Thorpe Blvd.
Prague, OK 74864
405-587-4591
Fax: 405-275-9442
Type of Counseling:
Prepurchase Counseling,
Default/Foreclosure Counseling,
HECM Counseling, Rental
Counseling

CREDIT COUNSELING
CENTERS OF OKLAHOMA,
INCORPORATED
210 E. Dewey

Sapulpa, OK 74066
918-224-8412
Toll-Free: 800-324-5611
Fax: 918-224-8759
Type of Counseling:
Prepurchase Counseling,
Default/Foreclosure Counseling,
HECM Counseling, Rental
Counseling
Affiliate of: NATIONAL
FOUNDATION FOR
CONSUMER CREDIT,
INCORPORATED

CENTRAL OKLAHOMA
COMMUNITY ACTION
ACENCY
600 E. Strothers
Seminole, OK 74888
405-382-1800
Fax: 405-275-9442
Type of Counseling:
Prepurchase Counseling,
Default/Foreclosure Counseling,
HECM Counseling, Rental
Counseling

CONSUMER CREDIT
COUNSELING SERVICE
Mid First Bank 330 N. Broadway
Shawnee, OK 74801
800-364-2227
Toll-Free: 800-364-2227
Fax: 405-789-5052
Email: lhoover@cccsok.com
Type of Counseling:
Prepurchase Counseling, Rental
Counseling, Default/Foreclosure
Counseling, HECM Counseling

CENTRAL OKLAHOMA
COMMUNITY ACTION
ACENCY
132 N. Bell
Shawnee, OK 74801
405-878-9500
Fax: 405-275-9442
Type of Counseling:
Prepurchase Counseling,
Default/Foreclosure Counseling,
HECM Counseling, Rental
Counseling

CENTRAL OKLAHOMA
COMMUNITY ACTION
ACENCY

510 W. Benedict
Shawnee, OK 74801
405-214-4455
Fax: 405-275-9442
Type of Counseling:
Prepurchase Counseling,
Default/Foreclosure Counseling,
HECM Counseling, Rental
Counseling

KI BOIS COMMUNITY
ACTION FOUNDATION,
INCORPORATED
301 E Main
Stigler, OK 74462
918-967-9050
Fax: 918-967-9025
Type of Counseling:
Prepurchase Counseling, Rental
Counseling, Default/Foreclosure
Counseling

STILLWATER HOUSING
AUTHORITY
807 S Lowry
Stillwater, OK 74074
405-372-4906
Fax: 405-372-1416
Email: sha@ionet.net
Type of Counseling:
HECM Counseling,
Default/Foreclosure Counseling,
Rental Counseling, Prepurchase
Counseling

CONSUMER CREDIT
COUNSELING SERVICE
Postal Plaza Building, 720 South
Husband, Suite 10
Stillwater, OK 74074
800-364-2227
Toll-Free: 800-364-2227
Fax: 405-789-5052
Email: lhoover@cccsok.com
Type of Counseling:
Prepurchase Counseling, Rental
Counseling, Default/Foreclosure
Counseling, HECM Counseling

CENTRAL OKLAHOMA
COMMUNITY ACTION
ACENCY
619 W. 12
Stillwater, OK 74074
405-624-2533
Fax: 405-275-9442

Type of Counseling:
Prepurchase Counseling,
Default/Foreclosure Counseling,
HECM Counseling, Rental
Counseling

**HOUSING AUTHORITY OF
THE CHEROKEE NATION**
1500 Hensley Drive
Tahlequah, OK 74465-1007
918-456-5482
Fax: 918-458-5018
Type of Counseling:
Default/Foreclosure Counseling,
Rental Counseling, Prepurchase
Counseling

**CONSUMER CREDIT
COUNSELING SERVICE**
Building 420
Tinker AFB, OK 73145
800-364-2227
Toll-Free: 800-364-2227
Fax: 405-789-5052
Email: lhoover@cccsok.com
Type of Counseling:
Prepurchase Counseling, Rental
Counseling, Default/Foreclosure
Counseling, HECM Counseling

**CREDIT COUNSELING
CENTERS OF OKLAHOMA,
INCORPORATED**
4646 S Harvard Ave
Tulsa, OK 741590450
918-744-5611
Toll-Free: 800-324-5611
Fax: 918-744-0232
Website: www.cccsofok.com
Type of Counseling:
Prepurchase Counseling, Rental
Counseling, Default/Foreclosure
Counseling, HECM Counseling
Affiliate of: NATIONAL
FOUNDATION FOR
CONSUMER CREDIT,
INCORPORATED

**COMMUNITY ACTION
PROJECT OF TULSA**
717 South Houston, Ste. 200
Tulsa, OK 74127
918-382-3200
Fax: 918-382-3213
Type of Counseling:

Prepurchase Counseling,
Default/Foreclosure Counseling
Affiliate of: NEIGHBORHOOD
REINVESTMENT
CORPORATION

**CREDIT COUNSELING
CENTERS OF OKLAHOMA,
INCORPORATED**
1 W. 36TH Street N
Tulsa, OK 74106
918-425-8289
Toll-Free: 800-324-5611
Fax: 918-428-7510
Type of Counseling:
Prepurchase Counseling,
Default/Foreclosure Counseling,
HECM Counseling, Rental
Counseling
Affiliate of: NATIONAL
FOUNDATION FOR
CONSUMER CREDIT,
INCORPORATED

**METROPOLITAN TULSA
URBAN LEAGUE**
240 E Apache Street
Tulsa, OK 74106-3799
918-584-5221
Fax: 918-584-3620
Type of Counseling: Rental
Counseling

**HOUSING PARTNERS OF
TULSA, INCORPORATED**
415 E. Independence
Tulsa, OK 74106
918-581-5711
Fax: 918-582-0397
Type of Counseling:
Prepurchase Counseling, Rental
Counseling, Default/Foreclosure
Counseling, HECM Counseling

**CONSUMER CREDIT
COUNSELING SERVICE**
1st National Bank Building, 1100
East Main, 3rd Floor
Weatherford, OK 73096
800-364-2227
Toll-Free: 800-364-2227
Fax: 405-789-5052
Email: lhoover@cccsok.com
Type of Counseling:

Prepurchase Counseling, Rental
Counseling, Default/Foreclosure
Counseling, HECM Counseling

**CENTRAL OKLAHOMA
COMMUNITY ACTION
ACENCY**
318 W. 4TH Street
Wewoka, OK 74884
405-257-3423
Fax: 405-275-9442
Type of Counseling:
Prepurchase Counseling,
Default/Foreclosure Counseling,
HECM Counseling, Rental
Counseling

OREGON

****CONSUMER CREDIT
COUNSELING SERVICE OF
LINN-BENTON**
214 NW Hickory Street
Albany, OR 97321-0381
541-926-5843
Toll-Free: 888-225-0009
Fax: 541-926-6731
Type of Counseling:
HECM Counseling,
Default/Foreclosure Counseling,
Rental Counseling, Prepurchase
Counseling
Affiliate of: NATIONAL
FOUNDATION FOR
CONSUMER CREDIT,
INCORPORATED

****CONSUMER CREDIT
COUNSELING SERVICE OF
COOS-CURRY,
INCORPORATED**
2110 Newmark Ave
Coos Bay, OR 97420-2957
541-888-7040
Fax: 541-888-7044
Type of Counseling:
HECM Counseling,
Default/Foreclosure Counseling,
Rental Counseling, Prepurchase
Counseling
Affiliate of: NATIONAL
FOUNDATION FOR
CONSUMER CREDIT,
INCORPORATED

CORVALLIS NEIGHBORHOOD HOUSING SERVICES, INCORPORATED
2797 NW 9th St
Corvallis, OR 97330
541-752-7220
Fax: 541-752-5037
Email: cnhs@proaxis.com
Type of Counseling:
Prepurchase Counseling
Affiliate of: NEIGHBORHOOD REINVESTMENT CORPORATION

CONSUMER CREDIT COUNSELING SERVICE OF LANE COUNTY, INCORPORATED
149 W 12th Ave Ste 100
Eugene, OR 97440
541-342-4459
Toll-Free: 888-830-7235
Fax: 541-342-5467
Email: cccslane@clipper.net
Website:
www.creditdebthelp.com
Type of Counseling:
HECM Counseling,
Default/Foreclosure Counseling,
Rental Counseling, Prepurchase
Counseling

CONSUMER CREDIT COUNSELING SERVICE OF OREGON-HILLSBORO
1050 SW Baseline Rd
Suite A8
Hillsboro, OR 97123-3873
888-875-2227
Fax: 503-408-6820
Type of Counseling:
HECM Counseling,
Default/Foreclosure Counseling,
Rental Counseling, Prepurchase
Counseling

OPEN DOOR COUNSELING CENTER
34420 SW Tualatin Valley Hwy
Hillsboro, OR 97123-5470
503-640-6689
Fax: 503-640-9374
Type of Counseling:
Default/Foreclosure Counseling,
Prepurchase Counseling, HECM
Counseling, Rental Counseling

CONSUMER CREDIT COUNSELING SERVICES OF SOUTHERN OREGON
740 Main St.
Klamath Falls, OR 97601
541-883-8118
Fax: 541-883-8118
Type of Counseling:
Prepurchase Counseling, Rental
Counseling

CONSUMER CREDIT COUNSELING SERVICES OF SOUTHERN OREGON
820 Crater Lake Ave., Ste. 202
Medford, OR 97504
541-779-2273
Fax: 5417796412
Type of Counseling:
Prepurchase Counseling, Rental
Counseling
Affiliate of: NATIONAL FOUNDATION FOR CONSUMER CREDIT, INCORPORATED

ACCESS INCORPORATED
3630 Aviation Way
Medford, OR 97501
541-779-6691
Toll-Free: 800-452-2463
Fax: 541-779-8886
Type of Counseling:
HECM Counseling,
Default/Foreclosure Counseling,
Rental Counseling, Prepurchase
Counseling

PORTLAND HOUSING CENTER
3233 NE Sandy Blvd.
Portland, OR 972322557
503-282-7744
Fax: 503-736-0101
Email: kburkert@teleport.com
Type of Counseling:
Default/Foreclosure Counseling,
Rental Counseling, Prepurchase
Counseling
Affiliate of: NEIGHBORHOOD REINVESTMENT CORPORATION

CENTRAL OREGON COMMUNITY ACTION AGENCY NETWORK

2303 SW First St
Redmond, OR 97756
541-548-2380
Fax: 541-548-6013
Type of Counseling:
Default/Foreclosure Counseling,
Prepurchase Counseling, HECM
Counseling

UMPQUA COMMUNITY ACTION NETWORK
2448 W Harvard Blvd
Roseburg, OR 97470
541-673-1789
Fax: 541-672-1983
Type of Counseling:
HECM Counseling,
Default/Foreclosure Counseling,
Rental Counseling, Prepurchase
Counseling

Pennsylvania

HISPANIC AMERICAN ORGANIZATION
136 S. 4th Street
Allentown, PA 18102
610-435-5334
Fax: 610-435-2131
Type of Counseling:
Prepurchase Counseling

ALLENTOWN NEIGHBORHOOD HOUSING SERVICES, INCORPORATED
239 N.10th Street
Allentown, PA 18102
610-437-4571
Fax: 610-437-9958
Email: Jjanisnhs@aol.com
Type of Counseling:
Default/Foreclosure Counseling,
Prepurchase Counseling
Affiliate of: NEIGHBORHOOD REINVESTMENT CORPORATION

HOUSING OPPORTUNITIES OF BEAVER COUNTY, INCORPORATED
650 Corporation St Ste 207
Beaver, PA 15009
724-728-7511
Fax: 724-728-7202
Email: hobc@timesnet.net
Website: www.hobc123.org

Type of Counseling:
Default/Foreclosure Counseling,
Prepurchase Counseling

BUTLER COUNTY HOUSING
AUTHORITY
111 S. Cliff Street
Butler, PA 16003-1917
724-287-6797
Fax: 724-287-7906
Type of Counseling:
Prepurchase Counseling,
Default/Foreclosure Counseling,
HECM Counseling, Rental
Counseling

CONSUMER CREDIT
COUNSELING SERVICE OF
NORTHEASTERN
PENNSYLVANIA
1400 Abington Executive Park
Suite #1
Clarks Summit, PA 18411
570-587-9163
Toll-Free: 800-922-9537
Fax: 570-587-9134
Email: cccsnepa@epix.net
Website:
www.websiteint.com/cccsnepa
Type of Counseling:
Prepurchase Counseling,
Default/Foreclosure Counseling,
HECM Counseling, Rental
Counseling
Affiliate of: NATIONAL
FOUNDATION FOR
CONSUMER CREDIT,
INCORPORATED

**SHILOH COMMUNITY
SERVICES, INCORPORATED
548 Canal Street
Easton, PA 18042
610-252-5538
Fax: 610-252-0928
Type of Counseling:
Prepurchase Counseling, Rental
Counseling, Default/Foreclosure
Counseling, HECM Counseling
Affiliate of: CONGRESS OF
NATIONAL BLACK
CHURCHES, INCORPORATED

NORTHERN TIER
COMMUNITY ACTION
CORPORATION

135 W 4th St
Emporium, PA 15834-1123
814-486-1161
Fax: 814-486-0825
Type of Counseling: Rental
Counseling, Prepurchase
Counseling

**SAINT MARTIN CENTER
1701 Parade Street
Erie, PA 16503-1994
814-452-6113
Fax: 814-456-7310
Email: DPESCH1@AOL.COM
Type of Counseling:
Prepurchase Counseling, Rental
Counseling, Default/Foreclosure
Counseling, HECM Counseling
Affiliate of: CATHOLIC
CHARITIES USA

GREATER ERIE COMMUNITY
ACTION AGENCY
18 W 9th St
Erie, PA 16501-1343
814-459-4581
Fax: 814-456-0161
Email: rllgeac@erie.net
Type of Counseling:
HECM Counseling,
Default/Foreclosure Counseling,
Rental Counseling, Prepurchase
Counseling

BOOKER T. WASHINGTON
CENTER
1720 Holland St
Erie, PA 16503-1808
814-453-5744
Fax: 814-453-5749
Type of Counseling:
HECM Counseling,
Default/Foreclosure Counseling,
Rental Counseling, Prepurchase
Counseling

BAYFRONT NATO,
INCORPORATED
312 Chestnut St
Erie, PA 16507-1222
814-459-2761
Fax: 814-455-2743
Email: Bmlkcenter@aol.com
Type of Counseling:

Prepurchase Counseling, Rental
Counseling, Default/Foreclosure
Counseling

SHENANGO VALLEY URBAN
LEAGUE
601 Indiana Ave
Farrell, PA 16121-1759
724-981-5310
Fax: 724-981-1544
Type of Counseling:
HECM Counseling,
Default/Foreclosure Counseling,
Rental Counseling, Prepurchase
Counseling
Affiliate of: NATIONAL
URBAN LEAGUE

CONSUMER CREDIT
COUNSELING SERVICE OF
WESTERN PENNSYLVANIA
2000 Linglestown Road, Suite
302
Harrisburg, PA 17110
717-541-1757
Toll-Free: 888-599-2227
Fax: 717-540-4670
Website: www.cccspa.org
Type of Counseling:
Default/Foreclosure Counseling,
HECM Counseling, Prepurchase
Counseling, Rental Counseling

URBAN LEAGUE OF
METROPOLITAN
HARRISBURG
2107 N 6th St
Harrisburg, PA 17110-2453
717-234-3253
Fax: 717-234-9459
Type of Counseling:
Default/Foreclosure Counseling,
Prepurchase Counseling

FAIR HOUSING COUNCIL OF
THE CAPITAL REGION,
INCORPORATED
2100 North 6th Street
Harrisburg, PA 17110-2401
717-238-9540
Fax: 717-233-5001
Email: hfhc@pa.net
Type of Counseling:
HECM Counseling,
Default/Foreclosure Counseling,

Rental Counseling, Prepurchase
Counseling

PENNSYLVANIA HOUSING
FINANCE AGENCY
2101 North Front Street
Harrisburg, PA 17105-8029
717-780-3800
Toll-Free: 800-342-2397
Fax: 717-780-3905
Type of Counseling:
Default/Foreclosure Counseling

INDIANA COUNTY
COMMUNITY ACTION
PROGRAM, INCORPORATED
827 Water St
Indiana, PA 15701-1755
724-465-2657
Fax: 724-465-5118
Email:
ICCAP@MAIL.MICROSERVE.N
ET
Type of Counseling:
HECM Counseling,
Default/Foreclosure Counseling,
Rental Counseling, Prepurchase
Counseling

ELK COUNTY HOUSING
AUTHORITY
424 Water Street Ext
Johnsonburg, PA 15845-1547
814-965-2532
Fax: 814-965-5616
Type of Counseling:
Rental Counseling

ARMSTRONG COUNTY
COMMUNITY ACTION
AGENCY
124 Armsdale Road Suite 211
Kittanning, PA 16201-0028
724-548-3405
Fax: 724-548-3413
Type of Counseling: Rental
Counseling
TABOR COMMUNITY
SERVICES
439 E King St
Lancaster, PA 17602-3004
717-397-5182
Fax: 717-399-4127
Email: kmmcdivitt@tabornet.org
Type of Counseling:

Prepurchase Counseling,
Default/Foreclosure Counseling,
HECM Counseling, Rental
Counseling

HOUSING OPPORTUNITIES,
INCORPORATED
133 7th St
Mc Keesport, PA 15134
412-664-1590
Fax: 412-664-0873
Email: HOIMAIN@AOL.COM
Type of Counseling:
Default/Foreclosure Counseling,
Prepurchase Counseling, HECM
Counseling
Affiliate of: HOUSING
OPPORTUNITIES,
INCORPORATED

CENTER FOR FAMILY
SERVICES, INCORPORATED
213 W Center St
Meadville, PA 16335-3406
814-337-8450
Fax: 814-337-8457
Type of Counseling:
HECM Counseling,
Default/Foreclosure Counseling,
Rental Counseling, Prepurchase
Counseling

TREHAB CENTER OF
NORTHEAST PENNSYLVANIA
10 Public Avenue
Montrose, PA 18801-0366
570-278-3338
Fax: 570-278-1889
Email: JCRONK@EPIX.NET
Type of Counseling:
HECM Counseling,
Default/Foreclosure Counseling,
Prepurchase Counseling

LAWRENCE COUNTY SOCIAL
SERVICES, INCORPORATED
241 W. Grant Street
New Castle, PA 16103-0189
724-658-7258
Fax: 724-658-7664
Email: dhennon@lawcss.org
Type of Counseling:
HECM Counseling,
Default/Foreclosure Counseling,
Rental Counseling, Prepurchase
Counseling

PHILADELPHIA COUNCIL
FOR COMMUNITY
ADVANCEMENT
100 N 17th St Ste 700
Philadelphia, PA 19103-2736
215-567-7803
Toll-Free: 800-930-4663
Fax: 215-963-9941
Email: philapcca@aol.com
Website:
www.nelsononline.com/pcca/
Type of Counseling: HECM
Counseling, Prepurchase
Counseling, Default/Foreclosure
Counseling

HOUSING ASSOCIATION
INFORMATION PROGRAM
658-60 N Watts St
Philadelphia, PA 19123-2422
215-978-0224
Fax: 215-765-7614
Type of Counseling:
Default/Foreclosure Counseling,
Rental Counseling, Prepurchase
Counseling

TENANTS' ACTION GROUP
OF PHILADELPHIA
21 S 12th St 12th Fl
Philadelphia, PA 19107-3614
215-575-0700
Fax: 215-575-0718
Type of Counseling:
Rental Counseling

PHILADELPHIA HOUSING
DEVELOPMENT
CORPORATION
1234 Market St 17th Fl
Philadelphia, PA 19107-3721
215-448-3137
Fax: 215-448-3133

NORTHWEST COUNSELING
SERVICE
5001 N Broad St
Philadelphia, PA 19141-2217
215-324-7500
Fax: 215-324-8753
Type of Counseling:
HECM Counseling,
Default/Foreclosure Counseling,
Rental Counseling, Prepurchase
Counseling

URBAN LEAGUE OF
PHILADELPHIA
251-53 S 24th St
Philadelphia, PA 19103-5529
215-451-5005
Fax: 215-451-5006
Email: rwsulp@aol.com
Default/Foreclosure Counseling,
Prepurchase Counseling, Rental
Counseling, HECM Counseling

NUEVA ESPERANZA,
INCORPORATED
4261 N. 5th Street
Philadelphia, PA 19140
215-324-0746
Fax: 215-324-2542
Email: motero@nueva.org
Type of Counseling:
Prepurchase Counseling,
Default/Foreclosure Counseling

**THE REINVESTMENT FUND
718 Arch Street Suite 300 North
Philadelphia, PA 19106
215-925-1130
Fax: 215-717-4627
Type of Counseling:
Prepurchase Counseling,
Default/Foreclosure Counseling
Affiliate of: THE HOUSING
PARTNERSHIP NETWORK

**ASOCIACION
PUERTORIQUENOS EN
MARCHA
600 West Diamond Street
Philadelphia, PA 19122
215-235-6070
Fax: 215-235-7335
Email: apmhc@philly.infi.net
Type of Counseling:
Prepurchase Counseling, Rental
Counseling
Affiliate of: NATIONAL
COUNCIL OF LA RAZA

GERMANTOWN SETTLEMENT
218 W. Chelten Avenue
Philadelphia, PA 19144
215-849-3104
Fax: 215-843-7264
Type of Counseling:
Default/Foreclosure Counseling,
Prepurchase Counseling, Rental
Counseling

Affiliate of: HOUSING
OPPORTUNITIES,
INCORPORATED

**MOUNT AIRY, U S A
6639-41 Germantown Ave
Philadelphia, PA 19119
215-844-6021
Fax: 215-844-9167
Type of Counseling:
Rental Counseling,
Default/Foreclosure Counseling,
Prepurchase Counseling
Affiliate of: HOUSING
OPPORTUNITIES,
INCORPORATED

PHILADELPHIA
NEIGHBORHOOD HOUSING
SERVICES, INCORPORATED
511 North Broad St 4TH Floor
Philadelphia, PA 19123
215-988-9879
Fax: 215-988-1297
Type of Counseling:
Prepurchase Counseling,
Default/Foreclosure Counseling
Affiliate of: NEIGHBORHOOD
REINVESTMENT
CORPORATION

INTERCULTURAL FAMILY
SERVICES, INCORPORATED
4225 Chestnut St
Philadelphia, PA 19104-3014
215-386-1298
Fax: 215-386-9348
Type of Counseling:
Rental Counseling, Prepurchase
Counseling, Default/Foreclosure
Counseling

NEW KENSINGTON
COMMUNITY DEVELOPMENT
CORPORATION
2513-15 Frankford Ave
Philadelphia, PA 19125-1708
215-427-0322
Fax: 215-427-1302
Email:
NEWKENWLIBERTYNET.ORG
Type of Counseling:
Default/Foreclosure Counseling,
Prepurchase Counseling

Affiliate of: HOUSING
OPPORTUNITIES,
INCORPORATED

CENTRO PEDRO CLAVER,
INCORPORATED
3565 N 7th St
Philadelphia, PA 19140-4401
215-227-7111
Fax: 215-227-7105
Email: centro@Libertynet.org
Type of Counseling:
Prepurchase Counseling,
Default/Foreclosure Counseling

**CONSUMER CREDIT
COUNSELING SERVICE OF
DELAWARE VALLEY
1515 Market St Ste 1325
Philadelphia, PA 19102
215-563-5665
Fax: 215-563-7020
Type of Counseling:
Default/Foreclosure Counseling,
Rental Counseling
Affiliate of: NATIONAL
FOUNDATION FOR
CONSUMER CREDIT,
INCORPORATED

HOUSING CONSORTIUM FOR
DISABLED INDIVIDUALS
4701 Pine Street
Philadelphia, PA
215-528-5056
Fax: 215-528-5848
Type of Counseling:
Rental Counseling, Prepurchase
Counseling, Default/Foreclosure
Counseling

**PHILADELPHIA
DEVELOPMENT
PARTNERSHIP
1334 Walnut St 7th Fl
Philadelphia, PA 19107
215-545-3100
Fax: 215-546-8055
Website: www.pdp-inc.org
Type of Counseling:
Prepurchase Counseling,
Default/Foreclosure Counseling,
Rental Counseling
Affiliate of: THE HOUSING
PARTNERSHIP NETWORK

UNEMPLOYMENT
INFORMATION CENTER
1201 Chestnut Street, #702
Philadelphia, PA 19107
215-848-0848
Fax: 215-557-6981
Type of Counseling:
Default/Foreclosure Counseling

ACORN HOUSING
CORPORATION
846 N Broad St 2nd floor
Philadelphia, PA 19130-2234
215-765-1221
Fax: 215-765-0045
Type of Counseling:
Default/Foreclosure Counseling,
Prepurchase Counseling
Affiliate of: ACORN HOUSING
CORPORATION

**DIVERSIFIED COMMUNITY
SERVICES
1210 South Broad Street
Philadelphia, PA 19146
215-336-3511
Fax: 215-551-4327
Type of Counseling:
Prepurchase Counseling,
Default/Foreclosure Counseling,
Rental Counseling
Affiliate of: HOUSING
OPPORTUNITIES,
INCORPORATED

ACTION HOUSING,
INCORPORATED
425 Sixth Ave Ste 950
Pittsburgh, PA 15219-1819
412-391-1956
Fax: 412-391-4512
Type of Counseling:
HECM Counseling,
Default/Foreclosure Counseling,
Rental Counseling, Prepurchase
Counseling
Affiliate of: THE HOUSING
PARTNERSHIP NETWORK

**OPERATION NEHEMIAH
235 Eastgate Drive
Pittsburgh, PA 152351413
412-704-1247
Fax: 412-244-3512
Type of Counseling:
Prepurchase Counseling

Affiliate of: CONGRESS OF
NATIONAL BLACK
CHURCHES, INCORPORATED

CENTER FOR INDEPENDENT
LIVING SW PA
7110 Penn Ave
Pittsburgh, PA 15208-2434
412-371-7700
Fax: 412-371-9430
Type of Counseling:
HECM Counseling,
Default/Foreclosure Counseling,
Rental Counseling, Prepurchase
Counseling

CONSUMER CREDIT
COUNSELING OF WESTERN
PENNSYLVANIA
2403 Sidney Street, Suite 40
Pittsburgh, PA 152222294
412-390-1300
Toll-Free: 888-599-2227
Fax: 412-390-1336
Website: www.cccspa.org
Type of Counseling:
HECM Counseling,
Default/Foreclosure Counseling,
Rental Counseling, Prepurchase
Counseling
Affiliate of: NATIONAL
FOUNDATION FOR
CONSUMER CREDIT,
INCORPORATED

GARFIELD JUBILEE
ASSOCIATION,
INCORPORATED
5138 Penn Ave
Pittsburgh, PA 15224-1616
412-665-5200
Fax: 412-665-5205
Email:
GARFIELD@HILLHOUSE.CKP.
EDU
Type of Counseling:
HECM Counseling,
Default/Foreclosure Counseling,
Rental Counseling, Prepurchase
Counseling

NEIGHBORHOOD HOUSING
SERVICES, INCORPORATED
355 5th Ave. Suite 1022, Park
Building
Pittsburgh, PA 15222-2407

412-281-9773
Fax: 412-232-3615
Type of Counseling:
Prepurchase Counseling
Affiliate of: NEIGHBORHOOD
REINVESTMENT
CORPORATION

URBAN LEAGUE OF
PITTSBURGH
One Smithfield St 3rd Floor
Pittsburgh, PA 15222-2222
412-227-4802
Fax: 412-227-4870
Email: league@hillhouse.ckp.edu
Type of Counseling:
HECM Counseling,
Default/Foreclosure Counseling,
Rental Counseling, Prepurchase
Counseling
Affiliate of: NATIONAL
URBAN LEAGUE

**NAZARETH HOUSING
SERVICES
285 Bellevue Road
Pittsburgh, PA 15229-2173
412-931-3510
Fax: 412-931-7255
Email: SRCINDY@JUNO.COM
Type of Counseling:
Prepurchase Counseling,
Default/Foreclosure Counseling
Affiliate of: HOUSING
OPPORTUNITIES,
INCORPORATED

ELDER-ADO, INCORPORATED
320 Brownsville Rd
Pittsburgh, PA 15210-2249
412-381-6900
Fax: 412-381-3797
Type of Counseling:
HECM Counseling

SCHUYKILL COMMUNITY
ACTION
225 N Centre St
Pottsville, PA 17901-2511
570-622-1995
Fax: 570-622-0429
Email: ECONOPP@PTD.NET
Type of Counseling:
Rental Counseling, Prepurchase
Counseling, Default/Foreclosure
Counseling, HECM Counseling

BERKS COMMUNITY ACTION
AGENCY BUDGET
COUNSELING CENTER
247 N 5th St
Reading, PA 19601-3303
610-375-7866
Fax: 610-375-7830
Type of Counseling:
HECM Counseling,
Default/Foreclosure Counseling,
Rental Counseling, Prepurchase
Counseling

**NEIGHBORHOOD HOUSING
SERVICES OF READING,
INCORPORATED
383 Schuylkill Ave
Reading, PA 19601
610-372-8433
Fax: 610-374-2866
Type of Counseling:
Prepurchase Counseling,
Default/Foreclosure Counseling
Affiliate of: NEIGHBORHOOD
REINVESTMENT
CORPORATION

UNITED NEIGHBORHOOD
CENTERS OF LACKAWANNA
COUNTY
410 Olive Street
Scranton, PA 18509
570-346-0759
Fax: 570-342-3972
Type of Counseling:
Default/Foreclosure Counseling,
Rental Counseling, Prepurchase
Counseling

**CATHOLIC SOCIAL
SERVICES
400 Wyoming Avenue
Scranton, PA 18503
570-207-2291
Fax: 570-341-1293
Type of Counseling:
Default/Foreclosure Counseling,
Prepurchase Counseling, Rental
Counseling, HECM Counseling
Affiliate of: CATHOLIC
CHARITIES USA

MERCER COUNTY
COMMUNITY ACTION
AGENCY
296 A St

Sharon, PA 16146-1241
724-342-6222
Fax: 724-342-6301
Type of Counseling:
Prepurchase Counseling,
Default/Foreclosure Counseling,
HECM Counseling
Affiliate of: HOUSING
OPPORTUNITIES,
INCORPORATED

TABLELAND SERVICES,
INCORPORATED
535 E Main St
Somerset, PA 15501-2108
814-445-9628
Toll-Free: 800-452-0148
Fax: 814-443-3690
Type of Counseling:
HECM Counseling,
Default/Foreclosure Counseling

PHOENIXVILLE HOMES
250 N. Main Street
Spring City, PA 19475
610-948-1797
Fax: 610-948-1765
Type of Counseling:
Prepurchase Counseling,
Default/Foreclosure Counseling

KEYSTONE LEGAL SERVICES,
INCORPORATED
2054 E College Ave
State College, PA 16801-7201
814-238-4958
Fax: 814-238-9504
Type of Counseling:
Default/Foreclosure Counseling,
Prepurchase Counseling

FAYETTE COUNTY
COMMUNITY ACTION
AGENCY
140 North Beeson Avenue
Uniontown, PA 15401
724-437-6050
Fax: 724-437-4418
Type of Counseling:
HECM Counseling,
Default/Foreclosure Counseling,
Rental Counseling, Prepurchase
Counseling

WARREN FOREST COUNTY
ECONOMIC OPPORTUNITY
COUNCIL
1209 Pennsylvania Ave W

Warren, PA 16365-1841
814-726-2400
Toll-Free: 800-231-1797
Fax: 814-723-0510
Type of Counseling:
Default/Foreclosure Counseling,
Rental Counseling, Prepurchase
Counseling, HECM Counseling

TRI-COUNTY PATRIOTS FOR
INDEPENDENT LIVING
69 E Beau St
Washington, PA 15301-4711
724-223-5115
Fax: 724-223-5119
Type of Counseling:
HECM Counseling, Rental
Counseling

COMMUNITY ACTION
SOUTHWEST
315 E Hallam Ave
Washington, PA 15301-3407
724-225-9550
Fax: 724-228-9966
Type of Counseling:
HECM Counseling,
Default/Foreclosure Counseling,
Rental Counseling, Prepurchase
Counseling

WASHINGTON COUNTY
HOUSING AUTHORITY
100 Crumrine Tower, Franklin
Street
Washington, PA 15301-6995
724-228-6060
Fax: 724-228-6089
Type of Counseling: Rental
Counseling

WASHINGTON-GREENE
COMMUNITY ACTION
CORPORATION
22 W High St
Waynesburg, PA 15370-1324
724-852-2893
Fax: 724-627-7713
Type of Counseling:
Default/Foreclosure Counseling,
Rental Counseling

CONSUMER CREDIT
COUNSELING SERVICE OF
LEHIGH VALLEY, INC
3671 Crescent Court East

Whitehall, PA 18052-0233
610-821-4011
Fax: 610-821-8932
Type of Counseling:
Default/Foreclosure Counseling,
Prepurchase Counseling, HECM
Counseling, Rental Counseling
Affiliate of: HOUSING
OPPORTUNITIES,
INCORPORATED

COMMISSION ON ECONOMIC
OPPORTUNITY OF LUZERNE
COUNTY
165 Amber Lane
Wilkes Barre, PA 18703-1127
570-826-0510
Fax: 570-829-1665
Type of Counseling:
Rental Counseling,
Default/Foreclosure Counseling

BUCKS COUNTY HOUSING
GROUP
2324 Second Street Pike Suite 17
Wrightstown, PA 18940
215-598-3566
Toll-Free: 866-866-0280
Fax: 215-598-1289
Email: rmilgram@bchg.org
Type of Counseling:
Prepurchase Counseling,
Default/Foreclosure Counseling

HOUSING COUNCIL OF YORK
116 N George St
York, PA 17401-1106
717-854-1541
Fax: 717-845-7934
Type of Counseling:
HECM Counseling,
Default/Foreclosure Counseling,
Rental Counseling, Prepurchase
Counseling

Puerto Rico

CONSUMER CREDIT
COUNSELING SERVICE OF
PUERTO RICO,
INCORPORATED
Bayamon Shopping Center
Office 6 2nd Fl
Bayamon, PR 00961
787-269-4100
Fax: 787-269-4153

Email: infor@cccspr.org
Website: www.cccspr.org
Type of Counseling:
Default/Foreclosure Counseling,
Prepurchase Counseling, HECM
Counseling

CONSUMER CREDIT
COUNSELING SERVICE OF
PUERTO RICO,
INCORPORATED
Calle Nazario #1A
Caguas, PR 00725
787-703-0506
Fax: 787-703-0580
Email: info@cccspr.org
Website: www.cccspr.org
Type of Counseling:
Prepurchase Counseling,
Default/Foreclosure Counseling,
HECM Counseling

CONSUMER CREDIT
COUNSELING SERVICE OF
PUERTO RICO,
INCORPORATED
Ave Fragoso 3 DS-5 Edif Tiri
Villa Fontana
Carolina, PR 00983
787-269-4100
Fax: 787-769-1360
Email: info@cccs.org
Website: www.cccspr.org
Type of Counseling:
Default/Foreclosure Counseling,
Prepurchase Counseling, HECM
Counseling

CEIBA HOUSING AND
ECONOMIC DEVELOPMENT
CORPORATION
Ave Lauro Pinero 252 alto
Ceiba, PR 00735-0203
787-885-3020
Fax: 787-885-0716
Type of Counseling:
HECM Counseling,
Default/Foreclosure Counseling,
Rental Counseling, Prepurchase
Counseling

CONSUMER CREDIT
COUNSELING SERVICE OF
PUERTO RICO,
INCORPORATED
Calle Mendes Vigo #208

Managuez, PR 00680
787-265-0480
Fax: 787-265-0560
Email: info@cccspr.org
Website: www.cccspr.org
Type of Counseling:
Default/Foreclosure Counseling,
Prepurchase Counseling, HECM
Counseling

CONSUMER CREDIT
COUNSELING SERVICE OF
PUERTO RICO,
INCORPORATED
4021Condominium Plaza Del
Sur Ste #1 Calle Carlos
Cartagena
Ponce, PR 00717
787-844-4550
Fax: 787-844-4540
Email: info@cccspr.org
Website: www.cccspr.org
Type of Counseling:
Default/Foreclosure Counseling,
Prepurchase Counseling, HECM
Counseling

CONSUMER CREDIT
COUNSELING SERVICE OF
PUERTO RICO,
INCORPORATED
1603 Ponce De Leon Ave. Stop
23 Cobian's Plaza, Suite GM-09
Santurce, PR 00909
787-722-8835
Toll-Free: 800-717-2227
Fax: 787-724-4142
Email: info@cccspr.org
Website: www.cccspr.org
Type of Counseling:
HECM Counseling,
Default/Foreclosure Counseling,
Rental Counseling, Prepurchase
Counseling

Rhode Island

**EAST BAY COMMUNITY
DEVELOPMENT
CORPORATION
150 Franklin Street
Bristol, RI 02809
401-253-2080
Fax: 401-253-6997
Type of Counseling:
Prepurchase Counseling

Affiliate of: CITIZENS'
HOUSING AND PLANNING
ASSOCIATION,
INCORPORATED

**COMMUNITY HOUSING
CORPORATION
25 West Independence Way
Kingston, RI 02881
401-782-4646
Fax: 401-783-6190
Email: act@netsence.net
Type of Counseling:
Prepurchase Counseling,
Default/Foreclosure Counseling
Affiliate of: CITIZENS'
HOUSING AND PLANNING
ASSOCIATION,
INCORPORATED

**CHURCH COMMUNITY
HOUSING CORPORATION
50 Washington Square
Newport, RI 02840
401-846-5114
Fax: 401-849-7930
Type of Counseling:
Prepurchase Counseling
Affiliate of: CITIZENS'
HOUSING AND PLANNING
ASSOCIATION,
INCORPORATED

BLACKSTONE VALLEY
COMMUNITY ACTION
PROGRAM, INCORPORATED
32 Goff Ave
Pawtucket, RI 02860-2928
401-723-4520
Fax: 401-723-3325
Type of Counseling:
Default/Foreclosure Counseling,
Prepurchase Counseling
Affiliate of: CITIZENS'
HOUSING AND PLANNING
ASSOCIATION,
INCORPORATED

**ACORN HOUSING
CORPORATION
807 Broad St., Suite 220
Providence, RI 02907
401-780-0500
Fax: 401-780-0826
Email: riacorn@acorn.org
Type of Counseling:

Prepurchase Counseling, Rental
Counseling, Default/Foreclosure
Counseling, HECM Counseling
Affiliate of: ACORN HOUSING
CORPORATION

**STOP WASTING
ABANDONED PROPERTY
439 Pine Street
Providence, RI 02907
401-272-0526
Fax: 401-272-5653
Email:
alcxnamzoff@hotmail.com
Type of Counseling:
Prepurchase Counseling
Affiliate of: CITIZENS'
HOUSING AND PLANNING
ASSOCIATION,
INCORPORATED

**PROVIDENCE
PRESERVATION SOCIETY
REVOLVING FUND
24 Meeting Street
Providence, RI 02903
401-272-2760
Fax: 401-273-9190
Type of Counseling:
Prepurchase Counseling
Affiliate of: CITIZENS'
HOUSING AND PLANNING
ASSOCIATION,
INCORPORATED

**HOUSING DEVELOPMENT
CORPORATION OF THE
NORTH END
481 Charles Street
Providence, RI 02904
401-351-3311
Fax: 401-351-4900
Email: hdcne@aol.com
Type of Counseling:
Prepurchase Counseling,
Default/Foreclosure Counseling
Affiliate of: CITIZENS'
HOUSING AND PLANNING
ASSOCIATION,
INCORPORATED

**ELMWOOD FOUNDATION
1 Trinity Square
Providence, RI 02907
401-273-2330
Fax: 401-274-3670

Type of Counseling:
Prepurchase Counseling
Affiliate of: CITIZENS'
HOUSING AND PLANNING
ASSOCIATION,
INCORPORATED

**ALLEN MINISTRIES
ENRICHING
NEIGHBORHOODS (AMEN)
161 Bellevue Avenue.
Providence, RI 02907
401-831-0367
Fax: 401-861-9492
Type of Counseling:
Prepurchase Counseling, Rental
Counseling
Affiliate of: CONGRESS OF
NATIONAL BLACK
CHURCHES, INCORPORATED

RHODE ISLAND HOUSING
AND MORTGAGE FINANCE
CORPORATION
44 Washington St
Providence, RI 02903-1721
401-751-5566
Fax: 401-243-0016
Type of Counseling: HECM
Counseling

RHODE ISLAND
DEPARTMENT OF ELDERLY
AFFAIRS
160 Pine St
Providence, RI 02903-3708
401-222-2858
Fax: 401-222-1490
Type of Counseling:
HECM Counseling, Rental
Counseling

URBAN LEAGUE OF RHODE
ISLAND
246 Prairie Ave
Providence, RI 02905-2333
401-351-5000
Fax: 401-454-1946
Type of Counseling:
HECM Counseling,
Default/Foreclosure Counseling,
Rental Counseling, Prepurchase
Counseling

WEST ELMWOOD HOUSING DEVELOPMENT CORPORATION
392 Cranston St
Providence, RI 02907
401-453-3220
Fax: 401-453-3222
Email: scw@aol.com
Type of Counseling:
Default/Foreclosure Counseling,
Prepurchase Counseling
Affiliate of: NEIGHBORHOOD REINVESTMENT CORPORATION

CONSUMER CREDIT COUNSELING SERVICE
535 Centerville Rd Ste 103
Warwick, RI 02886-4376
401-732-1800
Toll-Free: 800-781-2227
Fax: 401-732-0250
Website:
www.creditcounseling.org
Type of Counseling:
Default/Foreclosure Counseling,
Rental Counseling, Prepurchase
Counseling, HECM Counseling
Affiliate of: NATIONAL FOUNDATION FOR CONSUMER CREDIT, INCORPORATED

South Carolina

SUNBELT HUMAN ADVANCEMENT RESOURCES, INCORPORATED - SHARE
400 E River St
Anderson, SC 29624-2448
864-224-7028
Fax: 864-226-8636
Type of Counseling:
HECM Counseling,
Default/Foreclosure Counseling,
Rental Counseling, Prepurchase
Counseling

WATEREE COMMUNITY ACTIONS, INCORPORATED
637 Rutledge St
Camden, SC 29020-4237
803-432-3411
Fax: 803-432-3411
Type of Counseling:
Default/Foreclosure Counseling,

Rental Counseling, Prepurchase
Counseling

TRIDENT URBAN LEAGUE, INCORPORATED
656 King Street
Charleston, SC 294130249
843-965-4037
Fax: 843-965-4039
Type of Counseling:
Prepurchase Counseling

FAMILY SERVICES INCORPORATED
4925 Lacross St. Ste. 215
Charleston, SC 28406
843-744-1348
Toll-Free: 800-232-6489
Fax: 843-744-2886
Email:
dwalker@familyserviceschassc.com
Type of Counseling:
Prepurchase Counseling,
Default/Foreclosure Counseling,
Rental Counseling

CHESTERFIELD-MARLBORO ECONOMIC OPPORTUNITY COUNCIL, INCORPORATED
318-322 Front Street
Cheraw, SC 29520
843-320-9760
Fax: 843-320-9770
Type of Counseling:
Prepurchase Counseling,
Default/Foreclosure Counseling,
Rental Counseling

NATIONAL ASSOCIATION FOR THE ADVANCEMENT OF COLORED PEOPLE
1114 Blanding Street
Columbia, SC 29201
803-256-8771
Fax: 803-252-5999

PALMETTO LEGAL SERVICE
2109 Bull St
Columbia, SC 29201-2103
803-799-9668
Fax: 803-799-1781
Type of Counseling:
HECM Counseling,
Default/Foreclosure Counseling,

Rental Counseling, Prepurchase
Counseling

SOUTH CAROLINA STATE HOUSING FINANCE AND DEVELOPMENT AUTHORITY
919 Bluff Road
Columbia, SC 29201
803-734-2000
Toll-Free: 800-476-0412
Fax: 803-734-2356
Type of Counseling:
Prepurchase Counseling,
Default/Foreclosure Counseling

CONSUMER CREDIT COUNSELING SERVICE OF FAMILY SERVICE CENTER
1800 Main St
Columbia, SC 29201-2433
803-929-6666
Fax: 803-929-6665
Type of Counseling:
Default/Foreclosure Counseling,
Rental Counseling, Prepurchase
Counseling, HECM Counseling

WATEREE COMMUNITY ACTIONS, INCORPORATED
3220 Two Notch Rd
Columbia, SC 29202
803-786-4250
Fax: 803-786-4252
Type of Counseling:
Default/Foreclosure Counseling,
Prepurchase Counseling

SUNBELT HUMAN ADVANCEMENT RESOURCES, INCORPORATED - SHARE
121 E First Avenue
Easley, SC 29641-1628
864-859-2989
Fax: 864-859-1401
Type of Counseling:
HECM Counseling,
Default/Foreclosure Counseling,
Rental Counseling, Prepurchase
Counseling

SAVANNAH GROVE HOUSING COUNSELING PROGRAM
2620 Alligator Road
Effingham, SC 29541
843-662-7851

Fax: 843-662-3140
Type of Counseling:
Prepurchase Counseling
Affiliate of: CONGRESS OF
NATIONAL BLACK
CHURCHES, INCORPORATED

CAROLINA REGIONAL
LEGAL SERVICES
CORPORATION
279 W Evans St
Florence, SC 29503
843-667-1896
Toll-Free: 800-304-9939
Fax: 843-664-2406
Email: crls@logicsouth.com
Type of Counseling:
Default/Foreclosure Counseling,
Rental Counseling, HECM
Counseling

SUNBELT HUMAN
ADVANCEMENT RESOURCES,
INCORPORATED
1200 Pendleton St
Greenville, SC 29611-4832
864-269-0700
Fax: 864-295-6151
Type of Counseling:
HECM Counseling,
Default/Foreclosure Counseling,
Rental Counseling, Prepurchase
Counseling

URBAN LEAGUE OF THE
UPSTATE, INCORPORATED
15 Regency Hill Dr
Greenville, SC 29607-1230
864-244-3862
Fax: 864-244-6134
Email: hbarksdale@aol.com
Type of Counseling:
Default/Foreclosure Counseling,
Rental Counseling, Prepurchase
Counseling, HECM Counseling
Affiliate of: NATIONAL
URBAN LEAGUE

GREENVILLE COUNTY
HUMAN RELATIONS
COMMISSION
301 University Ridge, Suite 1600
Greenville, SC 296013660
864-467-7095
Fax: 864-467-5965
Type of Counseling:

Prepurchase Counseling,
Default/Foreclosure Counseling,
Rental Counseling, HECM
Counseling

PALMETTO LEGAL SERVICES
426 S Lake Dr
Lexington, SC 29072-3414
803-359-4154
Fax: 803-359-9351
Type of Counseling:
HECM Counseling,
Default/Foreclosure Counseling,
Rental Counseling, Prepurchase
Counseling

WATEREE COMMUNITY
ACTIONS, INCORPORATED
3 W Boyce St
Manning, SC 29102-3205
803-435-4337
Fax: 803-435-4338
Type of Counseling:
Default/Foreclosure Counseling,
Prepurchase Counseling

FAMILY SERVICES
INCORPORATED
4925 Lacross Road Suite 215
North Charleston, SC 29406-
843-744-1348
Fax: 843-744-2886
Type of Counseling:
Prepurchase Counseling,
Default/Foreclosure Counseling,
Rental Counseling

TRIDENT UNITED WAY
6296 Rivers Ave
North Charleston, SC 29419
843-740-9000
Fax: 843-566-7193
Type of Counseling:
HECM Counseling,
Default/Foreclosure Counseling,
Rental Counseling, Prepurchase
Counseling

PALMETTO LEGAL SERVICES
1557 Carolina St NE
Orangeburg, SC 29115-4925
803-533-0116
Fax: 803-531-5102
Type of Counseling:
HECM Counseling,
Default/Foreclosure Counseling,

Rental Counseling, Prepurchase
Counseling

SUNBELT HUMAN
ADVANCEMENT RESOURCES,
INCORPORATED - SHARE
204 N Fairplay St
Seneca, SC 29678-3216
864-882-3495
Fax: 864-885-0634
Type of Counseling:
HECM Counseling,
Default/Foreclosure Counseling,
Rental Counseling, Prepurchase
Counseling

WATEREE COMMUNITY
ACTIONS, INCORPORATED
13 S Main St
Sumter, SC 29150-5244
803-775-4354
Fax: 803-773-9782
Type of Counseling:
HECM Counseling,
Default/Foreclosure Counseling,
Rental Counseling, Prepurchase
Counseling

PALMETTO LEGAL SERVICES
207A North Washington St
Sumter, SC 29151
803-773-1471
Fax: 803-773-8765
Type of Counseling:
HECM Counseling,
Default/Foreclosure Counseling,
Rental Counseling, Prepurchase
Counseling

South Dakota

NEIGHBORHOOD HOUSING
SERVICES OF THE BLACK
HILLS, INCORPORATED
817 1/2 Main Street
Deadwood, SD 57732
605-578-1401
Fax: 605-578-1405
Type of Counseling:
Default/Foreclosure Counseling,
Prepurchase Counseling, Rental
Counseling, HECM Counseling

SOUTH DAKOTA HOUSING
DEVELOPMENT AUTHORITY
221 South Central

Pierre, SD 57501-1237
605-773-3181
Toll-Free: 800-540-4241
TTY/TDD: 605-773-6107
Fax: 605-773-5154
Website: www.sdhda.org
Type of Counseling:
Rental Counseling,
Default/Foreclosure Counseling,
Prepurchase Counseling

OGLALA SIOUX TRIBE
PARTNERSHIP FOR
HOUSING, INCORPORATED
Old Ambulance Building
Pine Ridge, SD 57770
605-867-1555
Fax: 605-867-1522
Type of Counseling:
Default/Foreclosure Counseling,
Prepurchase Counseling, Rental
Counseling

CONSUMER CREDIT
COUNSELING SERVICE OF
THE BLACK HILLS,
INCORPORATED
111 St. Joseph Street
Rapid City, SD 57701
605-348-4550
Toll-Free: 800-568-6613
Fax: 605-348-0107
Type of Counseling:
Default/Foreclosure Counseling,
Rental Counseling, Prepurchase
Counseling, HECM Counseling

BLACK HILLS LEGAL
SERVICES
621 6th St Ste 202
Rapid City, SD 577091500
605-342-7171
Fax: 605-348-5874
Type of Counseling:
HECM Counseling,
Default/Foreclosure Counseling,
Rental Counseling, Prepurchase
Counseling

SIOUX EMPIRE HOUSING
PARTNERSHIP
200 North Phillips Avenue STE.
303
Sioux Falls, SD 57104
605-339-0942
Fax: 605-339-0201

Type of Counseling:
Prepurchase Counseling, Rental
Counseling

EAST RIVER LEGAL SERVICES
335 N Main Ave Ste 300
Sioux Falls, SD 57104-6004
605-336-9230
Fax: 605-336-6919
Type of Counseling:
HECM Counseling,
Default/Foreclosure Counseling,
Rental Counseling

CONSUMER CREDIT
COUNSELING SERVICE-
LUTHERN SOCIAL SERVICES
705 E 41st St Ste 100
Sioux Falls, SD 57105-6025
605-330-2700
Fax: 605-357-0150
Type of Counseling:
HECM Counseling,
Default/Foreclosure Counseling,
Rental Counseling, Prepurchase
Counseling
Affiliate of: NATIONAL
FOUNDATION FOR
CONSUMER CREDIT,
INCORPORATED

Tennessee

CONSUMER CREDIT
COUNSELING SERVICE
Osborne Office Pk 6000 Bldg Ste
2300
Chattanooga, TN 37411
423-490-5620
Fax: 423-490-5624
Type of Counseling:
HECM Counseling,
Default/Foreclosure Counseling,
Rental Counseling, Prepurchase
Counseling

DEPARTMENT OF HUMAN
SERVICES CITY OF
CHATTANOOGA
501 W 12th St
Chattanooga, TN 37402-3852
423-757-5551
Fax: 423-757-4852
Type of Counseling:

HECM Counseling,
Default/Foreclosure Counseling,
Rental Counseling

**SOUTHEAST TENNESSEE
LEGAL SERVICES
414 McCallie Ave.
Chattanooga, TN 37402
423-756-4013
Fax: 423-265-4165
Email:
rfowler@setnlegalservices.org
Type of Counseling:
Prepurchase Counseling,
Default/Foreclosure Counseling,
Rental Counseling, HECM
Counseling
Affiliate of: WEST TENNESSEE
LEGAL SERVICES,
INCORPORATED

FAMILY AND CHILDREN'S
SERVICE OF CHATTANOOGA,
INCORPORATED
300 East 8th Street
Chattanooga, TN 37403
423-755-2822
Fax: 423-755-2897
Type of Counseling:
Prepurchase Counseling,
Default/Foreclosure Counseling,
Rental Counseling

**LEGAL AID SOCIETY OF
MIDDLE TENNESSEE AND
THE CUMBERLANDS
120 Franklin St.
Clarksville, TN 27040
931-552-6656
Fax: 931-552-9442
Email: pmack@lasmt.org
Type of Counseling:
Prepurchase Counseling,
Default/Foreclosure Counseling,
Rental Counseling, HECM
Counseling
Affiliate of: WEST TENNESSEE
LEGAL SERVICES,
INCORPORATED

CONSUMER DEBT
COUNSELING
1685 Ft. Campbell Boulevard,
Suite D
Clarksville, TN 370423513
Toll-Free: 800-966-3328

Fax: 314-647-1359
Type of Counseling:
Default/Foreclosure Counseling

**SOUTHEAST TENNESSEE
LEGAL SERVICES
85 Central Avenue NW
Cleveland, TN 37311
423-756-4013
Fax: 423-265-4164
Email:
rfowler@setnlegalservices.org
Type of Counseling:
Prepurchase Counseling,
Default/Foreclosure Counseling,
Rental Counseling, HECM
Counseling
Affiliate of: WEST TENNESSEE
LEGAL SERVICES,
INCORPORATED

**LEGAL AID OF SOCIETY OF
MIDDLE TENNESSEE
85 Central Avenue NW
Cleveland, TN 37311
931-552-6656
Fax: 931-552-9442
Type of Counseling:
HECM Counseling,
Default/Foreclosure Counseling,
Rental Counseling, Prepurchase
Counseling
Affiliate of: WEST TENNESSEE
LEGAL SERVICES,
INCORPORATED

**LEGAL SERVICES OF SOUTH
CENTRAL TENNESSEE
104 W. 7th Street
Columbia, TN 38402
931-381-5533
Fax: 931-381-5541
Email: pfrison@bellsouth.net
Type of Counseling:
Prepurchase Counseling,
Default/Foreclosure Counseling,
Rental Counseling, HECM
Counseling
Affiliate of: WEST TENNESSEE
LEGAL SERVICES,
INCORPORATED

**LEGAL AID SOCIETY OF
MIDDLE TENNESSEE AND
THE CUMBERLANDS
Null

Cookeville, TN 38503
931-528-7436
Fax: 931-528-9350
Type of Counseling:
Prepurchase Counseling,
Default/Foreclosure Counseling,
Rental Counseling, HECM
Counseling
Affiliate of: WEST TENNESSEE
LEGAL SERVICES,
INCORPORATED

WEST TENNESSEE LEGAL
SERVICES, INCORPORATED
208 s. Church St.
Dyersburg, TN 38024
901-285-8181
Fax: 901-285-8184
Type of Counseling:
HECM Counseling,
Default/Foreclosure Counseling,
Rental Counseling, Prepurchase
Counseling
Affiliate of: WEST TENNESSEE
LEGAL SERVICES,
INCORPORATED

**LEGAL AID OF SOCIETY OF
MIDDLE TENNESSEE
650 N. Water Avenue
Gallatin, TN 37066
615-451-1880
Fax: 615-451-1882
Type of Counseling:
HECM Counseling,
Default/Foreclosure Counseling,
Rental Counseling, Prepurchase
Counseling
Affiliate of: WEST TENNESSEE
LEGAL SERVICES,
INCORPORATED

WEST TENNESSEE LEGAL
SERVICES, INCORPORATED
113 W. Paris St.
Huntingdon, TN 38344
901-986-8975
Fax: 901-986-8977
Type of Counseling:
HECM Counseling,
Default/Foreclosure Counseling,
Rental Counseling, Prepurchase
Counseling
Affiliate of: WEST TENNESSEE
LEGAL SERVICES,
INCORPORATED

WEST TENNESSEE LEGAL
SERVICES, INCORPORATED
210 W Main St
Jackson, TN 38302-2066
731-285-8181
Email: wtlegal@usit.net
Type of Counseling:
HECM Counseling,
Default/Foreclosure Counseling,
Rental Counseling, Prepurchase
Counseling
Affiliate of: WEST TENNESSEE
LEGAL SERVICES,
INCORPORATED

CONSUMER CREDIT
COUNSELING SERVICE OF
GREATER KNOXVILLE,
INCORPORATED
2700 S Roan St Ste 212
Johnson City, TN 37601-7557
800-358-9231
Fax: 865-637-3637
Type of Counseling:
HECM Counseling,
Default/Foreclosure Counseling,
Rental Counseling, Prepurchase
Counseling

**AMERICAN CREDIT
COUNSELORS,
INCORPORATED
208 Sunset Drive, Suite 505
Johnson City, TN 37604
800 646-0042
Toll-Free: 800-646-0042
Fax: 540-366-7140
Type of Counseling:
HECM Counseling,
Default/Foreclosure Counseling,
Prepurchase Counseling, Rental
Counseling

**CONSUMER CREDIT
COUNSELING SERVICE OF
SOUTHWESTERN VIRGINIA,
INCORPORATED
2615 E. Center Street
Kingsport, TN 37664
800-926-0042
Toll-Free: 800-926-0042
Fax: 540-366-7140
Type of Counseling:
HECM Counseling,
Default/Foreclosure Counseling,

Prepurchase Counseling, Rental
Counseling

CONSUMER CREDIT
COUNSELING SERVICE OF
EAST TENNESSEE
1011 N. Broadway
Knoxville, TN 37917
865-522-2661
Toll-Free: 800-358-9231
Fax: 865-637-3637
Email: cccser@usit.net
Type of Counseling:
HECM Counseling,
Default/Foreclosure Counseling,
Rental Counseling, Prepurchase
Counseling

KNOXVILLE AREA URBAN
LEAGUE
1514 E. Fifth Avenue
Knoxville, TN 37917
865-524-5511
Fax: 865-525-5154
Email: rgiles@korrnet.org
Type of Counseling:
Default/Foreclosure Counseling,
Rental Counseling, Prepurchase
Counseling
Affiliate of: NATIONAL
URBAN LEAGUE

KNOX HOUSING
PARTNERSHIP,
INCORPORATED
900 E Hill Avenue Suite 270
Knoxville, TN 37921-6362
865-637-1679
Fax: 865-637-9713
Type of Counseling:
Prepurchase Counseling,
Default/Foreclosure Counseling
Affiliate of: NEIGHBORHOOD
REINVESTMENT
CORPORATION

MEMPHIS AREA LEGAL
SERVICES
109 N Main 2nd Fl
Memphis, TN 38103
901-523-8822
Fax: 901-843-6789
Type of Counseling:
Prepurchase Counseling, Rental
Counseling, Default/Foreclosure
Counseling, HECM Counseling

VOLLINTINE EVERGREEN
COMMUNITY ASSOCIATION
1680 Jackson Ave
Memphis, TN 38107-5044
901-276-1782
Fax: 901-276-1784
Type of Counseling:
HECM Counseling,
Default/Foreclosure Counseling,
Rental Counseling, Prepurchase
Counseling

CONSUMER DEBT
COUNSELING
1750 Madison Avenue, Suite 200
Memphis, TN 38104
901-276-2000
Toll-Free: 877-786-3328
Fax: 314-647-1359
Type of Counseling:
Default/Foreclosure Counseling

ASSOCIATED CATHOLIC
CHARITIES, INCORPORATED
1325 Jefferson Ave
Memphis, TN 38104
901-722-4700
Fax: 901-722-4791
Email: clifton@cathchar.org
Type of Counseling:
Default/Foreclosure Counseling,
Rental Counseling, Prepurchase
Counseling, HECM Counseling
Affiliate of: CATHOLIC
CHARITIES USA

**ACORN HOUSING
CORPORATION HOUSING
COUNSELING OFFICES -
MEMPHIS
1254 Lamar Ave, # 304
Memphis, TN 38104
901-274-8080
Fax: 901-274-8305
Type of Counseling:
Prepurchase Counseling, Rental
Counseling, Default/Foreclosure
Counseling
Affiliate of: ACORN HOUSING
CORPORATION

**LEGAL AID OF SOCIETY OF
MIDDLE TENNESSEE
526 N. Walnut Street
Murfreesboro, TN 37130
615-890-0905

Fax: 615-890-5274
Type of Counseling:
HECM Counseling,
Default/Foreclosure Counseling,
Rental Counseling, Prepurchase
Counseling
Affiliate of: WEST TENNESSEE
LEGAL SERVICES,
INCORPORATED

**VICTORY HOUSING
COUNSELING CENTER
3447 Brickchurch Pike
Nashville, TN 37207
615-226-9556
Fax: 615-226-9987
Type of Counseling:
Prepurchase Counseling,
Default/Foreclosure Counseling
Affiliate of: CONGRESS OF
NATIONAL BLACK
CHURCHES, INCORPORATED

RESIDENTIAL RESOURCES,
INC.
961 Woodland Street
Nashville, TN 37206
615-650-9779
Fax: 615-650-1253
Type of Counseling:
Default/Foreclosure Counseling,
Prepurchase Counseling, Rental
Counseling

CONSUMER DEBT
COUNSELING
2131 Murfreesboro Pike, Suite L2
Nashville, TN 37217
615-361-0710
Toll-Free: 877-786-3328
Fax: 314-647-1359
Type of Counseling:
Default/Foreclosure Counseling

WOODBINE COMMUNITY
ORGANIZATION
222 Oriel Ave.
Nashville, TN 37210
615-860-3453
Fax: 615-833-9727
Type of Counseling:
Prepurchase Counseling,
Default/Foreclosure Counseling

CITIZENS FOR AFFORDABLE
HOUSING

1719 West End Ave Ste 322W
Nashville, TN 37203-5120
615-321-5626
Fax: 615-321-5640
Email: cfah@gobot.com
Website: www.cfahi.gobot.com
Type of Counseling:
Default/Foreclosure Counseling,
Rental Counseling, Prepurchase
Counseling

**AFFORDABLE HOUSING
RESOURCES**
1011 Cherry Ave
Nashville, TN 37203
615-251-0025
Fax: 615-256-9836
Type of Counseling:
Default/Foreclosure Counseling,
Prepurchase Counseling
Affiliate of: NEIGHBORHOOD
REINVESTMENT
CORPORATION

**METROPOLITAN ACTION
COMMISSION**
1624 5th Ave N
Nashville, TN 37208-2243
615-862-8860
Fax: 615-862-8881
Type of Counseling:
Default/Foreclosure Counseling,
Rental Counseling, Prepurchase
Counseling

**LEGAL AID OF SOCIETY OF
MIDDLE TENNESSEE**
211 Union Street, Suite 800
Nashville, TN 37201
615-244-6610
Fax: 615-224-6186
Email: pmoct@lasmt.org
Type of Counseling:
HECM Counseling,
Default/Foreclosure Counseling,
Rental Counseling, Prepurchase
Counseling
Affiliate of: WEST TENNESSEE
LEGAL SERVICES,
INCORPORATED

**CONSUMER CREDIT
COUNSELING SERVICE OF
MIDDLE TENNESSEE,
INCORPORATED**
PO Box 160328

Nashville, TN 37216-0328
615-650-3116
Fax: 615-777-3414
Type of Counseling:
HECM Counseling,
Default/Foreclosure Counseling,
Rental Counseling, Prepurchase
Counseling

**HOUSING DEVELOPMENT
CORPORATION OF THE
CLINCH VALLEY**
Nations Bank Building 795 W
Main St., 2nd Floor
Oak Ridge, TN 37831
865-482-7345
Fax: 865-220-8645
Type of Counseling:
Default/Foreclosure Counseling,
Prepurchase Counseling, Rental
Counseling
Affiliate of: NEIGHBORHOOD
REINVESTMENT
CORPORATION

**LEGAL AID SOCIETY OF
MIDDLE TENNESSEE AND
THE CUMBERLANDS**
PO Box 5209
Oak Ridge, TN 37831
865-483-8454
Toll-Free: 800-483-8457
Fax: 865-483-8905
Email: hn0517@handsnet.org
Type of Counseling:
Prepurchase Counseling,
Default/Foreclosure Counseling,
Rental Counseling, HECM
Counseling
Affiliate of: WEST TENNESSEE
LEGAL SERVICES,
INCORPORATED

**WEST TENNESSEE LEGAL
SERVICES, INCORPORATED**
141 N. Third Street
Selmer, TN 38375
901-645-7961
Fax: 901-645-7963
Type of Counseling:
HECM Counseling,
Default/Foreclosure Counseling,
Rental Counseling, Prepurchase
Counseling
Affiliate of: WEST TENNESSEE
LEGAL SERVICES,
INCORPORATED

**LEGAL SERVICES OF SOUTH
CENTRAL TENNESSEE**
123 North Atlantic St.
Tullahoma, TN 37388
931-455-7000
Fax: 931-455-7003
Type of Counseling:
Prepurchase Counseling,
Default/Foreclosure Counseling,
Rental Counseling, HECM
Counseling
Affiliate of: WEST TENNESSEE
LEGAL SERVICES,
INCORPORATED

TEXAS

**CONSUMER CREDIT
COUNSELING**
241 Pine St Ste 101A
Abilene, TX 79601-5944
915-677-9323
Toll-Free: 800-527-0526
Fax: 915-673-0405
Type of Counseling:
Default/Foreclosure Counseling,
Rental Counseling, Prepurchase
Counseling

**CONSUMER CREDIT
COUNSELING SERVICE OF
GREATER DALLAS,
AMARILLO**
6300 I 40 West, Suite 106
Amarillo, TX 79106
800-878-2227
Toll-Free: 800-878-2227
Fax: 806-356-0677
Type of Counseling:
Default/Foreclosure Counseling,
Rental Counseling, Prepurchase
Counseling, HECM Counseling

**CATHOLIC FAMILY SERVICE,
INCORPORATED**
200 S Tyler St
Amarillo, TX 79101-1448
806-376-4571
Fax: 806-345-7911
Email: cfs@arn.net
Website:
www.catholicfamilyservice.org
Type of Counseling:
Default/Foreclosure Counseling,
Rental Counseling, Prepurchase
Counseling, HECM Counseling

Affiliate of: CATHOLIC
CHARITIES USA

CONSUMER CREDIT
COUNSELING SERVICE OF
GREATER DALLAS,
ARLINGTON
201 E Abram St, Ste 730
Arlington, TX 76010
817-461-2227
Fax: 817-460-0409
Type of Counseling:
Default/Foreclosure Counseling,
Rental Counseling, Prepurchase
Counseling, HECM Counseling

CONSUMER CREDIT
COUNSELING SERVICE OF
GREATER
DALLAS/ARLINGTON-
SOUTH
5850 West I-20, Suite 110
Arlington, TX 76017
817-572-2467
Fax: 817-572-0752
Type of Counseling:
Prepurchase Counseling, Rental
Counseling, Default/Foreclosure
Counseling, HECM Counseling

LEGAL AID OF CENTRAL
TEXAS
2201 Post Road Street #104
Austin, TX 78704
512-447-7707
Toll-Free: 800-369-9270
Fax: 512-447-3940
Type of Counseling:
Default/Foreclosure Counseling,
Rental Counseling, Prepurchase
Counseling

AUSTIN TENANTS' COUNCIL
1619 E. Cesar Chavez St.
Austin, TX 78702-4455
512-474-7007
Fax: 512-474-0197
Email: bruce@housing-rights.org
Type of Counseling: Rental
Counseling

TEXAS DEPARTMENT OF
HOUSING AND COMMUNITY
AFFAIRS
507 Sabine, Suite 900
Austin, TX 78701

512-475-3800
Fax: 512-472-8526
Type of Counseling:
Rental Counseling, Prepurchase
Counseling

CONSUMER CREDIT
COUNSELING SERVICE OF
GREATER FORT
WORTH/BEDFORD
4001 Airport Freeway, Ste 500
Bedford, TX 76021
817-283-4111
Fax: 817-283-4045
Type of Counseling:
Rental Counseling,
Default/Foreclosure Counseling,
Prepurchase Counseling

CONSUMER CREDIT
COUNSELING SERVICE OF
GREATER FORT WORTH/BIG
SPRING
1801 Virginia Ave. Suite 4
Big Spring, TX 79720
915-264-0321
Fax: 915-264-0321
Type of Counseling:
Default/Foreclosure Counseling,
Rental Counseling, Prepurchase
Counseling

COMMUNITY DEVELOPMENT
CORPORATION OF
BROWNSVILLE
901 East Levee Street
Brownsville, TX 78520-5804
956-541-4955
Fax: 956-982-1804
Type of Counseling:
Default/Foreclosure Counseling,
Prepurchase Counseling

CONSUMER CREDIT
COUNSELING SERVICE OF
GREATER FORT
WORTH/BROWNWOOD
300 N. Main, Suite C
Brownwood, TX 76801
915-643-3426
Fax: 915-643-3426
Type of Counseling:
Rental Counseling,
Default/Foreclosure Counseling,
Prepurchase Counseling

BRAZOS VALLEY
AFFORDABLE HOUSING
CORPORATION
1706 E. 29th St.
Bryan, TX 77805-4128
979-775-4244
Fax: 979-775-3466
Type of Counseling:
Prepurchase Counseling

CONSUMER CREDIT
COUNSELING SERVICE OF
GREATER FORT
WORTH/BURLESON
1161 SW Wilshire, Ste. 116
Burleson, TX 76028
817-295-3828
Fax: 817-295-4012
Type of Counseling: Rental
Counseling, Default/Foreclosure
Counseling, Prepurchase
Counseling

CONSUMER CREDIT
COUNSELING SERVICE OF
GREATER
DALLAS/CARROLLTON
3630 N. Josey Lane French
Quarter Executive Suite 20
Carrollton, TX 75007
972-242-6548
Fax: 972-570-5996
Type of Counseling:
Prepurchase Counseling, Rental
Counseling, Default/Foreclosure
Counseling

CONSUMER CREDIT
COUNSELING SERVICE OF
GREATER DALLAS/CEDAR
HILL
630 N. Hwy 67, Suite B-4
Cedar Hill, TX 75104
972-291-4754
Fax: 972-228-2992
Type of Counseling:
Prepurchase Counseling, Rental
Counseling, Default/Foreclosure
Counseling

**CONSUMER CREDIT
COUNSELING SERVICE OF
SOUTH TEXAS
1706 South Padre Island Dr
Corpus Christi, TX 78416
361-854-4357

Toll-Free: 800-333-4357
Fax: 361-854-1334
Website: www.cccsstx.org
Type of Counseling:
Default/Foreclosure Counseling,
Rental Counseling, Prepurchase
Counseling, HECM Counseling
Affiliate of: NATIONAL
FOUNDATION FOR
CONSUMER CREDIT,
INCORPORATED

CONSUMER CREDIT
COUNSELING SERVICE OF
GREATER DALLAS,
CORSICANA
200 N 13th St Ste 208
Corsicana, TX 75110-4674
800-886-2227
Toll-Free: 800-886-2227
Fax: 903-872-8097
Type of Counseling:
Default/Foreclosure Counseling,
Rental Counseling, Prepurchase
Counseling, HECM Counseling

WEST DALLAS
NEIGHBORHOOD
DEVELOPMENT
CORPORATION
2907 N. Hampton Rd.
Dallas, TX 75212
214-688-1596
Fax: 214-688-0499
Type of Counseling:
Prepurchase Counseling,
Default/Foreclosure Counseling,
Rental Counseling

CONSUMER CREDIT
COUNSELING SERVICE OF
GREATER DALLAS, NORTH
DALLAS
14110 Dallas Pkwy Plaza I Bldg
Ste 280
Dallas, TX 75240
972-387-2227
Fax: 972-866-6761
Type of Counseling:
Default/Foreclosure Counseling,
Rental Counseling, Prepurchase
Counseling, HECM Counseling

CONSUMER CREDIT
COUNSELING SERVICE OF

GREATER DALLAS OF
DALLAS
8737 King George Dr Ste 200
Dallas, TX 75235
800-783-5018
Toll-Free: 800-783-5018
Fax: 214-630-6805
Type of Counseling:
Default/Foreclosure Counseling,
Rental Counseling, Prepurchase
Counseling, HECM Counseling

DALLAS URBAN LEAGUE,
INCORPORATED
4315 S. Lancaster Rd
Dallas, TX 75216
214-915-4600
Fax: 214-915-4601
Email:
Clarene.Whitfi@dallasurbanleag
ue.com
Type of Counseling:
Default/Foreclosure Counseling,
Rental Counseling, Prepurchase
Counseling

DALLAS COUNTY HOME
LOAN COUNSELING CENTER
2377 N. Stemmons Freeway, Ste.
724
Dallas, TX 752072710
214-819-6060
Fax: 214-819-6069
Type of Counseling:
Prepurchase Counseling,
Default/Foreclosure Counseling,
Rental Counseling, HECM
Counseling

HOUSING COUNSELORS OF
TEXAS, INCORPORATED
501 Wynnewood Village
Shopping Center, #201
Dallas, TX 752241899
214-941-8222
Fax: 214-941-3598
Type of Counseling:
Default/Foreclosure Counseling,
Prepurchase Counseling, Rental
Counseling

DALLAS COUNTY
COMMUNITY ACTION
COMMITTEE,
INCORPORATED
611 E. Jefferson

Dallas, TX 75203
214-941-8712
Fax: 214-827-6584
Type of Counseling:
Default/Foreclosure Counseling,
Rental Counseling

CONSUMER CREDIT
COUNSELING SERVICE OF
GREATER DALLAS, ONE
NORTHPARK
8950 N Central Expy Suite 122
Dallas, TX 75231
214-363-4357
Fax: 214-363-3538
Type of Counseling:
Default/Foreclosure Counseling,
Rental Counseling, Prepurchase
Counseling, HECM Counseling

**ACORN HOUSING
CORPORATION
4415 San Jacinto St
Dallas, TX 75204-5087
214-823-9885
Fax: 214-823-0819
Type of Counseling:
Default/Foreclosure Counseling,
Prepurchase Counseling
Affiliate of: ACORN HOUSING
CORPORATION

**VECINOS UNIDOS
3603 N. Winnetka Ave.
Dallas, TX 75212
214-761-1086
Fax: 214-761-0838
Email: vecinosunidos@juno.com
Type of Counseling:
Prepurchase Counseling
Affiliate of: NATIONAL
COUNCIL OF LA RAZA

CONSUMER CREDIT
COUNSELING SERVICE OF
GREATER DALLAS, OAK
CLIFF
400 S Zang ST SUITE 1004
Dallas, TX 75208
214-943-2075
Fax: 214-943-4753
Type of Counseling:
Default/Foreclosure Counseling,
Rental Counseling, Prepurchase
Counseling, HECM Counseling

CONSUMER CREDIT
COUNSELING SERVICE OF
GREATER DALLAS
2710 North Stemmons Frwy
North Tower, Suite 1000N
Dallas, TX 75207
800-249-2227
Fax: 214-638-4398
Type of Counseling:
Prepurchase Counseling, Rental
Counseling, Default/Foreclosure
Counseling, HECM Counseling

CONSUMER CREDIT
COUNSELING SERVICE OF
NORTH CENTRAL TEXAS,
DECATUR
1411 S Hwy 51 Ste 7
Decatur, TX 76234
940-627-5235
Fax: 940-627-6981
Type of Counseling:
Default/Foreclosure Counseling,
Rental Counseling, Prepurchase
Counseling, HECM Counseling

CONSUMER CREDIT
COUNSELING SERVICE OF
NORTH CENTRAL TEXAS,
DENISON
101 E. Main Street, Suite 125
Denison, TX 75020
903-463-3298
Fax: 903-463-3573
Type of Counseling:
Prepurchase Counseling, Rental
Counseling, Default/Foreclosure
Counseling, HECM Counseling

**HOPE, INCORPORATED
415 E. Sherman
Denton, TX 76206
940-380-0513
Fax: 940-382-0609
Email: hope-inc@juno.com
Type of Counseling:
Prepurchase Counseling, Rental
Counseling, Default/Foreclosure
Counseling
Affiliate of: HOUSING
OPPORTUNITIES,
INCORPORATED

CONSUMER CREDIT
COUNSELING SERVICE OF

NORTH CENTRAL TEXAS,
DENTON
207 W Hickory St Ste 202
Denton, TX 76201-4156
940-382-0331
Fax: 940-387-0123
Type of Counseling:
Default/Foreclosure Counseling,
Rental Counseling, Prepurchase
Counseling, HECM Counseling

CONSUMER CREDIT
COUNSELING SERVICE OF
GREATER DALLAS, DESOTO,
LANCASTER
1229 Pleasant Run Rd., Ste 214
DeSoto, TX 75115
972-224-4786
Fax: 972-228-2992
Type of Counseling:
Prepurchase Counseling, Rental
Counseling, Default/Foreclosure
Counseling, HECM Counseling

CONSUMER CREDIT
COUNSELING SERVICE OF
GREATER
DALLAS/DUNCANVILLE
402 W. Wheatland Rd, Suite 116
Duncanville, TX 75137
972-709-1723
Fax: 972-709-8974
Type of Counseling:
Prepurchase Counseling, Rental
Counseling, Default/Foreclosure
Counseling, HECM Counseling

PROJECT BRAVO,
INCORPORATED
4838 Montana Ave
El Paso, TX 79903
915-562-4100
Fax: 915-562-8952
Type of Counseling:
Default/Foreclosure Counseling,
Rental Counseling, Prepurchase
Counseling, HECM Counseling

GUADALUPE ECONOMIC
SERVICES CORPORATION
221 N Kansas St Ste 1503
El Paso, TX 79901
915-577-0185
Fax: 915-577-0187
Type of Counseling:

Default/Foreclosure Counseling,
Rental Counseling, Prepurchase
Counseling

YWCA-CONSUMER CREDIT
COUNSELING SERVICE
1600 N. Brown St
El Paso, TX 79902-4725
915-577-2530
Fax: 915-533-8132
Type of Counseling:
Default/Foreclosure Counseling,
Prepurchase Counseling, HECM
Counseling
Affiliate of: NATIONAL
COUNCIL OF LA RAZA

YOUNG WOMENS CHRISTIAN
ASSOCIATION EL PASO DEL
NORTE REGION
1918 Texas Avenue
El Paso, TX 79901
915-533-2311
Fax: 915-774-5002
Type of Counseling:
Prepurchase Counseling,
Default/Foreclosure Counseling,
HECM Counseling
Affiliate of: NATIONAL
COUNCIL OF LA RAZA

CONSUMER CREDIT
COUNSELING SERVICE OF
GREATER FORT
WORTH/FORT HOOD
Bldg. 1 Rm 106, Family Support
Center
Fort Hood, TX 76544
254-532-4808
Fax: 254-532-4808
Type of Counseling:
Default/Foreclosure Counseling,
Rental Counseling, Prepurchase
Counseling

CONSUMER CREDIT
COUNSELING SERVICE OF
GREATER FORT
WORTH/FORT STOCKTON
1008 North Kansas # 9
Fort Stockton, TX 79735
915-336-3288
Fax: 915-550-8910
Type of Counseling:

Rental Counseling,
Default/Foreclosure Counseling,
Prepurchase Counseling

CITY OF FORT WORTH
HOUSING DEPARTMENT
1000 Throckmorton St
Fort Worth, TX 76102
817-871-7540
Fax: 817-871-7328
Type of Counseling:
Default/Foreclosure Counseling,
Rental Counseling, Prepurchase
Counseling

CONSUMER CREDIT
COUNSELING SERVICE OF
GREATER FORT
WORTH/EAST FORT WORTH
6737 Brentwood Stair Rd. Suite
130
Fort Worth, TX 76112
800-867-2227
Fax: 817-283-4018
Type of Counseling:
Rental Counseling,
Default/Foreclosure Counseling,
Prepurchase Counseling, HECM
Counseling

HOUSING OPPORTUNITIES
OF FORT WORTH
1305 W Magnolia Ave SUITE E
Fort Worth, TX 76104-4345
817-923-9192
Fax: 817-924-8252
Email: HOFW@SWBELL.NET
Type of Counseling:
Default/Foreclosure Counseling,
Prepurchase Counseling, Rental
Counseling, HECM Counseling
Affiliate of: HOUSING
OPPORTUNITIES,
INCORPORATED

CONSUMER CREDIT
COUNSELING SERVICE OF
GREATER FORT
WORTH/NORTHSIDE
2100 N. Main St. # 224
Fort Worth, TX 76106
800-867-2227
Fax: 817-283-4018
Type of Counseling:
Rental Counseling,
Default/Foreclosure Counseling,

Prepurchase Counseling, HECM
Counseling

CONSUMER CREDIT
COUNSELING SERVICE OF
GREATER FORT
WORTH/SOUTHWEST
4900 Overton Ridge # 213B
Fort Worth, TX 76132
800-867-2227
Fax: 817-283-4018
Type of Counseling:
Rental Counseling,
Default/Foreclosure Counseling,
Prepurchase Counseling, HECM
Counseling

**NEIGHBORHOOD HOUSING
SERVICES OF FORT WORTH,
INCORPORATED
2315 N Main St Ste 401
Fort Worth, TX 76106
817-624-9454
Fax: 817-624-0860
Email: nhsfw@swbell.net
Type of Counseling:
Prepurchase Counseling
Affiliate of: NEIGHBORHOOD
REINVESTMENT
CORPORATION

CONSUMER CREDIT
COUNSELING SERVICE OF
GREATER FORT WORTH
1320 South University, Suite 190
Fort Worth, TX 76107
817-732-2227
Toll-Free: 800-374-2227
Fax: 817-882-8623
Type of Counseling:
Prepurchase Counseling, Rental
Counseling, Default/Foreclosure
Counseling, HECM Counseling
Affiliate of: NATIONAL
FOUNDATION FOR
CONSUMER CREDIT,
INCORPORATED

CONSUMER CREDIT
COUNSELING SERVICE OF
GREATER FORT
WORTH/SOUTHEAST
2801 Miller Ave.
Fort Worth, TX 76104
800-867-2227
Fax: 817-283-4018

Type of Counseling:
Rental Counseling,
Default/Foreclosure Counseling,
Prepurchase Counseling, HECM
Counseling

CONSUMER CREDIT
COUNSELING SERVICE OF
NORTH CENTRAL TEXAS,
FRISCO
6817 Main Street
Frisco, TX 75034
972-377-2647
Fax: 972-542-3623
Type of Counseling:
Prepurchase Counseling, Rental
Counseling, Default/Foreclosure
Counseling, HECM Counseling

CONSUMER CREDIT
COUNSELING SERVICE OF
NORTH CENTRAL TEXAS,
GAINESVILLE
715 E. California
Gainesville, TX 76240
940-668-1967
Fax: 960-665-4707
Type of Counseling:
Prepurchase Counseling, Rental
Counseling, Default/Foreclosure
Counseling, HECM Counseling

CONSUMER CREDIT
COUNSELING SERVICE OF
GREATER DALLAS,
GARLAND
705 W Avenue B Ste 502
Garland, TX 75040-6229
888-843-2227
Toll-Free: 888-843-2227
Fax: 972-205-1029
Type of Counseling:
Default/Foreclosure Counseling,
Rental Counseling, Prepurchase
Counseling, HECM Counseling

CONSUMER CREDIT
COUNSELING SERVICE OF
GREATER DALLAS, GRAND
PRAIRIE
801 W Freeway Ste 240
Grand Prairie, TX 75051
972-642-3100
Fax: 972-237-0610
Type of Counseling:

Default/Foreclosure Counseling, Rental Counseling, Prepurchase Counseling, HECM Counseling

CONSUMER CREDIT COUNSELING SERVICE OF NORTH CENTRAL TEXAS, GREENVILLE
2304 Stonewall, Suite 210
Greenville, TX 75401-5759
903-455-4311
Fax: 903-455-2594
Type of Counseling:
Default/Foreclosure Counseling, Rental Counseling, Prepurchase Counseling, HECM Counseling

TEJANO CENTER OF COMMUNITY CONCERNS
6901 Brownwood
Houston, TX 77020
713-673-1080
Fax: 713-673-1304
Type of Counseling:
Prepurchase Counseling, Rental Counseling

AVENUE COMMUNITY DEVELOPMENT CORPORATION
2505 Washington Street, Suite 400
Houston, TX 77007
713-864-8099
Fax: 713-864-0027
Type of Counseling:
Prepurchase Counseling

CONSUMER CREDIT COUNSELING SERVICES OF THE GULF COAST AREA, INCORPORATED
4600 Gulf Freeway, Ste 500
Houston, TX 77023-3551
713-923-2227
Toll-Free: 800-873-2227
Fax: 713-394-3209
Type of Counseling:
Default/Foreclosure Counseling, Rental Counseling, Prepurchase Counseling

GULF COAST COMMUNITY SERVICE ASSOCIATION
5000 Gulf Frwy, Bldg 1
Houston, TX 77023-4634

713-393-4700
Fax: 713-393-4754
Type of Counseling:
Default/Foreclosure Counseling, Rental Counseling, Prepurchase Counseling, HECM Counseling

HOUSTON AREA URBAN LEAGUE
1301 Texas Ave.
Houston, TX 77002
713-393-8700
Fax: 713-393-8760
Email: philipi@haul.org
Website: www.haul.org
Type of Counseling:
Default/Foreclosure Counseling, Prepurchase Counseling, HECM Counseling, Rental Counseling
Affiliate of: NATIONAL URBAN LEAGUE

HOUSING OPPORTUNITIES OF HOUSTON INCORPORATED
2900 Woodridge Dr Ste 300
Houston, TX 77087
713-644-8488
Fax: 713-644-5054
Email: hoh@neosoft.com
Type of Counseling:
Default/Foreclosure Counseling, Prepurchase Counseling
Affiliate of: NATIONAL COUNCIL OF LA RAZA

**ACORN HOUSING CORPORATION
704 East 11 1/2 Street
Houston, TX 77008
713-863-9002
Fax: 713-863-1964
Type of Counseling:
Default/Foreclosure Counseling, Rental Counseling, Prepurchase Counseling
Affiliate of: ACORN HOUSING CORPORATION

**DOMINION COMMUNITY DEVELOPMENT CORPORATION
1102 Pinemont Dr.
Houston, TX 77018
713-957-2789
Fax: 713-957-3087

Type of Counseling:
Prepurchase Counseling, Default/Foreclosure Counseling, Rental Counseling, HECM Counseling
Affiliate of: CONGRESS OF NATIONAL BLACK CHURCHES, INCORPORATED

GREATER PARK PLACE COMMUNITY DEVELOPMENT CORPORATION
8130 Park Place Blvd.
Houston, TX 77207-2784
713-641-3462
Fax: 713-641-0847
Email: jgreen2281@aol.com
Type of Counseling:
Prepurchase Counseling, Default/Foreclosure Counseling, Rental Counseling

CREDIT COALITION
3300 Lyons Avenue, Number 203A
Houston, TX 77020-
713-224-7772
Fax: 713-224-7792
Type of Counseling:
Prepurchase Counseling, Rental Counseling, Default/Foreclosure Counseling

CONSUMER CREDIT COUNSELING - MID-CITIES
1500 Norwood Dr Bldg B Ste 203
Hurst, TX 76054-3604
800-374-2227
Toll-Free: 800-374-2227
Fax: 817-377-0036
Type of Counseling:
Default/Foreclosure Counseling, Rental Counseling, Prepurchase Counseling

CONSUMER CREDIT COUNSELING SERVICE OF GREATER DALLAS, IRVING
4322 N. Belt Line Rd. Ste B-207
Irving, TX 75038
972-255-0079
Fax: 972-570-5996
Type of Counseling:
Default/Foreclosure Counseling, Rental Counseling, Prepurchase Counseling, HECM Counseling

CONSUMER CREDIT
COUNSELING SERVICE OF
GREATER FORT
WORTH/KILLEEN
1711 E. Central Texas Expwy
#302
Killeen, TX 76541
800-219-2227
Fax: 254-628-2457
Website:
Type of Counseling:
Rental Counseling,
Default/Foreclosure Counseling,
Prepurchase Counseling

KINGSVILLE AFFORDABLE
HOUSING, INCORPORATED
1000 West Corral
Kingsville, TX 78363
361-592-6783
Fax: 361-595-1997
Type of Counseling:
Default/Foreclosure Counseling,
Rental Counseling, Prepurchase
Counseling

METRO AFFORDABLE
HOUSING CORPORATION
2000 San Francisco Ave.
Laredo, TX 78040
956-722-4521
Fax: 956-722-6561
Type of Counseling:
Prepurchase Counseling,
Default/Foreclosure Counseling,
Rental Counseling

**LAREDO-WEBB
NEIGHBORHOOD HOUSING
SERVICES, INCORPORATED
216 Bob Bulloch Loop
Laredo, TX 78046
956-712-9100
Fax: 956-712-9102
Email: ldonhs@icsi.net
Type of Counseling:
Default/Foreclosure Counseling,
Prepurchase Counseling
Affiliate of: NEIGHBORHOOD
REINVESTMENT
CORPORATION

CONSUMER CREDIT
COUNSELING SERVICE OF
NORTH CENTRAL TEXAS,
PARIS

2600 Lamar Ave Ste B
Leessburg, TX 75460
903-785-9888
Fax: 903-785-7296
Type of Counseling:
Default/Foreclosure Counseling,
Rental Counseling, Prepurchase
Counseling, HECM Counseling

CONSUMER CREDIT
COUNSELING SERVICE OF
GREATER FORT
WORTH/LEVELLAND
1001 8th Street, # 2
Levelland, TX 79336
806-894-8511
Fax: 806-785-2250
Type of Counseling:
Rental Counseling,
Default/Foreclosure Counseling,
Prepurchase Counseling

CONSUMER CREDIT
COUNSELING SERVICE OF
NORTH CENTRAL TEXAS,
LEWISVILLE
1165 S Stemmons Fwy Ste 263
Lewisville, TX 75067-5374
972-221-6798
Fax: 972-353-3118
Type of Counseling:
Default/Foreclosure Counseling,
Rental Counseling, Prepurchase
Counseling, HECM Counseling

CONSUMER CREDIT
COUNSELING SERVICE OF
GREATER DALLAS,
LONGVIEW
1800 NW Loop 281 Ste 201
Longview, TX 75064
800-577-2227
Toll-Free: 800-577-2227
Fax: 903-295-3315
Type of Counseling:
Default/Foreclosure Counseling,
Rental Counseling, Prepurchase
Counseling, HECM Counseling

CONSUMER CREDIT
COUNSELING SERVICE OF
GREATER FORT
WORTH/LUBBOCK
4010 82nd St. # 250
Lubbock, TX 79423
800-867-2227

Fax: 806-785-2250
Website: www.cccsfw.org
Type of Counseling:
Rental Counseling,
Default/Foreclosure Counseling,
Prepurchase Counseling

GUADALUPE ECONOMIC
SERVICES CORPORATION
1416 1st St
Lubbock, TX 79401-1312
806-744-4416
Fax: 806-744-7940
Type of Counseling:
Default/Foreclosure Counseling,
Prepurchase Counseling

CONSUMER CREDIT
COUNSELING SERVICE OF
MANSFIELD
209 N Walnut Creek Dr Ste D
Mansfield, TX 76063-1791
817-732-2227
Fax: 817-377-0036
Type of Counseling:
Default/Foreclosure Counseling,
Rental Counseling, Prepurchase
Counseling

MARSHALL HOUSING
AUTHORITY
1401 Poplar St
Marshall, TX 75671
903-938-0717
Fax: 903-938-0737
Type of Counseling:
Default/Foreclosure Counseling,
Rental Counseling, Prepurchase
Counseling

CONSUMER CREDIT
COUNSELING SERVICE OF
GREATER DALLAS,
MARSHALL
101 E Austin St Ste 209
Marshall, TX 75670-3301
800-577-2227
Fax: 903-295-3315
Type of Counseling:
Default/Foreclosure Counseling,
Rental Counseling, Prepurchase
Counseling

**CONSUMER CREDIT
COUNSELING SERVICE OF
NORTH CENTRAL TEXAS

901 N. McDonald, Suite 600
McKinney, TX 75070-0299
800-856-0257
Toll-Free: 800-856-0257
Fax: 972-542-3623
Type of Counseling:
Default/Foreclosure Counseling,
Rental Counseling, Prepurchase
Counseling, HECM Counseling
Affiliate of: NATIONAL
FOUNDATION FOR
CONSUMER CREDIT,
INCORPORATED

CONSUMER CREDIT
COUNSELING SERVICE OF
GREATER DALLAS,
MESQUITE
3939 Highway 80 Ste 302
Mesquite, TX 75150
972-681-2227
Fax: 972-681-9895
Type of Counseling:
Prepurchase Counseling, Rental
Counseling, Default/Foreclosure
Counseling, HECM Counseling

**MIDLAND
NEIGHBORHOOD HOUSING
SERVICES, INCORPORATED
300 E. Indiana, Ste 1
Midland, TX 79701
915-687-6647
Fax: 915-684-8293
Email: mnhs@planetlink.net
Type of Counseling:
Default/Foreclosure Counseling,
Prepurchase Counseling
Affiliate of: NEIGHBORHOOD
REINVESTMENT
CORPORATION

CONSUMER CREDIT
COUNSELING SERVICE OF
GREATER FORT
WORTH/MIDLAND
2500 N. Big Spring St. # 290
Midland, TX 79705
915-570-9011
Toll-Free: 800-374-2227
Fax: 915-684-3720
Type of Counseling:
Rental Counseling,
Default/Foreclosure Counseling,
Prepurchase Counseling

CONSUMER CREDIT
COUNSELING SERVICE OF
GREATER FORT
WORTH/MINERAL WELLS
116 SE First St.
Mineral Wells, TX 76067
940-325-2952
Fax: 817-599-0813
Type of Counseling:
Rental Counseling,
Default/Foreclosure Counseling,
Prepurchase Counseling

**AMIGOS DEL VALLE,
INCORPORATED
116 N Conway Ave
Mission, TX 78572
956-581-9494
Fax: 956-581-2210
Email: chino@main.rgv.net
Type of Counseling:
Prepurchase Counseling
Affiliate of: NEIGHBORHOOD
REINVESTMENT
CORPORATION

CONSUMER CREDIT
COUNSELING SERVICE OF
NORTH CENTRAL TEXAS,
MOUNT PLEASANT
1805 N. Jefferson St.
Mount Pleasant, TX 75456
903-577-9569
Fax: 903-575-0086
Type of Counseling:
Default/Foreclosure Counseling,
Rental Counseling, Prepurchase
Counseling, HECM Counseling

CONSUMER CREDIT
COUNSELING SERVICE
2626 John Ben Shepperd Pkwy
Bldg B Ste 103
Odessa, TX 79761-1956
800-374-2227
Toll-Free: 800-374-2227
Fax: 915-550-8910
Type of Counseling:
Default/Foreclosure Counseling,
Rental Counseling, Prepurchase
Counseling

CONSUMER CREDIT
COUNSELING SERVICE OF
GREATER
DALLAS/PALESTINE

1006 N. Mallard
Palestine, TX 75801
800-396-2227
Fax: 903-872-8097
Type of Counseling:
Prepurchase Counseling, Rental
Counseling, Default/Foreclosure
Counseling

COLONIAS DE VALLE
1203 E Ferguson St
Pharr, TX 78577
956-787-9903
Fax: 956-782-1016
Type of Counseling:
Prepurchase Counseling, Rental
Counseling

CONSUMER CREDIT
COUNSELING SERVICE OF
GREATER FORT
WORTH/PLAINVIEW
1900 W. &th St. Rm 201
Plainview, TX 79072
806-296-6167
Fax: 806-785-2250
Type of Counseling:
Rental Counseling,
Default/Foreclosure Counseling,
Prepurchase Counseling

CONSUMER CREDIT
COUNSELING SERVICE OF
NORTH CENTRAL TEXAS,
WEST PLANO
2301 Ohio Dr., Suite 295
Plano, TX 75093
972-985-2713
Fax: 972-519-9763
Type of Counseling:
Prepurchase Counseling, Rental
Counseling, Default/Foreclosure
Counseling, HECM Counseling

CONSUMER CREDIT
COUNSELING SERVICE OF
NORTH CENTRAL TEXAS,
PLANO
101 E Park Blvd Ste 757
Plano, TX 75074-5477
972-881-2887
Fax: 972-424-4815
Type of Counseling:
Default/Foreclosure Counseling,
Rental Counseling, Prepurchase
Counseling, HECM Counseling

CONSUMER CREDIT
COUNSELING SERVICE OF
GREATER DALLAS,
RICHARDSON
100 N Central Expy Ste 400
Richardson, TX 75080
972-437-6252
Fax: 972-234-0227
Type of Counseling:
Default/Foreclosure Counseling,
Rental Counseling, Prepurchase
Counseling, HECM Counseling

CONSUMER CREDIT
COUNSELING, Telephone
counseling
2235 Ridge Rd Ste 103
Rockwall, TX 75087-5142
214-638-2263
Fax: 214-638-4398
Type of Counseling:
Default/Foreclosure Counseling,
Rental Counseling, Prepurchase
Counseling

CONSUMER CREDIT
COUNSELING OF SAN
ANGELO
3115 Loop 306 Ste 102
San Angelo, TX 76904-5983
915-942-9156
Fax: 817-377-0036
Type of Counseling:
Default/Foreclosure Counseling,
Rental Counseling, Prepurchase
Counseling

CONSUMER CREDIT
COUNSELING SERVICE OF
GREATER FORT
WORTH/GOODFELLOW AIR
FORCE BASE
225 Fort Lancaster
San Angelo, TX 76908
915-954-3893
Fax: 915-947-1237
Type of Counseling:
Rental Counseling,
Default/Foreclosure Counseling,
Prepurchase Counseling

AVENIDA GUADALUPE
ASSOCIATION
1327 Guadalupe St
San Antonio, TX 78207
210-223-3151

Fax: 210-223-4405
Website: www.agatx.org
Type of Counseling:
Prepurchase Counseling

**SAN ANTONIO HOUSING
TRUST FOUNDATION
118 Broadway St
Suite 606
San Antonio, TX 78205-1945
210-735-2772
Fax: 210-735-2112
Website:
www.sahousingtrust.org
Type of Counseling:
Prepurchase Counseling,
Default/Foreclosure Counseling,
Rental Counseling
Affiliate of: THE HOUSING
PARTNERSHIP NETWORK

OUR CASAS RESIDENT
COUNCIL, INCORPORATED
3006 Gaudalupe Street
San Antonio, TX 782075162
210-433-2787
Fax: 210-433-2789
Type of Counseling:
Prepurchase Counseling,
Default/Foreclosure Counseling,
Rental Counseling

SAN ANTONIO
DEVELOPMENT AGENCY
115 E Travis
Suite 800
San Antonio, TX 78205
210-225-6833
Fax: 210-225-0233
Type of Counseling:
Default/Foreclosure Counseling,
Prepurchase Counseling

COMMUNITY ACTION
DIVISION CITY OF SAN
ANTONIO
115 Plaza de Armas
Suite 150
San Antonio, TX 78205
210-207-5910
Fax: 210-207-5914
Email: espencer@ci.sat.tx.us
Type of Counseling:
Default/Foreclosure Counseling,
Rental Counseling, Prepurchase
Counseling

**NEIGHBORHOOD HOUSING
SERVICES OF SAN ANTONIO,
INCORPORATED
851 Steves Ave
San Antonio, TX 78210-0339
210-533-6673
Fax: 210-533-0923
Type of Counseling:
Prepurchase Counseling
Affiliate of: NEIGHBORHOOD
REINVESTMENT
CORPORATION

CONSUMER CREDIT
COUNSELING SERVICE OF
NORTH CENTRAL TEXAS,
SHERMAN
200 N Travis St Ste 406
Sherman, TX 75090-0005
903-892-6927
Fax: 903-868-1367
Type of Counseling:
Default/Foreclosure Counseling,
Rental Counseling, Prepurchase
Counseling, HECM Counseling

CONSUMER CREDIT
COUNSELING SERVICE OF
GREATER FORT
WORTH/STEPHENVILLE
150 Harbin Dr. # 327
Stephenville, TX 76401
254-965-7454
Fax: 254-965-3841
Type of Counseling:
Rental Counseling,
Default/Foreclosure Counseling,
Prepurchase Counseling

CONSUMER CREDIT
COUNSELING SERVICE OF
NORTH CENTRAL TEXAS,
SULPHUR SPRINGS
521 Main Street, Suite 211
Sulphur Springs, TX 75480
903-439-1130
Fax: 903-438-0125
Type of Counseling:
Prepurchase Counseling, Rental
Counseling, Default/Foreclosure
Counseling, HECM Counseling

CONSUMER CREDIT
COUNSELING SERVICE OF
GREATER FORT
WORTH/SWEETWATER

119 E. 3rd St. # 303
Sweetwater, TX 79556
915-235-0222
Fax: 915-673-0405
Type of Counseling:
Rental Counseling,
Default/Foreclosure Counseling,
Prepurchase Counseling

CONSUMER CREDIT
COUNSELING SERVICE OF
GREATER FORT
WORTH/TEMPLE
1506 Paseo Del Plata # 100
Temple, TX 76502
254-771-1818
Fax: 254-771-0210
Type of Counseling:
Rental Counseling,
Default/Foreclosure Counseling,
Prepurchase Counseling

CONSUMER CREDIT
COUNSELING SERVICE OF
NORTH CENTRAL TEXAS,
TEXARKANA
4520 Summerhill Rd
Texarkana, TX 75503
903-792-1116
Fax: 903-792-1208
Type of Counseling:
Default/Foreclosure Counseling,
Rental Counseling, Prepurchase
Counseling, HECM Counseling

CONSUMER CREDIT
COUNSELING SERVICE OF
GREATER DALLAS, TYLER
1001 Loop 323 ESE Ste 250
Tyler, TX 75701
800-396-2227
Toll-Free: 800-396-2227
Fax: 903-581-6986
Type of Counseling:
Default/Foreclosure Counseling,
Rental Counseling, Prepurchase
Counseling, HECM Counseling

CONSUMER CREDIT
COUNSELING SERVICE OF
GREATER FORT
WORTH/WACO
6801 Sanger Ave. Suite 202
Waco, TX 76710
254-772-8626
Fax: 254-772-4037

Type of Counseling:
Rental Counseling,
Default/Foreclosure Counseling,
Prepurchase Counseling

**NEIGHBORHOOD HOUSING
SERVICES OF WACO,
INCORPORATED
922 Franklin Avenue
Waco, TX 76701
254-752-1647
Fax: 254-752-6472
Email: egreen@swbell.net
Type of Counseling:
Prepurchase Counseling
Affiliate of: NEIGHBORHOOD
REINVESTMENT
CORPORATION

CONSUMER CREDIT
COUNSELING SERVICE OF
GREATER DALLAS,
WAXAHACHIE
820 Ferris Ave Ste 375
Waxahachie, TX 75165
888-397-2227
Toll-Free: 888-397-2227
Fax: 972-923-1269
Type of Counseling:
Default/Foreclosure Counseling,
Rental Counseling, Prepurchase
Counseling, HECM Counseling

CONSUMER CREDIT
COUNSELING SERVICE OF
GREATER FORT
WORTH/WEATHERFORD
200 Palo Pinto # 107
Weatherford, TX 76086
817-599-0813
Fax: 817-599-0813
Type of Counseling:
Rental Counseling,
Default/Foreclosure Counseling

CONSUMER CREDIT
COUNSELING SERVICE OF
GREATER DALLAS, WICHITA
FALLS
4245 Kemp St. Suite 502
Wichita Falls, TX 76308-2129
800-380-2227
Toll-Free: 800-380-2227
Fax: 940-692-3239
Type of Counseling:

Default/Foreclosure Counseling,
Rental Counseling, Prepurchase
Counseling, HECM Counseling

Utah

CEDAR CITY HOUSING
AUTHORITY
364 South 100 East
Cedar City, UT 84720
435-586-8462
Fax: 435-865-9397
Type of Counseling:
Prepurchase Counseling,
Default/Foreclosure Counseling,
Rental Counseling

UTAH STATE UNIVERSITY -
FAMILY LIFE CENTER
493 N 700 E
Logan, UT 84321-4231
435-797-7224
Toll-Free:
TTY/TDD:
Fax: 435-797-7432
Email: tawnee@cc.usu.edu
Website: www.usu.edu/flc
Type of Counseling:
HECM Counseling,
Default/Foreclosure Counseling,
Rental Counseling, Prepurchase
Counseling

YOUR COMMUNITY
CONNECTION
2261 Adams Ave
Ogden, UT 84401-1510
801-394-9456
Fax: 801-394-9456
Type of Counseling:
HECM Counseling,
Default/Foreclosure Counseling,
Rental Counseling, Prepurchase
Counseling

**NEIGHBORHOOD HOUSING
SERVICES OF PROVO
91 West 200 South
Provo, UT 84601-
801-375-5820
Fax: 801-375-5966
Type of Counseling:
Prepurchase Counseling,
Default/Foreclosure Counseling

Affiliate of: NEIGHBORHOOD
REINVESTMENT
CORPORATION

COMMUNITY ACTION
SERVICES
257 East Center
Provo, UT 84606
801-373-7634
Fax: 801-373-8228
Type of Counseling:
HECM Counseling,
Default/Foreclosure Counseling,
Rental Counseling, Prepurchase
Counseling

**SALT LAKE
NEIGHBORHOOD HOUSING
SERVICES, INCORPORATED
622 West 500 North
Salt Lake City, UT 84116-3417
801-539-1590
Fax: 801-539-1593
Website: www.slnhs.org
Type of Counseling:
Default/Foreclosure Counseling,
Prepurchase Counseling
Affiliate of: NEIGHBORHOOD
REINVESTMENT
CORPORATION

SALT LAKE COMMUNITY
ACTION PROGRAM
764 S 200 W
Salt Lake City, UT 84101-2710
801-359-2444
Fax: 801-355-1798
Type of Counseling:
HECM Counseling,
Default/Foreclosure Counseling,
Rental Counseling, Prepurchase
Counseling

VERMONT

**CENTRAL VERMONT
COMMUNITY LAND TRUST
107 North Main Street
Barre, VT 05641
802-476-4493
Fax: 802-479-0020
Type of Counseling:
Prepurchase Counseling, Rental
Counseling

Affiliate of: NEIGHBORHOOD
REINVESTMENT
CORPORATION

**BRATTLEBORO AREA
COMMUNITY LAND TRUST
192 Canal Street
Brattleboro, VT 05301
802-254-4604
TTY/TDD: 802-254-4604
Fax: 802-254-4656
Email: esjohnson@bacl.org
Type of Counseling:
Prepurchase Counseling
Affiliate of: CITIZENS'
HOUSING AND PLANNING
ASSOCIATION,
INCORPORATED

BURLINGTON COMMUNITY
LAND TRUST
179 S Winooski Ave
Burlington, VT 05402-0523
802-660-0642
Fax: 802-660-0641
Email: admin@getahome.org
Type of Counseling:
Prepurchase Counseling,
Default/Foreclosure Counseling

CHAMPLAIN VALLEY OFFICE
OF ECONOMIC
OPPORTUNITY
191 North St
Burlington, VT 05402
802-660-3456
Fax: 802-660-3454
Email: bayder@together.net
Type of Counseling:
Prepurchase Counseling, Rental
Counseling
Affiliate of: CITIZENS'
HOUSING AND PLANNING
ASSOCIATION,
INCORPORATED

**GILMAN HOUSING TRUST
101 Main Street
Lyndonville, VT 05851
802-334-1241
Email: info@nekhome.com
Type of Counseling:
Prepurchase Counseling,
Default/Foreclosure Counseling,
HECM Counseling

Affiliate of: NEIGHBORHOOD
REINVESTMENT
CORPORATION

**LAMOILLE HOUSING
PARTNERSHIP
109 Professional Drive, Suite 1
Morrisville, VT 05661
802-888-5714
Fax: 802-888-3082
Email: lucy@pshift.com
Type of Counseling:
Prepurchase Counseling
Affiliate of: CITIZENS'
HOUSING AND PLANNING
ASSOCIATION,
INCORPORATED

**RANDOLPH AREA
COMMUNITY DEVELOPMENT
CORPORATION
PO Box 409
Randolph, VT 05060
802-728-4305
Fax: 802-728-4016
Email: RACDC@quest-net.com
Type of Counseling:
Prepurchase Counseling
Affiliate of: CITIZENS'
HOUSING AND PLANNING
ASSOCIATION,
INCORPORATED

**RUTLAND COUNTY
COMMUNITY LAND TRUST
128 Merchants Row, 6th floor
Rutland, VT 05701
802-775-3139
Toll-Free: 800-545-7989
Fax: 802-775-0434
Email: ekrcclt@sover.net
Type of Counseling:
Prepurchase Counseling
Affiliate of: CITIZENS'
HOUSING AND PLANNING
ASSOCIATION,
INCORPORATED

**ROCKINGHAM
COMMUNITY AREA LAND
TRUST
23 Pleasant St.
Springfield, VT 05156
802-885-3220
Fax: 802-885-5811
Type of Counseling:

Prepurchase Counseling
Affiliate of: NEIGHBORHOOD
REINVESTMENT
CORPORATION

**LAKE CHAMPLAIN
HOUSING DEVELOPMENT
CORPORATION
2 Federal Street, Suite 101
St. Albans, VT 05478
802-527-2361
Fax: 802-527-2961
Email: lchdcsta@together.net
Type of Counseling:
Prepurchase Counseling,
Default/Foreclosure Counseling
Affiliate of: CITIZENS'
HOUSING AND PLANNING
ASSOCIATION,
INCORPORATED

**RUTLAND WEST
NEIGHBORHOOD HOUSING
SERVICES
71 Marble Street
West Rutland, VT 05777
802-438-2303
Fax: 802-438-5338
Email: rwnhs@vermontel.com
Type of Counseling:
Default/Foreclosure Counseling,
Prepurchase Counseling
Affiliate of: NEIGHBORHOOD
REINVESTMENT
CORPORATION

Virginia

PEOPLE INCORPORATED
1173 W Main St
Abingdon, VA 24210-2428
540-623-9000
Fax: 540-628-2931
Type of Counseling:
HECM Counseling,
Default/Foreclosure Counseling,
Prepurchase Counseling

SENIOR CITIZENS
EMPLOYMENT AND
SERVICES, INCORPORATED
121 N Saint Asaph St
Alexandria, VA 22314-3109
703-836-4414
Fax: 703-836-1252

CONSUMER CREDIT
COUNSELING SERVICE OF
GREATER WASHINGTON
801 N Pitt St Ste 117
Alexandria, VA 22314-1765
703-836-8772
Fax: 703-548-7704
Type of Counseling: HECM
Counseling

CATHOLIC CHARITIES USA
1731 King St Ste 200
Alexandria, VA 22314-2720
703-549-1390
Fax: 703-549-1656

ARLINGTON AGENCY ON
AGING
1800 North Edison St.
Arlington, VA 22207-1955
703-228-5030
Fax: 703-228-5073
Type of Counseling: HECM
Counseling

ARLINGTON HOUSING
CORPORATION
2300 S 9th St S Ste 200
Arlington, VA 22204-2320
703-486-0626
Fax: 703-486-0653
Type of Counseling: Rental
Counseling, Prepurchase
Counseling

**CONSUMER CREDIT
COUNSELING SERVICE OF
SOUTHWESTERN VIRGINIA,
INCORPORATED
506 Cumberland Street
Bristol, VA 24201
800-926-0042
Fax: 540-366-7140
Type of Counseling:
HECM Counseling,
Default/Foreclosure Counseling,
Prepurchase Counseling, Rental
Counseling

PIEDMONT HOUSING
ALLIANCE
515 Park Street
Charlottesville, VA 22902-
434-817-2436
Fax: 434-817-0664
Website: www.avenue.org/pha

Type of Counseling:
Prepurchase Counseling,
Default/Foreclosure Counseling,
Rental Counseling

MONTICELLO AREA
COMMUNITY ACTION
AGENCY
1025 Park St
Charlottesville, VA 22901-3934
804-295-3171
Fax: 804-296-0093
Type of Counseling:
HECM Counseling,
Default/Foreclosure Counseling,
Rental Counseling, Prepurchase
Counseling

**CATHOLIC CHARITIES OF
HAMPTON ROADS,
INCORPORATED
3804 Poplar Hill Road, Suite A
Chesapeake, VA 23321
757-484-0703
Fax: 757-484-1096
Email: cchrcccs@aol.com
Type of Counseling:
HECM Counseling,
Default/Foreclosure Counseling,
Prepurchase Counseling, Rental
Counseling
Affiliate of: CATHOLIC
CHARITIES USA

**COMMUNITY HOUSING
PARTNERS CORPORATION
930 Cambria Street NE
Christianburg, VA 24073
757-422-9664
Fax: 757-425-5826
Type of Counseling:
Prepurchase Counseling
Affiliate of: THE HOUSING
PARTNERSHIP NETWORK

**CONSUMER CREDIT
COUNSELING SERVICE OF
SOUTHWESTERN VIRGINIA,
INCORPORATED
Tudor Square, Ste. 10 211
Roanoke St.
Christiansburg, VA 24073
800-926-0042
Toll-Free: 800-926-0042
Fax: 540-366-7140
Type of Counseling:

HECM Counseling,
Default/Foreclosure Counseling,
Prepurchase Counseling, Rental
Counseling

****CONSUMER CREDIT
COUNSELING SERVICE OF
SOUTHWESTERN VIRGINIA,
INCORPORATED**
First Union Bank Building Main
Street
Covington, VA 24426
800-926-0042
Toll-Free: 800-926-0042
Fax: 540-366-7140
Type of Counseling:
HECM Counseling,
Default/Foreclosure Counseling,
Prepurchase Counseling, Rental
Counseling

**CONSUMER CREDIT
COUNSELING SERVICE OF
GREATER WASHINGTON**
3927 Old Lee Hwy
Fairfax, VA 22030-2422
703-591-9020
Fax: 703-591-3927
Type of Counseling:
HECM Counseling,
Default/Foreclosure Counseling,
Prepurchase Counseling

**OFFICE FOR WOMEN
FAIRFAX COUNTY**
1200 Government Center Pkwy
Fairfax, VA 22035
703-324-5730
Fax: 703-324-3959

****CATHOLIC CHARITIES OF
HAMPTON ROADS,
INCORPORATED**
121 South Main Street
Franklin, VA 23851
757-562-6222
Fax: 757-562-3930
Type of Counseling:
Rental Counseling,
Default/Foreclosure Counseling,
Prepurchase Counseling
Affiliate of: CATHOLIC
CHARITIES USA

TELAMON CORPORATION
111 Henry St

Gretna, VA 24557-0500
804-656-8357
Fax: 804-656-8356
Type of Counseling:
Default/Foreclosure Counseling,
Rental Counseling, Prepurchase
Counseling

**HAMPTON REDEVELOPMENT
AND HOUSING AUTHORITY**
22 Lincoln St
Hampton, VA 23669-3522
757-727-1111
Fax: 757-727-1090
Email: hrha@aol.com
Type of Counseling:
Prepurchase Counseling,
Default/Foreclosure Counseling,
Rental Counseling

**CENTER FOR CHILD AND
FAMILY
SERVICE/CONSUMER CREDIT
COUNSELING SERVICE OF
HAMPTON ROADS**
2021 Cunningham Drive, Suite
400
Hampton, VA 23666-3375
757-826-2227
Fax: 757-838-8021

Type of Counseling:
HECM Counseling,
Default/Foreclosure Counseling,
Prepurchase Counseling
Affiliate of: NATIONAL
FOUNDATION FOR
CONSUMER CREDIT,
INCORPORATED

**CONSUMER CREDIT
COUNSELING SERVICE OF
GREATER WASHINGTON**
604 South King Street, Suite 007
Leesburg, VA 20175
703-777-3787
Fax: 703-548-7704
Type of Counseling:
HECM Counseling, Prepurchase
Counseling, Default/Foreclosure
Counseling, Rental Counseling

****AMERICAN CREDIT
COUNSELORS,
INCORPORATED**
Null

Lynchburg, VA 24502
800-646-0042
Toll-Free: 800-646-0042
Fax: 540-366-7140
Type of Counseling:
HECM Counseling,
Default/Foreclosure Counseling,
Prepurchase Counseling, Rental
Counseling

**LYNCHBURG COMMUNITY
ACTION GROUP,
INCORPORATED**
1310 Church St
Lynchburg, VA 24504-4604
804-846-2778
Fax: 804-845-1547
Type of Counseling:
Default/Foreclosure Counseling,
Rental Counseling, Prepurchase
Counseling

**SKYLINE COMMUNITY
ACTION PROGRAM,
INCORPORATED**
Old Elementary School Route
687
Madison, VA 22727
540-948-2237
Fax: 540-948-2264
Type of Counseling:
HECM Counseling,
Default/Foreclosure Counseling,
Rental Counseling, Prepurchase
Counseling

**CONSUMER CREDIT
COUNSELING SERVICE OF
GREATER WASHINGTON**
10629 Crestwood Dr
Manassas, VA 20109-3433
703-690-4779
Fax: 703-335-1632
Type of Counseling:
HECM Counseling,
Default/Foreclosure Counseling,
Prepurchase Counseling

**VIRGINIA COOPERATIVE
EXTENSION - PRINCE
WILLIAM OFFICE**
8033 Ashton Ave Ste 105
Manassas, VA 20109-8202
703-792-6287
Fax: 703-792-4630
Email: mleon@pwcgov.org

Website:
www.pwcgov.org/vce/html/pe
rsonal_finance.html
Type of Counseling:
Prepurchase Counseling,
Default/Foreclosure Counseling,
Rental Counseling, HECM
Counseling

****CONSUMER CREDIT
COUNSELING SERVICE OF
SOUTHWESTERN VIRGINIA,
INCORPORATED**
900 Starling Avenue
Martinsville, VA 24112
800-926-0042
Toll-Free: 800-926-0042
Fax: 540-366-7140
Type of Counseling:
HECM Counseling,
Default/Foreclosure Counseling,
Prepurchase Counseling, Rental
Counseling

**NORTHHAMPTON HOUSING
TRUST, INCORPORATED**
Lankford Highway Rt 13
Nassawadox, VA 23413-0814
757-442-4509
Fax: 757-442-7530
Email: veseehc@esva.net
Type of Counseling:
Default/Foreclosure Counseling,
Rental Counseling, Prepurchase
Counseling

**VIRGINIA EASTERN SHORE
ECONOMIC EMPOWERMENT
AND HOUSING
CORPORATION**
UPS Address is 10340, Lankford
Highway Birdsnest VA
Nassawadox, VA 23413
757-442-4509
Fax: 757-442-7530
Type of Counseling:
HECM Counseling,
Default/Foreclosure Counseling,
Rental Counseling, Prepurchase
Counseling

**CENTER FOR CHILD AND
FAMILY
SERVICE/CONSUMER CREDIT
COUNSELING SERVICE OF
HAMPTON ROADS`**

12891 Jefferson Avenue
Newport News, VA 23606
757-826-2227
Fax: 757-838-8021
Type of Counseling:
HECM Counseling,
Default/Foreclosure Counseling,
Prepurchase Counseling, Rental
Counseling

****CATHOLIC CHARITIES OF
HAMPTON ROADS,
INCORPORATED**
12829 Jefferson Avenue, Ste. 101
Newport News, VA 23608
757-484-0703
Fax: 757-484-1096
Email: CCHRCCCS@aol.com
Type of Counseling:
HECM Counseling,
Default/Foreclosure Counseling,
Rental Counseling
Affiliate of: CATHOLIC
CHARITIES USA

**NEWPORT NEWS OFFICE OF
HUMAN AFFAIRS**
6060 Jefferson Ave
Newport News, VA 23607
757-245-3271
Fax: 757-244-8146
Email: pcdcohainc.org
Type of Counseling:
HECM Counseling,
Default/Foreclosure Counseling,
Rental Counseling, Prepurchase
Counseling

**CENTER FOR CHILD AND
FAMILY
SERVICE/CONSUMER CREDIT
COUNSELING OF HAMPTON
ROADS**
Fort Eustis Building #601
Newport News, VA 23604
757-826-2227
Fax: 757-838-8021
Type of Counseling:
HECM Counseling,
Default/Foreclosure Counseling,
Prepurchase Counseling, Rental
Counseling

**CONSUMER FINANCIAL
COUNSELING OF
TIDEWATER, DIVISION OF**

**FAMILY SERVICES OF
TIDEWATER INCORPORATED**
222 W 19th St
Norfolk, VA 23517
757-625-2227
Fax: 757-640-8402
Type of Counseling:
HECM Counseling,
Default/Foreclosure Counseling,
Rental Counseling, Prepurchase
Counseling

****CATHOLIC CHARITIES OF
HAMPTON ROADS,
INCORPORATED**
1301 Colonial Avenue
Norfolk, VA 23517
757-625-2568
Fax: 757-625-5684
Email: CCHRCCCS@aol.com
Type of Counseling:
Default/Foreclosure Counseling,
Prepurchase Counseling, Rental
Counseling, HECM Counseling
Affiliate of: CATHOLIC
CHARITIES USA

THE STOP ORGANIZATION
2551 Almeda Ave
Norfolk, VA 23513-2443
757-858-1360
Fax: 757-858-1389
Type of Counseling:
HECM Counseling,
Default/Foreclosure Counseling,
Rental Counseling, Prepurchase
Counseling

**CRATER DISTRICT AREA
AGENCY ON AGING**
23 Seyler Dr
Petersburg, VA 23805-9243
804-732-7020
Fax: 804-732-7232
Email: Cccrater@aol.com
Type of Counseling: HECM
Counseling

**RESTON INTERFAITH,
INCORPORATED**
11484 Washington Plaza W
Suite 400
Reston, VA 20190
703-787-3100
Fax: 703-787-3046
Type of Counseling:
Rental Counseling

RICHMOND URBAN LEAGUE
101 E Clay Street
Richmond, VA 23219-1331
804-649-8407
Fax: 804-643-5724
Email: ulr@aol.com
Type of Counseling:
HECM Counseling,
Default/Foreclosure Counseling,
Rental Counseling, Prepurchase
Counseling
Affiliate of: NATIONAL
URBAN LEAGUE

HOUSING OPPORTUNITIES
MADE EQUAL,
INCORPORATED
2201 W. Broad Street, Suite 200
Richmond, VA 23220
804-354-0641
Fax: 804-354-0690
Type of Counseling:
HECM Counseling,
Default/Foreclosure Counseling,
Rental Counseling, Prepurchase
Counseling

COMMONWEALTH OF
VIRGINIA DEPARTMENT FOR
THE AGING
1600 Forest Ave Ste 102
Richmond, VA 23229
804-662-9333
Fax: 804-662-9354
Type of Counseling: HECM
Counseling

CAPITAL AREA AGENCY ON
AGING
24 E Cary St
Richmond, VA 23219-3733
804-343-3025
Fax: 804-649-2258
Type of Counseling: HECM
Counseling

**RICHMOND
NEIGHBORHOOD HOUSING
SERVICES, INCORPORATED
2712 Chamberlayne Avenue
Richmond, VA 23222-2634
804-329-2500
Fax: 804-329-2100
Type of Counseling:
Default/Foreclosure Counseling,
Prepurchase Counseling

Affiliate of: NEIGHBORHOOD
REINVESTMENT
CORPORATION

SOUTHSIDE COMMUNITY
DEVELOPMENT AND
HOUSING CORPORATION
1624 Hull Street
Richmond, VA 23224
804-231-4449
Fax: 804-231-3959
Type of Counseling:
Prepurchase Counseling, Rental
Counseling, Default/Foreclosure
Counseling, HECM Counseling

**COMMONWEALTH
CATHOLIC CHARITIES
1512 Willow Lawn Dr.
Richmond, VA 23230
804-285-5900
Fax: 804-285-9130
Email: comcathric@aol.com
Type of Counseling:
Prepurchase Counseling,
Default/Foreclosure Counseling,
Rental Counseling
Affiliate of: CATHOLIC
CHARITIES USA

TOTAL ACTION AGAINST
POVERTY IN ROANOKE
VALLEY
510 11th St. NW
Roanoke, VA 24017
540-777-2777
Fax: 540-777-2778
Type of Counseling:
HECM Counseling,
Default/Foreclosure Counseling,
Rental Counseling, Prepurchase
Counseling

CITY OF ROANOKE
REDEVELOPMENT AND
HOUSING COUNSELING
AUTHORITY
2624 Salem Tpke NW
Roanoke, VA 24017-5334
540-342-4561
Fax: 540-983-9229
Type of Counseling:
HECM Counseling,
Default/Foreclosure Counseling,
Rental Counseling, Prepurchase
Counseling

AMERICAN CREDIT
COUNSELORS
7000 Peters Creek Rd
Roanoke, VA 24019
540-366-6926
Toll-Free: 800-926-0042
Fax: 540-366-7140
Type of Counseling:
Default/Foreclosure Counseling,
Prepurchase Counseling, Rental
Counseling, HECM Counseling

**CATHOLIC CHARITIES OF
HAMPTON ROADS,
INCORPORATED
4855 Princess Anne Road
Virginia Beach, VA 23462
757-484-0703
Fax: 757-484-1096
Email: CCHRCCCS@aol.com
Type of Counseling:
Default/Foreclosure Counseling,
Prepurchase Counseling, Rental
Counseling, HECM Counseling
Affiliate of: CATHOLIC
CHARITIES USA

**CATHOLIC CHARITIES OF
HAMPTON ROADS,
INCORPORATED
1315 Jamestown Road, Suite 202
Williamsburg, VA 23185
757-875-0060
Fax: 757-877-7883
Email: CCHRCCCS@aol.com
Type of Counseling:
Prepurchase Counseling,
Default/Foreclosure Counseling,
Rental Counseling, HECM
Counseling
Affiliate of: CATHOLIC
CHARITIES USA

CENTER FOR CHILD AND
FAMILY SERVICE/
CONSUMER CREDIT
COUNSELING SERVICE OF
HAMPTON ROADS
1031 Richmond Road
Williamsburg, VA 23186
757-826-2227
Fax: 757-838-8021
Type of Counseling:
HECM Counseling,
Default/Foreclosure Counseling,

Prepurchase Counseling, Rental
Counseling

CONSUMER CREDIT
COUNSELING SERVICE OF
GREATER WASHINGTON
2971 Valley Ave Ste 2
Winchester, VA 22601-2631
800-747-4222
Fax: 540-948-7498
Type of Counseling:
HECM Counseling,
Default/Foreclosure Counseling,
Prepurchase Counseling

CONSUMER CREDIT
COUNSELING SERVICE OF
GREATER WASHINGTON
12662 B Lake Ridge Dr
Woodbridge, VA 22192
703-494-1014
Fax: 703-494-1594
Type of Counseling:
HECM Counseling,
Default/Foreclosure Counseling,
Prepurchase Counseling

Washington

ABERDEEN NEIGHBORHOOD
HOUSING SERVICES
710 E Market St
Aberdeen, WA 98520-3430
360-533-7828
Fax: 360-533-7851
Email: bmacfarlane@aberdeen-
nhs.com
Website: www.aberdeen-
nhs.com
Type of Counseling:
HECM Counseling,
Default/Foreclosure Counseling,
Rental Counseling, Prepurchase
Counseling
Affiliate of: NEIGHBORHOOD
REINVESTMENT
CORPORATION

HOMESIGHT OF KING
COUNTY
55 A. St
Auburn, WA 98001
206-723-4355
Toll-Free: 888-749-4663
Fax: 206-723-7137

Email:
Tenesha@HOMESIGHTWA.org
Website: www.homesightwa.org
Type of Counseling:
Prepurchase Counseling
Affiliate of: HOUSING
OPPORTUNITIES,
INCORPORATED

CONSUMER CREDIT
COUNSELING SERVICE OF
KITSAP COUNTY
2817 Wheaton Way Ste 206
Bremerton, WA 98310
360-373-9138
Toll-Free: 800-244-1183
Fax: 253-582-5158
Type of Counseling:
HECM Counseling,
Default/Foreclosure Counseling,
Prepurchase Counseling

CONSUMER CREDIT
COUNSELING SERVICE OF
OLYMPIC SOUTH SOUND
2451 NE Kresky Road
Chehalis, WA 98532-2436
253-588-1858
Toll-Free: 800-244-1183
Fax: 253-582-5158
Type of Counseling:
HECM Counseling,
Default/Foreclosure Counseling,
Prepurchase Counseling

CONSUMER CREDIT
COUNSELING SERVICE OF
GRAYS HARBOR COUNTY
3001 Ingham Street
Hoquiam, WA 98550
253-588-1858
Toll-Free: 800-244-1183
Fax: 253-582-5158
Type of Counseling:
HECM Counseling,
Default/Foreclosure Counseling,
Prepurchase Counseling

**CONSUMER CREDIT
COUNSELING SERVICES OF
THE TRI-CITIES
401 N. Morain Street
Kennewick, WA 99336
509-737-1973
Toll-Free: 800-201-2181
Fax: 509-737-9722

Type of Counseling:
Prepurchase Counseling,
Default/Foreclosure Counseling,
HECM Counseling, Rental
Counseling
Affiliate of: NATIONAL
FOUNDATION FOR
CONSUMER CREDIT,
INCORPORATED

PIERCE COUNTY,
DEPARTMENT OF
COMMUNITY SERVICES,
HOUSING PROGRAMS
8815 South Tacoma Way, Suite
211
Lakewood, WA 98499
253-798-7038
Toll-Free: 800-562-0336
Fax: 253-798-3999
Type of Counseling:
HECM Counseling,
Default/Foreclosure Counseling,
Rental Counseling, Prepurchase
Counseling

HOMESIGHT SNOHOMISH
COUNTY
22001- 66th Avenue West
Mountlake Terrace, WA 98043
206-723-4355
Toll-Free: 888-749-4663
Fax: 206-723-7137
Email:
tanesha@HOMESIGHTWA.ORG
Website: www.homesightwa.org
Type of Counseling:
Prepurchase Counseling
Affiliate of: HOUSING
OPPORTUNITIES,
INCORPORATED

CONSUMER CREDIT
COUNSELING SERVICE OF
THURSTON COUNTY
409 Cluster Way, Suite E
Olympia, WA 98502
360-943-5740
Toll-Free: 800-244-1183
Fax: 253-582-5158
Type of Counseling:
HECM Counseling,
Default/Foreclosure Counseling,
Prepurchase Counseling

CONSUMER CREDIT
COUNSELING SERVICE OF
CLALLAM COUNTY
3430 Highway 101 E
Port Angeles, WA 98362-9068
253-588-1858
Toll-Free: 800-244-1183
Fax: 253-582-5158
Type of Counseling:
HECM Counseling,
Default/Foreclosure Counseling,
Prepurchase Counseling

CONSUMER CREDIT
COUNSELING SERVICE OF
KITSAP COUNTY
18943 Caldart Ave
Poulsbo, WA 98370
253-588-1858
Toll-Free: 800-244-1183
Fax: 253-582-5158
Type of Counseling:
HECM Counseling,
Default/Foreclosure Counseling,
Prepurchase Counseling

CONSUMER CREDIT
COUNSELING SERVICE OF
PACIFIC COUNTY
408 Second St
Raymond, WA 98577-1710
253-588-1858
Toll-Free: 800-244-1183
Fax: 253-582-5158
Type of Counseling:
HECM Counseling,
Default/Foreclosure Counseling,
Prepurchase Counseling

**ACORN HOUSING
CORPORATION
5416 Rainier Avenue South
Seattle, WA 98118
206-723-5845
Fax: 206-723-8658
Type of Counseling:
Default/Foreclosure Counseling,
Prepurchase Counseling, Rental
Counseling, HECM Counseling
Affiliate of: ACORN HOUSING
CORPORATION

WASHINGTON STATE
HOUSING FINANCE
COMMISSION
1000 2nd Avenue, Suite 2700

Seattle, WA 98104
206-464-7139
Fax: 206-587-5113
Type of Counseling:
Prepurchase Counseling

HOMESIGHT
5117 Rainier Avenue South
Seattle, WA 98118
206-723-4355
Toll-Free: 888-749-4663
Fax: 206-760-4210
Email:
tenesha@homesightwa.org
Website: www.homesightwa.org
Type of Counseling:
Prepurchase Counseling
Affiliate of: HOUSING
OPPORTUNITIES,
INCORPORATED

URBAN LEAGUE OF
METROPOLITAN SEATTLE
105 14th Ave
Seattle, WA 98122-5558
206-461-3792
Fax: 206-461-8425
Type of Counseling:
Default/Foreclosure Counseling,
Rental Counseling, Prepurchase
Counseling, HECM Counseling

FREMONT PUBLIC
ASSOCIATION
1501 N. 45th St
Seattle, WA 98103
206-694-6700
Fax: 206-694-6777
Email: krisb@fremontpublic.org
Website:
www.fremontpublic.org
Type of Counseling:
Default/Foreclosure Counseling,
Rental Counseling, Prepurchase
Counseling, HECM Counseling

**NEW BIRTH COGIC
12643 Renton Avenue South
Seattle, WA 98108
206-772-6557
Fax: 206-772-4419
Type of Counseling:
Prepurchase Counseling
Affiliate of: CONGRESS OF
NATIONAL BLACK
CHURCHES, INCORPORATED

CONSUMER CREDIT
COUNSELING SERVICE OF
OLYMPIC-SOUTH SOUND
428 Birch St RM 12A
Shelton, WA 98584-1700
253-588-1858
Toll-Free: 800-244-1183
Fax: 253-582-5158
Type of Counseling:
HECM Counseling,
Default/Foreclosure Counseling,
Prepurchase Counseling

**SPOKANE
HOMEOWNERSHIP
RESOURCE CENTER
55 West Mission St Ste # 103
Spokane, WA 99201
509-343-7472
Fax: 509-343-7474
Type of Counseling:
Prepurchase Counseling

SPOKANE NEIGHBORHOOD
ACTION PROGRAMS
500 S. Stone
Spokane, WA 99202-3937
509-456-7105
Fax: 509-456-7159
Type of Counseling:
HECM Counseling,
Default/Foreclosure Counseling,
Prepurchase Counseling

THE MARTIN LUTHER KING
DEVELOPMENT
ASSOCIATION
1023 Martin Luther King, Jr.
Way
Tacoma, WA 98405
253-627-1099
Fax: 253-627-1187
Type of Counseling:
Prepurchase Counseling

CONSUMER CREDIT
COUNSELING SERVICE OF
OLYMPIC SOUTH SOUND
11306 Bridgeport Way SW
Tacoma, WA 98499
253-588-1858
Toll-Free: 800-244-1183
Fax: 253-582-5158
Type of Counseling:
HECM Counseling,
Default/Foreclosure Counseling,
Prepurchase Counseling

CONSUMER CREDIT
COUNSELING SERVICE OF
OLYMPIC-SOUTH SOUND
11306 Bridgeport Way SW
Tacoma, WA 98499-3005
253-588-1858
Toll-Free: 800-244-1183
Fax: 253-582-5158
Website: www.cccs-nw.org
Type of Counseling:
HECM Counseling,
Default/Foreclosure Counseling,
Prepurchase Counseling

COMMUNITY HOUSING
RESOURCE CENTER
3801-A Main Street
Vancouver, WA
360-690-4496
Fax: 360-694-6665
Type of Counseling:
HECM Counseling,
Default/Foreclosure Counseling,
Prepurchase Counseling

West Virginia

CONSUMER CREDIT
COUNSELING OF SOUTHERN
WEST VIRGINIA
735 S Kanawha St
Beckley, WV 25801-5626
800-869-7758
Fax: 304-255-2412
Type of Counseling:
HECM Counseling,
Default/Foreclosure Counseling,
Prepurchase Counseling

CONSUMER CREDIT
COUNSELING SERVICE OF
BLUEFIELD, INCORPORATED
Green Valley Retail Center
Bluefield, WV 24701-6282
304-325-5143
Toll-Free: 800-313-5097
Fax: 304-324-0375
Type of Counseling:
Prepurchase Counseling,
Default/Foreclosure Counseling,
HECM Counseling

**RELIGIOUS COALITION FOR
COMMUMITY RENEWAL -
JUBILEE HOUSING
1516 Washington Street East

Charleston, WV 25311
304-346-6398
Fax: 304-346-6417
Type of Counseling:
Prepurchase Counseling,
Default/Foreclosure Counseling,
HECM Counseling
Affiliate of: THE HOUSING
PARTNERSHIP NETWORK

WEST VIRGINIA HOUSING
DEVELOPMENT FUND
814 Virginia Street, East
Charleston, WV 25301
304-345-6475
Fax: 304-340-9941
Type of Counseling:
Prepurchase Counseling,
Default/Foreclosure Counseling,
Rental Counseling

CONSUMER CREDIT
COUNSELING SERVICE OF
THE KANAWHA VALLEY
8 Capitol St Ste 200
Charleston, WV 25301-2828
800-281-5969
Fax: 304-344-3871
Type of Counseling:
HECM Counseling,
Default/Foreclosure Counseling,
Rental Counseling, Prepurchase
Counseling

**COMMUNITY WORKS IN
WEST VIRGINIA
4710 Chimney Drive Suite 6
Charlestown, WV 25032-4148
304-965-2241
Fax: 304-965-2264
Email: housenwv@aol.com
Type of Counseling:
Default/Foreclosure Counseling,
Prepurchase Counseling
Affiliate of: NEIGHBORHOOD
REINVESTMENT
CORPORATION

CONSUMER CREDIT
COUNSELING SERVICE OF
NORTH CENTRAL WEST
VIRGINIA
115 S 4th St Ste 208
Clarksburg, WV 26302
304-623-0921
Toll-Free: 800-498-6681

Fax: 304-624-4089
Type of Counseling:
HECM Counseling,
Default/Foreclosure Counseling,
Rental Counseling, Prepurchase
Counseling
Affiliate of: NATIONAL
FOUNDATION FOR
CONSUMER CREDIT,
INCORPORATED

KANAWHA INSTITUTE FOR
SOCIAL RESEARCH ACTION
124 Marshall Avenue
Dunbar, WV 25064
304-768-8924
Fax: 304-768-0376
Type of Counseling:
Prepurchase Counseling

CONSUMER CREDIT
COUNSELING SERVICE, A
DIVISION OF GOODWILL
INDUSTRIES
1102 Memorial Blvd.
Huntington, WV 25701
304-522-4321
Toll-Free: 888-534-4387
Fax: 304-525-7038
Type of Counseling:
HECM Counseling,
Default/Foreclosure Counseling,
Rental Counseling, Prepurchase
Counseling

CONSUMER CREDIT
COUNSELING SERVICE OF
MID-OHIO VALLEY
2715 Murdoch Ave Rm B4
Parkersburg, WV 26101-1059
304-485-3141
Toll-Free: 888-785-1997
Fax: 304-485-3286
Type of Counseling:
Prepurchase Counseling, HECM
Counseling, Default/Foreclosure
Counseling
Affiliate of: NATIONAL
FOUNDATION FOR
CONSUMER CREDIT,
INCORPORATED

FAMILY SERVICE CREDIT
COUNSELING
51 11th St
Wheeling, WV 26003-2937

304-232-6733
Toll-Free: 800-220-3252
Fax: 304-233-7237
Type of Counseling:
HECM Counseling,
Default/Foreclosure Counseling,
Rental Counseling, Prepurchase
Counseling

Wisconsin

**NEIGHBORHOOD HOUSING
SERVICES OF BELOIT,
INCORPORATED
156 St. Lawrence Ave
Beloit, WI 53511
608-362-9051
Fax: 608-362-7226
Type of Counseling:
Default/Foreclosure Counseling,
Rental Counseling, Prepurchase
Counseling
Affiliate of: NEIGHBORHOOD
REINVESTMENT
CORPORATION

COMMUNITY ACTION,
INCORPORATED
1545 Hobbs Dr
Delavan, WI 53115-2027
262-728-8296
Toll-Free: 800-424-8297
Fax: 262-728-8294
Email: action@genevaonline.com
Type of Counseling:
Default/Foreclosure Counseling,
Rental Counseling, Prepurchase
Counseling

**NEIGHBORHOOD HOUSING
SERVICES OF GREEN BAY,
INCORPORATED
700 Cherry St
Green Bay, WI 54301
920-448-3075
Fax: 920-448-3078
Email: nhsbob@netnet.net
Type of Counseling:
Prepurchase Counseling,
Default/Foreclosure Counseling
Affiliate of: NEIGHBORHOOD
REINVESTMENT
CORPORATION

LEGAL SERVICES OF
NORTHEAST WISCONSIN,
INCORPORATED

201 West Walnut St, Suite 203
Green Bay, WI 54303
920-432-4645
Toll-Free: 800-236-1127
Fax: 920-432-5078
Type of Counseling:
Default/Foreclosure Counseling,
Rental Counseling

COMMUNITY ACTION,
INCORPORATED
2300 Kellogg Ave
Janesville, WI 53546-5921
608-755-2470
Toll-Free: 800-424-8297
Fax: 608-755-2246
Email: action@genevaonline.com
Type of Counseling:
HECM Counseling,
Default/Foreclosure Counseling,
Rental Counseling, Prepurchase
Counseling

**NEIGHBORHOOD HOUSING
SERVICES OF KENOSHA,
INCORPORATED
1119 60th St.
Kenosha, WI 53140
262-652-6766
Fax: 262-652-8108
Type of Counseling:
Prepurchase Counseling,
Default/Foreclosure Counseling
Affiliate of: NEIGHBORHOOD
REINVESTMENT
CORPORATION

URBAN LEAGUE OF GREATER
MADISON, INCORPORATED
151 E. Gorham Street
Madison, WI 53703
608-251-8550
Fax: 608-251-0944
Type of Counseling:
Default/Foreclosure Counseling,
Prepurchase Counseling, Rental
Counseling

COMMUNITY DEVELOPMENT
AUTHORITY OF THE CITY OF
MADISON
Madison Municipal Bldg.
Suite 318
215 Martin Luther King Jr. Blvd.
Madison, WI 53710
608-266-4675

TTY/TDD: 608-264-9290
Fax: 608-264-9291
Type of Counseling:
Prepurchase Counseling, Rental
Counseling

WISCONSIN HOUSING AND
ECONMIC DEVELOPMENT
AUTHORITY
201 W. Washington Ave
Suite 700
Madison, WI 53703-1728
608-266-7884
Fax: 608-267-1099
Type of Counseling:
Prepurchase Counseling, Rental
Counseling, Default/Foreclosure
Counseling

COALITION OF WISCONSIN
AGING GROUPS,
INCORPORATED
2850 Dairy Drive
Suite 100
Madison, WI 53718
608-224-0606
Fax: 608-224-0607
Email: carolmat@midplains.net
Type of Counseling: HECM
Counseling

**THE WISCONSIN
PARTNERSHIP FOR HOUSING
DEVELOPMENT
INCORPORATED
121 South Pinckney St.
Suite 200
Madison, WI 53703
608-258-5560
Fax: 608-258-5565
Website: www.wphp.org
Type of Counseling:
HECM Counseling,
Default/Foreclosure Counseling,
Rental Counseling, Prepurchase
Counseling
Affiliate of: THE HOUSING
PARTNERSHIP NETWORK

TENANT RESOURCE CENTER
1202 Williamson St. Suite A
Madison, WI 5370
608-257-0006
Fax: 608-286-0804
Type of Counseling: Rental
Counseling

**ACORN HOUSING
CORPORATION
152 W. Wisconsin Ave #731
Milwaukee, WI 53203
414-273-1905
Fax: 414-276-8191
Type of Counseling:
Prepurchase Counseling,
Default/Foreclosure Counseling
Affiliate of: ACORN HOUSING
CORPORATION

HOUSING RESOURCES,
INCORPORATED
4850 W. Fond du Lac Ave.
Milwaukee, WI 53216
414-272-3933
Fax: 414-272-3968
Type of Counseling:
Prepurchase Counseling

SOUTH COMMUNITY
ORGANIZATION
1635 South 8th Street
Milwaukee, WI 53204
414-643-7913
Fax: 414-643-5972
Type of Counseling:
Prepurchase Counseling,
Default/Foreclosure Counseling,
Rental Counseling

CAREER YOUTH
DEVELOPMENT,
INCORPORATED
2601 N. Martin Luther King
Drive
Milwaukee, WI 53212
414-264-6888
Fax: 414-264-5622
Type of Counseling:
Prepurchase Counseling, Rental
Counseling

WALKER'S POINT
DEVELOPMENT
CORPORATION
914 S 5th St
Milwaukee, WI 53204-1711
414-645-9222
Fax: 414-645-9386
Type of Counseling:
Default/Foreclosure Counseling,
Rental Counseling, Prepurchase
Counseling

**NEIGHBORHOOD HOUSING
SERVICES OF MILWAUKEE,
INCORPORATED
635 North 35th Street
Milwaukee, WI 53208
414-344-3013
Fax: 414-344-3196
Type of Counseling:
Prepurchase Counseling
Affiliate of: NEIGHBORHOOD
REINVESTMENT
CORPORATION

DANE COUNTY HOUSING
AUTHORITY
2001 W Broadway, #1
Monona, WI 53713-3707
608-224-3636
Fax: 608-224-3632
Website:
Type of Counseling:
HECM Counseling,
Default/Foreclosure Counseling,
Rental Counseling, Prepurchase
Counseling

THE RACINE/KENOSHA
COMMUNITY ACTION
AGENCY, INCORPORATED
2113 N. Wisconsin Street
Racine, WI 53402-
262-637-8377
Fax: 262-637-6419
Type of Counseling: Rental
Counseling

**CONSUMER CREDIT OF
RACINE
420 7th St
Racine, WI 53403-1222
262-634-2391
Fax: 262-635-7135
Type of Counseling:
Default/Foreclosure Counseling,
Prepurchase Counseling
Affiliate of: NATIONAL
FOUNDATION FOR
CONSUMER CREDIT,
INCORPORATED

NEIGHBORHOOD HOUSING
SERVICES OF RICHLAND
COUNTY, INCORPORATED
133 N Central Park Rm 220
Richland Center, WI 53581
608-647-4949

Fax: 608-647-8792
Email: nhsrcwi@ix.netcom.com
Type of Counseling:
Default/Foreclosure Counseling,
Prepurchase Counseling
Affiliate of: NEIGHBORHOOD
REINVESTMENT
CORPORATION

**CATHOLIC CHARITIES
BUREAU, INCORPORATED
1416 Cumming Ave
Superior, WI 54880-1720
888-831-8446
Toll-Free: 888-831-8446
Fax: 715-394-5951
Type of Counseling:
Default/Foreclosure Counseling,
Prepurchase Counseling
Affiliate of: CATHOLIC
CHARITIES USA

WAUKESHA COUNTY
DEPARTMENT OF AGING
25042 West Northview Rd
Waukesha, WI 53188
262-548-7848
Fax: 262-896-8273
Type of Counseling: HECM
Counseling, Rental Counseling

**CATHOLIC CHARITIES OF
THE DIOCESE OF LA CROSSE,
INC.
200 Washington Street
Wausau, WI 54403
715-849-3311
Toll-Free: 888-849-3311
Fax: 715-849-8414
Email:
dhutchinson@catholiccharitieslax
.org
Type of Counseling:
Prepurchase Counseling,
Default/Foreclosure Counseling,
Rental Counseling
Affiliate of: CATHOLIC
CHARITIES USA

Wyoming

INTERFAITH OF NATRONA
COUNTY, INCORPORATED
1514 East 12th Street, #303
Casper, WY 82601
307-235-8043

Fax: 307-235-8711
Type of Counseling: Rental
Counseling

CONSUMER CREDIT
COUNSELING SERVICE OF
NORTHERN COLORADO AND
SOUTHEAST WYOMING
2113 Warren Ave
Cheyenne, WY 82001-3739
800-424-2227
Fax: 970-229-0721

Website: www.cccsnc.org
Type of Counseling:
HECM Counseling,
Default/Foreclosure Counseling,
Rental Counseling, Prepurchase
Counseling

CONSUMER CREDIT
COUNSELING SERVICE OF
NORTHERN COLORADO AND
SOUTHEAST WYOMING
221 E Ivinson Ave, 2nd Floor

Laramie, WY 82070-3038
800-424-2227
Toll-Free: 800-424-2227
Fax: 970-229-0721
Website: www.cccsnc.org
Type of Counseling:
HECM Counseling,
Default/Foreclosure Counseling,
Rental Counseling, Prepurchase
Counseling

Help for Homeowners
Facing the Loss of Their Home *

For most families, a home is not only a significant financial investment but also a source of pride. The loss of a home, due to unexpected events such as unemployment, can be financially and personally devastating.

If you have been laid off or are facing unemployment, you can keep your home — if you know the right steps to take. The Department of Housing and Urban Development/ Federal Housing Administration, the Department of Veterans Affairs, the Department of Labor and the mortgage industry have worked together to produce important basic information — and key links to local groups and organizations — that can help you get through difficult times without losing your home.

Facing Money Problems

Financial problems are most often associated with the following life changes:

★ Loss of job
★ Cuts in work hours or overtime
★ Retirement
★ Illness, injury or death of a family member
★ Divorce or separation

If your family is facing any of these changes and cannot pay your bills, now is the time to look closely at what you owe and what you earn, eliminating unnecessary spending and reaching out for help if you still can't meet your financial obligations. Taking action now can help you protect your family from the loss of your home. This page was created to help you find advice, information, and web links that will help you keep your home.

STEPS TO TAKE WHEN YOU MAY NOT BE ABLE TO PAY YOUR MORTGAGE

➡ Contact Your Lender NOW!
➡ Talk To A Housing Counseling Agency
➡ Prioritize Your Debts

➡ Explore Loan Workout Solutions

➡ Are You Eligible For Disaster Relief/Military Options?

➡ Beware Of Predatory Lending Schemes

➡ Try Other Resources

CONTACT YOUR LENDER AS SOON AS YOU HAVE A PROBLEM

Many people avoid calling their lenders when they have money troubles. Most of us are embarrassed to discuss our money problems with others or believe that if lenders know we are in trouble, they will rush to collection or foreclosure.

Lenders want to help borrowers keep their homes. Foreclosure is expensive for lenders, mortgage insurers and investors. HUD/FHA, as well as private mortgage insurance companies and investors like Freddie Mac and Fannie Mae, require lenders to work aggressively with borrowers who are facing money problems.

Lenders have workout options to help you keep your home. However, these options work best when your loan is only one or two payments behind. The farther behind you are on your payments, the fewer options are available.

Do not assume that your problems will quickly correct themselves. Don't lose valuable time by being overly optimistic. Contact your mortgage lender to discuss your circumstances as soon as you realize that you are unable to make your payments. While there is no guarantee that any particular relief will be given, most lenders are willing to explore every possible option.

FINDING YOUR LENDER

Check the following sources for lender contact:
* ★ Your monthly mortgage billing statement
* ★ Your payment coupon book
* ★ Web links or customer service numbers found under "help for homeowners" lenders

INFORMATION TO HAVE READY WHEN YOU CALL:

To help you, lenders typically need:
* ★ Your loan account number
* ★ A brief explanation of your circumstances

★ Recent income documents (such as pay stubs); Benefits Statements from Social Security, Disability, Unemployment, Retirement, or Public Assistance. If you are self-employed, have your tax returns or a year-to-date Profit and Loss Statement available for referral)

★ List of household expenses

Expect to have more than one phone conversation with your lender. Typically, your lender will mail you a "loan workout" package. This package contains information, forms and instructions. If you want to be considered for assistance, you must complete the forms and return them to your lender quickly. The completed package will be reviewed before the lender talks about a solution with you.

CALL TODAY! The sooner you call; the sooner help is available. DO NOT IGNORE MAIL FROM YOUR LENDER

If you do not contact your lender, your lender will try to contact you by mail and phone soon after you stop making payments. It is very important that you respond to the mail and the phone calls offering help. If your lender does not hear from you they will be required to start legal action leading to foreclosure. This will substantially increase the cost of bringing your loan current.

Information For Families With FHA Loans

The **Federal Housing Administration (FHA)** provides a wide range of relief options for borrowers. There are many alternatives and ways to get help. These may include mortgage modifications, special forbearances, and other actions you can take to avoid foreclosure (See {http://www.hud.gov/foreclosure/index.cfm}).

HUD's National Servicing Center (See {http://www.hud.gov/offices/hsg/sfh/nsc/nschome.cfm}) works closely with customers who have FHA insured loans. Do you feel your lender is not responding to your questions? Do you need assistance contacting your lender? The NSC is ready to help!

Talk to a Housing Counseling Agency

If you don't feel comfortable talking with your lender, you should immediately contact a HUD-approved housing counseling agency and arrange an appointment with a counselor. A counselor will help you assess your financial situation, determine what options are available to you, and help you negotiate with your lender. A counselor will be familiar with the various work-out arrangements that lenders will consider and will know what course of action makes the most sense for you and your family, based on your circumstances. In addition, the counselor can call the lender with you or on your behalf to discuss a work-out plan. By meeting with a counselor before your mortgage payments are too far behind, you can protect yourself from future credit problems.

A good counselor will help you establish a monthly budget plan to ensure that you can  meet all of your monthly expenses, including your mortgage payment. Your personal financial plan will clearly show how much money you have available to make the mortgage payment. This analysis will help you and your lender determine whether a reduced or delayed payment schedule could help you. Also, a counselor will have information on services, resources, and programs available in your local area that may provide you with additional financial, legal, medical or other assistance that you may need.

To find out more about HUD-approved housing counseling agencies and their services, please call 1-888-466-3487 on weekdays between 9:00 am and 5:00 pm Eastern Standard Time. You can also get an automated referral to the three housing counseling agencies located closest to you by calling 1-800-569-4287. To look at the list of these HUD-approved agencies by state on the HUD web site at {http://www.hud.gov/offices/hsg/sfh/hcc/hccprof14.cfm }.

Many of these local housing counseling agencies are affiliates of national and regional housing counseling intermediaries. The websites for the HUD-approved **National and Regional Housing Counseling Intermediaries**, (See {http://www.hud.gov/offices/hsg/sfh/hcc/nrhci.cfm}), describe the full range of assistance offered, as well as maps showing location of their affiliates.

Prioritize Your Debts

For the unemployed, getting by will require a new, tightened budget. Prioritize your bills and pay those most necessary for your family: food, utilities and shelter.

Failing to pay any of your debts can seriously affect your credit rating. However, if you stop making your mortgage payments you could lose your house. Whenever possible, any income available after paying for food and utilities should be used to pay your monthly mortgage payments. If your employment income has been stopped or reduced, first consider eliminating or reducing your other expenses (such as dining out, entertainment, cable, or even telephone services). If that does not provide enough income, consider using other financial resources like stocks, savings accounts, or personal property that may have value like a boat or a second car. Take any responsible action that will save cash.

In addition to speaking with your lender, you may want to contact a nonprofit consumer credit counseling agency that specializes in providing help in restructuring credit payments. Credit counselors can often reduce your monthly bills by negotiating reduced payments or long-term payment plans with your creditors. The majority of credit counseling agencies are reputable and provide their services free of charge or for a small monthly administrative fee tied to a repayment plan. Beware of credit counseling agencies that offer counseling for a large upfront fee or donation.

For consumer debt advice contact the **National Foundation for Credit Counseling** (See: {http://www.debtadvice.org/})

Use the Internet to find a HUD-approved housing counseling (See: {http://www.hud.gov/offices/hsg/sfh/hcc/hcc_home.cfm}) or dial 1-800-569-4287 or TDD: 1-800-877-8339. These agencies can provide financial counseling or refer you to a local credit counseling agency.

When you call a consumer credit counseling agency, you will be asked to provide current information about your income and expenses. Make sure you ask if the agency has a charge before you sign any documents!

Preserve Your Good Credit

Do not underestimate the importance of preserving your good credit. Your future ability to purchase certain items, rent or buy a home, and complete other transactions often requires a credit check. Consumer credit agencies and your lender can help you explore solutions to keep your credit from getting blemished.

Maintaining good credit is even important for job hunters. When you apply for a job, the employer probably will check your credit report to determine:
- ★ whether you have been sued
- ★ have filed for bankruptcy
- ★ or have trouble paying your bills

Explore Loan Workout Solutions

First and foremost, if you can keep your mortgage current, do so. However, if you find that you are unable to make your mortgage payments, you may qualify for a loan workout option. Check with your lender to find out which of these options may be available.

If Your Problem Is Temporary - Call Your Lender

Reinstatement: Your lender is always willing to discuss accepting the total amount owed to them in a lump sum by a specific date. They will often combine this option with a Forbearance.

Forbearance: Your lender may allow you to reduce or suspend payments for a short period of time after which another option must be agreed upon to bring your loan current. A forbearance option is often combined with a Reinstatement when you know you will have enough money to bring the account current at a specific time in the future. The money might come from a hiring bonus, investment, insurance settlement, or a tax refund.

Repayment Plan: You may be able to get an agreement to resume making your regular monthly payments, in addition to a portion of the past due payments each month until you are caught up.

If it appears that your situation is long-term or will permanently affect your ability to bring your account current:

Mortgage Modification: If you can make the payments on your loan, but you do not have enough money to bring your account current or you cannot afford the total amount of your current payment, your lender may be able to change one or more terms of your original loan to make the payments more affordable. Your loan could be permanently changed in one or more of the following ways:
- Adding the missed payments to the existing loan balance.
- Changing the interest rate, including making an adjustable rate into a fixed rate.
- Extending the number of years you have to repay.

Claim Advance: If your mortgage is insured, you may qualify for an interest-free loan from your mortgage guarantor to bring your account current. The repayment of this loan may be delayed for several years.

If Keeping Your Home Is Not An Option - Call Your Lender

Sale: If you can no longer afford your home, your lender will usually agree to give you a specific amount of time to find a purchaser and pay off the **total amount owed**. You will be expected to obtain the services of a real estate professional who can aggressively market the property.

Pre-Foreclosure Sale or Short Payoff: If the property's sales value is not enough to pay the loan in full, your lender may be able to accept **less than the full amount owed**. This option can also include a period of time to allow your real estate agent to market the property and find a qualified buyer. Monetary help may also be available to pay other lien holders and/or help toward paying a few moving costs.

Assumption: A qualified buyer may be allowed to assume your mortgage, even if your original loan documents state that it is non-assumable.

Deed-in-lieu: Your lender may agree to allow you to voluntarily "give back" your property and forgive the debt. Although this option sounds like the easiest way out for you, generally, you must attempt to sell the home for its fair market value for at least 90 days before the lender will consider this option. Also, this option may not be available if you have other liens such as judgments of other creditors, second mortgages, and IRS or State Tax liens.

Resources For Finding A Real Estate Agent And Selling Your Home

If you need to sell your home, there will be many questions you have to answer. You will need to find how much your house is actually worth, and you will have to find a real estate agent you are comfortable with. The following resources will help:

International Real Estate Digest (See: {http://ired.com/buymyself/canale/art3.html})
National Association of Hispanic Real Estate Professionals (See:
    {http://www.nahrep.org/})
National Association of Realtors (See:
    {http://www.realtor.com/default.asp?hm=on&poe=realtor})
National Association of Real Estate Brokers, Inc. (See:
    {http://www.nareb.com/default.shtml})

The Homestore (See: {http://www.homestore.com/Finance/SellersGuide/
default.asp?lnksrc=REALR2LF2C0048})
Selling a Home (See: {http://www.hud.gov/selling/index.cfm})

Special Disaster Relief Options – Call Your Lender

If your property has been damaged by a natural disaster or if you have been called up
for active military duty or affected by a national tragedy, such as the terrorist acts of
September 11, 2001, there may be additional assistance available.

For additional information you may wish to view these links:

➡ Victims of a declared natural disaster area (See:
{http://www.hud.gov/offices/hsg/sfh/owning.cfm})
➡ Called back to Active Military Duty: Questions & Answers for Reservists,
Guardsmen and Other Military Personnel regarding The Soldiers' and Sailor's Civil
Relief Act of 1940 (See: {http://www.hud.gov/offices/hsg/sfh/nsc/qasscra1.cfm}).

HUD has a toll-free number for servicemen and women with questions concerning their
mortgage. For more information, call 1-888-297-8685 between the hours of 7 a.m. and 7
p.m. Central Standard Time on weekdays.

Beware of Predatory Lending Schemes

Most mortgage lenders are reputable and provide a
valuable service by allowing families to own a home
without saving the thousands or hundreds of thousands of
dollars necessary to buy it outright. However, a few,
unscrupulous lenders, especially those who make high risk
second mortgages, engage in predatory lending practices
that can increase the likelihood that a borrower will lose his or her home to foreclosure.
These abusive practices include making a mortgage loan to an individual who does not
have the income to repay it, charging excessive interest, points and fees or repeatedly
refinancing a loan without providing any real value to the borrower.

Borrowers facing unemployment and/or foreclosure are frequent targets of predatory
lenders because they are desperate to find any "solution" to their default.

Homeowners frequently receive refinance offers in the mail telling them that they have been "pre-approved" for credit based on the equity in their home. When you are wondering how you are going to pay your mortgage and other bills, it may appear very attractive to borrow against your house. But consider this, if you cannot make your current payments, increasing your debt, even if you get some temporary cash, will make it harder to keep your home.

BEWARE OF SCAMS:

Equity skimming: a buyer offers to repay the mortgage or sell the property if you sign over the deed and move out.

Phony counseling agencies: offer counseling for a fee when it is often given no charge.

Do not sign anything you do not understand. It is your right and duty to ask questions.

Information is your best defense against becoming a victim of predatory lending especially for a desperate homeowner!

Where to Report Suspected Predatory Lending – homeowners can either visit the Stop Mortgage Fraud web site (See: {http://www.stopmortgagefraud.com/}) or call 1-800-348-3931 to get information on what steps to take to file a complaint. Homeowners calling the 800 number will receive a brochure that contains information also found on the Web site.

FOR MORE INFORMATION ABOUT PREDATORY LENDING GO TO:

HUD's Predatory Lending Web Site:(See:
    {http://www.hud.gov/offices/hsg/pred/predlend.cfm})
Freddie MAC's Predatory Lending Web Site: (See:
    {http://www.freddiemac.com/homebuyers/bank/pred_lending.html})
Freddie MAC's "Don't Borrow Trouble" Web Site: (See:
    {http://www.dontborrowtrouble.com/})

Frequently Asked Questions (FAQ)

1. **How do I know who my lender is and how to contact them?**
   Look at your monthly mortgage coupons or billing statements for the name of your lender and contact information.

2. **I do not remember what type of mortgage loan I have, how can I find this information?**
   Look on the original mortgage documents or call your mortgage lender.

3. **Do I need to keep living in my house to qualify for assistance?**
   Typically, yes, but call your lender to discuss your specific circumstances and get advice on options that may be available.

4. **What type of information should I have ready to discuss with a lender?**
   Typical information requested by lenders in a workout package include:
   - Brief explanation of circumstances
   - Recent income documents
   - List of household expenses

5. **My employer has already announced layoffs within the coming months, what can I do now?**
   Through this website you have taken the first step toward educating yourself about available options. Determine if the layoffs will cause a financial hardship that will make it hard for your family to make your mortgage payments. If so, consider other resources that you have available to pay your mortgage. Review your spending habits and see where you can reduce spending. If you have a lot of consumer debt, consider contacting a nonprofit, consumer credit counseling agency. Take advantage of any employer offered resources. If you still believe that you will have trouble making your mortgage payments, contact your lender right away.

6. **Will there be any out-of-pocket expenses I will be responsible for if I am approved for a workout option?**
   Some workout options do include expenses that the borrower is expected to pay, for example, recording fees for a loan modification. Because, every situation is different you should contact your lender for more information. However, if a lender has no contact with a borrower and has to start foreclosure, the legal fees that the borrower will be expected to pay can be very expensive. To avoid unnecessary legal fees, call your lender as soon as you realize you are in trouble.

* This information was prepared through the collaborative efforts of HUD/FHA, the Department of Veterans Affairs, Department of Labor, Fannie Mae, Freddie Mac, and members of the mortgage industry

How Do I Check Out A Move?

Finding a new home can be a nightmare anytime. But what if you don't know the first thing about the area where you are relocating? A bank account and the local real estate ads aren't enough anymore to make the right decisions on a move. You need help. Uncle Sam has sympathy for those who have learned to hate cardboard boxes and unreal-estate agents.

When you move to a new town, there are things you should know before you settle on your dream house. Are some neighborhoods safer than others? What about the schools? Are they as good or better than the schools your children now attend? Are they asking too much for a house in this area? What about the mortgage options? Know the score for yourself. Don't depend on the real estate agent interested in seeing her commission for telling you everything.

A house selling in Washington, DC for $125,000 would only go for $62,000 in Columbus, Ohio. Know the value of homes in your potential city, so you don't pay an arm and a leg for something not worth a foot. There are many government resources to help you on your way to a successful move.

Here are some best-kept secrets to make any transition easier:

Moving Expenses As A Tax Deduction

You can write off many moving expenses if certain conditions are met. You can even deduct expenses of moving back to the United States if you retire while living and working overseas. Just call the IRS and ask for Publication 521, *Moving Expenses*, which outlines expenses you can and cannot deduct, explains what happens when your company pays for part of the move, details issues such as gas, food, and lodging during the move, and more. You can also download this publication from the web. Contact your local IRS office, or call the IRS Forms line at 800-829-3676, {www.irs.ustreas.gov}.

Get Your Moving Expenses Paid

If you have been laid off from work and are not likely to return to the same employer, you may be considered a dislocated worker. Dislocated workers are those who have been laid off from a job due to factory downsizing, reorganization, trade issues, military downsizing, and more. There are many services available to dislocated workers through the Title III Program which provides for retraining and readjustment assistance for dislocated workers. In many cases, funds are available to assist the dislocated worker in moving to a new location where the worker has a job offer. To become eligible for these services, you must contact your local State Employment Services office, your state's Dislocated Worker Unit, or the Job Training Partnership Act office (look in the blue pages of your phone book). Each local office has funds that they can disperse for a variety of services to the worker, including training, child care, job search services, and education. Contact Employment Training Administration, U.S. Department of Labor, Office of Worker Retraining and Adjustment Programs, 200 Constitution Ave., NW, Room N-5426, Washington, DC 20210; 202-219-5577; {www.doleta.gov/programs/factsht/edwaa.htm}.

Eliminate High Crime Cities

To find a safe little hamlet to raise Junior, you better do some research before you move. *Crime In The U.S.*, the Federal Bureau of Investigation's (FBI) annual report of violent and property crime, contains statistics for many towns with over 10,000 people, and can provide you with information such as the number of murders, robberies, assaults, burglaries, auto thefts, and more, but they do not rank cities. Many libraries carry this publication, or you can call the FBI for information on your city. Contact Criminal Justice Inf. Service Division, Federal Bureau of Investigation, 935 Pennsylvania Ave., NW, Washington, DC 20535-0001; 202-324-3000; {www.fbi.gov/ucr/ucr.htm}.

When Weather's Important

Weatherheads can take the chill out of moving by contacting Uncle Sam's Climatic Data Center, which can help you move to a sunny location through their book, *Comparative Climate Data* ($5, free online), covering weather data for 270 major locations. Pick a city and find out if it's warmer, colder, sunnier, or snowier than other cities. Contact National Climatic Data Center, National Oceanic and Atmospheric Administration, Federal Bldg., 151 Patton Ave., #120, Asheville, NC 28801-5001; 828-271-4800, Fax: 282-271-4876; {www.ncdc.noaa.gov/nedc.html}.

Move To A City With Lots Of Single Men

You can check out the singles scene anywhere in the country by contacting the Bureau of the Census. They keep some interesting figures regarding the population, such as the ratio of total number of single men to single women in metro areas. Give them a call to find out what areas of the country will improve your chances of finding that special someone...if that's what you're interested in. Contact Marriage and Family Statistics

Branch, Population Division, Bureau of the Census, Bldg. 3, Room 2353, Washington, DC 20233; 301-457-2465; {www.census.gov/population/www/}.

A Library Of Information

A wonderful resource for information about a town is its local library. Library workers, familiar with the area can answer questions such as the population change of the town over time, how the city operates, the city budget, and demographics. The library can also provide information on the history of a town, city parks and recreation facilities, school board information, community resources, and even election results. You can locate the local library by looking in the blue pages of the town's telephone directory, or take a look at nearly 700 public libraries online at {www.yahoo.com/reference/libraries/public_libraries/}.

Check Out The Town Business Scene

Local Chambers of Commerce can provide you with a wealth of information regarding a new town. They usually offer a map of the town, parks and recreation directories, walking tours, information about the type of government and the town's annual report, along with information on schools, real estate, and industry. You can also look through the Chamber's membership directory to see the types of industry located in the town to get a sense of the business climate. You can locate the Chamber of Commerce by looking in the blue pages of the local phone directory, or by contacting the city hall. To look for chambers on the web, try {www.worldchambers.com/}.

Salaries, Unemployment, And The Job Market

If you are looking for an overview of labor information, then the Bureau of Labor Statistics (BLS) is for you. The Bureau collects, processes, analyzes, and disseminates data relating to employment, unemployment, and other characteristics of the labor force; wages, other worker compensation; economic growth and employment projections; and more. BLS can refer you to experts within the Bureau who can answer your specific questions, provide you with historical information, and refer you to tables and charts for data. They can answer questions such as:

- What are the employment statistics and the outlook for a particular occupation?
- What is the unemployment rate for a state?
- What is the current wage for a word processor in Seattle, and what are the average benefits likely to be?
- What is the employment projection for a specific job?

Contact Office of Publications, Bureau of Labor Statistics, U.S. Department of Labor, 2 Massachusetts Ave., NE, Room 2863, Washington, DC 20212; 202-691-5200; {www.bls.gov/}.

Highway Looking Like A Parking Lot?

Want to know how many people own cars in your state? What about fatal and injury accident rates for the Nation's highways? Want to know the number of licensed women drivers or the ratio of licensed drivers to the population? What about highway finance or highway usage? An extensive list of publications is maintained by the Office of Highway Information Management. For information about your state or for ordering information, contact Office of Highway Information Management, Federal Highway Administration, U.S. Department of Transportation, 400 7th St., SW, Washington, DC 20590; 202-366-0650; {www.fhwa.dot.gov/ohim/}.

Don't Get Washed Out In A Flood

Know the law of the land before you sign on the dotted line. The Federal Emergency Management Agency publishes the *Flood Boundary Way Map* which shows the flood-prone areas within the community. Each map accompanies a study which shows directions in which flooding may occur. To obtain this map for your area of interest, call 1-800-358-9616. The *Flood Insurance Manual* has many useful sections for homeowners, including "How To Read A Flood Insurance Rate Map," which is a guide to help identify and understand key features of the Flood Insurance Rate Map. For this free publication, call 1-800-FEMA-MAP. Federal Emergency Management Agency, 500 C St., SW, Washington, DC 20472; 202-646-4600, {www.fema.gov/}.

Flood Insurance Made Simple

Some victims of the recent flood were covered under the government's National Flood Insurance Program (NFIP), but many were not. To find out if you qualify, get the free brochure, *Answers to Questions About The National Flood Insurance Program* which explains NFIP, and the type of assistance it provides. For information on rules, regulations, claims, and publications, contact National Flood Insurance Program at 800-480-2520. National Flood Insurance Program, 451 Hungerford Dr., Rockford, MD 20850; 800-611-6125; {www.fema.gov/diz98/98059.htm}.

How Not To Buy Swamp Land In Florida

Thinking about buying lakefront property in Arizona or a condo on a golf course in Florida? Before you send a dime to a land developer in another state, find out before you buy what your rights are from the following free publications: *Buying Lots from Developers* and *Before Buying Land.... Get The Facts*. There are several things a developer must do before a lot can be sold or leased. They must file a Statement of Record with the U.S. Department of Housing and Urban Development (HUD), containing full and current disclosure about ownership and more, and a printed Property Report must be delivered to each purchaser or lessee in advance of signing the contract or agreement. Contact Interstate Land Sales, Registration Division, U.S. Department of Housing and Urban Development (HUD), 451 7th St., SW, Room 9160, Washington, DC 20410; 202-708-1112; {www.hud.gov/fha/ils/ilshome.html}.

Make Sure Your Kid Learns The 3 R's

How do you choose the best schools for your child? What role do grandparents have in education today? Should you delay starting kindergarten if your child has a summer birthday? How do you motivate your middle school student? The ERIC Clearinghouse on Elementary and Early Childhood Education and the National Parent Information Network both are wonderful resources for all kinds of education questions. You can find the answers to these questions and many more at the websites. Contact ERIC Clearinghouse on Elementary and Early Childhood Education, University of Illinois at Urbana-Champaign, Children's Research Center, 51 Gerty Drive, Champaign, IL 61820-7469; 217-333-1386, Voice/TTY: 800-583-4135, {http://ericeece.org or http://npin.org}.

Rural Housing Help

For those who live or are considering moving to a rural area, the Rural Housing Service offers a variety of housing assistance. Direct loans are available to assist lower-income rural families obtain decent, safe homes, loan guarantees, home repair loans and grants, and rural rental assistance payments to name only a few of the programs. For more information, contact Administrator, Rural Housing Service, U.S. Department of Agriculture, 14th and Independence Ave., Room 5037, Washington, DC 20250; 202-720+-4323; {www.rurdev.usda.gov.rhs/index.html}.

Housing Finance Statistics

Monthly reports are compiled by the Program Evaluation Division of the U.S. Department of Housing and Urban Development (HUD) in areas relating to the mortgage market, securities, taxation, market trends, interest rates, among others. You can receive a free survey of mortgage lending activity and a survey of FHA and conventional mortgage rates. If you are interested in receiving information about these subjects or want to be placed on the mailing list, contact Program Evaluation Division, Mortgage Survey Information Center, Assistant Secretary for Housing, U.S. Department of Housing and Urban Development (HUD), 451 7th St., SW, Washington, DC 20410; 202-755-7470, ext. 145; {www.hud.gov/}.

How Much Did A House Sell For?

If you know when the current owner bought the house and how much they paid, you will be a better prepared negotiator. All this information is available at the county Recorder of Deeds. Other information available includes the legal description of the property located at the address, and the bank or company who financed the purchase. Also available at the county level is information on the property's assessed value, which is different from the appraised value, and the amount of taxes charged for the property. To locate the County Recorder of Deeds, look in the blue pages of the local telephone directory.

What's The Housing Market Like?

If you are planning on moving, it might be helpful to know some general information about the housing situation of a prospective area. The U.S. Department of Housing and Urban Development (HUD) and the Bureau of the Census have released the results of the American Housing Survey for the United States in 2000, the largest and most detailed survey of the Nation's housing stock. It provides information on national or regional housing conditions, markets, or policies. It presents detailed data on the characteristics of occupied and vacant housing units, including size, structural condition, housing costs and values, and indicators of neighborhood quality. It also provides basic demographic data on the age, sex, race, income, and mobility of householders. In addition to the Survey available for $5, results from 11 metropolitan areas have also been released ($5 each). For more information, contact HUD USER, P.O. Box 6091, Rockville, MD 20850; 800-245-2691, 301-251-5154 (DC metro area), {www.huduser.org/}.

Veterans Home Ownership

If you are a veteran or an unmarried surviving spouse, you can obtain VA-guaranteed loans for the purchase and refinancing of homes, condominiums and manufactured homes. You can usually do so without a down payment (except for manufactured homes). For eligibility and more information on VA loan guaranties, contact your regional VA office or contact Veterans Assistance Office, Department of Veterans Affairs, 810 Vermont Ave., NW, Washington, DC 20420; 800-827-1000; {www.va.gov/}.

The following publications are available to veterans:

- *Pointers for the Veteran Homeowner* - a guide for veterans whose home mortgage is guaranteed or insured under the GI Bill. (26-5)

- *To the Home-Buying Veteran* - a guide for veterans planning to buy or build homes with a VA loan. (26-6)
- *VA-Guaranteed Home Loans for Veterans* - helps you understand what the VA can and cannot do for the home purchaser. (26-4)
- *VA Direct Home Loans for Native Americans Living on Trust Lands.* (27-93-1)
- *Veterans Benefits for Older Americans.* (27-80-2)

Counseling for Homebuyers, Homeowners, and Tenants

To help reduce delinquencies, defaults, and foreclosures, the U.S. Department of Housing and Urban Development (HUD) provides free counseling to homeowners and tenants under its programs through HUD-approved counseling agencies. The counselors advise and assist homeowners with budgeting, money management, and buying and maintaining their homes. This is not just for HUD homes, but for all home buyers and owners. The amount of service available does vary for each counseling agency. For the counseling agency nearest you, contact your local HUD office of information, or National Servicing Center, U.S. Department of Housing and Urban Development, 500 W. Main St., Suite 400, Oklahoma City, OK 73102; 888-297-8685; {www.hud.gov/offices/hsg/sfh/hcc/hccprof14.cfm}.

Housing Discrimination

The U.S. Department of Housing and Urban Development (HUD) administers the law that prohibits discrimination in housing on the basis of race, color, religion, sex, and national origin; investigates complaints of housing discrimination; and attempts to resolve them through conciliation. Two common forms of discrimination are redlining and steering. Redlining is the illegal practice of refusing to originate mortgage loans in certain neighborhoods on the basis of race or ethnic origin. Steering is the illegal act of limiting the housing shown by a real estate agent to a certain ethnic group. If you have experienced housing discrimination, you should file a complaint with any HUD office in person, by mail, or by telephone at the numbers listed here. HUD refers complaints to state and local fair housing agencies. To receive a copy of the free publication *Fair Housing Act Regulations*, contact the Housing Discrimination Hotline at 1-800-669-9777. Contact Fair Housing Enforcement Division, Office of Fair Housing and Equal Opportunity, U.S. Department of Housing and Urban Development, Washington, DC 20410-2000; 800-669-9777; {www.hud.gov/offices/fheo/index.cfm}.

Mortgage Manuals

There are tons of houses out there begging for your attention, but getting your foot in the door shouldn't cost you an arm and a leg. Before you carry your cash across the threshold, check out the latest on mortgages, real estate brokers, and home financing through publications available at the Federal Trade Commission. Contact Federal Trade Commission, 6th and Pennsylvania Ave., NW, Washington, DC 20580; 202-326-2222, 877-FTC-HELP; {www.ftc.gov}.

Some of the titles include:

- *Getting a Loan: Your Home as Security*
- *Home Equity Credit Lines*
- *Home Equity Scams: Borrowers Beware!*
- *Home Financing Primer*
- *Lawn Service Contracts*
- *Mortgage Discrimination*
- *Mortgage Servicing*
- *Refinancing Your Home*
- *Reverse Mortgages*
- *Second Mortgage Financing*
- *Timeshare Resales*
- *Timeshare Tips*
- *Using Ads to Shop for Home Financing*

Crime In Your Neighborhood

The crime rate for a neighborhood can be a whole lot different than the rate for the entire city. You don't want to put your kid in a day care center near an outdoor drug market or buy a fast food franchise in an area where the crime rate is ten times the national average. Real estate agents can brag all they want about how a certain area has a low crime rate, but if you want the facts and not the opinion of a biased salesperson, you have to get local crime statistics. Your State Crime Statistics Office collects information or can tell you where to locate information like:

- The rate of auto thefts in your town
- The rate of robberies in your town
- Crime and arrest data by county

Before drawing conclusions from state crime data, a number of factors should be considered, including strength of local police departments, economic profile of the town, and attitudes of residents toward police and crime. Most states have publications that report crime and can produce computer printouts of specific topics.

STATE CRIME STATISTICS

Alabama
Criminal Justice Information Center
770 Washington Ave., Suite 350
Montgomery, AL 36130-0660
334-242-4900
http://acjic.state.al.us/alacrime.htm
This division publishes the *Crime in Alabama Annual Report*. Computer printouts of selected data are provided if the information is readily available. Special statistical analysis of data not found in the annual report is also provided. There is no cost for these services.

Alaska
Department of Public Safety
Information Systems
Uniform Crime Reporting Section
5700 E. Tudor Rd.
Anchorage, AK 99507
907-465-4322
www.dps.state.ak.us/
The *Crime in Alaska Annual Report* is free. Computer printouts are not provided at this time.

Arizona
Department of Public Safety
Uniform Crime Reporting Section
P.O. Box 6638
Phoenix, AZ 85005
602-223-2000
www.dps.state.az.us/
The department publishes the *Arizona Uniform Crime Annual Report*. Computer printouts of selected data are provided at no charge.

Arkansas
Crime Information Center
Uniform Crime Reporting Section
1 Capitol Mall, Room 4D 200
Little Rock, AR 72201
501-682-2222
www.acic.org/statistics/stats.htm
The Crime Information Center publishes an annual report on crime rates in Arkansas. Call or write for a free copy.

California
Department of Justice
Law Enforcement Information Center
Box 944255
Sacramento, CA 94244-2550
916-302-3360
http://caag.state.ca.us/cjsc/
Publications include the *Crime and Delinquency in California Report* and *Annual Criminal Justice Profile*, which are free upon request. Other publications, customized statistical reports, and statistical information on California are also available.

Colorado
Department of Public Safety
Division of Criminal Justice
700 Kipling St., Suite 1000
Denver, CO 80215
303-239-4442
www.state.co.us/gov_dir/edps/dcj/dcj.htm
Publications include *Community Corrections Annual Report*. The office does not provide crime statistics printouts upon request.

Connecticut
Department of Public Safety
Department of State Police
Uniform Crime Reporting Program
Crimes Analysis Division
P.O. Box 2794
Middletown, CT 06457-9294
860-685-8030
www.state.ct.us/dps/
Publications include the *Annual Uniform Crime Report*, *Crime in Connecticut Quarterly Report*, and the *Family Violence Report*.

Delaware
Delaware State Police
State Bureau of Identification
Statistical Services
P.O. Box 430
Dover, DE 19903-0430
302-739-5900
www.state.de.us/dsp/
This bureau publishes the *Crime in Delaware Annual Report*. Selected data runs are also available. Fees vary according to the complexity of the request.

District of Columbia
Metropolitan Police Department
Planning and Research Section (CRAS)
300 Indiana Ave., NW, Room 3125
Washington, DC 20001
202-724-4100
http://mpdc.dc.gov/info/districts/crstats.shtm
Computer printouts of selected data are provided with a Freedom of Information request. Information can be faxed right to you or mailed.

Florida

Department of Law Enforcement
Uniform Crime Reporting Section
Attn: FDL/FSAC
P.O. Box 1489
Tallahassee, FL 32302
850-410-7140
www.fdle.state.fl.us/index.html
This department publishes a four-page summary pamphlet of Florida crime statistics which is available at no cost. Computer printouts of selected data are available at no charge. Information that was included in previous annual reports is also available upon request.

Georgia

Georgia Bureau of Investigation
Georgia Crime Information Center
P.O. Box 370748
Decatur, GA 30037-0748
404-244-2840
www.ganet.org/gbi/
The Crime Information Center publishes an annual four-page summary of the *Georgia Criminal Justice Data Report*. Computer printouts of selected data are also provided upon request, generally at no cost.

Hawaii

Department of the Attorney General
Statistical Analysis Center
235 S. Beretania St., Suite 401
Honolulu, HI 96813
808-586-1150
www.cpja.ag.state.hi.us/rs/
A *Crime in Hawaii Annual Report* is published. Computer printouts of selected data are available depending upon the complexity of the request.

Idaho

Criminal Identification Bureau
P.O. Box 700
Meridian, ID 83680-0700
208-884-7000
www.isp.state.id.us/
The Crime Identification Bureau publishes an annual *Uniform Crime Reporting Program Report*. Computer printouts of selected data are provided free upon request. Some information is available on diskette or magnetic tape if you supply your own software.

Illinois

Department of State Police
Division of Forensic Services and Identification
Bureau of Identification
125 E. Monroe St., Room 103
P.O. Box 19461
Springfield, IL 62794-9461
217-782-7263
www.isp.state.il.us
Publications include the *Crime in Illinois Annual Report*. The office will re-run monthly special reports for individuals upon request. There is no charge for this service.

Indiana

Indiana State Police
Data Division
100 Indiana Government Center North
100 N. Senate, Room N340
Indianapolis, IN 46204-2259
317-232-8200
www.ai.org/isp/index.html
Although this office does not publish an annual report, it will provide individuals with computer printouts or copies of crime statistics. There is no charge involved in these instances. Data is also available on diskette or magnetic tape. Charges vary according to the complexity of the request. Detailed requests should be made in writing.

Iowa

Department of Public Safety
Field Services Bureau
Wallace State Office Bldg.
Des Moines, IA 50319
515-281-8494
www.state.ia.us/government/dps/index.html
This department publishes the *Iowa Uniform Crime Annual Report*.

Kansas

Statistical Analysis Center
Kansas Bureau of Investigation
1620 SW Tyler
Topeka, KS 66612
785-296-8200
www.ink.org/public/kbi/
The Statistical Analysis Center publishes the *Crime in Kansas Annual Report*. Computer printouts of selected data are free upon request if the data is available. If you provide your own magnetic tapes or diskettes the staff will transfer the data on to them at no extra cost.

Kentucky

State Police
Information Section
1250 Louisville Rd.
Frankfort, KY 40601
502-227-8700, ext. 359
www.state.ky.us/agencies/ksp/ksphome.htm

Publications include the *Crime in Kentucky Annual Report* and *Traffic Accident Facts Report*. Computer printouts of selected data are available in special circumstances, depending upon the request. Most printouts are free. Some accident data requires an additional charge.

Louisiana

Louisiana Commission on Law Enforcement
1885 Wooddale Blvd., Room 708
Baton Rouge, LA 70806-1511
225-925-4418
www.cole.state.la.us
This office provides statistics on crime to the general public such as basic index crimes and arrest information.

Maine

Department of Public Safety
Uniform Crime Reporting Division
18 Meadow Rd.
104 State House Station
Augusta, ME 04333-0104
207-287-3619
www.state.me.us/dps
Publications include the *Crime in Maine Annual Report*. Computer printouts of selected data is available on a limited basis, usually at no charge.

Maryland

Maryland State Police
Uniform Crime Reporting Unit
1201 Reistertown Rd.
Pikesville, MD 21208
Attn. UCR
410-486-3101
www.inform.umd.edu/ums+state/md_resources/mdsp/index.html
Publications include the annual *Crime in Maryland Report*. Computer printouts are not generally provided, but can be done upon special request.

Massachusetts

Executive Office of Public Safety
1 Ashburton Place, Room 2133
Boston, MA 02108
617-727-7775
www.state.ma.us/eops/
Publications include a *Hate Crime Statistics Report* and yearly crime comparison reports. Computer services are available.

Michigan

Department of State Police
7145 Harrison Rd..

Uniform Crime Reporting
Lansing, MI 48823
517-332-2521
www.msp.state.mi.us/index.html
The Uniform Crime Reporting Division publishes an annual *Michigan Crime Report*, which is free upon request. Computer printouts of selected data are also free.

Minnesota

Department of Public Safety
Bureau of Criminal Apprehension
1246 University Ave.
St. Paul, MN 55104-4197
651-642-0670
www.dps.state.mn.us/bca/bca.html
Publications include an *Annual Report* and the *Uniform Crime Report Summaries.*

Mississippi

Department of Public Safety
City of Jackson Police Department
P.O. Box 958
Jackson, MS 39205
601-987-1212
www.dps.state.ms.us/
Mississippi does not have a central agency for collecting crime statistics. Each county or city has a department of safety that keeps individual records of criminal data. Computer printouts are not available.

Missouri

State Highway Patrol
Technical Service Bureau
Criminal Records Division
P.O. Box 749
Truman State Office Bldg., Room 870
Jefferson City, MO 65102
573-526-6153
www.dps.state.mo.us/dps/mshp/hp.htm
The Criminal Records Division publishes an annual *Missouri Crime Index Report.*

Montana

Montana Board of Crime Control
3075 N. Montana Ave.
P.O. Box 201408
Helena, MT 59620-1408
406-444-3604
http://bccdoj.doj.state.mt.us
Free publications include the *Crimes of Montana Annual Report*. Computer printouts of selected data are provided upon written request.

Nebraska

Commission on Law Enforcement and Criminal
Justice
301 Centennial Mall South
P.O. Box 94946
Lincoln, NE 68509-4946
402-471-2194
www.state.ne.us/home/crime.com
The Commission publishes a *Crime In Nebraska Annual
Report* which is free upon request.

Nevada

Nevada Highway Patrol
Uniform Crime Report Division
555 Wrightway
Carson City, NV 89711-0585
775-687-5300
http://nhp.state.nv.us/index.htm
Nevada began compiling crime statistics in a
computer database in 1993. They publish an annual
report, which is available for $4.

New Hampshire

Department of Safety
Division of State Police
Uniform Crime Reports
10 Hazen Dr.
Concord, NH 03305
603-271-2575
www.state.nh.us/nhsp/contents.html
Publications include the *Crime In New Hampshire*
report. Computer printouts of selected data are
provided at no charge upon written request.

New Jersey

Department of Law and Public Safety
Division of State Police
Uniform Crime Reporting Unit
Box 7068
West Trenton, NJ 08628-0068
609-882-2000, ext. 2392
www.njsp.org/front.html
The *Crime In New Jersey Report* is published annually.
The office can supply computer printouts of selected
data.

New York

Division of Criminal Justice Services
4 Tower Place, 8th Floor
Albany, NY 12203-3702
518-485-7675
http://criminaljustice.state.ny.us/
This division publishes the *Crime and Justice Annual
Report* which is free upon request. Computer
printouts are available at no cost.

North Carolina

Division of Criminal Information
P.O. Box 629
Raleigh, NC 27602
919-716-6400
www.jus.state.nc.us/cleframe.htm
The *Crime in North Carolina Annual Statistics Report* is
available for a fee. Printouts of statistics already
collected in their annual report are provided at no
cost, if requests are reasonable. Individualized
computer runs can also be performed but may
become expensive. Costs vary according to the
complexity of the request.

North Dakota

State Crime Bureau
Bureau of Criminal Investigation
P.O. Box 1054
Bismarck, ND 58502-1054
701-328-5500
www.ag.state.nd.us
Publications include an *Annual Report* which is free
upon request. Computerized printouts of crime data
are available. In most cases the cost is minimal.
Detailed requests should be placed in writing.
Information can also be transferred to computer
diskette or magnetic tape if you supply the software.

Ohio

Governor's Office of Criminal Justice Services
Capitol Square
400 E. Town St., Suite 300
Columbus, OH 43215-4242
614-466-7782
www.ocjs.state.oh.us/
This office publishes a report entitled *Crime and Arrest
Data by County* which is free upon request. The office
does not provide computer printouts of selected data.

Oklahoma

Oklahoma State Bureau of Investigation
6600 N. Harvey, Building 6
Oklahoma City, OK 73116
405-879-2528
www.osbi.state.ok.us
The statistics unit publishes the *Crime in Oklahoma
Annual Report*. Computer printouts of selected data
are provided at no cost.

Oregon

State Executive
Law Enforcement Data System
955 Center St., NE, US20
Salem, OR 97301
503-378-3055

www.leds.state.or.us/
This division publishes the *Criminal Offenses and Arrests Annual Report*. Computer services are not available, but standard output reports can be obtained upon request.

Pennsylvania
Pennsylvania State Police
Commission on Crime and Delinquency
1800 Elmerton Ave.
Harrisburg, PA 17110
866-782-7711
http://ucr.psp.state.pa.us/UCR/ComMain.asp
The *Commission on Crime and Delinquency Annual Report* is free upon request. Computer printouts of annual data are also provided at no charge.

Rhode Island
Justice Commission
1 Capitol Hill
Providence, RI 02908
401-222-2620
www.rijustice.state.ri.us/sac/sac.htm
This department publishes the *Serious Crime in Rhode Island Annual Report*, which is free.

South Carolina
South Carolina Law Enforcement Division
Uniform Crime Reporting
P.O. Box 21398
Columbia, SC 29221-1398
803-896-7216
www.sled.state.sc.us
This division publishes *Crime in South Carolina* which is available for a fee. Free copies may be obtained from the Freedom of Information Office at 803-896-7013.

South Dakota
Division of Criminal Investigation
Statistical Analysis Center
500 E. Capitol St.
Pierre, SD 57501-5070
605-773-3331
www.sddci.com
Publications include a newsletter and annual and quarterly reports which are free upon request. Computerized printouts of selected crime data are available at no cost. Detailed requests should be made in writing. Information can also be transferred to computer diskette or magnetic tape if you supply the software.

Texas
Department of Public Safety
Uniform Crime Reporting Section
5805 N. Lamar Blvd.
P.O. Box 4087
Austin, TX 78765
www.txdps.state.tx.us/
Publications include the *Crime In Texas Annual Report*. Computer printouts of selected data are provided free, upon request.

Utah
Department of Public Safety
Bureau of Criminal Identification
4501 South, 2700 West
Salt Lake City, UT 84114
801-965-4461
http://publicsafety.utah.gov
Publications include the *Crime in Utah Annual Report* which is free upon request. Computer printouts of selected data are available, usually at no cost.

Vermont
Department of Public Safety
Vermont Criminal Information Center
103 S. Main St.
Waterbury VT 05671-2101
802-244-8786
www.dps.state.vt.us/cjs
The Criminal Information Center publishes the *Vermont Annual Crime Report* which is free upon request.

Virginia
Department of State Police
Uniform Crime Reporting Section
Records Management
P.O. Box 27472
Richmond, VA 23261-7472
804-674-2000
www.vsp.state.va.us/index.htm
The *Crime in Virginia Annual Report* is available for $5. Computer printouts of selected data are provided on a cost recovery basis.

Washington
Washington Association of Sheriffs and Police Chiefs
P.O. Box 826
2629 12th Court SW
Olympia, WA 98507
360-586-3221
www.waspc.org/
This organization produces the *Crime in Washington State Annual Report*, which is free upon request. Information that is not included in the annual report but readily accessible in their data banks is available to the public upon request.

WEST VIRGINIA

Department of Public Safety
Uniform Crime Reporting Division
725 Jefferson Rd.
South Charleston, WV 25306
304-558-2930
www.state.wv.us
The UCR Division publishes a *Crime in West Virginia Annual Report*. No computer services are available, but data can be retrieved manually and the staff will fill requests as needed.

Wisconsin

Office of Justice Assistance
Wisconsin Statistical Analysis Center
131 W. Wilson St., Suite 202
Madison, WI 53702-0001
608-266-3323
www.oja.state.wi.us/static

The Statistical Analysis Center publishes a free *Crime and Arrests Annual Report* which is available upon request. Computer printouts of selected data provided at no charge.

Wyoming

Criminal Justice Information Section
316 W. 22nd St.
Cheyenne, WY 82002
307-777-7181
http://attorneygeneral.state.wy.us/dci/index.html
Publications include the *Uniform Crime Annual Report*. Computer printouts of selected data are provided at no charge. The office will furnish special reports if the data requested is of the type they usually collect. These reports are usually in table or letter form. Services are free, unless there is significant computer programming involved. Complex requests should be made in writing.

Sample The State Statistics

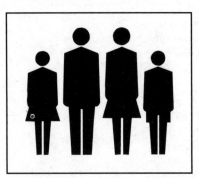

Every ten years, we all fill out the Census form and then what happens with all of that information? Approximately 1,300 organizations nationwide receive data from the U.S. Bureau of the Census and then disseminate that information to the public free of charge or on a cost recovery basis. These organizations are called state data centers and can provide you with specific information on your state or town. Want to move to a town full of twenty-somethings? Want to know the area with the most 20-year old houses which will need new roofs for your roofing business? Want to stay away from teenagers? Want to know the number of churches, hospitals, or recreational facilities in a town? You can sometimes even get information for a particular zip code. The data centers can provide you with information on specific reports they have available, customized searches that they can perform, and their free and fee schedules for particular information.

State Data Centers

Below is a roster of data centers in all 50 states as well as the District of Columbia, Puerto Rico and the Virgin Islands. Some of these Census Bureau information providers are based in state departments and agencies, universities, business colleges, and libraries.

Alabama

Center for Business and
Economic Research

University of Alabama
P.O. Box 870221
Tuscaloosa, AL 34587-0221
205-348-6191

Fax: 205-348-2951
http://cber.cba.ua.edu/asdc.ht
ml

Alabama Department of
Economic and Community
Affairs
Communication and
Information Division
P.O. Box 5690
401 Adams Ave.
Montgomery, AL 36103-5690
334-242-5525
www.adeca.state.al.us

Alabama Public Library Service
6030 Monticello Dr.
Montgomery, AL 36130
334-213-3900
800-723-8459
www.apls.state.al.us/

Alaska

Alaska State Data Center
Research and Analysis Section
Department of Labor
P.O. Box 25501
Juneau, AK 99802-5501
907-465-4500
Fax: 907-465-2101
http://146.63.75.50/research

Alaska State Library
Government Publications
P.O. Box 110571
Juneau, AK 99811-0571
907-465-2927
Fax: 907-465-2665
www.library.state.ak.us/asp/as
p.html

Dept. of Community and
Regional Affairs
Community and Business
Development
P.O. Box 110809
Juneau, AK 99811-0809
907-269-4521
Fax: 907-269-4539
www.dced.state.ak.us/cdb/hom
e.htm

Institute for Social and Economic
Research
University of Alaska
3211 Providence Dr.
Anchorage, AK 99508
907-786-7710
Fax: 907-786-7739

www.iser.uaa.alaska.edu/home.
htm

Arizona

Arizona Department of
Economic Security
Site Code 045Z
P.O. Box 6123
1789 W. Jefferson St., NE
Phoenix, AZ 85005
602-542-5984
www.de.state.az.us/links/econo
mic/webpage/ page2.html

Center for Business Research
College of Business
Administration
Arizona State University
Box 874011
Tempe, AZ, 85287-4011
480-965-3961
Fax: 480-965-5458
www.cob.asu.edu/seid/cbr/

Bureau of Business and
Economic Research
Bank One Center for Business
Outreach
College of Business
Administration
Northern Arizona University
Box 15066
Flagstaff, AZ 86011-5066
928-523-7313
Fax: 928-523-1612
www.cba.nau.edu/bber

Research Library
Dept. of Library Archives and
Public Records
1700 W. Washington, 3rd Floor
Phoenix, AZ 85007
602-542-4035
800-255-5841 (AZ)
www.dlapr.lib.az.us/

Economic and Business Research
Program
College of Business and Public
Administration
University of Arizona
McClelland Hall 204
Tucson, AZ 85721-0108
520-621-2155
Fax: 520-621-2150
http://ebr.eller.arizona.edu/Lib
rary/sdc.htm

Arkansas

State Data Center
UALR Institute for Economic
Advancement
2801 S. University Ave.
Little Rock, AR 72204
501-569-8530
Fax: 501-569-8538
www.aiea.ualr.edu/csdc/defaul
t.html

Arkansas State Library
1 Capitol Mall
Little Rock, AR 72201
501-682-2864
www.asl.lib.ar.us

Research and Analysis Section
Arkansas Employment Security
Division
P.O. Box 2981
Little Rock, AR 72203
501-682-3159
www.accessarkansas.org/esd/
labormarketinformation.htm

California

State Census Data Center
Department of Finance
915 L St.
Sacramento, CA 95814
www.dof.ca.gov/html/Demogra
p/druhpar.htm
916-445-3878

Sacramento Area COG
3000 S Street, Suite 300
Sacramento, CA 95816
916-457-2264
www.sacog.org/

Association of Bay Area
Governments
P.O. Box 2050
Oakland, CA 94604-2050
510-464-7957
Fax: 510-433-5557
www.abag.ca.gov

Southern California Association
of Govts.
818 W. 7th St., 12th Floor
Los Angeles, CA 90017-3435
213-236-1800
Fax: 213-236-1825
www.scag.ca.gov/census

San Diego Association of
Governments
Wells Fargo
401 B St., Suite 800
San Diego, CA 92101
619-595-5300
Fax: 619-595-5305
www.sandag.cog.ca.us/

State Data Center Program
University of
California-Berkeley
2538 Channing Way, #5100
Berkeley, CA 94720-5100
510-642-6571
Fax: 510-643-8292
http://ucdata.berkeley.edu

Colorado

Division of Local Government
Colorado Department of Local
Affairs
1313 Sherman St., Room 521
Denver, CO 80203
303-866-4147
Fax: 303-866-2660
www.dlg.oem2.state.co.us/dem
og/ demog.htm

Business Research Division
Graduate School of Business
Administration
420 UCB
University of Colorado-Boulder
Boulder, CO 80309-0420
303-492-8227
Fax: 303-492-3620
http://leeds.colorado.edu/brd/
index.cfin

Agriculture and Resource
Economics
Colorado State University
Clark B-320
Fort Collins, CO 80523-1172
907-491-6325
Fax: 970-491-2067
http://dare.agsci.colostate.edu

Documents and Department of
the Libraries
Colorado State University
Fort Collins, CO 80523-1172
303-491-1880
http://lib.colostate.edu/researc
h/colorado

Connecticut

Policy Development and
Planning Division
Connecticut Office of Policy and
Management
450 Capitol Ave.
MS#52ASP
Hartford, CT 06106-1308
860-418-6230
www.opm.state.ct.us

Government Information
Services
Connecticut State Library
231 Capitol Ave.
Hartford, CT 06106
860-757-6570
www.cslib.org/gis.htm

Connecticut Department of
Economic and Community
Development
Research Division
505 Hudson St.
Hartford, CT 06106
860-270-8165
www.state.ct.us/ecd/research/i
ndex.html

Center for Population Research
University of Connecticut
344 Mansfield Road, Unit 2068
Storrs, CT 06269-2068
860-486-9269

Delaware

Delaware Economic
Development Office
99 Kings Highway
P.O. Box 1401
Dover, DE 19901
302-739-4271
Fax: 302-739-2028
www.state.de.us/dedo/new_we
b_site/ frame_data_center.html

College of Urban Affairs and
Public Policy
University of Delaware
Graham Hall, Room 286
Academy St.
Newark, DE 19716
302-831-8406
www.udel.edu/suapp

District of Columbia

Data Services Division
Mayor's Office of Planning
801 N. Capitol St., NE, Suite 4000
Washington, DC 20002
202-442-7600
www.planning.dc.gov/main.shtm

Metropolitan Washington
Council of Governments
777 N. Capitol St., NE, Suite 300
Washington, DC 20002-4239
202-962-3293
www.mwcog.org/hspps/census
reports.html

Center for Neighborhood
Information Services
1825 K Street, Suite 710
Washington, DC 20006-1202
202-223-2598
Fax: 202-223-2604
www.dcagenda.org/pages/nis

Florida

Center for the Study of
Population
Institute for Social Research
654 Bellemy Bldg., R-93
Florida State University
Tallahassee, FL 32306-4063
850-644-7101
www.fsu.edu/~popctr

State Library of Florida
500 S. Bronough St.
Tallahassee, FL 32399-0250
850-245-6600
http://dlis.dos.state.fl.us/stlib/

State Data Center
Agency for Workforce
Innovation
Office of Workforce Information
Services
Labor Market Statistics
C&M Industrial Center, Bldg. B
4972 Woodville Highway
Tallahassee, FL 32311-0902
850-488-1048
Fax: 850-921-0776
http://lmi.floridajobs.org/censu
s2000/ index.htm

Georgia

Division of Demographic and
Statistical Services

Georgia Office of Planning and
Budget
270 Washington St., SW
Atlanta, GA 30334
404-656-3820
Fax: 404-656-3828
www.opb.state.ga.us/

University of Georgia Libraries
Government Documents, 2nd
Floor
Athens, GA 30602
706-542-0662
www.libs.uga.edu/govdocs/go
vdocs.html

State Data and Research Center
101 Marietta St., Suite 2550
Atlanta, GA 30303
404-463-1100
Fax: 404-463-1137
www.gadata.org

Gilbert Memorial Library
Government Information
Department
Georgia Institute of Technology
Atlanta, GA 30332-0900
404-894-4519
http://ibid.library.gatech.edu/
%7Egovweb

Hawaii
Hawaii State Data Center
Department of Business,
Economic Development, and
Tourism
Research and Economic Analysis
Division
#1 Capitol District Bldg.
250 S. Hotel St., 4th Floor
Honolulu, HI 96813
Mailing Address:
  P.O. Box 2359
  Honolulu, HI 96804
808-586-2423
www.hawaii.gov/dbedt/sdcrpt.
html

Information and
Communication Services
Division
State Dept. of Accounting and
General Services
P.O. Box 0150
1151 Punchbowl St.

Honolulu, HI 96813
808-586-1800
olepe.icsd.hawaii.gov/dags/icsd

University of Hawaii at Manoa
Information Technology Services
265 McCarthy Mall, Keller Hall
Honolulu, HI 96822-2302
808-956-2387
Fax: 808-956-2412

Idaho
Idaho Department of Commerce
700 W. State St.
P.O. Box 83720
Boise, ID 83720-0093
208-334-2470
800-842-5858
www.idoc.state.id.us/

Institutional Research
Room 319, Business Bldg.
Boise State University
1910 University Drive
Boise, ID 83725
208-385-1613
www.idbsu.edu/

The Idaho State Library
325 W. State St.
Boise, ID 83702
208-334-2150
Fax: 208-334-4016
www.lili.org/isl/

Center for Business Research
and Services
Campus Box 8044
Idaho State University
Pocatello, ID 83209
208-236-3049
Fax: 208-236-5960
www.isu.edu/departments/cbr/

Illinois
Census and Data Users Services
Department 4690
Campus Box 4950
6 Research Services Bldg.
Beauford and Fell St.
Normal, IL 61790-4950
309-438-5946
Fax: 309-438-2898
www.cadus.ilstu.edu/populatio
n.htm

Center for Governmental Studies
Northern Illinois University
Social Science Research Bldg.
138 N. 3rd St.
DeKalb, IL 60115
815-753-0934
www.nibidc.com/index.html

Chicago Area Geographic
Information Study
Department of Geography (M/C
092)
1007 W. Harrison St., Room 2102
University of Illinois at Chicago
Chicago, IL 60607-7138
312-996-5274
Fax: 312-996-6343
www.cagis.uic.edu/

Northeastern Illinois Planning
Commission
Research Services Department
222 S. Riverside Plaza, Suite 1800
Chicago, IL 60606-6097
312-454-0400
Fax: 312-454-0411
www.nipc.cog.il.us/

State Data Center
Division of Policy
Development/Planning &
Research
Department of Commerce &
Community Affairs
620 East Adams Street
Springfield, IL 62701
217-782-1381
Fax: 217-524-3701
www.commerce.state.il.us/
doingbusiness/research/factsan
d.htm

Indiana
Indiana State Library
Indiana State Data Center
140 N. Senate Ave.
Indianapolis, IN 46204
317-232-3733
Fax: 317-232-3728
www.statelib.lib.in.us/www/rl
/sdcmenu.html

Indiana Business Research
Center
Indiana University
Research Park 110

Kelly School of Business
501 N. Morton St.
Bloomington, IN 47404
812-855-5507
Fax: 812-855-7763
www.ibrc.indiana.edu

Indiana Business Research
Center
Kelley School of Business
Indiana University
Suite 210, 777 Indiana Avenue
Indianapolis, IN 46202
317-274-2979
Fax: 317-615-0031
www.ibrc.indiana.edu

Office of Research and
Technology
Indiana Dept. of Commerce
1 N. Capitol, Suite 700
Indianapolis, IN 46204
317-232-8959
www.ai.org/doc/index.html

Indiana Business Research
Center
Kelley School of Business
Indiana University
Suite 210, 777 Indiana Avenue
Indianapolis, IN 46202
317-274-2979
Fax: 317-615-0031
www.ibrc.indiana.edu

Iowa

State Library of Iowa
E. 12th and Grand
Des Moines, IA 50319
515-281-4350
800-248-4483
Fax: 515-242-6543
www.silo.lib.ia.us/datacenter

Center for Social and Behavioral
Research
221 Sabin Hall
University of Northern Iowa
Cedar Falls, IA 50614-0402
319-273-2105
Fax: 219-273-3104
http://csbsnt.csbs.uni.edu/dept
/csbr

Census Services
Iowa State University

303 East Hall
Ames, IA 50011-1070
515-294-8337
Fax: 515-294-0592
http://socserver.soc.iastate.edu
/census

Department of Sociology
University of Iowa
W140 Seashore Hall
Iowa City, IA 52242
319-335-2887
www.uiowa.edu/~soc/icpsr_fr
m.htm

Kansas

State Library
300 SW. 10th St., Room 343-N
Topeka, KS 66612-1593
785-296-3296
800-432-3919 (KS)
http://skyways.lib.ks.us/kansas
/ksl/ ref/cen01.htm

Division of the Budget
Room 152-E, Statehouse
Topeka, KS 66612-1504
785-296-2436
Fax: 785-296-0231
http://da.state.ks.us/budget

Research Institute
1541 Lilac Lane.
607 Blake Hall
The University of Kansas
Lawrence, KS 66044-3177
785-864-3701
Fax: 785-864-3683
www.ku.edu/pri/ab_ippbr/pri.
shtml

Center for Economic
Development and Business
Research
1845 Fairmont
2nd Floor, Devlin Hall
Wichita State University
Wichita, KS 67260-0121
316-978-3225
Fax: 316-978-3950
www.webs.wichita.edu/cedbr

Population and Research
Laboratory
Department of Sociology
204 Waters Hall

Kansas State University
Manhattan, KS 66506
785-532-6865
www.ksu.edu/sasw/

Kentucky

Urban Studies Institute
College of Business and Public
Administration
University of Louisville
426 W. Bloom St.
Louisville, KY 40208
502-852-7990
Fax: 502-852-7386
www.louisville.edu/ksdc

Governor's Office of Policy and
Management
Capitol Annex, 700 Capitol Ave.
Frankfort, KY 40601
502-564-7300
www.osbd.state.ky.us

State Library Division
Department for Libraries and
Archives
300 Coffeetree Rd.
P.O. Box 537
Frankfort, KY 40602-0537
502-564-8300
Fax: 502-564-5773
www.kdla.state.ky.us/

Louisiana

State Census Data Center
Office of Electronic Services
P.O. Box 94095
1051 N. 3rd St.
Baton Rouge, LA 70804
225-219-4025
www.state.la.us/demo.htm

Division of Business and
Economic Research
University of New Orleans
Lake Front
New Orleans, LA 70148
504-280-6240
Fax: 504-280-6094
www.uno.edu/~coba/dber/ind
ex.html

Economic Research Division
Louisiana Tech University
College of Business and
Administration

P.O. Box 10318
Ruston, LA 71272
318-257-3701
www.cab.latech.edu/public/cen
ters/ research/index.htm

Louisiana State Library
Referenced Bibliography Section
P.O. Box 131
Baton Rouge, LA 70821-0131
225-342-4913
www.state.lib.la.us/

Louisiana Population Data
Center
Department of Sociology
126 Stubbs Hall
Louisiana State University
Baton Rouge, LA 70803-5411
Mr. Charles Tolbert
225-578-5360
www.lapop.lsu.edu/

Louisiana Economic Assistance
Program (LEAP)
Center for Business and
Economic Research (CBER)
University of Louisiana at
Monroe
Monroe, LA 71209-6277
318-342-1215/1219
Fax: 318-342-1209
http://leap.ulm.edu

Maine
Maine State Planning Office
Census Data Center Program &
Maine Census Consortium
184 State Street
Augusta, ME 04330
Mailing Address:
  c/o 38 State House Station
  Augusta, ME 04333
207-287-2989
Fax: 207-287-6489
www.state.me.us/spo/census.ht
m

Maryland
Maryland Department of
Planning
State Data Center
301 W. Preston St.
Baltimore, MD 21201
Ms. Jane Traynham
410-767-4450

Fax: 410-767-4480
www.mdp.state.md.us/msdc

University of Maryland
UMCP McKeldin Library
4th Floor, Government
Documents
College Park, MD 20742
301-405-9165
Fax: 301-314-5651
www.lib.umd.edu/gov/govt_d
ocs.html

Enoch Pratt Free Library
Resource Center
Maryland Room
400 Cathedral St.
Baltimore, MD 21201-4484
410-396-1789
www.epfl.net/sirc/md

Small Business Development
Center
7100 Baltimore Ave., Suite 401
College Park, MD 20740
301-403-8300

Massachusetts
Massachusetts Institute for
Social and Economic Research
128 Thompson Hall, Box 37515
University of Massachusetts
Amherst, MA 01003-7515
413-545-3460
Fax: 413-545-3686
www.umass.edu/miser/

Massachusetts Institute for
Social and Economic Research,
McCormack Bldg.
1 Ashburton Place, Room 1004
Boston, MA 02108
617-727-4537
Fax: 617-727-4660
www.umass.edu/miser

Michigan
Michigan Information Center
Department of Management and
Budget
Census Data
George W. Romney Bldg.
10th Floor, 111 S. Capitol
Lansing, MI 48933
517-373-7910
www.state.mi.us/dmb/mic/

MIMIC/Center for Urban
Studies
Wayne State University
656 W. Kirby, Room 3057
Detroit, MI 48202
313-577-8996
Fax: 313-577-1274
www.cus.wayne.edu/mimic/

The Library of Michigan
Government Documents Service
P.O. Box 30007
717 W. Allegan St.
Lansing, MI 48909
517-373-1580
www.libofmich.lib.mi.us/

Minnesota
State Demographer's Office
Minnesota Planning
658 Cedar St., Room 300
St. Paul, MN 55155
612-296-2557
www.mnplan.state.mn.us/demo
graphy/index.html

Minnesota Population Center
Minnesota Data Center
University of Minnesota
271 19th Ave., South
537 Heller Hall
Minneapolis, MN 54555
612-624-4389
Fax: 612-626-8375
www.pop.umn.edu/index.html

Educational Resources Center
Department of Education
1500 Hwy. 36 West
Roseville, MN 55113
651-582-8719
http://cfl.state.mn.us/library/e
dures.htm

Metropolitan Council
Mears Park Center
230 East 5th Street
St. Paul, MN 55101
651-602-1000
www.metrocouncil.org/resource
s/resources.htm

Mississippi
Center for Population Studies
The University of Mississippi
Leavell Hall, Room 102

University, MS 38677
662-915-7288
Fax: 662-915-7736
www.olemiss.edu/depts/sdc

Div. of Research and
Information Systems
Department of Economic and
Community Development
1200 Walter Sillas Bldg.
P.O. Box 849
Jackson, MS 39205
601-359-3449
www.decd.state.ms.us/

Southern Mississippi Planning
and Development District
9229 Highway 49
Gulfport, MS 39503-4317
228-868-2311
Fax: 228-868-7094
www.smpdd.com

Missouri

Missouri State Census Data
Center
Missouri State Library
600 W. Main St.
P.O. Box 387
Jefferson City, MO 65102
573-526-7648
Fax: 573-751-3612
www.oseda.missouri.edu/mscd
c/

Office of Administration
124 Capitol Bldg.
P.O. Box 809
Jefferson City, MO 65102
573-751-2345
www.oa.state.md.us

Office of Social and Economic
Data Analysis
University of Missouri-
Columbia
602 Clark Hall
Columbia, MO 65211
573-882-7396
Fax: 573-884-4635
www.oseda.missouri.edu/index
.html

Geographic Resources Center
University of Missouri-
Columbia

Stewart Hall
Columbia, MO 65211
573-882-1404
Fax: 573-884-4095
www.msdis.missouri.edu/

Small Business Research
Information Center
University of Montana-Rolla
104 Nagogami Teerrace
Rolla, MO 65409-1340
573-341-4559
Fax: 573-341-6495
www.umr.edu/~tscsbdc

Center for Economic Information
207 Haag Hall
Univ. of Missouri-Kansas City
5100 Rockhill Road
Kansas City, MO 641110
816-235-2832
Fax: 816-235-5263
http://cei.haag.umkc.edu

Montana

Census and Economic
Information Center
Montana Department of
Commerce
P.O. Box 200501
1424 9th Ave.
Helena, MT 59620-0505
406-444-2896
Fax: 406-444-1518
http://ceic.commerce.state.mt.us

Montana State Library
1515 E. 6th Ave.
P.O. Box 201800
Helena, MT 59620-1800
406-444-3115
800-338-5087
http://msl.state.mt.us

Bureau of Business and
Economic Research
University of Montana
Gallagher Business Bldg.
32 Campus Dr., #6840
Missoula, MT 59812
406-243-5113
www.bber.umt.edu

Research and Analysis Bureau
Workforce Services Division

Montana Department of Labor
and Industry
P.O. Box 1728
Helena, MT 59624
406-444-2430
800-633-0229 (MT)
http://rad.dli.state.mt.us

Natural Resource Information
System
1515 East 6th Avenue
Helena, MT 59620-1800
406-444-5354
http://nris.state.mt.us/index.ht
ml

Nebraska

Center for Public Affairs
Research
Nebraska State Data Center
Peter Kiewit Conference Center,
#232
University of Nebraska at
Omaha
Omaha, NE 68182
402-554-2134/2132
www.unomaha.edu/~cpar

Governor's Policy Research
Office
P.O. Box 94601
State Capitol, Room 1319
Lincoln, NE 68509-4601
402-471-2414

Federal Documents Librarian
Nebraska Library Commission
The Atrium
1200 N. St., Suite 120
Lincoln, NE 68508-2023
402-471-2045
800-307-2665 (NE)
www.nlc.state.ne.us/

The Central Data Processing
Division
Dept. of Administration Services
Nebraska Department of
Economic Development
301 Centennial Mall S.
Lower Level
P.O. Box 95045
Lincoln, NE 68509-5045
402-471-4855
www.info.neded.org

Nebraska Department of Labor
550 S. 16th St.
P.O. Box 94600
Lincoln, NE 68509-4600
402-471-2518
www.dol.state.ne.us/

Department of Natural
Resources
301 Centennial Mall South
P.O. Box 94876
Lincoln, NE 68509-4676
402-471-3964
www.dnr.state.ne.us

Nevada
Nevada State Data Center
Nevada State Library and
Archives
Capitol Complex
100 N. Stewart St.
Carson City, NV 89701
775-684-3326
800-922-2880 (NV)
http://dmla.clan.lib.nv.us/docs
/nsla/sdc

New Hampshire
Office of State Planning
2-1/2 Beacon St.
Concord, NH 03301-4497
603-271-2155
Fax: 603-271-1728
www.state.nh.us/osp/sdc/sdc.
html

New Hampshire State Library
20 Park St.
Concord, NH 03301-6303
603-271-2060
www.state.nh.us/nhsl/index.ht
ml

New Jersey
New Jersey Department of Labor
Labor Planning and Analysis
P.O. Box 388
Trenton, NJ 08625-0388
609-984-2595
Fax: 609-984-6833
www.state.nj.us/labor/lra/njsd
c.htm

New Jersey State Library
U.S. Documents Office
185 W. State St.

P.O. Box 520
Trenton, NJ 08625-0520
609-292-6259
Fax: 609-984-7900
www.njstatelib.org/aboutus/SG
IS/libusdoc.htm/

Data and Statistical Services
Social Science Reference Center
Princeton University
One Washington Rd.
Princeton, NJ 08544
609-258-6052
www.princeton.edu/~sbwhite/
ssrcwebb.html

Edward J. Bloustein School of
Planning and Public Policy
Rutgers, The State University of
New Jersey
Civic Square Building
33 Livingston Avenue, Suite 300
New Brunswick, NJ 08901-1981
732-932-5475
http://policy.rutgers.edu

Rutgers University Computing
Services
CCIS-Hill Center
Busch Campus
258A Hill Center, Box 879
Piscataway, NJ 08854-0879
732-445-3137

New Mexico
Economic Development
Department
P.O. Box 20003
Santa Fe, NM 87504-5003
505-827-0264
www.edd.state.nm.us/

New Mexico State Library
Federal Documents
1209 Camino Carlos Rey
Santa Fe, NM 87507
505-476-97
www.stlib.state.nm.us/libraryse
rvices/statepubs/sg6.html

Bureau of Business and
Economic Research
University of New Mexico
1920 Lomas NE
Albuquerque, NM 87131-6021
505-277-6626

Fax: 505-277-7066
www.unm.edu/~bber

State Data Center
Department of Economics and
International Business
New Mexico State University
Box 30001, Dept. 3CQ
Las Cruces, NM 88003-8001
Dr. Kathleen Brook
505-646-2113
http://cbae.nmsu.edu/MainPag
e/Pub_Centers/Data_Center

New York
Cornell University
CISER Data Archive
201 Caldwell Hall
Ithaca, NY 14850
607-255-4801
Fax: 607-255-9353
www.ciser.cornell.edu/

Nelson A. Rockefeller Institute
of Government
411 State St.
Albany, NY 12203-1003
518-443-5522
Fax: 518-443-5788
http://rockinst.org

New York State Library
6th Floor, Cultural Education
Center
Empire State Plaza
Albany, NY 12230
518-474-3940
www.nysl.nysed.gov/

Office of Real Property Services
16 Sheridan Ave.
Albany, NY 12210-2714
518-486-5446
www.orps.state.ny.us/

State Data Center
Empire State Development
30 South Pearl Street
Albany, NY 12245
518-292-5300
Fax: 518-292-5806
www.empire.state.ny.us/data_h
ome.html

North Carolina
Division of State Library
109 E. Jones St.

Raleigh, NC 27699-4641
919-733-3270
Fax: 919-733-5679
http://statelibrary.dcr.state.nc.us

Institute for Research in Social
Science
University of North Carolina-
Chapel Hill
Manning Hall CB 3355
Chapel Hill, NC 27599-3355
919-962-0512
Fax: 919-962-4777
www.irss.unc.edu

Center for Geographic
Information
Office of State Planning
301 N. Wilmington St., Suite 700
Raleigh, NC 27601
919-733-2090
Fax: 919-715-0725
www.cgia.state.nc.us/

Office of State Budget and
Management
Data Service Unit
State Data Center
20321 Mail Service Center
Raleigh, NC 27699-0321
Location:
   5050 Administration Building
   116 West Jones
919-733-7061
Fax: 919-715-3562
http://sdc.state.nc.us

North Dakota

North Dakota State Data Center
North Dakota State University
Agribusiness and Applied
Economics, Room 424, IACC
P.O. Box 5636
Fargo, ND 58105-5636
701-231-7980
www.ndsu.nodak.edu/sdc

Division of Community Service
400 E. Broadway, Suite 50
Bismarck, ND 58502
701-328-2676
www.state.nd.us/dcs/tahome.h
tml

Department of Geography
University of North Dakota

Box 9020
Grand Forks, ND 58202
701-777-4246
Fax: 701-777-6195
www.und.nodak.edu/dept/Geo
g/mainpage.html

North Dakota State Library
Liberty Memorial Bldg.
604 East Boulevard Ave.
Department 250
Bismarck, ND 58505-0800
701-328-4622
800-472-2104
ndsl.lib.state.nd.us

Ohio

Office of Strategic Research
Ohio Department of
Development
P.O. Box 1001
77 High St., 27th Floor
Columbus, OH 43215
614-466-2115
Fax: 614-466-9697
www.odod.state.oh.us/osr/data
.htm

State Library of Ohio
274 E. First Ave.
Columbus, OH 43201
614-644-1971
http://winslo.state.oh.us/govin
fo/stgvtop.html

Cleveland State University
Northern Ohio Data and
Information Service
The Urban Center
Maxine Goodman Levin College
of Urban Affairs
Cleveland, OH 44115-2440
216-687-2209
http://nodisnet1.csuohio.edu/n
odis/index.html

Data Center
Department of Human and
Community Resource
Development
248 Agricultural Administration
2120 Fyffe Road
Columbus, OH 43210
614-688-8760
www.osuedc.org/current

Buckeye Hills-Hocking Valley
Regional Development District
Route 1, County Road 9
Box 299D
Marietta, OH 45750-9286
740-374-9436
Fax: 740-374-8038
www.seovirtual.com

Ohio Occupational Information
Division of Labor Market
Information
Ohio Department of Job and
Family Services
145 South Front Street
P.O. Box 1618
Columbus, OH 43216-1618
614-752-6865
http://lmi.state.oh.us/Index.htm

Oklahoma

Oklahoma State Data Center
Oklahoma Department of
Commerce
900 N. Stiles
Mailing Address:
   P.O. Box 26980
   Oklahoma City, OK
   73126-0980
405-815-5184
800-652-8779
www.odoc.state.ok.us/osdc.htm

Oklahoma Department of
Libraries
200 NE 18th St.
Oklahoma City, OK 73105
405-522-3335
www.odl.state.ok.us/usinfo

Center for Economic and
Management Research
The University of Oklahoma
Michael F. Price College of
Business
307 W. Brooks, Room 4
Norman, OK 73019-0450
405-325-2931
http://cemr.ou.edu/

Oregon

Oregon State Library
250 Winter St., NE
Salem, OR 97301
503-378-4277
Fax: 503-588-7119
www.osl.state.or.us/

Population Research Center
School of Urban and Public
Affairs
Portland State University
506 SW Mill-URBN 570J
Portland, OR 97207-0751
503-725-5159
Fax: 503-725-5162
www.upa.pdx.edu/CPRC

Office of Economic Analysis
155 Cottage St., NE, U20
Salem, OR 97301
503-378-4967
www.oea.das.state.or.us/popula
tion.htm

Documents Center
Main Floor Knight Library
1501 Kincaid Street
1299 University of Oregon
Eugene, OR 97403-1299
503-346-3070
Fax: 503-346-3094
http://libweb.uoregon.edu/gov
docs

Pennsylvania
Pennsylvania State Data Center
Institute of State and Regional
Affairs
Pennsylvania State University at
Harrisburg
777 W. Harrisburg Pike
Middletown, PA 17057
717-948-6336
Fax: 717-948-6754
http://pasdc.hbg.psu.edu/inde
x.html

Penn State University
Social Sciences Library
201 Paterno
University Park, PA 16801
814-865-4861
Fax: 814-865-1403
www.libraries.psu.edu/crsweb/
docs/govmain.htm

Rhode Island
Rhode Island Department of
Administration
Statewide Planning Program
One Capitol Hill
Providence, RI 02908-5873

401-222-7901
www.planning.state.ri.us

Office of Health Statistics
Rhode Island Department of
Health
3 Capitol Hill, Room 407
Providence, RI 02908-5097
401-222-2550
Fax: 401-273-4350
www.healthri.org/chic/statistic
s/home.htm

Rhode Island Economic
Development Corporation
One West Exchange St.
Providence, RI 02903
401-222-2601
Fax: 401-222-2102
www.riedc.com/

Office of Library and
Information Services
Department of Administration
One Capitol Hill
Providence, RI 02908
401-222-2726
Fax: 401-222-4195
www.lori.state.ri.us/lori

Population Studies and Training
Center
Brown University
P.O. Box 1916
112 George Street
Providence, RI 02912
401-863-2278
Fax: 401-863-3351
www.pstc.brown.edu

United Way of Southeastern
New England
229 Waterman Street
Providence, RI 02906
401-444-0600
Fax: 401-444-0635
www.unitedwaysene.org

South Carolina
South Carolina State Library
1500 Senate St.
P.O. Box 11469
Columbia, SC 29211
803-734-8026
www.state.sc.us/scsl/den

Office of Research and Statistics
South Carolina Budget and
Control Board
Rembert Dennis Building
Room 425
Columbia, SC 29201
803-734-3793
www.ors.state.sc.us

South Dakota
Business Research Bureau
School of Business
University of South Dakota
414 E. Clark
Vermillion, SD 57069
605-677-5287
605-677-5427
www.usd.edu/brbinfo/

Government Publication
South Dakota State Library
800 Governors Dr.
Pierre, SD 57501-2294
605-773-5241
800-423-6665
www.sdstatelibrary.com

Labor Market Information
Center
South Dakota Department of
Labor
420 S. Roosevelt, Box 4730
Aberdeen, SD 57401
605-626-2314
Fax: 605-626-2322
www.sdjobs.org/lmic

Office of Administration
Services
South Dakota Department of
Health
600 E. Capitol Ave.
Pierre, SD 57501-2536
605-773-5303
Fax: 605-773-5683
800-738-2301
www.state.sd.us/index.htm

South Dakota State University
Rural Sociology Department
Scobey Hall, Box 504
Brookings, SD 57007-1296
605-688-4899
Fax: 605-688-6354
www.abs.sdstate.edu:81/sociolo
gy/census_dat

TENNESSEE

Center for Business and
Economic Research
College of Business
Administration
University of Tennessee
Glocker Bldg., Suite 100
Knoxville, TN 37996-4170
865-974-5441
Fax: 865-974-3100
http://cber.bus.utk.edu/

TEXAS

Business and Industry Data
Center
Department of Economic
Development
P.O. Box 12728
1700 N. Congress Ave.
Austin, TX 78701
512-936-0292
www.bidc.state.tx.us

State Data Center
Department of Rural Sociology
Texas A & M University
2125 TAMU
College Station, TX 77843-2125
979-845-5115
Fax: 979-862-3061
http://txsdc.tamu.edu/

Texas State Library and Archive
Commission
P.O. Box 12927
Austin, TX 78711
512-463-5455
www.tsl.state.tx.us/

Texas Natural Resources
Information System
P.O. Box 13231
Austin, TX 78711-3231
512-463-8337
Fax: 512-463-7274
www.tnris.state.tx.us

UTAH

Office of Planning and Budget
116 State Capitol
Salt Lake City, UT 84114
801-538-1027
Fax: 801-538-1547
www.governor.state.ut.us/dea/

University of Utah
Bureau of Economic and
Business Research
1645 E. Campus Center Dr.,
Room 401
Salt Lake City, UT 84112
801-581-6333
Fax: 801-581-3354
www.business.utah.edu/BEBR/

Department of Community and
Economic Development
324 S. State St., Suite 500
Salt Lake City, UT 84111
801-538-8700
877-4UTDCED (488-3233)
www.dced.state.ut.us/

Department of Workforce
Services
140 E. 300 S.
P.O. Box 45249
Salt Lake City, UT 84145-0249
801-536-9786
Fax: 801-526-9238
http://wi.dws.state.ut.us

VERMONT

Center for Rural Studies
University of Vermont
207 Morrill Hall
Burlington, VT 05405-0106
802-656-3021
http://crs.uvm.edu/

Vermont Department of
Libraries
109 State St.
Montpelier, VT 05609-0601
802-828-3261
http://dol.state.vt.us/

VIRGINIA

Virginia Employment
Commission
Labor Market information
703 E. Main St.
Richmond, VA 23219
804-786-7496
www.vec.state.va.us/

Wheldon Cooper Center for
Public Service
University of Virginia
918 Emmet St. N., Suite 300
Charlottesville, VA 22903-4832

434-982-5582
www.ccps.virginia.edu/demogr
aphics

Virginia State Library
Documents Section
800 E. Broad St.
Richmond, VA 23219-8000
804-692-3562
www.lva.lib.va/us/

WASHINGTON

Forecasting Division
Office of Financial Management
450 Insurance Bldg.
Box 43113
Olympia, WA 98504-3113
360-902-0599
www.ofm.wa.gov/demographic
s.htm

Puget Sound Regional Council
1011 Western Ave., Suite 500
Seattle, WA 98104-1035
206-464-7532
www.psrc.org/

Social Research Center
Department of Rural Sociology
Washington State University
P.O. Box 644006
Pullman, WA 99164-4006
509-335-8623
www.ruralsoc.wsu.edu/

Department of Sociology
Demographic Research
Laboratory
Amtzen Hall 501A
Western Washington University
Bellingham, WA 98225-9081
360-650-3176
Fax: 360-650-7295
www.ac.wwu.edu/~drl/

Department of Employment
Security
LMEA
P.O. Box 9046
Olympia, WA 98507-9046
360-438-4804
800-215-1617
www.wa.gov/esd/lmea

CSSCR
University of Washington

145 Savery Hall, DK 45
Seattle, WA 98195
206-543-8110
Fax: 206-543-8670
http://julius.csscr.washington.edu/

Department of Sociology
Applied Social Data Center
Central Washington University
Ellensburg, WA 98926-7545
509-963-1300
Fax: 509-963-1308
www.cwu.edu/~asdc/home.html

West Virginia

West Virginia Development
Office
Research and Strategic Planning
Division
Capitol Complex
Bldg. 6, Room 553
Charleston, WV 25305
304-558-4010
Fax: 304-558-0362
www.wvdo.org/business/research.htm

Reference Library
West Virginia State Library
Commission
1900 Kanawha Blvd. East

Cultural Center
Charleston, WV 25305
304-558-2045
800-642-9021, #1
http://129.71.160.4

Office of Health Services
Research
WVU Health Science Center
Medical Center Dr.
P.O. Box 9140
Morgantown, WV 26506-9145
304-293-1080
www.hsc.wvu.edu/som/cmed/ohsr

Bureau of Business and
Economic Research
College of Business and
Economics
West Virginia University
P.O. Box 6025
Morgantown, WV 26506-6025
304-293-7832
www.be.wvu.edu/serve/bureau/data.htm

Wisconsin

Department of Administration
Demographic Services Center
101 E. Wilson St.
Madison, WI 53702

608-266-1927
www.doa.state.wi.us/dhir/boir/demographic

Applied Population Laboratory
Department of Rural Sociology
University of Wisconsin
1450 Linden Dr., Room 316
Madison, WI 53706
608-262-1515
Fax: 608-262-6022
www.ssc.wisc.edu/poplab/

Wyoming

Survey Research Center
University of Wyoming
P.O. Box 3925
College of Business Building
Laramie, WY 82071-3925
307-766-2030
www.uwyo.edu/src/

Department of Administration
and Information
Economic Analysis Division
1807 Capitol Ave., Suite 206
Cheyenne, WY 82002-0060
307-777-7504
Fax: 307-632-1819
http://eadiv.state.wy.us/

Highway Information Closer To Home

You can get more specific information on the roadways in your town by contacting your state Highway Department. Want to know how safe your corner is for kids? How many accidents occur on the beltway and when? How safe are the bike paths? Where are accidents most likely to occur?

Every state highway department has a database made up of reports completed by all law enforcement agencies which investigate accidents. In most instances, the computerized system can be searched and printouts provided by a number of variables including accident type, county, month of year, alcohol involvement, driver sex, age, and more. Some states provide these printouts free of charge, while others charge up to $150 per hour or require a Freedom of Information act request. Many states also publish an annual report, which is usually free.

Highway Department Offices

Alabama

Alabama Highway Department
Accident Identification and Surveillance Section
Traffic Engineering
1409 Coliseum Blvd.
Montgomery, AL 36130
334-242-6128
www.dot.state.al.us/default.asp
A report, *Alabama Traffic Accident Facts*, is available to individuals at no cost. The accident database can be searched, sorted, and a printout produced.

Alabama Department of Public Safety
500 Dexter Avenue
Montgomery, AL 36130
To view the reports, visit the Critical Analysis Reporting Environment at http://care.cs.ua.edu.

Alaska

Department of Transportation and Public Facilities
3132 Channel Dr.
Juneau, AK 99801-7908
907-465-3900
888-PLAN-DOT
www.dot.state.ak.us/
Publications include a free annual report. Accident database printouts are provided. You can download the information at their website.

Arizona

Arizona Department of Transportation
Traffic Records Section
2828 N. Central Ave., Suite 880
Phoenix, AZ 85004
602-712-7437
www.dot.state.az.us/
Publications include the *Arizona Motor Vehicle Crash Facts*. The accident database can be searched, sorted, and a printout provided at no charge. Their website has data that covers the past four years.

Arkansas

Arkansas State Highway and Transportation Department
Attn: Traffic Safety Section
P.O. Box 2261
Little Rock, AR 72203
501-569-2648

www.ahtd.state.ar.us/
Publications include an annual *State Accident Data Report*. Information from accident databases is not released on a routine basis.

California

Department of Transportation
Caltrans
Publications Unit
1900 Royal Oaks Dr.
Sacramento, CA 95815-3800
916-445-3520
http://caltrans-opac.ca.gov/publicat.htm
Publications include the annual *California Accident Data*. The accident database can be searched, sorted, and a printout provided on a cost recovery basis.

Colorado

Department of Highways
Staff Traffic Division
4201 E. Arkansas Ave., Room 172
Denver, CO 80222
303-757-9271
www.dot.state.co.us/Programs/Safety
This department's publications include: *Accidents by County*, and *Accidents by City*. Both are free. A report entitled, *Accidents by Rates*, is $5. The Department of Revenue issues standard summaries of motor vehicle reports for a nominal fee. Information from accident databases is not released as a general policy.

Connecticut

Department of Transportation
Bureau of Policy and Planning
Office of Inventory and Forecasting
2800 Berlin Turnpike
Newington, CT 06131-7546
860-594-2022
www.dot.state.ct.us/bureau/pp/pp.html
The accident database can be searched, sorted, and a printout provided at no cost. Requests should be in writing. Go to the website listed above to view the information online.

Delaware

State Police Headquarters
Delaware State Traffic Control Section

P.O. Box 430
Dover, DE 19903-0430
302-739-5969
www.state.de.us/
Publications include monthly and annual reports. The database can be searched, sorted, and a printout provided at no cost. Delaware's *Annual Traffic Statistical Report* can be viewed at their website.

District of Columbia

Traffic Studies
Department of Public Works
2000 14th St., NW, 6th Floor
Washington, DC 20009
202-727-1000
No listings are provided on a regular basis. General questions are answered over the telephone.

Florida

Department of Transportation
Safety Engineer Office
605 Suwannee St., MS 53
Tallahassee, FL 32399-0450
850-458-3546
www11.myflorida.com/safety/default.htm
To view reports, see
www.hsmv.state.fl.us/html/safety.html
Publications include the *Florida Traffic Accident Facts Report* which is free upon request. The accident database can be searched, sorted, and a printout provided, usually free of charge. If the department must perform a mainframe computer search, there is an additional charge.

Georgia

Department of Public Safety
Accident Reporting Section
P.O. Box 1456
Atlanta, GA 30371
404-624-7660
www.ganet.org/dps/index.html
Standard accident summaries and an annual report is free upon request. Copies of individual accident reports are also provided. The agency does not routinely provide computer printouts of accident data. You can view the *Georgia Traffic Accidents Report* at their website.

Hawaii

Department of Transportation
Public Affairs Office
869 Punchbowl St., Room 120
Honolulu, HI 96813
808-587-2160
www.state.hi.us/dot

General questions are answered over the phone. A publication entitled *Major Traffic Accidents in Hawaii* is available free of charge.

Idaho

Office of Highway Safety
Idaho Transportation Department
P.O. Box 7129
Boise, ID 83707-1129
208-334-8100
www2.state.id.us/itd/index.htm
Publications include the *Idaho Traffic Collisions* report, which is free upon request and is available for online searching. The accident database can be searched, sorted, and a printout provided. A broad search of the database is usually under $10, but fees vary depending upon the complexity of the request. A specific accident report is $4 plus tax and shipping.

Illinois

Department of Transportation
Division on Traffic Safety
3215 Executive Park Dr.
Springfield, IL 62794-9245
217-782-2575
http://dot.state.il.us/
Publications include an *Aggressive Driver/Smooth Operator*. The accident database can be searched, sorted, and a printout provided at no cost. The *Illinois Crash Facts and Statistics* report is available online and covers statistics from 1998 to the present.

Indiana

Governor's Council on Impaired and Dangerous Driving
Indiana Criminal Justice Institute
One North Capitol Avenue, Suite 1000
Indianapolis, IN 46204
www.in.gov/cji/research/traffic_data.htm
Publications include annual summaries of motor vehicle traffic accidents entitled *Crash Facts*. The report plus others on traffic safety are available at their website. The accident database can be searched, sorted, and a printout provided on a cost recovery basis

Iowa

Iowa Department of Transportation
Driver Services
Park Fair Mall
100 Euclid Avenue
P.O. Box 9204
Des Moines, IA 50306-9204
515-237-3153
800-532-1121

www.dot.state.ia.us/mvd/ods/index.htm
Publications include the *Iowa Crash Facts*. The accident database can be searched, sorted, and a printout provided for a cost recovery fee. It can also be searched online.

Kansas

Department of Transportation
Bureau of Traffic Safety
7th Floor DSOB
915 Harrison
Topeka, KS 66612
785-296-3756
www.ink.org/public/kdot/safety/index.html
Publications include the *Annual Kansas Accident Facts*, and an *Alcohol Related Accidents and Accidents by Driver Age Group Report*. These reports can be downloaded from their website.

Kentucky

State Police
Statistics Division
Records Branch
1250 Louisville Rd.
Frankfort, KY 40601
502-226-2169
www.state.ky.us/agencies/ksp/traffic.htm
Publications include a *Kentucky Traffic Accident Facts Annual Report*. The accident database can be searched for records dating back five years. A written request for information is required. These reports can also be viewed at the website listed above.

Louisiana

Department of Public Safety and Corrections
Highway Safety Commission
P.O. Box 66336
265 S. Foster Dr.
Baton Rouge, LA 70896
225-925-6991
www.dps.state.la.us/hwswww.nsf
The accident database can be searched, sorted, and a printout provided upon written request. It can also be downloaded from their website.

Maine

Department of Public Safety
Bureau of Highway Safety
164 State House Station
Augusta, ME 04333-0164
207-624-8756
www.state.me.us/dps/Bhs/homepage.htm
The accident database can be searched, sorted, and a printout provided at no cost upon request. A

publication entitled *Maine Highway Crash Facts* is available.

Maryland

State Highway Administration
Traffic Safety Analysis Division
7491 Connelly Dr.
Hannover, MD 21076
410-787-5822
www.sha.state.md.us/
The staff will supply data and selected excerpts from publications for reasonable requests. There is normally no charge, but fees are based on the amount of data requested and staff time involved.

Massachusetts

Governor's Highway Safety Bureau
10 Park Plaza, Suite 5220
Boston, MA 02116
617-973-8900
www.massghsb.com/safety_data.html
The Highway Safety Data report is available on-line for review and searching.

Michigan

Michigan State Police
Office of Highway Safety Planning
4000 Collins Rd.
P.O. Box 30633
Lansing, MI 48909-8133
517-322-6025
www.michigan.gov/msp/1,1607,7-123-1645_3501_4626---,00.html
Publications include *Michigan Traffic Crash Statistics*, and *Fatal and Serious Injury Traffic Crash Trends in Michigan*.

Minnesota

Department of Public Safety
Office of Traffic Safety
444 Cedar St., Suite 150
St. Paul, MN 55101-5150
651-296-3804
www.dps.state.mn.us/trafsafe/trafsafe.asp
Publications include *Crash Facts Report*. The report is available at the website listed above. This department does not provide accident database searches.

Mississippi

Department of Public Safety
Highway Safety
P.O. Box 958
Jackson, MS 39205
601-987-1212
www.dps.state.ms.us/

This department does not provide accident database searches. General questions are handled over the phone.

Missouri

State Highway Patrol
Division of Highway Safety
P.O. Box 104808
Jefferson City, MO 65110
573-751-4161
800-800-BELT
www.dps.state.mo.us/dps/mshs/hs.htm
Publications include the annual *Missouri Traffic Safety Compendium*. The accident database can be searched, sorted, and a printout provided upon special request. Fees vary and are based on a cost recovery basis.

Montana

Montana Department of Transportation
Traffic Safety Bureau
P.O. Box 201001
Helena, MT 59620-1001
406-444-7301
www.mdt.state.mt.us
Publications include their free *Problem Identification Paper*. The accident database can be searched, sorted, and a printout provided at no cost. It is also available online.

Nebraska

Department of Roads
Highway Safety Bureau
Accident Records
P.O. Box 94669
Lincoln, NE 68509
402-479-4645
www.dor.state.ne.us/highway_safety
Publications include the annual *Traffic Accident Facts Report*. The report is available online. The accident database can be searched, sorted, and a printout provided, usually at no cost.

Nevada

Department of Transportation
Safety Engineering
1263 S. Stewart St.
Carson City, NV 89712
702-888-7000
www.nevadadot.com
Publications include the annual *Nevada Crashes*. The accident database can be searched, sorted, and a table provided. This can be researched at their website.

New Hampshire

Department of Transportation
John O. Mortin Bldg.

P.O. Box 483
Concord, NH 03302-0483
603-271-3734
www.state.nh.us/dot
A *Fatal Accident Summary* is free to the public. The accident database can be searched, sorted, and a printout provided.

New Jersey

Department of Law and Public Safety
Division of Highway Traffic Safety
P.O. Box 048
Trenton, NJ 08625
609-633-9300
800-422-3750
www.state.nj.us/lps/hts
Publications include *Traffic Safety Facts Annual Report*. The department has a link to the Fatality Analysis Reporting System (FARS) where you can look up a report based on a set of data or create your own report.

New Mexico

Highway and Transportation Department
Traffic Safety Bureau
P.O. Box 1149
Santa Fe, NM 87504-1149
505-827-0427
www.unm.edu/~dgrint/tsb.html
Publications include the annual *New Mexico Traffic Crash Data Report*. The accident database can be searched, sorted, and a printout provided at no cost. Requests for data not found in the annual report should be placed in writing. Go to their website to view the data yourself.

New York

State Department of Motor Vehicles
Accident Safety Division
Research Bureau, Room 420
6 Empire State Plaza
Albany, NY 12228
518-473-5595
800-CALL-DMV
www.nydmv.state.ny.us/stats.htm
Publications include an annual *Accident Facts*, and the *Ten Year Accident Summary*. The accident database can be searched, sorted, and a printout provided. Fees vary according to the complexity of the request. Visit their website to view those and other reports.

North Carolina

Division of Motor Vehicles
Traffic Records Section
1100 New Bern Ave.

Annex Bldg., Room 101
Raleigh, NC 27697
919-715-7000
www.dmv.dot.state.nc.us/
Publications include a free report entitled *North Carolina Traffic Crash Facts Book*. To obtain a copy of the book, call 919-861-3062. A summary of the data is available at the DOT website. You will find traffic safety information at the Highway Safety Research Center website. The accident database can be searched, sorted, and a printout provided for a fee from: Highway Safety Research Center, CB 3430, UNC Campus, Chapel Hill, NC 27599; 919-962-2202; or online at <www.hrsc.unc.edu/>.

North Dakota

Department of Transportation
Drivers License and Traffic Safety Division
608 E. Boulevard Ave.
Bismarck, ND 58505-0700
701-328-2600
www.state.nd.us/dot/dl&ts.html
Publications include the *Vehicle Crash Facts*. This report is available at their website. The accident database can be searched, sorted, and a printout provided.

Ohio

Department of Public Safety
Public Information Office
P.O. Box 182081
Columbus, OH 43218-2081
614-466-4344
www.state.oh.us/odps/
Ohio publishes a number of safety-related publications, including *Traffic Crash Facts*, and *Facts and Figures*. You can view these at the website listed above.

Oklahoma

Department of Public Safety
Highway Safety Division
3223 N. Lincoln Blvd.
Oklahoma City, OK 73105
405-523-1571
www.dps.state.ok.us/ohso
Publications include the annual *Oklahoma Crash Facts Report*, which is free. You can download this report at their website. Computer printouts are available upon written request. Fees vary according to the complexity of the data search.

Oregon

Department of Transportation
Crash Analysis and Reporting Unit

Accident Data
Transportation Development Division
355 Capitol St., NE, Room 135
Salem OR, 97301
503-986-4232
888-275-6368
www.odot.state.or.us/tdb/accident_data/
Publications include an *Oregon Accident Rate Table*. This report can be downloaded at their website. The accident database can be searched, sorted, and a printout provided at no cost.

Pennsylvania

Department of Transportation
Department of Highway Safety and Traffic Engineering
Keystone Building
400 North Street
Harrisburg, PA 17120
717-783-0352
www.dot.state.pa.us
This office publishes a free report entitled *Crash Facts and Statistics*. The report will soon be available online. The accident database can be searched, sorted, and a printout provided. Fees vary according to the scope of the request. All requests should be made in writing.

Rhode Island

Department of Transportation
State Office Bldg., Room 251
Two Capitol Hill
Providence, RI 02903
401-222-3025 (Governor's Office on Highway Safety)
800-354-9595 (General Department of Transportation)
www.dot.state.ri.us
Standard tables of accident reports are published yearly and are available upon request. The accident database can be searched, sorted, and a printout provided upon special, written request. Individuals must first complete an open records request. Costs vary according to the actual research and computer time involved.

South Carolina

Department of Pubic Safety
Office of Highway Safety
Statistical Services Section
5400 Broad River Road
Columbia, SC 29212
803-896-9963
877-349-7187
www.scdps.org/ohs
Publications include the *South Carolina Traffic Collision Fact Book*. It can be viewed at their website. The

accident database can be searched, sorted, and a printout provided.

South Dakota
Department of Transportation
Accident Records
Becker-Hansen Building
700 E. Broadway Ave.
Pierre, SD 57501-2586
605-773-3868
www.sddot.com/pe/data/accident.asp
Publications include an annual *South Dakota Accident Report*. This and other reports can be found at their website. Be sure to look at all of their publications. Individual computer runs of selected data are provided generally at no cost.

Tennessee
Governor's Highway Safety Office
505 Deaderick Street, Suite 1800
Nashville, TN 37243
615-741-2589
www.tdot.state.tn.us
This office is responsible for collecting and analyzing traffic accident data. The accident database can be searched, sorted, and a printout provided.

Texas
Department of Public Safety
Accident Records Bureau
Box 15999
Austin, TX 78761-1599
512-465-2600
www.txdps.state.tx.us/administration/driver_licensing_control/arb.html
Publications include the *Motor Vehicle Traffic Accidents Report*. The accident database can be searched, sorted, and a printout provided for a cost recovery fee. This information is available online.

Utah
Department of Transportation
Division of Traffic Safety
4501 S. Constitution Blvd.
Salt Lake City, UT 84114-3200
801-965-4284
www.dot.utah.gov/ops/traff_saf/traff_saf.htm
Publications include *Utah Annual Safety Report* and *Accident Statistics*. These reports can be downloaded from the website. The accident database can be searched and printouts provided. Requests should be in writing and individuals must first complete a request form. Fees for computer printouts vary. Individuals may receive data within the last five years. Fees vary.

Vermont
Governor's Highway Safety Program
103 S. Main St.
Waterbury, VT 05671-2101
802-244-1317
www.dps.state.vt.us/cjs/ghsp.htm
Publications include an annual report entitled *Vermont Crash Data Book*. This report is also available online. The accident database can be searched, sorted, and printouts provided. Costs for individual searches vary depending upon the scope of the request. Requests should be made in writing.

Virginia
Department of Motor Vehicles
P.O. Box 27412
Richmond, VA 23269
866-DMVLINE (368-5463)
800-435-5137
www.dmv.state.va.us/webdoc/citizen/drivers/crash_facts.asp
Publications include an *Virginia Traffic Crash Facts Report*. The accident database can be searched, sorted, and printouts provided upon special, written request. There may be a charge depending upon the complexity of the information requested. You can search the report online at the website listed above.

Washington
Department of Transportation
Transportation Data Office
310 Maple Park Ave., SE
Olympia, WA 98504
360-705-7932
www.wsdot.wa.gov/ppsc/TDO/default.htm
Publications include the *Washington State Annual Collision Data Report*. Go to the website to view the report yourself. The accident database can be searched, sorted, and a printout provided. Most requests usually require only one hour of staff time.

West Virginia
Department of Highways
Traffic Engineering Division, Building 5
1900 Kanawah Blvd. E.
Charleston, WV 25305
304-558-3063
www.wvdot.com
Publications include the *West Virginia Crash Data Report* which is free. The accident database is not available to the general public.

Wisconsin
Department of Transportation
Traffic Accidents Section

P.O. Box 7919
Madison, WI 53707-7919
608-267-1847
608-266-2265
www.dot.state.wi.us/dmv/accident.html
Publications include a report entitled *Wisconsin Traffic Crash Statistics* which is free to the public. Computer printouts not normally available. Go to their website to view the above report.

Wyoming
Highway Safety Branch
Department of Transportation
5300 Bishop Blvd.
Cheyenne, WY 82009
307-777-4450
http://dot.state.wy.us
Publications include the *Wyoming Comprehensive Report on Traffic Accidents*. The accident database can be searched and printouts provided at no cost.

Go To School Before Your Kid Does

The difference between school districts and individual schools can be staggering. It's an important consideration that's bound to affect where you decide to live. Should you count on the information that you get from a real estate agent interested in selling you a house? No! If you are house hunting and have children in school, you can find all the answers to all of your questions simply by contacting both the State Department of Education and the local school district.

The amount spent per child, student-teacher ratio, tests scores, experience, and more are only some of the data available from these offices. Once you have compiled the information, you can make an informed choice on what school is best for your kids.

State Department of Education Offices

Alabama
Alabama Department of Education
50 N. Ripley
P.O. Box 302101
Montgomery, AL 36104
334-242-9700
www.alsde.edu/html/home.asp
The department produces the *School Report Cards*, *System Report Cards*, and the *State Report Card*. You can view the documents individually, or download the entire set from the website. The monthly newsletter, *Alabama Education News*, is also available.

Alaska
Alaska Department of Education and Early Development
Public Information
801 W. 10th St., Suite 200
Juneau, AK 99801-1894
907-465-2851
www.eed.state.ak.us/home.html
This office provides computer searches and printouts. Specialized requests should be placed in writing. Due to budget cuts, the *Annual Report* is no longer being published. Information such as the enrollment or

dropout rates can be found, however, in the *Alaska Public School District's Report Card to the Public*. The report can be viewed and downloaded from the website.

Arizona

Arizona Department of Education
Academic Standards and Accountability Division
1535 W. Jefferson
Phoenix, AZ 85007
602-542-5022
800-352-4558
www.ade.state.az.us/
The office publishes the *Arizona School Report Cards*, a detailed collection of information about each Arizona public school.

Arkansas

Arkansas Department of Education
IT-Information and Reporting
#4 Capitol Mall
Little Rock, AR 72201
501-682-1189
http://arkedu.state.ar.us
This office provides computer searches and information via printouts and diskettes to nonprofit organizations, only. Requests may be made directly over the telephone, but those of a complex nature should be placed in writing. There is no fee for services. Publications include *Report Card of Arkansas Schools*. This and other reports can be viewed online.

California

California Department of Education
721 Capitol Mall
P.O. Box 944272
Sacramento, CA 95814
916-657-2451
http://goldmine.cde.ca.gov/
or
Demographics Office
428 J Street, 2nd Floor
Sacramento, CA 95814
916-327-0219
http://goldmine.cde.ca.gov/demographics
The Educational Demographics Unit provides searches and printouts free of charge. The office's publications include: *School Profiles*, *Demographic Reports*, *California School District Data*, and *DataQuest*. All these reports are available online.

Colorado

Colorado Department of Education
Education Statistics and Data

201 E. Colfax
Denver, CO 80203
303-866-6600
www.cde.state.co.us/
This office provides computer searches on staff and student enrollment. The office publishes *Graduation Statistics*, and *Statewide Education Facts*. All this information can be found at their website.

Connecticut

Connecticut Department of Education
Public Information Office
165 Capitol Ave.
P.O. Box 2219
Hartford, CT 06145
860-713-6548
www.state.ct.us/sde/
This office provides information through computer analyses, printouts, and magnetic tapes, or it can be viewed online. The publication office publishes *Strategic School Profiles*, and comprehensive surveys of each Connecticut public school.

Delaware

Delaware Department of Education
Federal and Lockerman Sts.
P.O. Box 1402
Dover, DE 19903-1402
302-739-4601
www.doe.state.de.us/
The office provides board approved reports listing statistics on school enrollments, number of teachers, educational statistics, and teacher personnel reports. Titles include *Summary of Public Schools*, *Statistics for Delaware School Districts*, and *Delaware Education at a Glance*. Check out their website for a wealth of information.

Florida

Florida Department of Education
Education Information and Accountability Services
325 W. Gaines St., Room 852
Tallahassee, FL 32399-0400
850-487-2280
www.firn.edu/doe/eias/home0050.htm
Publications include *Statistical Briefs*, *Florida School Indicator Reports*, and *Graduation Rates*; all of which are available online.

Georgia

Georgia Department of Education
205 Jessie Hill, Jr. SE
Atlanta, GA 30334
404-656-2800
800-311-3627

www.doe.k12.ga.us/
The Administrative Technology Department provides information such as basic attendance and enrollment data, some financial information, types of enrollment, and the expenditure and cost per child. The publication *Georgia Public Education Report Card* is free and has a wealth of information on Georgia schools. All this information can be found at their website, and downloaded for free.

Hawaii

Hawaii Department of Education
Information Branch
P.O. Box 2360
Honolulu, HI 96804
808-586-3230
http://doe.k12.hi.us
Enrollment data can be obtained free of charge from this office. At present, computer diskettes and magnetic tapes are not available. Specialized requests should be placed in writing. Publications include the *Annual Financial Report* which may be obtained by calling 808-586-3230. There are many reports available for viewing at their website.

Idaho

Idaho Department of Education
P.O. Box 83720
Boise, ID 83720-0027
208-332-6800
www.sde.state.id.us/Dept
Their publications include financial summaries, an *Annual Statistical Report*, and *Accreditation Summary Report of Idaho Schools*. They also provide an *Educational Directory* and school profiles. These are all available online.

Illinois

Illinois State Board of Education
100 N. First St.
Springfield, IL 62777-0001
217-782-3950
www.isbe.state.il.us/research/Default.htm
The Research Division has compiled a variety of reports and publications. Their publications include *Annual Statistical Report of Illinois Public School Districts, School Directories,* and *School Report Cards.* Download them from their website, or call the number above.

Indiana

Indiana Department of Education
Accountability System for Academic Progress (ASAP)
Room 229, State House
Indianapolis, IN 46204-2798

317-232-0808
www.doe.state.in.us/
This office provides computer searches and printouts. Types of information available include enrollment figures, graduation rates, and teacher to pupil ratios. Their publications include the *Annual Performance Report, Expulsion Reports,* and *School Directory*. At their website you can choose the data you are interested in and create your own personal report.

Iowa

Iowa Department of Education
Bureau of Planning, Research and Evaluation
Grimes State Office Bldg.
Des Moines, IA 50319-0146
515-281-4837
www.state.ia.us/educate/
This office gathers and posts data and reports for viewing. Teachers' names and school addresses are released. Publications include the *Annual Condition of Education Report* and the *Basic Educational Data Survey (BEDS)*.

Kansas

Kansas State Department of Education
120 SE 10th Ave.
Topeka, KS 66612
785-296-3201
www.ksde.org/welcome_main.shtml
A variety of information can be looked up at their website for each school. This office provides computer searches and, on occasion, printouts. The office publishes the *Kansas Educational Directory, Education Matters,* and *School Building Report Card*. Most of these are available online.

Kentucky

Kentucky Department of Education
Division of Data Policy Management and Research
500 Mero Street
Frankfort, KY 40601
502-564-5279
www.kde.state.ky.us/
This office provides computer searches, printouts, and bulletins. Information such as *School Report Cards, School and District Profiles,* and the *Kentucky Schools Directory*. Check out their website for that and much more information.

Louisiana

Louisiana Department of Education
P.O. Box 94064
626 North 4th Street
Baton Rouge, LA 70804
225-342-4411
877-4LEAP21

www.doe.state.la.us/
The Division of Planning, Analysis & Information
Resources produces the *School Report Card* which is
posted at their website. They also have an Interact
with the Data feature where you can choose
information to compare schools. Publications include
the *Annual Financial* and *Statistical Report*.

Maine

Maine Department of Education
Station House 23
Augusta, ME 04333
207-624-6616
www.state.me.us/education/homepage.htm
Access reports such as the *Maine Educational
Assessment* and *Graduates On To Post-Secondary Schools*
from the Data Center to help make the best school
choice. Publications include *Students Educated at
Public Expense*, and *Maine Educational Staff*. All
publications are available on the website only.

Maryland

Maryland Department of Education
Office of Planning
Results and Information Management
200 W. Baltimore St.
Baltimore, MD 21201
410-767-0100
888-246-0016
www.msde.state.md.us/
This office produces the Maryland School
Performance Report that can be search by school,
system, or state data. Information is in categories
such as Student Performance and Participation with
more detailed subcategories.

Massachusetts

Massachusetts Department of Education
350 Main St.
Malden, MA 02148
781-388-3000
800-439-0183
www.doe.mass.edu
They produce and post the results of the MCAS
assessment test for each school. The School
Performance Ratings let you look at each school to see
how they fared in the state. Other statistical reports
are also available on-line. Enrollment figures,
attendance data, and drop-out reports are available.
Publications include: *School Facts*, *Children First*, and
Per Pupil Expenditures by Program.

Michigan

Michigan Department of Education
Information Center Data Services
608 W. Allegan St.

Hannah Bldg.
P.O. Box 30008
Lansing, MI 48933
517-373-3324
www.mde.state.mi.us/
You can do in depth research at this website, MEAP
scores, analysis of financial data, and more. They even
have a link to Standards & Poor for the School
Evaluation Service. This office provides computer
searches and printouts on a limited basis. Diskettes
are available. At present, there is no base charge for
services, but this would depend upon the extent of
the request. Publications include *Michigan School
Report*, *School District Data Book*, and *Michigan K12
Database*.

Minnesota

Minnesota Department of Education
Information and Technology Unit
1500 Highway 36 West
Roseville, MN 55113
651-582-8200
http://children.state.mn.us/
This office provides computer searches, printouts,
and diskettes, free of charge. Teachers' names and
school addresses are available on labels from the
Documents Division. *School District Profiles* can be
viewed online.

Mississippi

Mississippi Department of Education
P.O. Box 771
Jackson, MS 39205-0771
601-359-5615
www.mde.k12.ms.us
The office provides computer searches, printouts, and
magnetic tapes. The Office of Accountability
Reporting provides the *Mississippi Report Card* and the
Superintendents Annual Report which has data such as
Promotions and Non-Promotion, Dropouts, and
Public School Personnel. This and other publications
can be reviewed at their website.

Missouri

Missouri Dept. of Education School Data Section
P.O. Box 480
Jefferson City, MO 65102-0480
573-751-4212
http://services.dese.state.mo.us/
The Division of Improvement supplies *School Data*,
School Improvement Planning Profiles which lists
information concerning demographics, educational
performance and more. Also, check the results of the
Missouri Assessment Program to see the top 10
schools. Other publications include *At School Manuals*
and MAP Assessments, which can also be

downloaded from their site. Computer searches and printout requests are available.

Montana

Montana Office of Public Instruction
Capitol Station
Helena, MT 59620-2501
406-444-3656
www.opi.mt.gov/index.html
This office does not provide individual computer searches. However, information on grades kindergarten through twelfth is available in their *Montana School Directory. Database Files of Montana Schools* are available on the website for downloading and searching. Other information at their site includes *Education Profiles and Services* and MontCAs results.

Nebraska

Nebraska Department of Education
Data Center
P.O. Box 94987
Lincoln, NE 68509
402-471-2295
www.nde.state.ne.us/
This office's services include computer searches, printouts, and magnetic tapes. Fees vary depending upon the scope of the project. The office prefers that requests be in writing. The office publishes the *Nebraska Education Directory*, and *Nebraska Public School District Statistical Facts*. The office provides the *State of Schools Report* that can be downloaded from their website. All of these informative reports will give you what is needed to choose the school that is right for you.

Nevada

Nevada Department of Education
Office of Finance Accountability and Audit
400 W. King St.
Carson City, NV 89710
702-687-9200
www.nde.state.nv.us
This office provides computer searches and printouts based upon aggregated student demographic data. Requests should be placed in writing. Their publications include the *School Accountability Data*.

New Hampshire

New Hampshire Department of Education
Office of Information Services
State Office Park South
101 Pleasant St.
Concord, NH 03301-3860
603-271-3494
www.ed.state.nh.us

The Office provides computer searches and printouts. Information is also available on diskette or magnetic tape, depending upon the data requested. Teachers' names and school addresses are released under certain circumstances. The office has numerous Reports and Statistics available at their website. You can access information on enrollment, financial data, and student-teacher ratios.

New Jersey

New Jersey Department of Education
Office of Public Information
CN 500, 100 River View Executive Plaza
Trenton, NJ 08625
609-292-4041
www.state.nj.us/education/
Services include computer searches, printouts, and magnetic tapes upon individual request. There is no set fee for services, since it varies according to the scope of the request. This website has all of the information you need to compare schools. You can view the *School Report Cards*, compare school in other states, and use their Data Search and Analysis. You will also be able to look-up the *Statewide Assessment Reports*.

New Mexico

New Mexico Department of Education
Education Bldg.
Data Collection and Reporting Unit
300 Don Gaspar Ave.
Santa Fe, NM 87501-2786
505-827-6526
http://sde.state.nm.us/
This office provides computer searches and printouts free of charge. The office publishes the *Accountability Report, Dropout Report*, and the *New Mexico Educational Personnel Directory*. There are many reports and publications available to the public detailing information on the schools. The *District Report Card* and *School Fact Sheets* are just a few. They also maintain a rating of each school.

New York

New York Department of Education
Fiscal Analysis and Research Unit
Room 301, State Education Bldg.
Albany, NY 12234
518-474-5213
www.nysed.gov/
This office provides computer searches, printouts, and magnetic tapes. Recent Reports on school statistical data is available at this website. Not only will you find a report on each school, but also individual reports of *Most Improved Schools at Grade 4*

and Grade 8, Middle Math Results, and more. Some of the publications are *School District Fiscal Profiles* and *Statistical Profiles of Public School Districts*.

North Carolina

North Carolina Department of Public Instruction
301 N. Wilmington St.
Raleigh, NC 27601-2825
919-807-3300
800-663-1250
www.dpi.state.nc.us/
The Publication Office has an abundance of information online for you. The reports are on *Student Testing Results Evaluation and Analysis*, and *About North Carolina Schools*. Some of the Reports and Statistics can be downloaded such as the *ABCs School Report Card*. Other publications on topics like *Education Initiatives* and *Education Directory* can be obtained online or ordered from the above phone number.

North Dakota

North Dakota Department Education
Department of Public Instruction
600 E. Boulevard Ave.
Dept. 201, Floors 9, 10, and 11
Bismarck, ND 58505-0440
701-328-2260
www.dpi.state.nd.us/
This office provides computer searches and printouts. The *North Dakota Educational Directory* is available for $8, or it can be downloaded at their website. There are also eight different files from the directory that can be viewed separately; Statistical Summary and Directory Guide, Educational Directory, and more. Other publications include *School District Profiles* and *School Finance Facts*.

Ohio

Ohio Department of Education
25 S. Front St.
Columbus, OH 43215-4183
614-995-1545
877-644-6338
www.ode.state.oh.us
This office provides computer searches and printouts. Publications include *School District Profiles*, *State Composite Profiles*, and *Proficiency Test Data*. Not only can you view the Ohio Local Report Cards for the District, Buildings, and Community Schools, but they also have the Interactive Local Report Card. With this you can create your own report based upon the criteria you choose. Check out the enrollment and discipline data too.

Oklahoma

Oklahoma State Department of Education
Documents
2500 N. Lincoln Blvd.
Oklahoma City, OK 73105-4599
405-521-2293
www.sde.state.ok.us/home/default.html
This office provides computer searches and printouts. The department makes the *Report Cards for the State, District, and Sites* available to the public on-line. Some other publications they have available are the *Oklahoma Directory of Education*, *Test Scores*, and *School District Database*.

Oregon

Oregon Department of Education
School Finance, Data and Analysis
Public Service Bldg.
255 Capitol St., NE
Salem, OR 97310-0230
503-378-0203
www.ode.state.or.us/
This office provides computer searches and printouts. Fees vary, depending upon the scope of the project. Requests should be made in writing. This office provides the *District Profile Reports* which you can use to compare districts or similar schools. The *School Report Card* is available with information covering the past 3 years. Other publications include *District and School Mailing Labels* and the *School Directory*.

Pennsylvania

Pennsylvania Department of Education
Office of Data Services
333 Market St.
Harrisburg, PA 17126-0333
717-787-2644
www.pde.state.pa.us
This office provides computer searches and printouts. Requests should be placed in writing for complex data. The office publishes the *Status Report On Education In Pennsylvania, Public, Private and Non-Public School High School Graduates*, and *School Profiles*. School profiles will help you to evaluate a specific school or district in Pennsylvania. Data on available programs, enrollment, technology and resource, and test results are available. Some of the Statistical Reports they offer are, *Status Report on Education in Pennsylvania, Public, Private and Nonpublic Schools*.

Rhode Island

Information Works!
Rhode Island Department of Elementary and Secondary Education
255 Westminster St.

Providence, RI 02903-3400
401-222-4600, ext. 2231
www.ridoe.net
Information Works! lists all of the data on a school that you would hope to find. The *School Performance Grouping* lists schools by their performance and improvement over a 3 year period. For those and other reports on demographics and financial information, check out their website.

South Carolina

South Carolina Department of Education
1429 Senate St.
Columbia, SC 29201
803-734-8500
www.sde.state.sc.us
This office provides computer searches and printouts. Fees vary for the use of computer time, and are dependent upon the complexity of the request. Their list of publications includes: *Pupils in South Carolina Schools, School Crime Incident Report* and *Quick Facts about South Carolina Public Schools*. Their website posts *Report Cards* for each school in the state. It also has a list of high achieving schools. The Publications Office has test results for each school and district of up to 7 different assessment tests.

South Dakota

South Dakota Department of Education and Cultural Affairs
Office of Finance and Management
700 Governors Dr.
Pierre, SD 57501-2291
605-773-3248
605-773-4748
www.state.sd.us/
This office provides computer searches and printouts. Special requests should be placed in writing. The office publishes *Education in South Dakota: A Statistical Profile* and *An Educational Directory*. These are available online.

Tennessee

Tennessee Department of Education
Office of Accountability
6th Floor, Andrew Jackson Tower
710 James Robertson Parkway
Nashville, TN 37243-0375
615-532-4703
www.state.tn.us/education
This office does not normally provide computer searches, but will provide you with a free copy of their *Annual Statistical Report, School Directory*, or *21st Century Schools Report Card*. These are available at their website.

Texas

Texas Education Agency
Division of Public Information
1701 N. Congress
Austin, TX 78701-1494
Mailing Address:
    P.O. Box 13817
    Austin, TX 78711-3817
512-463-9734
www.tea.state.tx.us/
Publications include *Texas Education Directory and Snapshot: School District Profiles*. The *Comprehensive Annual Report on Texas Public Schools* provides information on the overall state of education in Texas. The *Accountability Data Tables* will give you a more in depth picture of each school or district. There is also a link to the *Comparable Improvement Report*.

Utah

Utah Board of Education
School Finance and Statistics Section
250 E. 500 S.
Salt Lake City, UT 84111
801-538-7660
www.usoe.k12.ut.us/
Publications available include the free *Superintendent's Annual Report*. All of the information is available from their website, including numerous statistical spreadsheets.

Vermont

Vermont Department of Education
Communications Department
State Office Bldg.
120 State St.
Montpelier, VT 05620-2501
802-828-3154
www.state.vt.us/educ/
This office provides information via printouts to profit and nonprofit organizations. The department publishes *Vermont School Report, Education Facts and Ratios, Standards for Vermont Educators* and *Student Performance Data*. These can be examined at their website.

Virginia

Virginia Department of Education
Office of Information Technology
101 N. 14th St., 22nd Floor
Richmond, VA 23219
804-225-2951
800-292-3820
www.pen.k12.va.us/Anthology/VDOE/
The office provides information via printouts and booklets. Requests for specialized information must be placed in writing. The office publishes the free

Superintendent's Annual Report, *The DOE Directory,* and *The Literacy Program Testing Data,* which are available online. This office makes available the *School Report* and results of the state's Assessment Tests at this website.

Washington

Washington Superintendent of Public Instruction
Data Administration
Old Capitol Bldg.
P.O. Box 47200
Olympia, WA 98504-7200
360-725-6370
www.wednet.k12.wa.us
This office provides information via printouts, diskettes, and computer tapes. Special requests should be placed in writing. Publications include *Dropout and Graduation Statistics, Minority Enrollment Report, Enrollment Facts in Washington State,* and *Enrollment by Grade Level by County,* which are available at their website. From the Washington State Education Profile, you can download WASL scores by district or school, demographic information, and more.

West Virginia

West Virginia Department of Education
WV Education Information System
Bldg. 6, 1900 Kanawha Blvd. E., Room 346
Charleston, WV 25305-0330
304-558-3927
http://wvde.state.wv.us/
This office provides computer searches and printouts. Although the staff does not normally provide information on diskette or magnetic tape, they can do so if you specify your required format. The office publishes an *Annual Educational Summary* and *West*

Virginia Report Cards. From the *Washington State Education Profile,* you can download WASL scores by district or school, demographic information, and more.

Wisconsin

Wisconsin Department of Public Instruction
Statistical Information Center
125 S. Webster
P.O. Box 7841
Madison, WI 53707-7841
608-266-3390
800-441-4563
www.dpi.state.wi.us/
The *School Performance Report* contains in depth information by school or district. Each category; academics, attendance and behavior, staff and money, demographics, has a number of sub-categories. That along with other reports such as *School Financial Data* and *SAGE Evaluation Reports* provides all of the information needed for parents. All of these are available from their website.

Wyoming

Wyoming Department of Education
Statistical Department
Hathaway Bldg., 2nd Floor
2300 Capitol Ave.
Cheyenne, WY 82002-0050
307-777-5252
www.k12.wy.us/wdehome.html
This office provides free statistical which are available online. Publications include *Enrollment History, Wyoming CAS Student Assessment Results,* and *School Directory.*

Housing Made Affordable

The U.S. Department of Housing and Urban Development (HUD) has several different programs available to help people become first time homebuyers, assist with the housing needs of the elderly and disabled, help people who are having trouble paying their mortgage, mortgage insurance for those deemed ineligible for FHA mortgage insurance, and even find subsidized rent for people who are struggling with their finances. In some cases, housing funds are made available through local community organizations. HUD also offers properties for sale through real estate brokers, and these homes can often be purchased for less than the going rate. Contact the HUD regional office near you for more information about HUD programs, or look at the HUD field office website at {http://www.hud.gov/directory/ascdir3.cfm}.

HUD Regional Offices

Regional Director
Office for New England
10 Causeway Street, Room 301
Boston, MA 02222-1092
617-994-8200

Regional Director
Office for Mid West
Ralph Metcalfe Federal Building
77 West Jackson Boulevard
Chicago, IL 60604-3507
312-353-5680

Regional Director
Office for Rocky Mountain Area
633 17th Street, 14th Floor
Denver, CO 80202-3607
303-672-5440

Regional Director
Office for New York/New Jersey

26 Federal Plaza
Suite 3541
New York, NY 10278-0068
212-264-1161

Regional Director
Office for Southwest
801 Cherry Street
Fort Worth, TX 76113-2905
817-978-5980

Regional Director
Office for Pacific/Hawaii
450 Golden Gate Avenue
San Francisco, CA 94102-3448
415-436-6550

Regional Director
Office for Mid-Atlantic
100 Penn Square East
Wanamaker Building

Philadelphia, PA 19107-3380
215-656-0600

Regional Director
Office for Great Plains
400 State Avenue, Room 200
Kansas City, KS 66101-2406
913-551-5462

Regional Director
Office for Southeast/Caribbean
40 Marietta Street
Five Points Plaza
Atlanta, GA 30303-2806
404-331-4111

Regional Director
Office for Northwest and Alaska
909 1st Avenue, Suite 200
Seattle, WA 98104-1000
206-220-5108

State Housing Assistance

Every state has a variety of programs to help with the construction and purchase of homes. Housing finance agencies (HFAs) have been created by states to issue tax-exempt bonds to finance mortgages for lower-income first-time home buyers and to build multi-family housing. Funds are also available for persons who take steps to make their homes more energy efficient, for home owners and landlords who remove lead paint from dwelling units, for houses without plumbing or those with plumbing that is dysfunctional, for handicapped persons, and to help landlords defray the costs of bringing low-income housing into compliance. In many states, elderly home owners  can look to the HFA to obtain financing and/or support services they need to remain in their homes and avoid institutionalization. Some of the states have more than one agency dedicated to housing, and many cities and counties have quasi-federal/ quasi-local housing authorities with addition programs.

Insurance: Car, Homeowner, and Health

Each state has its own laws and regulations for all types of insurance, including car, homeowner, and health insurance. The officials listed below enforce these laws. Many of these offices can provide you with information to help you make informed insurance buying decisions. If you have a question or complaint about your insurance company's policies,

contact the company in question first. If you do not receive a satisfactory response, then contact the state insurance regulator. They can answer many questions, including:

- What are some tips on how to choose an insurance policy?
- Are there consumer guides to different policies?
- What should you do if you have been unfairly treated by an insurance company?

State Insurance Commissioners

Alabama
Insurance Commissioner
201 Monroe St., Suite 1700
Montgomery, AL 36104
www.aldoi.org
334-269-3550

Alaska
Director of Insurance
P.O. Box 110805
Juneau, AK 99811-0805
907-465-2515
800-INSUR-AK
www.dced.state.ak.us/insurance

Arizona
Director of Insurance
2910 N. 44th St., Suite 210
Phoenix, AZ 85018
602-912-8400
800-325-2548
www.state.az.us/id/

Arkansas
Insurance Commissioner
1200 W. 3rd St.
Little Rock, AR 72201
501-371-2600
800-282-9134

www.accessarkansas.org/insurance

California
Commissioner of Insurance
300 S. Spring St., 13th Floor
Los Angeles, CA 90013
916-492-3500 (Sacramento)
213-897-8921 (Los Angeles)
800-927-HELP
www.insurance.ca.gov/docs/index.html

Colorado
Commissioner of Insurance
1560 Broadway, Suite 850
Denver, CO 80202
303-894-7499
800-930-3745
www.dora.state.co.us/insurance

Connecticut
Insurance Commissioner
P.O. Box 816
Hartford, CT 06142-0816
860-297-3800
800-203-3447
www.state.ct.us/cid/

Delaware
Insurance Commissioner
841 Silver Lake Blvd.
Dover, DE 19904
302-739-4251
800-282-8611
www.state.de.us/inscom

District of Columbia
Director of Insurance
810 First St., NE, Suite 701
Washington, DC 20002
202-727-8000
www.disr.washingtondc.gov/main.shtm

Florida
Insurance Commissioner
200 E. Gaines St.
Tallahassee, FL 32399-0300
850-413-3100
800-342-2762
www.doi.state.fl.us/

Georgia
Insurance Commissioner
West Tower, Suite 704
2 Martin Luther King, Jr. Dr.

Atlanta, GA 30334
404-656-2070
800-656-2298
www.inscomm.state.ga.us

Hawaii
Insurance Commissioner
250 S. King St., 5th Floor
P.O. Box 3614
Honolulu, HI 96811
808-586-2790
www.state.hi.us/dcca/ins

Idaho
Director of Insurance
P.O. Box 83720
Boise, ID 83720-0043
208-334-4250
800-721-3272 (complaints)
www.doi.state.id.us/

Illinois
Director of Insurance
320 W. Washington St.
Springfield, IL 62767-0001
217-782-4515
877-527-9431 (health)
866-445-5364 (toll-free)
www.state.il.us/ins/

Indiana
Commissioner of Insurance
311 W. Washington St.
Suite 300
Indianapolis, IN 46204-2787
317-232-2385
800-622-4461
www.ai.org/idoi/index.html

Iowa
Insurance Commissioner
330 Maple St.
Des Moines, IA 50319
515-281-5705
877-955-1212
www.iid.state.ia.us/

Kansas
Commissioner of Insurance
420 SW 9th St.
Topeka, KS 66612-1678
785-296-5865
800-432-2484
www.ksinsurance.org

Kentucky
Insurance Commissioner
215 W. Main St.
P.O. Box 517
Frankfort, KY 40602
502-564-3630
800-595-6053
www.doi.state.ky.us/kentucky

Louisiana
Commissioner of Insurance
P.O. Box 94214
Baton Rouge, LA 70804-9214
225-342-5900
800-259-5300
www.ldi.state.la.us/

Maine
Superintendent of Insurance
#34 State House Station
Augusta, ME 04333
207-624-8475
800-300-5000 (ME)
www.state.me.us/pfr/ins/ins_i
ndex.htm

Maryland
Insurance Commissioner
525 St. Paul Place
Baltimore, MD 21202
410-486-2000
800-492-6116
www.mdinsurance.state.md.us

Massachusetts
Commissioner of Insurance
One South Station
Boston, MA 02210-2208
617-521-7794
www.state.ma.us/doi

Michigan
Commissioner of Insurance
Insurance Bureau
P.O. Box 30220
Lansing, MI 48909-7720
517-373-0220
877-999-6442
www.cis.state.mi.us/ofis

Minnesota
Commissioner of Commerce
85 7th Place E, Suite 500
St. Paul, MN 55101
612-297-7161

800-657-3602 (complaints)
800-657-3978 (license status)
www.commerce.state.mn.us/pa
ges/InsuranceMain.htm

Mississippi
Commissioner of Insurance
1001 Woolfolk State Office
Building
501 N. Main St.
P.O. Box 79
Jackson, MS 39205
601-359-3569
800-562-2957
www.doi.state.ms.us

Missouri
Director of Insurance
301 W. High St.
P.O. Box 690
Jefferson City, MO 65102-0690
573-751-4126
800-726-7390
www.insurance.state.mo.us

Montana
Commissioner of Insurance
P.O. Box 4009
Helena, MT 59604-4009
406-444-2040
800-332-6148 (MT)
www.discoveringmontana.com/
sao/default.htm

Nebraska
Director of Insurance
941 O St., Suite 400
Lincoln, NE 68508-3639
402-471-2201
www.nol.org/home/ndoi/

Nevada
Commissioner of Insurance
788 Fairview Dr., Suite 300
Carson City, NV 89701-5491
775-687-4270
800-992-0900
http://doi.state.nv.us

New Hampshire
Insurance Commissioner
56 Old Suncook Rd.
Concord, NH 03301
603-271-2261
800-852-3416

http://webster.state.nh.us/insu
rance

New Jersey
Commissioner
Department of Insurance
20 W. State St.
P.O. Box 325
Trenton, NJ 08625-0325
609-292-5360
www.state.nj.us/dobi/index.html

New Mexico
Superintendent of Insurance
P.O. Drawer 1269
Santa Fe, NM 87504-1269
505-827-4601
800-947-4722
www.nmprc.state.nm.us

New York
Superintendent of Insurance
25 Beaver St.
New York, NY 10004
212-480-6400
800-342-3736 (in NY)
www.ins.state.ny.us/njins.htm

North Carolina
Commissioner of Insurance
P.O. Box 26387
Raleigh, NC 27611
919-733-2032
800-546-5664
www.ncdoi.com

North Dakota
Commissioner of Insurance
600 E. Boulevard Ave.
Dept. 401
Bismarck, ND 58505-0320
701-328-2440
800-247-0560 (in ND)
www.state.nd.us/ndins

Ohio
Director of Insurance
2100 Stella Court
Columbus, OH 43215-1067
614-644-2658
800-686-1526 (consumer)
800-686-1527 (fraud)
800-686-1578 (senior health)
www.ohioinsurance.gov

Oklahoma
Insurance Commissioner
P.O. Box 53408
Oklahoma City, OK 73152-3408
405-521-2828
800-522-0071
www.oid.state.ok.us

Oregon
Insurance Commissioner
350 Winter St., NE, Room 440
Salem, OR 97301
503-947-7980
800-722-4134
www.cbs.state.or.us/external/ins

Pennsylvania
Insurance Commissioner
1326 Strawberry Square
Harrisburg, PA 17120
717-787-2317
877-881-6388
www.insurance.state.pa.us

Rhode Island
Insurance Commissioner
233 Richmond St., Suite 233
Providence, RI 02903
401-222-2223
www.dbr.state.ri.us/insurance.h
tml

South Carolina
Chief Insurance Commissioner
P.O. Box 100105
Columbia, SC 29202-3105
803-737-6150
800-768-3467
www.state.sc.us/doi/

South Dakota
Director of Insurance
Insurance Bldg.
118 W. Capitol St.
Pierre, SD 57501
605-773-3563
www.state.sd.us/dcr/insurance/

Tennessee
Commissioner of Insurance
500 James Robertson Parkway,
4th Floor
Nashville, TN 37243-0565
615-741-2218
800-342-4029

www.state.tn.us/commerce/ins
urdiv.html

Texas
Insurance Commissioner
P.O. Box 149104
Austin, TX 78701
512-463-6169
800-578-4677
www.tdi.state.tx.us

Utah
Commissioner of Insurance
State Office Bldg., Room 3110
Salt Lake City, UT 84114
801-538-3800
800-439-3805
www.insurance.utah.gov

Vermont
Commissioner of Banking and
Insurance
89 Main St., Drawer 20
Montpelier, VT 05620-3101
802-828-3301
800-964-1784
www.bishca.state.vt.us/InsurDi
v/Insur_index.htm

Virginia
Commissioner of Insurance
Tyler Bldg.
1300 E. Main St.
P.O. Box 1157
Richmond, VA 23218
804-371-9741
800-552-7945
www.state.va.us/scc/division/
voi/webpages/homepageb.htm

Washington
Insurance Commissioner
P.O. Box 40255
Olympia, WA 98504-0255
360-753-7300
800-562-6900 (WA)
www.insurance.wa.gov

West Virginia
Insurance Commissioner
1124 Smith St.
P.O. Box 50540
Charleston, WV 25305-0540
304-558-3386

800-642-9004
www.state.wv.us/insurance

Wisconsin
Commissioner of Insurance
121 E. Wilson St.
Madison, WI 53702

608-266-3585
800-236-8517 (WI)
http://oci.wi.gov/oci_home.htm

Wyoming
Commissioner of Insurance
Herschler Building

3rd Floor, East
122 W. 25th St
Cheyenne, WY 82002
307-777-7401
800-438-5768 (WY)
http://insurance.state.wy.us/index.htm

Put Your Money In A Safe (Place, That Is)

Finding the right bank, savings and loan, or credit union means figuring out your own needs first. How much money can you keep on deposit and how many checks will you write? Examine your future loans and savings needs, as well as look at the convenience of the financial institution, its service charges, fees, and deposit and loan interest rates. Before making your final choice, make sure the institutions you're considering are federally insured. The offices listed below can answer such questions as:

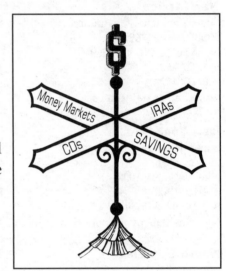

- what is a bank's asset size?
- what are all the banks in a state that are covered by their office?
- where is a particular bank located and where are its branches?

For information about a particular financial institution, contact one of the following offices:

National Banks (banks that have the word "National" in their names or the initials "N.A." after their names)
Comptroller of the Currency, Compliance Management, Department of the Treasury, 250 E St., SW, Washington, DC 20219, 202-874-5000; {www.occ.treas.gov}.

FDIC-Insured Banks
Division of Compliance and Consumer Affairs, FDIC, 550 17th St., NW, Washington, DC 20429, 877-ASK-FDIC, 202-942-3080, 800-934-3342; {www.fdic.gov}.

Savings and Loans
Office of Thrift Supervision, Department of Treasury, 1700 G St., NW, Washington, DC 20552, 202-906-6237, 800-842-6929; {www.ots.treas.gov}.

State Banks

Contact your State Government Banking Commissioner located in your state capital (see state by state listing below).

State Government Banking Commissioners

Alabama
Superintendent of Banks
401 Adams Ave., Suite 680
Montgomery, AL 36130
334-242-3452
www.bank.state.al.us

Alaska
Department of Community and
Economic Development
Division of Banking, Securities,
and Corporations
150 Third Street, Suite 217
Juneau, AK 99801
Mailing Address:
   P.O. Box 110807
   Juneau, AK 99811-0807
907-465-2521
www.dced.state.ak.us/bsc/home.htm

Arizona
Superintendent of Banks
2910 N. 44th St., Suite 310
Phoenix, AZ 85018
602-255-4421
800-544-0708 (toll free in AZ)
www.azbanking.com

Arkansas
Bank Commissioner
The Sedgwick Center
400 Hardin Road, Suite 100
Little Rock, AR 72211
501-324-9019
www.accessarkansas.org/bank

California
Commissioner of Financial
Institutions
State Banking Department
111 Pine St., Suite 1100
San Francisco, CA 94111-5613
415-263-8500
800-622-0620 (toll free in CA)
www.dfi.ca.gov

Colorado
State Bank Commissioner
Division of Banking
Denver Post Bldg.
1560 Broadway
Suite 1175
Denver, CO 80202
303-894-7575
www.dora.state.co.us/banking

Connecticut
Banking Commissioner
260 Constitution Plaza
Hartford, CT 06103
860-240-8200
800-831-7225 (toll free in CT)
www.state.ct.us/dob/

Delaware
State Bank Commissioner
555 E. Lockerman St.
Suite 210
Dover, DE 19901
302-739-4235
800-638-3376 (toll free in DE for complaints only)
www.state.de.us/bank/index.htm

District of Columbia
Commissioner of Banking and
Financial Institutions
1400 L Street, NW, Suite 400
Washington, DC 20005
202-727-1563
http://dbfi.dc.gov/main.shtm

Florida
Florida Department of Banking
& Finance
State Comptroller
101 East Gaines Street
Tallahassee, FL 32399-0350
850-410-9286
800-848-3792
www.dbf.state.fl.us

Georgia
Commissioner of Banking and
Finance
2990 Brandywine Rd., Suite 200
Atlanta, GA 30341-5565
770-986-1633
www.ganet.org/dbf/dbf.html

Hawaii
Commissioner of Financial
Institutions
Department of Commerce and
Consumer Affairs
P.O. Box 2054
1010 Richards St., Room 602A
Honolulu, HI 96805
808-586-2820
www.state.hi.us/dcca/dfi

Idaho
Department of Finance
P.O. Box 83720
700 W. State St., 2nd Floor
Boise, ID 83720-0031
208-332-8000
888-346-3378 (ID)
www.finance.state.id.us/home.asp

Illinois
Commissioner of Banks and Real
Estate
500 E. Monroe St.
Springfield, IL 62701
217-782-3000
877-793-3470
www.obre.state.il.us

Indiana
Department of Financial
Institutions
402 W. Washington, Room W066
Indianapolis, IN 46204
317-232-3955
800-382-4880 (toll free in IN)
www.dfi.state.in.us/

Iowa

Superintendent of Banking
200 E. Grand, Suite 300
Des Moines, IA 50309
515-281-4014
www.idob.state.ia.us

Kansas

State Bank Commissioner
700 Jackson St., Suite 300
Topeka, KS 66603-3714
785-296-2266
www.osbckansas.org

Kentucky

Commissioner
Department of Financial
Institutions
1025 Capital Center Dr.
Suite 200
Frankfort, KY 40601
502-573-3390
800-223-2579
www.dfi.state.ky.us/

Louisiana

Commissioner of Financial
Institutions
8660 United Plaza Boulevard
2nd Floor
P.O. Box 94095
Baton Rouge, LA 70804-9095
225-925-4660
www.ofi.state.la.us

Maine

Superintendent of Banking
#36 State House Station
Augusta, ME 04333-0036
207-624-8570
800-965-5235
www.state.me.us/pfr/bkg/bkg
_index.htm

Maryland

Commissioner of Financial
Regulation
500 North Calvert St., Room 402
Baltimore, MD 21202-2272
410-230-6100
www.dllr.state.md.us/finance

Massachusetts

Commissioner of Banks
One South Station

Boston, MA 02110
617-956-1500
800-495-2265
www.state.ma.us/dob/

Michigan

Commissioner of Financial &
Insurance Services
P.O. Box 30220
Lansing, MI 48909-7720
517-373-0220
877-999-6442
www.cis.state.mi.us/ofis

Minnesota

Department of Commerce
Division of Financial
Examinations
85 7th Place East, Suite 500
St. Paul, MN 55101-2198
651-296-2135
www.commerce.state.mn.us/pa
ges/FinancialServicesMain.htm

Mississippi

Commissioner of Banking and
Consumer Finance
P.O. Box 23729
Jackson, MS 39225-3729
601-359-1031
800-844-2499
www.dbcf.state.ms.us/

Missouri

Commissioner of Finance
P.O. Box 716
Jefferson City, MO 65102
573-751-3242
800-722-3321
www.ecodev.state.mo.us/financ
e/finhome.htm

Montana

Commissioner of Banking and
Financial Institutions
P.O. Box 200546
Helena, MT 59620-0546
406-444-2091
http://discoveringmontana.com
/doa/banking

Nebraska

Director of Banking and Finance
P.O. Box 95006
1200 N. Street

The Atrium, Suite 311
Lincoln, NE 68509-5006
402-471-2171
www.ndbf.org

Nevada

Commissioner of Financial
Institutions
406 E. Second St., Suite 3
Carson City, NV 89701-4758
775-684-1830
http://fid.state.nv.us

New Hampshire

Bank Commissioner
64B Old Suncook Road
Concord, NH 03301
603-271-3561
http://webster.state.nh.us/bank
ing

New Jersey

Commissioner of Banking
P.O. Box 040
Trenton, NJ 08625
609-292-5360
www.state.nj.us/dobi/index.ht
ml

New Mexico

Financial Institutions Division
722 St. Michael's Drive
Santa Fe, NM 87501
505-827-7100
www.rld.state.nm.us/fid/index.
htm

New York

Superintendent of Banks
Two Rector St., 118th Floor
New York, NY 10006-1894
212-618-6553
800-522-3330 (consumer)
800-832-1838 (small business)
www.banking.state.ny.us/

North Carolina

Commissioner of Banks
316 W. Edenton St.
Raleigh, NC 27603
Mailing Address:
    4309 Mail Service Center
    Raleigh, NC 27699-4309
919-733-3016
www.banking.state.nc.us/

North Dakota
Commissioner of Banking and
Financial Institutions
2000 Schafer St., Suite G
Bismarck, ND 58501-1204
701-328-9933
www.state.nd.us/dfi

Ohio
Superintendent of Financial
Institutions
77 S. High St., 21st Floor
Columbus, OH 43215-0121
614-728-8400
www.com.state.oh.us/odoc/dfi

Oklahoma
Bank Commissioner
4545 N. Lincoln Blvd., Suite 164
Oklahoma City, OK 73105-3427
405-521-2782
www.state.ok.us/~osbd/

Oregon
Administrator
Division of Finance and
Corporate Securities
350 Winter St., NE, Room 410
Salem, OR 97301-3881
503-378-4140
800-722-4134
www.cbs.state.or.us/dfcs/

Pennsylvania
Secretary of Banking
333 Market St., 16th Floor
Harrisburg, PA 17101-2290
717-787-2665
800-PA-BANKS (toll free in PA)
www.banking.state.pa.us/

Rhode Island
Director and Superintendent of
Banking
Dept. of Business Regulation
Division of Banking
233 Richmond St., Suite 231
Providence, RI 02903-4231
401-222-2405
www.dbr.state.ri.us

South Carolina
Commissioner of Banking
Calhoun Office Bldg.
Columbia, SC 29211
803-734-2001
www.lpitr.state.sc.us/gvtdir97/
p225.htm

South Dakota
Director of Banking
Division of Banking
217 1/2 West Missouri
Pierre, SD 57501-4590
605-773-3421
www.state.sd.us/dcr/bank/BA
NK-HOM.htm

Tennessee
Commissioner of Financial
Institutions
500 Charlotte Ave.
John Sevier Bldg., 4th Floor
Nashville, TN 37243-0705
615-741-2236
www.state.tn.us/financialinst/

Texas
Banking Commissioner
2601 N. Lamar Blvd.
Austin, TX 78705
512-475-1300
877-276-5554 (consumer hotline)
www.banking.state.tx.us

Utah
Commissioner of Financial
Institutions
P.O. Box 89
Salt Lake City, UT 84110-0089
801-538-8830
www.dfi.utah.gov

Vermont
Deputy Commissioner of
Banking
89 Main St., Drawer 20
Montpelier, VT 05620-3101
802-828-3307
www.bishca.state.vt.us

Virginia
Bureau of Financial Institutions
1300 E. Main St., Suite 800
P.O. Box 640
Richmond, VA 23218-0640
804-371-9657
800-552-7945 (toll free in VA)
www.state.va.us/scc/division/
banking

Washington
Department of Financial
Institutions
Division of Banking
210 11th Ave., SW, Room 300
P.O. Box 41200
Olympia, WA 98504-1200
360-902-8700
800-372-8303
www.dfi.wa.gov

West Virginia
Commissioner of Banking
1900 Kanawha Blvd. East
Bldg. 3, Room 311
Charleston, WV 25305-0240
304-558-2294
800-642-9056
www.wvdob.org

Wisconsin
Secretary of Financial
Institutions
345 W. Washington Ave., 4th
Floor
P.O. Box 7876
Madison, WI 53707
608-261-7578
800-452-3328
www.wdfi.org

Wyoming
Banking Commissioner
Division of Banking
Department of Audit
Herschler Bldg.
3 East, 122 W. 25th St.
Cheyenne, WY 82002
307-777-7797
http://audit.state.wy.us/bankin
g/banking.htm

Index

Hispanic community
  housing grants, 48
Historic preservation
  National Register of Historic Places, 486
  nonprofit organizations, 487
  renovation, 486
Home
  surviving the loss of, 647
Home buying
  books about, 332
  buyers rights, 329
  disabled persons, assistance for, 326
  down payment assistance, 316, 338
  financial assistance, 321, 322, 326, 329
  first-time buyers, 321
  free publications, 321, 322, 328
  Habitat for Humanity, 331
  homesteading, 328
  housing guides, 334
  mortgage payment assistance, 321, 322
  pre-purchase counseling, 322
  resource list, 339, 340
  seniors, assistance for, 326
Home Equity Conversion Mortgage Program, 27
Home financing, 337
Home improvement
  See home repair, 24
Home ownership vouchers, 18
Home repair, 22, 317
  energy efficiency, 27
  grants, 317
  loans, 18
  mortgages, 24
  Native Americans, 156, 158
Home repair programs, 99, 322, 324, 326, 335
  energy efficiency, 336
  energy-related repair assistance, 334
  grants, 335
  rural areas, 98
  volunteer organizations, 316, 333
  weatherization assistance, 340
Home sales
  appraisal, 339
Homeless
  shelter grants, 46
  supportive housing, 37
  veterans, 161
HomeSteps Asset Services
  foreclosed properties, 458
Hospitals
  mortgages, 30
Hotlines
  safe drinking water, 333
Housing
  counseling for homeowners, 663
  counseling programs, 503

discrimination, 338, 663
foreclosed properties, 457
market data, 662
mortgage manuals, 663
mortgage statistics, 661
property data, 662
rural, 661
state assistance, 696
veterans, 662
Housing and Urban Development, U.S. Department of, 325
  foreclosed properties, 457, 462
  HOME program, 61
  housing data, 662
  housing programs, 695
  housing research, 47
  regional offices, 696
  reverse mortgage, 366
Housing counseling agency, 649
Housing Counseling Clearinghouse, 503
Housing counseling programs, 43
  rural families, 110
Housing programs
  affordable housing, 108
  apartment buildings, 42
  areas hurt by defense cuts, 25
  city offices, 272
  county offices, 258
  disaster assistance, 20, 21
  federal government, 16
  foreclosed properties, 44
  Healthy Homes Initiative, 43
  law enforcement officers, 44
  low-income, 61
  multi-family housing, 16, 40, 44
  persons with AIDS, 41
  self-help, 110
  small cities, 49
  subsidies, 41
  teachers K-12, 54
  transitional, 359
Housing research, 47

I

Idaho
  banking commissioner, 701
  city housing offices, 283
  county housing programs, 262
  crime statistics, 666
  data centers, 673
  development programs, 186
  education department, 690
  energy assistance programs, 349
  fair housing hub, 369
  General Services Administration office, 474

L_____

M_____

Oregon
  banking commissioner, 703
  city housing offices, 302
  county housing programs, 267
  crime statistics, 668
  data centers, 678
  development programs, 235
  education department, 693
  energy assistance programs, 351
  fair housing hub, 371
  General Services Administration office, 475
  highway department, 686
  historic renovation, 498
  HOME program, 87
  homeowner programs, 234
  housing counseling agencies, 612
  HUD office, 377, 464
  insurance commissioner, 699
  public housing agencies, 435
  rent assistance programs, 345
  rental programs, 236
  rural development office, 143
  rural housing office, 484
  SBA district office, 479
  state weatherization agency, 343
  tax agency, 356
  U.S. Army Corps of Engineers office, 472
  VA office, 468

P_____

Pacific Islands
  community development programs, 51
Pennsylvania
  banking commissioner, 703
  city housing offices, 303
  county housing programs, 268
  crime statistics, 669
  data centers, 679
  development programs, 238
  education department, 693
  energy assistance programs, 351
  fair housing hub, 371
  General Services Administration office, 475
  highway department, 686
  historic renovation, 498
  HOME program, 88
  homeowner programs, 237
  housing counseling agencies, 613
  HUD office, 377, 465
  insurance commissioner, 699
  public housing agencies, 435
  rental programs, 239
  rural development office, 143
  rural housing office, 484
  SBA district office, 479
  state weatherization agency, 343

  tax agency, 356
  U.S. Army Corps of Engineers office, 472
  VA office, 468
Police. *See* law enforcement officers
Population
  statistics, 658, 670
Property, surplus, 473
Public housing
  demolition grants, 53
  eligibility, 373
  funding, 53
  revitalization grants, 53
  supportive services, 57
  voucher programs, 372
Public housing units
  mortgages, 29
Puerto Rico
  housing counseling agencies, 619
  General Services Administration office, 475
  HOME program, 89
  HUD office, 465
  public housing agencies, 438
  rural development office, 144
  rural housing office, 484
  SBA district office, 479
  VA office, 468

R_____

Radon, 332
Real estate
  land sales, 660
Renovation
  housing preservation grants, 99
Renovation, commercial
  tax credits, 487
Renovation, historic
  grants, 486
  loans, 486
Rental assistance, 17, 60, 361
  disabled persons, 360
  elderly, 360
  emergency, 346, 361
  public housing, 372
  rural areas, 100, 104
  security deposit, 359
  short-term, 344
  tax refunds, 360
  transitional, 359
  voucher programs, 59, 372
Rental housing
  for the elderly, 33
  loans, 103
  multi-family, 34
  rural areas, 104
  urban renewal areas, 33

Research
　housing, 47
Reverse mortgages, 27, 361
　features, 364
　types, 362
Rhode Island
　banking commissioner, 703
　city housing offices, 304
　crime statistics, 669
　data centers, 679
　development programs, 240
　education department, 693
　energy assistance programs, 351
　fair housing hub, 371
　General Services Administration office, 475
　highway department, 686
　historic renovation, 498
　HOME program, 90
　homeowner programs, 239
　housing counseling agencies, 619
　HUD office, 377, 465
　insurance commissioner, 699
　public housing agencies, 438
　rent assistance programs, 345, 347
　rental programs, 241
　rural development office, 144
　rural housing office, 484
　SBA district office, 479
　state weatherization agency, 343
　tax agency, 356
　U.S. Army Corps of Engineers office, 472
　VA office, 468
Rural areas
　housing programs, 97
Rural housing
　foreclosed properties, 481
　mortgages, 21
Rural Housing Service, 97, 325, 326, 661

S____

Scams, 655
　equity skimming, 655
　phony counseling agencies, 655
　where to report, 655
Self-help housing programs, 110
Seniors
　home buying assistance, 326
Single room occupancy, 40, 58
Small Business Administration
　foreclosed properties, 476
Social Services Department
　short term rent assistance, 344
South Carolina
　banking commissioner, 703
　city housing offices, 304

county housing programs, 268
crime statistics, 669
data centers, 679
development programs, 242
education department, 694
energy assistance programs, 351
fair housing hub, 371
General Services Administration office, 475
highway department, 686
historic renovation, 499
HOME program, 90
homeowner programs, 241
housing counseling agencies, 621
HUD office, 378, 465
insurance commissioner, 699
public housing agencies, 438
rental programs, 242
rural development office, 144
rural housing office, 484
SBA district office, 479
state weatherization agency, 343
tax agency, 356
U.S. Army Corps of Engineers office, 472
VA office, 468
South Dakota
　banking commissioner, 703
　city housing offices, 304
　crime statistics, 669
　data centers, 679
　development programs, 243
　education department, 694
　energy assistance programs, 351
　fair housing hub, 371
　General Services Administration office, 475
　highway department, 687
　historic renovation, 499
　HOME program, 91
　homeowner programs, 242
　housing counseling agencies, 622
　HUD office, 378, 465
　insurance commissioner, 699
　public housing agencies, 439
　rental programs, 243
　rural development office, 145
　rural housing office, 484
　SBA district office, 479
　state weatherization agency, 343
　tax agency, 357
　U.S. Army Corps of Engineers office, 472
　VA office, 468
Statistics
　crime, 664
　employment, 659
　population, 658
　transportation, 660

Y____